With the enormous famine and se
in our day as it also existed in the day of the prophet Amos (Amos 8:11), I heartily endorse the book on *Faithful Preaching: Preparing and Delivering Transformational Sermons* by Hershel Wayne House and Daniel Garland, for it offers the proper antidote for such a drought. Even though most will give lip service to expository preaching of the Word of God, in all too many instances the text serves merely as jumping-off point for the message. This work courageously urges that we return to carefully laying out portions of the Biblical text with their accompanying Biblical authority and visually illustrating how that could be done. Only this will quench the huge appetite for God's word that currently exists in the land.

Walter C. Kaiser, Jr.
President Emeritus
Gordon-Conwell Theological Seminary, Hamilton, MA

Wayne House & Daniel Garland have tackled one of the greatest needs of our day. Faithful preaching that leads to spiritual transformation is lacking in many contemporary churches. We need a return to biblical exposition that helps the listener discover the truth of the text and its proper application to real life. If you are serious about preaching, don't miss this incredible book.

Dr. Ed Hindson, D.Min., Th.D., D.Phil.
(Founding Dean & Distinguished Professor of Religion,
Liberty University School of Divinity)

Dr. Wayne House is one of the most unique and profound expositors that I know. I've had the privilege of sitting at his feet for the last 15 years. If anyone takes the time to listen to Dr. House, he can change your life forever. He is one of the preachers that I study on a regular basis.

Dr. Frank E. Ray, Sr.
New Salem Baptist Church, Memphis, TN

If anyone is called and committed to the interpretation in preaching of the Scripture, they will find Drs. House and Garland's new book, *Faithful Preaching,* an important book for their library. They have provided clear and accurate understanding of how to proclaim and preach the Bible. Someone who is called to the preaching of the gospel will find this book both theologically sound and practically useful.

Bishop Keith W. Reed, Sr.
Senior Pastor/teacher
Sharon Baptist Church, Philadelphia, PA

In a day when preaching has been marred by a topical or prosperity approach. Drs. House and Garland challenge us to speak as the prophets who said, 'thus saith the Lord.' They do this by urging their readers to learn to preach expository sermons, preaching that comes directly from the text of Scripture. They are able to do this in this outstanding work through careful, progressive presentation and abundant examples. I encourage all ministers who desire to be faithful to the preaching of the Word of God to read this book, and practice it.

Dr. Melvin V. Wade, Sr.
Pastor, Mount Moriah Baptist Church, Los Angeles, California
Former President of the National Missionary Baptist Convention of America

Wayne House and Dan Garland make the connection between developing a message from God and effectively delivering a sermon to people. Biblical preaching is a great need in a generation searching for truth, so I am very grateful for this fresh work on the greatest task of all: proclaiming the Word of God.

Dr. Jack Graham
Pastor, Prestonwood Baptist Church, Plano, Texas

This powerful and informative book will give the committed pulpiteer a comprehensive understanding of how to be a better expository preacher. It is a must read for those who take proclaiming God's Word seriously.

Dr. Tony Evans
Senior Pastor, Oak Cliff Bible Fellowship, Dallas, Texas

Faithful PREACHING

Preparing & Delivering Transformational Sermons

H. WAYNE HOUSE & DANIEL G. GARLAND

LAMPION Press

Faithful Preaching

Preparing and Delivering Transformational Sermons

Lampion Press, LLC, P. O. Box 932, Silverton, OR 97381

ISBN: 978-1-942614-07-4

Library of Congress Control Number: 2015914281

Formatting and cover design by Amy Cole, JPL Design Solutions

Printed in the United States of America

In memory of Arthur B. Whiting,
whose expository preaching method inspired this book
and produced generations of expository preachers

And to
Dr. Robert A. Williams, Jr., Dr. Larry L. Harris, Sr. (deceased),
and Dr. George Waddles, Sr., who have carried on
this tradition in WHW Ministries.

Faithful PREACHING

Contents

Part III
Delivering the Development
131

Part IV
Demonstrating the Discovery, Development, and Delivery of What God Meant by What He Said
151

Acknowledgments

Many people have input into the production of a book at its various stages. We must first of all acknowledge Arthur B. Whiting from whose method of, and passion for, preaching we have greatly benefited, though neither of us ever knew him personally. Next, we must express our appreciation for Milton Jones who was the instructor in homiletics at Western Seminary from whom we learned the Whiting Method. We also thank Dr. Dennis Wretlind for the use of his material on integrating exegesis into the Whiting Method.

Daniel Garland thanks the professors of Faith Evangelical Seminary, and its President, Michael Adams, under whom he earned the degree of Doctor of Ministry in Expository Communication, especially H. Wayne House under whom he wrote his dissertation on the Whiting Method of exposition. He is also indebted to his brother Hubert and V. Deane Keller for providing early examples of solid expositional preaching, and especially to his wife, Kathy, without whose faithful love, encouragement and support his contribution to the book would not have been made.

Special thanks to Elizabeth "Lizzie" Summers for her meticulous efforts in manuscript preparation and to Amy Cole for her exceptional formatting and design work and gracious spirit.

Preface

"Preach the Word!" was Paul's straightforward charge to his young assistant Timothy (2 Tim. 4:1-2), and this call has gone out to thousands of ministers of the Word of God since the original command was written. There can be no higher calling given to a servant of Christ than what Paul gave to Timothy.

The calling is honorable, though not all those who have received the call have honored the position. Failure has occurred notoriously in homes and communities when preachers have not been godly leaders. These are tragic shortcomings that are indicative of the on-going struggle with the flesh, the world, and the devil. What has often been passed over, however, is the failure of the man of God when standing in the pulpit, standing before the people of God, with the Word of God. Dealing unfaithfully with the biblical text is no less serious an ethical failure than any lapse into immorality. Those who are to be elders (bishops, overseers, pastors) in Christ's church must meet the high standards of character, given in 1 Timothy 3:1-7 and Titus 1:5-9, precisely because God has commissioned them to proclaim doctrine and give reproof, correction, and instruction in righteousness from the sacred text (2 Tim. 4:2; cf 2 Tim. 3:16-17). Failure to communicate the timeless truths of God's Word compromises the very purpose for which godly character is demanded of preachers.

In the west there is an abundance of Bibles available to most families, but few of these Bibles are being carefully studied. There are thousands of preachers in the pulpits, but there is a dearth of the proclamation of the words of God. Much of this is due to topical or applicational preaching that gives little consideration to the contextual meaning of the words of God found in the Bible. In our day, the tendency is to use Bible verses as a point of departure for a topic the preacher wants to communicate to his congregation, without ever explaining the author's intent. Application often does not come from the text being preached but from whatever practices the preacher desires for his congregants to follow. Of course, most preachers who follow this approach are well-intentioned but were never taught the importance of expositing the text of Scripture. It is our belief that the minister of Christ is obligated to explain the words of God to those under his care, and to derive the meaning of the sermon directly from biblical text.

Faithful Preaching sets forth in a careful and progressive manner the procedure for preparing and delivering expositional sermons. Chapter by chapter, the building blocks of biblical expositional preaching are provided and illustrated by graphics and charts. The chapters on sermon preparation and delivery use one sermon to show development throughout the book, but then also provide other sermon examples. The appendices give additional examples of sermons showing the application of the procedure to the variety of literature found in Scripture. Those who have limited knowledge of the Hebrew and Greek languages will be able to apply almost all of the techniques of sermon preparation, but there is additional help for those who can use the original languages of Scripture. God is pleased to honor His words when His imperfect but qualified servants are equipped and willing to communicate their true meaning. So "Preach the Word!"

Foreword

Scripture gives no set liturgy for public church services and no detailed manual on church polity. But whenever the Bible does deal with either corporate worship or the duties of church leaders, it always stresses the vital importance of Biblical preaching and teaching.

To qualify for service as an elder in the church, for example, a man must be "able to teach" (1 Tim. 3:2), because his primary duty as an elder and teacher is "holding fast the faithful word as he has been taught, that he may be able, by sound doctrine, both to exhort and convict those who contradict" (Titus 1:9).

Thus when Paul told Timothy, "Preach the word!" (2 Tim. 4:2), he was summarizing and emphatically declaring the heart of the agenda for both corporate worship and the leadership and oversight of the church. Likewise, when Paul gave his charge to the elders of the church at Ephesus and told them "to *shepherd* the church of God" (Acts 20:28), this is precisely what he had first and foremost in his mind: leading and feeding the flock through the ministry of God's Word.

That agenda does not change to suit whatever is fashionable in any given generation. As a matter of fact, Paul's instructions to Timothy plainly stipulated that a time would come when people "will not endure sound doctrine, but … they will heap up for themselves teachers; and they will turn their ears away from the truth, and be turned aside to fables" (2 Tim. 4:3-4). In times and cultures such as those (which would certainly include the shallow age in which we now live) every pastor's duty remains fixed and crystal-clear: "Preach the word…*in season and out of season*."

Years ago, when I originally sensed God's calling to pastoral ministry, my father (who was himself a preacher and the son of a preacher) gave me a Bible which he had inscribed with that simple text: "Preach the Word!" It was a simple reminder of every pastor's most crucial task, and that brief command from 2 Timothy 4 has remained a singular focus for me. I have never once thought to deviate from it.

Pastors nowadays are presented with an endless parade of fads and diversions—all claiming to be better means than biblical preaching for stimulating church growth or attracting people. Pollsters, church-growth experts, and even some seminary professors are solemnly warning us that preaching is truly out of season. The church is overrun, it seems, with self-styled experts telling church leaders how to be timely, trendy, and innovative. Biblical preaching is invariably their first target. They counsel pastors to preach shorter sermons with less biblical and doctrinal content and more cultural references. Many pastors today therefore devote inordinate amounts of time and energy to immersing themselves in pop culture and trying to keep up with the latest fads. (One young pastor told me with a straight face that he regarded going to the cinema as "sermon preparation," because he based so many of his messages on themes from hit movies.) Meanwhile, the study and proclamation of God's Word is in serious decline, even in some seminaries and historic churches that were once thought of as strong precisely because of their devotion to biblical preaching.

Blessed is the man who keeps preaching the Word, even when such preaching is supposedly out of season.

Like Wayne House and Dan Garland, I am convinced that the best method of preaching is expository. In other words, it is the kind of preaching that aims to draw the meaning and message *from the biblical text* and proclaim that truth with authority and passion—as opposed to merely using a phrase of Scripture for a sermon title; making a verse of God's Word into a jumping-off point for a topical treatment of something; or borrowing an idea or a story from the Bible as incidental illustrative material for a motivational talk.

Drs. House and Garland carefully outline one very effective method of expository preaching, and they show in thorough detail how to do it and do it well. Their explanation is replete with much valuable and practical help for how to understand the biblical text, how to think it through thoroughly, how to organize a sermon, and how to deliver it clearly and effectively. This is a welcome addition to the expository preacher's library, one of the finest new resources I have seen in years.

I love Dr. House's and Dr. Garland's passion for biblical exposition, their careful attention to the text of Scripture, and (above all) their devotion to the truth of Scripture. Those standout qualities—combined with remarkable giftedness as teachers and the ability to make almost any concept clear—are the main features that make this book so wonderfully valuable. The authors' commitment to expository preaching is contagious, too. That's why I'm delighted to see this book in print, and I hope it will find a large audience among pastors, young men still training for ministry, and even lay people with teaching duties in the church. If you are in such a role and are looking for help to make your ministry more effective, this could well be the most valuable book you will read all year.

JOHN MACARTHUR
Pastor-teacher of Grace Community Church in
Sun Valley, California, and president of the
Master's College and Seminary

CHAPTER 1

The Question: Why Expository Preaching?

Welcome to a consideration of what is arguably the highest privilege of all earthly endeavors–the solemn, authoritative proclamation of the Word of God.

Someone has said, "If God calls you to be a missionary, don't stoop to be a king."[1] The same advice applies to all who serve as God's ambassadors. But with great privileges—like speaking for God—come great responsibilities, among them, being as well prepared as possible.

The Urgent Need For A Systematic Approach To Preaching Biblical Texts

Speaking for God

Few evangelical Christians would deny the urgency of proclaiming the message of God's Word, the Bible. If its very words are God-breathed and "profitable" (2 Tim. 3:16-17 NKJV), then the value of communicating its timeless truth cannot be overestimated. Hearing the biblical text and understanding its meaning and relevant implications for life-change is the basis for faith (see Romans 10:16-17). And without faith, it is impossible to please God (Heb. 11:6). It is no wonder, then, that the apostle Paul addressed his understudy Timothy with this pressing imperative, which likewise commands all who would be God's spokespeople: "I charge you therefore before God and the Lord Jesus Christ, who will judge the living and the dead at His appearing and His kingdom: Preach the word! Be ready in season and out of season. Convince, rebuke, exhort, with all longsuffering and teaching" (2 Tim. 4:1-2 NKJV).

The problem is that sermons do not ring with God's *authority* simply because the preacher uses God's *Word*.[2] To ensure that *you* serve the Word, and not vice versa, you need an approach to sermon development and delivery that truly allows a text to speak for itself.

Adequate Methodology

Even those who praise biblical exposition as the indispensable means of faithfully communicating God's Word, do not always practice it. One reason that sermons that effectively communicate God's message are so scarce is ignorance of how to prepare and deliver them—especially in developing countries. Without a practical method for developing sermons from within a given Scripture text, preachers tend to speak on topics for which scriptural support is either out of context, incomplete, or missing altogether. As a result, people hear *human* reasoning instead of biblical truth. Not only does this disserve humanity by failing to meet real human needs, for which God's Word is uniquely adequate (see 2 Tim. 3:17), but it also dishonors God by misrepresenting Him.

The Whiting Method

To meet the urgent need for a systematic approach to preaching biblical texts, a British-born preacher and scholar named Arthur B. Whiting initiated a technique that came to be called the *Whiting Method*. This approach develops a text's theme from principles formulated on the basis of word studies. Though the original system was never published, a variety of professors, including Milton William Jones and Dennis O. Wretlind, have taught and made valuable modifications to it. (Their contributions will be discussed in Chapter 4.) In keeping with this refining process, this book will demonstrate that when the Whiting Method is used with all relevant contextual data, it is a valuable tool in helping preachers rightly interpret and proclaim the intended meaning of Bible texts. *Faithful Preaching* will help expositors develop and deliver the truth they discover, within the boundaries of the literary unit of Scripture under study.

Is Preaching Different from Teaching?

When Paul concluded his charge to Timothy to "preach the word" with the phrase "with … teaching" (2 Tim. 4:2), he raised for us an important question: What is the difference, if any, between expository *preaching* and *teaching*?

Exposition, The Common Bond of Biblical Preaching and Teaching

In his book *Biblical Preaching*, Haddon Robinson offers a definition of expository preaching that is consistent with a conservative view of Scripture and a commitment to interpretation that is faithful to the biblical text: "*Expository preaching*—the communication of a biblical concept, derived from and transmitted through a historical, grammatical, literary study of a passage in its context, which the Holy Spirit first applies to the personality and experience of the preacher, then through him to his hearers."[3] This definition (as well as that of Lawrence O. Richards and Gary J. Bredfelt, in their book, *Creative Bible Teaching*[4]) hardly distinguishes preaching from expository teaching. From the time of the New Testament's completion, preachers and teachers are essentially indistinguishable. Both are responsible for conveying the meaning and implications of God's written revelation (2 Tim. 4:2; 1 Tim. 4:11, 13). Preaching includes the same explanation of biblical truth for life-change that is normally associated with teaching or instruction. By the same token, the teacher's lesson plan, just as the preacher's sermon, should be structured to achieve the effect that the text was meant to have on the listener's mind, attitude, and behavior.[5] What *distinguishes* preaching from teaching is its authoritative appeal to the will in the context of corporate worship.[6] One might say that all preaching faithful to the text is expositional, but not all exposition is necessarily preaching.

The Distinctive Role of Expository Preaching[7]

Sermons are structured literary units crafted to impact listeners with what God has to say to them in the context of their meeting in His presence.[8] Reminding people of their responsibilities and solemnly charging them in the presence of God, the speaker worships God by letting Him speak (see 2 Timothy 2:14). With His solemn authority, preachers reprove, rebuke, encourage, correct, persuade, and comfort, as well as inform, explain, and motivate. (See Titus 2:15 and I Thessalonians 2:9-12.) Those present, then, worship God by giving attention to His message. (See I Thessalonians 2:13-16.) But who is adequate to fulfill the responsibilities of the high and holy privilege of ministering to these hearers? (See 2 Corinthians 2: 15-16; 3:5-6.)

Are Preachers Born or Made?

Bible scholar R. E. O. White once commented, "Good preachers are born, not made."[9] He then explained by adding, "Technique and teaching will never impart the gift." White balances these remarks, however, by stating, "Without guidance, the most earnest preacher of the gospel hacks away with a blunt knife at the most delicate of operations, his labour vastly increased, his effectiveness sadly decreased, by his lack of a method." If White is correct, books and courses on preaching can provide *part* of the guidance necessary for the development and effective use of God's gifts. But competent preachers are first *born* with *natural* abilities that training can't add. When they are later born from above (see John 3:3 NET), they receive spiritual gifts that training can't add to (see Galatians 1:15-24). Finally, they develop their natural abilities and spiritual gifts through training, without which these gifts and abilities would remain underdeveloped at best.

Is One Method of Sermon Preparation and Delivery Worthy of Universal Adoption?

Methods Are Variable

That this book presents an adaptation of the Whiting Method of homiletics is a testimony to the fact that methods are always various and variable. Richards and Bredfeldt wrote, "Methods are not an end. They are a means to an end."[10] Therefore, preachers should be flexible in their adoption and use of methods.

When the "end" is preaching the Word of God, to His glory, the best methods are likely to have a great deal in common. While no method should ever be used with slavish devotion, or touted as *the* method, what commends the Whiting Method is its step-by-step approach, which can be easily understood, remembered, and taught. It is built on respect for both the Scriptures' authority and the important role of the communicator. It is adaptable and transferable. It focuses on the biblical text from beginning to end, with no introduction of extraneous matter; thus it is exegetical[11] rather than eisegetical.[12]

The value of any systematic approach to preaching is demonstrated not by the greatest public speakers and scholars but by its ability to sustain even those of modest skill in faithful ministries over time. For more than thirty years, the writers have used the Whiting Method and found it beneficial as a means to the end of communicating God's message in the power of the Holy Spirit.

Does One Have to Know Greek and Hebrew to Preach the Word or Use This Method?

The biblical doctrine of the inspiration of Scripture is based on 2 Timothy 3:16 and means that the whole of Scripture is God-breathed and without error *in the original autographs*.[13] The Bible's authority extends equally to all parts and every word. So the ability to read and work in the original scriptural languages is not only advantageous to the preacher and teacher, but necessary in order to preach and teach with maximum confidence and command. But for those lacking formal training in Hebrew and Greek, there are many helpful tools today to assist in gaining much of the knowledge traditionally reserved for the person who reads the original languages.[14] Those who use these tools along with the English translation of the Bible may implement the Whiting Method and greatly benefit both themselves and their listeners.

PART I

Discovering What God Meant by What He Said

Part I of *Faithful Preaching* surveys certain assumptions and biblical principles on which we base our adaptation of the Whiting Method of homiletics.

Chapter 2, "The Charge: Speaking for God to a Contemporary Audience," explores the preacher's responsibilities. It presupposes that God exists, that the Bible is His word in His very words, and that God uses people to bridge the communication gap between the ancient text of Scripture and contemporary listeners.

Chapter 3, "The Channel: Representing God as His Mouthpiece," probes the preacher's roles and relationships. It presumes that God's message is always conveyed to people through the personalities of unique individuals that He has chosen and prepared.

Chapter 4, "The Challenge: Bridging the Communication Gap," explains how the Arthur B. Whiting Method of homiletics may be adapted and used to build a functional bridge for communicating God's message to listeners.

CHAPTER 2

The Charge: Speaking for God to a Contemporary Audience

Suppose you are to prepare and preach a sermon from 1 John 2: 1-2.[1] Your text, from the New King James Version, reads, "My little children, these things I write to you, so that you may not sin. And if anyone sins, we have an Advocate with the Father, Jesus Christ the righteous. And He Himself is the propitiation for our sins, and not for ours only but also for the whole world."

It doesn't take a theological education to notice that these are not your words to your audience. They were written rather than spoken, by an apostle, not by a modern preacher or teacher. The apostle and his readers were of a different nationality. They lived far away and long ago. Yet believing the passage to be the Word of God gives you confidence that its message is still relevant to you and your listeners. It also means that you will stand between God and your contemporaries as His spokesperson. But how can you and those you teach be sure that your sermon communicates God's message? Before embracing any method of sermon development or launching into the actual work of preparing a message, it is important to size up the multifaceted communication gap your sermon must bridge. This involves the issues of *authority, antiquity, relevance, meaning, delivery* and *connecting*.

The Authority of Scripture, It's Not Our Own

God Has Made Himself Known to Man

Anyone who would write or speak for God assumes an awesome responsibility (see James 3:1). To do so on one's own authority would be the height of presumption (see 1 Peter 4:10-11). But if God exists, and the Bible is His Word, then faithful communication of truth is not only possible, but is commanded, is desperately needed, and is the pinnacle of privilege (see John 17: 17; 2 Timothy 4:2; and Proverbs 29:18). The urgency of proclaiming God's Word is indicated by its very purpose. According to authors Lawrence Richards and Gary Bredfeldt, the Bible is meant to reveal the personal being of God, who transcends His creation but still chooses to be in close relation to it.[2] If this is true, then the importance of its message cannot be overstated. The words of J. I. Packer serve well: "What were we made for? To know God. What aim should we set ourselves in life? To know God. What is the 'eternal life' that Jesus gives? Knowledge of God… (John 17:3). What is the best thing in life, bringing more joy, delight and contentment than anything else? Knowledge of God."[3]

According to Scripture, things can be known about God by what He has created (Rom. 1:18-20), as things can be known about an artist by looking at his paintings.[4] But only through God's Son (Heb. 1:1-4; John 20:30-31), the Word in human form (see John 1:1, 14, and 18), and through the Bible, His Word in written human language (2 Tim. 3:16), may He be known in personal relationships.[5] Anything less than the authoritative declaration and accurate explanation of His own self-disclosure is powerless to bring sinful people into the intimacy of a right relationship with their Creator, and to bring immature saints to maturity in Christ.[6]

God's Word Meets Real Human Needs

Real human needs stem from the willful rejection of the knowledge of God (see Romans 1:18-20 and John 17:3). The Bible is God-given information about Him, for the purpose of meeting people's need to truly know Him as He is.[7] The Word of God is described as "living and active" because it expresses the discerning mind of the living God

(Heb. 4:12 NASB95). The apostle Paul commanded Timothy to "preach the word" (2 Tim. 4:2 NKJV). Adequately equipping God's people for every good work depends on the human ministries of teaching, reproof, correction, and training in righteousness, for which the God-breathed Scripture as a whole is profitable (2 Tim. 3:16)[8] Second Peter 1:21 says, "Men moved by the Holy Spirit spoke from God" (NASB95) (cf. Acts 4:25). It is precisely because He has put His words into the mouths of men that they need not (and dare not) put *their* words into the mouth of God!

Too often, however, Christian communicators forfeit God's authority by conveying their own messages rather than His, for at least three reasons: popularity, the precepts of men, and perversion of biblical texts. The remedy in every case is to remember that the source of one's sermon is the Scripture.

Popularity

The lure of popularity is a common pitfall, tempting both the compassionate preacher and the unconscionable one. It often results in attending to the felt needs of listeners. An extreme illustration is found in 1 Kings 22.

The question was whether Jehoshaphat, king of Judah, and Ahab, king of Israel, should go to battle against the Arameans at Ramoth-gilead. Some four hundred prophets agreed to tell King Ahab what they knew he wanted to hear: *Go to war! You'll win!* Their popularity with the king ranked higher than integrity before God.

But Micaiah was summoned for a second opinion. Under great pressure to maintain uniformity with the prophets who spoke favorably, "Micaiah said 'As the LORD lives, whatever the LORD says to me, that I will speak'" (v. 14 NKJV). In contrast to what his audience wanted to hear, Micaiah accurately predicted the defeat and death of Ahab. He also revealed that a deceiving spirit had been sent into the mouths of all the other prophets. The account shows that the real needs of people are met by the faithful proclamation of the Word of God, not by tickling their itching ears, which Paul condemned in 2 Timothy 4:3-4: "For the time will come when they will not endure sound doctrine, but according to their own desires, because they have itching ears, they will heap up for themselves teachers; and they will turn their ears away from the truth, and be turned aside to fables" (NKJV).

Precepts of Men

If popularity can pull preachers away from their calling and place them on their own authority, so can the precepts of men. But man's creation in God's likeness means that he has the ability to exercise judgment. Yet every individual has his own ideas of what is true, right, good, important, timely, moral, and appropriate (Isa. 53:6; Prov. 14:12; 16:25), and speaks out of what fills his heart (Matt. 12:34). Being spiritually dead (Eph. 2:1-2) as a result of his sin in Adam (Rom. 5:12), the natural man is neither willing nor able to respond positively to the things of God (1 Cor. 2:14). While this affects every aspect of man's being, it does not remove his ability to make decisions with accountability to God. Neither does regeneration guarantee that a believer will always speak and behave as a spiritual child of God. Because of sin, no one can be trusted, nor trust in himself, to speak for God as an independent agent (Jer. 17:5, 9). Not even Jesus, the sinless Son and Word of God in human form, spoke on His own initiative (see John 5:30; 8:28; 10:18; 12:49; and 14:10). At the conclusion of the Sermon on the Mount in the Gospel of Matthew, we read, "And so it was, when Jesus had ended these sayings, that the people were astonished at His teaching, for He taught them as one having authority, and not as the scribes" (7:28-29 NKJV; cf. Mark 1:22). According to Matthew 15:9, the scribes taught "AS DOCTRINES THE PRECEPTS OF MEN" (NASB95).

Perversion of Biblical Texts

In addition to the pressures of popularity and human precepts is the tendency of preachers and teachers to pervert the meaning of Bible texts when they are used to teach something other than what the biblical writer intended.[9] A 1993 article in *Christian Education Journal* warns readers of "an authority crisis" in Bible teaching and Bible-based curricula: "If the Bible is used only as a jump-off point for one's own objectives, the Bible's authority is being bypassed, because if a passage is not being used to teach what the Bible is teaching, the teacher stands only in his/her own authority. Too much of today's modern curriculum teaches only with human authority rather than with the authority of God. This then is the authority crisis in curriculum."[10]

Even teaching a truth from a Scripture that does *not* teach that truth is a form of false teaching! Author and exegete Walter Kaiser gives practical advice to those who would avoid this common error: "If the particular truth in which we are interested is indeed taught somewhere else in the Bible, then we must proceed immediately to that context for the message."[11]

Speaking for God, with His authority, means that we preach God's message, not our own. It requires the preacher to be willing to tell people what they need to hear rather than being swayed by popularity, human precepts, or perversions of the author's intended meaning.

In contrast with these three improper approaches, there is also a tendency on the part of some to wrongly think that biblical texts are ready-made sermons.

The Source Of One's Sermon

The text of Scripture provides the material from which a sermon is made, not the sermon itself.[12] First John 2:1-2, for example, is neither a sermon nor the outline of a sermon. If the charge to preach the Word to a contemporary audience meant simply to read or recite the text with good oral interpretation (or even running commentary), then this book would be both misleading and unnecessary. There is certainly value in the audible reading of God's Word as part of public worship,[13] and there are edifying ministries of the Word other than expository preaching and teaching.[14] Such ministries may even avoid the danger of putting human words into God's mouth. But sermons *are* human creations for communicating divine messages given in one setting to learners who live in a different setting. So for you to speak "as the oracles of God" (1 Pet. 4:11), you must recognize and do your part to bridge the contextual divide between the original audience and your own.

The Antiquity Of Scripture, The Communication Gap

The Bible was written long ago, in distant lands, to people of different languages, cultures, and history, whose specific responsibilities toward God are different from those to whom the modern teacher and preacher communicates.[15] In short, not a word of Scripture was addressed to the contemporary preacher or audience. Paul's imperative to "preach the word" requires that the herald first understand the author's intended meaning, in his setting and that of his addressees.[16] Only then can the timeless truth be extracted from its original situation and extended without distortion into the new and different situations of people living today. Those now sitting under the preaching of God's Word cannot help but regard the content of Scripture as ancient, foreign, distant, and difficult, as well as supernatural. If they are to hear what God has to say to them in terms that are current, familiar, near, understandable, and life changing, you must do all you can to bridge the communication gap.[17] (See figure 2-1.)

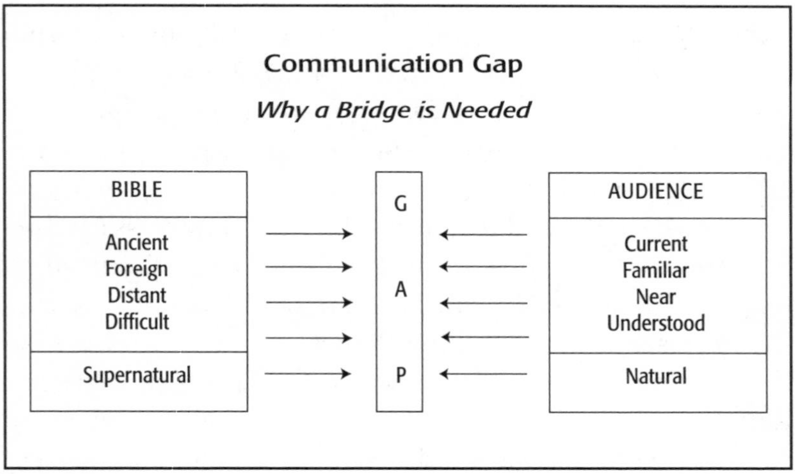

Figure 2.1

It is not enough that the speaker of biblical principles be personally convinced of their relevance. The successful minister must also help the audience overcome the natural bias against all that seems archaic and irrelevant in favor of the latest scientific discoveries and pop culture. It is good to remember the Bible's own claim to timeless relevance. Ezra the priest declared, "Forever, O LORD, Your word is settled in heaven" (Ps. 119:89 NKJV). The modern student of Scripture can learn to appreciate the unchanging truth and universal applicability of the Bible as Jesus and His apostles regarded the Hebrew Scriptures (see 2 Tim. 3:16-17).[18] Communicators of God's plan of the ages can also draw the attention of their listeners to archaeological discoveries that confirm the ancient record.[19] In the hands of the modern preacher, like you, the antiquity of biblical texts can give listeners a fixed point of reference for their personal navigation in a world of constant change. But their natural skepticism and need to be convinced are part of the communication gulf that you are charged to span. In the next chapter, we will consider the importance of the preacher as God's representative. Nothing is more convincing of the Bible's relevance and power to change lives than the changed life of God's spokespeople.[20]

In addition to being ancient, foreign, and distant, the Bible is uniquely difficult. Its sheer length, variety of literary styles,[21] and complexity set it apart. It is comprised of sixty-six books written in three foreign languages. It covers the span of time itself. It presupposes unseen and prehistoric realities that require faith (see Hebrews 11:3, 6). Most important, the Bible is of a supernatural character that necessitates spiritual understanding. "For prophecy never came by the will of man, but holy men of God spoke as they were moved by the Holy Spirit" (2 Pet. 1:21 NKJV). The faithful minister of the Word will take this aspect of the communication gap into account, prayerfully depending on the Holy Spirit for illumination and understanding of God's Word. The preacher will also anticipate that at least some listeners may be utterly insensitive to God, "dead in trespasses and sins" (see Ephesians 2:1-3 NKJV). Until the hearers are born from above[22] and receive the Spirit of truth (see John 14:1 7; 15:26; and 16:13; and 1 John 4:6), a speaker's accomplishments through relational and verbal bridge building will be limited. And until God changes the listeners' hearts, His message will be met with resistance, indifference, or rejection. (See Matthew 10:24-25 and Romans 3:10-18.) God's representatives must not seek to bridge this gap between spiritual life and spiritual death with the man-made solutions of the social sciences, personal charm, or entertainment.[23] Neither will they fail to craft their sermons as the best possible packages in which to deliver God's message to those whose hearts may be opened to receive it. (See Acts 16:14.)

When considering the Grand Canyon–size rift between the Scripture writers and the hearers of sermons, remember that even regenerate listeners (and speakers) have an enemy, against whose schemes they must be armed and stand firm (see Matthew 13:39; Ephesians 6:10-17; and 1 Peter 5:8). Possessing "ears to hear" (Matt. 13:9 NKJV) is the responsibility of the listener to God's message. Having hearts like soil that are well prepared to receive the broadcast Word of God is a spiritual condition, granted by God. Not even the Son of Man produced receptivity in His listeners simply by the content or delivery of His message (see verses 11-12, 23). There are aspects of the communication gap between God's Word and the congregation that only God can bridge. Therefore, you, as God's spokesperson, must carefully devote all available energy to the aspects of bridge building for which you are responsible to God: namely, diligent study of God's Word with dependence upon His Spirit. Your preaching may be the means God uses to open hearts, since "faith comes by hearing, and hearing by the word of God" (Rom. 10:17 NKJV).

Even at the time of writing, merely understanding the language, knowing the culture, and recognizing the genre did not ensure that the original readers, any more than contemporary readers, would grasp the meaning and application of the text.[24] Spiritual discernment was needed.

Character of Scripture, Written for Us but Not to Us

At least four characteristics of Scripture explain why spiritual discernment (1 Cor. 2:14-15) and diligent study (2 Tim. 2:15) are required of students of the Word: (1) the supernatural quality of Scripture; (2) the progress of revelation; (3) the distinction between the redemptive and kingdom programs of God; and (4) the fact that truth must be derived from what was revealed to others, in circumstances different from those of the contemporary preacher and congregation.

The Supernatural Quality of Scripture

The Bible is the result of the Spirit's revealing the mind of God to humanity (1 Cor. 2:10-13). Its supernatural quality is such that the unaided human mind cannot understand or accept it (vv. 12-14).[25] A person deprived of spiritual understanding, whether as a result of judgment, apostasy, or remaining spiritually dead in trespasses and sins, is walking in darkness. (See Isaiah 9:1; Lamentations 3:2; Luke 11:34-36; Ephesians 2:1-3; 1 Thessalonians 5:4-5; and 1 John 1:6-7.) With the illuminating work of the Holy Spirit, however, the believer is able to understand spiritual truth (1 Cor. 2:13, 15-16). The Bible then becomes a lamp to his feet and a light on his path (Ps. 119:105; 2 Pet. 1:19). This is why the apostle John denied the need of any other source of instruction than the Holy Spirit's anointing, which every believer has from the moment he or she believes (1 Jn. 2:27).

The Progress of Revelation

Written revelation was given step-by-step, as a parent's instruction of a child, giving only information appropriate for each stage of development.[26] Thus, God's Word, says author Robert Traina, "is moving, and moving steadily from the lower to the higher, from the lesser to the greater, from the partial to the total, from the temporary to the final."[27] Therefore, the Old Testament must never be interpreted as if it were the New Testament. The student of Scripture must discover whether a particular standard established in the Old has been abrogated, altered, or affirmed in the New Testament.

The Distinction Between the Redemptive and Kingdom Programs of God

What Stanley A. Ellisen called "the redemptive program"[28] of God, to justify lost sinners,[29] must not to be confused with what he termed "the kingdom program"[30] to restore man's rule on earth through Christ as the last Adam and heir to David's throne (1 Cor. 15:24-28, 45). Accordingly, you must be conscious of changes in the way God administers His earthly kingdom. What He expects from His people as a test of obedience and basis for blessing and reward, changes according to which covenant is in view.[31] God's justification of sinners, on the other hand, has always been by grace through faith in what is revealed about the person and work of Christ (Eph. 2:8-9).[32] This never changes. So truth pertaining to the believer's sanctification and rewards must be faithfully distinguished from truth pertaining to justification.[33]

The Derivation of Truth Revealed to Others

While all Scripture is profitable for the believer's thorough equipping for good works (2 Tim. 3:17), every truth it teaches must be derived from something said to someone else in different circumstances (1 Cor. 10:11). To preach with the authority of firsthand knowledge, there is no substitute for the study of God's Word for the purpose of first knowing and doing His will, then teaching it (see Ezra 7:10). The very passion to communicate is properly derived from changes the speaker is making as a lifelong learner continually growing into the likeness of Christ. (See Colossians 1:10 and Ephesians 4:15-16.) But first comes the hard work of study. Adequate preparation for the presentation of God's Word requires strenuous effort. In 2 Timothy 2:15, Paul writes, "Be diligent to present yourself approved to God, a worker who does not need to be ashamed, rightly dividing the word of truth" (NKJV). The word translated "be diligent," means "to take pains." "Rightly dividing," literally means "to cut straight." As a tentmaker, Paul would have had a special appreciation for the importance of accuracy in handling leather and other valuable fabric so that the pieces cut from it fit together. When a useful finished product was formed without unnecessary waste, the worker himself was approved. Skillful labor was required, not just good intentions, the right attitude, or the proper approach.[34]

The Interpretation of Scripture: God Meant Something By What He Said

The Single Meaning of Scripture

Confidence that *your sermon* communicates *God's message* requires an adequate philosophy of meaning. The Arthur B. Whiting Method of sermon development, an adaptation of which is presented in Chapter 4, assumes *literal hermeneutics*. *Hermeneutics* has been defined as "the science and art of Biblical interpretation."[35] It involves skillful observance of rules within a system that presupposes certain things about authority and the nature of language.[36] Literal hermeneutics assumes the single meaning of Scripture,[37] which was fixed by the writer's use of words in their original contexts.[38] Because of its contextual orientation, literal hermeneutics has been called the "historical-grammatical" approach to biblical interpretation.[39] A more complete description would be the "literal-grammatical-historical-cultural-literary-contextual interpretation." Though cumbersome, this compound expression reflects the fact that every contextual layer defines the meanings of the words in which they were written. (See figure 2-2.)

The Process of Literal Interpretation

I. Inductive: Specific to general
II. Exegetical: Meaning is "led out"
1. Words
2. Word Relations (Syntax)
3. Contexts (Immediate; Argument; Dispensation; Cultural)
4. Setting

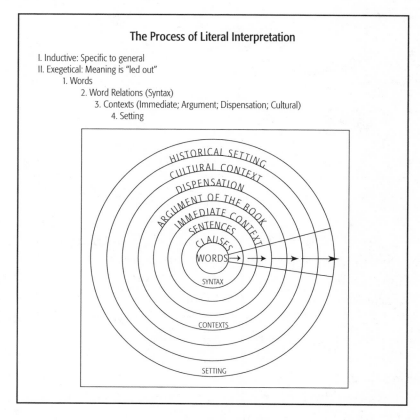

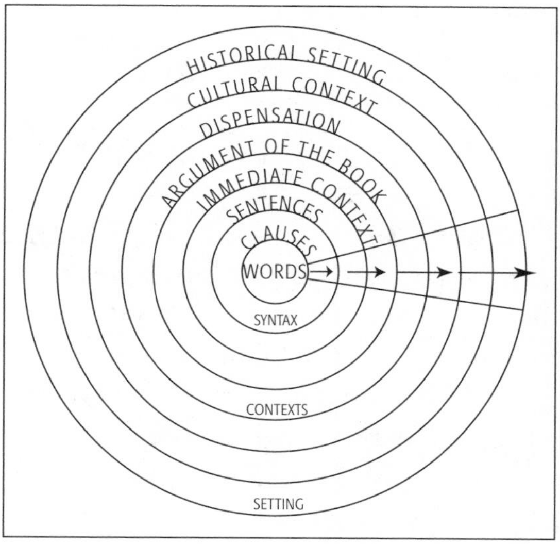

Figure 2.2

Guiding Theological Principles

Literal interpretation is guided by at least seven theological convictions about the nature of written revelation, briefly summarized in figure 2-3 and described as follows:[40]

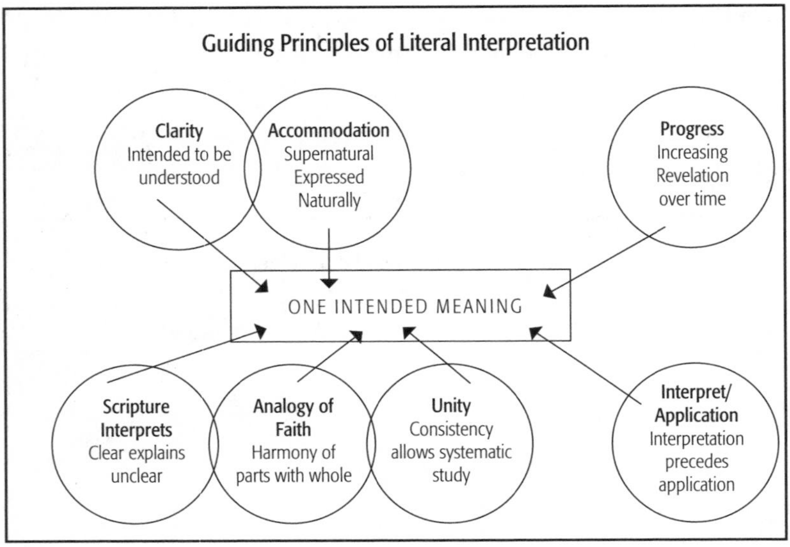

Figure 2.3

1. *The Principle of Clarity.* This principle holds that God communicated with man for the purpose of being understood. Thus, the single meaning of biblical texts is not only possible, but divinely intended. "By use of scientific philology and the illumination of the Spirit we arrive at the clarity of Scripture, and there is no need to resort to the Church," wrote Baptist theologian Bernard Ramm, explaining the Protestant view of clarity in contrast to that of Roman Catholicism.[41] Rather than looking for elaborate systems of codes, symbols, or keys to unlock hidden meanings, the interpreter guided by this principle will expect to discover what God disclosed through "the laws of language."[42] This does not mean that golden nuggets of truth all lie exposed on the surface of Scripture, but that they may be discovered by normal literary "mining" practices when illumined by the Holy Spirit.

2. *The Principle of Accommodation* refers to God's use of words to express supernatural realities in natural terminology so that people can grasp concepts that would otherwise be incomprehensible. Examples include references to God's having eyes (Gen. 6:8), arms (Ps. 44:3), wings (Ps. 91:4), etc. Without God's willingness to condescend to the limits of finite human understanding, there would be no clarity. The close association of these principles is represented in figure 2-3 by the overlapping circles.

3. *The Principle of the Progress of Revelation*, briefly discussed earlier in this chapter, refers to increasing revelation over time. While the Hebrew Scriptures are no less God-breathed, they are foundational to the New Testament built upon them. This principle is succinctly summarized in the following statement attributed to Saint Augustine (A.D. 354-430):

> *The New is in the Old contained,*
> *The Old is in the New explained.*
> *The New is in the Old latent.*
> *The Old is in the New patent.*[43]

4. *The "Scripture Interprets Scripture" Principle* refers to the claim of Martin Luther and other reformers that instead of appealing to the magisterium of the Roman Catholic church to provide the meaning of a biblical text, "the entire Holy Scripture is the context and guide for understanding the particular passages of Scripture."[44] In other words, the clearest passages of Scripture on a given topic or doctrine render the meaning of less-clear passages on the same subject.

5. *The Principle of the Analogy of the Faith* is closely related to the previous principle. It means that the correct meaning of a given passage will never contradict the teaching of Scripture as a whole on that point.[45]

6. *The Unity of Scripture Principle* assumes the integrity of revelation as given by one author. In the words of Bernard Ramm, this principle holds that "there is one system of truth or theology contained in Scripture, and therefore all doctrines must cohere or agree with each other."[46] While deductions must never be imposed upon a given text, this principle provides the basis for a systematic study of Scripture in

order to discover what "the Bible teaches" on a given topic or doctrine. It also provides a corrective of methods that assert multiple meanings in Scripture.[47]

7. *The Principle of Interpretation and Application* recognizes that, while a text has but one meaning, it may have many applications. Accordingly, the applications of a passage must never be confused with its interpretation, which must always precede its applications in the process of expositing the text of Scripture.[48]

Together, the guiding principles of literal hermeneutics should be appreciated for what they are, without expecting more than they can provide. Simply following them does not impart the skill needed to "play the game," any more than following the rules of tennis makes one a champion. By the same token, skillful play *without* rules is not tennis! This is the conclusion of David Neff's evaluation of I. Howard Marshall's book *Beyond the Bible*. In reference to historic Church councils and creeds, Marshall contends that in moving from revelation to doctrine, more is needed than rules of interpreting Scripture. Neff's conclusion has merit: "The rules for interpreting Scripture can take us only so far, but as Marshall and Vanhoozer demonstrate, we can learn a lot by watching great interpreters playing at their finest."[49]

Literal Interpretation

Literal interpretation stands in contrast to *allegorical interpretation*, which holds that the real, spiritual meaning of Scripture lies hidden beneath the actual words the writer used.[50] The disadvantage and danger of allegorical interpretation is that it provides no objective safeguard against a person's bringing *personal* prejudices and assumptions to the text. It allows the imposition of a theological system upon the text rather than allowing the text to correct the system.[51] William Ames (1576-1633) stated the case against allegorical interpretation with even greater brevity and poignancy: "Anything which does not mean one thing surely means nothing."[52]

Conversely, the great advantage of literal interpretation is its recognition that meaning is grounded in objective fact, thus eliminating the need for speculation and protecting the interpretive process against subjectivity. Literal interpretation is consistent with the inductive method of Bible study, which moves from observation of what the text actually says to a general principle on the basis of specific textual data.[53] Inductive Bible study is, in turn, consistent with the conservative view of Scripture itself, which holds that "God has communicated with us, in just the way we communicate with other people."[54] Respect for the normal, natural use of language recognizes the connotative[55] value of literary figures of speech, such as similes, metaphors, parables, analogies, puns, and even allegories.[56] However, unless there is good reason within a given Scripture passage to regard its language as figurative, words should be taken in their normal, natural sense.

An example of figurative language is found in Galatians 2:9. James, Cephas, and John are described as pillars of the Church in Jerusalem. Pillars physically support buildings. It is obvious that Paul, the writer, did not mean that these three men served the Church by holding up a physical structure. He clearly meant that the Church, as a spiritual structure, depended on these spiritual leaders as a building rests upon foundational posts. So, while the word translated "pillars" is used to picture another reality, this does not give the reader license to read into the word *pillars* a meaning foreign to it. The figurative meaning of language is related to, and governed by, its plain, literal sense.

The text of our model sermon, 1 John 2:1-2, refers to Christ as "an Advocate" (NKJV). Does John use the term *parakletos* in the plain-literal (and more general) sense to denote a person "called to one's side"?[57] The ESV reflects this interpretation, paraphrasing *parakletos*: "one who speaks to the Father in our defense." Rendering the idea behind the word, rather than translating it, makes for easier reading. But did John simply describe a function the Lord serves?

Another possibility is that John used the word as a figure of speech intended to vividly portray the Lord as the believer's defense attorney before the Judge in a court of law. By capitalizing *Advocate*, the translators of the New King James Version; New American Standard Bible; and New American Standard Bible, Updated Edition, indicate their understanding of the term as an official title. This would mean that Jesus' advocacy results from His *being* the believer's representative, which is an outcome of His being "Jesus Christ the righteous ... the propitiation for our sins" (1 Jn. 2:1-2 NKJV).

The point is, literal interpretation calls for an effort to investigate this question on the assumption that words mean something, and that it is the words of Scripture themselves that God breathed (see Matthew 5:18 and Luke 16:17), not the ideas with which people invest them.[58]

The fact that every fulfilled Bible prophecy recorded has been fulfilled *literally* strongly supports literal interpretation. None have been fulfilled in ways that required a spiritual, mystical, or subjective interpretation of the prediction. It has been well said, therefore, that "when the plain sense of Scripture makes sense, seek no other sense, lest it be nonsense."[59]

When literal interpretation is applied to biblical texts in the original language, the process is called *exegesis*.[60] This word comes from two Greek words that mean "to lead out." It describes the process of *leading out* the meaning of a word, phrase, clause, sentence, paragraph, etc., by observing the grammatical construction and ways in which words relate to each other in their various contexts. The opposite of exegesis is *eisegesis*, which refers to reading meanings *into* the text.[61]

The following diagram gives a schematic overview of the process of literal interpretation (see figure 2-4). Notice that the author's intended meaning in the original context is the "interpretation" determined by inductive Bible study. When the meaning is generalized and stated as a timeless truth, it is called a "principle." When the principle is extended into new and different situations without distorting the original meaning, the results are called "applications."[62]

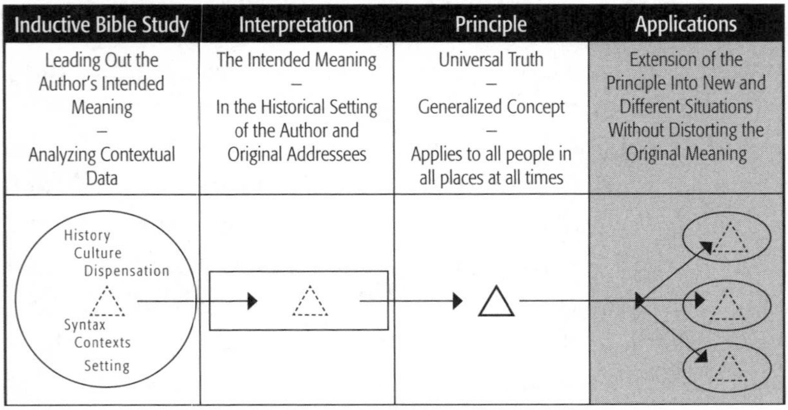
Inductive Bible Study
Interpretation
Principle
Applications
Leading Out the Author's Intended Meaning – Analyzing Contextual Data
The Intended Meaning – In the Historical Setting of the Author and Original Addressees
Universal Truth – Generalized Concept – Applies to all people in all places at all times
Extension of the Principle Into New and Different Situations Without Distorting the Original Meaning
History
Culture
Dispensation
Syntax
Contexts
Setting

Figure 2.4

Expository Communication, The Conveyance of God's Message

Discovering what God meant by what He said is the basis for expository preaching. *Homiletics* is a word used in reference to "the science and art of preparing and delivering the Word of God. It is the framing of the message. It is taking gold and putting a silver frame around it. It is conveying through the spoken word and through life, the words of truth."[63]

The following table shows the distinctions and relationships between hermeneutics, homiletics, and public speaking.[64] (See figure 2-5.)

To remove homiletics from figure 2-5 would imply public speaking of raw biblical data. This would be like serving uncooked agricultural products and calling it a meal. Walter Kaiser's assertion on this point is sure to receive the reader's "amen!":

> Nothing can be more dreary and grind the soul and spirit of the Church more than can a dry, lifeless recounting of Biblical episodes apparently unrelated to the present. The pastor who delivers this type of sermon, reflecting his seminary exegesis class, bombards his bewildered audience with a maze of historical, philological and critical detail so that the text drops lifeless in front of the listener.[65]

Hermeneutics	Homiletics	Public Speaking
Interpretation	**Preparation**	Presentation
Foundation	**Building**	Exhibition
Argument	**Arrangement**	Pronouncement
Grasping	**Grouping**	Giving
Outlook	**Outline**	Outlet

Figure 2.5

Homiletics without hermeneutics, on the other hand, could be like a very attractive plate of poisonous toadstools— pretty to look at but potentially deadly! And without public speaking, homiletics on the basis of good hermeneutics is like exquisite cuisine that is never brought from the kitchen to the patron of a restaurant. To nourish listeners with presentations of God's Word that are inviting, healthy, and easily digested, the expository communicator cannot neglect the essential bridge-building work of homiletics.

In his book *The Preacher's Portrait*, John Stott compares and contrasts the preacher's various roles and responsibilities according to Scripture. The imagery of a steward, or household manager, emphasizes the preacher as "the trustee and dispenser of another's person's goods."

> So the preacher is a steward of God's mysteries, that is, of the self-revelation which God has entrusted to men and which is now preserved in the Scriptures. The preacher's message, therefore, is derived not directly from the mouth of God, as if he were a prophet or apostle, nor from his own mind, like the false prophets, nor undigested from the minds and mouths of other men, like the babbler, but from the once revealed and now recorded Word of God, of which he is a privleged steward.[66]

Stott observes the various directions in which the preacher, as a steward, is to "be found faithful" (1 Cor. 4:2 NKJV). His trustworthiness is to be "to the householder who has appointed him to the task; … to the household who are looking to him for sustenance; and … to the deposit which is committed to his trust."[67]

Expository Communication, Connecting with Contemporaries

With respect to the steward's household, the better a speaker and audience know one another, the better the bridge that can be built from the Bible to the listener. In his excellent book *Teaching to Change Lives*, Howard G. Hendricks asserts, "You are not interested simply in inculcating principles; you want to infect people. Therefore, *the way people learn determines how you teach*."[68] Richards and Bredfeldt put the same idea this way: "Teach people, not just lessons. It is people we are called to serve. It is people Christ died to redeem. Be sure that it is the student who is your focus in teaching, not simply the delivery of Bible content."[69]

Though the apostle Paul may not have been well acquainted with anyone in his audience at Athens, his sermon in Acts 17 reflects audience analysis. "He begins in his students' world. He starts with where they live."[70] By referring to his observation of their idol "to an unknown God," Paul gained their attention and stimulated their interest in his declaration of the identity of the true and living God. When Paul addressed Jews, on the other hand, he proclaimed Christ as the one who fulfills the Hebrew Scriptures (Acts 24:14). Richards and Bredfeldt argue convincingly that Jesus knew people's needs and adapted His messages to meet them:

> Jesus geared His teaching to the needs and readiness of His students when He said, "1 have much more to say to you, more than you can now bear" (John 16:12). Jesus recognized the basic educational principle that the student's needs, interests, and readiness determines what is to be taught and how it is to be taught. Whether it was with Nicodemus (John 3), the woman at the well (John 4), the woman caught in adultery (John 8), Thomas in his doubt (John 20), or Peter in his guilt (John 21), Jesus understood human need and adjusted His approach accordingly.[71]

Jesus, Paul, and others certainly exemplify the principle of focusing the message meet their students' needs. It is doubtful that they would take issue with Hendricks's assertion: "Know your students. The more you know of their needs, the better able you are to meet them."[72] But, at the same time, while listeners' needs should certainly determine how the content of revelation is delivered, you cannot allow those needs to dictate the message itself. One who does so fails to serve the householder to whom he or she accounts as a steward, by failing to make the "deposit" of God's entrusted Word.

Ironically, when allowed to rule the roost, seeker sensitivity fails the very household the steward would please! As Richards and Bredfeldt state, "it is important for the creative Bible teacher to remember that basic human needs have not changed significantly over the millennia that have passed since the Scriptures were written."[73] This statement validates the needs theories of social scientists Abraham Maslow and Fredrick Herzberg, who hold that basic human needs (physical safety and relational needs) must be met before higher motivators (such as esteem and achievement) can be effectively addressed. Biblical communicators must distinguish between the *real* needs of people and the *desires* they often refer to as needs.

The constancy of real human needs partly explains why it is entirely possible to develop and deliver an effective sermon to complete strangers, as is often done by speakers at large gatherings and through the mass media. For this to occur, however, the speaker must establish a relational connection of some kind. The Son of God Himself, who alone explains the Father, did not do so from a distance, but came as a human being and tented among us (Jn. 1:18, 14). So Hendricks is on solid theological footing when he says to would-be Bible teachers, "You can impress people from a distance. But you can impact them only up close."[74] If the expository communicator is charged with building a bridge between the "then and there" of Bible times and the "here and now"[75] of his audiences, he must, as Haddon Robinson stated, "know his people as well as his message, and to acquire that knowledge he exegetes both the Scripture and the congregation."[76]

Summary and Conclusion

The Bible is God-given information about God for the purpose of making Him known to people, whose greatest need is to know Him in a life-changing, personal relationship. Granted the privilege of speaking for God to a contemporary audience, expository communicators are responsible for discovering what God meant by what He said. Yielding to the lure of popularity, the precepts of men, and the perversion of what passages actually teach, in part explains why sermons often communicate the preacher's message and authority, rather than God's.

When the source of one's sermon is the Scriptures, the preacher accepts the responsibility for bridging the communication gap created by its antiquity, difficulty, and foreignness to the listeners. The super-natural character of Scripture, the progress of revelation, the distinction between the redemptive and kingdom programs of God, and the derivation of truth revealed to others, call for spiritual discernment and skill.

Literal interpretation seeks the contextual meaning inductively, understanding that every word in the original language is God-breathed. In discovering the single meaning of texts, the interpreter is guided by theological assumptions about the nature of divine revelation. As principles are carefully drawn and extended into new and different situations of listeners, without distorting the original meaning, the preacher realizes the wedding of hermeneutics and public speaking and thus serves as a faithful steward and effective bridge builder.

What kind of messenger does God use to convey what He has to say from His Word to people living today? What is the nature of the messenger's role and relationships? Are *you* personally qualified to be the vehicle in which God is willing to transport what He meant in John 2: 1-2, to those willing to hear? These questions express the concerns of Chapter 3.

Discussion Questions

1. As different kinds of expository communication of Scripture, explain the differences between *preaching* and *teaching*.
2. How have you seen popularity, human precepts, or perversions of the Bible's text detract from a preacher's communication with God's authority? Give examples.
3. In your own words, what is the *communication gap*, and why does it exist?

4. Why is it so important to wed homiletics to hermeneutics?
5. Why do you agree or disagree that you can *impact people only up close*?
6. Explain the following terms:

hermeneutics	homiletics
inductive Bible study	exegesis
interpretation	allegorical interpretation
principle	applications

7. Explain the statement "Expository preachers are authoritative, not authoritarian."

CHAPTER 3

The Channel: Representing God as His Mouthpiece

Arthur B. Whiting once said, "Some consider only the message important, but the speaker makes the words of Scripture live. Homiletics is the method and the man, not just the method."[1] In keeping with this assertion, Donald Macleod wrote, "Preaching cannot be discussed apart from the preacher. It is time, then, for us to discover/rediscover the preacher: Who is he or she? In what are they involved? And why?"[2]

Chapter 2 answered these questions, in part.[3] Preachers build verbal and relational bridges to people far removed from the world and time of the Bible. But who, really, is qualified to speak for God? Is Howard Hendricks correct when he asserts, "What you *are* is far more important than what you say or do"?[4] If so, what kind of person can and does God use to articulate His message in a given generation? Let us begin by acknowledging His use of people—not only to speak for Him, but to be individual incarnations of His revelation.

God Uses People

According to Scripture, God has chosen to use people, as His spokespersons, or mouthpieces, to *reach* people. The writer of Hebrews began his epistle, "God, who at various times and in various ways spoke in time past to the fathers by the prophets, has in these last days spoken to us by His Son" (1:1-2 NKJV). Referring to His apostles (sent ones), Jesus prayed to the Father, "As You sent Me into the world, I also have sent them into the world" (John 17:18 NKJV). And in Romans 10:14-15, Paul asks, "How then shall they call on Him in whom they have not believed? And how shall they believe in Him of whom they have not heard? And how shall they hear without a preacher? And how shall they preach unless they are sent? As it is written: 'How beautiful are the feet of those who preach the gospel of peace, who bring glad tidings of good things!'" (NKJV).

Preachers are bearers of the message God sent them to communicate to others on His behalf. The human factor is not just the mechanism for sowing the Word like seed (see Matthew 13:3, 19); it is also the medium through which the Word is sent and received. As Hendricks noted, "God's method is always incarnational. He loves to take the truth and wrap it in a person."[5] With the exception of the apostles and prophets of the first-century Church, preachers convey God's message already inscripturated through the personalities of those chosen to write it. Again, it is the writer of Hebrews who asks, "How shall we escape if we neglect so great a salvation, which at the first began to be spoken by the Lord, and was confirmed to us by those who heard Him, God also bearing witness both with signs and wonders, with various miracles, and gifts of the Holy Spirit, according to His own will?" (2:3-4 NKJV).

To declare the meaning of a passage such as 1 John 2:1-2, then, is to relate revelation recorded by the apostle John. He was impacted as an eyewitness of the incarnate Son of God as well as guided infallibly by the Spirit of God. (See 2 Peter 1:21.) By the time the message is communicated to the contemporary audience, it will be filtered through one more personality, that of the preacher. (See figure 3-1.)

When Hendricks goes on to describe this process, he says of God, "He takes a clean individual and drops him or her in the midst of a corrupt society, and that person—because of what he knows, feels, and does—convincingly demonstrates the power of God's grace."[6] Assuming this is true, how *clean* must a person be? Exactly what kind of person can and does God use to articulate the truths of Scripture?

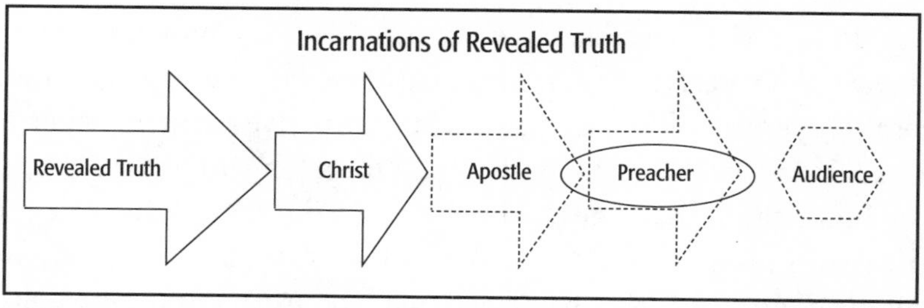

Figure 3.1

God Uses Imperfect People

According to Scripture, God uses whom He will to speak His word. He used Jonah—not just despite his uncooperative attitude, but partly *because* of it.[7] Long before that, the Lord used Balaam's donkey to speak for Him! (See Numbers 22). In Luke 19:40, Jesus declared that if those celebrating His triumphal entry into Jerusalem remained silent, the rocks would cry out. His point was that while God has chosen to speak through people, He is not limited to human agencies, let alone clean ones. In Philippians 1:18, Paul rejoiced that, whether in pretense or in truth, Christ was being proclaimed. Whether people preach out of selfish ambition or pure motives affects their reward, but not God's ability to use them.

Balaam was a false prophet, hired by Moab's king, Balak, to curse the Israelites (see Numbers 22-24). In his willingness to receive a diviner's fee, Balaam became a symbol of mercenary motivation in ministry (see 2 Peter 2:15). Yet despite Balaam's every intention and effort to curse God's people, Yahweh used him to bless His people instead. To this day, the Oracles of Balaam[8] stand as a testimony of God's ability to give His pure words through an impure vessel. Even the sinless Son of God became man by being conceived and born of a woman who confessed her need of a Savior (Luke 1:47). So God is not dependent upon human perfection in those who represent Him verbally.

Neither does one's credibility with students depend upon perfection. Hendricks says, "Kids aren't looking for a perfect teacher, just an honest one, and a growing one."[9] In fact, the teacher, he states, is "primarily a learner, a student among students."[10] If, as Hendricks also states, "failure is a necessary part of the learning process," then God can weave your past, forgiven sins into the fabric of your testimony to strengthen your credibility. David could not have penned either Psalm 32 or Psalm 51 without the pathos of a forgiven sinner.

Understand that these observations do not advocate or make light of sin in any way. The answer to Paul's question in Romans 6:1, "Shall we continue in sin that grace may abound?" (NKJV), is "Certainly not! How shall we who died to sin live any longer in it?" (v. 2 NKJV). Paul describes his own self-discipline in terms of a boxer who delivers eye-blackening blows to his own body: "I discipline my body and bring it into subjection, lest, when I have preached to others, I myself should become disqualified" (1 Cor. 9:27 NKJV).

God's spokespeople are naturally unnecessary, unworthy, inadequate, and unprofitable. They are unnecessary because, as we have seen, God can work apart from them. They are unworthy because they owe their existence, usefulness, and calling to God. In 1 Timothy 1:12-13, the apostle Paul stated, "I thank Christ Jesus our Lord who has enabled me, because He counted me faithful, putting me into the ministry, although I was formerly a blasphemer, a persecutor, and an insolent man; but I obtained mercy because I did it ignorantly in unbelief" (NKJV).

And God's spokespersons are naturally inadequate. Paul was quick to remind the Corinthians that neither he nor his co-ministers could boast of self-sufficiency: "Not that we are adequate in ourselves to consider anything as coming from ourselves," he said, "but our adequacy is from God" (2 Cor. 3:5 NASB95).

As finite mortals in unredeemed bodies, all preachers are unequal to their task apart from the adequacy that comes from God. They are unprofitable because their service never exceeds their duty. They can never repay their debt of love.

Still, those who speak *for* God are created, chosen, called, cleansed, and commissioned *by* God. Like the prophet Jeremiah and the apostle Paul, each of God's spokesmen has been formed in the womb for the task he would be given. In Jeremiah, the prophet quotes the words of Yahweh in describing his call to speak for God:

> Then the word of the LORD came to me, saying: "Before I formed you in the womb I knew you; before you were born I sanctified you; I ordained you a prophet to the nations." Then said I: "Ah, Lord GOD! Behold, 1 cannot speak, for I *am* a youth." But the LORD said to me: "Do not say, 'I am a youth: for you shall go to all to whom I send you, and whatever I command you, you shall speak. Do not be afraid of their faces, for I am with you to deliver you," says the LORD. Then the LORD put forth His hand and touched my mouth, and the LORD said to me: "Behold, I have put My words in your mouth. See, I have this day set you over the nations and over the kingdoms, to root out and to pull down, to destroy and to throw down, to build and to plan!" (1:4-10 NKJV)

Similarly, Paul said, "But when it pleased God, who separated me from my mother's womb and called me through His grace, to reveal His Son in me, that I might preach Him among the Gentiles, I did not immediately confer with flesh and blood, nor did I go up to Jerusalem to those who were apostles before me; but I went to Arabia, and returned again to Damascus" (Gal. 1:15-17 NKJV).

Luke refers to John the Baptist as "finishing his course" (Acts 13:25 NKJV). Paul told Timothy, "fulfill your ministry" (2 Tim. 4:5 NKJV). In his epistle to the Ephesians, Paul speaks of believers as God's "workmanship created in Christ Jesus for good works, which God prepared beforehand that we should walk in them" (2:10 NKJV). And author Andrew Blackwood once commented, "The preacher himself is God's 'poem' (another translation of the Greek *poiema, workmanship*, Eph. 2:10)."[11] So, as a minister of God's Word, before taking up the task of fashioning a sermon, recognize first that you are a "piece of work," God's creative composition. Your content and delivery should bear your signature, just as the writings of David, Peter, John, and Paul incorporate their unique personalities.

In addition to God's sovereign work of cleansing imperfect human beings and using them as His representatives, He also places them in the body of Christ according to His will (1 Cor. 12:4-11, 18).

God Gifts the Imperfect People He Uses

Assuming that one is among those given to Christ by the Father (see John 6:37; 10:16; 17:6, 24), he or she must also be given to the Church (Eph. 4:11) by Christ and/or be gifted to speak (see 1 Peter 4:11 and Romans 12:6-8). Those with the nonspeaking gifts, such as serving, giving, mercy, ruling, etc., are to specialize in the capacity of their spiritual gifts.[12] Those with speaking gifts, such as prophecy, exhortation, and teaching, as well as those given to the Church to equip the saints for service, including evangelists, pastors, and teachers, may or may not function in one of the two local church offices of elder/overseer and deacon (see 1 Timothy 3:1-13 and Titus 1:5-9). As illustrated in the following diagram, these designations result in a variety of speaking orientations, A through C-3.[13] (See figure 3-2.)

Depending on where an individual fits at a given time, his or her speaking ministry will be affected. Preaching elders may reprove, rebuke, and exhort with authority not exercised in the same way by a Sunday school teacher or street evangelist (see Titus 2: 15). (We encourage you to explore for yourself the relation between the kinds of ministers Christ gives to the Church, the nature of the speaking gifts, and implications of church offices. Such exploration is beyond the scope of this book.) But no matter how one's speaking gift can be described, when an imperfect but regenerate human is gifted to speak, the issue of character is paramount.

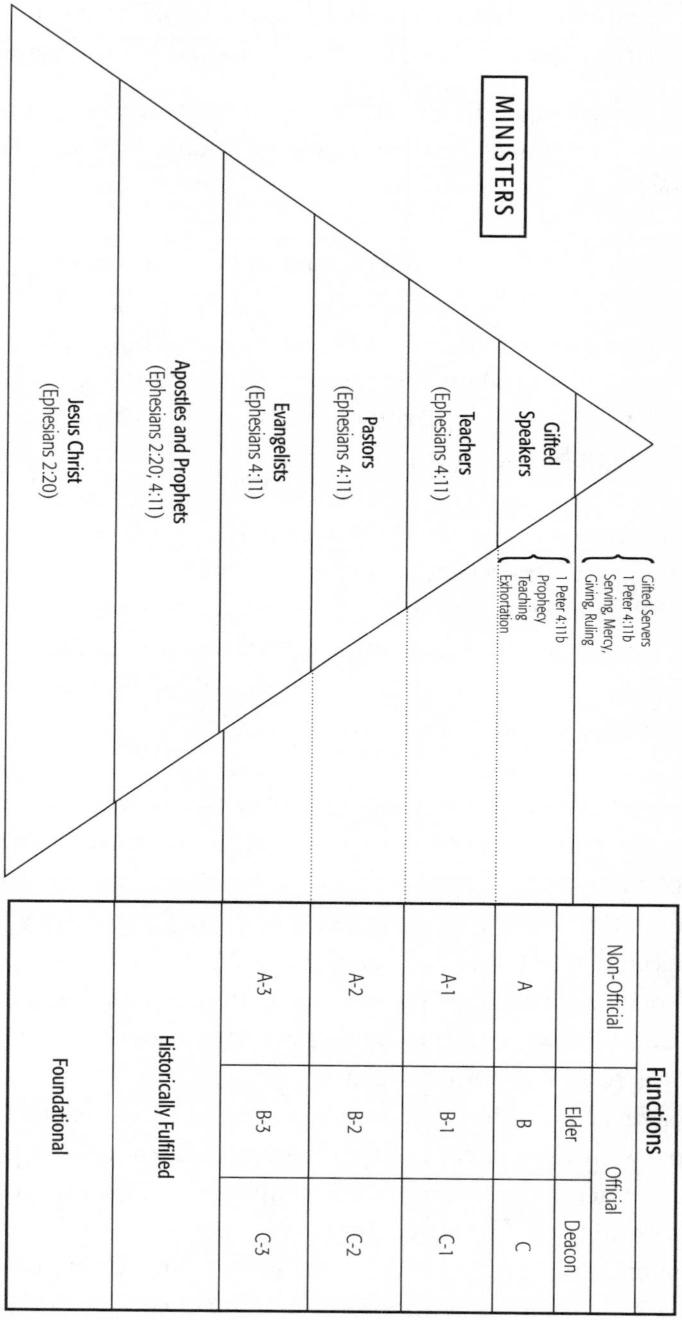
MINISTERS
Gifted Servers
1 Peter 4:11b
Serving, Mercy, Giving, Ruling
1 Peter 4:11b
Prophecy
Teaching
Exhortation
Gifted Speakers
Teachers
(Ephesians 4:11)
Pastors
(Ephesians 4:11)
Evangelists
(Ephesians 4:11)
Apostles and Prophets
(Ephesians 2:20; 4:11)
Jesus Christ
(Ephesians 2:20)
Functions
Non-Official
Official
Elder
Deacon
A
B
C
A-1
B-1
C-1
A-2
B-2
C-2
A-3
B-3
C-3
Historically Fulfilled
Foundational

Figure 3.2

God Deserves the Honor of Godly Character in the Imperfect People He Gifts and Uses[14]

Credibility is crucial to effective communication. Remo Fausti and Edward McGlone, in their book entitled *Understanding Oral Communication*, state:

> Many studies of source credibility have been conducted. They have identified three factors as the major determinants of the credibility of a public speaker: his perceived trustworthiness, his perceived expertness, and his general ability as a public speaker.
>
> Perceived trustworthiness refers to those personality traits which listeners associate with a speaker who has their best interests in mind. Whatever a speaker can do to create a friendly, helpful, ethical, generous, just and unselfish image should increase his credibility.[15]

In a word, the persuasive element they just described is *character*. From the standpoints of social science and philosophy, character may be thought of as part of nonverbal communication which either harmonizes with the words that are spoken, or creates dissonance resulting in distraction, distrust and confusion. John Milton Gregory's question applies to preachers perhaps more than to anyone else. He asks, "How can the teacher's manner fail to be earnest and inspiring when his subject matter is so rich in radiant reality?"[16]

Ancient philosopher Socrates summarized the essence of communication with the concepts he called *ethos*, *pathos*, and *logos*. "*Ethos* embraced character. *Pathos* embraced compassion. *Logos* embraced content."[17] According to Hendricks, Socrates thought of *ethos* as "establishing the credibility of the teacher—his credentials." He understood that who you are is far more important than what you say or do, because it *determines* what you say or do. Who you are as a person is your greatest leverage as a speaker, a persuader, a communicator. You must be attractive to those who would learn from you. They must trust you, and the more they trust you, the more you communicate to them."[18]

If it is true that "credibility always precedes communication,"[19] then part of earning the right to be heard involves your willingness to be vulnerable, to let people know your background, experiences, and struggles. Hendricks says, "Great teachers ... communicate *as* total persons, and they communicate *to* the total person of their hearers."[20] He is not exhorting speakers to add new dimensions to their speeches. Essentially, he is saying that great speakers recognize that "words account for only seven percent of everything we communicate to others,"[21] but listeners are attentive to the *other* 93 percent! So, though "content counts," say Richards and Bredfeldt, "[creative Bible teachers] know that ... it is students that they teach."[22] Knowing one's audience is critical. Perhaps this explains why Paul described his ministry with the church at Thessalonica as he did:

> So, affectionately longing for you, we were well pleased to impart to you not only the gospel of God, but also our own lives, because you had become dear to us. For you remember, brethren, our labor and toil; for laboring night and day, that we might not be a burden to any of you, we preached to you the gospel of God. You are witnesses, and God also, how devoutly and justly and blamelessly we behaved ourselves among you who believe; as you know how we exhorted, and comforted, and charged every one of you, as a father does his own children, that you would walk worthy of God who calls you into His own kingdom and glory. For this reason we also thank God without ceasing, because when you received the word of God which you heard from us, you welcomed it not as the word

> of men, but as it is in truth, the word of God, which also effectively works in you who believe. (I Thess. 2:8-13 NKJV)

The persuasive ability of any kind of interpersonal communication is enhanced when listeners perceive that the speaker can be trusted. So, your character is important in expository communication of Scripture, because you, the preacher, represent God to people. When your sermon fully communicates God's message, you are demonstrating the attributes of God that mortals can reflect.[23] But to the extent that your message is God's, but your character is ungodly, you misrepresent the one whose mission you are to fulfill. You fail to be the ambassador that Paul and his companions were (Eph. 6:20; 2 Cor. 5:20). Listeners leave with unworthy thoughts of God when those who speak for Him portray Him as other than He is. That this can be done through one's life as well as through one's language accounts for such clichés as "Practice what you preach," "Walk the talk," "Your actions speak so loudly that I can't hear your words," "People don't care how much you know until they know how much you care," etc.

From the standpoint of Scripture and theology, godly character is essential to an effective testimony, and an inseparable part of what it means to glorify God (1 Cor. 10:31-33). Speakers stand before their audiences as examples to be followed. Paul exhorted the Corinthians to imitate him as he also imitated Christ, and as children imitate their father (1 Cor. 4:14-16; 11:1). In Ephesians 5:1, he told his readers: "Be imitators of God as dear children" (NKJV). A comparison of these statements leads to the conclusion that to pattern one's life after Paul's was to be like Christ and God. Preachers of such exemplary character motivate teachable listeners to learn.

Demonstrating God's character in your behavior displays His attributes. This is what it means to glorify God, which is the chief end of man, according to the Westminster Confession of Faith.[24] As a creature made in God's likeness and saved by His grace, every believer owes it to God to present his or her body as a living sacrifice that is holy and acceptable, and to work toward achieving the life transformation that results from a mind constantly in the process of renewal (Rom.

12:1-2). How much more must this be true of the one seeking through the spoken word to present every man complete in Christ (Col. 1:28)! Because it is God who is at work in the believer, both to will and do His good pleasure (Phil. 2:13), the expository preacher has every reason to be a person of godly character, willing even to endure hardship (1 Tim. 4:6-16; 6:11; 2 Tim. 3:14; 4:5). But such character is not the result of personal determination alone. It is the fruit produced by the indwelling Holy Spirit when the believer yields to His control.

God Produces Godly Character in the People He Uses

The Holy Spirit's indwelling of the believer's body results from having once been baptized (placed) into the body of Christ as a member (1 Cor. 12:13: Rom. 12:1-5). Without His presence, a person cannot be "in the Spirit," or even belong to God (Rom. 8:9). This baptism in the Holy Spirit occurs at the moment one believes on the Lord Jesus Christ and is justified.[25] It is properly evidenced by baptism with water as soon after as possible. (See Acts 2:41; 9:18; 10:47-48; 16:15,33.)

As an expository preacher, you must not only be "spiritual" in this sense of having Christ in your life (Col. 1:27), but you must also be "spiritual" by continually being filled with (or controlled by) the Holy Spirit" (Eph. 5:18). The present passive imperative of the verb (pronounced *play-ra-oh*), "to fill," indicates the believer's responsibility to obey this command—continually—while depending upon the Holy Spirit, who exercises the control and produces His fruit (see Galatians 5:22-23).

Spirit-filled preaching, then, occurs when you, a regenerate individual, proclaim the Word of God, under His control. It is *anointed* in that the Holy Spirit in your life *is* God's anointing (see 1 John 2:27). This does not nullify your unique personality and style, nor does it render unnecessary your diligence as a student or your responsibility to maintain your "walk in the Spirit" (see Galatians 5:16, 25). On the contrary, a person is never more his true self than when he is fulfilling the purpose for which God created and called him.[26]

Personal growth that is Christlike integrates the physical, social, intellectual, and emotional aspects of one's personality by obedience to God's Word (I Thess. 5:23). In Luke 2:52 we are told, "And Jesus kept increasing in wisdom and stature, and in favor with God and men" (NASB95). Hendricks asserts that proper growth in any of these areas cannot be isolated from appropriate growth in all of them.[27] The Spirit-filled preacher never stops learning, growing and changing in greater conformity to Christ.[28] This accounts for the passion to communicate.[29] It also requires some kind of education.

Spirit-Filled Preachers Make Good Use of Natural Abilities

It has been said that "there are three kinds of preachers: those who you cannot listen to–they turn you off; those who you can listen to–they can be tolerated; and those who you must listen to–they demand attention."[30] The difference is not always a matter of spirituality. You also need to possess and develop natural abilities, including the capacities to think clearly and speak frankly and forcefully. A good speaker does not mumble, but enunciates every word. We will discuss these and other aspects of sermon delivery in further detail in Chapter 8.

The goal of any ongoing education, formal or informal, should be to enable you to understand and evaluate the contextual data of Scripture. This includes geographical, historical, dispensational, cultural, literary, grammatical, and syntactical information. Your ability to read and analyze the text in its original language shows respect for the fact that the very words of Scripture are inspired. Facility in Hebrew and Greek exegesis reduces dependence upon the expertise of others and enhances your ability to speak with the authority of firsthand information.

Summary and Conclusion

God has chosen to use imperfect people, whom He redeems, gifts, and places in the Church to be His spokespersons. The Holy Spirit produces His fruit in the life of these believers who, having been baptized in the Spirit at conversion, yield to His control through moment-by-moment obedience to His Word. As the Spirit works to conform them to the likeness of Christ, they will grow in every aspect of their personalities. Godly character enhances their credibility as preachers, makes their testimonies effective, and glorifies God by displaying His attributes. But in order to speak with skill and with the authority of an exegetical theologian, every preacher must be trained. The following diagram illustrates the qualified preacher. (See figure 3-3.)

The Qualified Preacher

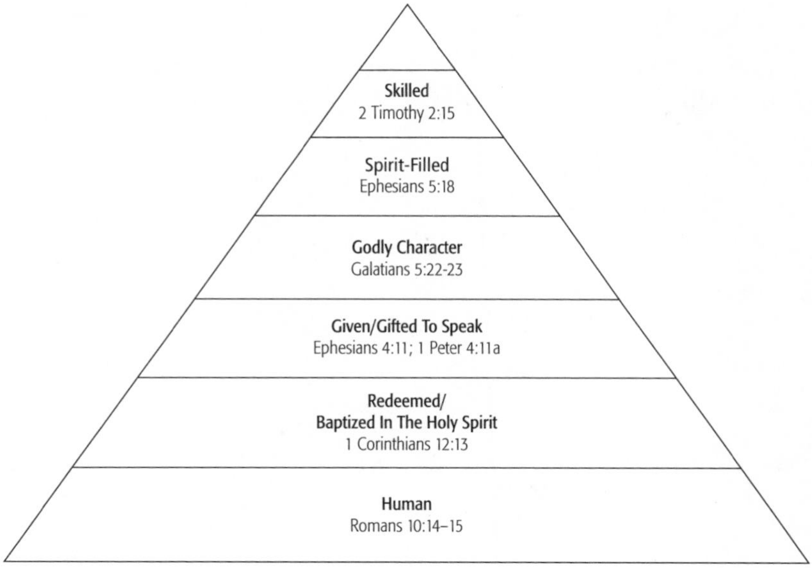

Figure 3.3

Discussion Questions

1. How would you explain, biblically, the apparent effectiveness of preachers who are later discovered to have been leading a double life of immorality?

2. How would you explain, biblically, the apparent ineffectiveness of preachers whose service appears to be faithful with respect to character?

3. Differentiate between baptism in the Holy Spirit, the filling of the Holy Spirit, and anointed preaching.

4. List the benefits of godly character in a minister of God's Word.

5. Describe how preaching can be affected by the type of minister one is, the spiritual gift a person possesses, and his or her relation to church office.

6. Evaluate the importance of a theological education for preachers, including study of the original languages.

CHAPTER 4

The Challenge: Bridging the Communication Gap

In Chapter 2 we demonstrated that bridging the communication gap requires discovering Scripture's intended meaning and then preparing for its delivery in terms of listeners' real needs. Chapter 3 emphasized the preacher as the channel through whom God makes Himself known to others. With this dual assignment of communicating God's message through your preachment and personality, you now need a good method by which to provide its package.

This chapter will demonstrate the usefulness of the Whiting Method of homiletics in helping you meet the *challenge*. As professor Milton Jones once said, "There are other systems of homiletics and other good preachers. The strengths of the Whiting System are its combination of exegesis and homiletics, and that its effectiveness has been proven over time." Before introducing the method, some information about its namesake may be helpful.

A Brief Biography of Arthur B. Whiting

Arthur B. Whiting was born in England and educated at Cambridge, then at Cliff College. There, he met and studied under Samuel Chadwick, a famous English preacher and professor of exegesis and homiletics.[2] Whiting later came to the U.S. and attended Moody Bible Institute, Pittsburgh Xenia Seminary, and Dallas Theological Seminary, where he studied under Lewis Sperry Chafer. Whiting taught at the Philadelphia Bible Institute and served at First Baptist Church,

New York, before proceeding to Biola College; Talbot Seminary; and Western Conservative Baptist Seminary in Portland, Oregon. While at Western Seminary, Whiting reoriented the curriculum to incorporate preaching with an exegetical emphasis.

In 1965, Milton William Jones presented a master of theology thesis at Western Conservative Baptist Seminary, entitled "An Investigation and Explanation of the Whiting System of Homiletics as a Practical Approach to Preaching." In his thesis, Jones stated, "The Method referred to in the thesis as the Whiting method, has come to the author from personal hours of instruction and involvement in homiletics from the homiletician, Dr. Arthur B. Whiting."[3] Milton Jones later became a professor of homiletics at Western Conservative Baptist Seminary and one of the lecturers under whose instruction we learned the system.[4]

Source of the Whiting Method

As a preacher, Chadwick discovered that to truly understand a passage of Scripture, he needed a solid study of the intricate parts of a passage, but "found that it was pedantic and boring. (Dry as ice and just as cold)."[5] He also recognized the need to bridge the gap between exegetical word studies and the expositional outline. Figure 4-1 represents an early depiction of his conception.

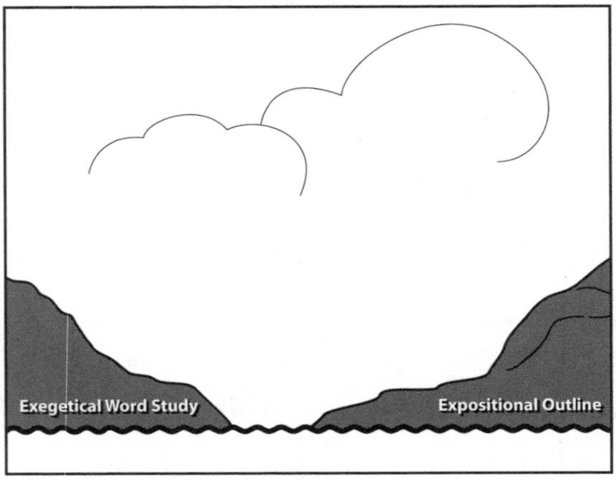

Figure 4.1

Whiting found that the principles of a passage provide the basis for the connecting link between exegesis and exposition. At the same time, he realized that principles alone did not provide a "roadway" to travel from one side to the other. (See figure 4-2.)

Whiting eventually discovered that a perfect roadway was provided by a statement of the principles in a single sentence called a "theme." (See figure 4-3.)

An Overview of the Method

The Whiting Method of homiletics may be described as a technique for producing an expository outline that develops a text's theme based on principles drawn from word studies. An hourglass is used to illustrate how exegetical data, including word studies, are summarized as principles before they are funneled into a theme, which is then broken down into an outline. (See figure 4-4.)

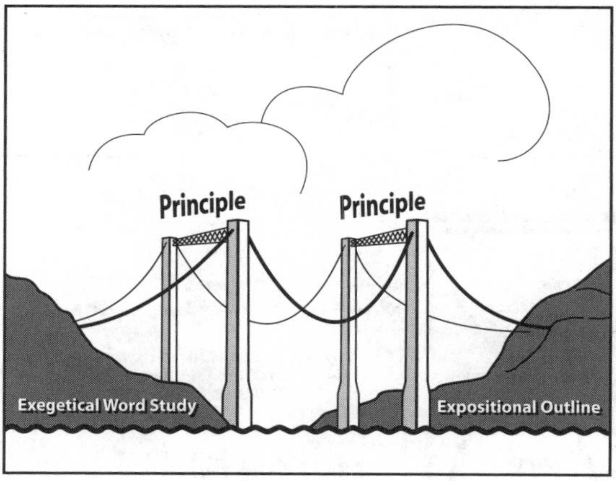

Figure 4.2

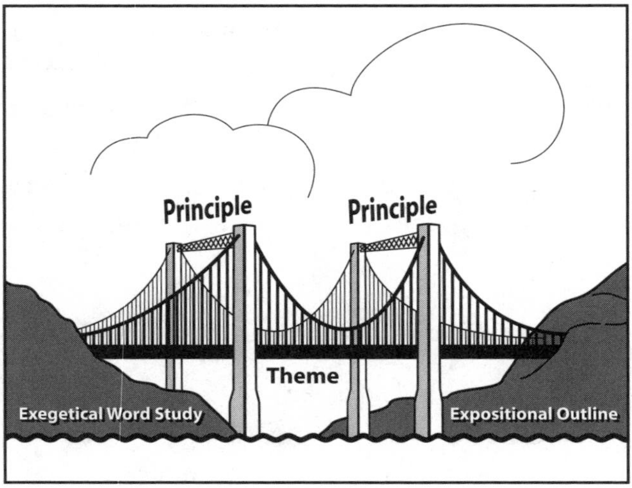

Figure 4.3

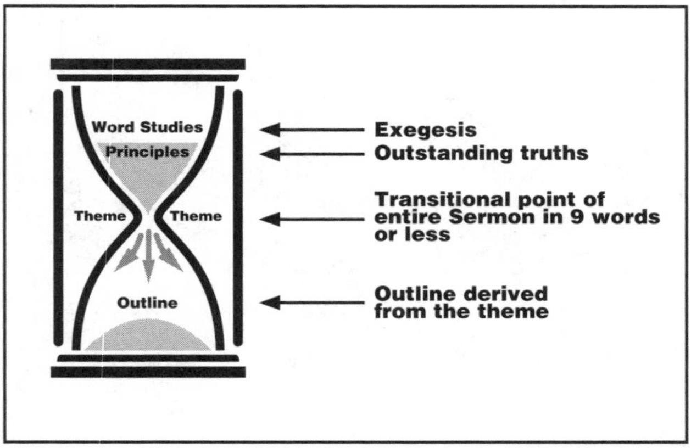

Figure 4.4

The Two Aspects of Sermon Preparation[6]

(See figure 4-5.)

The Elements of the Whiting Method

The *analysis* of a text begins with a determination of the text itself. Where does the author's unit of thought begin and end?[7] When these text boundaries are identified, the unit is called a *pericope*. Studying the words of the text within their contexts[8] is a process of taking apart what

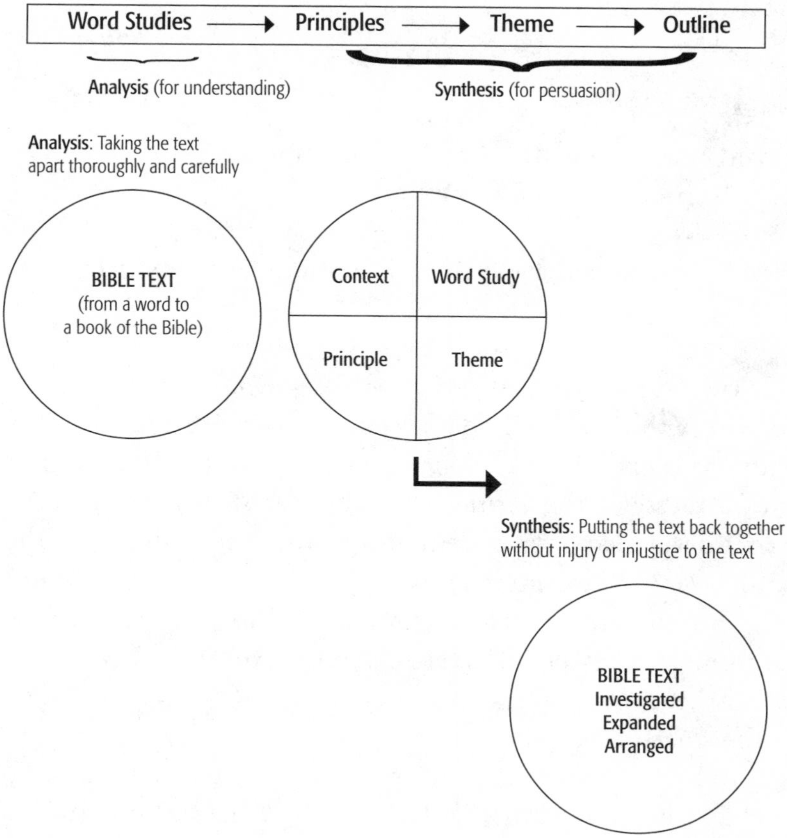

Figure 4.5

the Spirit of God superintended the writer to compose to express what He meant. The goal of textual analysis is to understand both the particles of meaning and the way they were assembled to form the whole thought of the writer. With this insight, the parts are then reassembled through a process called *synthesis* to produce statements of truth called *principles*. The principles are summarized in a single, epitomized principle called the *theme*. When the theme of a passage is divided into bitesize portions, the result is an *outline*. The outline traces the development of the theme from the text so that a sermon hearer can see from his own Bible what God's message is, and how he may be certain of it.

Analysis

The Text

The word *text* is from the Latin *textum*, meaning "woven." Whiting defined a sermon text as follows:

> "A text is that portion of Scripture out of which the message is woven."

Sermons may be *classified* as *topical*, *textual*, *expository*, or *devotional*. The Whiting Method seeks to expose the text of Scripture; therefore, it is expositional. When a single passage of Scripture is the basis of a message, the sermon is called *textual-expository*.[10] When a sermon is developed independent of the order and materials of the text, it is called *topical-expository*. However, when all of the Scriptures that relate to a topic are studied contextually, a more precise way to refer to the sermon developed is "textual-topical expository." In either case, expository sermons begin with texts.

The goal of expository preaching of a text, or topically related texts, is to bring the listener as close as possible to the meaning of the original text, in its context, in order to apply its unchanging truth to the listener's context. In view of this purpose, texts must be selected with care to include a complete thought. This unit of thought, or pericope, may consist of a single word, phrase, verse, paragraph, chapter, section, book, or group of books.[11]

A sermon could be preached on the *single word* "repent," in Matthew 3:2. Development might include a description of the original setting, the meaning of the original word, and the application of the principle. Paul's *phrase* describing Tychicus as "a beloved brother and faithful minister in the Lord," found in Ephesians 6:21 (NKJV), could be developed in connection with his relationship, service, and sphere. More commonly, a *verse* of Scripture, such as Luke 19:10, expresses a presentable thought: "For the Son of Man has come to seek and to save that which was lost" (NKJV). Usually, a *paragraph*, such as 1 John 2:1-2, will suggest itself as an appropriate sermon text. First Corinthians 13 is a good example of an entire *chapter* that lends itself to development in one sermon. A *section*, such as 2 Corinthians 8-9, has been surveyed under the heading "Holy Living Produces Holy Giving."[12] Entire books, such as Obadiah or Philemon, can be exposited as texts. It is even possible to proclaim the overall thrust of *groups of books*, such as the Pentateuch, synoptic Gospels, or the Epistles of John.[13]

Textual sermons are, by definition, limited to parameters within which a preacher finds it easier to focus the message and avoid wandering or speaking too broadly. Because textual sermons grow out of the structured thought that God Himself disclosed, they have the advantage of being more authoritative than purely topical sermons. This has the effect of stimulating the appetites of those who are genuinely interested in understanding what God has revealed rather than what a speaker may think. The sheer diversity of biblical literature and subjects provides the preacher of textual sermons with built-in variety and virility. Listeners are also able to remember and retrieve the points of sermons that were demonstrated from a text.

As a preacher, make sure that you carefully rely on the Holy Spirit when selecting texts. Develop the discipline of reading daily from the Bible and other Christian literature, and ideas for texts will come. It is also critical that you be intimately acquainted with your audience to determine when particular texts are most appropriate. Other determinants of text selection include preaching through books according to a long-term plan, seasonal days, personal experiences, natural disasters, world events, and the need for periodic preaching of classical passages.

Textual Analysis

Translation

Once you have selected a text, the process of textual analysis begins by translating it from the original language, or evaluating existing translations, depending on your abilities. This leads to the study of words in their various uses, relationships, and contexts.

Start by selecting and comparing translations classified as "essentially literal,"[14] such as the New King James Version (NKJV), New American Standard Bible, Updated Edition (NASB95), and the English Standard Version (ESV). Note any differences between them that may suggest the need for further study. (See figure 4-6.)

My little children, these things I write to you, so that you may not sin. And if anyone sins, we have <u>an Advocate</u> with the Father, Jesus Christ the righteous. (1 John 2:1 NKJV)

My little children, I am writing these things to you so that you may not sin. And if anyone sins, we have <u>an Advocate</u> with the Father, Jesus Christ the righteous. (1 John 2:1 NASU)

My little children, I am writing these things to you so that you may not sin. But if anyone does sin, we have <u>an advocate</u> with the Father, Jesus Christ the righteous. (1 John 2:1 ESV)

Notes:

1. These things I write (NKJV)	I am writing these things (NASU, ESV)
2. And if (NKJV, NASU)	But if (ESV)
3. Advocate (NKJV, NASU)	advocate (ESV)

Figure 4.6

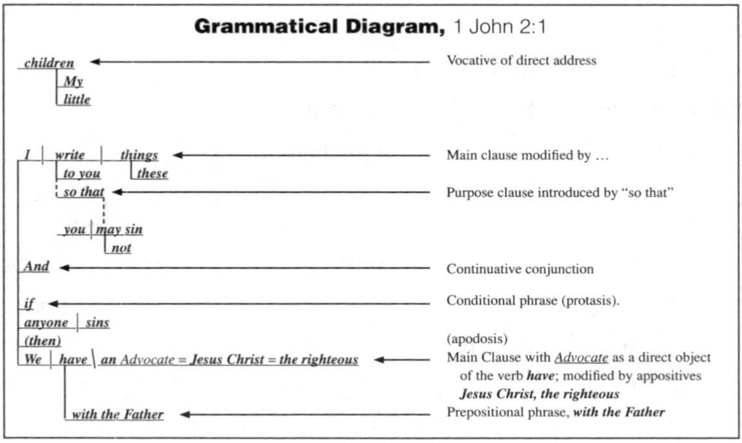

Figure 4.7

Diagram, Or Mechanical Layout[15]

Next, note the role of the word *advocate* in the sentence by diagramming the sentence, or making a mechanical layout. (See figures 4-7 and 4-8.)

Mechanical Layout, 1 John 2:1

My little children

I write these things
    to you
    so that you may not sin

and

    if
    anyone sins

    (then)

we have an Advocate = Jesus Christ the Righteous
    with the father

> A mechanical layout is a simpler way of showing the relationship between independent clauses and dependent clauses and phrases by indenting subordinate ideas.

Figure 4.8

Word Studies

A word study, as referred to in the Whiting Method, is the analysis of a word selected either because it (1) recurs in the text,[16] (2) is an unusual word (seldom if ever used in the Bible outside the text under study), or (3) is a difficult word that poses some kind of problem in grammatical construction or meaning. In 1 John 2:1, the words translated "advocate," and "propitiation:" require the kind of understanding and explanation that word studies can provide. (See figure 4-9.)

WORD STUDIES → PRINCIPLES → THEME → OUTLINE

Figure 4.9

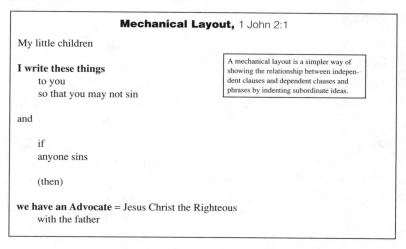

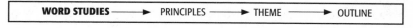

Tools

Word studies involve the use of various "tools," including lexicons, concordances, grammars, and theological dictionaries, for the purpose of grammatical analysis and determining the range of meanings.[17] Many of the tools needed to build a good theological library are available on Bible software such as the Logos.[18]

Range of Meaning

Grammatical analysis generally includes identification of the form, function, and syntax of the word under study. In contrast, the range of meaning for a New Testament word refers to the word's root meaning, its usage in Classical Greek, its treatment in the Septuagint, its use in the New Testament, and the meaning derived from these considerations. Such studies can be undertaken by non-language users (NLU), whose ability to study the text is limited to English, as well as those who are able to work in the original languages (LU).[19] However, the study of selected words from a passage provides only a small part of the data that is available only to the exegete.[20]

Advantages of Word Studies

The first and most obvious value of conducting word studies is that they help the student of Scripture understand the text, because a word's meaning is determined by its usage in context. Second, the information discovered often provides helpful illustrative material as well. A study of the word translated "Advocate" in 1 John 2:1, for example, opens the door to a courtroom, where a defense attorney represents the accused before a judge (see figures 4-10 and 4-11). Third, word studies build confidence in God's Word as listeners see that the very words He breathed were given intentionally, structured purposefully, and that their meaning can be established objectively.

[Note: The following material, marked LU (Language User), has some value for the non-language user (NLU) as well. Those who find the content too technical, however, are welcome to proceed to page 63.]

Advocate

Form

Masculine accusative singular noun

Function

Direct object of the verb "have," in the independent clause of 1 John 2:1a, joined to the first independent clause by "and," and therefore related to 1 John 2:1a.

Meaning
(English word)

The World Book Dictionary, 32.

"A person who speaks in favor; one who pleads or argues publicly for something, such as a proposal, belief, or theory; supporter." [<Old French *avocet*, learned borrowing from Latin advocatus, (originally) past participle of advocare summon , ad- to + vocare call]

(Greek word)
James Strong's *Exhaustive Concordance of The Bible*, 19.

#3875. παράκλητος par-ak'-lay-tos; an intercessor, console:--advocate, comforter, from #3874 παράκλησις , comfort, consolation, exhortation, entreaty, from #3870 παρακαλέω, beseech, call for, exhort, entreat, pray, from #3844 παρα, near, beside; and #2564 καλέω call,

W. E. Vine's *Expository Dictionary of New Testament Words*, 35; 208. "For 'Advocate' see 'Comforter.'"
5. PARAKLETOS (παράκλητος), lit., called to one's side, i.e., to one's aid, is primarily a verbal adjective, and suggests the capability or adaptability for giving aid. It was used in a court of justice to denote a legal assistant, counsel for the defense, an advocate; then, generally, one who pleads another's cause, an intercessor, advocate, as in I John 2:1, of the Lord Jesus. In the widest sense, it signifies a succourer, comforter.

Figure 4.10

The Integration of Exegesis and the Whiting Method

(See figure 4-12.)

The Whiting Method, as developed and taught by Milton Jones at Western Conservative Baptist Seminary, Portland, Oregon, was found to have a deficiency, which he addressed in a supplementary review sheet, dated September 21, 1972. The method of producing an expository outline that developed the theme of a text based on principles drawn from word studies was lauded for its value as far as it went. But, since there is far more to exegesis than word studies, a question arose as to the relation between exegesis and homiletics.

Colin Brown: *The New International Dictionary of New Testament Theology*, vol. I, 88ff. (excerpts follow)

Advocate, Paraclete, Helper

παράκλητος	παράκλητος (*parakletos*), helper, intercessor, advocate, paraklete.

"The noun *parakletos* is derived from the verbal adj. and means called [to one's aid]. It is first found in a legal context in the court of justice, meaning legal assistant, advocate (Demosthenes, 19, 1; cf. Lycurgus, Frag. 102)."

OT "Job's 'comforters' are called parakletores (plur. in Job 16:2 LXX; Acquila and Theodotion have parakletoi). The Heb. Is *m^{e}na^{a}mim*.It is significantly the only instance of the word in the LXX."

NT "1 Jn. 2:1 f. gives the term a soteriological character in calling 'Jesus Christ the righteous' our 'advocate' (parakletos) and 'propitiation' (hilasmos) "for the sins of the whole world . . .

"This restriction of the title to Jesus and the Spirit requires a theological interpretation of the term which is at the same time polemical.

"It is striking that the term parakletos is only found in the Johannine writings, and apart from 1 Jn. 2:1 it occurs only in the discourses (Jn. 14:16, 26; 15:26; 16:7; cf. 16:12ff)."

Meaning in Context

Advocate is a title belonging to "Jesus Christ" which name is in apposition to it. He not only comes to the aid of believers who sin, but is uniquely sent to fill this role as the believer's defense attorney before God the Father, as in a court of law.

Application and Contrasts

If the believer who sins did not have Jesus Christ as his counsel for the defense; or, if He were not Himself the righteous propitiation for his sins, a single sin would result in defeat and hopeless despair. With Him, however, there is every inducement never to sin, nor to give up when he does sin.

Figure 4.11

Jones described the relation of exegesis to homiletics as analogous to the lumber used to build a house. The value of lumber is very real but limited to its owner. When lumber is used to construct a home, however, it benefits all who enjoy the dwelling. In a similar way, the value of exegetical material is limited to the exegete until it has been used in the construction of a well-built sermon. Then it blesses all who hear it.[21] Jones's point was that the disciplines of exegesis and homiletics are not at odds with each other but complementary when properly joined.

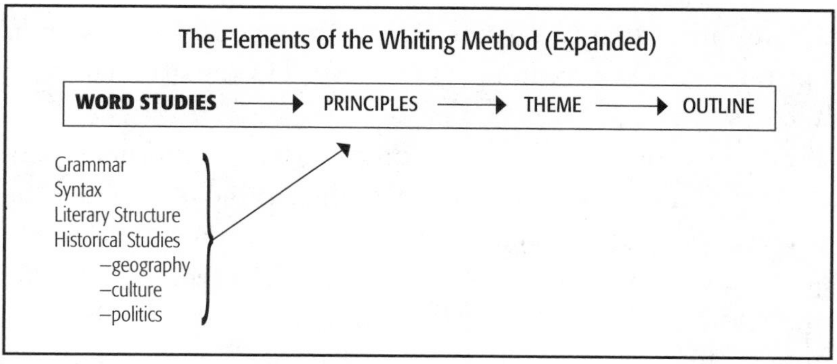

Figure 4.12

Let's take Jones's analogy a step farther. Just as homeowners typically do not attempt to display all of the lumber used to construct their homes, preachers should not display the exegetical resources used in a sermon's construction. With few exceptions, their listeners should be as unaware of the "nuts and bolts" of the sermon, as dinner guests are unaware of the floor joists and rafters of the dining room.

Jones goes on to extol the virtues of exegeting the text of an entire book before beginning a series of messages through the book. After noting the difficulty, in a three-year seminary curriculum, of training exegetical preachers at the same time that they are learning exegesis, Jones recommends that the student preacher learn the system by working within portions of Scripture "no smaller than a sentence and usually no larger (at this point) than a section" (i.e., from a chapter to a book in length).[22]

The next year, Dennis O. Wretlind presented a paper to Dr. W. Robert Cook, (of WCBS), in which the same issue was further addressed with an emphasis on the *preacher's preparation*. Wretlind offered practical suggestions for how a busy pastor could both prepare expository sermons based on solid exegesis of the original text and meet the time-consuming demands of other aspects of ministry.

In agreement with Jones's comments, Wretind observed that the seminary student learns to write sermons *before* finishing formal training in Hebrew and Greek exegesis. As a result, "the beginning point" of the Whiting Method is necessarily adapted to the abilities of beginning students.[23] Integral to the Whiting System of homiletics, however, is the assumption that "a sermon which speaks God's Word must be based primarily on the meaning of that Word in the original tongue in which it was inspired."[24]

Another problem Wretlind noted is that a preacher's personal passion for his message, and thus his ability to move others as he has been moved, is related to his direct contact with the original text, the joy of discovery, and independent work. If exegesis is defined as "the application of the laws of hermeneutics to the original text of Scripture with a view to declaring its meaning,"[25] then the goal must be to work as independently of secondary sources as possible. So you, the exegetical preacher, are responsible to sift the raw material of the text in order to (a) discern the adequacies and inadequacies of the different translations; (b) understand for yourself the meaning of the text, without being carried away by the opinions of others, which mayor may not be correct, and (c) declare your message with the authority of God.[26]

Basic Steps of Exegesis[27]

1. Read the text of the book or passage in the original Hebrew, Aramaic, or Greek in order to have the context of the language before [you] throughout the exegetical process.

2. Study the historical, geographical, [and] cultural contexts of the passage.

3. Analyze all the data in the text: literary genre and structure, words, quotations, figures of speech, parallel passages, grammatical observations, etc.

4. Record all information gained through the procedures of 1-3 above as it is gained. [See figures 4-13. 4-14, and 4-15a-b.]

Comparison of Exegesis with the Whiting Method[28]

(See figure 4-13.)

Example of a Grammatical Diagram from 1 John 2:1

(See figure 4-14.)

Example of a Word Study of παράκλητον, Advocate

(See figures 4-15a and b.)

Discussion of Select Exegetical Data That Contribute to the Formation of Principles

Only by reading the passage in the original language can you have a firsthand impression of John's fatherly tone indicated by the diminutive word for *child* and the first personal pronoun in the genitive (of relationship or possession) case. Tone is important in talking to people about sin.

Exegesis	Whiting Method
Exegesis calls for the study of *every* word according to the *selection* of which exegetical steps are appropriate.	The Whiting Method *selects* words for study on the basis of whether they are recurring, unusual, or difficult.
The *essentials* of exegesis and the Whiting Method are the same.	While the Whiting Method does not *emphasize* the historical study that is part of exegesis, study of the historical contexts is *implied* in the Whiting Method's basis upon literal interpretation.
Supplementing the Whiting Method with full and complete exegesis strengthens its integrity as a system.	

Figure 4.13

Τεκνία μου, ταῦτα γράφω ὑμῖν ἵνα μὴ ἁμάρτητε. καὶ ἐάν τις ἁμάρτῃ, παράκλητον ἔχομεν πρὸς τὸν πατέρα Ἰησοῦν Χριστὸν δίκαιον· 2 καὶ αὐτὸς ἱλασμός ἐστιν περὶ τῶν ἁμαρτιῶν ἡμῶν, οὐ περὶ τῶν ἡμετέρων δὲ μόνον ἀλλὰ καὶ περὶ ὅλου τοῦ κόσμου.

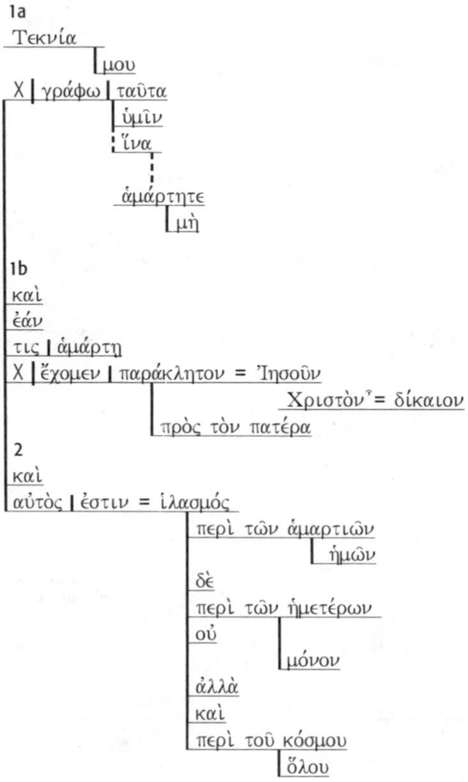

Tender, fatherly tone with diminutive of τεκνον, child, and 1st personal pronoun with the Genitive of Relationship or Possession.

Ταῦτα *these things* is ordered forward for emphasis.

Present Active Indicative of γράφω, 1st person singular, I am writing.

Negative purpose clause with second ingressive aorist of ἁμαρτάνω, subj., 2nd person plural, enter into sin. (Sin is not a necessary result of being in unredeemed bodies.)

Continuative conjunction.

Third class conditional clause with ἐαν (future probability) and 2 Aor. Act. Subj. 3ms, of ἁμαρτάνω forming the protasis, with indefinite pronoun, τις as the subject.

In apodosis, the Pres. Act. Ind, 1 Pl. of ἔχομαι, *we have* (includes the Apostle John).

Anarthrous Accus. Masc. Sing. Noun, παράκλατον, as the direct object of ἔχομεὶ.

Prepositional phrase modifying ἔχομεν functions adverbally (place).

Ιησοῦν Χριστόν, Jesus Christ is in apposition to παράκλατον and δίκαιον.

Anarthrous accusative, masculine, singular noun, *righteous*, stresses quality though definite by apposition.

Personal Translation

My little children, these things I am writing to you so that you might not ever sin; and if anyone should sin, we have an Advocate with the Father, Jesus Christ the righteous. And He is the satisfactory payment for our sins, and not for ours only, but also for the whole world.

Figure 4.14

Advocate
παράκλητος

Form

Masculine, accusative, singular noun

Function
Accusative of Direct Object, receiving the action of, or completing the meaning of, the verb ἔχομεν we have (Dana and Mantey, 92).

Root Meaning
From παρακαλέω "called to one's aid" in a judicial sense, hence, most frequently as a substantive, an advocate, pleader, intercessor, "a friend of the accused person called to speak in his character, or otherwise enlist sympathy in his favor (Abbott/Smith, 340–41).

Classical Usage
"Called to one's aid." In Latin, translated by the word *advocatus*. As a Substantive, used of "a legal assistant, advocate" (Liddell & Scott, 597).

Usage in the Septuagint
Used only once, in plural form, παρακλήτορες , in Job 16:2, where Job describes his friends as poor "comforters" (Septuagint, 677).
Found in Acquila and Theodotian as παρακλητοι (Hatch/Redpath, 1061; Colin Brown, Vol I, 88ff).
Translates Hebrew מְנַחֲמֵי , Piel ptc. m. pl. cs., from נחם ,
be sorry, repent, regret, be comforted, comfort (Bible Works).

Koine Usage
Originally, "one called in" to support, hence "advocate," "pleader," "a friend of the accused person, called to speak to his character, or otherwise enlist the sympathy of the judges" (Moulton and Milligan, 485).

New Testament Usage
Used in John 14:16 of the Holy Spirit as another παράκλητος , implying Jesus (who is speaking) as a παράκλητος. Also used of the Holy Spirit in John 14:26; 15:26; 16:7; and of Christ in 1 John 2:1 (Moulton and Geden, 758).

Originally meant in the passive sense, of being asked. The word came to mean "one who is called to someone's aid;" "one who appears in another's behalf, mediator, intercessor, helper" (Bauer, Arndt, and Gingrich, 623).

παράκλητος (*parakleetos*) meant in classical Greek merely *called to one's aid, assisting*, especially in a court of justice. Hence a *legal advisor or helper*. "But this falls short of the meaning it afterwards obtained: *viz*., not only of helping another to do something, but to help him *by doing it for him*. It is used only in John of the Holy Spirit's help (by Christ) in xiv. 16, 26; xv. 26; xvi. 7. And of Christ's help (by the Holy Spirit) in 1 John ii. 1" (Bullinger, 854).

Figure 4.15a

PARAKLETOS (παράκλητος), lit., called to one's side, i.e., to one's aid, is primarily a verbal adjective, and suggests the capability or adaptability for giving aid. It was used in a court of justice to denote a legal assistant, counsel for the defence, an advocate; then, generally, one who pleads another's cause, an intercessor, advocate, as in I John 2:1, of the Lord Jesus. In the widest sense, it signifies a succourer, comforter (W. E. *Vine's Expository Dictionary of New Testament Words*, 35, 208).

NT "1 Jn. 2:1 f. gives the term a soteriological character in calling 'Jesus Christ the righteous' our 'advocate' (*parakletos*) and 'propitiation' (*hilasmos*) for the sins of the whole world . . . This restriction of the title to Jesus and the Spirit requires a theological interpretation of the term which is at the same time polemical" (Colin Brown: *The New International Dictionary of New Testament Theology*, vol. I, 88ff).

Meaning in Context
Advocate is a title belonging to "Jesus Christ" which name is in apposition to it. He not only comes to the aid of believers who sin, but is uniquely sent to fill this role as the believer's defense attorney before God the Father, as in a court of law. His representation of the believer is not separated contextually either from His righteous character or His personal payment of the believer's debt, by which He satisfied the Father's just demand.

Application and Contrasts
If the believer who sins did not have Jesus Christ as his or her counsel for the defense; or, if Christ were not Himself *the righteous propitiation* for our sins, a single sin would result in defeat and hopeless despair. With Him, however, there is every inducement never to sin, nor to give up when one does sin. The believer has, in his or her favor, the solution referred to in the apodasis of the conditional clause in answer to the protasis, "If anyone sins."

Figure 4.15b

In 1 John 1, the Apostle has addressed those who deny a principle of sin within them (1:8). According to 1:10, some deny ever having committed a sin. Having referred to the universality of sin, John begins the second chapter with further explanation of the relationship between Christians and sin. His purpose in writing, that they never commit a single sin, is expressed with the ingressive aorist in the negative purpose-clause introduced with ἵνα.

Contrary to the apparent belief on the part of Gnostics influencing his readers, the Docetic faction of which made light of sin, John does not excuse sin on the part of believers as a human necessity. On the other hand, the third-class conditional statement in the protasis, if anyone sins, reassures those who will in all probability sin, of the secure standing they possess by the gift of Jesus as their righteous Advocate before the throne of God the Father. Not only does He stand in the unique position of their defense attorney at law, but the offering of himself as a satisfactory sacrifice (from a word study of ἱλασμος, propitiation) for sin gives a righteous standing to all for whom His self-sacrifice is efficacious, because He is qualitatively righteous [a nuance apparent only to those who are able to see that δίκαιος is anarthrous (without the article ὁ)].

If the ongoing work of Christ in heaven is the basis for the believer's assurance, His past cross-work on earth provided the basis of forgiveness for all in the world who will believe, and the basis of judgment for all who will not repent.

Figure 4.16

Making a personal translation also enables you to see why the New King James Version retained the slightly rougher word order in English, "These things I write," rather than the smoother "I write these things," as in the other versions we examined. By moving *tauta* forward in the sentence, John is stressing the content of his letter as that which calls for the explanation he is giving. For an example of exegetical notations, see figure 4-16.

Synthesis
The Formation Of Principles

The Elements Of The Whiting Method
(See Figure 4-17.)

According to the Whiting Method:[29]

> "A principle is an outstanding and abiding truth
> that is not limited to a moment in time."

WORD STUDIES	**PRINCIPLES**	THEME	OUTLINE

Figure 4.17

Outstanding

"Outstanding" describes a truth that is evidently prominent in importance from the perspective of the writer and his addressees. This calls for discernment. Except when quoting the devil or wicked people, everything the Bible says is assumed to be true. But not every true statement is equally germane to the argument of the book or purpose of the writer. While in no place to dismiss a scriptural truth as unimportant, you still can and must develop the art and skill of drawing principles that reflect author intent and support the thrust of the passage.[30] An outstanding truth in a passage is like a bearing wall in a building. It literally carries more weight than a nonbearing wall, though the latter is not unimportant.

Abiding

"Abiding," in the preceding definition refers to what Josh McDowell has called "absolute truth," which he defines as "that which is true for all people, for all times, for all places."[31] This is made explicit in the second half of the definition: "that is not limited to a moment in time." For these reasons, the statement of a "principle" should not employ proper nouns, which identify specific places or persons (other than those of God). Neither should it be stated in terms that date or otherwise restrict its universal application.

Prerequisites

Prerequisites for extracting a principle include (1) complete familiarity with the text under study; (2) careful, well-done analysis of grammar and meanings; and (3) compelling ability to think with the whole text in mind without arriving at vague generalities.[32] A useful technique for sifting the relevance of a text is to ask and answer questions on what has been called a truth sheet.

Use of Truth Sheets[33]

Asking and answering the questions *who, what, when, where, why*, and *how* in relation to a passage of Scripture is a simple and orderly way to be sure you have "covered all the bases" in the discovery of facts.

> Truth Sheets refer to the application of the six interrogatives to the text under study to produce statements of fact leading to principles.

The use of truth sheets simply formalizes a mental process that would otherwise tend to occur unconsciously, randomly, and incompletely. Truth sheets are comparable to a filter through which the text is poured to sift the hard facts as raw materials with which to construct principles.

Answering the question, *who?* provides the *identification of persons*. Answering the question, *what?* discovers the *transaction* of any *performance*. "When" describes the *duration* of the *period* of time involved in the passage. By asking *where?* the *location* becomes the focus. The *causation of production* is discovered in answer to the question, *why?* Finally, answering the question, *how?* divulges the *function* of any *procedure* that may be described in the text. (See figures 4-18 and 4-19.)

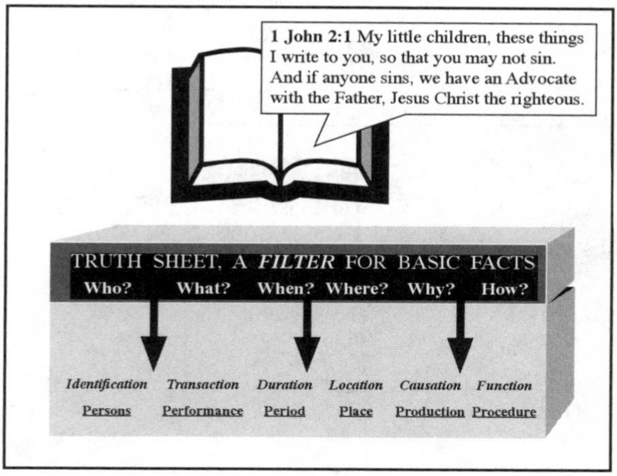

Figure 4.18

Completing a Truth Sheet for 1 John 2:1-2.[34] (See figure 4-19.)

From Basic Facts to Principles[35]

The basic facts written on the truth sheet form the basis for recording truths. Each truth should be recorded as a separate declaration, without any judgment regarding its importance or usefulness. Figure 4-20 shows examples from the truth sheet for 1 John 2:1-2.

Next, truths of the same vein are combined in a single, simple sentence. At this stage in the process, the focus should be on words of obvious, outstanding importance. (See figure 4-21.)

Minor, repetitive, subordinate, or implied truths not germane to the thrust of the passage should now be eliminated by crossing them out. The goal is to reword the statements of truth in two to six simple, clear statements. (See figure 4-22.)

Two to six principles should now be stated as positive certainties of universal truth. Before demonstrating how to state a principle positively, the following guidelines are offered to help the preacher avoid common pitfalls.

My little children, these things I write to you, so that you may not sin. And if anyone sins, we have an Advocate with the Father, Jesus Christ the righteous.
2 And He Himself is the propitiation for our sins, and not for ours only but also for the whole world. (NKJV)

TRUTH SHEET
STATEMENTS OF FACT LEADING TO PRINCIPLES

WHO? **IDENTIFICATION** **PERSONS**
–My little children
–Jesus Christ – Advocate, Righteous, Propitiation
–The whole world

WHAT? **TRANSACTION** **PERFORMANCE**
–Sin
–Advocacy of Jesus Christ
–Propitiation of Jesus Christ
–John's writing

WHEN? **DURATION** **PERIOD OF TIME**
–Now, John is writing
–Now, believers admonished not to commit sin at all
–Now, believers have an Intercessor, a Defense Attorney to plead their case
–Now, believers have a Propitiation for the judicial requirements of God's Law
–Future, both are true for the believer's Advocate and Propitiation

WHERE? **LOCATION** **PLACE**
–Believers are in unredeemed bodies on earth
–Christ is with the Father

WHY? **CAUSATION** **PRODUCTION**
–To urge believers not to sin at all
–To encourage believers that when they DO sin, they have a righteous Advocate
–To verify that Jesus Christ the Righteous has made a satisfactory payment of the penalty for all sin

HOW? **FUNCTION** **PROCEDURE**
–Jesus Christ the Righteous satisfied the judicial requirements of God's Law
–Jesus Christ is the voluntary atoning sacrifice for the whole world, which includes believers

Figure 4.19

- Believers need not sin.
- Believers sin.
- Christ is the answer to believers' sin problem.
- Christ is righteous.
- Christ is the believer's Advocate.
- Christ paid the penalty for the sins of the world.

Figure 4.20

- Believers need not sin, but do.
- Christ is the believer's righteous advocate.
- Christ paid the penalty for the sins of the world, including believers.

Figure 4.21

- Believers ~~need not~~ sin, ~~but do~~.
- ~~Christ is~~ the believer's righteous advocate.
- Christ paid the penalty for the sins of the world, ~~including believers~~.

Figure 4.22

- Believers sin, though they have the power to avoid sinning.
- Christ is a righteous Advocate for believers who sin.
- Christ paid for the sins of the world.

Figure 4.23

How Not to State a Principle[36]

A principle should not be stated:

1. as a question, such as *"Is there a solution to the problem of Christians sinning?"*
2. in the negative, such as *"Believers are not without advocacy when they sin,"*
3. using proper nouns (names of people or places), unless they are everlasting. For example. *"The apostle John wrote to encourage believers when they sin,"*
4. using personal pronouns, such as *"In Christ, you (or I) have an advocate with God the Father,"*
5. using compound sentences or complex sentence structure, such as *"Christ is a righteous advocate for believers who sin and paid the penalty for the sins of the world,"*
6. using unnecessarily difficult or many words, such as *"Christ is qualified to be the believer's advocate by virtue of His shed blood, which propitiated the sins of the world, including those of believers."*

How to State a Principle

Principles should be stated as positive certainties of universal truth (see figure 4-23).

From the Principles of a Passage to a Statement of its Theme[37]

> "The theme is the central truth of the passage expressed in a simple sentence."

Wording the Theme

In the Whiting Method, "the theme is the central truth of the passage expressed in a simple sentence." It states what Haddon Robinson calls "the big idea."[38] In the terminology of Richards and Bredfeldt, the theme is the "generalization" that tells the listener both what the author is talking about, and what he is saying about what he is talking about.[39] The theme is the condensation of all of the principles into a single sentence. But it is not to be worded in the abstract language of exegesis. Rather, the theme should be stated in the contemporary language of application. In this way, it fulfills the bridging role of Richards and Bredfeldt's "pedagogical idea."[40] An example from Philippians 2:3-8 follows. (See figure 4-24.)

Stating the Theme in the Contemporary Language of Application

Example from Philippians 2:3–8 ESV

3Do nothing from rivalry or conceit, but in humility count others more significant than yourselves. 4Let each of you look not only to his own interests, but also to the interests of others. 5Have this mind among yourselves, which is yours in Christ Jesus, 6who, though he was in the form of God, did not count equality with God a thing to be grasped, 7but made himself nothing, taking the form of a servant, being born in the likeness of men. And being found in human form, 8he humbled himself by becoming obedient to the point of death, even death on a cross.

Rather than stating the theme

"The Incarnation and death of Christ demonstrated His humility,"

a more *applicable* statement of the theme might be,

"Christ is the example of selfless service to others."

Figure 4.24

The Nature of an Effective Theme

As developed in the Whiting Method, the theme is a positive declaration, not a possibility, suggestion, or guess. It is the sermon in a nutshell. The theme is typically no more than nine words and is usually not alliterated. Themes should not consist of clichés, such as "The family that prays together stays together," or "God helps those who help themselves." A good theme will help you avoid extraneous material by expressing the single thought of the central thrust. This gives the message its greatest potential for impacting the listener's mind, will, and emotions. It also makes it easier for the listener to remember, providing a handle by which to recall the major points of the outline. Look at this example of a theme from 1 John 2:1-2 (see figure 4-25):

From Theme to Outline[41]

Main Headings

A good theme produces a good outline. It includes all the headings, but develops only the *main* headings of the outline (I, II, III, etc.), not the subheadings (A, B, C, etc.). An example from 1 John 2:1-2 follows. (See figure 4-26.)

Subheadings

In the following example, notice that the main headings and subheadings of an outline are referenced to verses (1, 2, etc.), and even parts of verses (1 a, 1 b, etc.). The small-case letters *a* and *b* refer to the subdivisions of a verse—usually according to clauses. This is to help the listener identify the specific portion of the text that supports a given point in the outline. In this way, the sermon is shown to be rooted in or growing out of the biblical text, not the preacher's imagination! By "clicking down" the (bolded) subheadings, A, B, C, etc., the listener is able to see a visual summary of what every portion of the text teaches *and* how it supports the main headings on which the theme rests. (See figure 4-27.)

Transition

Notice that a well-stated theme makes a good transitional sentence that gives continuity to the outline. (See figure 4-28.) The outline develops the theme, because the theme is limited to the text from which it was woven, and expresses a progression of thought, taking the listener from one "place" to another.

Theme of 1 John 2:1–2
When believers sin,
Christ is their righteous Advocate.

Figure 4.25

When Believers Sin,
Christ Is Their Righteous Advocate

When Believers Sin . . .
→ I. The Problem of Sinning Christians

. . . Christ Is Their Righteous Advocate
→ II. The Solution of Christ's Advocacy

Figure 4.26

Summary and Conclusion

The Whiting Method, while not the only strategy for sermon development, is commended for its wedding of exegesis and homiletics. Influenced by Samuel Chadwick, developed by Arthur B. Whiting and further refined by Milton William Jones and Dennis Wretlind, this system is most effective when principles are based on all of the exegetical data from textual analysis, rather than selected word studies alone. Therefore the benefits of the system are most fully realized by language users (LU). However, by using the research tools available in a quality theological library or computer software program, non-language users (NLU) can also make good use of the method. This is especially true if the passage is read in several reliable translations, if the text is diagrammed and/or laid out mechanically to note the way the words relate to each other (syntax), and if the historical setting is studied thoroughly.

Subheadings of the Sermon Outline

1 John 2:1–2

When Believers Sin, / Christ Is Their Righteous Advocate

I. The Problem of Sinning Christians 2:1a–b
- **A. Believers need not ever sin. (1a)**
- **B. Believers do sin. (1b)**

[Transition: "When believers sin, Christ is their Righteous Advocate"]

II. The Solution of Christ's Advocacy 2:1c–2
- **A. He is with the Father. (1c)**
- **B. He is righteous. (1c)**
- **C. He paid for our sins. (2a)**
- **D. He paid for the sins of the world. (2b)**

Figure 4.27

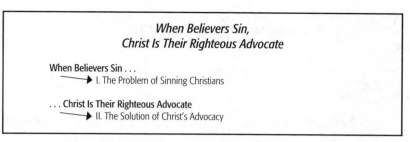

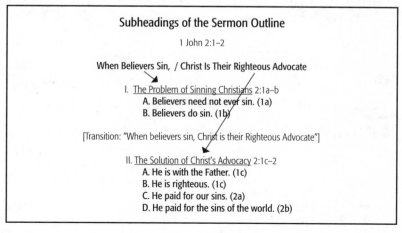

The Progression of Thought in a Well-Stated Theme

When believers sin, → Christ Is their righteous Advocate.

Figure 4.28

Whether evaluating existing translations (NLUs), or translating personally (LUs), use a *truth sheet* to sift relevant information. Compose three to six statements of timeless truths, called principles, by answering the six interrogatives (*who, what, when, where, why, how*). State the epitome of the principles, called the *theme*, by eliminating repetitious ideas and those of less importance. (The theme should be a single, positive, generalized sentence of no more than nine words.)

When worded in the language of the listeners, this encapsulated message enhances impact. Producing the main points of a good outline gives the listener a memorable handle by which to recall your sermon. When these are broken down into subheadings, indexed to the verses or portion of verses out of which they "grow," a listener is able to see that the message is God's, though the sermon is yours.

A well-stated theme provides an effective transitional statement. This helps the listener grasp the unity of the message. When the timeless truth is thus communicated, understood, applied, and implemented in the listener's life, you have used the Whiting Method to bridge the communication gap between the self-revealing God and those who desperately need to know Him intimately. In short, you have engaged in *delivering God's message in your sermon*. This is faithful preaching.

Discussion Questions

1. What are the two aspects of sermon preparation under which the elements of the Whiting Method may be arranged?

2. Define the following terms and describe their use or purpose.

   a. Text
   b. Word Study
   c. Truth Sheet
   d. Principle

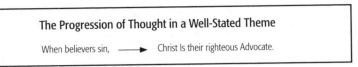

   e. Theme
   f. Outline

3. List several ways a principle should *not* be stated.
4. Describe the attributes of a well-stated theme.
5. For LU only: List some of the advantages of being able to use the biblical languages.
6. What did you find most helpful in this overview of the Whiting Method of homiletics?
7. List at least three questions that this introduction to the Whiting Method has raised for you.

PART II

Developing the Discovery

Part I of *Faithful Preaching* introduced an adaptation of the Whiting Method as a means of bridging the communication gap that exists between the text of Scripture and the contemporary audience of an expository preacher. Having discovered the meaning of the text in its context, and designed its packaging for delivery, you are ready to develop the actual content. Part II will address ways to assemble the components of the verbal bridge.

Chapter 5, "The Components of an Expository Sermon," deals with elements inherent to every presentation of God's Word. Regardless of your unique style and emphasis, certain factors enhance the effectiveness of any sermon introduction, body, illustration, conclusion, application, and invitation

Chapter 6, "The Classifications of an Expository Sermon," explores the kinds of expository sermons called for by the variety of biblical literature to be proclaimed. *Paragraph, chapter, book, doctrinal, biographical, parable, gospel,* and *typical* sermons all have their place in a balanced pulpit ministry.

CHAPTER 5

The Components of an Expository Sermon

Well-organized building materials, a good blueprint, and a competent builder are all parts that are necessary to construct a bridge that can effectively connect parties on opposite banks of a great divide. Yet these alone are not sufficient to build the bridge. Actual *work* must be done to assemble the parts so that they all fit together in a unified whole that is straight, strong, and inviting. The same is true of communicating ideas. This chapter concerns the purposes of the parts and how they are joined. Just as a physical bridge must be properly put together to serve its purpose, so must sermons.

Richards and Bredfeldt wisely observe that good planning does not displace Spirit-filled spontaneity; rather, it makes it meaningful:

> It is God's nature to plan … God designed His world by very exacting plans. He orders events by a master plan. And we as human beings made in His image have an innate tendency to make plans as well. We plan our days. We plan events. We plan travel. We plan our work. We plan our homes. We plan our lives. We plan worship services. We even try to plan our families. Should we not develop plans for teaching the Word of God as well?[1]

Planning for Success

Bridges vary in design to meet the needs and conditions of each span. Likewise, every sermon should be structured to reflect the literary genre and tone of the text. It should relate to the real needs of the particular people addressed. The truth must be communicated in a way that is natural to the speaker and responsive to the various learning styles of the listeners. The goal of every sermon should be to change the thinking, attitudes, and behavior of listeners to obedience to the revelation of God. This does not happen automatically, by accident, or in spite of poor planning. It has been said, "If you fail to plan, you plan to fail" and "If you aim at nothing, you hit it every time."

Even with planning, there are certain perils. When style is emphasized at the expense of substance, for example, the sermon becomes like the original Narrows Bridge in Tacoma, Washington. (See figures 5-1 a and b.) Built in 1940 to span Puget Sound, the bridge was celebrated as the world's third-longest suspension bridge. It was slender, elegant, and graceful. Yet just four months after it opened, the bridge collapsed in a windstorm, earning the name "Galloping Gertie."[2] Replaced in 1950, the new bridge, built to carry 60,000 cars per day, regularly handles 90,000![3] In a similar way, sermons that deliver sound content are better than those that are overly ambitious or structurally weak. When

Figure 5.1a

organization becomes an end in itself, the result can be too mechanical. For example, forced alliteration of an outline produces statements that are contrived or trite. Dazzling illustrations and excessive humor often detract from the thrust of God's message by "stealing the show." The desire to be profound or to impress people can tempt a preacher to use big words, complex sentence structure, and awkward or archaic expressions.

Good planning narrows the scope of the message, allowing the preacher to have a better grasp of a limited subject. It orders the presentation to accomplish strategic objectives without rambling. To hit a long-ranged target, a marksman uses a rifle rather than a shotgun. Similarly, the points of the message should be kept in proper proportion to the text, and ultimately contribute to a single goal. This gives the message integrity. Like a magnificent bridge, a well-structured sermon is more than a work of art; but it is not less!

Think of the listener as a lost traveler depending on the sermon for directions. Good organization causes the material to flow and makes it easier to follow, understand, and remember. Clear cognitive, affective, and behavioral lesson aims make the message more persuasive. Parts of a sermon include the *introduction, body, conclusion, application, and invitation.* These must be assembled with care. Though sermons begin with introductions, they are last to be prepared. According to Richards

Figure 5.1b

and Bredfeldt, one attribute of what they call "a good hook," is that it leads the student into the Word.[4] Until you know what you will communicate in the body of the sermon, you cannot effectively plan the best way to get people's attention or surface the need to which your text provides God's answer. So structuring begins with organization of the sermon's body.

The Body of the Message

The *body* is the main portion of the sermon. It is in the body that you will present the analysis of a passage for instruction, and the synthesis of its principles for persuasion. The body corresponds to the *book* part of Richards and Bredfeldt's *hook, book, look, took* (HBLT).[5] According to Haddon Robinson, the material may be arranged as it is developed *deductively*, beginning with the idea that the text supports; or *inductively*, building up to the idea on the basis of the textual data.[6] In either case, this is the portion of the sermon in which ideas are explained, propositions are proved, principles are applied, the story is told, and the subject is completed.[7] Because of its bulk and central purpose, the content of the sermon's body must be *adapted, divided, styled, ordered*, and *developed.*

Adapted

Adaptation is like shopping for clothing that fits both the person and the occasion. It reflects the style and substance of the text from which it is woven. It suits the preacher's gifts and abilities, *and* the nature of the audience. For example, the text of 1 John 2:1-2 was written by the apostle John when he was elderly. When he begins the second chapter, "My little children" (NKJV), the tone is fatherly. He firmly asserts that sin is darkness, the antithesis of the light in which a believer can and must walk in order to enjoy fellowship with God, who *is* light (1 John 1:5). The "blood of Jesus Christ His Son," John tells his readers, "cleanses us from all sin" (v. 7 NKJV). John is both firm and familial as he switches from writing in first-person singular, "My little children, these things *I* write to you" to first-person plural, "*we* have an Advocate with the Father" (1 John 2:1 NKJV, emphasis added). When he refers to "our sins," in verse 2, and for those of "the whole world" (NKJV), John includes himself. For a sermon to communicate God's message, you must also take the tone of John, who balances his emphasis on the gravity of sin with an emphasis on the marvelous grace of salvation.

Divided

Dividing the body of the sermon is necessary for adequate understanding and to carefully distinguish the vital force of the sections. In 1 John 2:1-2, for example, part of the text identifies the problem of sinning Christians. This builds the listener's sense of need for the solution of Christ's advocacy, given in the balance of the text. When given meaningful headings, the transition from one division of the sermon's body to another is clarified. In our sample sermon, the word *problem* in the first major division ("The Problem of Sinning Christians") anticipates the word solution in the second major division ("The Solution of Christ's Advocacy").

Styled

The body of the sermon is also *styled* for maximum impact, absorption, and memory. The use of words that start with the same letter is called *alliteration*.[8] The following sermon illustrates the use of an alliterated outline with partially alliterated subpoints. (See figure 5-2.)

Another device is called *tautophony*, or *assonance*. This is "the repetition of vowel sounds within a short passage of verse or prose."[9] Notice the use of assonance in the following sermon outline. (See figure 5-3.)

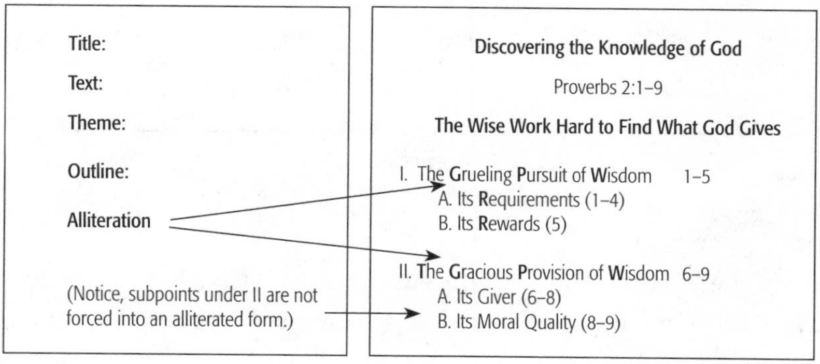

Figure 5.2

THE PRAYER GOD HEARS

Hebrews 5:5–10

God Listens To The Life Yielded To His Will

I. The Passionate Prayer of the Pious
   A. The **De**pendence of Humanity
   ⇕
   B. The **De**monstration of Humility
   ⇕
   C. The **De**termination of Honor

II. The Perfection of Divine Purpose
   A. The Deliverance of Salvation
   B. The Discipline of Sonship
   C. The Declaration of Success

Figure 5.3

Good headings are not just isolated labels or titles but statements with clear meaning. The use of questions in division headings can be distracting if it causes people to try to fill in the blanks rather than listen.

The following outline of the book of Jonah illustrates the importance of symmetry in stating the divisional headings of an outline. Note the consistent use of nouns on the right-hand side of the figure in contrast to the mixture of nouns and verbs on the left-hand side. (See figure 5-4.)

Poor Grammatical Balance	Good Grammatical Balance
I. Yahweh's Offer of Mercy to Sinners (phrase with noun)	I. Yahweh's Determination to Offer His Mercy to Sinners
II. God Delivers Repentant Pagans (clause with verb)	II. Yahweh's Deliverance of Repentant Pagans
III. The Compassionate LORD (phrase with adjective)	III. Yahweh's Demonstration of Compassion

Figure 5.4

Ordered

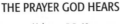

Ordering the body of the sermon will make it easier for you to remember what you have planned to say. It also makes it easier for the listener to follow. The order should be natural, flowing, moving, and varied. *Natural* order means that it corresponds to the text itself, or the logic of its progression is evident.[10] When one point of a sermon builds anticipation for the next, without sudden breaks, it is described as *flowing*. *Movement* toward a goal or conclusion is another important aspect of well-ordered material in the body of a sermon. *Varied* use of words to avoid repetition helps keep the listener engaged.

Developed

Every heading should have at least two subheadings, if it has any, says Jones.[11] "If a heading stands alone, then it should be included in the main heading from which it originates."[12]

The following outline (figure 5-5) is a model for structuring the body of the sermon.

Illustrations

Just because something is true, does not mean that it is clear. An *illustration* is a story, example, diagram, picture, object, or figure of speech that clarifies a concept by demonstrating what it is, how it works, or why it is important.

When Believers Sin, Christ Is Their Righteous Advocate

I. The Problem of Sinning Christians 2:1a–b
- A. Believers need not ever sin (1a)
- B. Believers do sin (1b)

II. The Solution of Christ's Advocacy 2:1c–2
- A. He is with the Father (1c)
- B. He is righteous (1c)
- C. He paid for our sins (2a)
- D. He paid for the sins of the world (2b)

Figure 5.5

For example, in John 17:20-21, Jesus prays for His disciples, "I do not pray for these alone, but also for those who will believe in Me through their word; that they all may be one, as You, Father, are in Me, and I in You; that they also may be one in Us, that the world may believe that You sent Me" (NKJV). The analogy of the unity of the Father and the Son to the unity of believers is difficult to conceptualize. Some sort of diagram or word picture may help people grasp the idea.

For instance, children are in their father's family tree, and their father's genes are in them. Genetically, then, there is a sense in which a father and his children are *in* one another. Similarly, you can be in water, yet also have water in you, as when you are in a swimming pool while also having some of the "pool" in you (water is in your mouth).

Illustrations have been compared to windows, which allow light to fill every room and make visible what would otherwise be unseen or shadowy. The use of the family tree and pool illustrations shed light on the concept of unity. Just as the use of color adds realism to media presentations, illustrations enhance sermons. At their best, they stimulate curiosity, imagination, and thought. Sometimes they are like the flashing lights of an alarm system that get people's attention. A good story or analogy can turn the ears of listeners into eyes with which to visualize the truth they hear. When they serve their purpose in clarifying God's message, they always point away from themselves to the object they illumine.[13]

But every analogy breaks down, and part of the skill of using illustrations is knowing their limitations and not over-pressing them.[14] As someone has said, "Illustrations were not made to walk on all fours." Like any good thing, they can be abused. This occurs when they dominate the truth. Windows too large, or too many, can structurally weaken a building. Likewise, illustrations that are too extensive, elaborate, entertaining, or memorable can weaken a sermon.

Skits and multimedia presentations are types of illustrations. In Matthew 18:1-5, Jesus stood a child before His disciples to demonstrate the kind of humble dependence upon God that is required for a person to enter the kingdom. To emphasize the importance of every member of the kingdom, He compared him to one lost sheep out of a hundred (vv. 12-14).

Illustrations help the listener consider a truth more objectively. In 2 Samuel 12:1-7, when the prophet Nathan told the story of a rich man who took a poor man's only ewe lamb, it caused David to judge his own sin against Uriah.

When illustrations actually illumine the truth of an otherwise abstract concept, they give you an opportunity to reinforce that truth by stating it differently. An example of this is the use of a *descriptive word*, such as Jesus' use of the word *sword*, in Matthew 10:34, to depict the divisive nature of the truth He brought to the earth. Literary *figures of speech* are another category of illustration, such as the shepherd/sheep imagery of Psalm 23 and John 10. Fifty-three figures of speech can be identified in the Sermon on the Mount in Matthew 5-7.[15] *Similes* and *metaphors* provide formal or implied comparisons to add emphasis, intensify feeling, or reveal the unknown by what is familiar.

Other forms of illustration include analogies, in which one thing is described by its similarity to another. *Anecdotes* are brief stories of an interesting, amusing, or biographical incident, used to make a point. Stories and poetry, whether fictitious or true, can effectively clarify ideas that would otherwise remain enigmatic or opaque.

Among the many sources of illustrations, the Bible is the most authoritative. A good example is the story of Joseph in Genesis 39:13 used to illustrate what Paul meant in 2 Timothy 2:22, by his command to "flee ... youthful lusts" (NKJV). The disadvantage of biblical illustrations is that their use may require explanation for those in the audience who are not familiar with them.

Personal observation of human nature and current events is one of the best sources of sermon illustrations, because it is fresh and personal. Its disadvantage is seen if "you had to be there" to appreciate the significance of the observation. Media reports of events and human interest stories can also be sources of illustrations. Biographies of people who exemplify good or evil can be very useful as long as they do not require too much time to explain. When gleaning illustrations from sports, songs, movies, and novels, make sure to avoid references to unwholesome sources.

Historical lessons, theological issues, the church hymnal, and developments in the arts and sciences can be used to good advantage. Books and websites that provide illustrations and humor can also be helpful, but personal discoveries are usually far more natural and effective.

The most important guideline for the use of illustrations in sermon development is that they actually shed light on important truth that would otherwise remain shadowy. They should not simply entertain, illustrate the obvious, or be too long or numerous. They should be simple (like clear glass, not stained glass!) and accurate (not "evangelastically" exaggerated or carelessly taken out of context). Statistical data has its place, but listeners may question how it was gathered and whether it is current or out-of-date.

Recording illustrations in the backs of books the preacher reads; on notepads kept in one's pocket, car, or nightstand; or in an electronic device, makes it possible to file them by subject and biblical text at a later date. The parables of Jesus indicate His attention to illustrative details as He observed life. The development of a hunter/gatherer's attitude regarding potential illustrations is a delight as well as a discipline for the expository preacher of God's Word.

Conclusion

The *conclusion* of a message follows the presentation and provides a résumé, succinctly gathering together everything said and drawing the message to a clear end. While a conclusion does provide the summary that ends a message, it should never consist of a statement that indicates that you're finished–especially if you're not! Rather, it adds the finishing touch that leaves a lasting impression and prepares the listener to decide what he or she is going to do in response. Sometimes simply repeating the theme of the sermon serves as an effective conclusion. The Whiting Method has identified several kinds of conclusions:

Formal

Formal conclusions actually restate the points and headings.[16] This tends to call undue attention to the mechanics of the presentation. If the outline is to be recapped, it can be paraphrased, reduced to a series of single words, restated in the vernacular of the day, stated in terms of inspirational ideals, or balanced with statements that convey a contrasting truth. For example, a message that has emphasized sin could be summarized with a reminder of God's forgiveness.

Informal

It is often best to conclude a sermon with an illustration. Other informal techniques include a personal testimony; an appropriate quotation; or a poem, prayer, challenge, rhetorical question, or song chosen for the purpose.

Effective conclusions have six features: they are *streamlined, simple, strong, short, skillful*, and they provide a *summary*. Conclusions must move without detours or stop signs. They are closure oriented and efficient in encapsulating the message. They consist of clear statements without big words. Good conclusions are stated with passion and conviction. Their wording is vivid, alive, energetic, and motivational. Since they should take no longer than two or three minutes to communicate, you must be skillful in preparing and delivering a summary that recalls the main points of sermon *without* introducing new ideas, arguments, or Scripture references.

Application

Application of the sermon refers to the threads of relevance that run throughout the sermon but are finally drawn together for personal appeal and action for both preacher and people. In terms of Richards and Bredfeldt's well-known *hook, book, look, took* (HBLT), application logically follows the *hook* (introduction), and *book* (body), with a *look* to the "*took*" (implementation) of the truth.[17] Richards and Bredfeldt distinguish between *self-guided applications*, in which the listener is on his own to perceive the text's implications, and the far preferable *guided self-application*, in which the hearer is led "to discover and grasp the relationship of the truth just studied to daily living."[18] These authors describe application as the navigational process in which a pilot lines up with the runway in order to land the plane at its destination. It clearly identifies the target, goal or objective.[19] From the standpoint of time, the application (*look*) marks a return from the past consideration of ancient revelation (*book*) to the present time, from which the introduction (*hook*) launched the message. Its implementation (*took*) will take place in the future. The following diagram illustrates what the authors refer to as "a trip through time."[20] (See figure 5-6.)

Expository preaching aims at changed lives on the part of people willing to respond mentally, affectively, and behaviorally to the revealed knowledge of God. Attributes of appropriate application have been described with the words *factual, fleshed-out, focused, fresh*, and *forceful.*

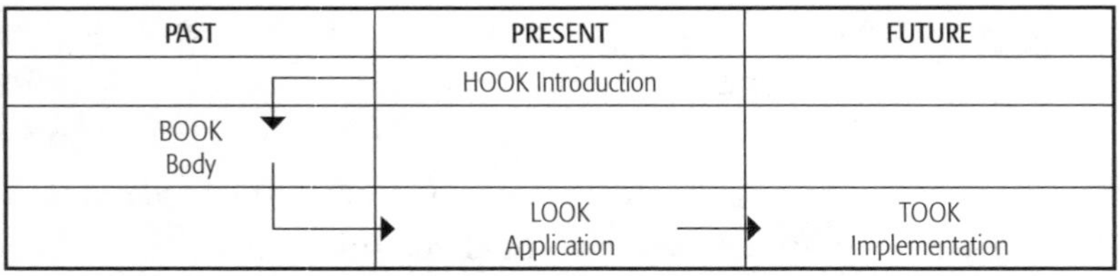

Figure 5.6[21]

Factual

Applications must accurately represent the actual claims of Scripture upon the individual. Just as you must vigilantly avoid reading meanings into the text of Scripture, you must also avoid the temptation to let applications be contorted by pressure from contemporary culture or sabotaged by your own hidden agenda. Many times exhortations on the basis of related principles taught elsewhere in Scripture will suggest themselves. But good application reinserts the very principle led out of its ancient context into the contemporary context without distorting its meaning. Put another way, good applications are those which the author would have made if he were writing today. For example, the requirement that elders be "blameless" in 1 Timothy 3:2 (NKJV) is explained by the list of character qualities that follows in the text. In applying the word blameless today, you will need to evaluate behaviors that were not moral issues at the time Paul wrote. Yet in doing so, you must be careful to avoid subjective judgments that reflect your own cultural biases. For example, ongoing addictions to illegal substances or Internet pornography clearly disqualify a man from the office requiring that he be *blameless*, while other less clear actions, such as body piercing or lottery gambling, may be debatable.

Fleshed-out

This attribute of good application is incarnational.[22] It looks to implement the principle in daily practice. It informs the listener's commitment to think, feel, and behave differently.

Focused

When an application zeroes in on particular issues of thought, attitude, and action, it is like the burning-hot concentration of sunlight as it passes through a magnifying glass held the right distance from an object. It is specific, pointed, and related to real needs; not diffuse, vague, or frivolous. As a result, it ignites change.

Fresh

Applications should avoid repeating tired, worn-out phrases and clichés. It may seem that virtually every sermon could be reduced to "trust and obey," or "read your Bible and pray," or "God is sovereign, but man is responsible." But this is not the time to generalize. Applications answer the question, "So what?" in the specific language of the listener's real circumstances.

Forceful

Finally, applications should pack a punch. Like the closing argument of a trial lawyer, a good application calls for the listener to render his or her verdict on the case just presented. It makes a short, pointed, simple appeal to the will. This should not be a high-pressure sales pitch, feisty challenge, or emotional manipulation. Neither does good application flatter or make outlandish promises. It simply guides the listener to accept the challenge of actually doing what he knows is in his own best interest. Forceful application urges him to explore, discover, and *do* what God wants him to do by exposing the contemporary implications of the timeless truth.

In the Whiting Method, guidelines for the development of good applications include their need to be *related* and *relational*. When they are related, they discreetly address specific needs of people as individuals without calling attention to particular individuals. Relational applications are communicated with the compassion of a preacher who is transparent about the impact of the truth on his own life, not that the sermon is *about* the preacher, but that he speaks to his audience as one of them.

Invitation

An invitation is simply the call for a particular personal response to God in light of His Word. Its purpose is to urge timely implementation of biblical principles while choices are clear. It is not necessarily an "altar call" to physically walk to a place of decision,[23] but an opportunity to decide on a change of thinking, feeling, and/or behaving.[24]

Invitations have been described as addressing the whole person, intellect, emotion, will, and conscience. Commending the argument of the discourse to the mind of the listener appeals to his *intellect*. Communicating the feeling of urgency to respond to the heart of God addresses the *emotions*. Calling for a conscious personal decision that is clear and specific, addresses the *will*. Appealing to the listener's heightened sense of right and wrong addresses his *conscience*.

Introduction

The introduction of a message precedes the theme and proof of the text. In Richard's and Bredfeldt's comparison of a Bible lesson to a plane flight, the goal of the introduction, or "hook," is to achieve liftoff with all passengers on board and en route to a safe landing at the desired destination.[25]

It has been said, "You only get one chance to make a first impression." This indicates the importance of the sermon introduction. Once the rest of the sermon has been prepared, you know the destination of the flight. The next task is to decide how best to sell tickets to prospective passengers. One of several dangers to avoid is overselling. This can easily result from preparing the introduction first. Jones has dubbed this problem as giving "a *Cadillac*—introduction to a *Ford*—body and conclusion."[26] Another problem is the tendency to preach your introduction rather than your sermon!

The introduction has been compared to the porch of a building, a stepping-stone, and a driveway.[27] It is only the entrance and should not be made so attractive that people won't move past it! Introductions are meant to prepare people to listen by getting and holding their attention. French general Napoleon once reportedly remarked, "The first five minutes of battle are decisive ones." It is during these early moments that a connection must be established between you and the people. The audience is deciding whether the message will be worth listening to based on what they perceive *you* to be. Introductions also let the audience in on what the sermon is about and awaken their interest in the subject.

Sometimes planes take off in the opposite direction of their destination due to weather conditions or airway traffic. Sermons, generally, should not. The best introductions are directly in line with the theme of the text.

A brief "introduction" offers a functional entryway to a home. It invites people to move, as directly as possible, from the front door to the dinner table. A similar sermon introduction can be described as *suggestive*, *simple*, and *relational*. It is *suggestive* in that it simply whets the appetite, as does a hors d'oeuvre, rather than spoiling the meal with too much food. It is *simple* because it only arouses the listener's curiosity, instead of overwhelming him or her with something too ornate or detailed. A simple introduction may state the title, give the reason for its choice, and tell its relation to life situations. Effective introductions are *relational* when they invite a warm audience response.

Ideas for introductions may be found in any number of possible sources. You may need to determine if the text is familiar, commonly misunderstood, controversial, or relevant to a current event. From the context, how does the Scripture passage fit the theme or argument of the chapter, book, etc.? What historical, geographical, and cultural settings might need to be explained to set up the sermon? On special days, including traditional holidays and anniversaries, seasonal or memorial emphases may suggest appropriate introductions. At Halloween, for example, it may be suitable in some settings to begin a sermon by temporarily putting on a mask to depict Satan's tactic of disguising his true identity (see 2 Corinthians 11:14), or the believer's tendency to masquerade in the mannerisms of the world (see Romans 12:2).

Newspaper and magazine articles can provide ways of taking people from what is presently on their minds to where their attention needs to move. (Media sources should first be checked for accuracy and relevance to the theme of the text.)

Other sources of introduction include the occasion for a guest speaker's invitation to speak. Personal observations of human nature or overheard conversations with one's barber, gas station attendant, fellow travelers, etc. can give the preacher a way to establish common ground. Finally, a variety of published sources of illustrations and humor are often indexed by subject and/or Scripture reference and can provide historical or hysterical "hooks."

Here, the sermon from Proverbs 2: 1-9, seen in an earlier example, is introduced with a bit of humor from a published source.[28] This is to get the listener's attention, cause him to chuckle, and start him or her thinking about the difference between human wisdom, which is merely *clever*, and divine wisdom, which is synonymous with *character*. (See figure 5-7.)

Textual introductions refer listeners to the passage under consideration. They set the stage for the message by giving the background for the text. Stories and skits are another type of introduction. (When using these, avoid being overly dramatic.) Another handy way to introduce a sermon is by using the text's topic as a *springboard*. Stating key problems that people face can build interest. Occasionally it is appropriate to simply announce the subject of the sermon, as in a more academic setting. You can also use a striking quotation as an introduction, but be sure to carefully identify the source and quote it accurately.

> **Discovering the Knowledge of God**
>
> Proverbs 2:1–9
>
> *John and Dave were hiking when they spotted a mountain lion staring at them. John froze in his tracks, but Dave sat down on a log, tore off his hiking boots, pulled a pair of running shoes from his backpack, and hurriedly began to put them on.*
>
> *"For crying out loud! You can't outrun a mountain lion!" John hissed.*
>
> *"I don't have to," said Dave, with a shrug. "I just have to outrun you."*
>
> There are many concepts of wisdom. Dave's wisdom was clever; but God's wisdom involves character. The proverbs before us today teach that **the wise work hard to find what God gives.**

Figure 5.7

(How many times has a quotation from German Reformation leader Martin Luther been mistakenly attributed to 1960s' Civil Rights leader Martin Luther King Jr.?)

Good introductions sometimes make use of rhetorical, challenging, or provocative questions, with pauses to allow people to ponder issues the sermon will later address. Beginning with a definition of a word, either from a dictionary or from your use of a key term, can also be a suitable introduction.

When comparing contrasting political views or doctrinal stances, do not unnecessarily alienate part of the audience by taking a potentially controversial personal position. By the same token, correcting a doctrinal error in an introduction requires skill to avoid leaving the impresssion that those believed to be in error are being personally attacked.

Object lessons, references to literature or movies, multimedia presentations, and songs are examples of other ways to introduce the sermon.

Avoid being abrupt in any sermon introduction. This can seem rude to listeners. It is also counterproductive to make excuses for either yourself or your subject. Dogmatism or erroneous facts can close people's minds. You should also avoid developing the introduction with multiple points that form a mini-sermon in itself. Also, using the same approach too often will certainly blunt its ability to hook the listener.

In composing introductions, determine exactly what you're trying to accomplish. Review the message to make sure the introduction actually *introduces* it! Whether you manuscript the entire message or not, write out the introduction, committing the first sentence of it to memory. Then deliver the introduction with the enthusiasm of one sold on what he is about to say.

Introducing 1 John 2:1-2

Following is one of many ways that the message of 1 John 2: 1-2 could be introduced. (See figure 5-8.)

Courtroom drama is a staple of American entertainment. Questions of justice seem to captivate the imaginations of TV viewers. But mention the phrase "defense attorney," and the name that jumps to mind may not be Perry Mason or Matlock, but Johnnie Cochran. Cochran led the so-called dream team that successfully won the acquittal of celebrity O. J. Simpson in 1995. Simpson, a famous football player, sports commentator, and actor, had been charged with murdering two people, including his wife. When the longest jury trial in California history ended, having involved 150 witnesses and costing $15 million, everyone seemed to have a different opinion.

People have a God-given capacity to make judgments. As a result of sin, they are also subject to the judgment of God. For Christians, sin raises tough questions. On one hand, how can those who sin stand before the God of absolute justice? On the other hand, if the blood of Jesus has cleansed them, why should it matter that they sin? The answer to these questions involves a greater courtroom drama than any on earth. You see, **when believers sin, Christ is their righteous Advocate.**

Figure 5.8

Summary and Conclusion

Like a bridge, every expository sermon consists of parts that have to be understood and put together carefully. For structural soundness, good planning is indispensable. The introduction, written last, gets attention and directs thought to the text for the truth that meets the needs it surfaces.

The body of a sermon must be structurally adapted to the preacher, the audience, and their circumstances. Dividing and subdividing the text distinguishes the vital forces that give the text its punch and make the sermon work. When these main points are styled and ordered, the flow of thought is unobstructed. When they are appropriate, illustrations help listeners pay attention and visualize abstract concepts.

Well-crafted conclusions give the audience a way to remember the gist of the sermon. This gives them a more condensed basis for deciding how to respond. Applications bring listeners back to the present from their consideration of timeless truths recorded in the context of the ancient past. They guide hearers in a process of self-application that results in commitment to implement changed thinking, attitudes, and actions in the future. The invitation simply calls individuals to timely action by appealing to their total personalities, minds, wills, emotions, and consciences.

Discussion Questions

1. What are clear and meaningful differences between a structured sermon and a presentation of God's Word that might be called a running commentary, devotional, exhortation, theological discourse, Bible talk, etc.?

2. Isn't a *good* unstructured presentation of a passage better than a structured homily that isn't as good? Are you convinced that the advantages of a well-built sermon are actually worth the effort it takes to build it? Do you truly believe that the average person who attends a preaching service really needs, wants, appreciates, and responds better to a polished, artistic sermon than to an informal talk?

3. Describe ways that the structural integrity of a sermon may be weakened.

4. List and describe the components of a sermon that must be understood and assembled.

5. Why should the sermon introduction be written last?

6. What are the advantages when the body of the sermon is adapted? divided? styled? ordered? developed?

7. Briefly describe the qualities of an effective conclusion by explaining what is meant by *streamlined, simple, short, summary*, and *skillful.*

8. What is meant by *factual,fleshed-out, focused, fresh*, and *forceful* when describing effective applications?

9. How is an invitation different from an altar call, and why do you agree or disagree that every sermon should have one?

10. Describe a good introduction.

CHAPTER 6

The Classifications of an Expository Sermon

Suspension bridges are only one kind of bridge, and not all of them are alike. The particular need and purpose of a bridge depends on many factors. As can be seen from this picture of the Sundial Bridge over the Sacramento River near Redding, California, the form and style of a bridge also reflect the imagination of the designer. (See figure 6-1.) The same is true of Scripture and should be true of sermons.

Kinds of sermons differ partly because, like the land of the Bible, the literature of the Bible varies dramatically. To treat God's Word as a paved parking lot with uniform spaces, in which answers to man's questions are neatly parked in accessible rows, is not only naive but dishonoring to the artistry of the Author. The infinite God has revealed Himself through the hills, valleys, rivers, cities, and deserts of diverse literature. Narrative, law, poetry, wisdom, and apocalyptic genres comprise a broad spectrum through which God has communicated His dual programs to redeem lost sinners and establish the reign of His Son upon the earth. The Word was written by people, and to people, who represent the full range of personalities, in circumstances that run the gamut of human experience. As a result, several types of sermons are needed in a pulpit ministry committed to declaring the whole purpose of God to all kinds of people. (See Acts 20:27.) They include the *paragraph sermon, chapter sermon, book sermon, doctrinal sermon, biographical sermon, parable sermon, gospel sermon*, and the preaching of *biblical types*.

Figure 6.1

The Paragraph Sermon[1]

The paragraph sermon is short enough for an intensive exegesis, but long enough for a sermon. It is practical and flexible enough for any situation.

The paragraph is the most frequently used unit for preaching, because a paragraph expresses a single unit of thought. Where it begins and ends is determined by the context. In narrative, paragraphs are often marked by references to time, called *temporal markers*. To determine the natural breaks in narrative, it is often helpful to read the text aloud. The texts of the Greek New Testament are usually more reliable in determining the limits of a paragraph than most English translations, which sometimes impose chapter divisions in the middle of a thought.[2] An example is found in the paragraph of 1 Corinthians 13:1-13, which actually begins with the second half of 12:31.

[Note: Non-language users may benefit from a perusal of figures 6-2 and 6-3 but are welcome to skip to the next section if they so desire.]

Language users will find that grammatical diagrams and/or mechanical layouts can be very helpful in identifying the subject, predicate, object, conclusion, etc., that express a complete idea.[3] (See figures 6-2 and 6-3.)

Paragraphs that deal with concrete subject matter are generally more "preachable" than those whose subjects are abstract or problematic, such as the baptism for the dead, in 1 Corinthians 15:29-34. The content of some paragraphs will suggest themselves for weddings, funerals, holidays, and other special occasions. Just make sure that your selections fit your stage of development as an exegete. For example, long or difficult paragraphs, such as 1 Peter 3:13-22, are better tackled when you have gained some experience.[4]

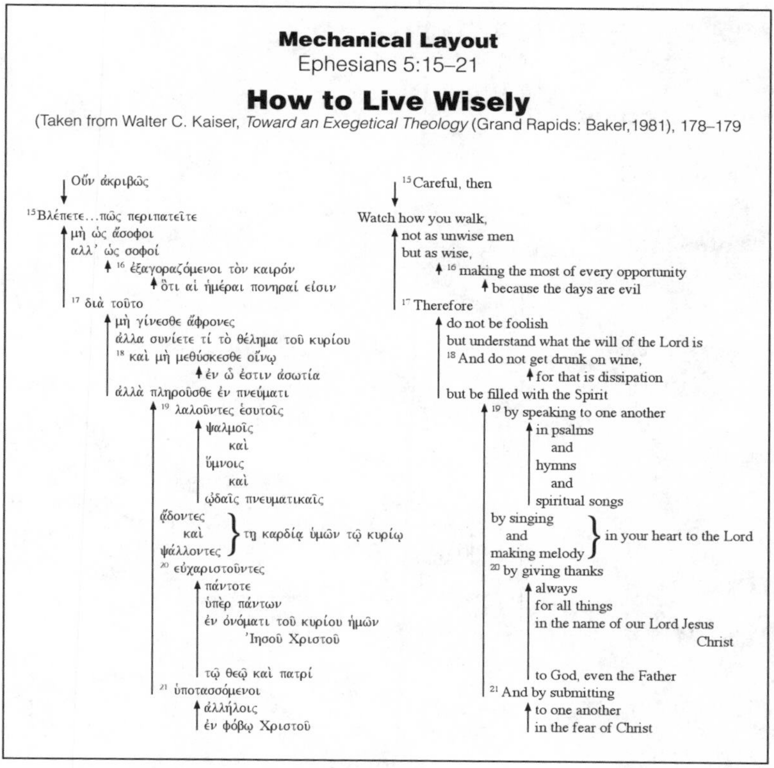

Figure 6.2

Grammatical Diagram,
Ephesians 5:15–21
How to Live Wisely

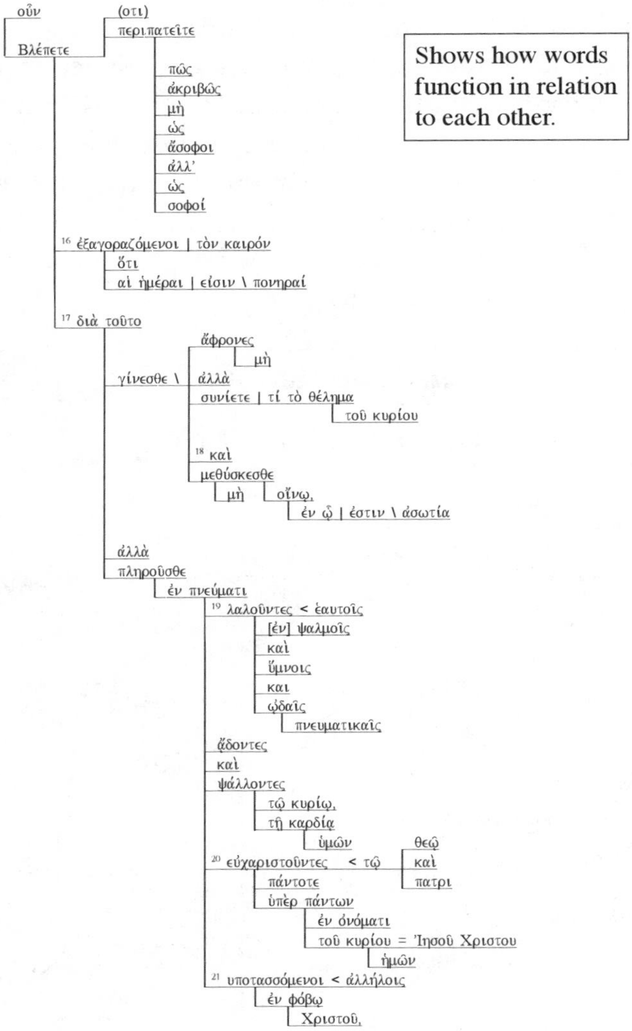

Figure 6.3

There are eight types of paragraph sermons.[5] *Narrative* paragraphs represent one episode that is part of a longer story, such as Abraham's offering of Isaac (Gen. 22:1-19). The parable of the lost sheep (Luke 15:3-7) is an example of a *discourse*. Isaiah 12:1-6 is a *poetic strophe*, or stanza, like the verse of a song. The apostle Paul's commendation of Epaphroditus, in Philippians 2:25-30, is called a *character sketch*. In 3 John 9, Diotrephes could be developed as a *career character*. An *event* is represented in the account of Jacob's wrestling with the Angel of Yahweh in Genesis 32:22-30. The apostle Paul's discussion of justification by faith, in Romans 3:27-30, is an example of a *doctrinal* paragraph sermon. *Problem paragraphs* include such passages as Matthew 19:3-9, where Jesus responds to a question (whether it is ever permissible to divorce and remarry).

The Chapter Sermon[6]

A chapter sermon is a textual expository message woven from the fabric of an entire chapter of the Bible. Chapter sermons confirm and utilize commonly accepted divisions of Bible books, which are thus easily identifiable and memorable as literary units. They can be developed and presented *on their own*, without being part of an ongoing series through the Bible book in which they are found, or they can be part of a series of great chapters on a topic, like giving (2 Cor. 8-9; Phil. 4, etc.); the rapture of the church (1 Thess. 4; 1 Cor. 15, etc); or rewards (1 Cor. 3; 2 Cor. 5). Several chapters of the Bible have been recognized as *classical* passages.[7] Examples include Genesis 2, "Why We Are What We Are"; Zechariah 4, "The Secret of True Strength"; 1 Corinthians 13, "The Love Chapter," and Hebrews 11, "The Hall of Faith."

Chapters, properly divided, lend themselves as texts for single sermons, especially when they concern a single subject. However, not every chapter is centered around a single person, place, event, or idea. Acts 16, for example, encompasses five separate accounts: The selection and circumcision of Timothy, Paul's Macedonian vision, Lydia's conversion, Paul and Silas's imprisonment, and the Philippian jailer's conversion. It is not impossible to preach all five of these accounts in one sermon, showing how they relate to Paul's second missionary journey, but chapter sermons usually develop an integrated whole.

Chapter sermons are developed by carefully reading the chapter and tracing the argument of the book to confirm proper chapter divisions and understanding the context. Next, the key portion of the chapter must be fully exegeted, noting how every element in the chapter supports the theme. Finally, the chapter must be clearly set in its historical, literary, and theological contexts. (See figure 6-4.)

The Book Sermon[8]

The text of a *book sermon* is an entire book of the Bible. Though they are the most difficult of all sermons to prepare, book sermons benefit both preacher and congregation. According to Jones, "it enables them to see a whole rather than such concentrated detail that the overall understanding is dissipated."[9] But there are obstacles to overcome in order to realize the advantages of preaching a whole book at a time. One is the listeners' predisposition to resist messages that they perceive as being too long. The very idea of covering even a one-chapter book, such as 2 John, Philemon, or Obadiah may seem daunting. However, the panoramic overview of whole books of the Bible is a very important part of a healthy pulpit ministry. It provides the contextual background necessary for interpreting texts within the book, and can be a good way to introduce a series of messages through a book of the Bible that may even be lengthy.

Example, Chapter Sermon

1 Corinthians 13

I.	Nature of Love	1–3
II.	Necessity of Love	4–7
III.	Nobility of Love	8–13

Figure 6.4

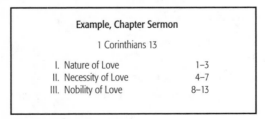

The large amount of text to be analyzed in most book sermons can also intimidate the preacher. It is best to prepare it over a period of several weeks, while working on less demanding sermons. Announcing an upcoming book sermon ahead of time, and encouraging the congregation to read the book several times in advance, can build interest and stimulate questions.

Becoming very familiar with the book's content by reading it several times in various translations (or, for LU, in the original text) will help you see where its natural divisions fall, and what verse or passage might suggest itself as most important to study thoroughly. Revelation 1:19 practically gives an outline for the entire book when it states, "Write the things which you have seen [ch.1], and the things which are [chs. 2-3], and the things which will take place after this [chs. 4-22]" (NKJV).

When preaching whole books, it is important to major on the author's reason for writing it. As the cast of a film supports the role of the star actor, tracing the thread, or threads, of minor themes is not only a legitimate part of analyzing the text, but is essential to the development of the book's "big idea."

A good way to build up to preaching book sermons is to tackle small ones first. For example, Dan once preached a series of messages entitled "Postcard Epistles," consisting of sermons on the one-chapter epistles of Philemon, 2 John, 3 John, and Jude. Figure 6-5 is an example of the development of 2 John.

Doctrinal Sermon[10]

The word *doctrine* is used here in reference to the collection and arrangement of the entire body of what the Bible teaches about a particular subject. A proper doctrinal sermon communicates the truth of divine revelation in a clear, cogent, concise manner, to evangelize the lost and edify the regenerate. First John 1:5-2:2, for example, deals with God's provision for the presence of sin.

In preaching doctrinal sermons, understand that they are to be *in*structive rather than *de*structive; your job is not to attack those who hold opposing views. Doctrinal sermons should develop a single, main idea, building upon elements that are clearly understood before progressing from one to another. The listener should be drawn to doctrinal preaching by the expectation of learning what God reveals about a subject, not the lure of slick titles or clever presentations.

The Truth of Love
2 John
Love Cannot Be Separated from Truth

I. Truth Binds Believers Together in Love	1–3
II. Truth Governs Believers' Walk in Love	4–6
A. Walking in Truth Determines Love for One Another	
B. Walking in Obedience Demonstrates Love for One Another	
III. Truth Makes Believers' Love Discriminating	7–13
A. Deceivers Are on the Loose	
B. Rewards Are on the Line	
C. Fellowship Is Limited by Doctrine	

Figure 6.5

Because doctrinal sermons are essentially textual-topical expository messages, only the Scripture text is more important than the sermon's subject. Therefore, the sermon's title can generate interest and stimulate curiosity—or fail to do so. Titles can also be useful for informing the public and preparing the congregation. Creating innovative titles helps broaden your own thinking about the message. Consider the following titles for their attention-grabbing quality. (See figure 6-6.)

Attention-Grabbing Titles of Doctrinal Sermons	
Noun and Phrase:	"Payday Someday!" (R. G. Lee)
The direct or indirect question:	"Why Do Bad Things Happen to God's People?" (Warren Wiersbe)
Heading and a question:	"Man: Why on Earth Was He Made?"
Double Title:	"Israel and the Future"
Direct Address:	"Let the Church Be the Church"
Clarity of sentence:	"Jesus Is a Friend of Sinners"
Using part of a text:	"'Not My Will'"

Figure 6.6

Every sermon should answer one question: "So what?" Since every doctrine answers questions, solves problems, and meets needs, always state the doctrine's purpose in your theme. For example, in Ephesians 5:18, the command to be filled with the Holy Spirit is parallel to the command to understand what the will of the Lord is (v. 17). Both are given in the context of conducting one's life wisely in evil days (vv. 15-16). The theme, then, of 5:18-20, could be stated, "*Living wisely in evil days requires the Spirit's control.*"

As noted in Chapter 2, the supernatural origin and spiritual quality of Bible doctrine make it difficult for immature believers to comprehend. (See Hebrews 5:11-14.) Its meaning may seem abstract. Its truth may have been obscured by false teaching or poor presentation in the past. So the clarity of doctrinal sermons is of utmost importance. It has often been said, "A mist in the pulpit is fog in the pew."[11] Since doctrinal sermons tend to be mentally demanding, they should be moderate in length.

Intellectual honesty is crucial to your credibility in preaching all kinds of sermons. It is especially important to avoid exaggeration, generalities, half-truths, inaccurate quotations, and jumping to conclusions when presenting doctrines that are invariably contradicted by opponents. When preaching doctrines of the future, exercise discipline to avoid sensationalism, and refuse to set dates or speculate about symbols. The simple, safe guideline is: never claim more than the Scriptures support.

After determining the topic of a doctrinal sermon, find and study every Scriptural reference to the subject. The goal is to discover how each passage relates to the doctrine. What contribution does it make? Group the verses according to the areas of doctrine and thought.

The Biographical Sermon[12]

Biographical sermons are of two kinds. *Objective* biographical sermons deal with the entire life cycle of a biblical character. They are often arranged chronologically so as to demonstrate God's ability to work in the listener's life as He has worked in the character's life. The life of John the Baptist shows God's use and praise of a man whose life seemed to end in defeat.

Subjective biographical sermons develop the story of someone's life according to themes and lessons determined by the preacher independently of explicit statements. For example, the life of Samson can be developed around the idea that he was a tragic hero. Lessons can be drawn from the life and death of Judas Iscariot.

The value of biographical sermons is that they reveal character. For example, in light of David's great sins, God still evaluates David as a man after His own heart (1 Sam. 13:14; Acts 13:22), a description that bears analysis.

Biographies relate the truth of God's Word to the daily lives of listeners who can identify with the characters studied. Whether they leave us in admiration and hope, or rebuked and without excuse, biographies utilize the method of the Holy Spirit to communicate truth through the experiences of real people. (See 1 Corinthians 10: 11.)

To prepare for biographical sermons, collect all of the biblical material needed to reconstruct the person's life. (Be careful not to confuse different individuals with the same name[13]) Then organize the material using some scheme. A chronological analysis of Moses' life reveals three periods of forty years. The life of Peter might be arranged in reference to before and after his critical denials of Christ. Jacob's story can be told on the basis of various experiences that are recorded. Joseph and Daniel might be described in terms of their dramatic changes in status. Outstanding lessons from the stories of characters such as Ruth, Esther, and Job provide another way to arrange the biblical information about them.

In synthesizing (generalizing, or principlizing) the biographical sermon, do not allow a character's reputation to prejudice your attitude. Lot, for example, must be evaluated on the basis of what Scripture actually says about him. Keep details in perspective so they do not overly influence people's perceptions. Obvious flaws in the good kings of Judah, for example, should not be allowed to obscure their overall character and influence. The life lesson of a character can also be spoiled by spending too much sermon time on a relatively minor point.

Pertinent questions that lead to the discovery of useful information make preparing biographical sermons similar to detective work. What sort of person is the subject? How did the subject come to have this character? What are the results of this individual's manner of life? What is the subject's national and cultural background?

Biographical sermons are an exception to the Whiting Method's rule forbidding the use of proper names in the statement of sermon themes. The following biographical sermon on Apollos is a good example of this application of the Whiting Method. (See figure 6-7.)

Title: God's Kind of Person
Texts: Acts 18:24–28; 1 Corinthians 16:12

Introduction:
Within the church there is an ongoing struggle between the mind and the heart, between head knowledge and doers of the Word of God, between orthodoxy and orthopraxy.

I. Apollos Was a Man of the Word
- A. He was a well-educated Greek (vv. 24–25) **MIND**
  1. He was a trained Greek from Alexandria (v. 24)
  2. He was mighty in the Word (v. 24)
- B. He was a faithful follower of Christ
  1. He was instructed in the way of the Lord (v. 25)
  2. He was fervent in Spirit (v. 25) **EMOTION**
- C. He was eager to teach the Word (v. 25) **WILL**
  1. He spoke accurately
  2. He spoke boldly, or openly (v. 26)
  3. He refuted the unbelieving Jews publicly (v. 28)

Theme: Apollos was a man of the Word and a servant to believers

II. Apollos Was a Servant to Believers
- A. He greatly helped the ones who believed (vv. 27–28)
  1. He longed to help believers (v. 27)
  2. He helped them in their Christian growth (v. 27)
  3. He helped them against their opposition (v. 28)
- B. He wanted to be beneficial to Paul at Corinth (1 Cor. 16:12)
  1. He delayed his trip to Corinth to avoid the party rivalry
  2. He would come to Corinth when Paul was fully recognized

Theme: Apollos was a man of the Word and a servant to believers

Figure 6.7

The Parable Sermon[14]

The parable sermon requires special consideration of the parable as a literary figure of speech. Zuck defines a parable as "a form of figurative language involving comparisons,"[15] a "true-to-life story to illustrate or illuminate a truth."[16] He adds, "Since parables are true to life, they differ from allegories and fables."[17]

In the New Testament, a parable is a fictitious narrative, true to life, designed for the purpose of teaching[18] a specific kingdom truth to those with receptive hearts, and to conceal them from those whose hearts are unreceptive to the truth presented (see Matthew 13:11-15). Thompson states, "In the context of prophecy a parable reveals something about a specific, crisis situation. Most parables in the Gospels interpret and illumine in some way the crisis situation created by the presence of Jesus."[19] Parables are persuasive in purpose, seeking to evoke a decision by presenting a critical choice. Parables perpetuate the truth by picturing it in such a way that it sticks in the mind, potentially convicting the unreceptive person when recalled at a later date.

Parables may be classified in various categories, including *parabolic sayings, similitudes, example-stories*, and *symbolic parables. Parabolic sayings* are short statements that could be expanded into figurative narrative. One example is found in Matthew 15:14, where Jesus said, "Let them alone. They are blind leaders of the blind. And if the blind leads the blind, both will fall into a ditch" (NKJV). Jesus used parabolic sayings mostly during his early ministry.[20]

A *similitude* is the expansion of a germ parable into a generalization. Similitudes describe familiar objects or phenomena for multiple, present application. An example is the parable of the ninety-nine sheep, in Luke 15:4-6. It is based on what any shepherd would do.

Example-stories are typical-case parables. They present a general truth by a specific example from the same realm. The Samaritan epitomized the good neighbor in the parable of Luke 10:30-37. Other examples include the rich fool (Luke 12:16-21), the rich man and Lazarus (Luke 16:19-31), and the Pharisee and the publican as they prayed in the temple (Luke 18:9-14).

Symbolic parables teach truths about relationships by describing things from everyday life. The prodigal son, in Luke 15, and the parable of the tares, in Matthew 13, are examples.

Parables are naturally persuasive, often incorporating facts, specifics, illustration, comparisons, contrasts, and testimony. The parables of Matthew 13, if not all New Testament parables, teach truth needed to properly understand how the Church relates to the kingdom of God during this time between the first and second comings of Christ (see

Matthew 3:10-17).[21] As does every good sermon, parables strike for a decision by appealing to the will.

To interpret a parable, the first step is to recover the original setting. To whom was the parable spoken, and under what circumstances? What can be learned from parallel passages, as well as from prologues, epilogues, etc.? What is the problem the parable was given to solve? It is usually stated in the context, but sometimes as far removed as the preceding chapter. What are the principle elements of the narrative? A mechanical layout (illustrated by figure 6-8) can help expose how the parable is structured. Who did what, when, where, how, and why? The goal is to seek the central truth. It is the solution to the problem at hand. Avoid trying to make the parable "walk on all fours." It is not an allegory, in which every detail has a representative meaning, but a story with one point, or a few points, of resemblance. Properly identifying the central truth makes it possible to determine which details actually contribute to the central truth, and which serve as "window dressing" to enhance and embellish it.[22]

The interpretation of a parable should be evaluated for proper perspective and balance. The central truth will never contradict the clear teaching of Scripture elsewhere. For example, interpreting the parable of the prodigal son (Luke 15:11-32) as teaching how a sinner may be justified could lead to the conclusion that a sinner may naturally come to his senses and come to God. This contradicts the doctrine of justification by grace alone, through faith alone, as taught in Romans 3:10 and Ephesians 2:1-10.

An interpretation that is consistent with the rest of Scripture is that the parable of the prodigal son, like the parables of the lost sheep and lost coin, teaches God the Father's concern for heirs of the Abrahamic covenant who are not enjoying its blessings. It answers the question of why Jesus spent so much time with sinners. Jesus had the Father's concern for disenfranchised Israelites. The religious leaders of Israel, like the prodigal's elder brother, did not. The fact that the prodigal was already the son of his father, is, therefore, a detail that contributes to the central truth. That the elder son failed to share his father's joy over the restoration of his wayward brother is another detail that enhances the central truth.

Finally, determine the intended appeal. What is the verdict for which the parable is appealing—not only to the intellect, but also the conscience and will?

Essential Elements of Various Parables

(1) **Good and Bad Fruit Trees,** Matthew 7:16–20.
Context: Sermon on the Mount, warning false teachers
Problem: How can you spot a false teacher?
Central Truth: The false teachers are those whose lives do not produce spiritual fruit

(2) **Bridegroom and Fasting,** Matthew 9:14.
Context: Disciples are not fasting
Problem: Why doesn't Jesus promote fasting?
Central Truth: Fasting on the part of the groomsmen is inappropriate as long as the Bridegroom is here!

(3) **New Patch and Old Garment,** Matthew 9:16.
Context: The parable of the Bridegroom's leaving has just been given.
Problem: Why will the Bridegroom be absent?
Central Truth: Israel is beyond repair and must be reformed!

(4) **New Wine in Old Wineskins,** Matthew 9:17
Context: Same
Problem: Same
Central Truth: Israel's history of inflexibility in response to the Holy Spirit has become crystallized.

Figure 6.8

The following statement by Ellisen summarizes proper interpretation of parables:

> It is, then, proper to consider the interpretation to be correct and complete if the historical context has not been distorted and the grammatical context has been duly expounded. The central truth will then correspond consistently with the basic elements of the story, and the significant details will enhance and enforce this central thrust. An indictment will usually be found, explicit or implicit, coupled with an appeal relative to the kingdom program. These basic elements will usually be seen, embroidered with details of realism which give the parable its uncontestable argumentative force.[23]

Examples of parables, given in figure 6-8, demonstrate the three essential elements to consider in preparing to preach the parables: the *context*, the *problem*, and the *central truth*.[24]

From the parables of Matthew 13, outlined in figure 6-9, a potential series of nine messages is indicated in bold-face type. (Though this figure reflects our theological perspective, the principles of the parables are true even if one holds to another theological perspective.[25])

Preaching the Parables

"The truths of the parables are to be applied to purposes of practical utility for current life situations and spiritual growth," says Ellisen.[26] But he gives three important precautions. First, allegorizing the parables, assigning meaning to insignificant elements, forfeits the power

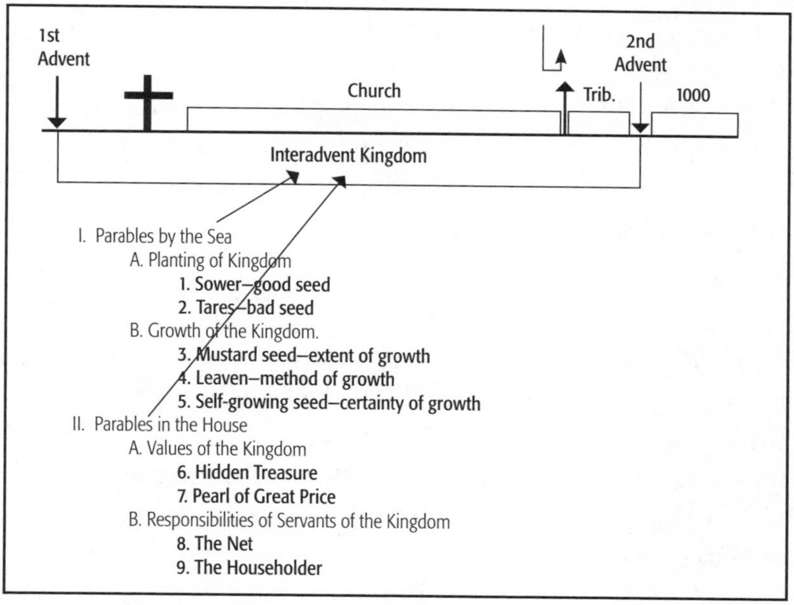

Figure 6.9

and blessing of the Holy Spirit and leaves the listener uncertain of the intended meaning. Second, preaching fragmented segments of the parables disrespects the unity of the figure and risks missing the central truth. Finally, application must proceed from proper interpretation.[27]

Stated positively, to properly preach the parables, you must observe dispensational distinctions, extract doctrine cautiously, and maintain simplicity.[28]

Dispensational Distinctions. You do not need to be a *dispensationalist* to appreciate the fact that the New Testament parables, when interpreted contextually, generally teach principles concerned with the responsibilities of believers within the household of faith. They generally do not deal with saving faith or eternal destiny.[29] When the central truth is discovered as the answer to a question or problem found within the context, it should be stated as a generalization. For example, the parable of the sower teaches the principle that God's Word is productive only in the hearts of individuals prepared to receive it.

Doctrine. Like "all Scripture," the New Testament parables are "profitable for doctrine" (2 Tim. 3: 16-17 NKJV). However, the doctrine gleaned from a parable must be balanced by the teaching of *every other* relevant passage of Scripture in its context.

Simplicity. The very nature of the parables is such that their meaning is simple, clear, and forthright to the *spiritually receptive*. "The further exposition strays from the natural and obvious meanings and indulges in intricate analogies, the less likely is the original intention served."[30]

The Gospel Sermon[31]

The gospel (or evangelistic) sermon is distinguished by its direct address to those who have not yet believed in the Lord Jesus Christ. It is further described by its intention to bring the listener to conviction of sin and willingness to receive the Bible's good news of forgiveness of sins and eternal life through faith in the Lord Jesus Christ. In light of Romans 1:16, the importance of such sermons can hardly be overstated: "For I am not ashamed of the gospel of Christ, for it is the power of God to salvation for everyone who believes, for the Jew first and also for the Greek" (NKJV). No person has been, or can be, saved apart from the Holy Spirit (Titus 3:5) and, with the exception of Adam and Eve, some human instrument (Rom. 10: 14). As important as evangelistic preaching is, the church primarily gathers for worship, not for evangelism. However, two facts bear consideration when discussing gospel preaching. First, unbelievers, including young children, visitors, and, possibly, those who falsely claim to believe in Christ, are often present at worship services. Second, expository preaching of the gospel occurs on occasions other than the church worship services, including special meetings and outreach activities.

There are distinct advantages to preaching messages designed to present the way of salvation. (See figure 6-10.)

Advantages of Preaching Messages Designed to Present the Way of Salvation

- Teaches the saved how to explain the gospel
- Wins some of the lost
- Clarifies the doctrine of salvation
- Gives insight into people's problems
- Alerts people to opportunities
- Keeps the pulpit *hot*

Figure 6.10

Areas covered by the gospel sermon include:

- the nature of man, guilt, and the consequences of sin
- the grace, power, and love of Christ
- the nature of salvation
- how to "receive Christ"
- how to escape sin's consequences
- an explanation of the "gospel" (1 Cor. 15:3–4)

Figure 6.11

The following areas should be covered by the gospel sermon. (See figure 6-11.)

The proper gospel message may be either topical-textual expository, or textual expository. *Topical-textual gospel sermons* present man's need of salvation because of sin, and God's provision in Christ. Like an evangelistic tract, they draw principles from a variety of relevant texts within their respective contexts. *Textual expository gospel sermons* develop these principles from the context of a *single* passage. Examples include Isaiah 53:4-6; John 3:16-21; and John 5:24-29.

Gospel sermons are adapted to various situations and circumstances but always address the consciences and wills of lost individuals.[32] They are straightforward, simple, and positively instructive. They are not clever, complex, or argumentative. If theological terminology must be used, it should be clearly explained and well illustrated. Your own testimony should be part of your presentation of the gospel, because it speaks of what you know to be true by personal experience. (See John 3:11; 4:22; Acts 2:32; 3:15-16; 22:3-21; 2 Corinthians 4:13-14; and 1 John 1:1-4.)

Preaching Old Testament Types[33]

Zuck defines a type as "an Old Testament person, event, or thing having historical reality and designed by God to prefigure (foreshadow) in a preparatory way a real person, event, or thing so designated in the New Testament and that corresponds to and fulfills (heightens) the type."[34]

Old Testament Types . . .

- Illustrate something future, but are *not* prophecy
- Consist of historical persons, objects or ceremonies, *not* visions or dreams
- Demonstrate divine appointment, *not* human concoction or imagination
- Are fulfilled in the New Testament, *not* the Old Testament
- Are distinguishable from other figures of speech

Figure 6.12

Ellisen describes how a *type* is distinguished from other kinds of revelation as follows (see figure 6-12):[35]

Unlike symbols, which were understood at the time they were given, types are more like pictures taken in the Old Testament and developed in the New.[36] Unlike parables, types are physical, not verbal. They are real, not fictitious. Unlike allegories, again, types are physical, not verbal, and bear only a few points of resemblance.

There are two kinds of Old Testament types: *innate* and *inferred*. *Innate types* are expressly identified as types in the New Testament, including typical people, things, and ceremonies. Examples of *typical people* are Adam (Rom. 5:14; 1 Cor. 15:22), Abel (Heb. 12:24), and Melchizedek (Heb. 5:6-10; 7:1-11). Examples of *typical things* include the sacrificial Lamb (John 1:29; Heb. 9:14), and manna in the wilderness (Ex. 16:14-30; John 6:34, 58). Manna pictured Christ in that it provided daily sustenance from heaven for the people of God in their time of need (Num. 11:8; John 6:51). It came down from heaven, was given by God as a free gift, and resulted in judgment when rejected (Num. 11). *Typical ceremonies* include offerings and feasts, most notably, Passover (Ex. 12; Lev. 23:4-8; 1 Cor. 5:7) and Sabbath (Lev. 23:1-3; Ex. 34:21; Heb. 4).[37]

Inferred types are not explicitly identified in the New Testament, but they parallel some aspect of Christ or New Testament truth with apparent intentionality on the part of the writer. Isaac is an example of an *inferred typical person*. Like Jesus, Isaac was his father's uniquely begotten son (Heb. 11:17; cf., John 3:16). His birth, too, was foretold, and his conception was miraculous. And, like Jesus, Isaac was offered by his father as a sacrifice, and voluntarily yielded to his father's purpose (Gen. 22). In these and other ways, Isaac provides an historic pattern and illustration of what God was determined to do in a greater way through the person of Christ. By the same token, important differences between a type and its fulfillment (antitype) often help to emphasize important truths by contrast. Jesus, for example, was not spared at the last moment, as Isaac was, but was actually slain as an offering for sin.

Joseph prefigured Christ by his father's love (Gen. 37:3), the record of his character without any mention of sin, his unjust suffering, his being hated and rejected by his brethren (Gen. 37:4, 8, 28; 39:17-18; Matt. 21:37-39; 27:19), his exaltation (Gen. 41), his Gentile bride (Gen. 41:45; Eph. 5:23), and his eventual recognition and reception by his brethren (Gen. 45:1-8; Zech. 12:10; Matt. 24:30).

Inferred *typical things* include:

- Noah's ark, resembling Christ as a place of deliverance from judgment (Gen. 6:17-18; Rom. 8:1; Heb. 6:18), having just one door (John 10:9), which God alone could shut (Gen. 7: 13; cf., John 10:28; Eph. 1:3); and

- cities of refuge (Num. 35; Heb. 6:8) which resembled Christ in that they were conspicuous and accessible to both Jews and Gentiles as long as the high priest lived (cf., Josh. 20:9; Gal. 3:27-29; Heb. 7:25; Rev. 22:17).

The history of interpreting Old Testament types reveals the problem of excess, finding types in virtually everything![38] This approach substitutes imagination for sound hermeneutical principles. It tarnishes the reputation of typology as a whole, and leads to false teaching. As someone has said, "the blessing does not justify the means." At the other extreme has been the problem of neglect, rejecting typology altogether.[39] This approach denies the artistry of biblical interpretation and ignores the value of "visual aids." Both theological liberalism and neoorthodoxy deny the unity of the Old and New Testaments, and so tend to view types simply as devices used by New Testament writers to illustrate Old Testament truth.

The mediating position recognizes legitimate types and has been thus called "the Golden Mean." Patrick Fairbairn (1805-1874) articulated this view, which was held during the apostolic period.[40] It holds that inferred types are validated by a consistent hermeneutical principle called "manifest analogy." The moderation of Fairbairn and more recent scholars is due to the development of principles that protect against extremes. Before surveying eight guidelines for interpreting types, Ellisen lists five reasons that the study of Old Testament types is valuable.

First, it refines and deepens one's understanding of the New Testament to observe how "the New is in the Old contained, and the Old is in the New explained."[41] Second, it deepens and broadens one's understanding and appreciation for the person and work of Christ throughout the Bible. Third, it serves as a biblical aid in teaching doctrine, especially in Christology and soteriology. Fourth, sound typology also has an apologetic value. It confirms divine inspiration by recognizing the prophetic character of the types. Fifth, principled typology emphasizes the value of the Old Testament for the believer today by demonstrating the unity of the whole Bible as given by a single author."[42]

Ellisen offers eight guidelines for interpreting Old Testament types.[43] First, the local setting of the type must be studied. "This forms the basis of the typical meaning, suggesting the purpose and character of the historical type."[44]

Second, applications must be based on the fulfillment of the type's purpose in history.[45] Third, the areas of resemblance and contrast between the type and antitype must be identified. These are usually found in the character, activity, or purpose of the type, often suggested by the New Testament. For example, while Abraham willingly offered his unique son, Isaac, God the Father actually sacrificed His.[46]

Fourth, this resemblance or contrast must be used to more sharply describe the type's analogy to the New Testament truth it anticipates.

Fifth, the type's quality as a *divine appointment* to prefigure New Testament truth (as opposed to a mere illustration or object lesson) must be emphasized.

Sixth, the analogy is not to be pressed or forced to *say* more than it was meant to from any point of resemblance.

Seventh, doctrines are not to be based on types alone, since, as Ellisen's handout states, "types are illustrations of doctrines taught in non-figurative language elsewhere."[47] Ellisen added that types challenge "the mind to accept or re-think a doctrine explicitly taught elsewhere, by showing how God foreordained and foreshadowed this truth in the times of the Old Testament shadows."[48]

Eighth, the advantage of New Testament hindsight in bringing into sharper focus the person and work of Christ must be recognized.

Preaching Old Testament types moves the student of Scripture in the *affective domain* of the heart, as well as addressing the *cognitive domain* of the head and the *behavioral domain* of the hands. It recognizes the value God Himself has placed on historical figures and word pictures. Types not only provide the mental images that colorfully portray the person and work of Christ, but do so in a way that carefully displays the sovereignty of God in fulfilling His plan of the ages!

The *film* exposed to the light of sanctified scholarship must be fully developed in the *darkroom* of your study, and appropriately displayed in the *gallery* of the congregation. Some of the most vivid pictures of the Lord Jesus Christ can only be seen in the Old Testament from the vantage point of New Testament hindsight.[49] Occasionally preaching a type, or series on the types, can change them from mere negatives in the minds of listeners to positive *proofs* that stimulate their desire for more. As preacher and people peer into the face of each portrait, they will revel in the sovereignty of the Artist. The decisions called for will be seen more clearly as part of one's well-reasoned service.

Summary and Conclusion

The rich variety of biblical literature, as well as the broad range of human needs, suggest the kinds of sermons surveyed in this chapter.

Paragraph sermons provide the mainstay, but there are no less than eight kinds! Doctrinal sermons are orderly presentations of what the Bible teaches on particular topics such as Scripture, man, sin, salvation, God, Christ, the Holy Spirit, Israel, the Church, and last things. They present a special challenge because they call for study of every passage of Scripture to determine how it relates to a particular truth. Chapter sermons must be carefully set in the context of the book. Book sermons help people see the big picture of a writer's theme and purpose, and how his book fits into the Bible as a whole.

Biographical sermons reveal character in ways that help people identify with the person whose life is under consideration.

Preaching the New Testament parables and Old Testament types, are specialties. Their interpretations and applications require careful observance of guidelines that yield rich rewards.

Gospel sermons are needed because there are usually unsaved people present in preaching services, and those who know the Lord need to see good examples of how the Bible's good news of eternal life through faith in Jesus Christ can be presented to those who don't yet know Him.

Discussion Questions

The following sermon is offered as an example of the Whiting Method. (See figure 6-13.) Answer the questions about this sermon to review the principles and guidelines in chapters 4-5.

1. What kind of sermon is it?
2. How is it styled?
3. Evaluate its use of typology.
4. How would you introduce, illustrate, and conclude such a sermon?

The Proof of Your Faith
Genesis 22:1–19

God Will Prove Your Faith in His Faithfulness to Provide

I. God Proves the Faith of His People (1–10)
- A. God Tested Abraham's Faith by Commanding Isaac's Sacrifice (1–2)
- B. Abraham Demonstrated Loyalty to God by Complete Obedience (3–10)
- C. God Proved Jesus' Commitment to His Word by Testing Him (Matt. 4:1–11)
- D. God Tests the Quality of Our Loyalty to Him (Rom. 5:3–4; 12:2; James 1:2–4; 1 Peter 1:6–7)

II. God Provides on the Basis of His Own Faithfulness (11–19)
- A. God Prevented Abraham from Harming Isaac (11–12)
- B. God Presented Abraham with a Substitute Lamb (13–14)
- C. God Promised to Keep His Covenant with Abraham (15–19)
  1. God swore by Himself (16)
  2. God honored Abraham's faith (18)
- D. God Blesses Us Through Our Faith in the Faithfulness of Christ (1 Cor. 1:9; Heb. 3:6)

Figure 6.13

PART III

Delivering the Development

Parts I and II were concerned with how to build the verbal bridge that conveys God's message through the unique agency of God's human instrument. Part III involves the assembly of the bridge to effectively transmit the truth.

Chapter 7, "The Characteristics of Effective Expositional Sermons," emphasizes the importance of messages that are authoritative, accurate, unified, organized, and passionate. Several styles of preparation are briefly examined and evaluated.

Chapter 8, "The Characteristics of Effective Expository Communicators," primarily deals with the preacher's need to be godly, relational and articulate.

CHAPTER 7

The Characteristics of Effective Expositional Sermons

A bridge can be a thing of breathtaking beauty, a photographer's delight, an artist's inspiration. But bridges are built primarily, not to admire, but to facilitate travel across barriers. One can argue that functionality *is* beautiful, but few would celebrate the design or appearance of a structure that didn't actually work. Different kinds of bridges work in different ways, but those that fulfill their purpose share common characteristics. They are structurally sound and well constructed of suitable materials. Despite radical differences in style and dimensions, every worthy bridge fulfills the same goal. A well-conceived design makes them all alike, in a manner of speaking. Similarly, all good sermons are alike in certain ways.

In this chapter we will briefly survey a few general characteristics of effective expositional sermons in conjunction with the Whiting Method of homiletics. Specifically, we will look at the pros and cons of three styles of preparation.

Sermons that do their job of bridging the communication gap all manifest the qualities of *authority, fidelity, order, movement, clarity*, and *passion*.[1] Each attribute contributes to the connection necessary to transmit timeless truth from the ancient world of the Bible to the contemporary world of your audience.

Authority

Not as the Scribes

Every effective expository preacher speaks with authority because the sermon communicates God's message. Unfortunately, there are many ways to squander and forfeit the effectiveness of divine authority. One way that even the least worthy speaker may steal the Creator's thunder is by relying on personal, human, finite expertise, knowledge, and wisdom. In accounting to the Author of Scripture, more than a few preachers might be asked the question God put to His servant Job: "*Who is this who darkens counsel by words without knowledge?*" (Job 38:2 NKJV).

With Job many speakers might be forced to admit, "You asked, 'Who is this who hides counsel without knowledge?' Therefore I have uttered what I did not understand, things too wonderful for me, which I did not know" (42:3 NKJV).

The effective power of God's Word is decimated by those who add their own puny authority to it, to "give it more oomph." Preachers have been accused of pounding the pulpit the hardest on the points of which they are the least certain. With dogmatism they have undermined their credibility. Or, in an attempt to humanly embellish, explain, defend, or politically correct the scriptural truth, they have diminished its impact.

Preachers also forfeit divine authority when they constantly quote (or plagiarize) the words of others. In these ways, the religious leaders of Israel provided the bland background against which the preaching of Jesus was all the more outstanding. Matthew 7:28-29 says, "And so it was, when Jesus had ended these sayings, that the people were astonished at His teaching, for He taught them as one having authority, and not as the scribes" (NKJV).

Not Authoritarian

To speak for God is to speak with His authority, not your own. As God the Son, Jesus could have spoken on His own authority. But as God the Son, with the addition of human nature, Jesus always did and said only what the Father initiated (see John 5:30; 8:28; 8:42; 12:49; 14:10). The only weapon He wielded against the devil's onslaught was the same "sword of the Spirit" with which the believer is armed: "the Word of God" (see Matthew 4:4 and Ephesians 6: 17).

Authoritative

Jesus and His apostles spoke what they knew by faith to be true. (See John 3:11; 4:22; and 2 Corinthians 4:13.) Accordingly, you should proclaim the things of which you are certain, based on prayerful study. Phrases such as "I think," or "I believe" express doubt or speculation that should be avoided. This is not to say that you should pretend to be sure about something uncertain. In fact, some texts present problems in which intellectual honesty requires the admitting of two or more possible solutions that must be decided on the basis of their merits. For example, one who interprets the days of Creation as literal, twentyfour-hour days would be remiss not to mention the bases on which some conservative scholars believe that the word *day* refers to longer periods of time.

Another example is found in 2 Kings 6:24-25. The sale of dove dung is mentioned in the context of a food shortage when the inhabitants of Jerusalem were under siege. This may or may not imply that dove droppings were eaten out of desperation. Author John Gray suggests that it refers to the use of bird manure for fuel.[2] Another possibility, noted in *Easton's Bible Dictionary*, is that "dove's dung" refers to "the seeds of a kind of millet, or a very inferior kind of pulse, or the root of the ornithogalum, i.e., bird-milk, the star-of-Bethlehem."[3] No matter what the correct interpretation, the point is clear: the besieged people of God were in dire straits! Though it may be impossible to say exactly what the author meant, a goal of the Whiting Method is to proclaim the point of the passage with the greatest possible confidence in the meaning of its supporting details.

Fidelity

Historical Accuracy

The fruit of faithful study is to "tell it like it is." Luke, the physician-historian and traveling companion of the apostle Paul, begins his Gospel with an emphasis on the historical accuracy of his research.

> Inasmuch as many have taken in hand to set in order a narrative of those things which have been fulfilled among us, just as those who from the beginning were eyewitnesses and ministers of the word delivered them to us, it seemed good to me also, having had perfect understanding of all things from the very first, to write to you an orderly account, most excellent Theophilus, that you may know the certainty of those things in which you were instructed. (1: 1-4 NKJV)

The need/desire of listeners to know the certainty of those things declared in expository preaching is met by those who are most effective. Like the book of Luke, the effective expository sermon should be painstakingly factual. When preaching the first eleven verses of Matthew 2, for example, the careful preacher will answer these questions: Were there really three magi who visited the Christ child in Bethlehem, or is this assumed because they brought *three* gifts? Were they *kings* ("We three kings of Orient are… ."), or did the hymn writer *assume* their royalty? Did they arrive at the manger along with the shepherds, or did they visit Jesus in a house more than a year later? When communicating God's Word, be careful to get the details right and explain what the average listener may not know.

For example, the gall given to Jesus on the cross fulfills the prophecy in Psalm 69:21. In Matthew 27:34, He refused to drink it, not because it tasted bad, but because it contained an opiate that would have lessened His pain. He was determined to endure the *full* punishment for sin, in the place of sinners—including the preacher and congregation!

Historically accurate sermon content enhances your ability to speak with God's authority. It also facilitates a single focus by keeping the sermon on track.

Unity

Focus. All effective sermons aim for a specific response, as if using a rifle rather than a shotgun. In the Whiting Method this is accomplished by developing the theme of a passage through the supporting outline that "grows" out of the text itself. An advantage of this approach is that it gives you a basis for emphasizing in the sermon what is emphasized in the text. As a result, the point of the sermon is the point of the biblical writer. This assumes intentionality on the part of the writer and implies your need to sort out what Kaiser calls the "authorial intent."[4] Though everything in the text is important, not everything in a given passage has equal prominence.

Integrity. The concept of unity also implies the connectivity and distillation of principles. In other words, the sermon not only "hangs together" structurally, so that it flows from one thought to the next, from beginning to end, but it has a center, like the nucleus of a cell. This organic unity of a sermon is especially important to its impact as a monologue. In the classroom or group Bible study, dialogue tends to decentralize the consideration of various principles in a passage, without adversely affecting its impact. A given discussion might, in this sense, involve several sermonettes. But when one person is speaking to a listening audience, the communication of a single, central, integrated, whole idea is the hallmark of the greatest effectiveness.

Order

Organization

When a sermon is centered in relation to its main thought, the *theme* of the passage, its organized development is very natural and beneficial. Every thought flows out of the one that precedes it, and the listener finds it easy to follow. A sense of progress toward a goal helps to gain and hold his attention. Regardless of the various learning styles represented in the congregation, an orderly presentation of truth helps listeners adapt the message to the way they learn.

Meaningfulness

In their book *Creative Bible Teaching*, Richards and Bredfeldt assert that "order and structure give meaning to information and ideas." To illustrate the point, they ask:

Which list of words is easier to remember? Which has more meaning?

1. dog, elephant, rabbit, mouse, whale, horse
2. mouse, rabbit, dog, horse, elephant, whale[5]

While the first list is random, the second moves from smaller to larger animals. In a similar way, sermon points that follow a logical sequence and are related to life experience are more apt to be understood and remembered.

Movement

Progress

Closely related to the organization of an effective expository sermon is its movement. People need to feel as if they are getting somewhere. If the concept of *order* is compared to a system of clearly marked surface roads, on-ramps, freeways, and exits, the concept of *movement* is comparable to the actual travel. No matter how desirable the destination, or how well mapped out the itinerary, a potential passenger will have little interest in riding with a driver who goes too slowly, gets stuck in traffic, takes a side trip or two along the way, or simply embarks on too long a journey for one day.

Impediments

External distractions, such as noise from nearby construction, a crying baby, or the persistent coughing of someone in the congregation, hinder a sermon's progress. Internal distractions, like hunger, anxiety, drowsiness, or preoccupation with relational difficulties, do the same. Whether external or internal, these things are not your responsibility as a preacher, because they are out of your control. Obstacles you *can* remove, however, include an excessive number of sermon points, too many details, unnecessary or ineffective illustrations, or too much time spent on minor issues.[6] In short, harness the power of condensation.

Economy

In her excellent book entitled *Words on Target*, author Sue Nichols emphasizes what she calls "the big three" qualities that emerge in successful writing. They are *economy, energy*, and *subtlety*. "Economy," she says, "means communicating without any unnecessary words. It means saying things quickly, using short words in short paragraphs."[7] The elements to be described or explained should be prioritized. Invariably, good material will be left on the *editing floor* so that what is most needful can be presented uncluttered. The length of time spent on each element of the sermon will be proportional to its importance.

Moderation

Effective expositors *moderate* their emotions so that the congregation is not worn out from too much gravity, levity, or sameness.

Clarity

Clear Thought

The words of R. E. O. White on the importance of clear thinking are sure to strike a responsive chord with any preacher:

> Usually we speak or write just as clearly as we think. When words dry up, and our writing runs into a tangle or becomes turgid and diffuse, the cure is to sit back and think out clearly what it is we are trying to say. When we have sorted out our muddled thinking, have corrected our preconceptions, hasty generalizations, hidden assumptions, false analogies, exaggerations and contradictions, then words come readily enough.[8]

Assumptions

Preachers who deliver sermons with impact are those who make it impossible for people *not* to understand the message. Without insulting the intelligence of their audiences, they are careful not to assume that their listeners know their Bibles, understand theological terminology, or have instant recall of statements made earlier in the message. Most important, they do not assume that their audience came to the gathering motivated to learn or even interested in the topic!

Good communicators know that people can't read their minds or always understand their words. They look for opportunities to provide visual aids, whether physical objects, projected images, handouts, body language, or picturesque speech. Without dumbing down God's message, they word their sermons for ease in understanding.

Passion

All preachers of effective sermons share this vital quality: *passion*, or strong feeling, both in relation to their personal motivation to communicate and their empathy for their listeners.

Compulsion to Communicate

In the introduction to his book *Teaching to Change Lives*, Hendricks says of the seven laws of the teacher, "If you boil them all down, these seven laws essentially call for a *passion to communicate*."[9] Such passion comes from the communicator's own growing edge of a life God is changing as he or she continues to learn, grow, and improve.[10] Paul described the apostles' passion as "the love of Christ [which] compels us" (2 Cor. 5:14 NKJV). Whether that was the apostles' love *for* Christ, or Christ's love, or both, the compulsion was affective.

Compassion for People

Not unrelated to the passion to communicate is the speaker's genuine compassion for those hurting and in need. This was the compassion modeled by the Lord Jesus in Mark 6:34: "Jesus … saw a great multitude and was moved with compassion for them, because they were like sheep not having a shepherd. So He began to teach them many things" (NKJV). You should certainly demonstrate the relationship every believer has to fellow members of the same body. In 1 Corinthians 12:26, Paul said, "If one member suffers, all the members suffer with it; or if one member is honored, all the members rejoice with it." This describes not mere sympathy, in which one feels sorry for another, but real empathy, in which one feels the pain of another. Caring enough to both weep with them and confront them in love comes from an experiential knowledge of God as one's own Father. (See Psalm 103:13; 1 Thessalonians 2:11; and Colossians 3:12-13.) Moses and Paul felt such compassion for the people of Israel that each expressed his willingness to forfeit his own enjoyment of God's blessings if by doing so he could secure God's blessings for His chosen people. (See Exodus 32:32 and Romans 9:3.)

Godly Zeal

When Jesus cleansed the temple, in John 2:17, He fulfilled the prophecy of Psalm 69:9, being consumed with zeal for Yahweh's house. In a similar way, Stephen was outspoken in his confrontation of those whom he said had always resisted the Holy Spirit (Acts 7:51). Sermons that change lives also demonstrate divine passion in the sense of loving what God loves and hating what He hates.

Styles Of Preparation

Manuscript

Advantages. Sermons written out word for word are *precise*. In the process of composing the script, you are able to work on all of the attributes of effective expository sermons discussed earlier in this chapter. You have time not only to pay careful attention to the unity, order, and movement of your message, but to vary the vocabulary, economize the wording, and polish the delivery by rehearsing it from a fixed script. Once you have the manuscript well enough in mind, you may use it merely as a prompt, glancing at it for the gist of what you have written, with freedom to depart from it.

Disadvantages. Manuscripts take a great deal of time to prepare, and, unless kept from the congregation's view, their appearance can distract the listener, giving the impression that you are presenting a paper or lecture rather than speaking, as Andrew Blackwood put it, "from heart to heart and eye to eye"[11] in the Spirit. Further, in poor lighting or during outdoor occasions (weddings, funerals, camp meetings, etc.), where wind may be a factor, extensive notes can be hard to read and manage. They tend to restrict spontaneity and can even tempt you to read your message, which is fine for radio, but not for the pulpit.

Memorization

Advantages. Memorized messages can be presented with the dramatic style and freedom of movement of a stage performer. They have all of the advantages of a manuscript without the problem of hiding, seeing, or managing extensive notes. Memorizing certain parts of a sermon, such as introductions, illustrations, or conclusions allows precise wording and good eye contact.

Disadvantages. In addition to the obvious time and effort it takes to memorize a sermon of any length is the possibility of forgetting your lines! Unforeseeable interruptions can present a dilemma as to where and how to start again. And, like a manuscript, memorized sermons can seem canned, impersonal, and inflexible.

Extemporaneous

Advantages. Many would agree that extemporaneous preaching provides the preacher with the best of both worlds.[12] With minimal notes to keep you moving through your outline, remind you of your theme and illustrations, etc., you are free to speak as the words come to mind. There are no conspicuous notes in your way or in view of the congregation, and less worry about losing your place. As long as you are thoroughly prepared, your delivery is likely to be more natural and convincing and will allow for flexibility. An excellent way to prepare to preach is to manuscript a sermon, working hard on its wording, but then leave it in the study and take only the outline into the pulpit.

Disadvantages. Forgetting something you planned to include, including something that would have been better left out, and repeating yourself are among the disadvantages of speaking freely within the guidelines of limited notes. Sermons can also run longer—or shorter—than you intended.

Summary and Conclusion

Effective expositional sermons are not the result of following strict rules, but they do exhibit common qualities. They communicate *divine* authority, not yours or someone else's. As a result, they are both factual and faithful to historical reality. Avoiding egotistical sideshows or demagoguery eliminates digressions that cloud your sermon's reflection of the single focus and integrity of the text. As a unit, the sermon is obviously dissectible. Orderly arrangement of your material makes it meaningful to the listener. As it efficiently moves toward a definite goal, the listener feels a sense of progress and accomplishment. Distractions are minimized and emotions are varied and controlled. Rather than assuming the listener's knowledge of, or interest in, the Bible and theology, express your ideas in ways that make misunderstanding practically impossible. With divine compulsion to communicate, you will empathize with the listener and demonstrate zeal for God's glory.

Whether you prepare a manuscript, memorize your sermon, or speak from limited notes will depend on your personal preference and the occasion. There is no biblical right or wrong, and all three styles have been used effectively by expository preachers. After assessing the advantages and disadvantages, however, it seems that most effective expository preachers speak extemporaneously.

Discussion Questions

1. In what ways did Jesus teach, not as the scribes, but with authority?
2. Without mentioning names, describe how you have witnessed the forfeiture of divine authority on the part of a contemporary preacher.
3. Why is *historical accuracy* so important to a sermon that aims to change people's *hearts*?
4. Why do you agree, or disagree, that organic unity is more important in a sermon than in a classroom discussion?

5. What is meant by "the economy of words"? What happens if concision is taken too far?
6. Using Peter's sermon in Acts 2, Stephen's sermon in chapter 7, and Paul's sermon in chapter 17, identify examples of passion as described in this chapter.
7. What is your chosen style of sermon preparation, and why?

CHAPTER 8

The Characteristics of Effective Expository Communicators

The human component of bridges that effectively span the communication gap is marked by certain qualities. Like the substance of effective sermons, the servants who deliver and model them with impact generally are *godly, relational*, and *articulate*. They recognize that a sermon is not good on its own, but only as it is well communicated. At the same time, godly expositors realize that they are prominent, not preeminent. Their value and importance is directly proportional to the extent that their sermons communicate God's message. A comment by author Donald Demaray on Jonathan Edwards, the persuasive preacher of the Second Great Awakening, will serve as a disclaimer for this chapter:

> Some of Edwards' sermons were over two hours long, which is not so uncommon in a day and age more leisurely than ours. Nonetheless, it is probably true that his delivery was dull at times. His voice was weak and not very commanding. He lacked many pulpit graces. He read his manuscripts; and one author, observing Edwards' nearsightedness, pictures him as clutching his papers in one hand, holding a candle in the other, and staring down the words as he read.[1]

Yet Edwards's weaknesses are mentioned to draw attention to an important fact: "The Holy Spirit overcomes weaknesses and handicaps, and develops the natural abilities of God's servants."[2] (This does not mean that Edwards might not have communicated even more effectively if he had been strong in his areas of weakness.)

Godly

Godliness describes the life of a God-centered person, whose thoughts, feelings, and actions reflect conscious dependence upon and reverent response to God. Godly thinking precedes godly action (see Romans 12:2). To be godly, you must accept yourself for who God has made you, and then act naturally, speak directly, and be real (see Romans 12:3).[3] But self-acceptance does not mean self-reliance. And godly communicators are not to ask God to empower their own messages for the glory of the preacher. Rather, they rely on the power of the Holy Spirit to deliver *His* message for *His* glory. Consider how Paul requested prayer from the Church at Ephesus: "[Pray] always with all prayer and supplication in the Spirit, being watchful to this end with all perseverance and supplication for all the saints—*and for me, that utterance may be given to me, that I may open my mouth boldly to make known the mystery of the gospel, for which I am an ambassador in chains; that in it I may speak boldly, as I ought to speak*" (Eph. 6:18-20 NKJV, emphasis added).

In view of their dependent role, the people God uses engage in the intellectual discipline of meditating on the Word of God, prayerfully brooding over the implications and significance of principles drawn from the passage (see Colossians 4:2-4). They exercise good judgment in deciding how best to deliver their discovery of what God meant by what He said. They avoid grumbling about the congregation. Being transparent and vulnerable about their own weaknesses and struggles not only keeps them taking God more seriously than themselves, but it also endears them to those able to identify with them. It also disarms potential adversaries.

God-centeredness gives you credibility as a preacher, which Richards and Bredfeldt identify as the first of several characteristics of all great teachers. Citing the research of David W. Johnson and Frank P. Johnson, they name six factors that influence credibility: *reliability of information, purity of motives, warmth and friendliness, reputation, expertise*, and *passion*.[4]

Relational

By *relational* we mean that you do not simply preach sermons; you serve people. You establish and nurture a bond of commonality, using your entire personality to impact the entire personality of each of your listeners. Every individual in the audience should feel that you are talking directly to him or her. You accomplish this by getting and holding their attention with a creative introduction and good eye contact. Appropriate smiles, gestures, and a friendly tone all *say* that the message is not just about God, or about you, but about the listeners. The people are not there to observe your performance. Rather, *you* are there so that *they* will better know, love, and serve the true and living God for the rest of their lives. Vivid words, purposeful actions, vocal variety, and visual displays are other ingredients noted by Richards and Bredfeldt, as part of a style that delivers.[5] None of these factors dictates a particular style, but all are incorporated by effective preachers, whether they stand behind an opaque pulpit, rove with a lapel microphone, project visuals onto a screen, or sit on a stool![6]

Relational preachers greet people with genuine interest in the things that are interesting to them. They don't just turn on the charm while standing before others, but take the initiative in getting acquainted and making themselves available for further contact and help.[7]

Articulate

The Voice

According to an old saying, "Many a sip is lost between cup and lip."[8] A drink spilled at the last possible moment before it would have been drunk might as well have not been poured. The same is true of the spoken word. If everything about the sermon is wonderful *except* that people can't hear it, understand it, or stay awake, it is like the original Narrows Bridge to Gig Harbor from Tacoma, Washington, which spilled cars into Puget Sound when it collapsed. Speaking too softly, rapidly, indistinctly, or monotonously can put people to sleep. But when used well, your voice is your best tool. The most effective way of gaining and holding attention is by speaking with appropriate modulation or variety.

Inflection

Deliberate changes or modulations in the speaker's tone of voice are known as *inflection*. Use upward modulation to express a question, indecision, uncertainty, doubt, or suspense. Use downward modulation to suggest firmness, determination, certainty, finality, and confidence. The most effective way to ensure appropriate voice modulation, however, is not by thinking about it, but by genuine enthusiasm for what you have to say. Hendricks says, "If you really believe and feel your message, it will show. You'll use good gestures." He further asserts, "The most effective communication always includes an *emotional* ingredient—the *feeling* factor, the excitement element."[9] This is not a new assertion. Jonathan Edwards's philosophy of preaching emphasized that, within intellectual structure, a strong appeal to the emotions was the key for unlocking a volitional response.[10]

Rate

The rate at which you speak should correspond to the thoughts you are expressing. Weighty matters, such as the theme or application, should be spoken slowly for clarity and emphasis. Short and quick speech, on the other hand, can communicate excitement or surprise. Varying the rate of speech makes it more interesting to listeners.

Pitch

While there are notable exceptions, a voice pitched too high can communicate weakness, irritation, youth, or nervousness. Using the lower range of your voice is generally preferable for communicating assurance, poise, strength, maturity, and confidence.

Movement

Whether it consists of hand and arm gestures, taking a few steps, use of visual aids (such as PowerPoint), pausing momentarily, or simply changing your voice, movement is the primary way to get and *hold* the attention of your audience.

Language

Effective communicators of God's Word not only speak distinctly, but they choose their words carefully and pronounce them with good diction. Avoid slang and "hip" language. Express yourself naturally, without a "preacher's twang." And definitely stay away from coarse jesting, cursing, and all expletives.

Summary and Conclusion

Effective expository communicators are godly, relational, and articulate. Though they are prominent in the pulpit, God is obviously preeminent in their thoughts, words, and behavior. As a result of who they are in relation to God, they care about the people to whom their entire personalities form part of the communicative bridge. Their speech is energized by their passion for God and the message He has given to them. Their compassion for their listeners and genuine interest in their spiritual and eternal well-being is expressed in their appropriate use of the voice, body, and language.

Discussion Questions

1. Describe the preacher, or preachers, whose sermons have had the greatest impact on your life. How were they like, or unlike, the profile presented in this chapter?

2. Why, biblically, do you agree or disagree that transparency and vulnerability on the part of an expositor of Scripture enhances effective communication?

3. Why, biblically, do you agree or disagree that the most effective communication always includes an emotional element?

4. Why, biblically, do you agree or disagree that, though God can use whomever He will, those who exhibit the characteristics of effective expository communicators could be even more useful as His spokespersons?

PART IV

Demonstrating the Discovery, Development, and Delivery of What God Meant by What He Said

Chapter 9, "Preaching from the Pentateuch," briefly introduces the nature of Hebrew narrative. It surveys the Hebrew Scripture, Pentateuch, and the book of Exodus. A sample sermon is presented from Exodus 20:1-17, entitled "God's Prescription for Right Relationships."

Chapter 10, "Preaching Historical Narrative," introduces the nature of story, plot, and archetype. To show how a sermon may be structured to match the story, a sample sermon is presented from the book of Ruth, entitled "The Hidden God Who Is in Control."

Chapter 11, "Preaching the Poetic Books," introduces the nature of hymnic literature. A sample sermon is presented from Psalm 113, entitled "Telling the Greatness of God."

Chapter 12, "Preaching Old Testament Prophecy" introduces the nature of biblical prophecy, relating prophecy to the biblical covenants and extending the meaning of a text into new contexts. From Zechariah 4:1-7, a sample sermon is presented, entitled "God's Work, God's Power."

Chapter 13, "Preaching the Gospels and Acts," surveys the nature of the Gospel genre and the book of Acts. The historical background, literary analysis, and theological understanding of each book is summarized. Sample sermons are presented from John 3:10-16, "Why the Son Descended"; Acts 6:1-7, "The Value and Importance of Official Service in the Church"; and Luke 10:25-37, "Action or Apathy?"

Chapter 14, "Preaching the Epistles," surveys the nature of the Epistle genre and twenty-two New Testament Epistles, with attention to their historical background, literary analysis, and theological understanding. A sample sermon is provided, entitled "The Excellence of Love," from 1 Corinthians 13.

Chapter 15, "Preaching the Revelation," undertakes questions of genre, approaches to interpretation, historical background, literary analysis, and theological understanding. A sample sermon from Revelation 1:1-8 is offered, entitled "The Revelation of Jesus Christ."

CHAPTER 9

Preaching from the Pentateuch

The Imperative

The imperative to preach the Word of God certainly applies to the first five books of the Bible, since they form its foundation. Rooted in the rich soil of mostly historical narrative grow the major themes of the Bible. And yet the Pentateuch[1] is often neglected in the pulpit ministry of even expository preachers. This may be due to a lack of confidence in the relevance and integrity of the Hebrew Scriptures as a whole, or ignorance of the basic structure and message of the books of Moses in particular. This chapter will demonstrate how to use the Whiting Method of homiletics to develop a sermon from the Pentateuch. In doing so, the historical, cultural, and dispensational rings of context will be emphasized rather than the grammatical analysis emphasized in Chapter 4. To help you understand and appreciate the foundational role of the Pentateuch, the following is a brief overview of the Old Testament as a whole.

Overview of the Hebrew Scriptures

Its Relevance

In his *Survey of Old Testament Introduction*, Gleason Archer notes that the New Testament writers referred to the Old Testament as a single, composite whole, ultimately authored by God Himself.[2] Archer explains his assertion by saying, "The New Testament writers regarded the entire Hebrew Scriptures as a testimony to Jesus Christ, the perfect

Man who fulfilled all the Law; the Sacrifice and High Priest of the ritual ordinances; the Prophet, Priest, and King of whom the prophets foretold; and the Lover whom the poetical books described."[3]

As noted in the discussion of types in Chapter 6, events recorded in the Old Testament were seen by New Testament writers as prefiguring New Testament realities. The crossing of the Red Sea foreshadowed Christian baptism (1 Cor. 10:1-2). The conquest of Canaan under Joshua was divinely intended to picture the spiritual rest into which Christians enter by faith (Heb. 3-4). Calling Israel out of Egypt pointed to Jesus' experience recorded in Matthew 2:15. Thus, the New Testament gives convincing evidence that the Hebrew Scriptures constituted a coherent and integrated organism, focused on the dual themes of redeeming lost sinners and reclaiming God's kingdom on earth.

Its Structure

The Hebrew arrangement (referred to in Matthew 5:17; 7:12; etc., as the *Law and the Prophets*) includes the *Law* (of Moses), the *Prophets* (i.e., former prophets: Joshua, Judges, Samuel, Kings; and latter prophets: Isaiah, Jeremiah, Ezekiel, and the Twelve), and the *Writings*. The books referred to as the Writings consist of the Poetic Books of Job, Psalms, and Proverbs; the *Rolls*, including Song of Solomon, Ruth, Ecclesiastes, Esther, and Lamentations; and the *Histories*, including Esther, Daniel, Ezra, Nehemiah, and Chronicles.

When the Hebrew Scriptures were translated into Greek at Alexandria, Egypt, in the third century B.C., the books were arranged as they are in modern translations. This first translation became known as the *Septuagint* (LXX, for short) for the seventy-two men involved in making it (LXX being the closest round number). Five books of Law and twelve books of History (totaling seventeen) are followed by the five books of the Major Prophets and twelve books of the Minor Prophets (totaling seventeen). The five books of Poetry at the center have been thought of as forming the "heart" of the body of the Old Testament. The resulting symmetrical pattern of 17–5–17 is illustrated in figure 9-1.[4] That the Word of God can be so arranged demonstrates something of the order and balance we would expect in the written revelation of the Author of creation and redemption.

General Overview

The Hebrew Scriptures reveal God's Plan to redeem lost sinners and reclaim His kingdom on earth through His Son of promise (see Genesis 3:15 and 1 Corinthians 15:24).[5]

The Books of Law and History are mostly narrative of God's work in past events on behalf of one nation, Israel, which Yahweh formed by His sovereign grace. Having called Abram into a covenant relationship with Him, Yahweh began to fulfill His promises to bless Abram and to bless all nations through the nation (Israel) that would come from him. The Pentateuch has been related to Israel as follows.[6] (See figure 9-2.)

Law & History	Poetry	Prophecy
5	5	5
12		12
17		17
Retrospective	Introspective	Prospective

Figure 9.1

The Pentateuch in Relation to the Nation of Israel		
1. Genesis:	Israel *selected*	from idolatry
2. Exodus:	Israel *saved*	from Egypt
3. Leviticus:	Israel *set apart*	from world and flesh
4. Numbers:	Israel disciplined for *service*	from Sinai wanderings
5. Deuteronomy:	Israel's Law *surveyed*	for blessing in Canaan

Figure 9.2

The twelve books of History cover Israel from her conception to the time of the prophet Malachi. The five books of Poetry express the fact that a life of meaning, purpose, skill, and beauty depends on enjoying a right relationship with God. Finally, the seventeen books of Prophecy proclaim God's judgment of sin and future restoration of His covenant people, Israel.[7]

The Pentateuch

Authorship

Critics have theorized that the Pentateuch is a compilation of writings, edited after the Babylonian captivity, by *different* authors recording various stages in the development of Israel's religion.[8] But Jesus referred to Moses as the Lawgiver in John 5:46-47; 7:19-23; and many other places. Also, the books of Moses demonstrate a continuity of content, theme, purpose, and style that is consistent with a single author.[9] The consecutive history found in the Pentateuch is but one of many factors confirming its unity. One book takes up where the other leaves off. Other indications of single authorship include the progressive spiritual development from Genesis through Deuteronomy and smoothness of transition from one book to the next. Finally, the Pentateuch gives evidence of an inverted parallelism, or chiasmus (a symmetrical arrangement of literary units in which the first set is matched by the second set in reverse order, producing a prominent center for emphasis).[10] (See figure 9-3.)

Genesis and Deuteronomy concern the formation of the universe and nation of Israel, while Exodus and Numbers have to do with the ordering of the nation. The prominent center created by this parallel design is the book of Leviticus, which calls upon God's people to reflect His holiness.[11]

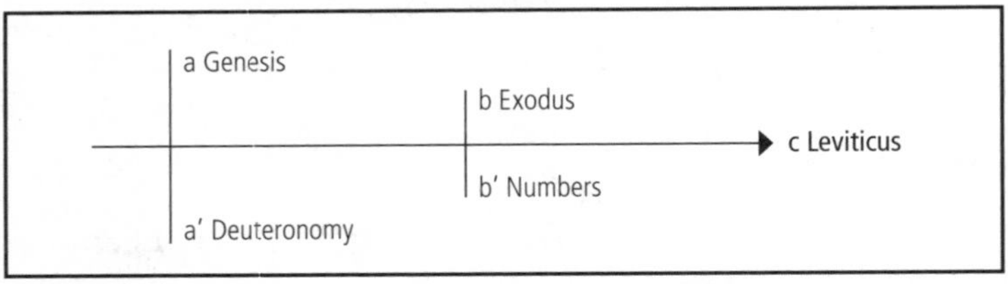

Figure 9.3

Dominant Themes

Gary Derickson, in a lecture demonstrating the importance and contribution of the Pentateuch to Old Testament theology, identified these dominant themes: God's sovereignty, judgment, faithfulness, holiness, and redemption. He further states that, cosmically, the Pentateuch provides the only rational explanation of the origin of the universe.

Ethnically, it alone accounts for the diversity of nations. Religiously, the books of Moses document the beginnings of man's sin and redemption, the nation and covenants of Israel, and God's plan of the ages. Historically, Genesis alone covers a greater span of time than all sixty-five other books put together![12] (See figure 9-4.[13])

Covenants

A biblical covenant is a formal agreement in which God promises to do certain things on behalf of humanity.[14] With the exception of the Mosaic covenant (explanation to follow), all of the biblical covenants depend only on the faithfulness of God for their fulfillment.

The Adamic covenant refers to God's promise in Genesis 3:15 to crush the head of the serpent by the heel of the Seed of the woman. It has been called the *protevangelium* because it provides the basis for hope that God would send a human to deliver man from sin and reestablish his rule on earth.

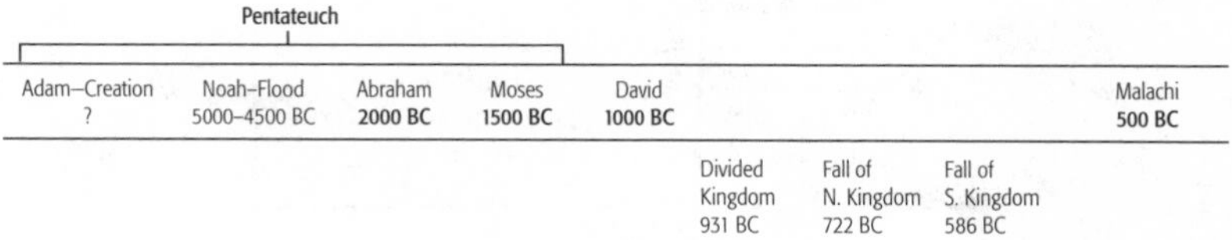

Figure 9.4

The Noahic covenant, in Genesis 9, provides the biblical basis for human government by authorizing the use of deadly force in upholding justice.

God's covenant with Abraham in Genesis 12 (and repeated in chapters 13, 15, 17, 18, and 22) forms the central set of promises. As shown in figure 9-5, the Abrahamic covenant is based on the redemptive and kingdom promises of the Adamic and Noahic covenants.

The promise to Abraham of personal blessing is the basis for the temporary Mosaic covenant. The Mosaic covenant, the heart of which is formed by the Ten Commandments, was replaced by the new covenant of Jeremiah 31, which promised the internalization of God's righteousness in the hearts of God's people. The New Covenant is ratified by the blood of Jesus Christ (compare Jeremiah 31:31 and Matthew 26:28; Mark 14:24; Luke 22:20; and 1 Corinthians 11:25), and obedient believers in Christ are already enjoying its personal, spiritual blessings through the indwelling Holy Spirit (see Galatians 3:27-28).

The land covenant in Deuteronomy 28-30, guarantees Israel the land promised to Abram, and sets forth the conditions of blessing in the land.

The Davidic covenant of 2 Samuel 7:16 is built on the Noahic covenant of human government, and promises the permanent, universal rule of a descendant of David upon his throne.

The following summary of biblical covenants shows the unique conditionality of the Mosaic covenant with regard to the nation of Israel. (See figure 9-5.)

Identification of the Biblical Covenants

1. Adamic, Genesis 3—redemption; rulership
2. Noahic, Genesis 9—governmental
3. Abrahamic, Genesis 12; 13; 15; 17; 18; 22
4. **Mosaic, Exodus 19:24—conditional blessing**
5. Land, Deuteronomy 28–30—land guaranteed
6. Davidic, 2 Samuel 7–Kingship guaranteed forever
7. New Covenant, Jeremiah 31–Replacing the Mosaic

Figure 9.5

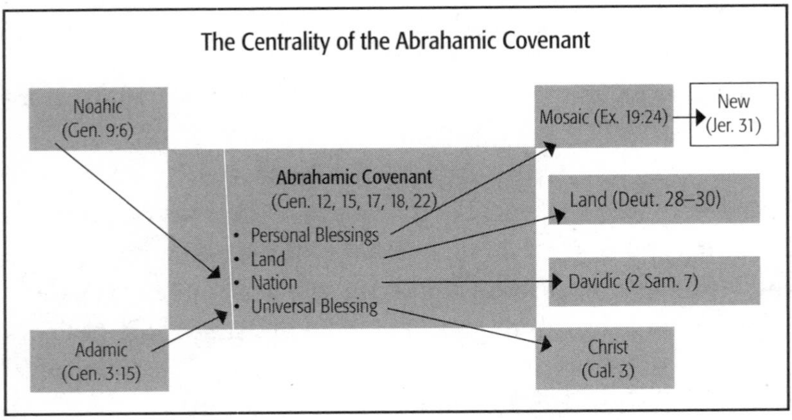

Figure 9.6

The following graphic, adapted from Stanley Ellisen, shows how the Abrahamic covenant is central to the other covenants of Scripture. (See figure 9-6.)

Summary of the Pentateuch By Book[15]

Derickson's succinct descriptions of the books of Moses, listed below, provide a basic summary of the Pentateuch.

1. **Genesis:** God's word … created a perfect world order and brought judgment and blessing upon its inhabitants, preserving a line through whom blessing would come.
2. **Exodus:** God's preparation of Israel for nationhood … is accomplished through His deliverance of the nation to Himself, entrance into a national covenant, and their constructing of a tabernacle.
3. **Leviticus:** The holiness of God … demands holy worship and conduct from His people.
4. **Numbers:** Israel's preparation for entering Canaan, under God's leadership … involved national organization, discipline, and provision of additional laws amid God's blessings.
5. **Deuteronomy:** Israel's call to covenantal faithfulness … results in God's blessing rather than punishment on the basis of His covenant.

Preaching the Law

Establishing the Text

The first step in preparing a sermon from the Pentateuch is to identify where the selected passage fits into the scheme of the Pentateuch as a whole. What is the role of the particular book in which the passage is found? This can be done by making, or referring to, good outlines of the books. For example, the Ten Commandments are found in the book of Exodus. An overview of the Pentateuch indicated that Exodus has to do with the ordering of the nation of Israel. It is based on the formation of the nation in Genesis. It anticipates the climactic emphasis on holiness in Leviticus. Exodus is parallel to the book of Numbers, which deals with the organization of the nation in the Sinai wilderness before entering the land promised to Abraham in Genesis. Before even looking at the text of Exodus 20, then, its placement in the Pentateuch indicates its purpose of establishing the basis for a right relationship with God on the part of a nation He has called to be set apart from the world as an agency of universal blessing.

Where does the passage fit in relation to the argument of the book? An outline of Exodus serves to further pinpoint the Ten Commandments in their context. The word *exodus* is Greek and means "the way out." The book of Exodus concerns Israel's deliverance from bondage in Egypt and development in the wilderness as a nation in a covenant relation with their Creator and Redeemer, Yahweh. Israel's redemption and organization as a theocratic nation establishes principles for the way God deals with believers in the church age of grace (1 Cor. 10:11). In short, the theme of Exodus is "Israel's redemption and organization as a theocratic nation."[16] It may be outlined as follows. (See figure 9-7.)

From the outline of Exodus, it is apparent that the Ten Commandments form the foundational bridge between God's redemption of Israel in chapters 1-19, and Israel's worship of God in chapters 25-40.

The specific text is established by determining the boundaries within which the writer expresses a complete thought. In the case of the Ten Commandments, each command is a paragraph, but the paragraphs are bound by identifiable markers of time, place, or persons, in the text.[17] Observing these indicators is called *establishing the text.* The Ten Commandments are introduced by the statement "And God spoke all these words, saying …" (Ex. 20:1), indicating a change in speaker. In verse 18, the speaker changes again, from God to Moses, who narrates the people's response to all they witnessed. Thus Exodus 20: 1-17 is marked by who is speaking.

Identify Points of Emphasis

By listing observations from the text, it is possible to identify the Ten

Commandments' chiastic structure.[18] They begin and end by addressing how a person *thinks*. Second, and second to last, is an emphasis upon what a person *says*. This leaves, accentuated in the center, the focus on what a person *does*. Right words and deeds come from right thoughts.

Outline of Exodus

I. Exodus	1–19
God separates the nation to Himself	
II. Law	**20–24**
God enters into covenant	
III. Tabernacle	25–40
God builds His throne room	
A. Instruction (25–31)	
B. Obstruction [Golden Calf] (32–34)	
C. Construction (35–40)	

Figure 9.7

Another observation is that man's relations with God are balanced by man's relations with man. The fact that man's relations with God come first is also significant. Good human relations depend on a proper relation to God. Other observations can be made and should be listed as you develop the truth sheet discussed in chapter 4.[19]

Identify the Literary Genre

Within the text, the kind of literature must be identified. Among the possibilities are prose, historical narrative, wisdom literature, and apocalyptic literature. *Historical narrative* is a type of prose, the genre of stories, in which a variety of *archetypes*[20] (or *plot motifs*) may be represented. *Hebrew poetry* employs parallelism, in which the thought of the second line either repeats, completes, contrasts, or highlights the thought of the first line, for emphasis and emotional appeal. *Wisdom literature* includes poetry, but is distinguishable by its sustained argumentation for conclusions about spiritual, ethical, and moral issues. *Apocalyptic literature* is highly symbolic in depictions of unseen and future events impossible to know apart from divine disclosures to the prophet.

The Ten Commandments are written in prose, the straightforward literature of historical narrative, records, and law. As prose, there are two kinds of law. *Apodictic* law consists of assertions or demands based on grounds.[21] *Causal* law states the consequences of an action as the effect of its cause.[22] The Ten Commandments are primarily *apodictic*, stating what is required of God's people on the basis of His having redeemed them.

The Author's Meaning

The meaning of biblical narrative is determined by the writer, not the reader. Through Moses, God gave the revelation of His holiness in the identifiable form of international treaties between kings (*suzerains*) and their subjects (*vassals*). This observation alone precludes reading the Ten Commandments as a means of justifying sinners. According to their form, the Ten Commands stipulate the basic obligations imposed upon and accepted by a ruler's subjects. At issue is not whether the relationship between the parties exists or continues, but whether those under the authority of their ruler enjoy his blessings or endure his curses. In the case of God and Israel, the question was whether the nation would appropriate or forfeit the blessings of the Abrahamic covenant, prospering in the land of promise and being a blessing to the nations.[23]

Following the pattern of the Hittites in the fourteenth and thirteenth centuries B.C., the Mosaic covenant is *dated* in Exodus 19:1-2. Next, the activity of the king, or *suzernin*, is described in terms of His geographical setting. Then Moses, as the mediator of the covenant, is described in terms of his title and activity (19:3-25). The actual covenant is preceded by a *preamble* in 20:1 that emphasizes the majesty and power of the King, God. A *historical prologue* describes previous relations between the king and his subjects, to produce thanksgiving and trust in subjects' hearts. In Exodus 20:2 the people are told, "I am the LORD your God, who brought you out of the land of Egypt, out of the house of bondage" (NKJV). Note that the nation belonged to God not on the basis of their performance, but *His*![24]

The Ten Commandments are *stipulations* that state specific, basic conditions for blessing (20:3-17). These are followed by detailed demands and other provisions for placing the record of the treaty on display in the temple for public reading. *Covenant ratification* involved the people's acceptance of the terms of the contract in oral and written form. It was sealed with blood and finalized by participation in a covenant meal (24:11).[25]

To correct the popular misconception that the Law was antithetical to the grace of God, the *Nelson Study Bible* states:

> The Law was benevolent instruction from God Himself. It was God's direction, like an outstretched hand, pointing out the way one should take on the road of life. The Israelites were in an enviable position. God had demonstrated His love for them by saving them. He had shown His faithfulness to His promises to their parents, Abraham and Sarah. He had formalized His relationship with them in a treaty and promised to make them His special people. Finally He even gave them instructions for how to live. They were at peace with their Creator.[26]

Sermon Development

As noted earlier, the sermon should reflect the structure and tone of its biblical text. With this in mind, the following sermon outline is offered as an example. (See figure 9-8.)

Sample Sermon

Introduction (hook)

In the 1981 movie *Chariots of Fire*, two elderly deans of the University of Cambridge discuss the zeal of one of their student-athletes named Harold Abrahams. Abrahams, who is Jewish, has just left the room after passionately defending his controversial use of a professional coach in preparation for the 1924 Olympics. Shaking his head, one of the deans expresses his disapproval of Abrahams' perceived arrogance, saying of his Jewish student and his heritage, "A different mountain, a different God."

God's Prescription for Right Relationships
Exodus 20:1–17

Right Treatment of God and People Cannot Be Separated

I. Right Treatment of God 1–12
  A. In Thought
    1. **No other gods** (whom to worship)
    2. **No graven images** (how to worship)
    B. In Words
      3. **No useless mention of God's Name** (reverence)
      C. In Actions
        4. **Keep the Sabbath holy** (God's time)
        5. **Honor parents** (God's representatives)

II. Right Treatment of People 13–17
      C.' In Actions
        6. **No murder** (respecting life in God's likeness)
        7. **No adultery** (respecting one's family)
        8. **No theft** (respecting ones property)
    B.' In Words
      9. **No slander** (respecting one's character)
  A.' In Thought
    10. **No coveting** (respecting one's desires)

Figure 9.8

To many Christians the Ten Commandments represent the harsh Law of Moses received on Mount Sinai, in contrast to the friendly grace of God revealed in Jesus on Mount Calvary! But do the two mountains represent different gods?

Properly understood, Sinai, where Moses received *God's* Law, and Calvary, where Christ was crucified "by the predetermined plan … of God" [Acts 2:23 NASB95], represent different purposes of the same God. Their purposes are *complementary*, not *competitive*. They are in conflict only when one or the other is misunderstood. Both concern right relationships. Sinai gives the prescription; Calvary fills it!

Body (book)

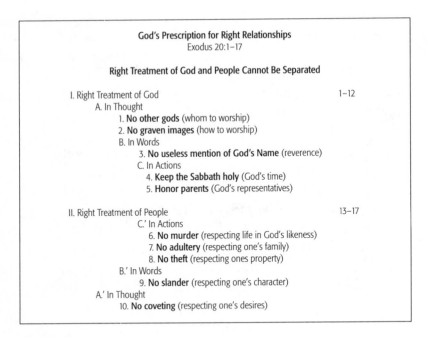

According to Exodus 19:1, the Law was given "in the third month after the children of Israel had gone out of the land of Egypt." [NKJV] It had taken two months to bring the people to the place where God appeared to Moses and declared Himself to be the "I AM," from the burning bush. At that time, God had also given Moses a sign. According to Exodus 3:12, God would bring Moses and the people of Israel to this location at the base of Mount Sinai, where they would worship Him. What a profound wonder it must have been for Moses to realize the fulfillment of God's promise!

As for the people, they had seen the power of God in operation. After bringing a series of miraculous plagues on Egypt, He had brought them through the Red Sea on dry land, destroyed the pursuing Egyptian army, led them with the cloud and pillar of fire, and miraculously provided food and water. Now they needed to understand the holiness of God.

Having received the Ten Commandments on the mountain, Moses came down to the people and spoke to them, teaching them God's Law.

What is the point of the Law, anyway? One way to state it is that: *Right treatment of God and people cannot be separated.*

I. Right Treatment of God

Notice, in verses 1-2, who initiated the communication of God's Law, and on what basis.

> And God spoke all these words, saying: "I am the Lord your God, who brought you out of the land of Egypt, out of the house of bondage." (NKJV)

In keeping with the known pattern of international treaties by which kings ordered the conduct of their subjects. God identifies Himself. He reminds the Israelites that He delivered them from slavery in Egypt. The people have God to thank for their well-being and very existence. They belong to Him on the basis of what He has done for them. They have every reason to embrace the terms He is about to state for the order and meaning to their already-existing relationship.

The first two commands concern right treatment of God *in thought*. Obedience to these Laws is in the realm of the heart and mind. Having learned idolatry in Egypt. Israel was now given the first stipulation for blessing. It concerned whom to worship: "*You shall have no other gods before Me*" [v. 3 NKJV]. This demand is reasonable because He is the only true and living God. The demand is compassionate because every person, place, object, or idea that might be exalted in God's place is false, disappointing, and ultimately disastrous.

The problem with idolatry is unreality, and it is as real today as it was in the days of Moses. If modern Christians were not capable of breaking this commandment, to their own detriment, the apostle John would not have said, at the end of his first epistle. "*Little children keep yourselves from idols*" [5:21 NKJV].

Most of us do pretty well at avoiding bowing down to carved statues. Yet we still often worship the creations of God in His place: the human body, pleasure, our children, friends—even physical life. God wants to spare us the let-down from promoting such things to the level of their own incompetence.

Having addressed whom Israel was to worship, God next addresses *how to worship*, prohibiting the dishonorable practices they had learned from the Egyptians. Beginning again with verse 4, we read:

> "You shall not make for yourself a carved image—any likeness of anything that is in heaven above, or that is in the earth beneath, or that is in the water under the earth; you shall not bow down to them nor serve them. For I, the Lord your God, am a jealous God, visiting the iniquity of the fathers on the children to the third and fourth generations of those who hate Me, but showing mercy to thousands, to those who love Me and keep My commandments." [Ex. 20:4-6 NKJV]

What's so bad about setting something before us that represents God and reminds us to worship Him? God is incomparable. Nothing people can make or discover can adequately portray what He is like. Every attempt to do so reduces Him in one's thoughts to someone other than (therefore, less than) He is. Having created us for personal intimacy with Him, no object can take His place.

God did not deliver Israel in order to collect tribute from them, as if He needed something from them, but for the *personal* relationship they needed with Him. God is jealous for His name, because He is worthy of our love and service.

His willingness to deal with people for generations according to their love for Him, or lack of it, demonstrates His long-term commitment to His covenant people for their good. He honors His end of the bargain whether they do or not.

Jesus would later state that a man speaks out of what fills his heart. So, having addressed the heart, God moves to man's treatment of God *in words*. In verse 7, we read:

> "You shall not take the name of the Lord your God in vain, for the LORD will not hold him guiltless who takes His name in vain." [NKJV]

A person's *name* in this context is his reputation. It stands for all that is true of him. God revealed Himself in the personal name *Yahweh*, the "I AM" of Exodus 3:14. It speaks of His being eternally the God who depends on no one and nothing outside of Himself for existence. It is the name by which He signs His covenants, binding Himself to the good of His people. To treat His name lightly is to fail to demonstrate reverence for His very being. It hurts His testimony among the unsaved. Invoking the name of God in an attempt to manipulate the outcomes of events reduces it to a charm. Such abuses make a person liable for punishment for the good of the community and preservation of God's honor.

Beginning with verse 8 the movement from thoughts to words is extended to right treatment of God *in deeds*. To *keep the Sabbath holy* as a steward of God's time involves not only resting on the seventh day, as God rested from His creative work on the seventh day, but also working the other six days! The text says:

> "Remember the Sabbath day, to keep it holy. Six days you shall labor and do all your work, but the seventh day is the Sabbath of the Lord your God. In it you shall do no work: you, nor

> your son, nor your daughter, nor your male servant, nor your female servant, nor your cattle, nor your stranger who is within your gates. For in six days the LORD made the heavens and the earth, the sea, and all that is in them, and rested the seventh day. Therefore the LORD blessed the Sabbath day and hallowed it." [vv. 8-11 NKJV]

God, though He lives beyond the boundaries of time, has acted and rested in time, setting the example that is beneficial for all but obligatory only for Israel under the covenantal relation.

To *honor parents* relates to right treatment of *God* because parents are *God's representatives* to their children. Verse 12 says:

> "Honor your father and your mother, that your days may be long upon the land which the Lord your God is giving you." (NKJV)

To *honor* parents means to treat them with respect. It implies a child's obedience, as Paul applies this principle in Ephesians 6:1. Absolute obedience to parents was not intended, because the other commandments applied to the child as well. So Paul limits his charge for obedience to parents with the phrase "in the Lord" (NKJV.) There are rare instances in which a child may have to disobey a parent in order to obey God. But then it is a "can't," rather than a "won't." The overarching principle is that *right treatment of God and people cannot be separated.*

The sixth commandment begins a new division in which the focus has shifted from right treatment of God to …

II. Right Treatment of People

The symmetrical development of these covenantal stipulations is instructive in itself. The vertical responsibilities (people to God) are balanced by the horizontal (people to people), but in the proper order. Unless a person is *godly*, he or she cannot be *neighborly* in the truest sense. In fact, failure to demonstrate compassion toward people in need indicates a problem in a person's relationship with God, as the parable of the good

Samaritan shows. By the same token, crimes against humanity, such as David's sin with Bathsheba, are ultimately, as David later confessed, against God, and God only. Another example is young Joseph. When tempted by Potiphar's wife, he answered, "How then can I do this great wickedness, and sin against God?" (Gen. 39:9 NKJV). *Right treatment of God and people cannot be separated.*

The sixth command, in verse 13, "*You shall not murder*" (NKJV), remains in the category of *actions*. Actions are emphasized in the arrangement of the Ten Commandments as the expression of what is in the heart. God cares about people and property. So be careful to avoid the philosophy that minimizes the importance of *stuff* in its emphasis upon what is considered *spiritual*. Remember that God, who is *Spirit*, made all the *stuff* there is!

The command to not murder does not outlaw killing people in self-defense, national defense, or in the execution of capital criminals. Neither is this command in conflict with Genesis 9:6, which says, "*Whoever sheds man's blood, by his blood shall be shed; for in the image of God He made man.*" Man owes his life to God. This is the most basic biblical argument against abortion and doctor-assisted suicide.

The seventh command, in verse 14, "*You shall not commit adultery*" (NKJV), concerns the boundaries of marriage within which God has safeguarded the act of procreating life in His image. It is a provision respecting one's family. It also honors the marriage covenant as establishing a relationship intended to reflect God's own promise keeping. *Right treatment of God and people cannot be separated.*

The eighth command, in verse 15, "*You shall not steal*" (NKJV). Theft disrespects God's ownership of all things. It is the rejection of His providence in meeting people's needs according to His will. More obviously, stealing is failure to treat others the way one would want to be treated. Today, people's "innocence"; intellectual property, or ideas; and identities are often stolen, as well as their wealth.

When God said, "*You shall not bear false witness against your neighbor*" (v. 17 NKJV), He addressed the basis of Israel's legal system. The confirmation of what is true by the testimony of two or three witnesses depends on their truthful reporting. Those who lie on the witness stand undermine justice and can ruin the reputations of those they slander.

This ninth command, forbidding *slander*, is back in the domain of words. It matches the prohibition against abusing God's name, in verse 7. The very ability to express oneself verbally is a godlike quality. With this power, people are able to confess faith in God's revelation, and bless God and others. When this privilege is abused, it reflects badly on the original Communicator, in whose likeness we were made.

The tenth command, recorded in verse 17, returns to the sphere of *thought*. It has to do with a person's mental appetite for what belongs to others.

> "You shall not covet your neighbor's house; you shall not covet your neighbor's wife, nor his male servant, nor his female servant, nor his ox, nor his donkey, nor anything that is your neighbor's." (NKJV)

Coveting is harboring inordinate selfish desires for things God has not given. It often leads to theft. But even when it doesn't, the spirit of discontent is an affront to the wise providence and generosity of God. In Colossians 3:5, Paul equated greed with idolatry. In Hebrews 13:5-6 the writer says:

> Let your conduct be without covetousness; be content with such things as you have. For He Himself has said, "I will never leave you nor forsake you." So we may boldly say: "The Lord is my helper; I will not fear. What can man do to me?" (NKJV)

Conclusion

The point of these core commands is that God deserves to have His people reflect what He is like in their relationships with Him and one another. He demands their obedience not only because they owe it to Him, but because it is essential to the life of spiritual prosperity which

He graciously offers them. In short, *right treatment of God and people cannot be separated.*

Applications (look)

Throughout the text, the commands address the individual Israelite. National obedience depended on what every man, woman, young person, and child did individually. The same is true of us.

If you have not yet come to Christ, you need to understand four things about the Law. First, no one is saved by keeping it. Salvation from the penalty of sin was never the purpose of the Law. In Romans 3:20, Paul wrote, "Therefore by the deeds of the law no flesh will be justified in His sight, for by the law is the knowledge of sin" (NKJV).

Second, the Law is like God's straightedge, against which even the best of people are shown to be crooked, or sinful. James said, "For whoever shall keep the whole law, and yet stumble in one point, he is guilty of all" (2:10 NKJV).

Third, without the righteousness revealed in God's Law, there is no hope of eternal life, only the certainty of eternal punishment. In Matthew 5:20, Jesus said, "Unless your righteousness exceeds the righteousness of the scribes and Pharisees, you will by no means enter the kingdom of heaven" (NKJV).

Fourth, Christ has fulfilled the righteousness demanded by the Law; and God puts His righteousness to the account of anyone who simply believes in Him. In Romans 3:21-26, Paul writes:

> But now the righteousness of God apart from the law is revealed, being witnessed by the Law and the Prophets, even the righteousness of God, through faith in Jesus Christ, to all and on all who believe. For there is no difference; for all have sinned and fall short of the glory of God, being justified freely by His grace through the redemption that is in Christ Jesus, whom God set forth as a propitiation by His blood, through faith, to demonstrate His righteousness, because in His forbearance God had passed over the sins

> that were previously committed, to demonstrate at the present time His righteousness, that He might be just and the justifier of the one who has faith in Jesus. (NKJV)

Although the believer in Jesus Christ is not obligated to keep the Ten Commandments as a condition for covenantal blessing, the righteousness of Christ, which is put to the believer's account by faith in Him, fulfills the moral demands of this very law. Until a person comes to faith in the Christ of Mount Calvary, the Law of Mount Sinai is an indispensable tool to make him aware of his need of a Savior. In Galatians 3:24, Paul compares the Law to a child's tutor, whose job it was to bring the child to the point of legal heirship.

Invitation (took)

If God has used His Law to make you aware of your need of the Savior, I urge you to put your trust in Him today. He is God's Son in human form, who died in your place and rose again. The Bible says, "Believe on the Lord Jesus Christ, and you will be saved" (Acts 16:31 NKJV).

If you have already trusted in Jesus as God's payment for the penalty of your sins, I invite you to confess to Him any sins He has brought to your awareness through this consideration of the Ten Commandments. First John 1:9 says, "If we confess our sins, He is faithful and just to forgive us our sins and to cleanse us from all unrighteousness" (NKJV).

Finally, be encouraged to use the Law "lawfully," as Paul put it in 1 Timothy 1:8 (NKJV). It is not a means of saving grace, but a way of showing people their need of it. In the words of Harold Abrahams' academic advisors, there are indeed two mountains. But the one and only God designed Sinai to prepare His people for Calvary so that through faith in Christ, they might enjoy the blessings of right relationships forever stated in the Ten Commandments. *Right treatment of God and people cannot be separated.*

Summary and Conclusion

The Hebrew Scriptures comprise a unified part of the written revelation of God and rest upon the foundational Books of Moses, the Pentateuch. The unity, order, and symmetry of the Old Testament books and of the Pentateuch reflect God as their ultimate Author. The Books of Moses form a chiasmus that emphasizes the holiness in which God's covenant people must relate to Him.

The biblical covenants are related through the promises God made to Abraham. The Mosaic covenant alone was conditional upon the people's obedience. It is replaced by the new covenant, already ratified by the blood of Jesus Christ. In the Holy Spirit, believers in Christ enjoy the personal blessings promised to Abraham. Israel will participate in other features of the new covenant in the Davidic kingdom to come. The Law, recorded in the book of Exodus, was a gracious provision from God. Its revelation of how Israel was to enjoy true prosperity in the land of promise encodes the right treatment of God and people that is fulfilled in the Christian through the Holy Spirit.

Preaching the Law begins with establishing the text and identifying points of emphasis and literary genre. The author's meaning is discovered by attention to the historical, cultural, and dispensational rings of context, as well as to grammatical analysis of the text.

Discussion Questions

1. In your own words, why should we preach from the Hebrew Scriptures in general, and from the Pentateuch in particular?
2. How would you argue for the single authorship of the Pentateuch, if challenged?
3. Trace the provisions of the Abrahamic covenant from the foundational covenants with Adam and Noah, to the covenants given later.
4. Why is it so important to understand the conditional nature of the Mosaic covenant and its replacement with the new?

5. List three aspects of sermon development by the Whiting Method that you felt were exemplified in the sample sermon on Exodus 20:1-17.

6. List three weaknesses of the sample sermon, in view of your understanding of the Whiting Method.

CHAPTER 10

Preaching Historical Narrative

People like stories, because they are *living* a story. Stories about people enrich the lives of listeners and readers, who are able to experience life vicariously through characters who are more or less like themselves. When true stories are told about real people, they are part of history. They provide an instructive pattern for comparison and contrast. When God is the author of true stories about real people, the historical lessons reveal truth about a person's relationship with Him and with other people that could not be communicated as well any other way. In short, stories are personally relational; true stories are historical, and the story of God's relations with people is revelatory.

The Pentateuch tells the origin of the universe, man, sin, and salvation through God's covenant people, Israel. The subsequent books of history (Joshua through Esther) tell the story of how God keeps the promises of His covenants, but does so through the stories of a lot of people with whom we can identify. The various accounts are unified by the plan and purpose of the God who is in control of both the events and their recording. His revelation is conveyed through many stories written by numerous people in the variety of ways in which stories are told and life is experienced. Each pattern of storytelling, then, has a place and purpose in communicating the spiritual truths that are grounded in "His-story" and desperately needed by all kinds of people in all types of circumstances.

In an attempt to explain why Bible stories are so often relegated to children's books and Sunday school and neglected from the pulpit, Steven Mathewson offers four reasons: First, compared to the New

Testament Epistles, the stories of Old Testament history seem to pack little significance for the amount of space they take up. Second, those who identify themselves as "New Testament preachers" have a tendency to see the value of Old Testament narrative as merely *illustrative* of New Testament truth rather than *foundational.* Third, the length of Old Testament history and the difficulty of the biblical languages can be overwhelming. And fourth, stories do not naturally lend themselves to the analytical outlines of rigid homiletical systems.[1]

Of particular relevance to the Whiting Method of sermon development is Mathewson's comment "The analytical outline approach presses the story into a mold that often works against it, especially when the outline points are alliterated or parallel."[2]

This chapter highlights some important considerations in developing sermons that reflect the form of the narrative text in the historical books of the Bible. These considerations include a brief overview of the Historical Books not covered in Chapter 10, a survey of some ways in which stories are structured, and a development of a sample sermon on the book of Ruth.

Overview of the Historical Books

Narrative, the literary genre of stories, is found in other books of the Bible besides the twelve books of history. However, an overview of the biblical books of Joshua through Esther indicates a consistent emphasis, which deserves attention when developing sermons from one of these books, such as the book of Ruth. Bruce Wilkinson and Kenneth Boa introduce the Historical Books with the following summary:

> These books describe the occupation and settlement of Israel in the Promised Land, the transition from judges to the monarchy, the division and decline of the kingdom, the captivities of the northern and southern kingdom, and the return of the Remnant.

> The historical books break into three divisions: (1) the theocratic books (Joshua, Judges and Ruth), (2) the monarchical books (Samuel, Kings and Chronicles), and (3) the restoration books (Ezra, Nehemiah, Esther).[3]

This categorical description of the Historical Books provides a helpful way to think through their content in relation to the time period in which the recorded events occurred. According to Wilkinson and Boa, the *Theocratic Books* cover events when God alone ruled His people, prior to the era of the kings, between 1405 and 1043 B.C. The *Monarchical Books* deal with the times of the kings, from Saul until the Babylonian captivity, 1043 and 586 B.C.. The *Restoration Books* pertain to the postexilic events between 605 and 536 B.C..[4]

Not only are the history books arranged to cover periods of time in an orderly fashion, but their collective message is that God is faithful to fulfill what Moses recorded in the book of Deuteronomy, particularly chapters 28-30. The history of Israel demonstrates the blessings of obedience to the revelation of God, and the curse of disobedience. The consistency of this theme is apparent in Derickson's message statements, arranged below under the categories and dates of Wilkinson and Boa.[5]

The Theocratic Books, 1405-1043 B.C.

1. **Joshua:** Israel's conquest and distribution of the land ... *resulted from following God's lead* through Joshua and from obedience to His commands.

2. **Judges:** The evil not purged from the land when Israel occupied it ... overcame the people while *God repeatedly raised up* deliverers to combat with evil.

3. **Ruth:** *The sovereign care of God* in Naomi's and Ruth's lives ... came through both divine agency and the human agency of Boaz.

The Monarchical Books,[6] 1043-586 B.C.

4. **Samuel:** *God's rule over Israel … was mediated* through Samuel, then Saul, and finally through David.

5. **Kings:** *God's blessings and curses upon Judah and Israel* … came in accordance with His covenant and as a result of either faith and obedience, or rebellion.

6. **Chronicles:** *God's blessing (with victory and peace) or cursing (with defeat and exile)* … resulted from Judah's spiritual commitment or rebellion (reflected in its treatment of the temple).

The Restoration Books, 605-536 B.C.[7]

7. **Ezra:** *God's blessing in response to obedience and national purity…* enabled the people to rebuild His temple and obey His law through the support of both the kings of Persia and princes of Judah.

8. **Nehemiah:** *God's restoration of the nation…*was accomplished through the leadership of Nehemiah.

9. **Esther:** *The sovereign care of God in preserving His chosen people …* is demonstrated in His working through circumstances and exaltation of key persons in order to nullify the attempt of their enemies to destroy them.

The historical continuity and theological consistency in the overall message of these books are what one would expect from writers who are moved by the Holy Spirit (see 2 Peter 1:21). They give the expository preacher a contextual basis for drawing the principle that a given story was actually intended to teach. By practicing what Walter Kaiser calls the *syntactical-theological method*,[8] the faithful expositor avoids the twofold danger of presenting historical facts without their theologyical significance[9] and separating the spiritual meaning from its basis in history.[10] For example, the meaning conveyed by the writer of Ruth, and the significance preachers find in that meaning, will fit with the historical facts, the revelation of God to that point in history, and the overall message of the history books.[11] Because stories are told in certain ways, however, the Whiting Method must be applied with particular attention to their structure and shape, and the sermon must be developed in such a way as to reflect that pattern.

The Nature of Stories

Stories seem easy enough to tell, and even easier to listen to. But to decipher the storyteller's intended meaning is often difficult, though not impossible. In discussing how to identify the overall plan and purpose of biblical books, for example, Walter Kaiser states, "The most difficult pattern of all to determine is in those cases where the major portion of a book, if not its entire text, is made up of narrative materials."[12] According to Kaiser, the interpreter must often "make his decision on the basis of what details were *selected* for inclusion and how they were *arranged* by the writer."[13] Kaiser is not saying that everything excluded from a narrative is unimportant. In fact, the provident hand of God, who isn't mentioned in the book of Esther, is made all the more prominent by His unseen involvement in the outworking of events.

Archetypes

One way to analyze the literature of biblical stories is to identify which of several possible plot patterns, known as *archetypes*, is found in them.[14] The archetype of the overall story is sometimes referred to as the *plot motif*. The archetypes found in various episodes within the story are sometimes called *type scenes*.[15] Among the most prominent archetypes in Scripture are the *hero*, *epic*, *tragedy*, and *comedy*.

Hero

According to Leland Ryken, hero stories are the most common archetype in narrative.[14] He describes them as follows: "Hero stories focus on the struggles and triumphs of the protagonist. The central hero or heroine is representative of a whole group and is usually a largely exemplary character, at least by the end of the story. The hero or heroine's destiny is an implied comment about life and reality."[17]

It is important to understand that the stories of Bible heroes include the record of faults and failures to teach a positive ideal by negative example.[18] David's sin with Bathsheba is an obvious case in point. Just because the Bible records something a hero says or does, doesn't stamp his or her behavior with divine approval.[19]

A subclass within the archetype of the hero is the *epic*, described by Ryken as "long narrative, a hero story on a grand scale," which is sufficiently expansive to represent a nation or produce self-awareness on the part of society as a whole.[20] Ryken's examples include the covenant theme of the Pentateuch, the Exodus, the life of David, the book of Revelation, and the Bible as a whole.[21]

Tragedy

Tragedy, says Ryken, "portrays movement from prosperity to catastrophe."[22] He describes the pattern by which such stories unfold as: dilemma / choice / catastrophe / suffering / perception / death.[23] When it involves a prominent figure, such as a king or ruler, he is called a *tragic* hero.[24] Saul and Samson are among the surprisingly few examples of tragedy in the Bible.[25]

Comic Plots

Comedies refer not to stories that are funny but to those having happy endings.[26] The protagonist moves through a series of obstacles to eventual triumph over them. Ryken notes, "In comic stories the protagonist is gradually assimilated into society (in contrast to tragedy, where the hero becomes progressively isolated from society). The typical ending of a comedy is a marriage, feast, reconciliation, or victory over enemies."[27] The plot has been described as "U-shaped,"[28] because the action moves from favorable circumstances through adversity and back to circumstances made even more favorable by the experience of loss or opposition. Most Bible stories fall into this category, including the stories of Job, Ruth, and even Jesus![29]

Common Elements

All stories, according to Steven Mathewson, revolve around four key elements: "plot, characters, setting, and point of view."[30] Discovering the meaning of Old Testament stories requires the exegetical preacher to look at them "through the lens of each element."[31] Such analysis can be incorporated into the development of the truth sheets discussed in Chapter 4. Simply ask and answer such questions as: *Who* are the characters? *What* is the plot? *When* did the events occur? *Where* does the action occur? *Where* is the writer in relation to the events he records? *How* is the story set? *Why* is the story told?

Another important idea to bear in mind in analyzing stories is the way they "combine to form larger narrative structures."[32] Using the story of Samson and Delilah, Thompson explains, "In biblical narrative originally independent stories lose their autonomy and become subordinated and integrated into a larger coherent whole. Consequently, the examination of one small story leads into the larger narrative structure in which it occurs,"[33]

Plot

Political pundits, detectives, and reporters sometimes tell us to "follow the money" if we want to understand why things happen the way they do. In a similar way, the key to understanding biblical narrative is to "follow the action." According to Mathewson, "plot refers to action. It consists of a sequence of events that usually hinges on a conflict or crisis. The events in the story move through this conflict or crisis toward some kind of resolution."[34] This organization of information about events tends to take one of several possible forms, which Mathewson calls *plot shape*.[35] He identifies the flow of action in a plot as progressing through four main stages: (1) exposition, (2) crisis, (3) resolution and (4) conclusion.[36] While it is not necessary or always possible to pinpoint the transition from one element of the plot to another, it is important to follow the general movement.

Exposition refers to the information provided to set the stage. In the book of Ruth, this information is found in chapter 1.

> Now it came to pass, in the days when the judges ruled, that there was a famine in the land. And a certain man of Bethlehem, Judah, went to dwell in the country of Moab, he and his wife and his two sons. The name of the man was Elimelech, the name of his wife was Naomi,

> and the names of his two sons were Mahlon and Chilion–Ephrathites of Bethlehem, Judah. And they went to the country of Moab and remained there. (vv.1-2 NKJV)

Understanding the story of Ruth requires that one know something about the period of the judges. Because of Israel's failure to execute God's judgment and exterminate the inhabitants of Canaan, the people were constantly subject to idolatry, anarchy, and harassment by enemies. Israel had not yet taken Jerusalem from the Jebusites (see Judges 1:21) and didn't have a king. Judges 17:6 states, "In those days there was no king in Israel; everyone did what was right in his own eyes" (NKJV). God raised up rulers known as *judges* to deliver the people from ruin when they lapsed into disobedience to the Mosaic covenant and reaped the promised consequences. When they repented, there was restoration and rest until the next relapse into sin. Seven such cycles have been identified. From the vantage point of the first readers of the story, this would have raised an important question: Without the stability of the monarchy in Jerusalem, who was looking out for the well-being of individual Israelites?

Due to a famine, Elimelech, whose name means "God is my King," leaves Bethlehem ("house of bread"), in the land of God's promises, to go and live among the people of Moab, who were forbidden to enter the assembly of Israel and with whom the Israelites were forbidden to intermarry. These facts are the exposition that sets up the story.

Crisis refers to "the complication, the conflict, or the tension"[37] that creates the question to be answered or the problem to be solved in a story. When it reaches its highest level of intensity, the crisis is sometimes called "the climax or peak moment."[38] In Ruth 1:3-5 the picture of moral chaos as a result of bad judgment is further darkened by the deaths of all the husbands: "Then Elimelech, Naomi's husband, died; and she was left, and her two sons. Now they took wives of the women of Moab: the name of the one was Orpah, and the name of the other Ruth. And they dwelt there about ten years. Then both Mahlon and Chilion also died; so the woman survived her two sons and her husband" (NKJV).

As bad as things were going for the bereft women, the husbands' deaths provide the turning point toward conflict resolution.

Resolution is first hinted at by Ruth's unexpected commitment to Naomi to cling to both her and the God Naomi has remembered only for the purpose of complaining about her losses. When the two return to the house of bread in the land of promise, it just *happens* to be the time of barley harvest. Ruth just *happens* to glean in a field owned by a near kinsman who just *happens* to be willing to redeem Ruth by paying Naomi for her land and to forfeit to his son the land he might have inherited.

The *conclusion* of a story often takes the form of an *epilogue*, which sums up the outcome, tying up the loose ends. The story of Ruth concludes with the acknowledgment that Ruth the Moabite is better to Naomi than seven sons. This is an amazing statement from a widow bereaved of her sons in a culture in which sons were highly prized and the Moabites were cursed. The story ends with Naomi caring for the grandson who, from the viewpoint of the storyteller (possibly Samuel), is in the line of King David!

Conclusions often clarify the writer's purpose in writing. Ellisen describes the purpose of Ruth as the portrayal of a pastoral love scene of faithfulness in the midst of a time of sin, idolatry, and infidelity—and *that* involving a woman from Moab! She became one of two Gentile women mentioned in David's genealogy, the other being Rahab the harlot. The story demonstrates Yahweh's concern for the people of the nations that will one day be blessed through the promised Seed of the woman, Israel's Messiah![39] Gregory Trull's summation is more succinct: Ruth is a "story of love and loyalty leading to a Royal Line."[40]

Characters

Old Testament stories, like any other, have a central character known as the *protagonist*.[41] The main adversaries who work against the central character are known as *antagonists*.[42] The characters who accentuate the central character are known as *foils*.[43] Then there are any number of minor characters whose roles are less important. When preparing to preach historical narrative according to the Whiting Method, the *who* question on the truth sheet should be expanded to identify the major *and* minor characters. For example, in the book of Ruth, see figure 10-1.

After analyzing each character's role from a literary standpoint, you can now evaluate them in light of the historical information provided. How are the characters described? (Ruth is a Moabitess. Is this a significant fact?) What does each one do? What is the meaning of each character's name? (Naomi means "pleasant," which explains why she asked people to call her Mara ["bitter"] instead of Naomi upon her return to Bethlehem.) How do the characters converse and interact? (In Ruth 1:14, Orpah *kissed* Naomi, but Ruth *clung* to her and said, "Your God [will be] my God" [v.16 NKJV].)

Character Classification of Ruth	
Major:	*[Hidden: Yahweh]* Ruth and Boaz – Protagonists Naomi – Foil
Minor:	Elimelech, Mahlon, Chilion, Orpah

Figure 10.1

According to author Ronald Hals, the writer of Ruth mentions the name of God no fewer than twenty-five times in eighty-five verses.[44] Kaiser further observes:

> In nine of these references God's name is used in a prayer asking for blessing on one of the major characters in the book. It is significant that each of the major characters is the object of at least one such prayer. Even more striking is the fact that, without interrupting the flow of the narration, the writer goes on to show by implication that in each case the prayer was answered.
>
> Thus restraint and reticence dominate the author's style in that he does not openly moralize or editorialize on what has (or has not) taken place. This makes the conclusion all the more dramatic and powerful. The major and minor incidents in the life of this family are all under

the providential care of God and included in the history of salvation.[45] The "thread of God's plan" is woven directly "into the tapestry of everyday events."[46] That he directs even the smallest details of our lives is a motif which recurs throughout the Book of Ruth.[47]

Setting

As mentioned previously, the setting of the story begins in Moab, where three husbands die, and progresses on to Bethlehem, where Ruth is redeemed and Naomi's hope is restored.

Point of View

To correctly understand the meaning of a story, you must identify the point of view from which it is told. This sometimes shifts. Mathewson describes the storyteller's perspective as *focalization*.[48] If the narration is from the reader's perspective, he calls it *external focalization* because the reader (from outside the story) knows things about the characters that the characters don't know about themselves.[49] If the story is told from the character's point of view, the perspective is that of *internal focalization*, because the reader is at the mercy of what the characters (insiders) reveal about themselves.[50] If the narrator speaks or writes from his own perspective, Mathewson calls it *zero focalization*, because both the outsider/reader and the insider/character depend on the narrator, who is in charge of what he reveals about the characters.[51]

Shifts in focalization are often indicated by verbs of perception, describing what the storyteller sees, hears, or knows.[52] When the narrator reveals his own heart on a matter, there is no doubt that he is in charge of the story.[53] One of the most common indicators of a change in perspective is when the word translated "behold" is used.[54] Sometimes the story is told from the perspective of God, who knows all things.[55] The story of Job, for example, begins with information about Satan's challenge, that only God could know and which is never told to Job.

Sample Sermon

The following sermon notes on the book of Ruth do not represent the usual format of the Whiting Method. It is included here partly to demonstrate your freedom to adapt your sermon within the basic Whiting Method principles. The Whiting Method simply establishes a point of reference from which you can depart, if desired, according to your own preaching style or for variety, but still be confident that the exegetical bases are covered. Approaching the story of Ruth as a play or movie is one way to reflect the way the story is actually told in Scripture. It eliminates points of an analytical outline that might be distracting as well as unnecessary.

Notice that the sermon begins with an introduction and survey of the entire book of Ruth. This can be thought of as a reconnaissance flight at high altitude. Next, from closer range, the sermon is developed around the central character, whose name, Yahweh, is explained. Circling at a lower altitude, the writer refers to the prayers of the characters to show God's faithfulness in answering them. Finally, God's providence in everyday life is acknowledged as the basis for great encouragement to the contemporary audience.

The Hidden God Who is in Control

Ruth 1-4
God Can Take Bad Decisions and Use Them for Good

Introduction:

This book is a story written in the time of David or Solomon about real people and events that occurred about two hundred years before, in the period of the judges. Not everything that happened in the lives of the people in the book is included, so the author of the book of Ruth selected details that developed the theme or idea he wished to teach in the book. Ruth is a theological book, not just a nice story.

Survey of the Book of Ruth:

Introduction	Setting the Scene	1:1-5
Scene I	The Road to Bethlehem	1:6-18
Interlude 1	*Arrival in Bethlehem*	1:19-22
Scene II	The Field of Boaz	2:1-17
Interlude 2	*Ruth's Report*	2:18-23
Interlude 3	*Naomi's Plan*	3:1-5
Scene III	The Threshing Floor of Boaz	3:6-15
Interlude 4	*Ruth's Report*	3:16-18
Scene IV	The Gate of Bethlehem	4:1-12
Conclusion	A Son Is Born	4:13-17
Genealogical	Appendix	4:18-22

Development of the Book of Ruth

Major Character: Not Ruth, Naomi, or Boaz, but Yahweh!
Theme: *God can take bad decisions and use them for good.*

Theme Developed:

Names of God in the Book:

Yahweh—Covenant Name of God, "He who is and will be" for His people; cf. Ex. 3:14, the God of faithfulness, used seventeen times.

God—Basic meaning is "He who is great or mighty," refers in this book to the God of Israel three times and to the God of Moab one time.

Almighty—Used in the two verses where Naomi speaks and says that Yahweh came against her.

Direct References to God:

Prayer:

Naomi prays for Ruth to receive kindness from Yahweh and that she may find a home and a husband (1:8-9).

In 2:20, Yahweh's kindness to Ruth is mentioned.

In Boaz she receives the latter request.

The Benediction of Boaz by Naomi (2:19-20) and of Ruth by Boaz (3:10).

Finds fulfillment in story's happy ending.

Prayers for family's prosperity (4:11-12, 14b).

Fulfilled in that couple's great-grandchild.

Became David the king.

Boaz prays that Ruth may find shelter under the wings of Yahweh (2:12).

Fulfilled in Ruth's request for Boaz to do the part of the next of kin (3:9) where "wing," or "skirt," is the same word. Here Boaz became the answer to his own prayers.

God's Actions:
Narrator speaks and has the action of Yahweh, initiating the movement of the story (1:6).
Narrator shows action of Yahweh, bringing the story to a happy ending (4:13).
Naomi mentions God's action against her (1:13, 20-21).
Naomi mentions God's action of favor (2:20).
Women of Bethlehem report God's goodness (4:14).

Indirect References to God:
"Blessed," in 2:19, implies *by Yahweh*.
Ruth "happened to come to the…field [of] Boaz" (2:3 NKJV) (even so-called accident attributed to Yahweh).
Scheme of Naomi and actions of Ruth (3:1-13)

Conclusion:

The story speaks to us. In the various events of our lives, we seldom see spectacular acts of deliverance and provision. But God is there, taking care of His world and fulfilling His plan for His children according to His schedule.

Summary and Conclusion

True stories about real people are part of His-story. When God superintends their recording, these various accounts of biblical history reveal truth about personal relationships with God and others. They not only illustrate New Testament truth but are part of its foundation. The books of Joshua through Esther comprise a unit of Scripture–most of which requires an understanding of how the stories of historical narrative are structured.

The content of the Historical Books is generally arranged chronologically, from the theocracy of Israel to its monarchy and postexilic restoration. Each of the books by itself, and the sum of them all together, demonstrates God's faithfulness to bless or curse His people according to the provisions in the Mosaic covenant. As theological history, never present Old Testament narrative as a mere record of human experience without its theological meaning and practical significance. Likewise, never proclaim its spiritual lessons apart from their basis in history.

Analyze the literature of all biblical stories with respect to their *archetype*, *plot*, *point of view*, and *characters*. Archetypes refer to various plot patterns, such as *hero*, *epic*, *tragedy*, and *comedy*. The *plot*, or sequence of action, usually involves (1) an *exposition* that sets the stage, (2) a *crisis* that presents a problem, (3) the *resolution* that resolves the tension, and (4) a *conclusion* that summarizes the results. *Focalization* concerns whether the story is told from the perspective of the reader, characters, or narrator. Observing shifts in the point of view from which the story is told is essential to good understanding.

When a character is central to the story, he or she is classified as a *major character*. Stories generally have two or three kinds of major characters, the *protagonist*, who is the main subject of the action; the *foil*, whose character serves to heighten the effect of the central character; and the *antagonist*, who stands in opposition. *Minor characters* are not unimportant but are less prominent than major characters. In addition to observing each character's role in light of the factual information selected and arranged, always seek to understand what the story teaches about God. The story of Ruth is really about God's care of His people despite chaotic times in which they are unaware that He is acting to fulfill His plan and purpose.

Discussion Questions

1. Do you agree that Bible stories tend to be neglected in expository preaching? If so, what do you believe is the main reason?
2. What is the point of the Historical Books, and what is the point of their *having* a point?
3. Why is it equally important to avoid preaching the stories of the Old Testament as mere history, and to avoid teaching spiritual lessons without reference to their basis in history?
4. Explain what is meant by an *archetype*, and tell why Ruth is a *comedy*.
5. Explain in your own words:

    a) plot:
    b) exposition:
    c) crisis:
    d) resolution:
    e) conclusion:

6. Explain the difference between internal and external focalization .
7. Explain the following:

    a) protagonist:
    b) antagonist:
    c) foil:
    d) minor character:

8. Why do you agree or disagree that Yahweh is the main character in the book of Ruth?

CHAPTER 11

Preaching the Poetic Books

The books of Job, Psalms, Proverbs, Ecclesiastes, and the Song of Solomon are classified as the books of *poetry*, or the Poetic Books. Because of its poetic quality, Lamentations, traditionally grouped with the Major (longer) Prophets, is also included in this brief survey. These six books contain most of the Hebrew poetry of the Bible but also include *wisdom* and some *prophetic* literature. The primary distinction of these six books, five of which are appropriately located in the heart of the body of Scripture, is that their contents express the heights and depths of mental and emotional responses to God's greatness in the context of the toughness of life. For this reason their expository proclamation meets the needs of people who wonder how to process perplexity, persecution, and pain, as well as how to express prayer and praise to the sovereign God.

Wisdom Literature

The Wisdom Literature of Job, Proverbs, and Ecclesiastes is "characterized ... by the stance of a narrator who pictures himself as a wise man declaring his observations about human experience."[1] As a literary genre, it is distinguishable by its sustained argumentation for conclusions about spiritual, ethical, and moral issues. Whereas human wisdom says, "Know yourself," God's wisdom says, "Know God" (see James 3:17-18).

Job

Overview

The author of the book of Job is unknown. Jewish tradition favored Mosaic authorship, but Job 32:16-17 seems to indicate that Elihu is the author. Other possible writers are Solomon and Job himself.[2] The events recorded in Job seem to be during the time of the patriarchs, Abraham, Isaac, and Jacob.[3] The setting is thought to be southeast of Israel, where good grazing made Job a wealthy man.

Job "is a comic narrative comprised of elements of wisdom, drama, lyric and tragedy."[4] As introduced in Chapter 10, *comedy* refers to its "U-shaped plot in which events begin in prosperity, descend into tragedy, and rise suddenly to a happy conclusion."[5] Though the story is told as if it were a play, James refers to Job not as a fictitious character, but as a man who actually lived (5:11). The book bearing his name is known as a *theodicy*, "a work that attempts to reconcile God's goodness and sovereignty with the existence of evil and suffering in the world."[6] A literary analysis reveals Job 28:1-28 as the prominent center.[7] Its lesson is that God does not explain His ways to man (see Romans 11:33-36). Nowhere in the narrative is Job even told about the dialogue between God and Satan, in chapters 1 and 2. Without this knowledge, Job cursed the day of his birth, crying from his pain. This speech in chapter 3 serves as a foundation for God's discourse in chapters 38-41.

Job and his friends all shared the same philosophy of life, namely that God blesses the righteous and curses unrighteousness. They differed only in how they viewed Job! Job contended for his own righteousness. The book's writer, in fact, refers to him as "perfect" (1:1 KJV). (His "perfection" described not a sinless life, but his standing in right relationship with God.) His friends, however, judged him to be *un*righteous by the fact that he was suffering. Elihu defended God as greater (a correct but incomplete response). God does not explain.[8]

Figure 11-1 outlines the book.[9]

Job

God allows the righteous to suffer for His own good purposes

I. The Prologue	1–2
II. The Dialogue	3–42:6
A. Dialogue-Dispute (3–27)	
B. Job's Discourses (28–31)	
C. Elihu's Defense of God (32–37)	
D. God's Rebuke and Challenge (38–42:6)	
III. The Epilogue	42:7–17

Figure 11.1

Interpretive Notes

In producing the truth sheets on the book of Job, it is especially important to keep track of your answers to these questions: *Who* is speaking? *What* are the issues? *How* does it fit into the argument?[10] *What* is Yahweh's perspective? Then note other observations and lessons. For example, Job 1:7-12 indicates that Satan has access to the throne of God, where he accuses the "brethren" (Rev. 12:10 NKJV). This means that he has not yet been cast down to the earth. Like a dog on a leash held in God's hand, Satan can do no more harm than God allows for the accomplishment of His purpose, which is for the believer's ultimate good!

Job gives a unique view into the relationship of Satan to God and Satan's enmity toward men. It teaches the need for repentance on the part of even the most righteous of persons. It also shows that divine discipline of God's children is ultimately constructive, that He is worthy of implicit trust, and that He commands men apart from material rewards.

With regard to judging whether it is punishment or development, any trial should be evaluated on the basis of the character being tried. To assume that a person is being punished simply because he is enduring a trial is to miss a lesson from Job. (See Matthew 4:1 and James 5:11.)

On the subject of trusting, note that God's closing speech in chapters 38-41 is a response to Job's speech in chapter 3. It says, in effect, that there are no "mistakes" in this world. Everything is under God's good control. As Derickson once told a roomful of college students, "Trust is not in knowing answers, but confidence in the one who knows even though He has not told me. God is to be trusted without understanding

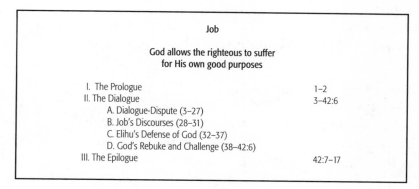

His ways. God is worthy to be served apart from any 'perks' or external incentives. God does reward the righteous … in the end."[11]

Preaching Job

If Job is preached as a series of messages, be sure to maintain clarity on where the text is in relation to the drama as a whole. Job may be preached by stating questions raised in the story and then answering them by an inductive approach to the text.

Proverbs

Title

The English word *proverbs* comes from two Latin words, *pro* ("instead of") and *verba* ("words"). A proverb is a short, catchy, memorable statement that summarizes a wise principle *in the place of many words*. The Hebrew word translated "proverb," *mashal*, conveys the idea of a governing life principle expressed by comparing two or more things.[12]

Authorship and Date

Solomon is mentioned as the author of most of the Proverbs (1:1; 10:1; 25:1). He either wrote or dictated chapters 1-25 and may be the one called "King Lemuel" in 31:1.[13] According to 1 Kings 4:32, Solomon spoke as many as three thousand proverbs that were probably recorded in the official records of the day. After God fulfilled His promise to give Solomon a wise heart (I Kings 3:12), Solomon became the most prominent among a class of sage men who sought and collected time-honored truisms about life during the Golden Age of Wisdom, 1000–700 B.C.

Literary Forms

Proverbs appear in at least four forms: (1) individual units; (2) clusters of maxims on a particular theme; (3) expanded units, called *epigrams*; and (4) sonnets expressing the stages of a thought in progress.[14] The *motto*, or overarching principle, of the book of Proverbs is: "The fear of the LORD is the beginning of knowledge [or wisdom]" (1:7; 9:10 NKJV).

Argument

"Courtiers proclaim that Yahweh has established and upholds a righteous order in which a man lives."[15] It is the end or outcome that reveals the truth about a course of action, not the way it may appear at a moment in time.[16]

Structure

The collection is introduced so that the reader will appreciate the relevance and urgency of learning and implementing its wisdom.[17] The two-part introduction serves to "hook" the reader. And though the proverbs look disconnected, there appears to be an order to their arrangement.[18] (See figure 11-2.)

Interpretive Issues[19]

To properly understand Proverbs, at least six issues must be addressed. First, *proverbs* must be distinguished from *promises*. While some promises are sprinkled among the proverbs (such as 3:5-6), proverbs are generalizations about life, to which there are notable exceptions. For example, though there is no better way to live a long life of prosperity on earth than to practice the principles of Proverbs 3:1-10, exceptions include John the Baptist and the Lord Jesus Christ. These men realized the principle only in a spiritual and eternal way not apparently envisioned by Solomon.

Words concerning wisdom	1–9
Proverbs of Solomon	10–22
→ Sayings of the wise men	23–24
Proverbs of Solomon	25–29
Words concerning wisdom	30–31

Figure 11.2

Second, "the fear of the LORD" must be understood. It includes both a willingness to obey His Word and a wholesome fear of the consequences of disobedience. It is not a beginning point beyond which a person progresses, but the foundational principle for understanding and applying all other principles. (See John 7:17.)

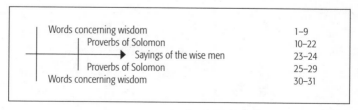

Third, wisdom and folly are personified as two kinds of women. There is a reason that Wisdom is exemplified by the industrious, faithful wife and mother of Proverbs 31. She nurtures the fear of Yahweh in her son's heart partly by honoring the authority of her husband. In stark contrast, Folly is portrayed as the immoral woman, who, by seducing the sons of others, asserts her fearless independence of the authority of God and man.

Fourth, Proverbs often compares or contrasts two aspects of two things, as in Proverbs 14:1. Not only is the wise woman compared/contrasted to the foolish, but their actions are compared as well. (See figure 11-3.)

Fifth, it is important to avoid the false distinction between the sacred and the secular. Proverbs generally describes "horizontal," human relationships, demonstrating that wisdom is ultimately behavioral (see James 3:13-18), and that civility, and all of life, is a concern to God.

Sixth, the characters of Proverbs must be understood in relation to one another.[20]

The wise woman builds her house,
But the foolish tears it down with her own hands.

Figure 11.3

The Simple: One who is gullible and easily misled. All start out untested, untaught, unlearned. The Simple "walk in the counsel of the wicked" (Ps. 1:1a NASB95) and either become wise or foolish.

The Fool: One who is dull and obstinate. He ignores the pursuit of wisdom. He is closed to reason but insists on making his views known publicly. He "stands in the path of sinners" (Ps. 1:1b NKJV). Without repentance, fools become mockers.

The Mocker: One who is contemptuous. He is not only foolish and proud, but obstructs the way of wisdom for others. Mockers "sit in the seat of scoffers" (Psalm 1:1c NASB95) .

The Wise: Open and obedient heart toward God, eager to follow His instruction. The wise takes correction (see 15:31) and pays attention to biblical commands (see 10:8). The wise "delight … in the law of the LORD" (Ps. 1:2 NASB95).

General Principles Underlying the Proverbs[21]

1. *Cause and Effect.* Obedience to God's moral law is generally beneficial, and disobedience is generally destructive (see Galatians 6:7).
2. *Good and Evil.* Redefining good and evil does not change what they are in the judgment of God (see Malachi 2:17).
3. *Worldly Influence.* The love for the Father and the lusts of the world are mutually exclusive (see 1 John 2:15).
4. *Self-deceit.* Self-centeredness and self-reliance are natural results of the fall of man into sin (see Jeremiah 17:9). It is consistent with fallen human nature to blame others, save oneself, determine truth on one's own, and demand the meeting of felt needs.
5. *Godly Minority.* The godly are often outnumbered, tempted by the rationale that "everybody's doing it," and in need of realizing their "majority" with God by living in light of biblical standards (see John 17:18-21).
6. *Absolute Truth.* Truth is the same for all people in all places and at all times.[22]

Preaching the Proverbs

Proverbs can be preached in a topical-expository manner. This requires that every proverb and related passage of Scripture be identified, interpreted in its context, and its meaning related to the overarching theme by means of an outline. For example, the present writer (Dan) once preached a sermon on the proverbial sluggard, using an outline from a subject study by Derek Kidner as a guide.[23] (See figure 11-4.) Such an approach is legitimate only if the passages are studied in their respective contexts and proper credit is given to the source of any organizational aid used.

The Proverbs can also be preached textually, as illustrated in figure 11-5.

The Sluggard
Proverbs
A Soft Way Leads to a Hard End

I. The Sluggard's Character
  A. He will not begin things (6:9–10)
    1. He does not even *commit* to refusal!
    2. He deceives himself
    3. His opportunities slip away
  B. He will not finish things (12:27; 19:24; 26:15)
  C. He will not face things
    1. He believes his own rationalizations (26:13–16)
    2. He avoids discomfort (20:4)
  D. He is restless
    1. He is dissatisfied (13:4; 21:25–26)
    2. He is helpless in the tangle of his life (15:19)
    3. He is wasteful (18:9)
    4. He is a worthless employee (10:26)
II. The Sluggard's Lessons
    1. Be a self-starter, like the ant (6:6–8; Heb. 4:11)
    2. Work when it is time to work (6:8; John 9:4)
    3. Putting things off catches up with you when it's too late (6:10–11, Luke 12:40)
    4. The soft way is harder in the end (12:24; Luke 16:19–25)
    5. Disorder can become irreversible (24:30–34, Rev. 20:15).

Figure 11.4

Ecclesiastes

"Ecclesiastes" is the Latin form of the Greek word meaning "the preacher." The Hebrew title, *Quoheleth*, signifies the chair or teacher of an assembly. Ironically, "preachers" so often fail to preach the book of "the preacher" because they perceive it to be cynical, fatalistic, or existential. In reality, it puts human endeavor into proper perspective. It teaches us to enjoy life, since it is the gift of God, but to enjoy it *responsibly*, since we will give an account to Him.

Author

The phrase "son of David, king in Jerusalem" (1:1 NKJV) indicates that Solomon is the writer. He is thought to have written this near the end of his life after having strayed from the Lord and experienced the disillusionment of sinful pursuits.

Theme

"Satisfaction can be found only by fearing God and keeping His commandments."[24]

Wisdom Shouts Ignored
Proverbs 1:8–33

Individuals Are Responsible to Seek the Wisdom God Gives

I. The Enticement of Sinners	8–19
A. The bland benefits of parental guidance (8–9)	
B. The bitter bite of sinful adventure (10–19)	
II. Wisdom's Shouts of Warning	20–23
A. Why personified as a woman? (20)	
B. Why depicted as a city? (20–21)	
C. Why the negative response? (22)	
D. Why the generous offer? (23)	
III. The Foolish Neglect of Wisdom	24–33
A. Why wisdom laughs (24–27)	
B. Why wisdom hides (28–30)	
C. How waywardness is established (31–32)	
D. How wisdom is enjoyed (33)	

Figure 11.5

Outline

(See figure 11-6.)

Ecclesiastes*

"Satisfaction can be found only by fearing God and keeping His commandments."

I. Prologue: All is futility	1:2
II. Poem on futility in physical order: The cycles of nature illustrate a lack of completion, novelty, remembrance, profit	1:3–11
III. By investigation and observation, Quoheleth proves all is futile	1:12–11:16
IV. On youth and old age	12:1–8
V. Epilogue	12:9–14

* Outline can be followed by noting the summary appraisal: "All is vanity and striving after wind."

Figure 11.6

Argument

Bruce Waltke states, "Although Quoheleth denies that one can observe a moral order in the creation, he affirms a wise, good, and just God rules over all."[25]

Key Phrases

"Vanity" refers not to what is bad, but to what is fleeting and incapable of being held on to. It is the word by which Abel was appropriately named, and means "vapor." "Under the sun" refers to all that makes up life but has no eternal significance in and of itself. "Striving after wind" amounts to wasting time.

Principles

Despite how life may seem, based on human experience, God is *wise, good*, and *just*. He is wise in that He has a plan (3:10; 7:14). God is good in having given creation to man as a gift to be enjoyed (2:24; 3:13-14). God is just in that there is a day of retribution and rewards (3:16-17; 11:9-10).

Conclusion

The *didactic* wisdom literature, including the book of Job and Psalms 37 and 49, as well as the *reflective* wisdom literature of Job and Ecclesiastes, proclaim by faith that there is a just God upholding an ethical order. The reflective books, however, demonstrate that man cannot discover this order in the creation through observation and experience. The author-editor of Job, however, contends that there is sufficient evidence of God's greatness and sublimity to render man inexcusable for his arrogance against the Creator and his failure to walk humbly before Him.[26]

Psalms

The Psalms comprise prayers and poems collected from roughly 1500 to 500 B.C. They were originally set to music accompanied by the plucking of stringed instruments. They lead the reader through the depths of despair to the heights of joy as Yahweh proves His faithfulness to provide, protect, deliver, sustain, and comfort His covenant people.

Authors of the Psalms

More than a dozen songwriters are represented in Israel's hymnal, sometimes called *The Psalter*. Ellisen's list in figure 11-7, based on inscriptions, indicates both the variety of composers and the preponderance of King David's contribution.[27]

Authorship of the Psalms

David wrote 73 psalms: 3–9; 11–32; 34–41; 51–65; 68–70; 86; 101; 103; 108–110; 122; 124; 131; 133; 138–145. Psalm 2 is attributed to David in Acts 4:25.

Asaph wrote 12 psalms: 50; 73–83.

Sons of Korah wrote 9 psalms: 42, 44–45; 47–49; 84–85; 87.

Solomon wrote two psalms: 72, 127.

Heman, Psalm 88

Ethan, Psalm 89

Moses, Psalm 90

Jeremiah, Psalm 137

Haggai and **Zechariah**: Psalms 146–147

Ezra: Psalm 119

Hezekiah: Psalms 120–134

The rest are called orphaned Psalms

Figure 11.7

Arrangement

Like the Pentateuch, the Psalms were written on five scrolls. Ezra is believed to have arranged the Psalms according to a progression of thought and by the usage of the names of God.[28] They were divided as follows. (See figure 11-8.)

The Five Books of Psalms			
Book	**Psalms**	**Author**	**Names of God**
Book I	1–41	David	Yahweh
Book II	42–72	David	Elohim
Book III	73–89	Asaph	Yahweh-Elohim
Book IV	90–106	Anonymous	Yahweh
Book V	107–150	Various	Yahweh

Figure 11.8

According to Ellisen, "each Book of Psalms concludes with a doxology, an affirmation of praise to God found in the last verse or two of the concluding psalm."[29] "In the case of Book V the entire last poem, Psalm 150, is the concluding doxology."[30] Books I and II are composed primarily of Davidic psalms. Book III includes psalms of Asaph, Psalms 73-83, and of the sons of Korah,[31] Psalms 84-88. Books IV and V include anonymous psalms, along with a few by David and others.[32]

Types of Psalms[33]

The variety of biblical psalms include *songs of praise, royal psalms, thanksgiving* (national and individual), *lament* (national and individual), *imprecatory*, and *penitential.*

Songs of praise to God (or hymns) are generally structured with an introduction, body, and conclusion. The body usually gives the reason that God should be praised, typically introduced by words translated "for" ("because," e.g., 96:4; 106:1) or "who" (e.g., 103:3; 104:2). (See figures 11-9 and 11-10.)

Examples of *royal psalms* include 2:1-6; 5:2; 10; 18:1-4; 24:7-10; and 93. These psalms sometimes emphasize the universal and absolute reign of Yahweh, as does Psalm 93. Other times they proclaim the rule of Messiah, as does Psalm 24.

National psalms of thanksgiving typically celebrate Yahweh's deliverance of Israel. For example, Psalm 124: 1-5 says:

If it had not been the LORD who was on our side,"
Let Israel now say–
If it had not been the LORD who was on our side,
When men rose up against us,

Psalm 103		
Intro:	1–5	Command to Praise
Body:	6–19	Reason we should praise Yahweh
Conclusion:	20–22	Command to Praise

Figure 11.9

Psalm 8		
Intro:	1	Praise
Body:	2–8	Rationale for Praise
Conclusion:	9	Praise

Figure 11.10

Then they would have swallowed us alive,
When their wrath was kindled against us;
Then the waters would have overwhelmed us,
The stream would have gone over our soul;
Then the swollen waters
Would have gone over our soul." NKJV

The characteristic common to *individual psalms of thanksgiving* is the expression of gratitude for personal deliverance out of some calamity, for example, Psalm 30:2-3:

O LORD my God, I cried out to You,
And You healed me.
O LORD, You brought my soul up from the grave;
You have kept me alive, that I should not go down to the pit. NKJV

Psalms of lament express negative emotions either of the individual or nation. Such psalms often express a prayer of disorientation[34] They are recognizable by expressions of grief, need, or complaint. They generally follow the pattern shown in figure 11-11.

In developing truth sheets, read psalms of lament in their literary and historical contexts. Ask *how* they reflect ancient Semitic expressions of grief and regret. Seek to understand the cause of the lament, asking *why*? *What* the psalm teaches about God is of utmost importance to understand. Also, seek to discover *how* the lament appeals to the emotions.

National psalms of lament differ only in the sense that the complaints by God's people because of calamity and feeling forsaken by God are expressed corporately. Often these psalms contain lengthy descriptions of the people's affliction, as in Psalm 44.

Patterns of Lament in Psalms 3, 5, 6, and 7
I. Invocation (Pss. 3:1–2; 5:1–7; 6:1; 7:1a)
II. Plea to God for help (Pss. 6:2–5; 7:1b)
III. Complaints (Pss. 3:1–2; 5:8–10; 6:6–7; 7:2)
IV. Confession of Sin or an Assertion of Innocence (Pss. 3:3–6; 6:8–9; 7:3–5)
V. Curse of Enemies (imprecation) (Pss. 3:7–8; 6:10; 7:6–9)

Figure 11.11

Imprecatory psalms utter God's curses upon His enemies, as in Psalm 69:22-28. They express the justice in which God avenges Himself, thus giving both legitimate expression to the righteous indignation of believers today and freedom from the temptation to take one's own revenge. (See Romans 12:19-20.)

Penitential psalms express repentance of sin. The most well-known example is Psalm 51, in which David confesses his sin with Bathsheba.

Headings

Many of the psalms begin with a superscription (or inscription). In the Hebrew Bible, it is the first numbered verse. In most English translations the superscription is unnumbered, often in a contrasting font, and appears as the title. Most readers do not understand that superscriptions are part of the God-breathed text. Others simply don't agree. However, these introductory statements often provide helpful historical allusions that describe the setting. Often they give the names of biblical persons involved in the experience or writing of the psalm. They sometimes tell the reader what kind of psalm it is. This provides a tremendous clue into how the psalm should be interpreted. For example, when preaching Psalm 3, you should first study its historical setting in 2 Samuel 15-17, indicated in the superscription, and convey this to the audience in the introduction or body of the message.

Hebrew Structure

The psalms are structured in a variety of ways, including *recurring refrains*, *acrostics*, and *parallelism*.[35] Recurring refrains form what is called an *inclusio*, in which a central idea is enveloped within similar statements. For example, see Psalm 46:7-11 in figure 11-12.

The statement "The LORD of hosts is with us" clearly forms a refrain. The note in the *Nelson Study Bible* shows how recognizing an in*clusio* of this psalm suggests a theme or point of emphasis for the preacher: "The pairing of the words 'the Lord of hosts' with 'the God of Jacob' in both verses, praises the Almighty, the Commander of heaven's armies for choosing to live with the descendants of Jacob, His people. Who could protect His people better?"[36]

Other examples of *inclusio* include Psalm 49:12, 20. (See figure 11-13.)

An *acrostic* is accomplished when every line begins with the succession of letters of the alphabet, as in Proverbs 31:10-31. In the Bible's longest chapter, Psalm 119, each of eight lines in every paragraph begins with the same letter of the Hebrew alphabet, in succession. (See figure 11-14.)

Inclusio, Psalm 46:7–11

7**The LORD of hosts is with us; the God of Jacob is our refuge.** Selah 8Come, behold the works of the LORD, who has made desolations in the earth. 9He makes wars cease to the end of the earth; He breaks the bow and cuts the spear in two; He burns the chariot in the fire. 10Be still, and know that I am God; I will be exalted among the nations, I will be exalted in the earth! 11**The LORD of hosts is with us; the God of Jacob is our refuge.** Selah (NKJV)

Figure 11.12

Inclusio, Psalm 49:12, 20

12Nevertheless man, though in honor, does not remain; he is like the beasts that perish.

These similar statements *frame* the central idea developed within them, that human life is fleeting and dependent upon God for any sense of permanence.

20A man who is in honor, yet does not understand, is like the beasts that perish.

Figure 11.13

As exciting as this may be to the serious Bible student, take care not to dwell on the mechanics of poetic structure, such as inclusio and acrostics. Derickson exhorts young preachers, "Don't stand up and preach on acrostics. But, in the midst of preaching, let people have insight into what God has chosen to do. Mention it in passing to praise God and motivate people to appreciate His character. Point out, as a tour-guide, what they could not otherwise see. People might otherwise be robbed of the riches of the medium as well as of the message. It has an aesthetic as well as utilitarian purpose."[37]

Parallelism refers to various ways in which the pairs of lines in Hebrew poetry (also called *couplets* or *cola*) work together to enhance the impact of their meaning. Parallelism can be complete, as in Psalm 103, or incomplete. Incomplete parallelism is an example of what is called *anacoluthon*. It sometimes signals an emotional state in which the writer is too excited, distracted, or simply forgetful to follow through on the structural scheme he began.

Parallelism also can be *internal* or *external*. Internal parallelism refers to how the second of two lines of poetry affects the first. Examples include *synonymous*, *antithetic*, *synthetic*, *emblematic*, *climactic*, and *inverted parallelism* known as *chiasmus*.

Psalm 119:1–8

אַשְׁרֵי תְמִימֵי־דָרֶךְ הַהֹלְכִים בְּתוֹרַת יְהוָה 2
אַשְׁרֵי נֹצְרֵי עֵדֹתָיו בְּכָל־לֵב יִדְרְשׁוּהוּ
3 אַף לֹא־פָעֲלוּ עַוְלָה בִּדְרָכָיו הָלָכוּ
4 אַתָּה צִוִּיתָה פִקֻּדֶיךָ לִשְׁמֹר מְאֹד
5 אַחֲלַי יִכֹּנוּ דְרָכָי לִשְׁמֹר חֻקֶּיךָ
6 אָז לֹא־אֵבוֹשׁ בְּהַבִּיטִי אֶל־כָּל־מִצְוֺתֶיךָ
7 אוֹדְךָ בְּיֹשֶׁר לֵבָב בְּלָמְדִי מִשְׁפְּטֵי צִדְקֶךָ
8 אֶת־חֻקֶּיךָ אֶשְׁמֹר אַל־תַּעַזְבֵנִי עַד־מְאֹד

Note: The Hebrew alphabet begins with the letter Aleph, א, as do each of the first 8 lines of poetry in Psalm 119. The next 8 lines begin with the second letter Beth, ב, and so on throughout the psalm.

Figure 11.14

Synonymous parallelism achieves amplification by repeating in a slightly different way in the second line what was stated in the first. Sometimes the first statement is general and the second more specific. Psalm 18:5 is an example:

The sorrows of Sheol surrounded me;
The snares of death confronted me. (NKJV)

In *antithetic* parallelism, the second line is a negative of the first line, not a contradiction. Look for an adversative conjunction, such as "but," as in Psalm 1:6.

> *For the LORD knows the way of the righteous,*
> *But the way of the ungodly shall perish.* (NKJV)

In *synthetic* parallelism the line or lines following the first line advances or completes the thought expressed in the first line. A good example is found in Psalm 1:1.

> *Blessed is the man who walks not in the counsel of the ungodly, Nor stands in the path of sinners, Nor sits in the seat of the scornful.* (NKJV)

Emblematic parallelism sets up a comparison by use of a simile often translated "like" or "as," or by use of a metaphor, which makes a comparison without these words. Psalm 1:3 is an example of emblematic parallelism with a simile: "He shall be like a tree planted by the rivers of water" (NKJV). "He" is compared, or paralleled, with "a tree" by the word translated "like." Another good example is found in Psalm 42:1, where David says "As the deer pants…so pants my soul" (NKJV).

Climactic parallelism, as its name implies, builds up to a climax, as in 92:9. (See figure 11-15.)

c) All the workers of iniquity shall be scattered.
b) For behold, Your enemies shall perish;
a) For behold, Your enemies, O LORD,

Figure 11.15

Inverted parallelism is also called *chiasmus*, because the order of comparison in the first line is reversed in the second line, creating a pattern that resembles the Greek letter (*chi*, pronounced "key"). The resulting pattern is a-b-b′-a′. (See figure 11-16.)

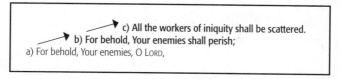

Psalm 91:14 (NKJV) is a good example of a chiasmus. (See figure 11-17.)

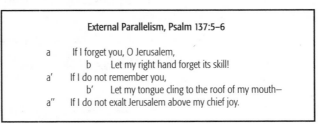

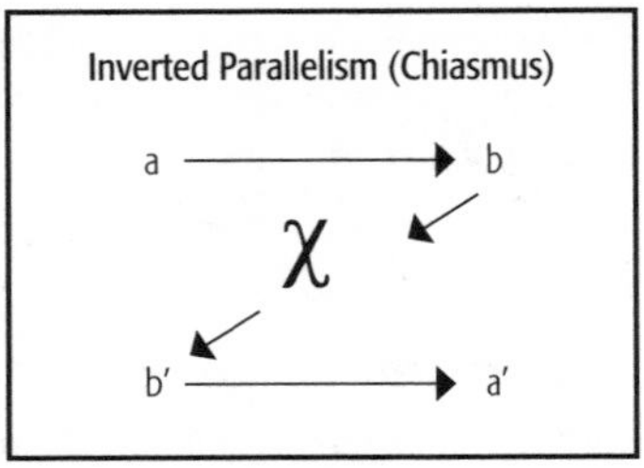

Figure 11.16

a Because he has set his love upon Me,
b therefore I will deliver him;
b′ I will set him on high
a′ because he has known My name.

Figure 11.17

It is clear from the chiastic structure of this verse that the Psalmist has narrowed the concept of loving God (a) to knowing His name (a'). *External parallelism* involves more than a single verse, providing both variety and an aid to memorization. A good example is Psalm 137: 5-6, which also illustrates the inverted parallelism (chiasmus) just discussed. (See figure 11-18.)

External Parallelism, Psalm 137:5–6

a If I forget you, O Jerusalem,
b Let my right hand forget its skill!
a′ If I do not remember you,
b′ Let my tongue cling to the roof of my mouth–
a″ If I do not exalt Jerusalem above my chief joy.

Figure 11.18

Preaching the Psalms

A sample sermon on Psalm 113 is outlined at the end of this chapter. The following outline by Gregory V. Trull, adapted and presented in figure 11-19, suggests a series of messages that could be entitled "Messiah in the Psalms."[38]

Messiah in the Psalms

Messiah the Son
- Ps. 2
  –Coronation Song for Israel's kings
  –Ultimately fulfilled in Jesus Christ

Messiah's Rejection
- Ps. 69:8–9 *Zeal of Messiah*
  –Zeal of Messiah brought rejection to David
  –Ultimate rejection in Christ
- Ps. 41:9 *Betrayal of a Friend*
  –David betrayed by one at the royal table
  –Christ betrayed by one at the Last Supper

Messiah's Death
- Ps. 34:19–20 *No bones broken*
  –Image of Passover Lamb
  –Literally fulfilled in Jesus (John 19:36)
- Ps. 22 *Agony of Crucifixion*
  –Abandonment (v. 1)
  –Water poured out (v. 14)
  –Gambling for clothes (v. 18)
  –Pierced hands and feet (v. 16)

Messiah's Resurrection
- Ps. 16:10 *Messiah Will Not Face Decay*
  –Only Jesus did not decay in grave (Acts 2:31)

Messiah's Reign
- Ps. 72:11, 17 *Universal Reign of Blessing*
- Ps. 110:1–3, 5–7 *Messiah, the Warrior King*
- Ps. 110:4 *Messiah the King-Priest* (Heb. 7:13–14)

Figure 11.19

Song of Solomon

The Song of Solomon expresses the intensely passionate love between King Solomon and a young girl. Their mutual admiration and eager anticipation of consummating their relationship physically are stated with respect for the bonds of marriage within which human sexuality is properly celebrated.[39]

Background

In Hebrew the Song of Solomon was called "The Song of Songs Which Is Solomon's."[40] Jerome's Latin translation (Vulgate) named the book "Canticles," Songs.[41] Both Jewish and Christian scholars generally agree that Solomon is the author.[42] Though the book is never mentioned by another biblical writer, it describes royal luxuries in keeping with Solomon's authorship indicated in 1:1 and by a total of seven mentions of his name.[43] The use of some Persian and Greek words may be explained by Solomon's acquaintance with other cultures.[44]

Literary Form

The introduction to the Song of Solomon in *The Nelson Study Bible* indicates several literary features of the poetry. First, the Song is a lyric *idyll*, a type of love song that is unique in the Bible.[45] Second, speeches and events do not necessarily follow in chronological order.[46] "At times the story line remains suspended while the audience views scenes from earlier or yet untold incidents."[47] Third, "in addition to the two characters that carry the story line–the Shulamite and King Solomon, a group of women interrupt certain scenes with brief musical speeches or warnings. Solomon uses the chorus to make transitions from one scene to another, as well as to add emphasis to important themes."[48]

Interpretation

Perhaps because of its erotic language, with no mention of God, the Song of Solomon has been interpreted in a variety ways in an apparent attempt to discover a spiritual meaning. According to author Craig Glickman, this has resulted in the writing of more commentaries on the Song than on any other book of the Bible, with no view enjoying wide acceptance.[49] For example, it has been viewed by some as an allegory without an historical basis, "representing Jehovah's love for Israel in the Old Testament and Christ's love for His church in the New Testament."[50] Others, with respect for its historical basis, have seen it as a type of Christ's love for the Church, with limited points of similarity.[51] Still others have viewed Solomon's song as a drama, which was acted out.

Attempts to read spiritual meaning into the Song may stem from a low view of the material creation, including the human body and sexual love. Taken literally, however, the Song was held in high regard by the Jews. It was the first of the "rolls" (*Megilloth*) read in the synagogue on the eighth day of the Feast of Unleavened Bread.[52] That the Jews took a naturalistic view of the Song is evident from a tradition mentioned in the *Nelson Study Bible*: "Because of its explicit language, ancient and modern Jewish sages forbade men to read the book before they were thirty (and presumably kept women from reading it at all)."[53]

Theology

"The Song of Solomon provides an example of how God created male and female to live in happiness and fulfillment. People are created as sexual beings."[54] "God ordained marriage from the beginning of creation: Man and woman were to become one flesh (Gen. 2:25)."[55]

Message

The message of the Song is simple, says Derickson: "Human love and marriage are beautiful in their emotional and physical expressions."[56] He elaborates with four statements that put sex in divine perspective. This is a major contribution of the poem.

- Sex is a gift from God.
- Sex is God's design.
- Sex is most beautifully expressed within boundaries.
- Sex is holy, and should be treated as such.

Outline (See figure 11-20.)

The Song of Solomon *Exaltation of Married Love*	
Courtship	1–2
Ceremony	3–4
Commitment	5–8

Figure 11.20

Preaching the Song of Solomon[57]

The Jews' tradition of restricting access to the Song of Solomon shows that they understood its natural meaning. While this suggests due caution in proclaiming its message to a mixed audience of all ages, the book must not be abandoned in the pulpit. At least three aspects of its message are desperately needed today.

First, it represents a high view of woman as man's full equal, without blurring the important distinction of their respective roles. The mutuality of the lovers' passion is demonstrated by the matching of reciprocal speeches. Solomon and his bride are equally in love, ready to initiate and enjoy physical intimacy.

Second, romantic love involves painful separation as well as the joy of intimacy. Without interpreting the book as an allegory, it can be used to illustrate the longing of the bride of Christ to be united with Him when He comes for His Church.

Third, the message that sexual love is good in marriage, but not before, is needed more today than ever. The warning is sounded no less than three times, "I charge you, O daughters of Jerusalem ... do not stir up nor awaken love until it pleases" (2:7; 3:5; and 8:4 NKJV).

Lamentations

Like the appendix of a book, Jeremiah's poetic Lamentations seems to provide material that doesn't properly fit within his prophecy. Like the appendix of the human body, Lamentations seems like a small, bitter organ that the reader could live without. It has been called "the saddest book in the Bible."[58] Who wants to listen to five movements of a funeral dirge? And yet, the book of Lamentations displays hope in the midst of heartbreak, which everyone needs at some point in life. Its record of, and response to, Jerusalem's fall to Babylon in 586 B.C. (see Jeremiah 29 and 52) serves as a warning to return to God in faith and to trust Him to restore them someday.

Structure and Message

Structured as a chiasm, the book takes the reader from grieving, to confession, to trust. (See figure 11-21.) As an alphabetic acrostic, it demonstrates order, even in the chaos of grief. Its overall lesson, says Derickson, is: "When suffering, trust in God's faithfulness to demonstrate mercy."[59]

Preaching Lamentations

Lamentations lends itself to a *book sermon* in which chapters 1-2 and 4-5 may showcase the central poem in chapter 3. The key verses are 3:22-25, which shine all the brighter in the dark night of personal and national distress–politically and spiritually:

> Through the LORD's mercies we are not consumed, because His compassions fail not. They are new every morning; great is Your faithfulness. "The LORD is my portion;" says my soul, "Therefore I hope in Him!" The LORD is good to those who wait for Him, to the soul who seeks Him. (NKJV)

Often referred to as "the weeping prophet," Jeremiah may be seen as a type of Christ, who wept over the same city centuries later (Matt. 23:37-38). As "a Man of sorrows and acquainted with grief" (Isa. 53:3 NKJV), Jesus is one from whom modern preachers and their listeners cannot afford to hide their faces. Lamentations, therefore, provides a needed reminder that God keeps His word in judging sin. It demonstrates that it is not ungodly to suffer as a consequence of the sins of others. In fact, ministers need to enter (and own) the suffering of those to whom they would minister. As one who wept bitterly, Jeremiah also teaches all men that it is not unmanly to show emotions. His book grants the believer "permission" to mourn, to outwardly express the inward pain of loss. But the contrition it teaches is more than the bitter

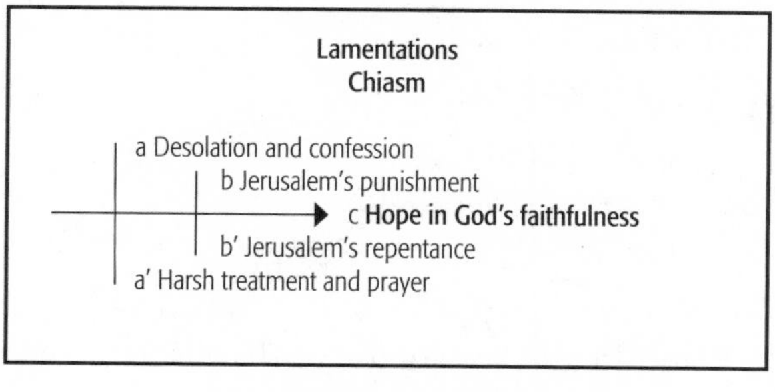

Figure 11.21

remorse of Judas Iscariot, recorded in Matthew 27:3. Confession of sin is an essential part of healing. (See 1 John 1:9.) Finally, the book illustrates the blessed comfort known only to those who mourn sin and its consequences. (See Matthew 5:4.) It illustrates the joy of the believer who sorrows not as those "who have no hope" (1 Thess. 4:13 NKJV).

Preaching Hebrew Poetry of Scripture

An important part of analysis is observing the author's literary arrangement of the text. In this way you can work to present the natural outline of the text rather than impose an artificial one upon it.

Sample Sermon on Psalm 113

Telling The Greatness Of God
Psalm 113

The Hallel, Psalms 113-118, all command the praise of Yahweh, "Hallel-u-jah"

1-3 Introductory statement of what is to be done by servants of Yahweh
- Command, not a request
- But what is praise?
  - Praise must be done in community
  - Thanksgiving can be done in private
  - Saying the word *Praise* does not accomplish the task
  - Praise is excited, public boasting
  - We sometimes exaggerate when boasting of grandchildren, etc.
  - When extolling God's virtues, we can never exaggerate
  - You can never say enough
- The Name of Yahweh is to be praised.
  - Name refers to reputation or character; His person and work
    - LORD in all caps stands in the place of the proper name of God, Yahweh
  - Follows the Jewish tradition to avoid pronouncing

the name they were not to take in vain, by
substituting Adonai, correctly
translated "Lord."

Blessed be the name: now and perpetually

Servitude is a high or lowly honor depending on who is served

Nothing is higher privilege than to be the servant of Yahweh

From east of sun to the west, is every place; the whole earth

4-9b Body

Sovereignty of Yahweh (transcendent)

High above all nations

Above the heavens

Incomparability of God

Tenderness of Yahweh (immanent)

Humbles Himself (Man naturally exalts himself)

God has to look "down" to look at what we regard as the highest "up"

The combination of truth is unique to Hebrew/Christian Monotheism

9c Conclusion: Praise Yah

Mercy toward a barren woman (which was a cultural shame)

At our best, we should realize that we owe praise to God for everything we are and have.

Summary and Conclusion

The books of Job, Psalms, Proverbs, Ecclesiastes, and Song of Solomon represent most of the Hebrew poetry in Scripture. Together, they express the heart and mind of man as he relates to God's greatness while experiencing the toughness of life.

Job demonstrates the need to trust and obey God even though He does not explain His ways.

Proverbs promotes the fear of God as the foundational principle of all others. The proverbs emphasize the sayings of wise men as generalizations to demonstrate God's maintenance of ethical order in a world made chaotic by sin. The simple need not become fools, and fools need not become mockers. By heeding the warnings of wisdom and yielding to her wooing, the simple may become wise.

Ecclesiastes stresses the inability of man to catch and keep a satisfying sense of purpose apart from the responsible enjoyment of life as a gift from God.

The Psalms generally lead the reader from the depths of despair to the heights of joy as Yahweh reveals His faithfulness to provide for, protect, deliver, sustain, comfort, and bless His covenant people. Different kinds of psalms express, through a variety of poetic structures, the praises, complaints, thanksgiving, lament, confession, and hope of God's covenant people. In addition, substantial hymnic literature, found in the book of Psalms alone, anticipates the sonship, rejection, death, resurrection, and reign of Messiah.

The Song of Solomon is an explicit love song about the courtship, ceremony, and commitment of King Solomon and a young Shulamite woman. It communicates important truths needed by youth and adults of both sexes. Among them are the equality of women and men, the pain of separation between lovers, and the appropriateness of arousing sexual passions only after a couple has married. While not an allegory, the love song does illustrate some aspects of the relationship between Christ and the Church as His bride.

Lamentations, while easy to neglect, reflects the bitter sorrows of sin and features God's faithfulness to His covenant people. It encourages the confession of sin and demonstrates the comfort and joy known only by those who mourn the effects of sin, as did Jeremiah and Jesus.

Sermons from scriptural Hebrew poetry should reflect the arrangement and structure of the text.

Discussion Questions

1. List the books of wisdom, and state in your own words what distinguishes Wisdom Literature.

2. Beside Hebrew poetry, describe in your own words what the poetic books all have in common.

3. What is one good way to preach Job, according to this chapter?

4. If preaching through the book of Job, what must the preacher be especially careful to do, and why?

5. Why do you agree or disagree that the book of Proverbs is compiled in an orderly fashion?

6. Explain your understanding of the motto of Proverbs given in 1:7. What does it mean … and not mean?

7. Describe two ways to preach the Proverbs according to this chapter.

8. According to this chapter, what does the phrase in Ecclesiastes "all is vanity" mean?

9. Describe each of the following kinds of Psalms:

   a. Songs of Praise
   b. Royal Psalms
   c. Thanksgiving (national/personal)
   d. Lament (national/personal)
   e. Imprecatory
   f. Penitential

10. Explain in your own words the meaning of these:

    a. Inclusio
    b. Acrostics
    c. Parallelism
       –Synonymous
       –Antithetic
       –Synthetic

–Emblematic
–Climactic
–Inverted (Chiasmus)

11. What is the difference between *internal* and *external* parallelism?
12. Why would you preach from the Song of Solomon, and how?
13. Why would you preach from Lamentations, and how?
14. Identify three strengths in the sample sermon on Psalm 113, and three weaknesses, based on your understanding of the Whiting Method and this chapter.

CHAPTER 12

Preaching Old Testament Prophecy

The Nature of Old Testament Prophecy

The Seventeen books of Isaiah through Malachi include most, but not all, of the prophetic literature of the Old Testament. Moses referred to himself as a prophet and predicted the coming of one (Christ) as a prophet like him, from among the people, to whom they must listen. (See Deuteronomy 18:15 and Acts 3:22 and 7:37.) As noted in Chapter 9, the Jews also regarded the books of Joshua, Judges, Samuel, and Kings as *former prophets*. Throughout the historical narrative of the Old Testament, some words of many of the speaking prophets have been recorded, including those of Nathan, Ahijah, Jehu, Elijah, Elisha, Shemaiah, Hanani, and Huldah.[1] In Acts 2:30, Peter refers to David as a prophet, having predicted the resurrection of Christ in Psalm 16:10. But even if "prophetic literature" was limited to the four major and twelve minor writing prophets, it would comprise no less than one quarter of the word Paul commanded Timothy (and the Church) to proclaim! (See 2 Timothy 4:2.)

The Prophets

Speakers for God

The basic idea of a prophet is one who speaks for God. But, while modern preachers speak for God by declaring the meaning and relevance of revealed truth, they do not prophesy as direct recipients and communicators of divine revelation, as did the biblical prophets. Such spokesmen were divinely chosen and given God's message. Wilkinson and Boa list "dreams, visions, angels, nature, miracles) and audible voice"[2] as ways God used to reveal His will and words to them. Burdened with the word of Yahweh,[3] the prophets discharged their responsibility by telling it forth (*forthtelling*). Because they represented the covenantkeeping God of history, their message also involved *foretelling* future events. In Isaiah 41:21-23, the challenge issued to Israel serves to remind the nation of their dependence upon God's revelation:

> *"Present your case." says the* LORD.
> *"Bring forth your strong reasons," says the King of Jacob.*
> *"Let them bring forth and show us what will happen;*
> *let them show the former things, what they were,*
> *that we may consider them,*
> *and know the latter end of them;*
> *or declare to us things to come.*
> *Show the things that are to come hereafter,*
> *that we may know that you are gods;*
> *yes, do good or do evil,*
> *that we may be dismayed and see it together."* (NKJV)

In Daniel 2:28, Daniel declares the power of God to know and declare through His prophets things that are future and unseen: "But there is a God in heaven who reveals secrets, and He has made known to King Nebuchadnezzar what will be in the latter days. Your dream, and the visions of your head upon your bed, were these ..." (NKJV).

Recipients of Revelation

British scholarship tends to regard the prophets as people of extraordinary human intuition or psychic gifts.[4] But according to Scripture, the prophets were ordinary people whom God called to be His mouth pieces (oracles) (see James 5:16-18 and 2 Peter 1:21). The Bible's denunciation of Balaam as a *false prophet* was made not on the basis that his predictions proved false, but that he led the people counter to God's will.[5]

Monitors of Covenant Responsibilities

The prophets simply announced what God would do, in keeping with His covenants with Israel, to provide universal blessing through one man. The consequences of obedience and disobedience spelled out in the Mosaic and land covenants (see chapter 9) were *predictable* based on both the general provisions of the covenants and specific revelation to the prophets concerning details and timing of God's judgment and restoration.

Because they spoke with divine authority primarily to the people with whom God had entered into covenant, the prophets served as watchmen for the nation. Their warnings and promises were also meant to motivate the holy living emphasized in the Pentateuch. The prophets also looked forward to the kingdom blessings of the coming Messiah.[6] Because God's warnings and promises related to material blessings and curses in the land, they are not to be explained away in favor of spiritual lessons. According to Ellisen, God's covenants are meant to: (1) reveal and guarantee God's redemptive purposes in His Eternal Covenant;[7] (2) reveal and guarantee God's Kingdom purposes through His chosen nation Israel; and (3) provide a faith basis for personal relationships with God.[8]

In addition to pronouncing judgments and consolation based on existing covenants, the new covenant is revealed in Jeremiah 31:33-34. As noted in chapter 8, the new covenant replaced the only temporary (Mosaic) covenant given by God, with one in which He graciously provided forgiveness of sin and inner guidance by the indwelling Holy Spirit. The Abrahamic covenant, which preceded the Mosaic covenant by five hundred years, is unilateral, unconditional, and still in force! Because the Church participates in the blessings of the *new* covenant, ratified by the blood of Christ, it is essential that preachers exposit the *old* covenant (Old Testament) prophecies in which it is rooted. (See Matthew 26:28 and Galatians 3:8.)

The Character of Prophecy

The Prophetic Message

A proper understanding of six features of biblical prophecy will correct common misconceptions about it. First, it was given to be understood.

Though one must be regenerate to truly appropriate the theological truth of Scripture and know it existentially (see 1 Corinthians 2:14-15), the unregenerate mind may comprehend it *intellectually*, because symbols used are often explained.[9]

Second, biblical prophecy often blends near and far things together. For example, the first and second comings of Christ are described as a single event in Isaiah 9:6. Jesus illustrated the necessity of discerning the partial fulfillment of a single statement of prophecy when, in the synagogue at Nazareth, He read from Isaiah 61. Stopping in the middle of verse 2, He said, "Today this Scripture is fulfilled in your hearing" (Luke 4:21 NKJV). The second half of verse 2, which Jesus did not read, pertained to the day of God's vengeance, which will not be fulfilled until He comes again.

Third, biblical prophecy is definite. Isaiah mentioned Cyrus 150 years in advance (44:28; 45:1). Josiah was named 300 years in advance (1 Kin. 13:2). Whereas sixteenth-century physician and astrologer Nostradamus[10] is celebrated for predictions thought to have come true only occasionally, God's prophets were accurate 100 percent of the time (see Deuteronomy 18:22).

Fourth, the speaker/writer of biblical prophecy was aware of the content and its implications. That they were not simply channeling information as a conduit is evident in their emotional involvement, reasoned explanations, and willingness to suffer for the truth they communicated. (For an example of this, see Jeremiah 1:17-19.)

Fifth, biblical predictions communicate knowledge of things that could only be known by revelation. For example, the seventy weeks of Daniel's prophecy (Dan. 9:24-27) reveal the length of time between the rebuilding of the temple in Jerusalem and the crucifixion of Israel's Messiah.[11]

Sixth, the predictions of biblical prophecy were relevant at the time that they were given. They were not merely forecasts that would eventually prove true, but warnings, judgments, and promises of restoration and of Messiah that met present needs.[12]

In view of these six features, a good working definition of biblical prophecy is: God's revelation of His eternal plan and purpose, provided in a written history of events before they occur in time and space.

Difficulties in Interpreting Prophecy

The literature of biblical prophecy in general, and apocalyptic literature[13] in particular, is rich in figurative language and symbolism that often challenge the interpreter's ability to understand and explain them.[14] For example, the description of Ezekiel's vision of wheels within wheels (Ezek. 1) may indicate that he saw the throne of God.[15] But it would be difficult to reach this conclusion based on the immediate context alone, and this interpretation neglects all of the details that would enable one to draw a picture of what Ezekiel saw.

The chronological gaps between what is often referred to as the *near* and *far* fulfillments of prophecies present another problem. For example, in His First Advent, Jesus fulfilled the prophecy of Isaiah 9:6 that a Child would be born and a Son given. But His shouldering of the mantle of government appears to refer to something yet in the future. However, the promise of Christ's reign was not irrelevant to those in whose time it was not fulfilled. Rather, it motivated holy living just as the anticipation of Christ's coming for His Church is meant to motivate holiness in the life of the New Testament believer. (See 1 John 3:1-3.)

Another challenge is understanding the geopolitical setting in which prophecies are given. The interpretation of Isaiah 6:1, for example, depends on the reader's awareness of the nature of King Uzziah's reign. Uzziah's death sets the stage for Isaiah's vision of the glory of the exalted, ever-living King, whose sovereignty is absolute, universal, and eternal.

Discerning how a prophecy is fulfilled also presents a challenge. Consider six scenarios: (1) Some Old Testament predictions, (e.g., Jeremiah 47) are clearly fulfilled in the Old Testament itself. But (2) others were not fulfilled until the New Testament. For example, the birth of Jesus in Bethlehem fulfilled Micah 5:2. (3) Old Testament prophecy may be fulfilled *partially*, or in one sense, but not fully, as it will be in the future. Isaiah 35, for example, refers to millennial glory, some miraculous aspects of which were fulfilled in the first coming of Christ. The resulting *tension* is sometimes referred to as the "already-not-yet" phenomenon. (4) Some Old Testament predictions *still* have not been fulfilled, in any sense, such as the creation of new heavens and a new earth, predicted in Isaiah 65:17-25. (5) Some New Testament predictions have been partially fulfilled. In Matthew 24 Jesus made predictions that have been accomplished "already-not-yet." Finally, (6) there are New Testament predictions that have yet to be fulfilled, such as 2 Peter 3.

Finally, the rabbinic method of interpreting the fulfillment of prophecy is important to understand. Arnold G. Fruchtenbaum explains that, in the rabbinic tradition of *Drash*, a prophecy was said to be fulfilled on the basis of only one point, or a few points, of resemblance among many points of nonresemblance. He cites, for example, Acts 2:16-21, where Peter referred to the outpouring of the Holy Spirit as that which Joel prophesied in Joel 2:28. In point of fact, *nothing* prophesied in Joel 2:28 occurred on the day of pentecost. There is no record that sons and daughters in Israel prophesied, that old men dreamed dreams, or that young men saw visions. In reality, the significant event of tongues-speaking that *did* occur on the day of pentecost is not even mentioned by Joel. The only point of connection is that Joel speaks of an outpouring of the Holy Spirit, an event that occurred on the day of pentecost, and the reason Peter quotes the Joel text.[16]

Primary Considerations in Preaching Old Testament Prophecy

In preparing to preach from the Prophetic Books of Scripture, you must pay careful attention to at least four areas: *historical background, literary analysis, theological understanding*, and *preaching points*.

Historical Background

The sermon on Isaiah 6:1-13, shown in figure 12-1 , illustrates how important the setting of a passage can be to its proper exposition and proclamation. The sermon is entitled "Putting Our Worldview in Order." Based on the first four verses, the sermon begins by stressing the importance of "knowing who God is:" The chapter begins with a statement of historical fact that is easy for the modern reader to breeze past while searching for some striking truth of spiritual depth and practical relevance. Yet, failure to understand this opening statement decimates the impact it would have had on its original readers. The phrase "In the year that King Uzziah died," does far more than date the vision that Isaiah goes on to describe. It provides the contrasting background against which the subject of Isaiah's vision must be understood and proclaimed.

In developing a truth sheet from this passage, you must apply the six interrogatives to Judah's long-time King Uzziah, as well as to Yahweh, whose glory Isaiah is allowed to see. *Who* was Uzziah? *What* distinguished him from other kings? *When* did he die? *Where* did Uzziah live and reign? *Why* was his death worth mentioning? While good commentaries can be helpful, and checking them *after* you have done your own analysis of the text is an important step, an exhaustive concordance[17] should be your primary source of biblical information about Uzziah. Consider the story of Uzziah as told in the historical literature of 2 Kings 15:1-5.

> In the twenty-seventh year of Jeroboam king of Israel, Azariah the son of Amaziah, king of Judah, became king. He was sixteen years old when he became king, and he reigned fifty-two years in Jerusalem. His mother's name was Jecholiah of Jerusalem. And he did what was right in the sight of the LORD, according to all that his father Amaziah had done, except that the high places were not removed; the people still sacrificed and burned incense on the high places. Then the LORD struck the king, so that he was a leper until the day of his death; so he dwelt in an isolated house. And Jatham the king's son was over the royal house, judging the people of the land. (NKJV)

The names Azariah and Uzziah refer to the same king of Judah.[18] For no less than fifty-two years, he reigned in Jerusalem. In addition to enjoying an extraordinarily long reign, he did what was right in the sight of Yahweh. Yet, Yahweh struck him with leprosy for one sin. The account in 2 Chronicles 26:16-21, goes to the heart of the matter. In short, prosperity brought pride, which led to the king's sin in the temple (see figure 12-1, point I. A.).

> But when he was strong his heart was lifted up, to his destruction, for he transgressed against the LORD his God by entering the temple of the LORD to burn incense on the altar of incense. So Azariah the priest went in after him, and with him were eighty priests of the LORD–valiant men. And they withstood King Uzziah, and said to him, "It is not for you, Uzziah, to burn incense to the LORD, but for the priests, the sons of Aaron, who are consecrated to burn incense. Get out of the sanctuary, for you have trespassed! You shall have no honor from the LORD God." (NKJV)
>
> Then Uzziah became furious; and he had a censer in his hand to burn incense. And while he was angry with the priests, leprosy broke out on his forehead, before the priests in the house of the LORD, beside the incense altar. And Azariah the chief priest and all the priests looked at him, and there, on his forehead, he was leprous; so they thrust him out of that place. Indeed he also hurried to get out, because the LORD had struck him. King Uzziah was a leper until the day of his death. He dwelt in an isolated house, because he was a leper; for he was cut off from the house of the LORD. Then Jotham his son was over the king's house, judging the people of the land. (NKJV)

It is in stark, shocking contrast to the man the Judeans would have properly looked up to for generations that Yahweh is seen as the "indescribably Holy One" (see figure 12-1, point I. B). Isaiah continues:

> I saw the Lord sitting on a throne, high and lifted up, and the train of His robe filled the temple. Above it stood seraphim; each one had six wings: with two he covered his face, with two he covered his feet, and with two he flew. And one cried to another and said: "Holy, holy, holy is the LORD of hosts; The whole earth is full of His glory!" And the posts of the door were shaken by the voice of him who cried out, and the house was filled with smoke. (6:1-4 NKJV)

The visible glory of the thrice-holy, ever-living, self-existent God (Yahweh) is to be appreciated against the dark backdrop of the king whose long reign of military, political, and domestic success ended ingloriously. In the light of this breathtaking comparison, Isaiah realizes his own need of personal cleansing.

House's sermon outline in figure 12-1 emphasizes the passage's historical background:

Putting Our Worldview in Order
Isaiah 6:1–13

I. Knowing Who God Is	1–4
A. The Importance of the Historical Setting to Isaiah's Vision (2 Kings 15:1–5; 2 Chronicles 26:16–21)	
• Prosperity Brought Pride	
• Uzziah's Sin in the Temple	
B. God the Indescribably Holy One	
II. Knowing Who We Are	5
A. Personal Reflection as We View God	
B. Personal Acceptance of Our Sinfulness	
III. Knowing Forgiveness Apart from Works	6–7
A. Recognition of Sin	
B. Undeserved Favor from God	
IV. Knowing Our Mission in View of Forgiveness	8
A. God's Desire to Interact with His People	
B. Our Need to Follow Forgiveness with Commitment	
V. Knowing That Judgment Often Precedes Redemption	(9b–13)

Figure 12.1

Literary Analysis

Sidney Greidanus emphasizes the importance of the literary analysis of prophetic texts in his book *The Modern Preacher and the Ancient Text*. He says, "Anyone reading the latter Prophets will soon discover and be frustrated by the lack of a chronological structure. This is not to say that prophetic books have no structure at all but that they have a different structure from what we have come to expect in Western literature, and even to some extent in Hebrew narrative."[19]

With regard to identifying the principle by which prophets organized their material, author Gene Tucker expresses a basic fact to bear in mind: "The prophets, as all other creative individuals, were part of a tradition, and they used the language and the forms of expression of their own time and place."[20] Tucker contends that instead of looking for a prophetic genre per se, we should be "looking for that continuity which should aid us in understanding each individual."[21] He concludes that most prophetic literature consists of accounts, prayers, or speeches. An *account* refers to information the prophet reports—often in first-person or third-person narrative.[22] According to Tucker, "relatively few *prayers*—words directed by man to God—are found in the prophetic books."[23] "Most of the units within the prophetic books fall under the general category of speeches in which the prophet himself addresses Israel, a group within Israel, an individual, or a foreign nation." These speeches are usually "not long formal compositions," but "brief and poetic utterances."[24] He identifies as *messenger speech* that which is often introduced by the words "Thus says the Lord."[25] The content of these speeches includes direct words from God, or *oracles*, and announcements (or pronouncements) of judgments and promises.[26]

Some prophetic material, such as the book of Ezekiel, is organized chronologically according to when the oracles were delivered. Haggai and Zechariah are also developed chronologically. The compilation of visions and oracles usually reflect a degree of topical arrangement as well, according to Greidanus, oracles of judgment being followed by oracles of salvation.[27]

Both prose and poetry are found in prophetic literature, but Von Rad states, "While there arc exceptions, the prophets' own way of speaking is, as a rule, in poetry: that is to say, it is speech characterized by rhythm and parallelism. In contrast, passages in which they are not themselves speakers but are the subjects of report, are in prose."[28]

With regard to poetic forms, various kinds of parallelism were discussed in Chapter 10. An example of *external parallelism* is found in the book of Hosea. According to Dorsey, the content of Hosea is arranged as a chiasm.[29] (See figure 12-2.)

Recognizing the prominent center formed by this inverted parallelism will enable you to organize your sermon to communicate God's message. The rhetorical structures of *internal* parallelism, discussed in Chapter 10, also "reinforce, sharpen and extend the meaning of the passage."[30] Prophetic material is especially rich in metaphors (like Hosea's husband-wife picture of Yahweh and Israel), and deliberate overstatements called *hyperboles* (such as Amos's calling the rich women of Samaria "cows of Bashan" [4:1 NKJV]).

Hosea
Salvation
Israel's Spiritual Adultery and Yahweh's Unconditional Love

a Israel is God's wayward wife: he will cause her to return home (1:1–3:5)
  b Condemnation of Israel's spiritual prostitution and idolatry (4:1–5:7)
    c Condemnation for political faithlessness and corruption and empty sacrifices (5:8–6:11a)
      d **CENTER: Israel has not returned to Yahweh** (6:11b–7:16)
    c′ Condemnation for political faithlessness and corruption . . . (8:1–9:7b)
  b′ Condemnation of Israel's spiritual prostitution and idolatry (9:7c–10:15)
a′ Israel is God's wayward son: (11:1–14:9)

Figure 12.2

Theological Understanding

While paying attention to all of the historical background and literary structure of a prophetic text, don't forget that, as Greidanus puts it, "the primary concern of Scripture is to acquaint us with God, his word, his will, his acts."[31] Although "in prophetic literature, the theocentric emphasis is so evident that it is hard to ignore," says Greidanus, "sometimes the central thrust is overlooked because preachers concentrate on the person of the prophet."[32] While it is possible to make a prophet such as Jonah the subject of a biographical sermon, this is not the viewpoint of the material itself.

Preachers can also become distracted by absorption with the details of apocalyptic predictions and their fulfillment in the distant future, thus missing the meaning of the prophecy to its immediate audience. Greidanus cautions, "When preaching on Old Testament prophecy, one ought not to move too quickly to the New Testament. For example, while Jesus Christ ultimately fulfills the type of Israel as a suffering servant of Yahweh, in Isaiah 53, to make the prophecy *only* about Him, and not about the nation, misses the point that the people associated with Christ have a servant-role to play.[33] The following diagram represents the servant of Yahweh as described by Delitzsch.[34] (See figure 12-3.)

The theological meaning of a passage is understood by using its various rings of context to answer what the text teaches about the character and work of God. It is the generalization about God that has timeless, universal application. In other words, it is a divine principle.

The theological meaning of Isaiah 6:1-13 might be stated as follows: Yahweh, in contrast to corruptible majesty of human kings, is glorious in absolute holiness and independent existence. The theological meaning of Hosea is that God is intolerant of spiritual adultery and yet faithful in extending His mercy to His undeserving people when they repent.

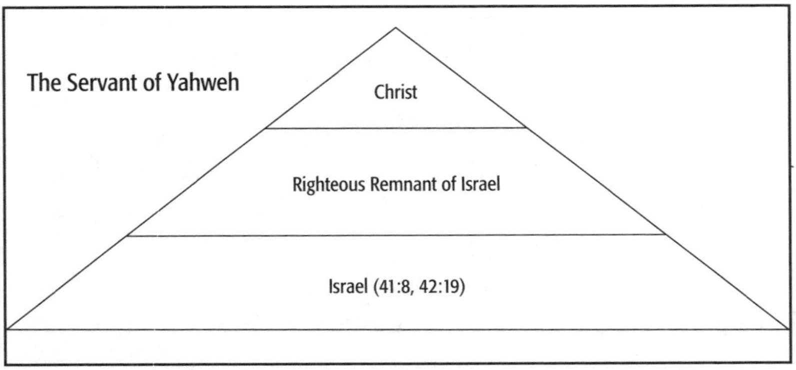

Figure 12.3

Preaching Points

Kaiser suggests four improper ways of preaching the prophetic texts of Scripture.[35] Each amounts to some form of taking the text out of context. One is directly applying a person's name or character in a prophetic text to a current social ill (e.g., applying 1 Kings 21 to "the Ahabs of our day"). Another is to select an action in the prophecy and use it as a launchpad to teach something unrelated to the context (e.g., "linking Ahab's aggrandizement with *institutional* systems like socialism, welfarism ... and the government in general").[36] A third abuse is taking advantage of a statement that serves as a motto or springboard from which to bounce to numerous cross-references. For example, a preacher who sets out to preach against women's liberation might launch his salvos from the conveniently worded statement in 1 Kings 21:7, "I [Jezebel] will give you the vineyard of Naboth the Jezreelite" (NKJV). A fourth way to miss the author's intent is to treat a text's content as a parable (a fictitious story with a spiritual meaning), for example, treating the account of Jezebel's confiscation of Naboth's vineyard as if it were only a story told to illustrate the unlawful seizure of private property by the state, when, in fact, it is an historical example of it.

To help you avoid these abuses, Kaiser suggests that your sermon reflect the conditional aspect of prophecy. He states, "Preaching from the prophets can have a great contemporary appeal if we emphasize repentance as the condition for experiencing the favor of God."[37] While this is generally true in principle, be careful not to apply warnings and promises issued to Israel as if they were addressing the Church. Old Testament prophecy was written *for* us but not *to* us.

Books of Prophecy
Isaiah

Historical Background

Isaiah was the son of Amoz, who, according to Jewish tradition, was King Amaziah's brother.[38] If the tradition is true, Isaiah was the first cousin of King Uzziah.[39] Isaiah's wife was called a prophetess in Isaiah 8:3. The name of their son, Maher-shalal-hash-baz, means "Swift is booty, speedy is prey," and is thought to symbolize the imminent plunder of the Northern Kingdom by Assyria, as Isaiah prophesied in chapters 1-39.[40] The name of his second son, Shear-Jasub, means "A remnant shall return," and relates to the deliverance promised in chapters 40-66.[41]

The superscription (verse 1) of the book indicates that Isaiah prophesied mainly in Jerusalem in close connection with kings Ahaz and Hezekiah. He is called "the prince of Old Testament prophets," and "the evangelical prophet," because his writing provides the broadest scope of theology in the Old Testament and emphasizes the good news of Messiah.[42]

The date of writing is about 740-690 B.C., after receiving his commission the year King Uzziah died (740 B.C.; see Isaiah 6). He probably spoke the prophecies of chapters 1-35 during the reigns of Uzziah, Ahaz, and Hezekiah, and the latter chapters (40-66) during the evil reign of Manasseh.[43] According to Freeman:

> The material prosperity of the two kingdoms produced the unusual social and moral evils, as well as religious declension, which inevitably results under such circumstances. The wealth and luxury which resulted from their economic prosperity, together with the spirit of optimism created by their military successes, produced an attitude of carnal security in the two capitals, which was also rebuked by Isaiah's contemporary, Amos (760-753).[44]

Literary Analysis

As noted above, Isaiah is arranged with an emphasis on judgment in the first thirty-nine chapters, and deliverance in the last twenty-seven chapters. Chapters 36-39 have been described as an *historic interlude*[45] forming the turning point of the book. With the threat of Assyria averted in chapters 36-37, the threat of Babylon, predicted in chapters 38-39, was the result of Hezekiah's sinful treaty with them. But beginning with chapter 40, the emphasis changes to the deliverance God will ultimately bring through His obedient, suffering Servant.

Theological Understanding

The prophet emphasizes both God's overall control of and His willingness to work through chosen servants, including the remnant of Jacob, but even the Gentile king Cyrus, and ultimately, Messiah. In 7:14, the prophecy of a virgin's conception was given as a sign to wicked King Ahaz. In 9:6, the prophecy of Messiah was given both as judgment and consolation when Israel had rejected God's Word. The events recorded in chapters 13-23 are fulfilled during Manasseh's rule.

Preaching Points

The reader is confronted with the need to be part of a faithful remnant that God will deliver. Hezekiah's sin of making a treaty with Babylon explains the division of the book and was recorded in both Kings and Chronicles because it was so critical. In a nutshell, one little sin cost the nation its freedom. Chapters 40-66 emphasize blessing with the return from captivity. In this section, Persian king Cyrus is named 150 years in advance.

Called God's "anointed," in Isaiah 45:1 (NKJV), Cyrus is a type of the Messiah. Messiah, though made to suffer, would fulfill the type of Yahweh's servant, which national Israel had failed to be.[46] Of major importance is the fact that chapters 60-66 contain promises to Israel of restoration and blessing that prove that the Jews' rejection of Christ did not result in final rejection of Israel!

Jeremiah

Historical Background[47]

The name Jeremiah means "whom Yahweh establishes" and fits the story of his prophetic calling and service to the Lord. Jeremiah's prophecies were compiled by an assistant named Baruch (36:4). Jeremiah was a priest, son of Hilkiah, and lived in the priestly town of Anathoth, about three miles north of Jerusalem (1 Chr. 6:60). He was chosen before he was born and received his call when quite young. Because of the threatening times, he was not allowed to marry (16:1-4). Jeremiah was appointed to stand against kings, princes, priests, and false prophets of Judah (1:18). He began his ministry in the thirteenth year of

Josiah's reign (626 B.C.), during the early part of Josiah's reformation and about five years before the books of the Law were found in the temple by Hilkiah. His ministry continued through the eleventh year of Zedekiah, when the Southern Kingdom was taken into captivity in 586 B.C.

With Babylon emerging as world empire over Egypt and Assyria, Jeremiah prophesied during the worst period of Jewish history. He lived through at least four national tragedies. First, Josiah's assassination at Megiddo (609 B.C.) brought national mourning similar to that for U.S. presidents Lincoln and Kennedy. (See Zechariah 12:11.) Second, Nebuchadnezzar's siege of Jerusalem began in 605 B.C. Many captives, including Daniel, were taken, and Judah began to be destroyed by the Babylonians, Moabites, and Ammonites (2 King 24: 1-4). Third, Jerusalem fell to Nebuchadnezzar in 597. King Jehoiakim, Ezekiel, and many temple treasures were taken captive. Fourth, Jeremiah was imprisoned in 587, and Jerusalem was destroyed one year later. Religiously, Josiah's reforms came too late to spare the Southern Kingdom from rampant idolatry as a result of foreign alliances.

Literary Analysis

Arranged logically, not chronologically, most of Jeremiah is autobiographical. Chapters 7-10 consist of a series of sermons.[48] Most famous is the *temple sermon*, in which God's destruction of the temple is stated as inevitable. Chapters 11-18 present Jeremiah's *covenant sermon*, which teaches that God keeps His covenant even though the people didn't keep theirs. (Compare 2 Timothy 2:13.)

Theological Understanding

Chapter 31 announces the new covenant, of which believers in Christ today enjoy a foretaste through the blessings of the indwelling Holy Spirit.[49] The provisions of the new covenant include forgiveness of sins, universal knowledge of Yahweh, and universal possession of the Holy Spirit. Jeremiah demonstrated faith in God's promise to restore a remnant to the land by buying a field there.

Preaching Points

Chapter 17 concerns idolatry, Sabbath breaking, and injustice. A society is measured partly by how it treats its dependent members.

Comfort is found in chapters 30-33. When the wicked prosper, as did Babylon, it is only a matter of time until God judges them.

God is faithful to honor those who honor Him. (See 1 Samuel 2:30.) When thirty-five despised Rechabites, whose father prohibited them from drinking wine, sowing seed, planting a vineyard, or building a house, obeyed their father's command, they were praised not for obeying the content of his command but for their steadfastness as an example to Judah. Likewise, the life of Ebed-Melech, an Ethiopian eunuch, was spared when others were slain, because he had rescued Jeremiah. God's faithfulness extends to His people even when they are under judgment, and He will bless those who wait patiently for His restoration.

Jeremiah himself was a type of Christ, who similarly predicted the destruction of Jerusalem by the Romans, and is called the "weeping prophet," foreshadowing Christ as the Man of Sorrows, who contended with the same religious hostility and also wept over Jerusalem (Luke 19:41).

Ezekiel

Historical Background

The name Ezekiel means "God is strong," or "God strengthens." Though Ezekiel's name is not found elsewhere in Scripture, it is mentioned in 1:3 and 24:24, confirming his authorship of the book. A priest, the son of Buzi, Ezekiel was born about 622 B.C. and was taken captive with Jehoiachin in 597 B.C. For five years he lived among the captives by the River Chebar before he began to prophesy at the age of thirty. Ezekiel was married, but his wife died when the siege of Jerusalem began, about 588 B.C. (24:1, 15-18). He ministered in his own hometown, where the elders came to hear him (14:1; 20:1, 3). His prophecy was written about 592-570 B.C. (see 1:2-3, 29:17). As Jeremiah prophesied in Jerusalem, and Daniel at the royal court in Babylon, Ezekiel spoke to the colony of captives.

Literary Analysis

Ezekiel is arranged according to the sequence in which he received and delivered his oracles, or words from the Lord. Following the call of Ezekiel in chapters 1-3, there are warnings for Judah in chapters 4-24 and prophecies against the nations in chapters 25-32. From chapters 32 on, the prophecies turn to Israel's restoration in the land with a glorious new temple.

Theological Understanding

Ezekiel spoke of God's willingness to restore His repentant people and be their Good Shepherd in a new Jerusalem, which would rise again with unparalleled splendor. As a priest, Ezekiel emphasized the new temple and its worship. His refrain is "'Then you shall know that I am the LORD'" (15:7 NKJV). Ezekiel is known for his use of signs and visions. He is the prophet of the "Spirit," whom he mentions more than twenty-four times. In Ezekiel 47:21-23, God's justice is evident in His refusal to dispossess the Gentiles assimilated into the tribes of Israel.

Preaching Points

Ezekiel's role as a watchman illustrates the principle that successful ministry is measured by faithfulness, not results.

Daniel

Historical Background

The name Daniel means "God is my Judge." The Jews classed the book of Daniel among the *Writings* rather than with the *Prophets* because he was considered a statesman rather than a preacher.[50] Born about 625 B.C., presumably of royal blood (see Daniel 1:3-6 and 2 Kings 20:18), he was brought to Babylon in 605 B.C. with the first deportees. Daniel was a contemporary of Jeremiah, having grown up during the reformation of Josiah. He ministered in the royal court of Babylon while Ezekiel ministered among the captives. Daniel prophesied from 603 (see Daniel 2:1) until about 535 B.C. (see 10:1), through the Babylonian reign into the Persian era. He served under four kings, including Nebuchadnezzar, Cyrus, and Darius, and was prime minister twice. At least one of the kings under whom Daniel served, Nebuchadnezzar, came to faith in Yahweh. Daniel would have known Zerubbabel and may have influenced Cyrus to allow the return of the captives to Jerusalem.[51]

Literary Analysis

Daniel is naturally divided between the accounts of personal triumphs that show God's control over people (chs. 1-6), and prophecies that demonstrate God's control over history (chs. 7-12). Interestingly, chapters 2 and 7, in which the time frame of Gentile world domination is outlined, were written in Aramaic, the language of the Gentiles.

Theological Understanding

Daniel was written to explain the *times of the Gentiles*, that is, God's sovereign tolerance of Israel's domination by Gentile world rulers.

Preaching Points

As a prophet, Daniel's personal deliverances illustrate God's sovereign control of events. Daniel and his friends were not the only young men taken captive. But they were the only ones who stayed true to God. Kidnapped, and possibly castrated, they were in dire straits from a human perspective. From God's standpoint, they were on assignment in a strategic position to fulfill God's purpose.

Hosea

Historical Background

The name Hosea is a pronunciation of Joshua, which means "salvation" or "deliverance." The book is dated by the reigns of our four southern kings (Uzziah through Hezekiah), 755 to 725 B.C. When Hosea prophesied against the Northern Kingdom, Israel was increasingly threatened by Assyria to the east and in political decline after its most prosperous period under Jeroboam II. Morally, the kingdom was approaching its lowest point. A band of priests committed murder (6:9), people were sacrificing their children, and worship had become polluted with prostitution! (See Hosea 4:11-14; 5:3-4; 6:10; 7:3-5; and 2 Kings 14-17.) Freeman notes that "the people confounded the worship of Yahweh with Baal, while calf worship was prevalent on every hand. The nation rejected God and trusted in foreign alliances (8:9-10)."[52]

Literary Analysis

The content of Hosea is arranged as a chiasm.[53] (See figure 12-2.) The prominent center emphasizes Israel's unfaithfulness to Yahweh.

Theological Understanding

Hosea's marriage to a wife he knew would be unfaithful to him symbolized Yahweh's rejection and subsequent restoration of Israel. Yahweh's covenant keeping is not dependent upon the faithfulness of His covenant people, but upon His faithfulness to His oath.

Preaching Points

The prophecy of Hosea illustrates God's unconditional love for those with whom He has entered into a covenant relationship. It also shows the devastating effects of sinning against God with the love of false gods, His intolerance of the idolatrous behavior, but also His commitment to His people.[54]

Joel

Historical Background

The name Joel means "Yahweh is God." This lends emphasis to the statement in 2:27, "Then you shall know that … I am the LORD your God" (NKJV; 3:17 reads similarly). Joel, son of Pethuel (1:1), prophesied in Judah and Jerusalem. His frequent references to priests suggest that he, too, may have been a priest.

That Joel probably wrote around 835 B.C. is consistent with several facts: First, his attitude, writing style, and language are much like those of Amos rather than the prophets who wrote after the exile. Second, he is much quoted by Amos, Isaiah, and Micah. Third, in Joel, the enemies of Judah are Philistia, Egypt, Greece, and Edom, not Assyria or Babylon. The absence of any mention of a king or princes suggests the time when Josiah was the under-age king overseen by Jehoiada, the high priest.

Politically, the elders and priests seem to be dominating the scene (1:13-14). Internationally, Judah was being pestered by neighboring Tyre, Sidon, and Philistia, who raided the land and sold the people as slaves to Greece. Religiously, the sins were indifference and drunkenness. This suggests that Joel may have prophesied after Jehoiada and Joash had purged the land of Baal worship. If so, he would have been a contemporary of Elisha in Israel.

Literary Analysis

The book is naturally divided into two parts, chapters 1-2 predicting a plague of locusts as a foretaste of judgment, and chapters 3-4 promising future restoration and hope.

Theological Analysis

Joel emphasizes the outpouring of the Holy Spirit in the day of the LORD,[55] to which Peter compares Pentecost (Acts 2:16-20). The book teaches that judgment is to bring repentance (Joel 2:12-13) and that timely repentance brings assurance of restoration (vv. 25-26).

Preaching Points

Although God's judgment in the Day of Yahweh (Joel 1:15) could no more be averted than the devastating scourge of locusts (vv. 3-4), this judgment was to bring repentance. Joel's message was that a remnant would be delivered, including every individual who calls on the name of Yahweh (2:32). Today, as then, timely repentance assures restoration.

Amos

Historical Background

Amos was from the village of Tekoa, six miles south of Bethlehem, where he served not as a priest or trained prophet, but as a manager or owner of large herds of livestock (Amos 1:1; 7:14).[56] The meaning of his name, "burden" or "burdensome," also describes the heavy load of oracles God had given him to deliver against the Northern Kingdom and surrounding nations. Ellisen notes that Amos was the first prophet described as one who employed visions and predicted Israel's doom.[57] Freeman describes the political and moral setting in which Amos wrote:

> The nation's unprecedented prosperity and luxury, together with their sinful indulgences, ease and idleness were indictive of national decay and moral depravity.
>
> Israel's moral corruption is described by the prophet as: carnal security (6:1); scorn of judgment for sin (v. 3a); violence and oppression (v. 3b); indolence (v. 4a); wanton luxury and gluttony (vv. 4b, 6b); idle pleasures (v. 5); drunkenness (v. 6a; cf.4:1); lack of compassion (v. 6b).[58]

Literary Analysis

Amos consists of three groups of oracles in nine chapters, arranged in a chiasm, with chapter 5 forming the prominent center for emphasis. (See figure 12-4.)[59] According to Tucker, "two basically different genres, superscription and motto, have been combined to serve together as the introduction of the Book of Amos."[60] Thus oracles against Judah, Israel, and the surrounding nations are unified under one title.[61]

Freeman observes:

> The second section, chapters 3-6, consists of three sermons against Israel for her sins. The sermons of judgment are easily perceptible since each begins with the prophetic formula "Hear this word" which stands at the head of chapters 3, 4 and 5. Each of the three denunciations is concluded with an emphatic "therefore" (3:11; 4:12; 5:16; 6:7) which announces the nation of judgment to follow.[62]

The third cluster of judgments, in chapters 7-9, include five visions: the locusts (7:1), fire (7:4), a plumb line (7:7), a basket of summer fruit

(8:1), and the altar (9:1).[63] The prophecy concludes with a promise of restoration and glory for Israel.

As for its placement in the canon and relation to the other prophecies, Amos's message amplifies Joel 3:16, which says, "The LORD also will roar from Zion" (NKJV).[64] Obadiah, in turn, builds on Amos 9:12, "that they may possess the remnant of Edom" (NKJV).[65] (See figure 12-4.)

Theological Understanding

Amos emphasizes and defends God's righteousness in judging Israel in view of her social injustices, moral degeneracy, and apostasy.[66] (See Amos 9:1 and Hebrews 10:26.) Amos is known for several classical passages, including 3:3 ("Can two walk together, unless they are agreed?" [NKJV]) and 7:7 ("Thus He showed me: Behold, the Lord stood on a wall made with a plumb line, with a plumb line in His hand" [NKJV]. Eight times Amos says, "Thus says the LORD."

Amos
The righteousness of God in Judging Israel

a General Judgments on the Nations	1–2
b Destruction of Bethel's idolatry	3
c Condemnation of Decadent Women and False Worship	4
d CENTER Call to repentance and lament	5
c′ Condemnation of Decadent Men and False Worship	6
b′ Destruction of Bethel's Idolatry	7
a′ Symbolic Judgment on Nations	8–9

Figure 12.4

Preaching Points Amos teaches that (1) there is a universal morality (chs. 1-2), (2) God delights to share His plans with His servants (3:7), and (3) insincere worship is an insult to God (4:4-5).

Obadiah

Historical Background

Obadiah, a common Old Testament name, means "servant" or "worshipper of Yahweh." Nothing is known of the prophet Obadiah or the date of his writing. Because its content is the doom of Edom (descendants of Esau), it is believed to have been written in a time when Israel was oppressed by the Edomites. Several factors favor a date around 845 B.C. First, the order in which Obadiah was placed in the Old Testament books suggests an early date of writing. It is also possible that Amos and Jeremiah quote Obadiah. It was during the reign of Jehoram and the ministry of Elisha that Edom revolted against her subjection to Judah and became her permanent enemy (2 Kings 8:22). Arabia and Philistia raided Judah (2 Chr. 21:16-17). If the early date is accurate, Obadiah is (a) the first writing prophet and (b) the first to introduce the day of the LORD.[67]

Literary Analysis

According to Dorsey, "The structure of the Book of Obadiah serves to reinforce its message. The balancing of the portrayal of proud Edom's future fall (units a and b) with the declaration of fallen Israel's future rise and ascendancy over Edom (units b' and a') highlights the theme that Yahweh will right the wrongs that Edom has committed against Israel by reversing the fortunes of the two nations.[68] See figure 12-5.[69]

Obadiah
Servant of Yahweh
God Knows How to Humble the Proud

a Proud Edom will be defeated (1–4)
    b Edom will be completely plundered (5–7)
        c Edom's population will be slaughtered (8–11)
            d **CENTER: Indictment of Edom** (12–14)
        c' Edom and the nations will be judged (15–16)
    b' Israel will regain what it has lost (17–18)
a' Humbled Israel will be victorious (19–21)

Figure 12.5

Theological Understanding

The prophecy of Obadiah pictures the history of Israel. Edom's judgment typifies God's attitude toward all pride and His determination to destroy the enemies of Israel. Edom was built on the cliffs of Mount Seir, which was impregnable to men but vulnerable to God, who humbles the proud (cp. Obadiah 1:3-4, Amos 9:2). (See figure 12-6.)

Preaching Points

Obadiah was written to proclaim the doom of Edom for her pride, hatred, and mistreatment of the Jews, and the eventual glory of Israel (1:10, 15). The Israelites were commanded not to hate (show less esteem for) the Edomite, "for he is your brother," said Deuteronomy 23:7 (NKJV). Yet the Edomites' hatred of Jews became a symbol for all hostility against Jews. Herod, an Edomite, mistreated Christ. By A.D. 70, there was only a remnant of Edomites. God promised to tear down any attempts they make to rebuild (Mal. 1:3-4). In Obadiah 1:12-14, where God expresses displeasure with Edom for their maltreatment of their "brother Jacob" (v. 10 NKJV), the words translated "Do not" (NASB) suggest "You should not [have]," as expressed variously in the King James, New King James, and New International Versions.

Several lessons can be drawn from Obadiah. First, the struggle between Jacob and Esau began in the womb. It was fueled by favoritism based on man's choice rather than God's choice. Second, pride is dangerous. As Proverbs 16:18 (NKJV) states, "Pride *goes* before destruction, and a haughty spirit before a fall."

Figure 12.6

Jonah

Historical Background

The name Jonah means "dove" and fits his mission as a messenger of peace. Jonah was the son of Amittai, from Gath Hepher in Zebulon (modern el-Meshad), four miles north of Nazareth. He was recognized as a prophet during the early reign of Jeroboam II, 793-753 (2 Kings 14:23-25). If he wrote the book of Jonah later in life, a probable date is around 765 B.C.[70]

Critics have rejected the historicity of Jonah because of their disbelief in the miraculous events recorded in the book. But conservative scholars believe in the historical nature of the book for at least three reasons. First, nothing in the book contradicts historical reality or suggests that the literature is a parable, legend, or allegory. Second, Jewish tradition has always regarded the book to be historically factual. Third, Christ referred to Jonah's being swallowed by the fish and Nineveh's repentance as historical fact[71] (Matt. 12:40-41; Luke 11:29-30).

Politically, Israel lived in constant fear of flash attacks from Syria and Assyria. Assyria was on the rise as a world power. Its capital city, Nineveh, had a population of 600,000 inside an outer wall some sixty miles in circumference. As the first foreign missionary, Jonah addresses the Northern Kingdom with the account of his mission to Nineveh, its archenemy.

Literary Analysis

On the structure of Jonah, Dorsey writes:

> Most people reading the Book of Jonah recognize that the book is composed of a series of episodes. There appear to be seven, each marked off for the audience by shifts in setting, genre and characters. These seven episodes are arranged in chronological order. But a secondary parallel arrangement scheme is also relatively conspicuous. The first three episodes (Jonah's first commission, his first experience with the pagans,

and his first prayer) are matched by the second three episodes (his second commission, his second experience with the pagans, and his second prayer) in an a-b-c, a´-b´-c´ configuration. Following these six episodes is Yahweh's lesson for Jonah, which concludes the book. The seven episodes of the book thus exhibit a parallel arrangement: a-b-c, a´-b´-c´, d.[72] (See figure 12-7.)[73]

Theological Understanding

The book is an object lesson to show Israel God's concern for the lost in contrast to Israel's lack of compassion. Thus, while Obadiah emphasizes God's vengeance, Jonah demonstrates His mercy. Jonah further serves to typify the death, burial, and resurrection of Jesus Christ from the dead in that both were in the place of death for parts of three days and nights (Matt. 12:40).

Jonah

Dove

God's Concern for the Lost in Contrast to Israel's Lack of Concern

a Jonah's commissioning and flight (1:1–3)
  b Jonah and the pagan sailors (1:4–16)
    c Jonah's prayer (1:17–2:10)
a' Jonah's recommissioning and obedience (3:1–3a)
  b' Jonah and the pagan Ninevites (3:3b–10)
    c' Jonah's prayer (4:1–4)
d Yahweh's lesson for Jonah (4:5–11)

Figure 12.7

Preaching Points

Jonah teaches that convenient circumstances often attend the way of disobedience to God (1:3). People should willingly obey God, as do His other creatures, the storm, the great fish, the shade plant, and the worm. The story demonstrates once for all that missions is obedience in extending *God's* compassion for the lost, not one's own compassion. But He can work through a person in spite of himself. And God honors the genuine repentance of anybody. Nevertheless, God is as interested in the work He is doing in His servants as in what He is doing *through* them.

Micah

Historical Background [74]

The name Micah means "Who is like Yahweh?" (see Micah 7:18). Micah was from Moresheth, twenty miles southwest of Jerusalem, on the border with Philistia. He is the only minor prophet whose writing ministry addressed both kingdoms, though he mainly prophesied to the Southern Kingdom of Judah. Hezekiah's memory of Micah's prophecy spared Jeremiah's life Jer. 26:18). Micah prophesied around 725 B.C., during the reigns of Jotham, Ahaz, and Hezekiah. To understand the nature of Micah's ministry, it is beneficial to compare and contrast him with his contemporary, Isaiah:

- Both warn of invasion.
- Both speak of Judah's deliverance from Assyria.
- Both speak of Judah's captivity in Babylon.
- Both foresee millennial blessings after regathering and national repentance.
- Both speak of Messiah, Isaiah foretelling His virgin conception, and Micah, His place of birth (5:2).

Differences between Isaiah and Micah include the facts that, whereas Isaiah spoke to the upper class, Micah wrote to the common people, with the touch of a "country preacher" (like Amos).[75] Isaiah concerned himself with the political life of Judah, but Micah wrote of religious and social issues. Finally, while Isaiah's prophecy includes surrounding nations, Micah's is confined to the people of Israel and Judah.

Literary Analysis

According to Dorsey, "Careful analysis of the book's layout reveals a seven-part symmetric arrangement … that is artful and at the same time highlights Micah's central themes, particularly (1) Israel's social sins, (2) the moral failure of its leadership, and (3) the ultimate establishment of Yahweh's own benevolent kingship over the land."[76]

(See figure 12-8.)[77]

Micah
Who Is Like Yahweh?

Both Kingdoms Will Be Judged and Delivered by Messiah

a Coming defeat and destruction (1:1–16)
  b Corruption of the people (2:1–13)
    c Corruption of the leaders (3:1–12)
      d **CENTER: Glorious Future Restoration**
    c′ Corruption of leaders (6:1–16)
  b′ Corruption of the people (7:1–7)
a′ Future reversal of defeat and destruction (7:8–20)

Figure 12.8

Theological Understanding

In 6:8, the prophecy asks what Yahweh requires of a person. The answer emphasizes heart righteousness. Another classic question in 7:18, "Who is a God like You?" emphasizes Yahweh as a pardoning God like no other.

Preaching Points

Micah's purpose was to warn of approaching judgment on both kingdoms for their idolatry and injustice, and the eventual deliverance Messiah would bring. He prophesied Bethlehem as the birthplace of Jesus, seven hundred years before Caesar's decree for David's descendants to register there, resulting in its fulfillment (5:2; see Luke 2:1-4). When preaching the book of Micah, emphasize not only the precise fulfillment of predictive prophecies, but also the theological understanding stated under the previous heading.

Nahum

Historical Background

The name Nahum means "consolation" and corresponds with the prophet's ministry. The town of Capernaum in Galilee is named *caper* ("town of") *naum* (Nahum), and is thought to have been named for the prophet who made his home there. Nahum may have escaped the northern captivity and fled to Judah, where he prophesied against Nineveh for the purpose of consoling Judah at a time of temporary reform. Though there are two possible dates of writing, Nahum most likely wrote during the reign of Hezekiah, around 700 B.C. Nahum prophesied against the same city of Nineveh that had repented seventy-five years earlier in response to Jonah's reluctant mission. The city was later destroyed by Nebopolassar in 612 B.C. In keeping with the meaning of his name, Nahum writes as if the action was taking place at the time of writing, yet doesn't mention a single sin of Judah!

Literary Analysis

Because 1:2-10 reflect an incomplete acrostic, various theories seek to explain the composition of Nahum. John Paterson notes a suggestion that the book is a prophetic liturgy but doubts that it was written by the same person at the same time.[78] Dorsey, on the other hand, finds seven units arranged in a chiasm around a center that emphasizes "lament over fall of Nineveh, the Lions' den" (2:11-13). He suggests that Nahum's use of a 4 + 3 pattern echoes a Hebrew dirge, "reinforcing the sense of eulogy over Nineveh's demise."[79] So viewed, the "opening vision is an effective attention-getting device, and it also introduces the issue of the cause of Nineveh's fall, to which Nahum will subsequently return." (See figure 12-9.)

Nahum
Consolation

God's Judgment and Destruction on Nineveh and Assyria

a Yahweh...avenges his enemies (1:2–10)
b Yahweh will destroy Nineveh (1:11–15)
c Vivid description of the attack upon Nineveh (2:1–10)
d **CENTER: Lament over fall of Nineveh (2:11–13)**
c′ Vivid description of the looting of Nineveh (3:1–7)
b′ Nineveh will be destroyed (3:8–13)
a Nineveh likened to a destructive force of nature (3:14–19)

Figure 12.9

Theological Understanding

According to Nahum, Nineveh's destruction shows that delayed judgment of sin is not to be mistaken as divine approval of it. God's justice and omnipotence made His eventual obliteration of Nineveh inevitable. At the same time, God is intimately acquainted with those who seek refuge in Him (1:7). In chapter 2 the destruction and exile of Nineveh as the result of a flood is seen as divine judgment. Chapter 3 emphasizes Nineveh's cruelty by the absence of anyone to grieve her annihilation.

Preaching Points

As a basis for never taking their own revenge, believers need to know that they can count on God to take vengeance against His enemies (Rom. 12:19). They are not to think that God is slow about His promise (see 2 Peter 3:8-9).

Habakkuk

Historical Background

According to Wilkinson and Boa, "The only explicit time reference in Habakkuk is to the Babylonian invasion as an imminent event (1:6; 2:1; 3: 16)."[80] "The most likely date for the book is in the early part of Jehoiakim's reign (609-597 B.C.). Jehoiakim was a godless king who led the nation down the path of destruction (cf. 2 Kings 23:34-25:5; Jer. 22:17)."[81] The name Habakkuk, meaning "to embrace," fits well his engagement of Yahweh in prayer with questions (1:2; 3:2). "He is concerned over the unchecked iniquity and widespread corruption in Judah which seems to go unpunished."[82] When he learns of Yahweh's intention to use the Babylonians to punish Judah, the prophet questions God's use of an executioner more wicked than Judah.

Literary Analysis

"The linear layout of the Book of Habakkuk, beginning with the negative and closing with the positive, suggests that the purpose of the book is to take the audience from confusion and despair to clarification and hope."[83] As Dorsey views it, the book is centered around 2:1-5, where the righteous are said to live by faith. (See figure 12-10.)[84]

Theological Understanding

Speaking to God about men sets Habakkuk apart from most of the prophets who spoke to people about God. The book shows the destruction of the enemies of the Southern Kingdom as the inevitable result of the holiness of God (1:13).

Preaching Points

Habakkuk's statement in 2:4, "But the just shall live by his faith" (NKJV) articulates a principle of physical survival in the coming Babylonian onslaught. The apostle Paul applied it to New Testament believers. (See Hebrews 10:38 and Paul's reference's to Habakkuk 2:4 in Romans 1:17 and Galatians 3:11). In Habakkuk 2:20, the prophet's reference to Yahweh in His holy temple calls for silence before Him as Judge. The great declaration of Habakkuk in 3:17-18, "Though the fig tree may not blossom … Yet I will rejoice in the LORD," emphasizes the fact that God Himself, not His material blessings, is the proper motivation for worship.

Habakkuk
To Embrace

The Righteous Must Wait for God to Destroy Jerusalem's Enemies

a Habakkuk's first complaint about Yahweh's justice (1:2–4)
b Yahweh's response to Habakkuk's first complaint (1:5–11)
c Habakkuk's second complaint about Yahweh's justice (1:12–17)
d **CENTER: the righteous will live by faith (2:1–5)**
c′ Yahweh's answer to second complaint, five woes (2:6–20)
b′ Yahweh's final answer (3:1–15)
a′ Habakkuk's psalm (3:16–19)

Figure 12.10

Zephaniah

Historical Background

The great-great-grandson of King Hezekiah, Zephaniah was a distant cousin to King Josiah and probably had an influential role in Josiah's reforms (see Zephaniah 1:1). He is the only minor prophet with royal blood. He wrote around 625 B.C.[85] The name Zephaniah means "Yahweh hides" and harmonizes with the statement in Zephaniah 2:3: "Seek the LORD, all you meek of the earth, who have upheld His justice.

Seek righteousness, seek humility. It may be that you will be hidden in the day of the LORD's anger" (NKJV). At the time, Josiah's reforms are not connecting with the people. Jerusalem was deserving of judgment for rampant idolatry and adultery in which even the prophets and priests participated despite various punishments (3:7). Zephaniah wrote the most detailed genealogy in the Minor Prophets.

Literary Analysis

According to Dorsey, Zephaniah is usually divided into seven major units that exhibit a symmetrical pattern:

> The announcement of coming judgment in the first unit is balanced by the announcement of coming restoration in the final unit. The condemnation of Jerusalem's princes and wealthy people in the second unit is balanced by the condemnation of the wicked princes and leaders of Jerusalem in the next-to-last unit. The description of the terrible day of Yahweh in the third unit is balanced by the depiction of Yahweh's judgment against the nations in the third-to-last unit. The book's fourth, central unit, is Zephaniah's call to repentance.[86]

(See figure 12-11.)[87]

Theological Understanding

In 1:14, the prophet warns, "The great day of the LORD is near; it is near and hastens quickly" (NKJV). In 2:3, he urges the people to "seek the LORD." God always provides a way of escape from judgment if it is taken in time (Zeph. 2:1-3; 1 Cor. 10:13).

Preaching Points

Zephaniah encourages righteous living in view of God's judgment of the world and restoration of Judah. This book teaches that failure to maintain separation from the world leads to spiritual compromise and judgment (1:4-5; see 2 Kings 17:33). If a community is not missionary *minded*, it soon becomes a mission *field* (see Zephaniah 1:6).

Haggai

Historical Background

The name Haggai means "festive" and fits the prophet Haggai's promotion of building the temple and resuming the observances of Israel's feasts (Ezra 5:1, 6:14). Haggai is the first of three "restoration prophets," meaning that he, along with Zechariah and Malachi, ministered in Judah to those who returned from the Babylonian captivity. Haggai may have been born in Babylon and also been one of the first to return to Jerusalem with Zerubbabel. His prophecy is the most precisely dated, written in the second year of Darius's reign, between September 1 and December 24, 520 B.C.

Zephaniah
Yahweh Hides

The Day of the LORD and the Judgment of Judah

a Coming judgment upon the wicked of Jerusalem (1:2–6)
    b Coming judgment of corrupt leaders (1:7–13)
        c Yahweh's judgment of all nations: (1:14–18)
            d **CENTER: Call to repentance (2:1–3)**
        c′ Yahweh's judgment of all nations (2:4–15)
    b′ Coming judgment of corrupt political leaders (3:1–7)
a′ Coming restoration of Jerusalem and its fortunes (3:8–20)

Figure 12.11

Zerubbabel was governor of Judah, and Joshua was the high priest. After nearly fifty thousand captives returned to Jerusalem from Babylon, the rebuilding of Jerusalem and the temple was halted by a decree by Artaxerxes (Cambyses) in 529 B.C. (Ezra 4:21). The people then began to accept the impossibility of observing temple worship and feasts and turned their attention to personal interests. At the urging of Haggai and Zechariah, however, the people resumed the work, which then won the support of Darius I.[88]

Having returned just seventy years after the first deportation (606), the temple was completed in 516 B.C., just seventy years after its destruction in 586. Thus the prophecy of seventy years of captivity was fulfilled from two points of view.

Literary Analysis

This book is a collection of five dated messages, together with a narrative episode, which are arranged in chronological order. (See figure 12-12.)

Haggai
Festive

A Call to Rise Up and Build the Temple

a Message of rebuke (1:2–11)
b Report of people's response (1:12–15)
c Message of encouragement (2:1–9)
d Message of promise (2:10–19)
e Message about Zerubbabel's significance (2:20–23)

Figure 12.12

Theological Understanding

Haggai teaches that there is no true prosperity out of God's will (1:6). Also, while contamination from sin comes by touch, the same is not true of holiness (2:13).

Preaching Points

Haggai's purpose in writing was to convict the people of neglecting the temple reconstruction in favor of their own interests, and to indicate that such neglect was the cause of their drought and economic depression. His resounding refrain is "Consider your ways" (1:5, 7 NKJV), because the people were saying, "The time has not come, the time that the LORD's house should be built" (1:2 NKJV). In 2:9, the people were to be motivated by God's promise that "the glory of [the] latter temple [would] be greater than the former" (NKJV). A preachable principle from 1:2 is that temptation to spiritual neglect is ever present.

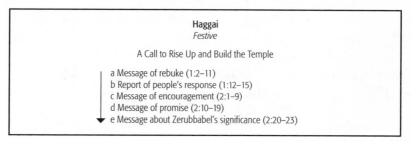

Malachi

Historical Background[89]

The name Malachi means "my messenger" and aptly describes the prophet himself, the priest of 2:7, the messenger of the covenant, and Messiah's forerunner in 3:1. Malachi was the last prophet before John the Baptist, whose coming he predicted. The burden of Malachi's revelation is so prominent in the book that the prophet himself remains in the shadows. Malachi wrote about 430 B.C., after the temple had been rebuilt. Enough time had elapsed for worship to have become a formal, empty routine. Politically, the nation was under Artaxerxes I, the Persian king who allowed Ezra and Nehemiah to return to Jerusalem. Despite experiencing several revivals, including that of Ezra in 445 B.C., the returned exiles were demoralized, certain that God had let them down by not ushering in the promised age of Messiah. They proudly and bitterly questioned God's love and commitment to justice.

Literary Analysis

Dorsey regards the arrangement of Malachi as effective in highlighting the book's main points:[90]

> The first and last units in the symmetry (positions of prominence) underscore the point that Yahweh rewards faithfulness and punishes wickedness … the two fold condemnation of the priests and people for cheating and robbing Yahweh with their inferior offerings, in the second and next-to-last units, draws attention to this theme. And the double coverage of the key role of the Levites in renewal, in the third and third-to-last units, highlights their importance in Israel's religious life. In addition, the placement of the call to repentance at the center of the book's symmetric arrangement emphasizes the key role that repentance must play if the people are to receive God's forgiveness and blessing![91]

(See figure 12-13.)[92]

Theological Understanding

Malachi emphasizes the greatness of God in writing to correct the haughty attitude of his readers. Though he assures them of Yahweh's love, he also presents Yahweh's case against His people for their sinful attitudes and formal religion.

Malachi
My Messenger

God's Love and Israel's Haughtiness

a Yahweh is just: He loves the faithful remnant of Israel (1:2–5)
b Priests and people have cheated Yahweh in their offerings (1:6–14)
c In the past Levi served in righteousness (2:1–9)
d **CENTER: Stop being faithless! (2:10–16)**
c′ In the future Yahweh's messenger will come (2:17–3:6)
b′ People have robbed Yahweh in tithes and offerings (3:7–12)
a′ Yahweh is just: He will reward the righteous but utterly destroy the wicked (3:13–4:3)

Conclusion: Day of Yahweh (4:4–6)

Figure 12.13

Preaching Points

According to Malachi, the pride and arrogance of the people's lifeless, formal worship was the result of their failure to love God in response to His love for them.

Zechariah

Historical Background

Zechariah was one of the prophet-priests. His name means "Yahweh remembers," and complements the prophet's emphasis on Israel's future restoration and cleansing through the redeeming work of the Messiah. Zechariah was the son of Berechiah, a priest whose name means "Yahweh blesses." The name of his grandfather, Iddo, means "the appointed time." Thus, in order, the three names mean: "the appointed time … Yahweh blesses … Yahweh remembers.[93] Zechariah began to prophesy about two months after Haggai began, so the setting was the same. Chapters 1-8 were written between October 520 and November 518. Chapters 9-14 were written probably after 480 B.C. According to Jewish tradition, Zechariah was slain in the sanctuary. His death was recalled by Jesus in Matthew 23:35 and Luke 11:51 .

Literary Analysis

Zechariah consists of seven messages that are chronologically arranged. (See figure 12-14.)

Symmetric Arrangement (Promised Restoration Is Reason to Repent and Rebuild)

I. The Repentance of Israel — **1:1–6**

II. The Rebuilding of Israel's Temple in Jerusalem — **1:7–8:23**

A. CONSOLATION (1–4)
- A Four Riders, Horns, Craftsmen (1)
  (Patrol of Earth with Jealousy for Jerusalem)
  - B Man with a **Measuring Line** (2)
    (Israelis return from Babylon)
    - C Cleansing of Joshua, High Priest (3)
      (**Purging of the Priesthood**)
      - ***Golden Lampstand and Two Olive Trees** (4) (Israel as Light of the World Under Messiah as Priest and King)

Text for Sample Sermon → *Golden Lampstand and Two Olive Trees

B. CONDEMNATION (5–6)
    - C' The Flying Scroll (5:1–4)
      (**Purging of the People**)
  - B' Woman in a **Measuring Basket** (5:7)
    (Iniquities **return to Babylon**)
- A' Four Chariots (6:1–8)
  (**Patrol** of Earth with Judgment of Nations)

C. TWO MESSAGES (7–8)
1. Rituals without Righteousness (7)
2. Fasts will become Feasts (8)

III. The Restoration of Israel's Kingdom — **9–14**

TWO BURDENS (9–14)

1. First Coming and Rejection
   - Human world conqueror and Divine Prince of Peace (9:1–17)
   - Divine Prince of Peace, Deliverer of His People (10:1–12)
   - Israel's Rejection of the Good Shepherd (11:1–17)
   - Israel's Deliverance and National Conversion (12)
2. Second Coming and Reign
   - Israel's National Cleansing (13:1–9)
   - Return of Christ in Glory (14:1–7)
   - Millennial Reign (14:8–21)

Figure 12.14

*This paragraph on the Golden Lampstand and two Olive trees is the text for the sample sermon that follows.

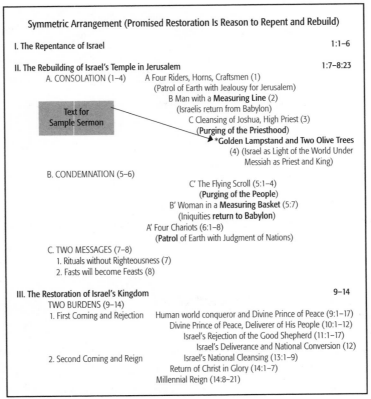

Theological Understanding

Like Isaiah, Zechariah is a great *messianic* prophet. Whereas Daniel was focused on the prophecy of Gentile world domination, Zechariah and Haggai were focused on the temple, reemphasizing the prophecies of Joel and Zephaniah concerning the coming day of the LORD. Zechariah correlates all of the previous prophecies about the restoration of Israel in the land under the Messiah—including Messiah's work in both His first and second comings.

Preaching Points

Zechariah's prophecy is distinguished by the prevalence of visions, information about angels, and a detailed picture of Israel's future. He wrote to encourage those who had returned from exile to Babylon to trust in Yahweh, by painting a meticulous portrait of future restoration. In interpreting the eight night visions, understand that they form a chiasm emphasizing the power of the Holy Spirit. (See figure 12-14.)[94]

Sample Sermon
God's Work, God's Power

Zechariah 4:1-7
Man Does God's Work / Only By God's Power

I. Revelation of God's Power 1-3
    A. The Prophet's Arousal
        1. by a speaking angel (1a)
        2. as if from sleep (1b)
    B. The Prophet's Description
        1. a golden lampstand (2)
            a. a bowl on top
            b. seven lamps
            c. forty-nine supply tubes
        2. two olive trees (3)
            a. one on right side of bowl
            b. one on left side of bowl

II. Request by God's Prophet 4-5
III. Reassurance for God's People 6-7
   A. Yahweh's Word to Zerubbabel (6)
      1. not by might
      2. not by power
      3. by God's Spirit
   B. Yahweh's Warning to Obstacles (7a)
      1. a great mountain of opposition to be flattened
      2. Zerubbabel to personally finish what he starts
   C. Yahweh's People to celebrate God's grace (7b)

Summary and Conclusion

Unlike modern preachers, who proclaim the message of established texts, the prophets received messages directly from God. But like today's ministers of the Word, they were ordinary people whom God chose and called to bear His message of judgment and hope in keeping with the stipulations of His covenants and His ability to predict the future in detail with absolute accuracy. The fulfillments of some of their predictions have already been recorded. Others are yet to be fulfilled. All were taken seriously by the New Testament writers and must not be dismissed, or spiritualized, by preachers today.

Among the challenges facing interpreters of prophetic literature are figurative language, understanding of the geopolitical situation, chronological gaps, and the various ways that predictions can be fulfilled. But the prophetic word is understandable and relevant. Even when the fulfillment of predictions would not occur in the lifetimes of those who heard them, they served to motivate repentance and provide the hope needed at the time.

In preparing to preach from Old Testament prophecy, give special consideration to the historical background, literary analysis, theological understanding, and preaching points of the particular book and passage under study. Familiarity with the basic message of each book will give you a framework within which to develop the message of a given text.

Isaiah urged his readers in the Southern Kingdom of Judah to trust in Yahweh rather than turn to other nations for help, because He promised to restore Judah after judging her.

Jeremiah's unpopular message that it was too late to ward off the Babylonian captivity by repentance is balanced by the promise of the new covenant, in whose spiritual blessings the Church is already participating.

As a priest, **Ezekiel** emphasized the new temple and its worship. While focused on the departure and return of God's glory, Ezekiel's role as a watchman illustrates the principle that successful ministry is measured by faithfulness, not results.

As a prophet, **Daniel's** personal deliverances illustrate God's sovereign control of events. The content of his prophecy demonstrates Yahweh's control over the domination of Israel and the world by Gentile nations.

Hosea's marriage to an unfaithful wife symbolized Yahweh's rejection and subsequent restoration of Israel. Yahweh's covenant keeping does not depend upon the faithfulness of His covenant people, but upon His faithfulness to His oath.

Joel compares the coming Day of Yahweh to the unstoppable onslaught of locusts. But he also predicts the future outpouring of the Holy Spirit, which was partially fulfilled at Pentecost. The book teaches that judgment is meant to inspire repentance, and that timely repentance brings assurance of restoration.

Amos vindicates the righteousness of God in judging His people. His prophecy emphasizes the existence of a moral plumb line by which God holds His people accountable.

Obadiah's prediction of the doom of Edom demonstrates God's ability to humble the proud.

Jonah records the phenomenal repentance of Nineveh in response to God's compassion and mercy for the lost, qualities not shared by the prophet or his people.

According to **Micah**, the ultimate cure for social injustice and idolatry is the coming of a deliverer "who is like Yahweh." This deliverer would be born in Bethlehem.

The book of **Nahum** reveals that Nineveh's destruction shows that delayed judgment of sin is not to be mistaken as divine approval of it.

Habakkuk teaches that the holy justice of Yahweh makes His punishment of Israel's enemies inevitable, and that He is to be worshipped for who He is, not what He bestows.

Zephaniah encourages righteous living in view of God's judgment of the world and restoration of Judah.

Haggai shows that neglecting the ministries of the Spirit can result in the loss of material blessings and bring God's discipline, which in turn leads to the blessings of a restored relationship.

Zechariah wrote to encourage those who had returned from the Babylonian exile to trust in Yahweh. He does this by giving a detailed picture of future restoration.

Malachi emphasized that the pride and arrogance of the people's lifeless, formal worship was the result of their failure to love God in response to His love for them.

A sample sermon from Zechariah shows how to develop a paragraph from a minor prophet for a modern audience. People today, as in the time of Zechariah, cannot do God's work without the power that He supplies by His Holy Spirit, portrayed in the vision of the candelabra supplied with oil from living olive trees.

Discussion Questions

1. Compare and contrast the ancient prophet and the modern preacher. Describe ways in which they are similar as well as different.

2. If the prophets primarily monitored the attitudes and behavior of the descendants of Jacob in relation to the old (Mosaic) covenant, by what rationale can their messages be applied to people living in the church age of grace?

3. What is meant by near and far fulfillments of prophecy, and what is one example?

4. What is meant by the "already-not-yet" tension in relation to prophecy?

5. In what sense was Joel 2:28 fulfilled at Pentecost?
6. How does the meaning of Isaiah 6:1 depend on an under standing of the historical background?
7. According to Von Rad, did the prophets usually speak in prose or poetry?
8. In preaching Old Testament prophecy, why is it important not to move too quickly to New Testament applications or fulfillment?
9. Identify and describe two or three improper ways of preaching prophetic texts of Scripture, as suggested by Walter Kaiser.
10. What sin, committed by King Hezekiah, explains the division of the book of Isaiah?
11. Which of the minor prophets predicted the birthplace of Christ?
12. Which book of the Major Prophets is known for his use of signs and visions?
13. In view of Daniel's emphasis upon the *times of the Gentiles*, what is significant about the language of chapters 2 and 7?
14. Whose prophecy taught that Yahweh's covenant keeping is not dependent upon the faithfulness of His covenant people, but upon His faithfulness to His oath?
15. Which of the minor prophets emphasizes the outpouring of the Holy Spirit in the day of the Lord?
16. Whose prophecy is distinguished by the prevalence of visions and a detailed picture of Israel's future?
17. How does a knowledge of the geography of Petra help a person understand the message of Obadiah?
18. Why do conservative scholars insist on the historicity of Jonah?
19. Describe the state of Jewish society at the time that Jeremiah wrote.

20. What attributes of God does the book of Nahum emphasize?
21. Whose prophecy emphasizes the fact that God Himself, not His material blessings, is the proper motivation for worship?
22. Who is the first of three restoration prophets?
23. Describe the times and message of Malachi.
24. Which of the minor prophets repeats, "Thus says the LORD," eight times?
25. Find two strengths and two weaknesses in the sample sermon on Zechariah 4:1-7.

CHAPTER 13

Preaching the Gospels and Acts

Throughout this book, much has been made of bridge building as an analogy for effective expository communication of God's Word. When your sermon is developed from one of the four Gospels or from the book of Acts, your very text is a like a plank from the bridge God has provided between the Old Testament prophecy and New Testament instruction for the Church. Using such *bridge material* to construct a sermon that communicates God's message will require you to think as a first-century Jew would in biblical times. In preaching the Gospels, you must put yourself in the place of those living under the Law in the presence of the promised Messiah, who spoke of the Church in the future. In preaching the Acts, you must be mindful of the transitional nature of the book. To treat the Gospels or Acts as other than the bridge they form is to confuse things that are, in reality, separate, or to deny the connection of things that are, in reality, related.

References to the kingdom must be carefully understood in terms of which aspect is being discussed. You must view historical facts through the lens of the writer's literary composition in order to discern his theological intent. Having discussed the Hebrew Scriptures in the last four chapters, a consideration of the Gospels and Acts must now begin with an introduction to the New Testament.

Introduction to the New Testament

The words *New Testament* refer to the new covenant ratified by the blood of the Messiah and put into effect by His death. (See Matthew 26:28;

Mark 14:24; Luke 22:20; 1 Corinthians 11:25; and 2 Corinthians 3:6.) It is *new* in relation to the Mosaic covenant, which it replaced as the basis for fellowship with God (Jer. 31:31; Heb. 8:8, 13; 9:15-17; 12:24). Entrance into the new covenant with God by faith in His Son Jesus the Messiah has both redemptive and kingdom implications (1 Pet. 2:7-9). Twenty-seven books written in *Koine* (common) Greek, from about A.D. 45 to 95, are called the *New Testament*. Each book of the New Testament makes its own distinct contribution to the revelation of God's plan to reclaim lost sinners and reestablish His rule on the earth (see Genesis 3:15; 12:1-3; 2 Samuel 7:8-17; Jeremiah 31:31; Hebrews 2:5-9). Regarding their recognition as Scripture, authors Wilkinson and Boa say,

> The New Testament books were separately circulated and gradually collected together. Their inspiration and apostolic authority guaranteed them a place in the canon of Scripture as they were set apart from other writings in the early church. As these books were copied and distributed throughout the Roman Empire, they were eventually placed in a standard order (more logical than chronological).[1]

The New Testament is Christ-centered. It includes the historical books of Matthew, Mark, Luke, John, and Acts; the Epistles of Paul, Peter, John, James, Jude, and Hebrews; and the Revelation. The historical books concern the person and work of Christ as the fulfillment of Old Testament prophecy and the foundation of the church, as He continues His work through His Spirit-filled people. The Epistles instruct, correct, and encourage churches and individual believers in Christ to realize their freedom not only from the *penalty* of sin (Rom. 8:1; Titus 2:11), but also from the *power* of sin (Rom. 6-7; Titus 2:12) as they look forward to freedom from the very *presence* of sin at Christ's coming for His Church (Titus 2:13). The Revelation was written to promote the worship of Christ in view of His exaltation in glory, His authority in the Church, and His coming again to finally destroy His enemies, redeem the faithful remnant of Israel, and reign on the earth.

In preaching the New Testament, keep in mind both its continuity with the Hebrew Scriptures and its revelation of the Church as distinct from Israel.

The Gospels

"Gospel"

The word *gospel* is from the Old English *godspel*,[2] translated from the Greek (euaggelion), which means "good news." Eventually the term was applied to the titles of the first four books of the New Testament because they are about Jesus, the subject of the Bible's good news.[3] In 1 Corinthians 15:1-5, the apostle Paul writes:

> Moreover, brethren, I declare to you the *gospel* which I preached to you, which also you received and in which you stand, by which also you are saved, if you hold fast that word which I preached to you–unless you believed in vain. For I delivered to you first of all that which I also received: that *Christ died for our sin according to the Scriptures, and that He was buried, and that He rose again the third day according to the Scriptures*, and that He was seen by Cephas, then by the twelve. [emphasis added] (NKJV)

Genre

The writers of the four accounts of the life of Christ–Matthew, Mark, Luke and John–have been called *evangelists*, though their writings addressed those who were already regenerate, not the lost. The four Gospels teach theology primarily through biographical narrative, sermons, sayings, parables, and apocalyptic literature.[4] Ryken, in explaining the importance of discovering the genre of a Gospel passage, says, "It usually provides the best descriptive framework for organizing a given unit. And sometimes the correct interpretation of a unit depends on identifying the precise genre of the passage."[5] According to Greidanus, the essential, distinguishing characteristic of the Gospel genre is information intended for declaration, to elicit faith in the listener/reader.[6] "Thus the gospel genre may be characterized as proclamation of the good news of the kingdom of God that has come in the person of Jesus Christ," he concludes.[7] Genre classification "sets the expectations of interpreters and determines the questions they ask of the text ... Thus genre designation is an initial step in interpretation."[8] So, before considering the questions to ask of the text, briefly examine their basic proclamation.

Kerygma

The *kerygma* refers to the common content of the apostles' proclamations of the gospel. According to *Baker's Dictionary of Theology*, the common apostolic gospel included: "(1) a historical proclamation of the death, resurrection and exaltation of Jesus, set forth as the fulfillment of prophecy and involving man's responsibility; (2) a theological evaluation of the person of Jesus as both Lord and Christ; (3) a summons to repent and receive the forgiveness of sins."[9] In addition, Jesus' baptism by John, His miracles, and His sayings are mentioned often in the Gospels. The irreducible minimum of the content of the gospel, which Paul says he received from the Lord's disciples, is the deity, death, and resurrection of Christ (1 Cor. 15: 3-4).[10]

Not all have appreciated the kerygmatic character of the gospel genre as its distinguishing mark. When reduced to mere history or simple literature, the Gospels have failed to win critical acclaim.

Criticism

The Gospels have been subjected to scholarly examination on two levels, *higher criticism* and *textual* (or *lower*) *criticism*. Higher criticism concerns such issues as authorship, date, literary structure, origins, and content of Scripture. When used with caution, higher criticism can be helpful in interpreting Scripture.[11] When it subjects the Bible to the limitations of human understanding and subjective judgment of unbelievers, however, higher criticism undermines faith in the historicity, authenticity, and authority of the Gospel accounts. Textual criticism, a necessary step of exegesis, attempts to establish the original text by comparing manuscript evidence. *Source criticism*, as a subset of higher criticism, contends with what is called the *synoptic problem*.[12] It seeks to answer two questions: (1) Why does a text in Matthew, Mark, or Luke appear to be duplicated in one or all of the others? and (2) Why are there differences in accounts of the same events?[13]

The *documentary hypothesis* assumes that Mark wrote first, followed by Matthew, Luke, and then John. It leads *redaction critics* (those who would *edit* the text) to assume that Matthew altered Mark's original, and that Luke used Matthew, plus an "L" document.[14] A conservative view of Scripture rejects this assumption, based on the fact that all of the church fathers believed that Matthew was written first. They even quoted from it as authority for the Church. Further, Paul treated Luke's writing as being on par with Scripture, and taught that the Gospels were written with the authority of the apostles, who were given to the Church (Eph. 2:20; 4:11). Mark was informed by Peter. Luke was informed by Paul.

The apostle John himself indicates that the Gospel writers *selected* historical material from all that *could* have been said, then arranged and adapted it according to the particular purposes for which they wrote.[15] This explains both the similarities and differences in the content of the Gospels. By no means must this lead to the conclusion reached by some critics, that the historical data was manufactured to support preconceived doctrines.

"Ultimately, the issue of reliability is a matter of faith in God's word,"[16] says Greidanus. Such faith is reasonable, because the facts presented in the Gospels are reasonable and as well-established as any in history.[17] The historical accuracy of the Gospels is crucial to their purpose and was easily checked by those who first heard the kerygma. The historicity of the Gospels is believable on the bases that they were (a) written relatively soon after the events they record, (b) based on eyewitness accounts, (c) accepted by the apostles, and (d) ensured to have been accurately recorded by the Holy Spirit's superintendence.[18] Greidanus, summarizing how the Gospels were compiled and why they can be trusted, says, "They relate actual historical events to proclaim their good news. Even though they write their accounts in a special, kerygmatic style, the evidence for their historicity is sufficient for approaching the Gospels with confidence in their reliability."[19]

Yet to reduce the Gospels to history alone misses the purpose for which the writers chose, organized, and adapted their material. In completing truth sheets for sermons on the Gospels, you must ask yourself: "Why did the author relate this incident? Why did he include it in his Gospel? What did he intend to convey? What kind of response did he expect from his hearers?"[20]

Preaching the Gospels

Text Selection

Preaching texts (or *pericopes*) are recognized by observing the writer's use of rhetorical devices discussed earlier in this book, including repetition, inclusion, parallelism, and chiasm. The goal is to identify a literary unit. Whether a paragraph or a longer portion of Scripture, the text must convey a complete thought. Using a *synopsis* (meaning "see together") makes it is easy to compare and contrast the content of a given text with parallel accounts in other Gospels. This is helpful in discovering the particular purpose of the writer of the text under study.[21] But such analyses should never seek to import into the text something the writer deliberately left out.

When the material of the Gospels is rearranged and collated into a single chronological account, the product is sometimes called a *harmony* of the Gospels.[22] While harmonies aid in understanding where the events of a given text fit into a chronology of Jesus' life, remember that this is *not* how the Spirit of God directed any of the Gospel writers to present the material. The goal of the biblical text is not to produce a movielike, comprehensive mental image of the life and times of Christ as much as it is to emphasize one aspect at a time. But examining a Gospel text in light of parallel accounts or harmonies will answer the questions that will help you determine the writer's intent.

The Right Questions

Greidanus poses excellent questions that can be easily incorporated into the truth sheet–making process:

> Is [the preaching text] found in other Gospels? If not, does its inclusion in this Gospel ... point to the author's interests and purposes? If it is found in another Gospel but in a different context. does the different arrangement of the preaching text shed light on the purpose of its author? Has the author "added or omitted anything? What verbal changes has he made? Are they merely stylistic? Are they more substantive?[23]

Using this approach with Matthew 8:18-27 provides a good example of its value. The emphasis of this passage is on *discipleship*, but Matthew contains intervening stories that Mark and Luke do not include. (See Mark 4:35-41 and Luke 8:22-25.) Why? How does adding these accounts serve Matthew's theological purpose? What purpose is served by Matthew's use of the words "Master," "Teacher," and "Lord"? The story of the wind and waves was given, following Matthew's accent on discipleship, to emphasize complete submission to the lordship of Christ. It stressed the worthiness of Jesus to be followed despite the surprising difficulty in doing so.

Interpretation

Gospel texts are properly interpreted in light of the life situations of both the characters *in* the story and the writer *of* the story. To accomplish this, you must carefully consider the historical background, literary analysis, and theological understanding of the passages.

Historical Background

"Historical interpretation seeks to understand the text as it was understood by its original audience."[24] It provides "the only objective point of control against subjective and arbitrary interpretations."[25]

Literary Analysis

Literary analysis is concerned with how the text is structured to convey its message. How does the text fit into the argument of the book? If it is narrative, the scene, characters, dialogue, and plot must be understood. If the text is apocalyptic, or discourse, be alert to such figures of speech as repetition, inclusion, chiasm, parallelism, double entendre, irony, and the use of the passive voice in reference to the unseen hand of God.[26]

Theological Analysis

Since the Gospels are about the person and work of Jesus Christ, every passage should be interpreted in light of what the writer intended to say about Him. While many other colorful characters in the Gospels might be the subjects of a good biographical sermon, they are simply the supporting cast. If they are allowed to outshine the Star, more than the writer's intent is missed! For example, the parable of the good Samaritan (Luke 10:30-37), given by Jesus and recorded by Luke, was not written merely to promote human compassion on the horizontal plane. Jesus, who had earlier been derisively called a "Samaritan" (John 8:48), is the one who, unlike the uncompassionate priest and Levite (religious leaders of Israel), demonstrated the Father's concern. The parable is about who Jesus is, not just about being a good neighbor.

Matthew

Historical Background

"Matthew is the gospel written by a Jew to Jews about a Jew," say Wilkinson and Boa. "Matthew is the writer, his countrymen are the readers and Jesus Christ is the subject."[27] The writer, identified in the title, *Kata Matthaion* ("according to Matthew"), was also called Levi (Mark 2: 14; Luke 5:27). Matthew's authorship and its early date of writing (before the fall of Jerusalem in A.D. 70) have been rejected by scholars who assume the priority of Mark's Gospel and the impossibility of Jesus predicting Jerusalem's ruin.[28] However, Guthrie concludes that "there is no conclusive reason for rejecting the strong external testimony regarding the authorship of Matthew.[29] Whether or not he originally wrote his Gospel (or notes for it) in Aramaic, as some have suggested, the Greek edition was most likely written in Antioch, Syria, between A.D. 58 and 68.[30] The son of Alphaeus, Matthew bore the social stigma of a publican, collecting taxes in Capernaum for the Roman government (Mark 2:14).

Literary Analysis

Greidanus identifies five teaching sections, all having to do with the kingdom of heaven:

1. The law of the kingdom (5-7)
2. Preachers of the kingdom (10:5-42)
3. Parables about the kingdom (13:1-52)
4. Life in the kingdom (18:1-35)
5. The consummation of the kingdom (24:1-25:46)[31]

The chiastic structure of Matthew places the parables of the kingdom of chapter 13 at the prominent center for emphasis.[32] (See figure 13-1.[33])

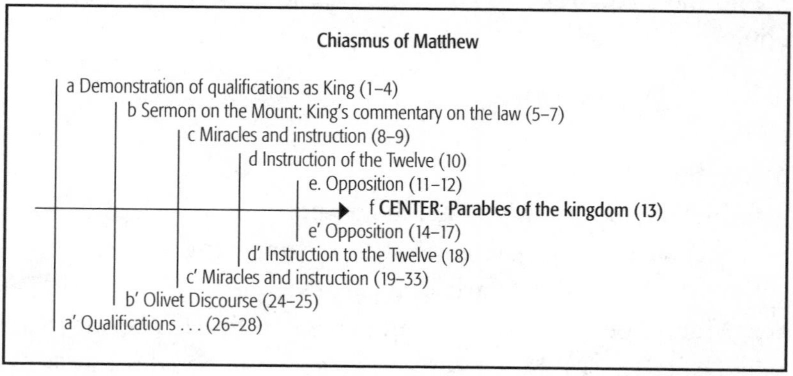

Figure 13.1

Theological Understanding

Matthew wrote to present Jesus as Israel's messianic King, beginning with David's son. He also explains to the followers of Jesus the postponement of His rule on David's throne as a result of His rejection by Israel's leaders, and describes the nature of His present rule in the hearts of those who receive Him.

There is a great emphasis on Gentiles in Matthew. He mentions the magi (2:1), Christ's church (16:18), church discipline (18), and "all the nations" (28:19 NKJV).[34] Tenney explains this frequent emphasis: "Matthew's Gospel is admirably suited to a church which was still closely related to Judaism, though becoming increasingly independent of it. It breathes the atmosphere of Messianism, yet it has a message for 'all the world.'"[35] He adds, "The Theme of the Gospel of Matthew is announced by its opening words: 'The book of the generation of Jesus Christ, the son of David, the son of Abraham' (Matt. 1:1)."[36] Even in the genealogy designed to show Jesus' descent from King David, Gentiles are prominent. Boaz, for example, was the son of a Canaanite prostitute, and Ruth was a descendant of Moab. The mention of Tamar and Bathsheba is also important to Matthew's purpose, as was his omission of the names of certain bad kings. Jesus is the King of Gentiles as well as of Jews, but entering and participating in His future Davidic (millennial) kingdom is conditional. It is the reward for the faithfulness of those who have received, by faith, the free gift of deliverance from the consequences of their sins.

Mark

Historical Background

Many writers believe that Mark is the earliest of the synoptic Gospels.[37] But whether or not it is the earliest, it is surely the shortest and simplest. The writer is John Mark, Barnabas's cousin (Col. 4:10), whose mother, Mary, opened her home in Jerusalem as a meeting place for believers (Acts 12:12). Based on Peter's greeting to Mark as "my son," in 1 Peter 5:13 (NKJV), Peter may have been the one to lead Mark to faith in Christ. If Mark was the "certain young man" in Gethsemane who followed Jesus wearing only a linen cloth (Mark 14:51-52 NKJV), then he was an eyewitness of some events about which he wrote. But it is generally assumed that Peter was the source of Mark's information, lending the Gospel his apostolic authority.[38]

Mark accompanied Saul and Barnabas on their missionary journeys but left early to return home to Jerusalem (Acts 13:13). Because Paul then refused to allow Mark to join him and Barnabas on their second journey, Barnabas took Mark and went to Cyprus, while Paul took Silas to Syria and Cilicia (Acts 15:36-41). About twelve years later, though, Mark was with Paul in his first imprisonment (Col. 4:10, Philem. 24). At the end of his life, Paul sent for Mark, commending him for his beneficial service (2 Tim. 4: 11).

Mark's authorship of the Gospel that bears his name was accepted by the early church without exception. He is thought to have written before A.D. 70, since Jesus' prediction of the temple's destruction is treated as unfulfilled in Mark 13:2. The most likely date is sometime between A.D. 55 and 65.[39]

Early tradition indicates that Mark was written to a Roman audience, from Rome.[40] This would explain why he did not include the genealogy of Christ, references to the Law, Jewish customs, fulfilled prophecies, and other items that would not have been meaningful to Gentiles. He also explained several Aramaic words, the language of the Jews, and sometimes substituted Latin words in their place[41]

Literary Analysis

Mark emphasizes the service and suffering of Jesus, punctuating his quick-moving, action-packed account with the word translated "immediately" some forty times.[42] His style is described as "*a popular literary style*, even though it does not rise to the literary standards of the highly educated."[43] The theme of Mark is stated in Mark 10:45: "For even the Son of Man did not come to be served, but to serve, and to give His life a ransom for many" (NKJV). Chapters 1-8 primarily concern Jesus' miracles in Galilee, with chapters 9-16 emphasizing His teaching on His way to the cross. Aune notes that "only once is a storyunit presented out of chronological sequence as a 'flashback': the story of John the Baptist's fate in Mark 6:17-29."[44]

At Caesarea Philippi, after Peter's great confession of faith, in answer to Jesus' question, "Who do you say that I am?" Jesus began to teach them that He would be betrayed into the hands of men and killed, but after three days He would rise again (9:31). The turning point is Jesus' transfiguration, recorded in the middle of the Gospel (9:1-8). Greidanus credits M. Philip Scott for recognizing the chiastic structure of Mark, adapted in figure 13-2.[45]

Theological Understanding

Mark's Gospel begins and ends with declarations of Jesus' deity. As noted in the literary analysis, the turning point begins with 8:27, where Jesus asks, "Who do men say that I am?" (NKJV). This leads to the Father's pronouncement at the Transfiguration, "This is My beloved Son. Hear Him!" (9:7 NKJV). Having demonstrated that He was the Son of God by His miracles (chs. 1-8), and having had that demonstration confirmed by the Father's declaration, Jesus teaches His way to the cross, where a *Roman* centurion would state the truth that Mark wrote his Gospel to establish: "Truly this Man was the Son of God!"

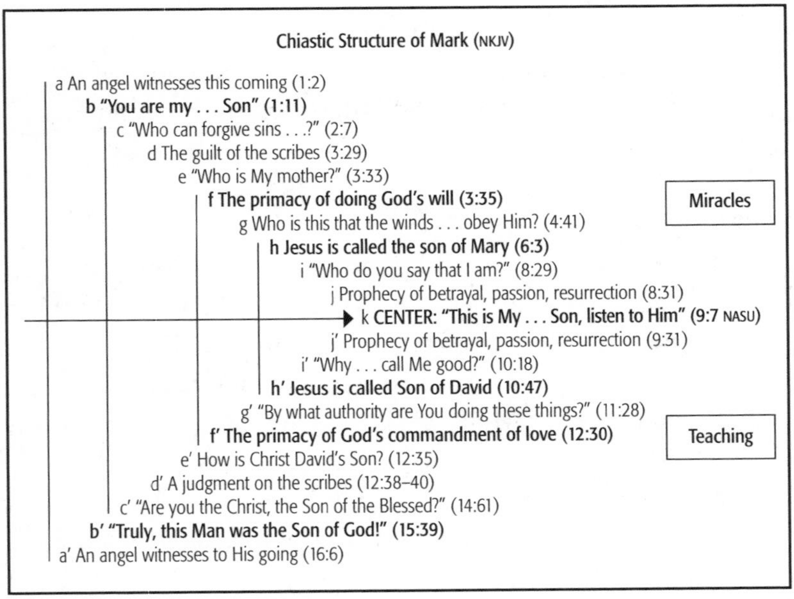
Chiastic Structure of Mark (NKJV)
a An angel witnesses this coming (1:2)
b "You are my . . . Son" (1:11)
c "Who can forgive sins . . .?" (2:7)
d The guilt of the scribes (3:29)
e "Who is My mother?" (3:33)
f The primacy of doing God's will (3:35)
g Who is this that the winds . . . obey Him? (4:41)
h Jesus is called the son of Mary (6:3)
i "Who do you say that I am?" (8:29)
j Prophecy of betrayal, passion, resurrection (8:31)
k CENTER: "This is My . . . Son, listen to Him" (9:7 NASU)
j' Prophecy of betrayal, passion, resurrection (9:31)
i' "Why . . . call Me good?" (10:18)
h' Jesus is called Son of David (10:47)
g' "By what authority are You doing these things?" (11:28)
f' The primacy of God's commandment of love (12:30)
e' How is Christ David's Son? (12:35)
d' A judgment on the scribes (12:38–40)
c' "Are you the Christ, the Son of the Blessed?" (14:61)
b' "Truly, this Man was the Son of God!" (15:39)
a' An angel witnesses to His going (16:6)
Miracles
Teaching

Figure 13.2

Jesus commanded people not to tell about His miracles for several possible reasons. First, He was not seeking publicity. Whenever it came, it made it more difficult for the people. Second, the timing of when He disseminated Church truth was critical. Also, when demons were testifying, their witness had a negative effect.

Luke/Acts

Historical Background

According to the opening statements of the third Gospel, its writer was not an eyewitness to the accounts he records. He was, instead, a well educated historian who certifies the accuracy of his documentation of *others'* eyewitness accounts. His purpose was to establish the historical facts on which the faith of a prominent young man named Theophilus ("Friend of God") might rest.[46] His orderly presentation of the evidence makes a convincing argument that the historical Jesus of oral tradition is indeed the Son of the only true God, the Savior of all men, and worthy of universal worship.

Luke's authorship of the third Gospel is deduced on the basis of two connections: First, the "we sections" of the book of Acts identify its author as Luke the physician (Col. 4:10-14), who accompanied Paul on some of His missionary journeys.[47] Second, the introduction to the book of Acts indicates that it is part two of a two-part series.[48] Acts 1 takes up where Luke 24 leaves off. Writing to the same Theophilus, the writer of Acts refers to the "former account," which almost certainly is the third Gospel: "The former account I made, O Theophilus, of all that Jesus began both to do and teach, until the day in which He was taken up, after He through the Holy Spirit had given commandments to the apostles whom He had chosen, to whom He also presented Himself alive after His suffering by many infallible proofs, being seen by them during forty days and speaking of the things pertaining to the kingdom of God" (1:1-3 NKJV).

If Luke is the writer of both Luke and Acts, as has been traditionally understood, then the date of his writing can be fixed at about A.D. 60 based on three reasonable assumptions. First, enough time must have elapsed between the resurrection of Christ and the writing of Luke's Gospel for the eyewitness accounts of others to have circulated and for Theophilus, a Gentile, to have been attracted to Christianity.[49] Second, the Gospel was written prior to Acts. Third, the fall of Jerusalem, which

Jesus prophesied in Luke 19:41-44 and 21 :20-24, was not mentioned as fulfilled. (It took place in A.D. 70.)[50]

If these assumptions are correct, then Luke is unique among the Gospels in predicting the fall of Jerusalem,[51] and its author is the only Gentile writer of a New Testament book.[52] His Gospel must be read as the logically ordered work of a Gentile writing to a Gentile in order to provide a basis for his faith in Christ. Its profitability for teaching in the Church is, therefore, certified.

Literary Analysis

The "orderly account" Luke presents is arranged more logically than chronologically. The organizing principle is, in the words of Tenney, "the central concept of Jesus as a member of humanity who lived the perfect and representative life of the Son of man through the power of the Holy Spirit."[53] Luke's thesis is stated in 19:9-10: "And Jesus said to [Zacchaeus], 'Today salvation has come to this house, because he also is a son of Abraham; for the Son of Man has come to seek and to save that which was lost'" (NKJV). It suited this purpose of Luke to expand on Jesus' journey from Galilee to Jerusalem, to which Luke devotes the bulk of his writing (9:51-19:27).[54] As literature, Luke is highly praised for its artistic beauty and masterful use of the Greek language.[55]

Thompson follows Charles Talbert in observing in Luke-Acts "a definite chain of authority, with each successor imitating his predecessor: the sequence moves 'from the faithful among the Jewish people, symbolized by John the Baptist … , to Jesus, and from Jesus to the Twelve.' Then from the Twelve, who were sent out by Jesus, the chain of authority passes to Paul and the churches which he founds. Those who belong to that chain are given in Luke an exemplar character."[56]

Greidanus views the structure of both Luke and Acts as consisting of three major parts marked by changes in geography. This may be illustrated as follows. (See figure 13-3.[57])

Theological Understanding

The Gospel of Luke emphasizes the humanity of Christ; His birth; infancy; and compassion for women, children, and the disenfranchised of society. Referring to the Holy Spirit more times than Matthew and

Luke What Jesus began to do and teach:	**Acts** What Jesus continues to do through the people He indwells:
Introduction: Preparation for the Ministry of Jesus (1:5–2:52)	
I. The Ministry in **Galilee** (4:14–9:50)	I. The Ministry in **Jerusalem** (1:12–7:60)
II. The Ministry between **Galilee and Jerusalem** (9:51–19:27)	II. The Ministry in **Judea and Samaria** (8)
III. The Ministry in **Jerusalem** (19:28–23:56)	III. The Ministry to the **End of the Earth** (9:1–28:31)
Conclusion: Consummation of the Ministry of Jesus (24:1–53)	

Figure 13.3

Mark combined.[58] Luke provides the theological basis for how Gentiles, as well as Jews, can participate in the blessings of Abraham. Luke's own skills as an historian, physician, and writer of literature serve to emphasize the nobility of humanity when redeemed by the Son of Man. As Luke follows the movement of Christianity from Galilee to Jerusalem, and from Jerusalem to Rome and the end of the earth, he also stresses the personal progress of discipleship. Leon Morris states, "It is probably significant that Luke speaks a number of times of Christianity as 'the way' (A9:2; 19:9, 23; 22:4; 24:14, 22); sometimes also he refers to it as 'the way of the Lord' (A18:25) and 'the way of God' (A18:26) … It draws attention to Christianity as a whole way of life, not simply as a means of satisfying religious impulses."[59]

The book of Acts was written in Rome, probably before A.D. 64, since there is no mention of the Neronian persecution that occurred after the burning of Rome. Luke maintains his focus on the Spirit in which Christ continues His work through the people He indwells (see Acts 6:10).[60] Acts is a history of the birth and building of the church between A.D. 33 and 62. When interpreting the book, pay careful attention to where a given passage fits into the context of transition from the temporary to the permanent indwelling of the Spirit, and from a focus upon Israel to the equality of Gentiles as full participants in the church. Learn to ask and answer the question, "How was God working at this juncture?"

Not everything *described* in the book of Acts is necessarily *prescribed* for the Church to follow. A helpful guideline is given in the saying, "Apostolic practice points to apostolic principle." This means that the apostles did what they did for a reason. The reader must seek to understand the underlying principle that gave rise to a particular practice rather than dismiss the record of what was done as a mere description of a bygone era. For example, does Luke's record of the casting of lots to determine Judas's replacement (Acts 1:26) simply *describe* what the apostles did? Or does it *prescribe* the way in which matters must be decided today? The underlying theology is that the sovereign God met the apostles' need for direction in a decision that they were biblically responsible to make. The principle of prayerful obedience to Scripture is never outdated and can be honored without necessarily following the Jewish custom of casting lots. (Proverbs 16:33 states, "The lot is cast into the lap, but its every decision is from the LORD" [NKJV].) On the other hand, consider the apostolic practice of baptizing new believers. The fact that every baptism recorded in Acts is *described* as having been done immediately upon the person's confession of faith in Jesus Christ indicates an urgency to obey that is dishonored by unnecessary delays.

John

Historical Background

The fourth Gospel was written by John the apostle after the synoptics, between A.D. 70 and 90. John was evidently a Galilean Jew who may have been one of the disciples of John the Baptist until he was called to follow Jesus at the outset of His public ministry (1:19-51).[61] After the ascension of Jesus, John is mentioned as a pillar of the church at Jerusalem (Gal. 2:9). According to tradition, he later went to Ephesus. He wrote his three epistles and Revelation while in exile on the island of Patmos (Rev. 1:9). John's purpose in writing his Gospel was to supplement the synoptic Gospels with a different emphasis.

Literary Analysis

In contrast to Matthew, Mark, and Luke, John structures his Gospel to emphasize the descent of the Word, who became flesh, and His ascent to glory[62] after having manifested the life that is in the Father, died for the sins of the world, and risen from the grave.

In the first part of John's Gospel, chapters 2-12, John records seven miracles that Christ performed publicly. Each one pointed to His deity as the Master of His creation and was associated with a discourse in which Jesus identified Himself with Yahweh (The I AM...Who Is). He says, for example, "I Am the Bread of life," "I Am the Light of the world," etc. In this way, John lays the basis for his reader's saving faith in Christ.

In chapters 13-20, John records the words and events that prepare Christ's people to live the abundant and fruitful lives of joy and unity in the Holy Spirit until He comes to take them home.

The following diagram represents another way to trace the development of John's Gospel. (See figure 13-4.[63])

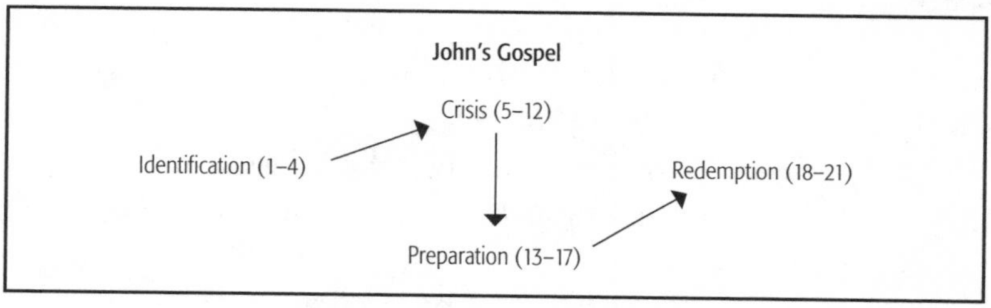

Figure 13.4

Theological Understanding

John 1:1-18 emphasizes the deity of Christ. He is the uncreated Creator, yet He is distinct from the Father, whom He came into the world to *exegete*! The living Word became flesh to bring light, life, and love to all who receive Him by faith. The statement of John's purpose in 20:30-31 is usually misunderstood as a message of how sinners may be justified.[64] But John writes about eternal life–not in terms of how to get it, but how to be enjoying it now[65]: "And truly Jesus did many other signs in the presence of His disciples, which are not written in this book; but these are written that you may believe that Jesus is the Christ, the Son of God, and that believing you may have life in His name" (NKJV). John writes so that those of His readers who have, in fact, believed that Jesus is the Christ, the Son of God, might, "by [continually] believing," "keep on having [the quality of] life [that is] in His name."[66]

Sample Sermon # 1
Why The Son Descended

John 3:10-16
The Son of God Came Down to Lift Men Up To Glory

I. The Witness of Heavenly Things (10-13)
  A. The Understanding of Spiritual Truth Is a Personal Responsibility (10)
  B. The Witness of Spiritual Truth Must Be Received (11)
  C. Christ is the Revealer of Heavenly Things (12-13)

II. The Gift of Eternal Life (14-16)
  A. Pictured in the Serpent
    1. Lifted up (14)
    2. Looked to with faith in God (15)
  B. Provided in the Son (16)
    1. Because the Father Loved the World
    2. Because the Son is Uniquely Begotten

Sample Sermon #2
The Importance of Official Service in the Church

Acts 6:1-7
Official Service Reflects the Lord and Advances His Mission

I. The Mission of the Church (1,7)
  A. The Spread of God's Word (7)
  B. Increasing the Number of Disciples (1, 7)
  C. Obedience to the Faith (7)

II. The Management of the Church (1-6)
  A. Leaders Attack Problems (1b-3)
  B. Leaders Apply Principles (2)
  C. Leaders Establish Priorities (3-4)
  D. Leaders Delegate Power (3, 6)
  E. Congregations Participate (5-6)

Sample Sermon #3
Action or Apathy: What We Need To Learn From the Good Samaritan Story

Luke 10:25-37 (NKJV)

Introduction:

Why I like this parable:

It concerns a lawyer, which, having been a law professor for a number of years, has interest for me in his method of argument and perspective.

It reveals how a person approaches the task of interpreting the Bible, whether in a normal sense or a spiritualizing sense.

It reveals the heart of humans, who are able to find so many ways to avoid the plain requirements of Christ.

It demonstrates that the task of the Christian does not end with traditional religious service but goes beyond our words to actions, similar to God.

I. Good Questions Can Have Bad Motives (v. 25)
   Luke 10:25: And behold, a certain lawyer stood up and tested Him, saying, "Teacher, what shall I do to inherit eternal life?"
   A. The Example of the Lawyer
      "What must I do to inherit eternal life?" *Seeking to test Him.*
   B. Other Examples in the Bible
      1. "Why does He still find fault? For who has resisted His will?" (Rom. 9:19) *Seeking to place blame on God for man's condemnation.*
      2. "Why have you made me like this?" (Rom. 9:20) *Seeking to blame God for our own sinfulness.*
      3. "Why did I not die at birth? Why did I not perish when I came from the womb?" (Job 3:11) *Questioning God's goodness and direction in his life.*
   C. How and Why Have We Questioned God?
      1. Why did God let this happen to me?
      2. Why did God take my loved one?
      3. What are our motives?

II. Good Answers Can Have Inadequate Application (vv. 26-28)
Luke 10:26: He said to him, "What is written in the law? What is your reading of it?"
Luke 10:27: So he answered and said, "'You shall love the LORD your God with all your heart, with all your soul, with all your strength, and with all your mind,' and 'your neighbor as yourself.'"
Luke 10:28: And He said to him, "You have answered rightly; do this and you will live."
   A. The Lawyer's Response: A Great and Theologically Correct Answer
      1. This lawyer had his understanding of Old Testament theology down pat.
      2. He did not understand, however, the implications that arose from his theology.
   B. How Do We Respond?
      1. Sometimes we fail to do what is right because we do not have our theology straight: this is ignorance.
         a. Not being baptized
      2. Sometimes we fail to do what is right in spite of having good theology: this is slothfulness, if not rebellion.
         a. Failing to see God's control in our lives when we have a flat tire

III. People Sometimes Have Improper Responses to God's Direction (v. 29)
Luke 10:29: But he, wanting to justify himself, said to Jesus, "And who is my neighbor?"
   A. The lawyer, after being confronted with his own understanding of truth, sought to alleviate his guilt.
   B. Our attempts:
      1. There's not enough time in the day.
      2. Somebody else will do it.
      3. Be warmed, and be fed.
      4. It won't make a difference.
      5. I would, but …

IV. God's Teaching on Fulfilling the Second Table of the Law: Love Your Neighbor as Yourself (vv. 30-35)

Luke 10:30: Then Jesus answered and said: "A certain man went down from Jerusalem to Jericho, and fell among thieves, who stripped him of his clothing, wounded him, and departed, leaving him half dead." Luke 10:31: "Now by chance a certain priest came down that road. And when he saw him, he passed by on the other side."

Luke 10:32: "Likewise a Levite, when he arrived at the place, came and looked, and passed by on the other side."

Luke 10:33: "But a certain Samaritan, as he journeyed, came where he was. And when he saw him, he had compassion."

Luke 10:34: "So he went to him and bandaged his wounds, pouring on oil and wine and he set him on his own animal, brought him to an inn, and took care of him."

Luke 10:35: "On the next day, when he departed, he took out two denarii, gave them to the innkeeper, and said to him, 'Take care of him; and whatever more you spend, when I come again, I will repay you.'"

A. How Not to Interpret a Parable, Particularly This One

"A **certain man** went down from Jerusalem to Jericho"; **Adam himself** is meant;

Jerusalem is the heavenly city of peace, from whose **blessedness Adam** fell;

Jericho means the moon, and signifies our **mortality**, because it is born, waxes, wanes, and dies.

Thieves are the **devil and his angels**.

"Who **stripped him**," namely, of his immortality; and beat him, by persuading him to sin; and left him **half-dead**, because **insofar as man can understand and know God, he lives, but insofar as he is wasted and oppressed by sin, he is dead**; he is therefore called half-dead.

The **priest and Levite** who saw him and passed by, signify the **priesthood** and **ministry of the Old Testament**, which could profit nothing for salvation.

Samaritan means "**Guardian**," and therefore the Lord Himself is signified by this name.

The **binding** of the wounds is the **restraint of sin**.
Oil is the **comfort of good hope**; **wind** the **exhortation to work with fervent spirit**.
The **beast** is the **flesh in which He deigned to come** to us.
The **being set upon the beast** is **belief in the incarnation** of Christ.
The **inn** is the **Church**, where travelers returning to their heavenly country are refreshed after pilgrimage.
The **morrow is after the resurrection** of the Lord.
The **two pence** are either the **precepts of love or the promise of this life and of that which is to come**.
The **innkeeper** is the **apostle (Paul)**. The supererogatory payment is either his counsel of celibacy or the fact that he worked with his own hands, lest he should be a burden to any of the weaker brethren when the Gospel was new, though it was lawful for him to live by the Gospel.

B. Possible Responses to the Wounded Man in the Story
  1. The wounded man made a bad decision: this road was treacherous.
     a. Do we hold that against him and use this as an excuse not to help?
     b. We are not talking about professional beggars who are making lots of money and simply too lazy to hold down a job. The beggars helped by Christ and the apostles were truly in need (usually blind or lame), with no one to help them.
  2. Should We Respond as the Priest and Levite? (people highly conscious of their religious responsibilities)
     a. Religiosity without compassion Too busy in doing God's work (the first table of the Law) to obey God's commands toward fellow humans (the second table of the Law): Are these really in conflict?

        This really is an illustration of what Christ sought to teach to the leaders and people throughout His whole ministry.

1) The leaders especially saw themselves exempt from their need to have compassion on others and help them, because they were trying to center on God's detailed laws on purity, to the exclusion of helping one's neighbor.
2) Christ's example:
    a) Sabbath versus caring for infirm
    b) Sabbath versus disciples being hungry
    c) Paying all the monetary requirements of the Law, but leaving responsibilities of other things (mercy, compassion. justice) undone

3. The Samaritan interrupted his busy life to help someone who probably despised him.
    a. Samaritans and Jews did not get along well.
    b. The Samaritan not only saw and expressed concern but went the extra mile.

V. The Question [s Turned Around: From "Who is *my* neighbor?" to "Who is neighbor?" (v. 36)
Luke 10:36: "So which of these three do you think was neighbor to him who fell among the thieves?"
    A. You can find your neighbor when you are willing to be neighborly.
    B. You don't have to scour the forests to find a neighbor, but simply respond to those whom God reveals along your daily journey.

VI. Christ's command is short but unequivocal:
Go and do the same as the good Samaritan (v. 37)
Luke 10:37: And he said, "He who showed mercy on him."
Then Jesus said to him, "Go and do likewise."*

*Scriptures in this outline are from the New King James Version.

Summary and Conclusion

The Gospels and Acts are themselves *bridge material* in their role of linking the old and new covenants. Be careful to treat these historical books of the New Testament as connecting links that have continuity, while at the same time recognizing the things that must be kept separate. The Gospels teach theology through a variety of literary genre, but are distinguished by their contribution to what was proclaimed by the early church, the *kerygma*. If reduced either to mere historical accounts or stories, the Gospels are misunderstood. In reality they are historical stories, which must be understood by appreciating why their factual information was selected and arranged the way it was by a particular author.

When selecting sermon texts, be sure they express a *complete* thought, or literary unit. Comparing a text with parallel accounts in other Gospels will help you determine the given author's intent. Harmonies of the Gospels can also help establish a temporal framework within which to view a given text. Proper interpretation of a text depends on asking the right questions when completing a *truth sheet* as part of the Whiting Method. Put yourself in the life situations of both the characters of the narrative and the writer. To do this, you must carefully consider the historical background, literary analysis, and theological understanding of the writer and those about whom he is writing. To preach from the Gospel of Matthew, pay attention to the kingdom emphasis of the book. How does the text fit into Matthew's purpose of explaining to Gentiles as well as Jews the nature of the kingdom during this time in which the King is not reigning on David's throne? The chiastic structure of the book focuses attention on the parables, which address this very issue of the inter-Advent kingdom.

Mark must be appreciated for its reflection of Peter's influence of the content, and the Roman audience which he addresses. It also has a chiastic structure centered in the Father's declaration of Jesus' sonship at the Transfiguration. The record of miracles leading up to this point demonstrates His supernatural character as God. The record of His teaching on the way to the cross emphasizes His servanthood.

Luke and Acts are best understood as two parts of a whole. The emphasis of his Gospel upon the perfect humanity of Christ suited his Greek audience (represented by Theophilus), who needed to know that Israel's Messiah also deserved the worship of Gentiles, since He "came to seek and to save that which was lost" (Luke 19:9-10 NKJV). Luke's Gospel and the book of Acts are both structured with three major parts marked by changes in geography. The concept of movement toward the goal of mature discipleship also seems to be reflected by Luke's emphasis upon Christianity as "the way." Acts traces the birth and building of the Church as the ongoing work of Christ, by His indwelling Holy Spirit. Always interpret texts in Acts in view of what God is doing at the time. The book is transitional, and what is *described* (practices) is not always *prescribed*, so wisely seek the *abiding principles* which underlay the apostles' *practices*.

John's Gospel, written later than the synoptics, is concerned with who Jesus is as the living Word who became flesh, to demonstrate the truth, life, and love of the Father. John emphasizes the enjoyment of eternal life through the continual exercise of faith in Jesus, whose worthiness of such trust was attested by the seven signs John records, and by the statements and discourses in which Jesus claims equality with Yahweh.

Discussion Questions

1. Explain, in your own words, what is meant by *New Testament*. In relation to what is it new, and how so?

2. Explain the difference between the *gospel* and the *Gospels*.

3. What is meant by the following terms?

   a. Kerygma
   b. Higher criticism
   c. Textual criticism
   d. Source criticism
   e. Synoptic problem

4. What is the objective when selecting a text from the Gospels or Acts for preaching? (What determines its parameters?)

5. What are some of the interpretive questions that are particularly important to ask of Gospel texts?

6. Whose life situation must the preacher seek to understand when interpreting the Gospels, and why?

7. Describe the concerns of each of the following:

    a. Historical background
    b. Literary analysis
    c. Theological understanding

8. Explain the value of recognizing chiasmus in the structure of Matthew and Mark.

9. Give several reasons for concluding Lukan authorship of the third Gospel and Acts.

10. Describe several ways in which the Gospel of John differs from the synoptics.

11. Find two commendable qualities and two negative observations about each of the sample sermons provided in this chapter.

CHAPTER 14

Preaching the Epistles

Introduction

Compared to the gulf that separates the modern Bible student from the world of the Old Testament, the Gospels, and Acts, the New Testament Epistles are closer to home. They would seem to call for a verbal bridge that is simpler for the preacher to construct. The Epistles consist of letters sent to churches and individual Christians with whom we find it easier to identify. In many cases their recipients were Gentiles–sometimes even Europeans! Their contents address many of the same problems with which we are still dealing in this church age. If the recipients of John's first epistle were living in the "last hour" (1 John 2:18 NKJV), we are more so. So, less effort would seem to be required to demonstrate the relevance of their content. When interpreting the New Testament Epistles, we have only (what Greidanus calls) "one horizon," not two, on which to focus our attention.[1]

While all of these observations may be true, it would be easy to exaggerate the ease of preaching the Epistles. For one thing, they are more closely related to the Gospels than one might imagine.[2] Ryken says, "Everything considered, the New Testament epistles are an extension of the Gospels. Both were written by authoritative Christian leaders and both existed to explain the life and teachings of Jesus."[3] Also, while the narrative of much of the Old Testament, Gospels, and Acts presents its challenges to the interpreter, the Epistles present difficulties of their own.[4] They tend to be more didactic, technical, and abstract, if not less personable. Again, it is Ryken who states, "The personality of the writers is much less important than the religious content of their letters. The writers, indeed, do not write primarily as individual persons but in their roles as apostles–as the conveyors of divine truth in a manner reminiscent of the Hebrew prophets."[5] Of the Epistles, Greidanus writes, "They are full of detailed truth and careful shades of meaning. In them every single word is full of significance. Expounding them therefore calls for hard work by the preacher before he can even begin to put a message together."[6]

On the other hand, the Epistles have a quality that has been called "situational immediacy," meaning that they were written not as essays in systematic theology, but in response to specific people living in real places and struggling with common problems. For this reason, the amount of space given to an issue may be disproportional to its importance apart from a local controversy or specific question (e.g., the discussion of celibacy in 1 Corinthians 7, or tongues in 1 Corinthians 12-14).

Our goal again in this chapter is to survey the basic factors of historical background, literary analysis, and theological understanding so that the reader will have a handle on how to use the Whiting Method to prepare sermons to deliver God's message.

The Genre of Epistle

Epistle

Most of the New Testament books (twenty-one of twenty-seven) are classified as epistles. The word epistle is a transliteration of the Greek word ἐπιστολή (*epistole*, pronounced *ep-is-tol-ay*), which means "a written message."[7] While the New Testament Epistles bear the marks of private letters occasioned by specific issues, they were evidently written with a consciousness of apostolic authority (see Romans 1:1; 1 Corinthians 1:1; 2 Corinthians 1:1; 2 Thessalonians 3:14, etc.) and intended for circulation (I Thess. 5:27; Col. 4:16). That the Epistles were written in response to particular concerns, however, takes them out of the category of *theological treatises*.[8] In other words, they are not systematic, abstract, exhaustive treatments of the subjects they address.

Rather, they are always focused on, and therefore somewhat limited by, their applicability to the situation either of the writer or his readers. According to Aune, "the overlap between letter and speech suggests two important dimensions for understanding the former. First, oratory was very important in the Greco-Roman world and rhetoric occupied a central role in ancient education."[9] In this way, the Epistles are more like sermons—especially those that were dictated to a scribe.[10] Ryken states, "Paul, moreover, composed most of his letters orally while dictating them to a secretary. As a result, New Testament epistles and oratories show great similarity in style."[11] Because this is true, when the Epistles are understood in the context of the historical situation of both writer and reader, their relevance for preaching today is often obvious.

Literary Devices

Like the Gospel genre, the Epistles include various other literary forms. According to Greidanus, "we find the narrative genre in Gal 1:13-2:21; apocalyptic in 1 Thess 4:13-5:11; a hymn in Phil 2:6-11; and wisdom in Gal 5:9; 6:7; 1 Cor. 15:33; and 2 Cor. 9:6."[12] In addition, Greidanus finds a liturgical formula in 1 Timothy 3:16, a creedal affirmation in Colossians 1:15-20, lists of vices and virtues in Romans 1:29-31 and Galatians 5:22-23, clusters of imperatives in Colossians 3, and reliance on figurative language.[13]

With regard to Paul's use of sources, Guthrie states that "the passages from the Epistles point to a primitive substratum on which the major Pauline doctrines were based…The most important passage is 1 Corinthians xv. 1-7 where the apostle clearly states that he preaches what had been delivered to him. The same emphasis is found in Romans i:4, viii. 34 … Dodd finds two other aspects of primitive preaching, eschatology (Rom. i.16; I Thes. i. 10) and the work of the Holy Spirit in the believer (Gal. iv. 6)."[14]

Paul may also have been influenced by early catechetical forms that appear in his writings as "faithful sayings," according to Guthrie,[15] who also observes the incorporation of hymnic literature into Paul's writing: "The apostle recognized the value of rhythmic expressions of Christian truth and would not have regarded these, as some scholars have tended to do, as steps away from the nobler heights of creative thinking towards a stereotyped formality. But hymns are more easily remembered than abstract statements of truth (e.g. 1 Cor. xiii.)."[16]

Virtually every rhetorical device discussed in this book appears in the Epistles. For examples, Greidanus observes Paul's use of *dialogue*, or *diatribe*, as he argues his points with an imaginary opponent who poses pertinent questions in passages such as 1 Corinthians 15:35-36. He notices Paul's sevenfold *repetition* of the word "one" in Ephesians 4:4-6 (see NKJV), and how it builds to the *climax* with his threefold repetition of the word "all" in verse 6.[17] "Grace and peace," are sometimes used to form an *inclusio*, unifying the text it encircles. An example of *chiasm* is found in 1 Corinthians 12, 13, and 14, in which chapter 13 forms the prominent center emphasizing love, between 12 and 14, which both discuss spiritual gifts.[18] Other examples include various kinds of parallelism,[19], antithesis,[20] and metaphor.[21] When recognized and understood, figures of speech not only enhance the interpretation of a passage but provide the preacher with an abundance of illustrative material to enlighten his listeners.

Form

According to Greidanus, letters at the time of the apostles typically consisted of an introduction, a body, and a conclusion. Wilkinson and Boa comment on the New Testament adaptation of this simple form:

> This shell was filled with the richness of revelation, and a transformation took place that makes it appropriate to call these writings epistles as well as letters. Their literary quality and length distinguished them from ordinary letters. Even Philemon (355 words) is considerably longer than the usual letters of Paul's day which easily fit on one sheet of papyrus. Paul's epistles required a number of these sheets to be joined and rolled into scrolls.[22]

In addition to being greater in length and spiritual depth, Paul's epistles added the elements of thanksgiving and exhortation.[23] Observing the resulting pattern helps the interpreter outline the argument of the book to see where the parts fit into the whole, and where an element may have been omitted, added, or changed for some reason.[24]

(See figure 14-1.[25])

Typical First-Century Letter	Typical Pauline Epistle
Introduction: (sender, addressee, greeting)	Opening: (sender, addressee, greeting)
	Thanksgiving
Body	Body
	Exhortation
Conclusion: (Greetings, prayer sentence, sometimes a date)	Closing: (Peace wish, greetings, warning, benediction)

Figure 14.1

Epistle of James

Historical Background

The Lord's half-brother James (see Galatians 1:19) wrote the earliest epistle, around A.D. 44-46, not long before the Jerusalem Council, over which he presided (see Acts 15: 13). Tenney establishes that "the church was still within the general circle of Judaism before it [became] an independent movement."[26] This was during the phase in which the Church was reaching out to Gentiles (Acts 11:19-15:35), and probably before Paul's first missionary journey.

Literary Analysis

James has been compared to the book of Proverbs and to the Sermon on the Mount because it deals with the practical application of supernatural wisdom to ethical behavior. Wilkinson and Boa's describe the writing:

> James writes with a very concise. authoritative, and unvarnished style. Combining pithy maxims of Wisdom Literature with the impassioned rhetoric of Amos, James' pointed barbs are born out of an uncompromising ethical stance. His

> Greek is of a good quality and he communicates his thoughts effectively by means of vivid imagery (especially from nature), illustrations, and figures of speech. This is a formal and sometimes severe epistle, authoritatively written and full of imperatives (54 in 108 verses).[27]

Theological Understanding

When James asserts that faith by itself is dead, he does not mean that it is nonexistent or that his readers, whom he calls "my beloved brethren," (James 1:16; 1:19; 2:5) are not justified. He rather urges his readers to demonstrate the reality of their faith by performing the good works it produces. "James wrote this incisive and practical catalog of the characteristics of true faith to exhort his Hebrew-Christian readers to examine the reality of their own faith ... James also rebukes those who succumb to the pursuit of worldly pleasure and wealth rather than God, and encourages patient endurance in light of the coming of the Lord."[28]

Epistles of Paul Before His Imprisonment

Galatians

Historical Background

If "the churches of Galatia" (1:2 NKJV) refers to those of Lystra, Iconium, and Pisidian Antioch, planted by the apostle Paul on his first missionary journey, then the epistle may have been written as early as A.D. 48. This would explain why no mention is made of the decision of the Jerusalem Council which dealt with the same issue of Judaizers attempting to mix the gospel of grace with works of the Law.[29] Paul seems to have written from Syrian Antioch.

Literary Analysis

Paul develops his argument beginning with personal vindication, in chapters 1-2, and moves to his polemical presentation in 3-4, before concluding with practical application in 5-6.

Theological Understanding

Tenney views Paul's epistle to the Galatians as "a protest against corruption of the gospel of Christ."[30] The theological impact of this "Magna Charta of spiritual emancipation,"[31] as it has been called, can hardly be overstated. According to Radmacher, Allen, and House, "in the whole Bible, there is no more passionate, comprehensive, yet concise statement of the truth of the gospel than Galatians. Salvation through faith in Jesus Christ alone (2:16; 3:11, 12). No work can earn salvation. Paul's succinct refutation of the Judaizers in this letter has transformed the lives of many–from Martin Luther to John Wesley."[32]

The Christian life is lived not by keeping rules, suppressing the flesh, eradicating the sin nature, or by *self*-crucifixion, but by realizing one's *co*crucifixion with Christ.

1 and 2 Thessalonians

Historical Background

Paul is thought to have written both of his epistles to the church at Thessalonica, from Corinth, within a few months of each other, in A.D. 50-52. Launstein explains the apostle's movement as follows:

> Following the Macedonian vision at Troas, Paul went to Philippi where the Gospel met with some success. This success resulted in persecution and imprisonment. After their release from prison they went through Amphipolis and Apollonia (Acts 17:1) and came to Thessalonica, where they stayed at least for three Sabbaths, and maybe up to six weeks. While Paul was in Athens he sent Timothy back to Thessalonica to check on their spiritual welfare (I Thess. 3:1-2). Paul went to Corinth (Acts 18:1) where Timothy and Silas joined him (Acts 18:5). Timothy reported to Paul concerning the Thessalonian believers and Paul then wrote the first epistle.[33]

Literary Analysis

Tenney describes the content of 1 Thessalonians as twofold: "praise for the steadfastness of the Thessalonians under persecution by the Jews and the correction of certain errors and misunderstandings that had grown up among them."[34]

Second Thessalonians communicates Paul's consolation concerning the Lord's return in chapter 1, correction concerning the Second Coming in chapter 2, and commands in view of the Second Coming in chapter 3.[35]

Theological Understanding

Whereas Galatians addressed the problem with Jewish Christians, 1 Thessalonians deals with Gentile converts to Christianity who need correction and instruction regarding sexual morality, social conduct, the state of dead believers, and church discipline. Though James had mentioned the Lord's coming in James 5:7-8, the Thessalonian epistles have the earliest full discussion of the coming of the Lord for His Church.[36] Paul's purpose is primarily to comfort his readers with instruction of Christ's coming *for* His saints.

The second epistle was written to correct some misunderstandings regarding the day of the Lord. Some in the church had stopped working for a living. Paul's remedial instruction informs the church about the Antichrist and tells of Christ's coming *with* His saints.

1 and 2 Corinthians

Historical Background

Without any training in the Hebrew Scriptures, the church at Corinth presented Paul with nagging problems that stemmed from their pagan background.[37] Located on the narrow isthmus that connected the main part of Greece with the island of Achaia, Corinth was a crossroads city of some 700,000 people at the time when Paul wrote.[38] It was known for the Isthmian games, its love of philosophy, and for the sexual immorality that was fostered by the worship of Aphrodite.[39] Having planted the church on his first missionary journey, Paul's concern for their spiritual maturity became the occasion for writing to them while staying in Ephesus in A.D. 55. In his first letter he commends Apollos for having had a good ministry there. (See Acts 18:24; 19:1; and 1 Corinthians 1:12; 3:4-6, 22; 4:6; and 16:12.) The church must have had a visit from Peter as well, or it is unlikely that they would have formed a Cephas party, as is indicated in 1 Corinthians 1:12.

In 1 Corinthians 5, Paul refers to having written an earlier letter concerning the church's need to separate themselves from professing believers who continued in immorality.[40] Having heard rumors of their unsatisfactory response to the first letter, and also wanting to thank them for the gift they had sent to him in Ephesus by Stephanas, Fortunatus, and Achaicus, Paul writes what has survived as 1 Corinthians.

Second Corinthians was written from Macedonia around A.D. 57, partly to express Paul's relief upon Titus's good report of their response to the letter we call 1 Corinthians, and to defend his apostleship against opponents in the church.[41] Paul also urges the Corinthians to follow through on their commitment to contribute to the needs of the saints in Jerusalem, and to prepare them for a third visit during which he hopes there will no longer be a need to speak to them with the severity required in his letters.

Literary Analysis

The content of 1 Corinthians is arranged in the order in which Paul addressed the problems reported to him. Chapters 1-4 concern division in the church. Chapters 5-6 deal with the resulting disorder. Chapters 7-14 are devoted to various difficulties the church is facing. Paul concludes his epistle by clarifying the doctrine of the resurrection of Christ.

Harvey cites Charles Talbert's work on the Corinthian correspondence in noting that chiasmus, inclusion, ring-composition, and the ABA' pattern "alert us to expect numerous examples of oral patterning in 1 Corinthians."[42]

The unevenness and rugged style of 2 Corinthians reflects the emotional interaction of Paul with his readers.[43] It is personal to the point of being almost autobiographical. The very factors that make 2 Corinthians difficult to outline or arrange under a single theme also account for its great value as a commentary on the nature of a minister and his ministry. Paul's defends his ministry in chapters 1-7. He upholds his collection for the saints in chapters 8-9. He defends his apostolic authority in chapters 10-13.

Theological Understanding

First Corinthians is about the life and problems of a carnal local church. Paul's purpose is to deliver the church from division and disorder. Paul skillfully addresses people proud of their wisdom, oratory, and liberty. He shows the practical implications of the centrality of Christ for their concepts of wisdom, sexual morality, discipline, marriage, worship, spiritual gifts, love, and the resurrection.

Second Corinthians reveals the nature of the ministry and the authority of the minister. If Paul had not experienced opposition and conflict, and then felt the need to speak of it from his heart, we would not have the record of God's self-disclosure of the God of all comfort (1:3-4), the fragrance of Christ (2:15), the letter written on human hearts (3:3), the believer's transformation from glory to glory (3:18), the believer's treasure in earthen vessels (4:7-10), the Christian's new creation (5: 17), the ministry of reconciliation (5:18-20), the importance of spiritual separation from unbelievers (6:14), the ministry of giving as Christ gave (8:9; 9:7), and the sufficiency of God's grace (12:9).

Romans

Historical Background

Written by Paul from Corinth in A.D. 57, the Epistle to the Romans was occasioned by Paul's plan to visit the church at Rome (Acts 19:21).[44] He wrote partly to solicit support for his plans to take the gospel to Spain (Rom. 15:24), but primarily to firmly establish the Roman believers in the apostolic teaching of God's plan of salvation for Gentiles as well as for Jews (1:16). It is evident from Romans 1:13 and 15:22, that Paul had been hindered on more than one occasion from visiting Rome, where he had several friends. How the church in Rome was established is unknown. [45]

Literary Analysis

Romans is mostly didactic material, but rich in a variety of literary devices, including dialogue and parallelism, to which the preacher must be alert. Greidanus says, "Rom 3:27-31 provides a compact example of this Hellenistic debating style: 'Then what becomes of our boasting? It is excluded. On what principle? On the principle of works? No, but on the principle of faith ... Do we then overthrow the law by this faith? By no means! On the contrary, we uphold the law' (cf. Rom 2-3, 1 Cor 9, Jas 2)."[46] He further observes that Romans 4:25 is a good example of antithetic parallelism: "*Who was put to death for our trespasses* and *raised for our justification*."[47]

Antithesis, prominent in the Epistles, is exemplified in Romans 5:12-21 and 8:18-39.[48] Other literary and rhetorical devices should be analyzed with the caution suggested by Harvey's comment: "Welch thinks that Romans contains little in the way of chiastic structure. On the other hand, Jouette Bassler identifies instances of ring-composition in her analysis of Romans 1:16-2:29; and Peter Ellis analyzes the entire letter using ABA' and 'chiastic' formats."[49]

Theological Understanding

Romans is clearly and carefully laid out to set forth the good news of how the righteousness of God is needed by all kinds of men, imputed through faith, imparted by the Holy Spirit, consistent with God's program for Israel (past, present, and future), and lived out in service. Douglas Moo, while calling the book a "treatise," or "tractate," states that "Romans is far from being a comprehensive summary of Paul's theology."[50] He concludes, "Romans, then, is a tractate letter and has at its heart a general theological argument, or series of arguments."[51] It emphasizes the power of the gospel (1:16-17); the depravity of man (1:18-32); the universal need of God's righteousness (2-3); the importance and adequacy of faith in appropriating God's righteousness (4-5); the principles, problems, and power of holy living, (6-8); God's sovereignty over Israel's temporary rejection and future restoration (9-11); and the practice of righteousness (12-15).

Epistles of Paul from Prison (Acts 21:17-28:31)

In four of Paul's epistles, Philemon, Ephesians, Colossians, and Philippians, he makes reference to his bonds or chains. The traditional view is that Paul wrote these letters from prison in Rome, between the mid-to-late 50s and the early 60s, though some say he wrote them from Caesarea Maritima, where he was held before being shipped to Rome.[52] References to "Caesar's household" (Phil. 4:22 NKJV) and the praetorian guard (Phil. 1:13), as well as the freedom with which he was visited by friends, tilt the balance in favor of the traditional view. Ellisen notes:

> Though in prison, [Paul] had a measure of liberty, living in "his own hired house, and received all that came in unto him" (Acts 28:30). His opposition at this time was not from the Roman government but from the Jews. Eight workers were present with Paul at this time: Tychicus, Onesimus, Aristarchus, Mark, Jesus Justus (of the circumcision); Gentiles were Epaphras, Luke and Demas (Col. 4:7-14)[53]

Philemon

Historical Background

Onesimus, Philemon's escaped slave, had stolen from his master and run away to Rome, where somehow he met Paul and was won to faith in Christ (Philem. 10). According to Colossians 4:9, he was a native of Colosse. Paul sent him back to Philemon with a request that he be welcomed and forgiven. Paul promised to pay whatever Onesimus owed to Philemon. According to Guthrie, "it has traditionally been supposed that Philemon was a member of the Colossian church, who had in some way been converted to Christianity through the agency of Paul (cf. verse 19)."[54]

Literary Analysis

The letter, though brief and "intensely personal," is also quite theologycal in its illustration of the doctrine of Christian forgiveness.[55] This observation lends weight to the suggestion by U. Wicket that this is "not so much a private letter, but … an apostolic letter about a personal matter."[56] Ellisen outlines the epistle with three divisions: Paul's plea for Philemon (1-7), Paul's plea for Onesimus (8-21), and Paul's plan for himself (22-25).[57]

Harvey notes that the repetition of the word translated "refresh," in verses 7 and 20, "frames the letter-body of Philemon." The repetition of the word "appeal" in verses 8-10, and of "owe" in verses 18-19, form word chains that heighten emphasis.[58]

Theological Understanding

Tenney finds in Philemon "all the elements of forgiveness: the offense (11,18), compassion (10), intercession (10, 18, 19), substitution (18, 19), restoration to favor (15), and elevation to a new relationship (16)."[59] Not only does Paul illustrate what Christ has done for the believer, but he exemplifies the way Christians should treat one another in turn. (See Colossians 3:12-17.) On the matter of slavery, Guthrie's comment is insightful:

> This Epistle brings into vivid focus the whole problem of slavery in the Christian Church. There is no thought of denunciation even in principle. The apostle deals with the situation as it then exists. He takes it for granted that Philemon has a claim of ownership on Onesimus and leaves the position unchallenged. Yet in one significant phrase Paul transforms the character of the master-slave relationship. Onesimus is returning no longer as a slave but as a brother beloved (verse 16). It is clearly incongruous for a Christian master to "own" a brother in Christ in the contemporary sense of the word, and although the existing order of society could not be immediately changed by Christianity without a revolution … the Christian master-slave relationship was so transformed from within that it was bound to lead ultimately to the abolition of the system.[60]

Finally, there is a model for Christian diplomacy in Philemon. Paul appeals to a man whom he could simply order with the authority of his office as an apostle.

Ephesians

Historical Background

Paul took advantage of Onesimus's return to write other letters, which were sent with him and a messenger named Tychicus (Eph. 6:21; Col. 4:7-9) to churches in other cities in Asia, namely Ephesus, Colossae, and Philippi. The writing of these letters was probably in A.D. 60-61.[61] Guthrie describes Ephesians as a circular letter, sent to Laodicea, Paul's spiritual testament, an introduction to Paul's body of writing, intended as a philosophy of religion for the whole Christian world, and as a general safeguard against the spread of the Colossian heresy.[62]

Literary Analysis

Developmentally, Ephesians divides in half, with chapters 1-3 establishing the believer's position in God's sight, and chapters 4-6 emphasizing the believer's walk on earth. As mentioned earlier in this chapter, Ephesians 4:4-6 exemplifies the rhetorical devices of repetition and climax, and Ephesians 6:11-17 is an extended metaphor, in which the armor of a Roman soldier is used to picture the implements of spiritual warfare provided to the believer in Christ.[63] In tone, Ephesians is calm and thoughtful (like Romans), in contrast to Colossians, which expresses strong emotion (like Galatians)[64] Wilkinson and Boa state, "Ephesians abounds with sublime thought and rich vocabulary, especially in chapters 1-3, where theology and worship are intertwined. Many regard it as the most profound book in the New Testament."[65]

Theological Understanding

Ephesians addresses the Church as the universal body of believers rather than responding to a local church issue.[66] The emphasis is on the power of God, the unity of all who are positioned "in Christ" and the need to behave in accordance with what is true of the believer as a result of God's gracious work in his behalf. There is a relatively cool development of such profound doctrines as election, predestination, salvation by grace, eternal security, the church, unity, spiritual gifts, being filled with the Holy Spirit, marriage and family relationships, and spiritual warfare.

Colossians

Historical Background

Colosse, located about one hundred miles east of Ephesus, was a minor city at the time of Paul. Though it had little influence on others, it was greatly influenced by Oriental merchants from the East who passed through the city on their way to Rome.[67] Tenney describes the Colossians as "Phrygian Gentiles (1:27), whose religious antecedents were highly emotional and mystical."[68] Paul had never visited the church that Epaphras founded there.[69] The letter appears to have been prompted by a report brought to Paul by Epaphroditus. Guthrie describes the heresy threatening the Colossian church. "It advocated a rigid observance of the Jewish law together with severe asceticism. There may also have been some form of sun-worship linked with an esoteric doctrine of angels."[70] He surmises that the Colossian error was more like that of the Essenes than the Gnostics.[71]

Literary Analysis

Critics have doubted that Paul wrote Colossians based on differences in its style and theological emphasis from his so-called *main* letters.[72] The argument for his authorship is maintained by others, however, because the specific falsehoods taught in Colosse evoked a stronger tone in response than he used in Ephesians.[73]

Theological Understanding

Colossians is Christological, positively presenting an accurate knowledge of the person and work of Christ as the antidote to error.[74] Guthrie notes the emphasis on the headship of Christ as Paul's basis for strongly opposing the ascetic tendencies in Colosse:

> The Christian is rather to hold to the Head (ii. 19). He is risen with Christ (ii. 12, iii. 1 ff) and should therefore live the risen life. It requires self-mortification (iii. 5), but Paul recognizes the clear distinction between this and rigid asceticism. The Christian is called upon to "put on" the new man (iii. 10) as well as to "put off" the old; positive action is linked with prohibition, in contrast with rigid asceticism which always tends to overstress the negative to the neglect of the positive.[75]

Philippians

Historical Background

Marshall notes that "Philippi was the first major town in ancient Macedonia to be visited by Paul and Silas when they crossed over into Europe from Asia (Acts 16:11-40)."[76] Paul's letter of friendship, fellowship, and thanks is thought to have been penned some ten years later. During this time since the conversions of Lydia and her household (Acts 16:14-15) and the Philippian jailer and his family (Acts 16:31-34), there had been a good response to the gospel. Paul writes in response to the church's loyalty and financial gift.

Literary Analysis

Paul's epistle to Philippi was written more like Romans than Ephesians, perhaps because Philippi was European, not Asian.[77] The most personal letter of Paul not addressed to specific individuals, it is replete with first-personal pronouns.[78] Greidanus observes that Philippians 2:1-11 is a textual unit that contains an ancient hymn.[79] It should not be broken up, but understood as a whole.

Theological Understanding

Philippians is about the joy and responsibility of sharing in the gospel of Christ. Sharing in prayer is the focus of 1:1-11. Sharing in persecution is the concern of 1:12-2:11. Sharing in people's lives is the issue in 2:19-30. Sharing in proper goals is the emphasis of chapter 3; and sharing in practical needs is the subject of chapter 4. Marshall says, "In the main part of the letter that begins in Philippians 1:12 ... Paul relates his experiences in such a way as to provide encouragement for the readers in their trying circumstances."[80]

Pastoral Epistles

According to Homer Kent, "the designation 'Pastoral Epistles' is appropriate for the letters to Timothy and Titus because they contain instruction for pastoral work in churches."[81] But the title is relatively recent,[82] and it is worth noting that Timothy and Titus are never called *pastors* or *elders* (who are charged with the responsibility of shepherding God's flock [1 Pet 5:1-3]).[83] They appear to have functioned as apostolic representatives with authority delegated to them by Paul. Tenney, commenting on the circumstances under which these relationships were developed, says, "Within the range of the Pastoral Epistles there was probably some lapse of time. 1 Timothy pictures Paul as traveling and active, counseling his young lieutenant concerning his pastoral duties. Titus is quite similar in its outlook. 2 Timothy, however, is definitely a terminus, for Paul evidently was confident that he would not survive the winter."[84]

1 Timothy

Historical Background

Hendriksen describes the circumstances under which Paul wrote his first epistle to Timothy. "Hence, about the year 63 Paul, having recently departed from Ephesus where he had left Timothy, and being now in Macedonia (1 Tim. 1:3), tells Timothy *how to administer the affairs of the church*."[83] According to Tenney, "the organization of the church had increased in complexity. Offices had become fixed and were sought by some as affording desirable eminence, so that the prestige of the office rather than its usefulness became the chief objective."[86]

Of Timothy, the *Nelson Study Bible* says,

> Timothy was a native of Lystra in Phrygia (Acts 16: 1-3). His father was Greek, and his mother, Eunice, and grandmother, Lois, were godly Jewish women (2 Tim. 1:5; 3:14, 15). It was through the influence of these women that Timothy learned the Hebrew Scriptures as a child. Paul calls Timothy a "true son in the faith" (1:2), suggesting that he was converted during Paul's first missionary visit to Lystra (Acts 14:6, 19).[87]

Literary Analysis

Because of the very personal style and conversational tone of 1 Timothy, it is not easy to outline. If organized under the general theme or heading "The Work of the Ministry,"[88] however, the three-point outline suggested by Radmacher, Allen, and House serves to trace its development. First Timothy 1:1-20 provides reminders in ministry. *Regulations* in ministry are the concern of 2:1-3:16. The remainder of the book, 4:1-6:21, deal with *responsibilities* of the ministry[89]

Theological Understanding

First Timothy 3:15 summarizes the main purpose of the letter: "I write so that you may know how you ought to conduct yourself in the house of God, which is the church of the living God, the pillar and ground of the truth" (NKJV). "The church is God's primary vehicle for accomplishing His work on earth (Matt. 16:18-20)."[90]

Titus

Historical Background

After Paul left Ephesus, he went to Macedonia, and may have sailed from there to Crete. Having spent some time in Crete, Paul left Titus to organize the unruly church, which reflected the careless, lazy, greedy, and divisive culture for which the islanders were known (Titus 1:12). Titus was a Gentile convert to Christianity from the days of Paul's first missionary journey. When Paul and Barnabas attended the Jerusalem Council, Titus was used as an example of a Greek who did not need circumcision (Gal. 2:1, 3). He is commended as Paul's representative to the church at Corinth (2 Cor. 7:6-16), and for his effectiveness in raising funds in Macedonia (2 Cor. 8:16, 19, 23).

Literary Analysis

Titus is known for its summary of New Testament doctrine stated almost as a formulated creed. "The word 'sound ' implies that a recognized standard of doctrine had been acknowledged, to which correct life and teaching must conform."[91]

Theological Understanding

In the greeting, Titus 1:1-4, Paul "puts all that follows into a spiritual context. The practical and ethical instructions that follow must be understood in its light, and the author continually reminds us of this."[92] The central themes of Christian salvation are compacted into what Tenney calls "a veritable doctrinal digest."[93] Yet Marshall is correct in his assertion that "the letter has a limited purpose, and it will not cover the whole of Christian life and experience. It is slanted in a particular direction to deal with particular problems, and therefore we are not to expect a full exposition of Christian theology from it."[94]

2 Timothy

Historical Background

The circumstances under which Paul wrote his final epistle, 2 Timothy, are quite different from those of the other "pastoral epistles." He is in prison, charging his understudy with the sobering responsibility of withstanding false teachers as a gentle warrior.

Literary Analysis

"The apostle uses everyday illustrations from army life, athletics and agriculture to show that service requires self-discipline, and Timothy must therefore be prepared for some hardship (ii. 3-6)."[95]

Theological Understanding

In view of his own years of faithfully serving the Lord, and seeing the increasing apostasy and persecution on the horizon, Paul instructs Timothy in areas of both his personal and his public life. If 1 Timothy was about the work *of* the ministry, and if Titus was about the work *in* the ministry, then 2 Timothy is about the work *of* the *minister*.[96] Chapter 2 presents a successful ministry as one that is reproducing (2:1-2), enduring (2:3-13), studious (2:14-18), and holy (2:19-26).[97] Not surprisingly, Paul emphasizes Christ and His work to prepare the way for the believer to follow Him to glory. Wilkinson and Boa summarize this emphasis as follows: "Christ Jesus appeared on earth, 'abolished death and brought life and immortality to light through the gospel' (1:10). He rose from the dead (2:8) and provides salvation and 'eternal glory' (2:10); for if believers 'died with *Him*' they will 'also live with *Him* ' (2:11). All who love His appearing will receive the 'crown of righteousness' (4:8) and 'reign with *Him*' (2:12)."[98]

Epistles of the Suffering Church
1 Peter

Historical Background

Peter wrote his first epistle in about A.D. 65-67, a few years after Rome began persecuting Christians. His readers in the provinces of Asia Minor had not yet felt the full effects of this threatening violence but were in need of a crash course in how to face it. They are formed in elder-led congregations (5:1) whose ministries are carried out by the members who are gifted to serve and speak (4:10-11).

Literary Analysis

First Peter is structured with the use of imperatives (thirty-four of them between 1:13 and 5:9),[99] which express a sense of informality and urgency on the part of a man convinced that Christians have a faith worth suffering for! Marshall notes that the word translated *suffer* occurs no less than twelve times, "more than any other book in the New Testament."[100] The epistle breaks down into a twofold outline in which the believer's position is emphasized in 1:1-2:10, and the believer's conduct is emphasized in 2:11-5:14.

Theological Understanding

Peter speaks of the sufferings of Christ in 2:23, 3:18, 4:1, 4:13, and 5:1. He speaks as an eyewitness who knew his own failure until he was impacted by the Resurrection he mentions in 1:3. He speaks of the love of Christ in 1:8 as one who had been asked, "Simon, son of Jonah, do you love Me?" NKJV (see John 21:15-19). He exhorts the elders to tend the flock of God, having been told by Christ, "Shepherd my sheep" (see John 21:16-17). He commands his readers to gird themselves with humility (5:5), having watched Jesus wrap the towel around Himself before washing the disciples' feet–including his! (John 13:5-17).[101]

Throughout the epistle, the sufficiency of God's grace (cf. 2 Cor. 12:9) is also emphasized, as Tenney explains:

> In addition to the theme of suffering that pervades the epistle there is the counter-theme of "the true grace of God" (5:12). Suffering should be met with grace and should develop grace in the individual. The term appears in the greeting (1:2), as the summary of the message of the prophets (1:10), as the expectation of the future (1:13), as the pattern for conduct under abuse (2:19, 20; Greek text), as the fullness of the blessings that come in answer to prayer (3:7), as the equipment for spiritual service (4:10), and as the favor which God shows to those who wait on Him humbly (5:5).[102]

Hebrews

Historical Background

Hebrews was written before A.D. 70, since the temple sacrifices are spoken of in 10:11 in the present tense. If the writer's identity had to be known in order to understand his writing, God would have revealed it, but such is not the case. More important to the interpretation of the text is the fact that it was written to second-generation Jewish Christians, who, under the threat of persecution, were tempted to return to the sacrificial system under the Mosaic Law.

By the time the epistle was written, its readers had been Christians long enough to become teachers (5:12), to lose their leaders to death (13:7), and to have forgotten "former days" in which they had been more faithful (10:32 NKJV). With the danger of persecution imminent (Heb. 10:32-36; 12:4), the writer's purpose is to demonstrate the superiority of Christ and the Christian faith to those shadowy types of Christ which He fulfilled. The epistle assumes a knowledge of the Old Testament in Greek (Septuagint), without which it cannot be understood.

Literary Analysis

Though written in polished Greek, with quotations from the Septuagint, the epistle is written like the oration of one who is steeped in the Old Testament Scriptures. Ellisen's outline of Hebrews is adequate to demonstrate the organization of the writer's argumentation. The author's opening statement concerns "the glory and sufficiency of Christ's person," in 1:1-4:13. Next, he sets forth "the glory and sufficiency of Christ's priesthood," in 4:14-10:18. Finally, in 10:19-13:25, he shows "the glory and sufficiency of Christ's program."[103]

Theological Understanding

In demonstrating the supremacy of Jesus Christ over all of the elemental laws, institutions, and ceremonies that point to Him, the writer confirms the temporary nature of the Mosaic covenant. Like scaffolding used in erecting a building, the Law had served its covenantal purpose. The end, to which the Jewish sacrificial system was a means, is Jesus! Those who know Him have no good alternative to moving on to maturity, by faith, as did their Hebrew ancestors. Hebrews not only gives the reader better understanding of the Old Testament, but also a critical message for all who are in need of greater endurance of faith.

Epistles to Combat Heresies

The final five epistles of the New Testament were all written to correct false teaching that had arisen from within the church as well as from without.

2 Peter

Historical Background

In his farewell to the Ephesian elders, recorded in Acts 20, Paul predicted the very thing that was happening when Peter wrote his second epistle: "For I know this, that after my departure savage wolves will come in among you, not sparing the flock. Also from among yourselves men will rise up, speaking perverse things, to draw away the disciples after themselves" (vv. 29-30 NKJV). The operative words, in relation to 2 Peter, are "from among yourselves." Peter begins his second chapter saying, "But there were also false prophets among the people, even as there will be false teachers among you, who will secretly bring in destructive heresies, even denying the Lord who bought them, and bring on themselves swift destruction" (2:1 NKJV).

While Jude speaks of outsiders who sneaked undetected into the fellowship of believers (1:4), the false teachers in 2 Peter are described as apostate believers (2:1, 20-22). Though their specific errors are not identified per se, the text itself indicates that a low view of Scripture led to a denial of Christ's return and resulted in a permissive, immoral lifestyle. (See 1:4; 2:1-3; 3:3-4.)[104] Peter's readers seem to be the same as those identified in his first epistle, since he refers to this letter as his second (3:1).

Second Peter was written just before the apostle's death, about A.D. 67 or 68, probably from Rome.[105] The dark, cold environment of a jail cell, without the assistance of an amanuensis, accounts for the rougher style of Greek than that found in 1 Peter.

Literary Analysis

"There is a decided difference of vocabulary and style between 1 and 2 Peter. The second epistle is written in a more labored and awkward

Greek. Perhaps a different amanuensis was employed, or possibly Peter transcribed it himself."[106] The letter can be outlined with these three points: the reminder to grow (1), the reminder of false teachers (2), and the reminder of the day of the Lord (3).

Theological Understanding

If, in contrast to Jude, Peter is addressing the problem of *regenerate* heretics, whose judgment for false teaching leaves them worse off (in this life) than when they believed (2 Pet. 2:21-22), the epistle contributes to the doctrine of salvation by grace alone. At the same time, it stresses the importance of true, experiential knowledge of the truth for a rich entrance into the eternal kingdom of the Lord (1:5-11). Knowing the truth, revealed by God to men set apart for the purpose of recording it, is the antidote to false teaching (1:19-21). Realizing the faithfulness with which God keeps His promises to rescue the righteous and judge the wicked is the key to holy living (2:9; 3:11).

Jude

Historical Background

Whoever the audience to whom Jude wrote, and whatever their ethnic composition may have been, their progress in the faith was being threatened by false teaching introduced by unbelievers. The error Jude addresses seems to be "an antinomian version of Gnosticism."[107] The Lord's half-brother, Jude did not believe in Jesus until after the resurrection (John 7:5; see Acts 1:14).

Literary Analysis

George Lawlor notes Jude's love of the triad, or speaking in triplets. He states, "The author seems to miss scarcely a single opportunity to express himself in this unique threefold manner."[108] In verse 1, for example, "Jude," "servant," and "brother," make up a triad, as do the words "called," "beloved," and "kept."[109] In verse 2, Jude joins "mercy, peace, and love" (NKJV). Lawlor cites no fewer than eighteen instances of this technique, which he says "has no parallel anywhere else in the New Testament Scriptures."[110]

Also noteworthy is the unreserved language with which Jude denounces the false teachers. This is indicative of the intolerance with which Jesus rebuked the scribes and Pharisees (see Matthew 15:1-14 and 23:1-26). This serves as a warning to modern Christians tempted to embrace the political correctness of our pluralistic society.

Regarding Jude's quotation of noncanonical sources, Tenney says, "The apocryphal works were sometimes used to illustrate certain principles for those who regarded them with reverence."[111] That truth was found in such sources in no way implies that they were considered inspired. The same is true of Paul's quotation of the poet Aretas in Acts 17:28, and of the Cretan prophet quoted in Titus 1:12.

Theological Understanding

Jude's reference to "the faith which was once for all delivered to the saints," in verse 3 (NKJV), identifies a completed body of truth.[112] No new content of the Christian faith was needed or is possible. It is a faith worth fighting for!

Jude strikes the crucial balance in emphases between the believer's *responsibility* to contend for the faith (v. 3) and keep himself in the love of God, looking for His mercy (v. 21), on the one hand, and the believer's *preservation* by Jesus Christ (v. 1), who is able to present him faultless before God (v. 24), on the other.

A careful examination of Jude indicates significantly different wording regarding the nature and destiny of the false teachers he describes. In contrast to those of Peter's second epistle, they are clearly unregenerate and destined for eternal damnation (v. 13).

1, 2, and 3 John

Historical Background

In reference to 1 John, Guthrie states, "It is impossible to grasp the purpose of the Epistle until something has been said about the background of thought to which it belonged."[113] First John was probably written in Ephesus after the Gospel of John but before the persecution that began in Rome under Domitian in A.D. 95,[114] since nothing is said about persecution. Most likely, it was sent to the Asian churches surrounding

Ephesus over which John had some oversight.[115] From what he says in 2:7, 18-27; and 3:11, John's readers were well-established believers. Their enjoyment of fellowship with God and with one another, however, was threatened by those who denied the reality of the incarnation of Christ. The Gnostic belief that spirit and matter can have no real connection led to the false conclusion that fellowship with God is independent of how one behaves in his body. John writes to denounce this error by assuring his readers of the truth by which they could also know with certainty that they were having fellowship with God, i.e., enjoying eternal life.

Second and Third John were purportedly written at about the same time, but were addressed differently. The "elect lady" of 2 John seems to refer to a church, but its identity is impossible to ascertain.[116] Third John was addressed to a man named Gaius, whose identity remains a mystery. Guthrie says, "It is not possible to be any more specific than this, but as it has already been shown that this Epistle is closely related both to 1 John and 2 John and as these Epistles are fairly reasonably assigned to an Asian destination, it may be supposed that Gaius' church was one of the circuit of Asiatic churches under the general supervision of the apostle John."[117]

Literary Analysis

The structure of 1 John is difficult to outline but may be best pictured as a triangular spiral in which he moves from doctrine (a), to morality (b), to community (c), to doctrine (a'), to morality (b'), to community (c'), to doctrine (a"), to morality (b"), to community (c"), and so forth.

Theological Understanding

First John contributes greatly to the understanding of fellowship in the family of God.

Doctrine: Fellowship in the family of God depends on the incarnational facts that Christ is real (1:1-4), that Jesus is the Christ (2:18-29), and that eternal life is in God's Son (5:1-12).

Morality: The practice of righteousness is walking in the light (1:5-10), which is obedience to God (2:3-6), which is proven by love for fellow believers (2:7-11), and results in a hope leading to purity in this life (3:1-10). This is an objective basis for knowing that one has (is enjoying) eternal life (5:13-21).

Community: It is impossible to love God and the world (system) at the same time (2:12-17). Love for God is demonstrated by the believer's compassion (3:11-18), which produces confidence before God (3:19-24), and is shown by obedience to God (5:1-12).

Second John stresses that love cannot be separated from truth. Truth binds believers together in love (1-3). Truth governs believers' walk in love (4-6). Truth makes believers' love discriminating (7-13).

Third John stresses that by faithful love, believers show they are of the truth.

Sample Sermon
The Excellence of Love

1 Corinthians 13:1-13
Love Excels Gifted Ministries in Priority, Performance, and Permanence

I. The Priority of Love in Relation to Gifted Ministries (1-3)
   A. Tongues
   B. Prophecy
   C. Merciful Deeds
II. The Performance of Love in Relation to People (4-7)
   A. How "Love is"
   B. What "Love does not" do
   C. What Love Does
III. The Permanence of Love in Relation to Faith and Hope (8-13)
   A. Lasting (8)
   B. Complete (9-11)
   C. Consummate (12-13)

Summary and Conclusion

While less "bridge work" may be required for you to convey God's message from the New Testament epistles to the contemporary listener, the Epistles present their own challenges. An epistle is a letter written with apostolic authority in response to a particular concern, which determines the scope of its theological development. Epistles include other genre and employ most of the rhetorical devices found in other biblical literature. In form, New Testament epistles tend to follow the pattern of an adaptation of the typical first-century letter.

James was written first, probably before Paul's first missionary journey. James confronts churches at a time when most Christians were Jewish. He employs many imperatives in his application of divine wisdom to his listeners' need to demonstrate the reality of their faith.

Next came the epistles that Paul wrote before his imprisonment. These include Galatians, 1 and 2 Thessalonians, 1 and 2 Corinthians, and Romans. Galatians is a protest against the Judaized attempts to corrupt the pure gospel of grace. Sanctification is the result of realizing the believer's crucifixion with Christ, not of keeping rules. The letters to the Thessalonians were written to clarify misunderstandings about the coming of the Lord *for* His saints, and of His return to earth *with* them. The epistles to the Corinthians were written to deliver a carnal local church from division and disorder by addressing the practical implications of the centrality of Christ (in 1 Corinthians), and defending Paul's apostleship (in 2 Corinthians).

Romans explains how the righteousness of God, needed by all men, is appropriated by faith, demonstrated practically by the power of the indwelling Holy Spirit, and evident in God's program for Israel.

From prison in Rome, Paul wrote Philemon, Ephesians, Colossians, and Philippians. In his personal letter to Philemon, Paul shows how Christians are to forgive as they have been forgiven in Christ. Ephesians presents Christ as the head of His body, the Church, and exhorts the believer to behave in keeping with his position "in Christ." Colossians is much like Ephesians, but emphasizes the headship of Christ over all things as a basis to combat asceticism. Philippians is about the joy and responsibility of sharing in the gospel of Christ.

The so-called *Pastoral Epistles* include 1 Timothy, Titus, and 2 Timothy, and deal with the conduct of church life. First Timothy shows that the church is the primary agency through which God is working in the world today. Titus summarizes Christian doctrine for a young man charged to establish order in the churches of Crete. In his final epistle,

2 Timothy, Paul gives the reader a look into the heart of a minister as he charges Timothy.

The epistles of the suffering church include 1 Peter and Hebrews. First Peter encourages churches of Asia Minor to realize the grace of suffering. Hebrews prods Jewish Christians to go on to maturity in Christ in view of His glory and sufficiency.

The last five epistles of the New Testament were written to combat heresies: 2 Peter, Jude, and 1, 2, and 3 John. While 2 Peter addresses the problem of believing false teachers, Jude denounces those who are unbelievers. Both books, however, promote the truth as the antidote to error. John's epistles confront the error of Gnosticism with the implications of the Incarnation.

A sample sermon on 1 Corinthians 13 provides an example of how a chapter from the Epistles can be prepared using the Whiting Method.

Discussion Questions

1. What factors make the verbal *bridge* between the New Testament Epistles and the modern audience easier to *construct* than that between other biblical literature and today's audience?

2. What bridge-building challenges do the Epistles pose compared to other biblical literature?

3. What are the marks of a New Testament Epistle that distinguish it from a personal letter?

4. How does an understanding of the background and literature of James affect the way you would preach it?

5. If Paul wrote letters to the Corinthian church that have been lost, can we say that the canon of Scripture is complete? If so, how?

6. What ministry needs might motivate you to preach from 2 Corinthians on the basis of its content?

7. Why do you agree or disagree with Douglas Moo that Romans is far from being a comprehensive summary of Paul's theology?

8. Why do you agree or disagree with the assertion that Paul's *intention* in writing Philemon was to teach principles of forgiveness?
9. Describe important similarities and differences between Ephesians and Colossians.
10. Why would it be proper or improper to preach a sermon using Philippians 2:5-8 as your text?
11. Which of the Pastoral Epistles would be especially appropriate for teaching doctrine to a new members class, and why?
12. Which of the Epistles would provide preaching texts that are especially appropriate for those who are suffering, and why?
13. Why do you agree or disagree that Peter and Jude address false teachers with different eternal destinies?
14. Explain your understanding of the Gnostic problem against which John's first epistle was written.
15. List two strengths and two weaknesses in the sample sermon outline of 1 Corinthians 13.

CHAPTER 15

Preaching the Revelation

The unique importance of final words is often mentioned by way of introduction to the Great Commission passages of Matthew 28:19-20, Mark 16:15-18, Luke 24:44-50, and Acts 1:8. However, the last recorded words of Jesus are not found in the Gospels or Acts. They are found in the Revelation of Jesus Christ, who says, "Surely, I am coming quickly" (Rev. 22:20 NKJV). Nothing is more urgently needed today than the obedient worship and hope that depend on a vision of Christ as He is in glory.

Yet the Bible's last book is often neglected in the pulpit ministry because of uncertainty about its nature and purpose. For the untaught, to understand the meaning of its symbols and Old Testament references is a daunting task. The responsibility of choosing between vastly different systems of interpretation is intimidating. Horrific descriptions of cataclysmic destruction and human carnage are abhorrent to the imagination. The sensationalism of preachers who have abused the Revelation to draw crowds and impress them with their ingenuity is repulsive. But none of these is a valid reason to ignore God's latest Word. So this chapter is dedicated to encouraging you to preach the book of Revelation with appropriate confidence and humility.

Introduction to the Book of Revelation

Title

The editors of our English translations have generally entitled the book The Revelation of John. But the Greek text simply begins with the words translated "The Revelation of Jesus Christ." The first word, translated "revelation," is transliterated "apocalypse."[1] In modern vernacular, it is sometimes used to refer to the cataclysmic destruction of the world. But the word simply means "to uncover or disclose." The content of the revelation is centered on Jesus Christ. It comes from the Father to the Son, and from the Son to John, by an angel. (Note for the preacher: This chain of communication is instructive. God chooses to mediate a message He could have delivered more directly. In communicating His messages, God is pleased to work through personal agencies, including you!)

The book begins: "The Revelation of Jesus Christ, which God gave Him to show His servants–things which must shortly take place. And He sent and signified it by His angel to His servant John, who bore witness to the word of God, and to the testimony of Jesus Christ, to all things that he saw" (1:1-2 NKJV).

The "things" John saw, "things which must shortly take place," refer to events that will occur quickly or in rapid succession once they begin. This is the meaning of the word translated "shortly." Verse 3 promises a special blessing for those who read and heed the things John wrote, because they could begin to occur at any moment. Verse 4 reiterates that John is the channel.

Historical Background

With regard to authorship, Guthrie writes, "Although the author calls himself only 'John', it was traditionally assumed that this John was the apostle."[2] After a lengthy discussion of objections to the authorship of the apostle John,[3] Guthrie concludes that the traditional view is better than the alternatives.[4]

Addressed to seven churches in the Roman province of Asia (1:4), the Revelation was written during a time of Roman persecution of Christians (1:9; 2:10, 13), probably near the end of the reign of Domitian (A.D. 81-96). This was the testimony of Irenaeus, disciple of Polycarp, disciple of John.[5]

Radmacher, Allen and House state:

> Reliable historical sources dating from the second century A.D. place the apostle John in Ephesus and ministering throughout the province of Asia from about A.D. 70-100 … John was undoubtedly placed on the island of Patmos because of his Christian testimony. He was released after eighteen months by Emperor Nerva (A.D. 96-98), after which the apostle returned to Ephesus to resume his leadership role there.[6]

Genre

In *Preaching Old Testament Prophecy*, Robert Thomas views the Revelation as a genuinely prophetic document, which has apocalyptic elements, i.e., "when the message was passed on to the prophet in the form of visions." He further states, "The literary genre of inspired writings was not the choice of the human author, but was an inevitable result of the manner in which God chose to reveal his message to the prophet."[7]

The Revelation certainly meets Greidanus's criteria for identifying prophetic literature. First, it is from God and about God.[8] As we have seen, it is not ultimately *from* John or ultimately *about* the future. Second, as prophecy was generally addressed by the writer to his contemporaries, John writes to the seven churches of Asia Minor.[9]

The message of prophecy is never just to satisfy curiosity or fuel speculation. It always has immediate application to those who hear it (e.g., "Worship God! For the testimony of Jesus is the spirit of prophecy" [Rev. 19:10 NKJV]). Third, as prophetic literature is generally about the kingdom,[10] the book of Revelation concerns the kingdom in its universal aspect (1:5; 17:14; 19:6; 20:11), "continuity with the past" (1:5, 19; 4:11; 5:9,12; 12:1), the "coming King" (19:7), and "progressive fulfillment" (20:4).[11]

The Revelation has the apocalyptic elements identified by Leland Ryken, which include: contrast of good and evil; an angelic interpreter; prose, not poetry; looking to end times; use of symbolism (concrete images to represent something else); animal characters (living creatures, lamb, horses, etc.); and colors (white versus red).[12]

At the same time, the Revelation has characteristics in common with the Epistles. It was addressed to churches by an apostle to meet their needs at the time.

Interpretation[13]

Walvoord outlines the basic approaches that have been taken in interpreting the Revelation. The *allegorical approach* spiritualizes the text, denying a literal millennial reign of Christ or any historical relevance. *Preterists* view the Revelation as a symbolic history of events completed in the past.[14] The *historical approach* views the Revelation as a symbolic representation of Church history, culminating with the return of Christ. Futurists view Revelation 4-22 as predictive of "things which will take place after these things" (1:19 NKJV) (i.e., subsequent to the things Jesus describes as occurring at the time).

Literary Analysis

More than perhaps any other biblical book, understanding the literary structure of the Revelation is crucial to its interpretation. According to Leland Ryken, "the book of Revelation is the most carefully structured long work in the Bible."[15] This does not mean that scholars agree on the principle by which it is organized.

Guthrie surveys no fewer than seven theories that have been presented to explain the arrangement of John's material.[16] They range from the assumption that it is the "patchwork" of editors, to a supposition that the Revelation is an impressionistic work of poetry. Others find the symbolism itself to furnish the key to understanding the book's meaning. According to this theory, "the number seven, Jewish liturgy, and astrology (the signs of the Zodiac),"[17] provide clues that the reader must use to find a meaning beyond the normal use of words. Still others view the writing as a drama, a song with seven choruses, a series of visions that must be rearranged, or a liturgy moving the reader from one focus of attention to another in a progression of worship.

In our judgment, each of these views errs by its preoccupation with form. John's use of the number seven in structuring his material is obvious, but it is a means to the end that the urgent message he has to communicate might be more easily understood and remembered.

The literal approach to interpreting Scripture, discussed in chapter 2, assumes that the meaning of John's message is one that he understood and expected his readers to understand–not in isolation from the context of the entire Bible, but as the culmination of its message.

John appears to have organized his material according to several literary devices or techniques. First is a system of contrasts between good and evil. To paraphrase Ryken:

> Satan is opposed to God and Christ. The followers of the beast are set against the saints. The whore of Babylon is seen in opposition to Israel and the virginal bride of Christ. The dragon is against the Lamb. The unholy trinity (the dragon, the beast from the sea, and the beast from the earth) oppose the Trinity. The dragon's angels oppose Michael's angels. Heaven is seen in contrast to the bottomless pit, and the New Jerusalem, in contrast to Babylon. Time is opposed to eternity, and the deliverance of believers is contrasted with the destruction of God's enemies.[18]

Second, John organizes the myriad details of his content into groups of seven and lists them in a series. Again quoting Ryken, "There is a prologue, a series of six sevenfold units, and an epilogue, as the following outline demonstrates."[19] (See figure 15-1.[20]) Ryken notes: "An awareness of this structural principle makes the work as a whole easy to remember and allows the reader to pick up the flow of action at any point and have a general grasp of what is happening."[21]

Third, instead of ordering his record of events chronologically, John moves in a line through a variety of things toward an ultimate destination or goal. In a way that fascinates the careful observer, John follows the same sequence of events that Jesus presented in His Olivet Discourse, Matthew 24. The following table shows this relationship in connection to Revelation 6. (See figure 15-2.[22])

Fourth, John makes more use of archetypes than any other biblical writer. Many terms for elemental, human experiences are used, including *life, death, blood, lamb, dragon, beast, light, darkness, earth, heaven, water, sea, sun, war, harvest, white, scarlet, bride, throne, jewels*, and *gold.*[23] Ryken further notes John's references to rising, associated with spiritual goodness, and falling, associated with spiritual evil; heaven is high and light; the bottomless pit is low and dark.[24]

John's Six Series of Sevens

Prologue (1)
1. Seven Churches (2–4)
2. Seven Seals (5–8)
3. Seven Trumpets (8–11)
4. Seven Signs (12–14)
5. Seven Bowls (15–16)
6. Seven Events of Final Judgment (17–22:5)
Epilogue (22:6–21)

Figure 15.1

Matthew 24	Revelation 6
(1) Wars and rumors of war (vv. 4–8)	4 Seals: Conqueror, war, famine, death (vv. 1–8)
(2) Persecution of Christ's followers (vv. 9–10)	5th Seal, martyrs (vv. 9–11)
(3) Appearances of false prophets and false messiahs (vv. 11–28)	
(4) Great natural disasters (v. 29)	6th Seal, terror (vv. 12–14)
(5) A final judgment (vv. 29–31)	Wrath of the Lamb (vv. 15–17)

Figure 15.2

Fifth, several type patterns are prominent in the Revelation, including the damsel in distress, delivered by the hero who kills the dragon (cf. ch. 12); the wicked witch, who is finally exposed; the marriage of the triumphant hero to his bride (cf. ch. 18); the celebration of the wedding feast (cf. ch. 19); a place glittering with jewels, in which the hero and his bride live happily ever after (cf. ch. 21); and the journey of the narrator to supernatural realms, where he encounters spiritual beings and returns to human life newly equipped (cf. 22:10-21). One could argue that these motifs are represented not because life is imitating art, but because John is describing the saga of cosmic history from which literary motifs are taken.

Recognizing each of these methods for what it is enhances an understanding of *how* John was superintended by the Holy Spirit to communicate with maximum impact and memorable quality. However, the actual outline John follows is given in Revelation 1:19, where he is told, "Write the things which you have seen, and the things which are, and the things which will take place after this" (NKJV). Walvoord comments:

> The things referred to as having already been seen are those contained in chapter 1 where John had his preliminary vision. This vision, of course, introduces the main subject of the entire book, Jesus Christ the glorious coming King. The second division, "the things which are," most naturally includes chapters 2 and 3 with the seven messages Christ delivered to the churches. This contemporary situation gives the historical context for the revelation which follows. The third division, "the things which shall be hereafter," would naturally include the bulk of the book which was to be prophetic as anticipated in 1:3 in the expression "the words of this prophecy."[25]

Theological Understanding

Leon Morris's description of the content of the Revelation as communicating "a theology of power" reflects the futurist view of one who interprets Scripture literally. Says Morris, "The writer is saying, in effect: 'You are seeing only part of the picture. If you could look behind the scenes, you would see that God is working his purpose out and that in his own good time he will completely overthrow all evil. The salvation he worked out at Calvary will not fail to achieve its final aim.'"[26]

In view of increasing persecution of Christians, John assured his readers that the Lord Jesus is bringing history to a glorious, purposeful climax. Jesus is seen in glory, directing the churches, judging the world, and bringing righteousness to the earth in fulfillment of biblical prophecies. The believer is thus given every reason to worship God and serve Him faithfully.

With regard to the present and future work of Christ, He is seen as the Head, giving direction to the local manifestations of His body, the Church, in chapters 2-3. His righteous judgment is described as "the wrath of the Lamb" in 6:16 (NKJV). It encompasses the sinful world in chapters 6, 8, 9, 14, and 16-18. He is coming for His bride, with whom He will rule the earth for a thousand years, according to 20:2-6.

The person and work of Christ, as viewed in John's present and future, are grounded in His past, completed works of creation and redemption. These include: His death and resurrection (1:5); His ascension (12:5); His gracious offer of eternal life to all who will repent (2:5 and 9:20-21), based on the shed "blood of the Lamb" (12:11 NKJV); His worthiness of worship based on His creation of all things (4:11); and His redemption of all kinds of people (5:9).

The power of the Holy Spirit is prominent in John's reception of visions and in the ultimate victory of Christ and His saints over Satan, demons, and the people they control. The royal priesthood of believers is prominent in their worship around the throne of God in heaven (4:10-11); in their prayers, which are ever before the throne of God (5:8; 8:3-4); and by their share in Christ's reign (20:4-6).

The closure of the canon of Scripture is another important theological consideration. Thomas writes, "This is a canonizing of the book of Revelation parallel to the way the Deuteronomy passage [4:1] came to apply to the whole OT canon. Use of the canonical model is equivalent to saying that there was no more room for inspired messages."[27]

Preaching the Revelation

In view of the peculiarities of the Revelation, several cautionary notes are in order when preparing to preach it.[28]

First, make sure that you choose a text on the basis of its communication of a complete thought.

Second, always ask what a given symbol typically means in the literature accessible to the original readers–particularly the Old Testament, to which the Revelation makes hundreds of allusions, and of which the Revelation is the climactic conclusion.

Third, ask what the passage teaches about God, His attributes, His plan, and His purpose. What is made known about the person and work of the Lord Jesus Christ? How does the text shed light on the nature of man and his purpose, role, and responsibilities? How is the passage related to messianic prophecies and their fulfillment?

Fourth, in developing the theme, ask what the prophet is asserting. In stating the principle that expresses the text's main thrust, reflect the form and tone of the text. If the text is confrontational, demanding, picturesque, comforting, and so forth, so should be the sermon. Restate the textual theme in terms of the "here and now." How is the textual theme confirmed, contrasted, fulfilled, balanced, deepened or expanded, etc., by the whole of Scripture?

Fifth, in applying the message, ask how the needs of the contemporary audience differ from those of the original audience.

Sixth, in delivering the message, maintain humility, objectivity, compassion, and reverence. If John fell as a dead man at the feet of Christ in glory (1:17), you, too, should exhibit appropriate fear as you nevertheless faithfully proclaim His message with boldness (1:19). Maintain objectivity. Avoid sensationalism, speculation, dogmatism, and disrespect for those with opposing views. And be careful not to exhibit callous indifference–let alone glee–in response to graphic descriptions of God's punishment of the wicked. The human toll, environmental impact, and eternal consequences of natural disasters and divine judgments recorded in the Revelation should make us sensitive to our listeners' needs for the comfort of salvation.

Seventh, preach worshipfully–but *preach* it! The Revelation is given to exalt the Lord Jesus Christ and move the reader to glorify Him in the heartfelt worship of the redeemed.

Sample Sermon
The Revelation of Jesus Christ

Revelation 1:1-8
The Ruler Of Earth's Kings Is Coming!

I. The Introduction to the Book and Its Blessings (1-3)
    A. The Revelation of Jesus Christ Is Designed to Make Secrets Known (1)
    B. The Revelation of Jesus Christ Is for His Bondservants
    C. The Revelation of Jesus Christ Is from the Father
    D. The Revelation of Jesus Christ Is a Blessing
II. The Introduction to the Subject and His Sovereignty (4-8)
    A. Christ Is the Source of Peace-Producing Grace
        1. Faithful witness
        2. Firstborn from the dead
        3. Ruler of the kings of the earth
        4. Him who loves us
        5. Him who released us from our sins by His blood
        6. Him who made us a kingdom of priests
        7. To whom be eternal glory
    B. Christ Is Coming with the Clouds
        1. His Fulfillment of Messianic Prophecy (Zech. 12:10)
        2. His Majesty as Eternal God

Summary and Conclusion

In spite of its unique importance as God's final word, the Revelation has been neglected by many preachers, partly as a result of its abuse by some. However, having come, as it did, from the Father to the Son, and from the Son to John, by way of His angel, the book promises a special blessing to those who hear and heed its message of events that will unfold rapidly.

As prophecy, with both epistolary and apocalyptic elements, the Revelation was addressed by the apostle John to churches expected to understand its meaning and current relevance to them.

Of several approaches that have been taken to interpreting the Revelation, the futuristic view is the only one that takes literally the things that are promised and have not yet taken place.

Many attempts to explain the rationale for how John's material is arranged have failed to *see the forest for the trees*! The literal approach does not dismiss the importance of literary analysis, but regards it as a means to the end of enhancing the reader's understanding and memory of the content of the Revelation. John himself gives the outline for his work in 1:19, which orients the reader to its movement from the past to the present, and to the future.

Since the content of the book is centered in Jesus Christ, it is not surprising that it provides a wealth of Christological understanding, from His person and work to His gracious inclusion of faithful believers in His rule.

Preaching the Revelation calls for courage and for special care in selecting the text, interpreting symbols, and dealing with Old Testament references. Focus on what your passage teaches about God, Christ, man, and the kingdom. Make sure your theme reflects the form and tone of the text. Adapt your applications carefully to your contemporary listeners, and deliver your sermon with humility, objectivity, compassion, and reverence.

Discussion Questions

1. Explain the reasons that you agree or disagree with the assertions made in this chapter for both the importance and neglect of the Revelation.
2. Why is it important to understand the correct title of the book?
3. In what ways is the Revelation prophetic, apocalyptic, and epistolary?
4. Which principle of organization do you believe best explains the arrangement of John's material, and why?
5. How can symbolism be adequately recognized for its value without eclipsing the understandable meaning of the text?

6. List several aspects of the present and future work of Christ that are unveiled in the Revelation.

7. Which of the guidelines for preaching the Revelation do you think will be most beneficial to you personally, and why?

Appendix

Outlining from the Nestle-Aland *Novum Testamentum Gracece*[1]

The *section*, consisting of any number of paragraphs, is indicated by an extrawide spacing from the preceding text, e.g. between Romans 4:25 and 5:1, and Acts 21:14 and 21:15.

The *paragraph*, which is indicated by indentation, begins with a majescule (capital letter). It may consist of one or more sentences.

The *subparagraph*, which is a division within a paragraph, also begins with a majuscule (e.g. Romans 5:15, 18). Where there is one subparagraph, there will always be another, and each may consist of one or more sentences.

The *sentence* usually begins with a miniscule (small letter), unless, of course, it happens to be the first sentence of a paragraph or subparagraph. All sentences end with a full stop (American "period"). CAUTION: a sentence beginning with a proper name will naturally be capitalized but may or may not commence a new subparagraph.

The *colon*: The parallel (grammatically and therefore logically) clauses (cola) within a sentence are separated by a raised dot (·). See Romans 6:5-7 for a sentence of three parallel clauses separated by two raised dots, or colon marks. CAUTION: The colon also introduces certain direct quotations, which are often subordinate (not parallel).

The *comma* separates the subordinate clauses and lesser phrases within a sentence or clause. These are more for easy reading than for logical division and can be neglected in analysis.

Sample Textual-Expository (Paragraph) Sermon (Manuscript Style)

Christ Our Advocate
1 John 2:1-2

Courtroom drama is a staple of American entertainment. Questions of justice seem to captivate the imagination of TV viewers. But mention the phrase *defense attorney* and the name that jumps to mind may not be Perry Mason or Matlock, but Johnnie Cochran. Cochran led the "dream team" that successfully won the acquittal of celebrity O. J. Simpson in 1995. Simpson, a famous football player, sports commentator, and actor, had been charged with murdering two people, including his wife. When the longest jury trial in California history ended, involving 150 witnesses and costing $15 million, everyone seemed to have his own opinion.

People have a God-given capacity to make judgments. As a result of sin, they are also subject to the judgment of God. For Christians, sin raises tough questions. On one hand, how can one who sins stand before the God of absolute justice? On the other hand, if the blood of Jesus has cleansed them, why should it matter that they sin? The answer to these questions involves a greater courtroom drama than any on earth. It begins with:

I. The Problem of Sinning Christians, found in 1 John 2:1

> "My little children, I am writing these things to you so that you may not sin." [NASB95]

John was believed to be about ninety when he penned these words. The word translated "little children" indicates that John regarded himself as the spiritual father of people who were still trustfully looking up to him and learning from him. John is the only New Testament writer to use this diminutive form of the word for children, and of his eight uses of this word, this is the only time he attaches the pronoun *my* to it. This indicates the personal affection he feels for his readers and his sense of responsibility for their spiritual well-being.

In the original language, the words *these things* are pushed forward in the sentence for emphasis. Referring to his act of *writing* in the present tense, John announces his current awareness of the reason he has taken pen in hand and expressed the thoughts found in chapter 1. His purpose is that his readers *may not sin*. The clause could be translated *that you may never sin*.

Here's a news flash! Believers need not *ever* sin. Contrary to popular opinion among many Christians, sin is not a necessity. Being human does not require that we sin. Satan would love to have us all think that sin in the life of a believer is normal, natural, usual, to be expected, and therefore acceptable behavior. But it isn't. Even though "everybody docs it," it's not OK.

Of the several words used for "sin" in the New Testament, this is the one that means "to fall short of the mark." The devil would like for us to think that sin is just a part of what it means to be human. But that's not what our baptisms portrayed. Our baptisms told everyone who observed them, or who would later hear about them, that we are now able to operate by the supernatural power in which Jesus lives, and is alive in us!

Where did we ever get the idea that we're being true to ourselves when we sin? Where in the Bible does it say that our weaknesses, faults, and failures are the common denominator of Christian s, the basis for our bond in men's groups, ladies' groups, and youth groups? Nowhere! The fact is, every believer is a saint, and what we have in common is Christ, by His indwelling Spirit and the Word of God.

The words *these things* could refer to the content of the entire epistle. More likely, they are the statements just made in chapter 1. There, John addressed those who deny a principle of sin within them. In 1:8, he says, "If we say that we have no sin, we are deceiving ourselves and the truth is not in us" [NASB95] .

The fact is, every believer on earth lives in an unredeemed body. Even John himself contended with a principle of sin that Paul called "the flesh." Having a body of sin does not mean that the body itself is evil or that we who are living in our old bodies *have* to slip into these old ruts of our presalvation days. It *does* mean that those ruts are there, and that we are fully capable of behaving like the people we were as the children of Adam. This is one of the "these things" that John has written to his readers.

Another of the "these things" is found in 1:10, where he says, "If we say that we have not sinned, we make Him a liar and His word is not in us" [NASB95] . In verse 8, the issue was denying the presence of a sinful tendency in our bodies. But here, in verse 10, the issue is denying ever having given in to that tendency. In other words. John is talking about people who deny ever having committed an act of sin.

John's point is that there is a principle of sin operating in the physical body of every Christian, and that every last one of us has chosen to obey it on occasion. We didn't *have to*, but we *did*.

Now, between verse 8, which speaks of our sinful *tendency*, and verse 10, which speaks about our acts of sin, John tells the benefit of agreeing with God about our sins when we commit them. He says. "If we confess our sins, He is faithful and righteous to forgive us our sins and to cleanse us from all unrighteousness" [NASB95]. At this point, we modern readers may be saying to ourselves, "If *everyone* has a principle of sin operating in his unredeemed body; and if *everybody* occasionally slips and acts like the person he was before God made him new; and if all you've got to do to enjoy restored fellowship with God when you sin is to agree with Him that your pride, or lust, or theft, or outburst of anger was wrong, then what is the big problem when we sin?" We may be especially prone to think this way when we read those Scriptures that describe our secure position before God. Ephesians 1:7, for example says, "In Him we have redemption through His blood, the forgiveness of our trespasses" [NASB95].

Many years ago I attended some meetings at which the main speakers were teaching that 1 John 1:9 refers to a person's initial confession of sin, and not to a spiritual discipline to observe throughout one's Christian life. It seemed as if they were saying that to be constantly vigilant about sin in your life is a negative preoccupation that actually leads to a vicious cycle of sin. Their solution to the pesky problem of sinning Christians was simply to rest in the positional truth that we stand forgiven by Christ's finished work on the cross. In other words, don't worry about the acts of sin that we all commit as Christians, because they can't affect our relationship with God.

Many of us seem to have adopted a similar attitude. But there is an important difference between our relationship with God, which *is* secured by Christ's finished work on the cross, and our enjoyment of that relationship, which must be maintained by walking in the light, as He Himself is in the light. There's a difference between position and fellowship. The apostle John is talking about fellowship, and he's addressing people like most of us, who already have a relationship with God, in which we are children in His Forever Family, but who often forfeit the joy of reveling in the abundant spiritual life.

John was combating that religious error called Gnosticism. The Gnostics were infected with the false idea that spirit and matter have no real connection. They denied that the eternal Word of God had ever actually come to earth as a physical human being. This is why John, in the first four verses of 1 John, goes to such lengths to emphasize that he and the other apostles heard, saw, gazed at, and handled the Word of God.

Those who denied that God actually took a physical body also denied that anything they might do in their physical bodies had any effect on their spiritual lives. To the Gnostic, a person had fellowship with God through exclusive, experiential knowledge of mysterious truth, not by how they conducted themselves in their bodies.

But John said, in verses 5-7 of chapter 1, "This is the message we have heard from Him and announce to you, that God is Light, and in Him there is no darkness at all. If we say that we have fellowship with Him and yet walk in the darkness, we lie and do not practice the truth; but if we walk in the Light as He Himself is in the Light, we have fellowship with one another, and the blood of Jesus His Son cleanses us from all sin." [NASB95]

According to John, fellowship with God has everything to do with how we are behaving in our bodies. It is precisely because we all still *tend* to sin, and have all committed *acts* of sin, that we must be careful *not* to sin. We dare not downplay the importance of our deeds, as the Gnostics did.

The second part of 2:1 begins by saying, "And if anyone sins" [NASB95]. This is essentially an admission that believers do sin. We don't have to, but we do. John wrote the "these things" of chapter 1 so that his readers, including us, might never enter into sin. But knowing that we all do, he prepares to tell us the solution to our problem.

Notice, he does not dismiss the issue as *no big deal* ... nor does he tell us that we can clean up our own messes by just mending our ways. No. Our sinning as Christians is *such* a big deal that we need help that only God Himself can provide! John says in effect, *when believers sin, Christ is their righteous Advocate.*

The ministry of the risen Savior on our behalf should not lead us to make light of sin, but to realize how seriously God takes it.

The last part of verse 1, along with verse 2, tells us four important things about...

II. The Solution of Christ's Advocacy

> "And if anyone sins, we have an Advocate with the Father, Jesus Christ the righteous" [NASB95].

The word translated "Advocate" in the New King James and New American Standard is the Greek word from which we get the English word *paraklete*. In some contexts it has the idea of one who is called to the side of another to render whatever aid is needed. But here it describes Jesus as a defense attorney in a court of law.

The New King James and New American Standard Versions actually capitalize Advocate as an official title. Other versions render the word by describing what an advocate does so that their readers will not have to learn a new word. But the original language implies what Jesus *does* by emphasizing who He *is* in relation to the believer who sins. Jesus is the One who intercedes for the believer and pleads his case, appealing to the Father on his behalf.

The words "we have" are in the present tense: *we are having*. Every Christian–including you and me–has a court-appointed legal counsel who is *for* him, on his side, making his case and winning it!

To say in response, "Well then, that settles it. My sins really *aren't* an issue. I can do whatever I want to, and my Daddy's lawyer will get me off," is to completely miss the point. Just consider how seriously the triune God takes our sins: that each of us *needs* legal representation, and that it is *provided* by the risen Savior, should bring us to our knees in humble repentance and thanksgiving.

There are four things about the believer's Advocate, in verse 2, that are very significant. First we're told that He is *with* the Father. In other words, having accomplished His purpose in coming to earth, Jesus who died, was buried, and rose again has ascended and is exalted in glory, at the Father's right hand. None of this would be true if He were not the Father's full equal as God the Son, or if His mission had not been successful.

Could we possibly have representation with the Father that was more apt to win our case? No, but more is said about Him!

Second, He is "Jesus Christ righteous." The absence of the article, translated "the" in the original language, stresses the quality or character of righteousness. It describes the exalted Lord as qualified to stand His ground before the Father because, as a Man, He fulfilled the Law of God on behalf of everyone who trusts in Him.

Third, verse 2 says, "And He Himself is the propitiation for our sins" [NASB95]. Not only is Christ our defender, with legal standing in the Father's presence, but He is also the propitiation for our sins. This means that His intercession on our behalf is based on a satisfactory payment, also made on our behalf–which consisted of His own sacrificial death.

Defense attorneys don't normally take the place of the clients they represent and pay the penalty they owe. But Jesus did. The only human being who fulfilled the Law (not only by not breaking it, but by fulfilling its positive demands) also paid the penalty for those who, by breaking one commandment one time, were guilty of all.

Fourth, in addition to His being with the Father, being righteous, and being the One who personally satisfied the Father's just requirement by enduring the essence of eternal hell in our place, He did so in the place of every man, woman, young person, and child of Silverton, Oregon; the U.S.; and the world.

At the end of verse 2, John adds: "and not for ours only, but also for those of the whole world" [NASB95]. Our Advocate satisfied the Father's just demands on behalf of the sins of every human being. This doesn't make everybody "saved," but it makes them savable by faith. Christ's death will not secure anyone's salvation apart from the faith that every person of mental competence is responsible for putting in Christ. This is why missionaries are sent all over the world. For people to hear the good news, other people must be sent to tell them. But it makes little sense to run around and tell everyone about the good news of Jesus Christ, or to support those who do, if, at the moment, you and I are in denial about the toll sin is taking in our own lives. Look up at verse 3 of chapter 1. Speaking for himself and all of the apostles—*sent ones*—John says, "what we have seen and heard we proclaim to you also, so that you too may have fellowship with us; and indeed our fellowship is with the Father, and with His Son Jesus Christ" [NASB95]

Fellowship with the Father, and with everyone else who is having fellowship with the Father, is why the Father sent His Son and why our Lord's "sent ones" told us about Him. It is why we must tell others. But we won't share what we aren't enjoying. That is one reason that John wants his readers, who are already saved from the penalty of sin, never to sin as Christians. That is why God has made a provision for us when we do. Just think about how seriously He takes our sins. According to this text, *when believers sin, Christ is their righteous Advocate*. If you have not yet believed in Christ, you have an opportunity right now that you cannot count on having this afternoon, tomorrow, or next week. I urge you to receive forgiveness of your sins and eternal life by believing on the Lord Jesus Christ as having died for your sins and risen again.

If you already believe in Him but have not been baptized as He commanded, that is an issue of fellowship, whether you realize it or not. I urge you to take this important first step of biblical discipleship.

If you are a baptized believer who has been living a careless life, not taking your sins as seriously as God does, think not only about the work Christ has done, but what He *is doing* to stand before the Father in your defense! Can you really continue with *business as usual*?

Finally, if you are a baptized believer who, though imperfect, is enjoying fellowship with God, confessing your sins, and confident of the cleansing of His Son's blood, will you join me in thanking Him for Christ our Advocate?

Gracious Father, thank You for Jesus Christ the righteous, who is representing us. Thank You for the life He lived, the death He died, and for the efficacy of His blood to cleanse us from all unrighteousness. As we walk in the light of Your fellowship, may we also have fellowship with one another, and may that include those You have sent us to win with the good news of Christ. In His Name, we pray. Amen.

Sample Textual-Topical Expository Sermon (Manuscript Style)

Judas's Real Estate
Matthew 27:6-10, Acts 1:15-20

One of the most effective lenses through which God allows us to see something of His magnificence is that of human rebellion and failure. It is like the dark glass that allows a person to observe the dazzling corona of the sun without damage to the eyes. For example, in the international war against terrorism, it may seem that the enemies of peace are like pieces of the puzzle of God's plan and purpose that seem to have been malformed, ill conceived. But whether you're talking about tyrants or traitors, the Antichrist or Judas, even Satan and his demons, these persons-no less than we-are under the control of God for His ultimate glory. As Psalm 76: IO says in effect, *God causes the wrath of man to praise Him.*

This does not mean that we should celebrate the wrath of man. But we should rest in the fact that the worst men and devils can do is just as useful a thread in the tapestry God is weaving as the genuine worship of men and angels! Nowhere is this important principle better demonstrated than in the story of Judas's real estate. And, as we get involved in it, ask yourself, what is *my* real estate? What is the true condition of my soul? With respect to the piece of property associated with Judas Iscariot, the Bible refers to it in three ways. The first is as:

I. The Field of Blood

Beginning with Matthew 27:6 in the New King James Version, we read:

> But the chief priests took the silver pieces and said, "It is not lawful to put them into the treasury, because they are the price of blood." And they consulted together and bought with them the potter's field, to bury strangers in. Therefore that field has been called the Field of Blood to this day. Then was fulfilled what was spoken by Jeremiah the prophet, saying, "And they took the thirty pieces of silver, the value of Him who was priced, whom they of the children of Israel priced."

This is one of two traditions that explain the naming *of the Field of Blood*. The price of the parcel was the blood money of the Prince of glory. What is especially interesting about this is the priests' sudden conscience. These are the same religious leaders who offered Judas thirty pieces of silver. I'm sure they carefully weighed it out so as not to be more or less than the amount they had set. Somehow these Bible teachers were blind to the fact that the price they put on Jesus' head was exactly the amount prophesied centuries earlier in Zechariah. And somehow, they had no scruples about the use of God's money to hire a snitch and condemn an innocent man. That did nothing to offend their sense of honor.

If you say it is because they sincerely thought they were serving God in expediting the arrest of one they believed to be making false claims to deity, then you have to account for another detail. Up in verse 4, when confronted with Judas's own admission that he had "sinned by betraying innocent blood" [NKJV], they neither denied that he was right nor launched an investigation into the facts. Instead, as if they agreed with him, they said, "What is that to us? You see to it!" [NKJV]

After Judas threw down the coins in the temple, the next scene in the story is pathetic: Learned, grown men, down on their hands and knees, looking for, and picking up, each of the same thirty pieces of silver that they had so carefully weighed out to buy the death of Jesus . "Oh, here's one! Here's another!" But now, all of a sudden, they regarded this money as tainted–not by *them* or by *their* actions, of course, but by Judas's betrayal of Jesus, who was crucified. Now they must sanitize it by some pious act of generosity.

You and I do not have to be into money laundering to do a similar thing. Instead of repenting of some wrong that we know, or should know, we have committed, we simply try to do something religious, thinking that our devotion will make up for it. Like the chief priests, we may also try to balance our guilt by placing the blame on someone else, as they did with Judas. There is nothing like ministry to anesthetize a nagging conscience. Many people have entered the ministry or gone to the mission field in order to offer God some service in the place of needed repentance of sin. But, as Samuel exhorted Saul in 1 Samuel 15:22, *to obey is better than sacrifice*. So beware of yourself and of others when you see great and meticulous attention being given to the letter of the law. Straining at a gnat while swallowing a camel often signals a vain attempt to redeem oneself and salve a guilty conscience. Be sure you are always constrained by the love of Christ, and that your ministry is never to work off a guilt complex.

The other note I make is from verse 7 and has to do with the purchase of a strangers' cemetery. We're told that the priests "consulted together and bought with [the coins] the potter's field, to bury strangers in" [NKJV].

One of the reasons I believe that the apostles appointed elders in the churches they established is that there is generally safety in the counsel of many. But there is no safety in the counsel of unqualified elders! The fact that the unrepentant architects of Jesus' murder were able to agree on a plan for His blood money shows that the value of a consensus depends on the character of those who are consenting!

The word *strangers* is thought to refer at least to Jews from outside of Jerusalem who happened to die there, and probably includes Gentiles. Burial was an issue because the Pharisees believed in a bodily resurrection. The burning of bodies, and spreading of ashes, was considered one of the worst ways to desecrate the remains of another human being.

A possible reason that a potter's field was considered a desirable location for a cemetery is that holes had probably been dug to get clay to make pottery. Ironically, the apostle Paul refers to our bodies as earthen vessels, or clay pots, in 2 Corinthians 4:7. (In fact, you may have known a few *crackpots* over the years!) But there is a more significant reason that the potter's field was chosen for a graveyard.

The second tradition that explains the naming of the field of blood is found in Acts 1, verses 18-19. There, it is clear that this same piece of real estate was named for Judas's spilt blood! Beginning with verse 18, and reading through verse 19, we have the following statements of the apostle Peter when he met with the 120 in Jerusalem, just before the Day of Pentecost: "Now this man purchased a field with the wages of iniquity; and falling headlong, he burst open in the middle and all his entrails gushed out. And it became known to all those dwelling in Jerusalem; so that field is called in their own language. Akel Dama, that is, Field of Blood" [NKJV].

It is stated in Matthew 27:5 that Judas hung himself. Although it is not actually said that he did it in the vicinity of the Potter's Field that the religious leaders purchased, or that his body was found there, it is strongly implied by the fact that this became another explanation of how the field of blood got its name.

By the way, it is often speculated that when Judas hung himself, either the rope or the tree branch to which it was tied, broke. Later, his disemboweled body was found on what we can imagine were the rocks below, the very picture of perdition, which means "destruction," or "damnation."

With regard to the suicide, to die at ones own hands graphically demonstrates that sin is naturally self-destructive. Proverbs 14:12 says, "There is a way that seems right to a man, but its end is the way of death" [NKJV]. Regarding the symbolism, it seems highly significant that Judas's own blood was spilled on the very real estate that Jesus' blood money went to purchase. This illustrates the principle of the harvest that Paul wrote in Galatians 6:7-9: "Do not be deceived, God is not mocked; for whatever a man sows, that he will also reap. For he who sows to his flesh will of the flesh reap corruption, but he who sows to the Spirit will of the Spirit reap everlasting life. And let us not grow weary while doing good, for in due season we shall reap if we do not lose heart" [NKJV]

That there is poetic justice in Judas's end, in contrast to the empty tomb of Jesus, is not meant to make us giddily happy. But it does provide reassuring evidence of a moral order. God does judge sin and reward righteousness, whether in this life or in the life to come.

The second way in which Judas's real estate is discussed in Scripture is in terms of ...

II. The Potter's Field

Beginning again with Matthew 27:7, we read:

> And they consulted together and bought with them the potter's field, to bury strangers in. Therefore that field has been called the Field of Blood to this day. Then was fulfilled what was spoken by Jeremiah the prophet, saying, "And they took the thirty pieces of silver, the value of Him who was priced, whom they of the children of Israel priced, and gave them for the potter's field, as the LORD directed me." [NKJV]

The phrase *potter's field* was first used in Jeremiah 18. The prophet was told that Israel was like clay in the hand of a potter. In chapter 19, Jeremiah was instructed to buy an earthenware jar and take it out to the Valley of Hinnom, which was at the entrance of the dump where they threw the broken jars. There Jeremiah prophesied against the nation. This was the very place where the Israelites had offered up their baby boys as burnt offerings to the false gods Baal and Molech. God directed Jeremiah to use the potter as a picture of God Himself, who can do what He pleases with the nations—including Israel—which are like clay jars.

The second time we read of the potter's field is in Zechariah 11:12-13, where God speaks through Zechariah: "Then I said to them, 'If it is agreeable to you, give me my wages; and if not, refrain.' So they weighed out for my wages thirty pieces of silver. And the LORD said to me, 'Throw it to the potter'–that princely price they set on me. So I took the thirty pieces of silver and threw them into the house of the LORD for the potter" [NKJV].

Zechariah prophesied the rejection of Christ right down to the price of His betrayal! Because he uses the imagery of Jeremiah's prophecy, Matthew attributes his words to the better-known prophet. He sees the priests' purchase of the field, using Jesus' blood money, as fulfilling God's command of Zechariah. That command, to throw the ridiculous payment to the potter, was a vivid demonstration of God's utter displeasure with their estimate of His Son! In other words, when the priests bought the land that was both *the field of blood* and *the potter's field*, they were unknowingly showing *God's* contempt for their contempt for His Son, Jesus! It was as if God was saying, *To hell with your money!* and even used their hands to put it there!

Judas's real estate, then, was *the field of blood* that shows how the wicked get caught in their own trap. It was also *the potter's field*, which reveals God's ability to use His enemies to doom themselves. And there is one more aspect of Judas's real estate that we cannot afford to ignore. As we noted from Jeremiah 19:2, it was also …

III. The Valley of Hinnom (or Gehenna)

The location of Judas's real estate is associated with the ravine southwest of Jerusalem, where King Ahaz had led the people in burning their children in the worship of false gods. It became the garbage dump, where the bodies of criminals were thrown without burial. It is where the precious body of our Lord Jesus would have been discarded had God not provided the tomb from which He arose in victory.

As far back as Isaiah, this valley had been a word picture for the actual punishment of the wicked. Isaiah 30:33 speaks of it as being set on fire by the breath of Yahweh, like a torrent of brimstone. Isaiah described the torment of that awful place with words that look beyond the physical real estate of Judas, to the real estate of everyone who dies in unbelief. In Isaiah 66:24, Yahweh describes the demise of the wicked dead with words Jesus applied to Gehenna: "Their worm does not die, and their fire is not quenched. They shall be an abhorrence to all flesh"

[NKJV]. The book of Mark repeats most of these words in chapter 9, verses 44, 46, and 48.

The Lord Jesus referred to the eternal lake of fire as *Gehenna*, into which, Revelation 20:14 says, death and Hades will ultimately be thrown. So Judas's real estate, at the entrance of the Valley of Hinnom, is in the area that pictures hell.

There are at least five ways we can apply the overarching principle of these accounts, that *God causes the wrath of man to praise Him*.

1. At the very least, it ought to fortify our respect for the Word of God, whose sixty-six books are one. With regard to its Old and New Testaments, Dr. Henrietta Mears liked to say, "The New is in the Old contained; the Old is in the New explained."[2]

The Bible is one book with one author and one theme. How else could more than forty writers from all walks of life, over a period of sixteen centuries and in three different languages, predict with such precision the acts performed by rebellious people, and have it fulfill a single purpose?

2. At the sight of hell–even the brief and poetic glimpse from the texts we've considered–we ought to thank God for loving us in such a way that He gave His one-of-a-kind Son, that whoever believes in Him will not follow Judas into the pit of eternal destruction but will instead realize His merciful deliverance and eternal dwelling in the presence of God. By the grace of God, you can know that your real estate is in heaven, where Christ is preparing a place for you, and from which He is going to come, anytime now, and take us home. As Paul and Silas told the Philippian jailer, "Believe on the Lord Jesus Christ, and you will be saved, you and your household" [Acts 16:31 NKJV].

3. Our brief tour of these cursed grounds should make sin less of an attractive nuisance. I'm much more likely to toy with sin if I think of it as a potent weapon that empowers me, like a .44 Magnum pistol, than if I realize it is powerless against God's purpose.

As the Lord told Saul from heaven, "It is hard for you to kick against the goads" [Acts 26:14 NKJV]. The Bible also says that the way of the transgressor is hard. Since God causes even the vengeful anger and spiteful rebellion of man to result in His praise, ultimately–since the day is coming when every knee will bow and every tongue confess that Jesus is Lord, to the glory of God the Father—why settle for calling Him "Rabbi" now, as Judas did? In view of the futility of thwarting God's purpose, why not surrender the members of our bodies like captured weapons, and commit ourselves to live for Him?

4. The lessons of Judas's real estate should make us bow before our Maker and confess: "Thou art the Potter; I am the clay." It ought to lead each of us to yield to Him with an attitude that says, "*Have Thine own way, Lord.*" If you have been struggling with a particular area of obedience to the will of God. I invite you to surrender to Him now. In the quiet of your heart, just say, *Not my will, but Thine be done.* Those are the words that Jesus said on your behalf, and God saved Him out of the death that is worse than any prospect you may be dreading in the will of God.

5. Instead of fretting over the events of this life that you *don't* control—the performance of your retirement funds, a loved one's illness, the threat of terrorism–make sure you're honoring the Lord in the things you *do* control. If the actions of God's enemies are under His control to the degree indicated in these passages, without any coercion of people against their will, don't you think the same is true of your unsaved spouse or boss, and of whoever seems to be standing in the way of your progress toward proper goals? Even the heads of terrorist organizations and rogue states arc like clay in the hands of their Potter, and *God causes the wrath of man to praise Him.*

Sample Doctrinal Sermon
Authority in the Church

Christ Governs His Church as Congregations Yield to the Spiritual Guides they Affirm

I. All Authority Resides in Christ *Exclusively*
   A. He has been given all authority in heaven and on earth (Matt. 28:18).
   B. He is the Head of the Church, His body (Col. 1:18; Eph. 5:22-24).

C. He is the Shepherd of the Church, God's flock (John 10:11-16; Heb. 13:20).
D. He is the High Priest of the Church, a priesthood (1 Pet. 2:9; Heb. 2:17-31).
E. He is the Vine upon whom the branches depend (John 15).

II. Christ Resides in All Believers *Equally*
A. He indwells the Church, His temple (1 Cor. 3:16-17).
B. He indwells believers individually (Rom. 8:9; 1 Cor. 6:19).
1. All believers are members of one another in the body of Christ (Rom. 12:4-5; 1 Cor. 12:12-13).
2. All believers have a capacity for understanding the Word of Christ (1 John 2:20, 27; 1 Cor. 2:15; Col. 3:16).
3. All believers are empowered to minister as priests (1 Pet. 2:5, 9; Rom 12:1; James 5:16).
4. All believers are gifted to serve one another (Rom. 12:6-8).
5. All believers are to participate in the selection and affirmation of biblical officers (Acts 6:1-6; 1 Thess. 5:12-13; 1 Tim. 3:10; Heb. 13:17).
6. All believers are to participate in the discipline of erring members and elders (Matt. 18:15-20; 1 Cor. 5:12-13; 1 Thess. 5:14; 2 Thess. 3:14; 1 Tim. 5:19).

III. Qualified Officers Serve as Christ's *Executives*
A. Only those recognized by the congregation for their spiritual maturity and exemplary character are charged with the responsibility to shepherd the flock of God (Acts 20:17, 28; 1 Tim. 3:1-7; Titus 1:5-9; 1 Peter 5:1-4; Heb. 13:7, 17).
B. The authority of elders
1. Managers of God's household (1 Tim. 3:5)
2. In charge of those allotted to their care (1 Pet. 5:3)
3. Possess authority, that must not be abused (1 Pet. 5:3)
4. Authorized to "let no one despise" their exhortation and rebuke (Titus 2:15)
5. Accountable to Christ for those responsible to submit to them (Heb. 13:17)

Sample Biographical Sermon (Manuscript Style)

A Man Called Andrew
John 1:35-42

Meet Andrew. He's not a big-name Christian, like Peter, Paul, or Mary. He's like most of us, whose ministries are little celebrated and mostly behind the scenes. Yet, by identifying with Andrew we are motivated in four areas: our priorities, our preparation for ministry, our pursuit of Jesus Christ, and our personal relationships with others.

Andrew is a Greek name that means "manly." Manliness can be thought of not only as maleness, but as describing the maturity of a faithful follower of Christ regardless of sex.[3] In this sense, the subject of our study lived up to the meaning of his name, and so can everyone of us who will.

The fact that he had a Greek name is interesting, since John 1:44 indicates that he was from Bethsaida, the fishing village on the northern shore of the lake called Galilee, and the brother of Simon (Peter), a Jew. This may indicate that Andrew and his family were not in isolation from the world in their day, but rubbed shoulders with unbelievers, like we know at school and work.

Andrew lived in the shadow of his brother, Peter. Both were fishermen by trade. The brothers apparently formed a partnership with James and John. Fishing was physically demanding. If Andrew shook your hand, you would have felt his calluses and strength from long hours of rowing and handling fish nets. He worked hard for a living, like most of us.

Mark 1:29 refers to the house of Simon and Andrew, near the synagogue in Capernaum. The reference to Peter's mother-in-law, in the next verse, indicates that Peter was married. Living with his married brother, who would become the lead disciple and spokesman for the twelve apostles, Andrew seems to have been overshadowed.

Though less prominent than Peter, Andrew was his own man, a disciple of John the Baptist. This observation leads us to consider the first way in which Andrew challenges us:

I. Our Priorities

Beginning with John 1:35, we read:

> Again, the next day, John stood with two of his disciples. And looking at Jesus as He walked, he said, "Behold the Lamb of God!" The two disciples heard him speak, and they followed Jesus. Then Jesus turned, and seeing them following, said to them, "What do you seek?" They said to Him, "Rabbi" (which is to say when translated, Teacher), "where are You staying?" He said to them, "Come and see." They came and saw where He was staying, and remained with Him that day (now it was about the tenth hour). One of the two who heard John speak, and followed Him, was Andrew, Simon Peter's brother.

To have been a disciple of John, Andrew would have had to sacrifice lots of hours and potential income from his fishing business. He would have put spiritual concerns ahead of material interests. From what we have read, there is reason to believe that if Andrew were living today, he would be an active member of a local church-something any believer can be. You and I do not have to be a Peter, Paul, or Mary to be faithful, available, and teachable! You simply have to put first things first.

The second hallmark of Andrew's character is that he was a prepared man. And his readiness to act in response to divine direction challenges us in the area of …

II. Our Preparation

Andrew would have been baptized by John, indicating his repentance of sin and identification with John's message of the kingdom. He was committed to receiving Messiah on His terms. He was living up to the light (truth) that he had. You don't have to be a prominent leader to do that. And yet, having become a faithful follower in response to divine revelation is the most important quality of a godly leader. It qualified Andrew to lead a man to Christ who would far outshine Andrew in greatness. The first step in bringing others to Jesus is to make sure we are practicing all that we know to be true. You and I cannot expect to lead others into receptivity to spiritual things that we do not have ourselves. *Faithful followers of Christ bring others to Him.*

A third principle we can draw from the life of Andrew is found in verses 35-37. Here we are told that he and another of John's disciples followed Jesus. Consider, then …

III. Our Pursuit of Jesus

John the Baptist got the attention of the religious leaders of Israel. A delegation of priests and Levites were sent from Jerusalem to ascertain whether he claimed to be the Christ, Elijah, or the *Prophet*. In John 1:23, the Baptist indicated his role as the Messiah's forerunner, and the next day he identified Jesus as the Lamb of God, who takes away the sin of the world. In John 1:34, John says of Jesus, "I have seen and testified that this is the Son of God" [NKJV]

Andrew was one of two men who acted in response to John's identification of Jesus as the Lamb of God. When asked, "What do you seek?" Andrew was the one who asked where Jesus was staying. When invited to come and see, Andrew and his companion (probably John the Evangelist) came and saw. He was not a mere hearer of the prophetic word, but one who acted on it with a proper sense of self-interest. Andrew sought to know Jesus personally. In a similar way, you and I need to pursue Christ for our own benefit before attempting to introduce others to Him. The personal pursuit of God logically follows hearts that have been prepared on the basis of the right priorities. Acting with a sense of desperate personal need logically precedes the invitation of others to join us.

One reason that our witnessing is often weak, sporadic, or nonexistent, is that our own experiences of God are weak, sporadic, or nonexistent. If we are letting the Lord Jesus meet our deepest longings for truth and grace, we will not hesitate to bring others to meet Him. *Faithful followers of Christ bring others to Him.* Andrew didn't hesitate. He ran and got Peter, and this brings us to the fourth area of challenge:

IV. Our Personal Relationships

In verses 41-42, we read, "He first found his own brother Simon, and said to him, 'We have found the Messiah' (which is translated, the Christ). And he brought him to Jesus. Now when Jesus looked at him, He said, 'You are Simon the son of Jonah. You shall be called Cephas' (which is translated, A Stone)" [NKJV] .

Andrew did what anyone of us can do. He began with the person nearest to him who did not know Christ. The words translated "found" and "brought" imply that Andrew went to some effort. Whether Peter was wary, reluctant, or quite willing, we aren't told. But having expended the time and energy to look for Peter and to locate him, Andrew also did whatever may have been necessary to help Peter overcome any reticence to come with him to Jesus.

In the same way, to bring your family member, friend, or acquaintance to Jesus may take some persistent effort. And in the same way, your friend could be the next Billy Graham, D. L. Moody, Charles Spurgeon, Martin Luther, or Mother Teresa! Your friend could be another Andrew, Priscilla, or Dorcas. God used Andrew to make introductions between Jesus Christ and Peter, who would later express the confession of faith on which Christ would build His Church! It would be Peter, not Andrew, who walked on the water. Peter was first to enter the empty tomb of Jesus. It was Peter whose sermon at Pentecost was used to gather in three thousand people all one day. And it was Peter who used the keys of the kingdom to open the doors of evangelism to every ethnic group. But where would Peter have been without the faithful witness of his less flamboyant brother, Andrew?

Bible students have noticed that each time Andrew is mentioned in this Gospel, he is bringing someone to Jesus. In chapter 6, it is Andrew who brings the boy with the loaves and fish to the Lord. In 12:22, it is Andrew again who goes to Jesus with a request on the part of some Greeks who wanted an interview with Him. No wonder Andrew was made the patron saint of both Russia and Greece. But as the Scripture paints his portrait, he is a manly man, and he challenges each of us in the areas of our priorities, preparation, pursuits, and personal contacts.

I first got acquainted with Andrew in 1982, when the Billy Graham Crusade came to Boise, Idaho, and our small church participated in that effort. We learned that as big a name as Billy has, eight out of every ten persons who respond to his invitation to trust Jesus Christ were brought to the crusade, not by his name, but by a Christian friend who cared about them.

Even Andrew may be a big-name Christian in contrast to you and me. But his willingness to introduce those near him to Jesus Christ gives us an example that we can follow, if only we will. If you have not yet come to Christ, you can do so today. Simply believe in the Lord Jesus Christ and you will be saved [Acts 16:31]. To believe *in* Him is to trust Him as the Son of God who came as a man, lived a sinless life, offered Himself as the sacrifice and died in your place, to pay the penalty of your sins, and who rose again.

If you know the Lord Jesus as your Savior today, it is probably because someone was willing to be an "Andrew" to you. In any case, God confronts us in this passage with the life of a man who serves as an example to us. *Faithful followers of Christ bring others to Him.*

Sample Gospel Sermon (Manuscript Style)

From Death to Life
John 5:24-29

About 1930, the Communist leader Bukharin journeyed from Moscow to Kiev. His mission was to address a huge assembly. His subject, atheism. For a solid hour he aimed his heavy artillery at Christianity, hurling argument and ridicule. At last he was finished and viewed what seemed to be the smoldering ashes of men's faith. "Are there any questions?" Bukharin demanded. A solitary man arose and asked permission to speak. He mounted the platform and moved close to the Communist. The audience was breathlessly silent as the man surveyed them first to the right, then to the left. At last he shouted the ancient Orthodox greeting, "CHRIST IS RISEN!" The vast assembly arose as one man, and the response came crashing like the sound of an avalanche, "HE IS RISEN INDEED!"[4]

Today, hundreds of people pass by Lenin's mausoleum in Moscow's Red Square and view the corpse of a father of Communism. The nation has a body on its hands and is not quite sure what to do with it. Such is not the case with Christians–once committed to mental asylums in the former Soviet Union, for their belief in God. While Lenin has obviously passed from the state of life to death, the believer in Jesus Christ has passed from death to life.

Beginning with John 5:24, and concluding with verse 29, our Lord speaks of life as freedom from judgment. He says in effect that

I. Believers are Spiritually Free from God's Judgment Now

"Most assuredly, I say to you, he who hears My word and believes in Him who sent Me has everlasting life, and shall not come into judgment, but has passed from death into life." [NKJV]

The "death" Jesus is talking about at the end of verse 24 is spiritual death. Spiritual death is separation from the love of God. It is the consequence of our choice, in Adam, to disobey God. Romans 5:12 explains: "Therefore, just as through one man sin entered the world, and death through sin, and thus death spread to all men, because all sinned" [NKJV].

According to history, I was born in the state of California. But according to Scripture, I was also born in the state of death. Ephesians 2:1-2 tells us: "And you He made alive, who were dead in trespasses and sins, in which you once walked according to the course of this world, according to the prince of the power of the air, the spirit who now works in the sons of disobedience." [NKJV]

The Bible's good news is that a person can move from one state to another. Just as definitely as I moved out of California and crossed the state line into Oregon in 1973, I also passed out of the state where I was subject to the death penalty and into the state where "there is therefore now no condemnation for those who are in Christ Jesus" [Rom. 8:1 NKJV].

How do I know? I know it because God's Word assures me that Jesus and His words are absolutely trustworthy. John 5:24, in the New

American Standard Version, begins with the words "Truly, truly." This signals the great importance and reliability of what follows. And the first thing I'm told about my new state is that I passed into it permanently. It happened when I heeded the message of Jesus Christ, recorded in the Bible. I believed the Father who sent Him. I began depending on God the Father as having loved the world of people–including me–in such a way that He gave His unique Son, Jesus, that whoever believes in Him should not perish but have eternal life.

Eternal life is not just natural life that never ends. It is a relationship with God in which I am no longer subject to judgment, because He punished Jesus His Son for my sins, in my place. Isaiah 53:6 describes the believer when it states, "All we like sheep have gone astray; we have turned, everyone, to his own way; and the LORD has laid on Him the iniquity of us all" [NKJV]. But not only did Jesus take the punishment for my sins; His own righteousness was put to my account so [hat God the Father relates to me as He relates to Jesus! Second Corinthians 5:21 says of the Father, "For He made [Christ] who knew no sin to be sin for us, that we might become the righteousness of God in Him" [NKJV].

When John 5:24 says of me, "has passed," it translates the perfect tense, which speaks of action that was completed in the past, with a result that continues to present. The result is life free from judgment–permanently. *Spiritual life is freedom from judgment.*

My possession of this life is not only *permanently* but also *presently*. In verse 25, Jesus goes on to say, "Most assuredly, I say to you, the hour is coming, and now is, when the dead will hear the voice of the Son of God; and those who hear will live" [NKJV]. The "hour" that "now is" refers to the present, when those still under God's judgment "hear the voice of the Son of God" in the sense of heeding the Bible's good news. This could include you, this very moment. Perhaps you are finally able to understand, and willing to receive, the work God has accomplished for you through His Son. God's promise is that "those who hear will live." In other words, you, too, will pass out of the state of condemnation and into the state of freedom from God's judgment already poured out on Jesus in your place!

This spiritual relocation takes place *permanently, presently*, and also *personally*. Verses 26-27 tell us that it all depends on the Son's relationship to the Father, and upon our relationship to the Son.

"For as the Father has life in Himself, so He has granted the Son to have life in Himself, and has given Him authority to execute judgment also, because He is the Son of Man." [NKJV]

"The Son of Man" is Jesus' favorite title. It identifies Him not only as a fellow human being, but as the Messiah who is God the Son in human form. His coming was anticipated with this title in Daniel 7:13-14, where He is said to be given dominion, glory, and a kingdom.

Since the believer was judged in union with Him at Calvary, and has already been raised spiritually with Him in glory, he or she has received life very *personally*, because *life is freedom from judgment*. No wonder the Lord says, in John 8:36, "Therefore if the Son makes you free, you shall be free indeed" [NKJV].

Verses 28-29 of our text advance the thought from the believer's spiritual freedom from God's judgment *now*, to the fact that …

II. Believers Will Be Physically Free from God's Judgment Later

> "Do not marvel at this for the hour is coming in which all who are in the graves will hear His voice and come forth." [NKJV]

If you have already crossed over the border from the state of death into the state of spiritual life, *permanently, presently*, and *personally*, then it should not be particularly marvelous or hard to accept the concept of a resurrection *physically*. In fact, verse 28 teaches resurrection for all the dead–including unbelievers–even Lenin! But the prospect of mere resurrection is no reason to be encouraged, because there are two kinds of resurrection, and only one is good. Verse 29 states, "those who have done good, to the resurrection of life, and those who have done evil, to the resurrection of condemnation" [NKJV]. The "good" is to have heard Jesus' words and believed Him who sent Him. It may include all of the deeds that give evidence of having believed. The "evil" is to have rejected

Jesus. It may include the deeds that confirm a person's unbelief. But the issue is whether or not a person has believed in Christ.

Physical freedom from God's judgment, then, is simply the result of spiritual freedom from His judgment, which already belongs to anyone who simply trusts in Jesus. The question is whether you are spiritually dead or alive. Do you possess permanently, presently, and personally the spiritual freedom from judgment that results in the physical freedom from judgment? If you're not sure, you can make certain right now. Simply believe on the Lord Jesus Christ, and you will be saved. You will receive as a free gift the *life* that is *freedom from judgment.*

Sample Textual-Expository Sermon (Example Of Preaching A Chapter, A Psalm, And Prophetic Literature) Springs Of Thanksgiving

Isaiah 12:1-6
Remembering Our Redemption Produces Praise And Proclamation

I. Praise (1-3)
  A. Thanks for comfort in place of anger (1)
  B. Trust in response to God's powerful deliverance
    1. The believer's song of salvation (2)
    2. The believer's source of joy (3)
II. Proclamation (4-6)
  A. Telling every people group about Yahweh
    1. His name (4a)
    2. His deeds (4b)
    3. His majesty (4c)
  B. Trumpeting the Lord's triumph
    1. Singing of His glory (5a)
    2. Spreading His reputation (5b)
    3. Shouting His greatness (6)

Sample Expository Book Sermon the Book of Jude Believers are to Contend for the Faith In Light of Ungodly Men in the Church

Introduction

I. The Reason for Contending
    A. Because they are the elect of God (1)
        1. Loved in God (1a)
        2. Kept for Jesus Christ (1b)
    B. Because ungodly men crept in (4)
    C. Because of the tendency to defect (5-11)
        1. A reminder of general occurrences of apostasy (5-7)

Illustration

            a. Exodus (5)
            b. Flood (6)
            c. Sodom and Gomorrah (7)
        2. An account of specific apostasy (11)
            a. Like the way of Cain (1la)
            b. Like the way of Balaam (11b)
            c. Like the rebellion of Korah (11c)

Transition Sentence:

Believers are to contend for the faith in light of ungodly men in the Church

II. Ungodly Men in the Church
    A. Their deeds revealed (4,8-10)
        1. They changed the grace of God (8a)
        2. They rejected authority (8b)
        3. They reviled heavenly beings (8c, 9)
        4. They reviled like raging animals (10a)
    B. Their character revealed (12, 13, 16)

Illustration

        1. Pride (12a)
        2. Death (12b)
        3. Shame (13a)
        4. Darkness (13b)
        5. Dissatisfaction (16a)

6. Arrogance (16b)
7. Deceit

C. Their Judgment Foretold (14-15)
1. Occurs at the Lord's return (14)
2. Purpose to judge ungodliness (15)

Application:

III. "*How does a believer contend for the faith in light of ungodly men in the church?*"

A. Remember the words of the apostles (17-19)
1. Based on knowledge of Christ (17)
2. Warn of mockers in the end time (18)
3. Warn of godless men (19)

B. Keep one another in the love of God (20-21)
1. By building one another(20a)
2. By praying in the Holy Spirit (20b)
3. By waiting for eternal life (21)

C. Have mercy on those perishing (22-23)
1. Those who are wavering (22)
2. Those who are being destroyed (23a)
3. Those who are defiled (23b)
    a. In fear of defilement (23ba)
    b. In hate toward defilement (bb)

D. Be assured of victory (24-25)
1. The protecting God (24)
2. The saving God (25a, b)
3. The eternal God (25c)

Conclusion:

Principles:

1. The elect are loved in God.
2. The elect are kept for Jesus Christ.
3. Believers are to contend for Christian doctrine.
4. Ungodly men infiltrate the church.
5. Ungodly men can be a danger to believers.
6. Believers are to be reminded of the apostles' words

Theme:
Believers are to contend for the faith in light of ungodly men in the Church.

Introduction:
The book of Jude has been slighted considerably in Christian circles in these latter days, and yet no book in the New Testament speaks more to our generation than this small letter. It may be slighted by some because they feel that the importance of a book is determined by its length. Others may feel that because of its negative character, having stern warnings and rebukes, other New Testament books are to be preferred for reading and study, but Jude possesses a quality of life and concern throughout. Those who are tolerant to perverters of the faith will find the book of Jude distasteful, for its warnings are severe and uncompromising against defectors from the truth of Jesus Christ. To those of us, though, who approach the book of Jude with receptive hearts and the mind of the Spirit, Jude's words will be as clear and helpful as they were two thousand years ago. Jude teaches that *believers are to contend for the faith in the light of ungodly men in the Church.*

Conclusion:
If believers will be careful to recognize those who sow discord among them, and if they will rely on God, they will be doing the will of God, for *believers are to contend for the faith ill the light of ungodly men in the Church.*

Notes

Chapter 1

1. Source unknown.
2. The Second Helvetic Confession of 1566, initiated in 1561 by Swiss reformer Heinrich Bullinger (1504-1575), asserts that "the preaching of the Word of God is the Word of God." The explanation, "when this Word of God is now preached in the church by preachers lawfully called, we believe that the very Word of God is proclaimed," seems to confuse the absolute authority of Scripture itself with a questionable concept of ecclesiastical authority. In our view, whether or not one's sermon communicates God's message depends upon the proper development and delivery of the textual principles. (John M. Cromarty, "Bullinger and the Second Helvetic Confession," *Our Banner* [June 1976]. http://www.pcea.asn.au/bullingr.html.)
3. Haddon W. Robinson, Biblical Preaching (Grand Rapids: Baker, 1980), 30.
4. Lawrence O. Richards and Gary J. Bredfeldt, *Creative Bible Teaching* (Chicago: Moody.1998). 61ff.
5. Richards and Bredfeldt's well-known model for structuring lessons for creative Bible teaching involves "Hook, Book, Look, Took," and promotes the stating of lesson aims, based on the generalized meaning of the text, that are *cognitive, affective*, and *behavioral.* (Richards and Bredfeldt, *Creative Bible Teaching*, 160. 138ff).
6. R. E. O. White said. "Only when preaching is made an act of worship, in which divine truth is explored and shared from faith to faith, in the power of the Holy Spirit, with a view to persuasion and decision, then indeed divine things can happen and the Word of God be glorified." (R. E. O. White, *A Guide to Preaching* [Grand Rapids: Eerdmans, 1973], 11.)
7. See Walter L. Liefeld, *New Testament Exposition* (Grand Rapids: Zondervan, 1984), 3-24.
8. In the words of Merrill F. Unger, expository preaching is "preaching that expounds the Scriptures as a coherent and coordinated body of revealed truth." (Unger, *Principles of Expository Preaching* [Grand Rapids: Zondervan, 1955].), 48.
9. White, *A Guide to Preaching*, 3.

10. Richards and Bredfeldt, *Creative Bible Teaching*, 195.
11. *Exegesis* is "leading out"of a text what is in the text.
12. *Eisegesis* is "leading into" the text what is not there.
13. See Benjamin B. Warfield, *The Inspiration and Authority of the Bible* (Philadelphia: Presbyterian and Reformed Publishing, 1970); and Clark H. Pinnock, *Biblical Revelation* (Chicago: Moody. 1971),
14. Recommended Bible software includes Logos, Bible Works, QuickVerse, and Accordance.

Chapter 2

1. Though a variety of texts will be used to elucidate or illustrate various components of sermon preparation, 1 John 2:1-2 will serve as the text for a model sermon throughout the introductory chapters.
2. Richards and Bredfeldt, *Creative Bible Teaching*, 25.
3. J. I. Packer, *Knowing God* (Downers Grove, IL: InterVarsity Press, 1973), 33.
4. Richards and Bredfeldt, *Creative Bible Teaching*, 25.
5. Ibid.
6. Paul tells Timothy that it is the sacred writings that are able to give him the wisdom that leads to salvation through faith, which is in Christ Jesus (2 Tim. 3:13-15). In Romans 1:16, the gospel is said to be the "power of God to salvation for everyone who believes" (NKJV). God's Word never fails to accomplish the purpose for which He sends it (Isa. 55:11).
7. Richards and Bredfeldt, *Creative Bible Teaching*, 33, 35.
8. In Colossians 1:28 the presentation of every man complete in Christ is declared as the purpose for which Paul and the other apostles proclaimed Christ, "teaching every man and admonishing every man."
9. "In fact, the more committed we are to the authority of Scripture, the more dangerous it is to read the narratives incorrectly. There is no greater abuse of the Bible than to proclaim in God's name what God is not saying. God commands us not to bear false witness," (Robinson, quoted by Steven D. Mathewson, *The Art of Preaching Old Testament Narrative* (Grand Rapids: Baker, 2002], 12.)
10. Richards and Bredfeldt, *Creative Bible Teaching*, 62, quoting John H. Walton, Laurie Bailey, and Craig Williford, "*Bible-Based Curricula and the Crisis of Scriptural Authority*," Christian Education Journal 13, no. 3 (1993): 85.
11. Walter C. Kaiser Jr., *Toward all Exegetical Theology: Biblical Exegesis for Preaching and Teaching* (Grand Rapids: Baker, 1981),70.
12. Nothing in Scripture indicates that the Lord's Sermon on the Mount in Matthew 5-7 (or the sermons of Peter, Stephen, and Paul, recorded in the book of Acts) includes every word that was spoken or was intended to be repeated verbatim to modern audiences.

13. When Paul tells Timothy to give attention to reading (1 Tim. 4:13), he also mentions exhortation and doctrine, implying the ministry of the public reading of Scripture, as indicated in the New International Version, and by italics in the New American Standard Bible and New American Standard Bible. Updated Edition.
14. Memorization, meditation, recitation, singing, prayer, and exhortation represent biblical uses of Scripture apart from the authoritative declaration of its meaning from the original context to people in a different context (Ps. 1:2; 119:11).
15. See Leland Ryken, *The Word of God in English* (Wheaton, IL: Crossway, 2002).
16. "The Second great need for a science of hermeneutics is *to bridge the gap between our minds and the minds of the Biblical writers.*" (Bernard Ramm, Protestant Biblical Interpretation [Grand Rapids: Baker, 1980], 4)
17. See Roy B. Zuck, *Basic Bible Interpretation* (Wheaton: Victor, 1991), 16-18.
18. That the Old Testament was the "Bible" of Jesus and His apostles is often forgotten, according to Halvor Ronning, tour guide and founder of the Home for Bible Translators in Jerusalem, Israel.
19. For example, the early date of the Exodus and conquest of Canaan (1446-1406 B.C.), indicated by the biblical chronology, is supported by the discovery of remnants of the collapsed wall of Jericho in the destruction layer dated with pottery that Garstang concluded was not found after 1400 B.C. (Bryant G. Wood, "The Walls of Jericho," *Bible and Spade* [Spring 1999]: 35-42.)
20. See the relationship benveen Paul's personal testimony and the passion and purity of his motivation to preach (1 Cor. 15:9-11; Gal 1:11-23).
21. See Leland Ryken, *How to Read the Bible as Literature* (Grand Rapids: Zondervan, 1984).
22. In John 3:3-8, 16 the word ἄνωθεν may best be translated as "above," as in this context, rather than as "again" or "anew," as it is sometimes translated.
23. In Galatians 1:10, Paul contrasts striving to please men with being a "bond servant" of Christ (NKJV).
24. Scriptural evidence that God's Word needed to be explained in order for the writers' contemporaries to understand it includes the fact that Ezra and other priests helped the people understand the Law after it was publicly read. Nehemiah 8:8 says they "gave the sense" and "helped them to understand the reading" (NKJV). In Matthew 13:10-11, Jesus indicated that one reason He spoke in parables is that the ability to know the mysteries of the kingdom of heaven was not granted to all. The writer of Hebrews 5:12 refers to readers who remained in need of teaching on the elementary principles of the oracles of God, even after the time when they should have become teachers. Also, Peter refers to Paul's writings as containing "some things hard to understand" (2 Pet. 3:16 NKJV).
25. See Ronald B. Mayers, *Balanced Apologetics* (Grand Rapids: Kregel, 1984), 52-53.
26. Ramm. *Protestant Biblical Inerpretation*, 101-2.

27. Robert Traina, *Methodological Bible Study* (Wilmore, KY: Asbury Theological Seminary, 1952), 156.
28. Stanley A. Ellisen, *3 Worlds in Conflict* (Sisters, OR: Multnornah, 1998), 24.
29. The "seed" of "the woman" was to be bruised on the heel, according to Genesis 3:15, an apparent reference to the temporary death of Christ, who, as the Suffering Servant of Isaiah 53, fulfilled Yahweh's promise to Abraham in Genesis 12:3: "In you all the families of the earth shall be blessed" (NKJV). (See Galatians 3:7-9, 26-29.)
30. Ellisen, *3 Worlds in Conflict*, 23.
31. A clear example of changes in the administration of God's kingdom program on earth is found in His instruction to Peter to kill and eat creatures formerly forbidden for the sake of ceremonial cleanliness (Acts 10:13-15).
32. See Lewis Sperry Chafer, *Salvation* (Grand Rapids: Zondervan, 1917), 31-39; and Earl D. Radmacher, *Salvation* (Nashville: Word. 2000), 113-28.
33. The doctrines of justification, sanctification, and glorification are related but distinct, and not to be confused. (See 1 Thessalonians 1:9-10 and Titus 2:11-14.) Confusing justification and sanctification leads to misunderstanding both grace and works (Rom. 11:6).
34. "The right attitude or approach to the Bible is not all that is necessary for understanding its meaning ... There is a right and a wrong way to build. Furthermore, certain skills must be developed before a person, through using the right method, can build properly. So it is with understanding the Bible." (J. Robertson McQuilkin, *Understanding and Applying the Bible* [Chicago: Moody, 1984], 14.)
35. Ramm, *Protestant Biblical Interpretation*, 1.
36. Ibid.
37. "To determine the single meaning is the objective of biblical interpretation. Otherwise, the fancy of the interpreter, or the preconceptions he imposes on the text, becomes the authority." (McQuilkin, *Understanding and Applying the Bible*, 66)
38. E. D. Hirsch makes a helpful distinction between *meaning* and *significance*. Meaning, or implication, is *in* what the author wrote, and doesn't change, while significance speaks of the relationship of meaning to things, and does change. (E. D. Hirsch, "Validity in lnterpretation [New Haven and London: Yale, 1967], 63.) Even Old Testament types exemplify the single meaning of Scripture in that they epitomize the truth fulfilled in the New Testament.
39. "The historical and grammatical principle. This is inseparable from the literal principle. The interpreter must give attention to *grammar*, to *times, circumstances, and conditions* of the writer of the biblical book; and to the *context* of the passage." (Ramm, *Protestant Biblical Interpretation*, 55.)
40. 40. For a fuller explanation of these principles, see Ramm, *Protestant Biblical Interpretation*, 97ff.; Zuck, *Basic Bible Interpretation*. 9-26; and Elliot E. Johnson,

Expository Hermeneutics: An Introduction (Grand Rapids: Zondervan. 1990), 31-53.

41. Ramm, *Protestant Biblical Interpretation*, 98.
42. Ibid.
43. Henrietta C. Mears, *What the Bible Is All About* (Ventura, CA: Regal, 1999), 23.
44. Ramm, *Protestant Biblical Interpretation*, 105.
45. See ibid., 107ff, for a good discussion of how this principle relates to various theories regarding the unity of Scripture.
46. Ibid., 197ff.
47. Ramm, on ibid., pages 111ff, discusses the unity of Scripture as a corrective to interpretation methods that assert a plurality in the meaning of Scripture, including allegory, cults, and Protestant Pietism.
48. Ibid., 113.
49. David Neff, "Hermeneutics, Anyone?" *Christianity Today* 49, no. 11 (2005): 92.
50. See Zuck, *Basic Bible Interpretation*, 44-45.
51. Ramm, *Protestant Biblical Interpretation*, 115.
52. William Ames, *The Marrow of Theology*, ed. and trans. John D. Eusden (Boston: Pilgrim, 1968), 188.
53. "The word 'inductive' means to go from specific details to a general principle." (Richards and Bredfeldt, *Creative Bible Teaching*, 63.)
54. Ibid., 30. The authors distinguish the conservative view of Scripture from the liberal view, which treats the Bible as a record of human attempts to find God in the normal events of life; and from the neo-orthodox view, which asserts that the Bible becomes the Word of God to those who encounter Him through it.
55. *Connotation* is "a meaning in addition to or apart from the thing explicitly named or described by a word." *Denotation*, by contrast, refers to that which is marked out plainly. (*Webster's New American Dictionary*)
56. In Galatians 4:24-31. Paul states that he is speaking allegorically in his reference to Hagar and Sarah as representatives of Mount Sinai and Jerusalem. Interpreting this allegory is not to be confused with the allegorical interpretation of Scripture in general For a good discussion of allegorical interpretation, see Traina, *Methodological Bible Study*. 172-74. Also see Zuck, *Basic Bible Interpretation*, 143-68.
57. W. E. Vine, *Expository Dictionary of New Testament Words*, 4 vols. (Old Tappan, NJ: Revell, 1940), 1:208.
58. See the work of Arnold Fruchtenbaum, who sets forth the four ways in which New Testament writers quote the Old Testament, including the Rabbinic method of drash, which applies a passage to only one point of similarity. (Arnold G. Fruchtenbaum, "Rabbinic Quotations of the Old Testament and How It Relates to Joel 2 and Acts 2," www.pre-trib.org/article-view.php?id=2.)
59. Source unknown.

60. Ramm, *Protestant Biblical Interpretation*, 115; Zuck, *Basic Bible Interpretation*, 20.
61. Ramm, *Protestant Biblical Interpretaion*, 115.
62. Note: More complete, "working definitions" for these terms will be given in Chapter 4. Also see Zuck, *Basic Bible Interpretation*, 279-92; and Walter C. Kaiser and Moises Silva, *An Introduction to Biblical Hermeneutics* (Grand Rapids: Zondervan, 1994), 271-83. For a good discussion of the basis of valid applications, see Johnson, *Expository Hermeneutics*, 224-64.
63. Arthur B. Whiting. as quoted by William Milton Jones, Professor of Homiletics (class handout, Western Conservative Baptist Seminary, 1971-1975).
64. This table by S. F. Logsdon was taken from Richard Parke. unpublished "Complete Class Notes for PTH 201" (Western Conservative Baptist Seminary, 1972), 2.
65. Kaiser, *Toward an Exegetical Theology*, 19.
66. John R. W. Stott, *The Preacher's Portrait* (Grand Rapids: William B. Eerdmans Publishing Co., 1961), 17.
67. Ibid., 32.
68. Howard Hendricks, *Teaching to Change Lives: Seven Proven Ways to Make Your Teaching Come Alive* (Sisters, OR: Multnomah. 1987), 39.
69. Richards and Bredfeldt, Creative Bible Teaching, 321.
70. Ibid., 153.
71. Ibid., 94-95.
72. Hendricks. *Teaching to Change Lives,* 93.
73. Richards and Bredfeldt, Creative Bible Teaching, 93.
74. Hendricks, *Teaching to Change Lives,* 94.
75. Richards and Bredfeldt, Creative Bible Teaching. 64.
76. Robinson, Biblical Preaching, 27.

Chapter 3

1. Whiting, as quoted by Jones (class handout, 1974).
2. Donald Macleod, *The Problem of Preaching*, (Philadelphia: Fortress, 1987), 23.
3. "Others may perceive the preacher as a thinker, quiet man of prayer, avid reader, a heavenly minded man, a spiritual psychiatrist, strong leader, good mixer, onc who understands finances, and a good communicator. But his usefulness as a reliable steward (1 Cor. 4:1-2), trusted ambassador (2 Cor. 5:19-20) and credible witness (Acts 1:8; 26:16) depends on his integrity as a man of God." (Jones, class handout, 1974).
4. Hendricks, *Teaching to Change Lives*, 74 .
5. Ibid.
6. Ibid.
7. The first foreign missionary, Jonah, was used, in spite of himself, to show God's concern for Gentiles, in contrast to Israel's lack of concern.

8. "The Oracles of Balaam" refers to Balaam's prophecies found in Numbers 23-24.
9. Hendricks, Teaching to Change Lives, 35.
10. Ibid., 17.
11. Andrew W. Blackwood, *The Fine Art of Preaching* (Grand Rapids: Baker, 1976), introduction by Ralph G. Turnbull.
12. James 3:1 warns that not many should be teachers due to the stricter judgment they will incur.
13. For discussion on the differences between ministries and offices, see Alexander Strauch, *Biblical Eldership* (Littleton: Lewis and Roth, 1995), 101-17; 175-80; Earl D. Radmacher, *The Nature of the Church* (Portland: Western Baptist Press, 1972), 269-99; Robert L. Saucy, *The Church in God's Program* (Chicago: Moody, 1972), 127-65; and Jay E. Adams, *Shepherding God's Flock* (Grand Rapids: Zondervan, 1986).
14. See Unger, *Principles of Expository Preaching*, 56-63.
15. Remo P. Fausti and Edward L. McGlone, *Understanding Oral Communication* (Menlo Park, CA: Cummings, 1972), 176.
16. Hendricks. *Teaching to Change Lives*. 84.
17. Ibid., 86.
18. Ibid.
19. Ibid., 95.
20. Ibid,. 87.
21. Ibid., 76.
22. Richards and Bredfeldt, *Creative Bible Teaching*, 109.
23. The attributes of God are commonly differentiated as *communicable* and *non-communicable*. Noncommunicable attributes include His omniscience, omnipotence, omnipresence, and eternality, which man will never manifest. God's communicable attributes, however, describe the divine nature that believers *can* manifest, including grace, mercy, peace, love, patience, kindness, etc. (W. Robert Cook, *Systematic Theology in Outline Form*, vol. 1 [Portland: Western Baptist Seminary Press, 1970], 54-58. Also see Stephen Charnock, *The Existence and Attributes of God* [Minneapolis: Central Baptist Theological Seminary, 1797; repr., Minneapolis: Klock & Klock. 1977], and A. W. Tozer, *The Knowledge of the Holy* [New York: Harper Collins, 1961].)
24. See www.reformed.org/documents/wcf_with_proofs/.
25. See Acts 11:15-18 for evidence of Gentiles believing and being baptized in the Holy Spirit with the apostles' indwelling at Pentecost.
26. Consider Moses in Exodus 4:11-12, and Jeremiah in Jeremiah 1:5-10.
27. Hendricks, *Teaching to Change Lives*, 25.
28. As Hendricks asserts, "if you stop growing today, you stop teaching tomorrow." (Ibid., 60.)

29. Hendricks made the following statement relative to the Seven Laws of the Teacher (Teacher, Education, Activity, Communication, Heart, Encouragement, and Readiness): "If you boil them down, these seven laws essentially call for a passion to communicate." (Ibid, 15.)
30. Whiting, as quoted by Jones (class handout, 1974).

Chapter 4

1. Jones, lecture, 1974.
2. After seven years of unfruitful preaching, British-born Samuel Chadwick (1860-1932) reportedly burned all of the sermons he had prepared over that period. Turning to prayer to revitalize his ministry, Chadwick began to see remarkable conversions, which he later attributed to the "gift of Pentecost." He concluded, "Destitute of the Fire of God, nothing else counts: possessing Fire, nothing else matters." (www.homestead.com/ephesusfwb/files/fire2.doc) It was as principal of Cliff College, a Methodist training school for preachers, that Chadwick wrote his famous book *The Way to Pentecost* (Fort Washington, PA: Christinn Literature Crusade, 2001), published after his death in 1932. It is not necessary to adopt Chadwick's nineteenth-century Wesleyan Pentecostalism to agree that effective preaching must be both Spirit filled and true to Scripture. Indeed, one cannot truly have one without the other.
3. Jones, "An Investigation and Explanation of the Whiting System of Homiletics as a Practical Approach to Preaching," (master's thesis, Western Conservative Baptist Seminary, 1965), 12.
4. Undoubtedly, refinements have been made by virtually every student who has implemented the system and adapted it based on personal abilities and style. Ron Allen, Duane Dunham, Dennis Wretlind, H. Wayne House, Rev. Ron Harper, and Rev. Norm Carlson have all taught the Whiting Method and contributed to its development.
5. Jones, lecture, 1970.
6. Jones, "An Investigation and Explanation of the Whiting System," 34.
7. As sample sermons from various literary genres arc developed in chapters 8-15, indicators of where a text begins and ends will be identified by various markers.
8. As was illustrated in Figure 2-3, the context of a biblical passage may be thought of as concentric circles beginning with words and extending to clauses, sentences, immediate context, argument of the book, dispensation, culture, and history.
9. Whiting, as quoted by Jones, "An Investigation and Explanation of the Whiting System," 5.
10. According to Whiting, "The textual-expository sermon is one in which the message is prepared within the confines and order of a given text." (Ibid., 48.)
11. Ibid.
12. Ibid., 36.

13. Ibid.
14. "An *Essentially Literal* translation 'strives to translate the exact words of the original-language text in a translation, but not in such a rigid way as to violate the normal rules of language and syntax' of the translation language." (Ryken, *The Word of God in English*, 19.)
15. For help on diagramming see Lee L. Kantenwein, *Diagrammatical Analysis* (Winona Lake, IN: BMH Books, 1979).
16. For example, the word translated "spirit," in Romans 8 recurs.
17. Suggested resources for word studies for non-language users include, for word studies: Kenneth Wuest, *Word Studies in the Greek New Testament*, vol. 1-3 (Grand Rapids: Eerdmans, 1973); A. T. Robertson, *Word Pictures in the New Testament*, vol. 1-6 (Nashville: Broadman, 1930); Donald J. Wiseman, cd., *Tyndale Old Testament Commentaries* (Downers Grove, IL: Intervarsity Press, 1976); Hershel H. Hobbs, *Preaching Values from the Papyri* (Grand Rapids: Baker, 1964); F. F. Bruce, *The New International Commentary on the New Testament* (Grand Rapids: Eerdmans, 1971). For grammatical help, see Nigel Turner, *Grammatical Insights into the New Testament* (Edinburgh: T & T Clark, 1965); Ronald A. Ward, *Hidden Meaning in the New Testament* (Old Tappan, NJ: Revell, 1969).
18. Helpful Bible software includes Libronix, BibleWorks, Accordance, and QuickVerse.
19. See explanation in the introduction.
20. Without the ability to read the text in its original language, a preacher forfeits a wealth of information, including (in the Greek New Testament) emphasis based on word order, the presence or absence of the article, figures of speech, synonyms not used, Hebraisms, etc.
21. Jones, "The Relation of Exegesis to Homiletics" (supplementary review sheet, Western Conservative Baptist Seminary, September 21, 1972).
22. Ibid.
23. Dennis O. Wretlind, "Greek Exegesis and The Whiting System of Homiletics: The Preacher's Preparation" (paper presented to Dr. W. Robert Cook, Western Conservative Baptist Seminary, December 10, 1973).
24. Ibid., 7.
25. Ibid.
26. Ibid., 7-8.
27. Wretlind, "Principles of Exegesis in the Greek New Testament" (class syllabus for NT 201, Western Conservative Baptist Seminary. 1973).
28. Adapted from Wretlind, "Greek Exegesis," 11-14.
29. Jones, "An Investigation and Explanation of the Whiting System," 7,31.
30. Brevard S. Childs all but dismisses the explanation of biblical material on the basis of timeless, universal ideas, describing this approach as an "idealistic philosophy." This would be true if the principles were imposed upon the text rather

than exegetically induced from it. So we agree with Childs's statement, "In sum, the thematic approach to Biblical Theology cannot be dismissed categorically, but its success depends largely on how critically and skillfully it is employed." See Brevard S. Childs, *Biblical Theology of the Old and New Testaments* (Minneapolis: Fortress Press, 1992), 15-16.

31. Josh McDowell, *Right from Wrong* (Dallas: Word, 1994), 17.
32. Jones, "An Investigation and Explanation of the Whiting System," 31.
33. Ibid.
34. H. Wayne House, syllabus for Expository Preaching, Faith Evangelical Seminary, 2004.
35. Jones, "An Investigation and Explanation of the Whiting System," 32.
36. Adapted from ibid.
37. Ibid., 6, 33.
38. Robinson. *Biblical Preaching*, 31.
39. Richards and Bredfeldt, *Creative Bible Teaching*, 86.
40. Ibid., 133.
41. Jones, "An Investigation and Explanation of the Whiting System," 37.

Chapter 5

1. Richards and Bredfeldt, *Creative Bible Teaching*, 152.
2. www.ketchum.org/tacomacollapse.html.
3. http://en.wikipedia.org/wiki/Galloping_Gertie.
4. Richards and Bredfeldt, *Creative Bible Teaching*, 155-56.
5. Robinson, *Biblical Preaching*, 156.
6. Ibid., 125-33.
7. Ibid.
8. Jones, '"An Investigation and Explanation of the Whiting System," 39.
9. http://en.wikipedia.org/wiki/Assonance.
10. There may be exceptions, when it makes sense to start at the end of a text and work backward to the beginning, but this is unnatural and would require a good, easily explainable reason.
11. Jones, "An Investigation and Explanation of the Whiting System," 49.
12. Ibid.
13. Ibid., 24.
14. Stephen Farris asserts, "There is a fundamental analogy between Bible and contemporary world that gives life to sermons of vastly different styles." He views the preacher's creativity in discovering such analogies as connecting the relevance of a passage to the audience. See Stephen Farris, *Preaching That Matters* (Louisville: Westminister John Knox Press, 1998), 24.
15. Ibid. Also see Kaiser, *Toward an Exegetical Theology*, 123-24, for a concise listing and description of figures of speech.

16. Jones, "An Investigation and Explanation of the Whiting System," 51.
17. Richards and Bredfeldt, *Creative Bible Teaching*, 157.
18. Ibid.
19. Ibid., 157, 150.
20. Ibid., 157, 159.
21. This diagram is an adaptation of one that appears in ibid., 160.
22. See figure 3-1 for an illustration of the concept of incarnating the truth.
23. The introduction of formal invitations is generally attributed to Charles Grandison Finney (1792-1875), often assailed by some Christians for his overemphasis on man's free will and his Palagian interpretation of man's nature. Around 1835, Finney took the *mourner's seat* practice that Eleazar Wheelock had used in 1741 and called it the *anxious seat*. The anxious seat was "a front pew left vacant where at the end of the meeting 'the anxious may come and be addressed particularly ... and sometimes be conversed with individually."(J. I. Packer, "Puritan Evangelism," www.apuritansmind.com/Puritan%20 Evangelism/JIPackerPuritanEvangelism.htm.) In about 1815, however, Asahel Nettleton, (1783-1844), a Calvinist, introduced the prayer room, which later became known as the inquiry room, and home visitation to counsel those concerned about their souls. For a good defense of Finney against alleged attacks by Calvinists, see Jim Stewart, "No Uncertain Sound," www.gospeltruth.net/ nouncertain.htm. For a good analysis of how both Nettleton and Finney have affected modern evangelism, see Rick Nelson, "How Docs Doctrine Affect Evangelism? The Divergent Paths of Asahel Nettleton and Charles Finney," www.founders.org/FJ33/article1.html.
24. Example of an invitation in Scripture: God to man: "Where are you?" (Gen. 3:9). Other examples include Exodus 32:26; Joshua 24:15; 2 Chronicles 34:30-32: Nehemiah 9:38; Matthew 4:19; Luke 19:5; Acts 2:40; 19:8,26; and 26:28; and Revelation 22:17.
25. Richards and Bredfeldt, *Creative Bible Teaching*, 149.
26. Jones, "An Investigation and Explanation of the Whiting System," 55-56.
27. Ibid.
28. 28. James S. Hewett, ed., *Illustrations Unlimited* (Wheaton: Tyndalc, 1988),452.

Chapter 6

1. See Appendix for a sample Paragraph Sermon.
2. See Appendix, Galen Currah, "Outlining from the Nestle-Aland *Novum Testamentum Graece*" (handout, Western Conservative Baptist Seminary, ca. 1973). Used by permission.
3. Kurt Aland's *Synopsis Quattuor Evangeliorum* (New York: American Bible Society), which places side by side the Greek texts of parallel Gospel accounts, is a useful tool in understanding passages from the synoptic Gospels.

4. In what sense Christ went in the Spirit and proclaimed to the spirits in prison who were disobedient in the days of Noah; and how Noah's delivery by the ark relates to a saving effect of baptism, have been described as among the most difficult passages to interpret in the entire Bible. (William Barclay, *The Letters of James and Peter* [Edinburgh: St. Andrew Press, 1958], 275) For a careful analysis of various views, see Wayne Grudem, "Christ Preaching Through Noah: 1 Peter 3:19-20 in the Light of Dominant Themes in Jewish Literature," *Trinity Journal* 7 (1986): 2.
5. The number and description of paragraph sermons discussed here are taken from Jones, "Supplement to Notes" (handout, ca. 1975).
6. See Appendix for a sample chapter sermon.
7. See G. Campbell Morgan, *Great Chapters of the Bible* (Old Tappan, NJ: Fleming H. Revell, 1935) and Tom Carter, *Spurgeon's Commentary on Great Chapters of the Bible* (Grand Rapids: Kregel), 1998.
8. See page 175 for a sample sermon on the book of Ruth, and page 354 for a sample sermon on Jude.
9. Jones, "An Investigation and Explanation of the Whiting System," 69.
10. See Appendix for a sample doctrinal sermon.
11. Original source unknown.
12. For a sample biographical sermon, see page 345 of the Appendix.
13. For example, there are eight Judases mentioned in Scripture.
14. For a sample sermon on a parable, see page 276. For a good discussion of "The Expositor and the Interpretation of Parables," see Unger, *Principles of Expository Preaching*, 186-200.
15. Zuck, *Basic Bible Imerpretation*, 194.
16. Ibid.
17. Ibid.
18. Hence the familiar refrain in such passages as Luke 8:8, "He who has ears to hear, let him hear!" (NKJV)
19. Leonard L. Thompson, *Introducing Biblical Literature: A More Fantastic Country* (Englewood Cliffs, NJ: Prentice-Hall, 1978), 256.
20. See the list "The Parables of Jesus" in Zuck, Basic *Bible Interpretation*, 198.
21. Zuck, *Basic Bible Interpretation*, 204, 210.
22. Ibid., 211-19.
23. Stanley A. Ellisen (class handout. Western Conservative Baptist Seminary).
24. Ibid.
25. For example, Childs refers to N. A. Dahl's "The Parables of Growth." He says, "Dahl attempts to recover an apologetical dimension of these parables which are offered in specific criticism of Jesus' ministry. How could this be the kingdom when the signs are so insignificant? How could his kingdom succeed when so many followers have fallen away? The parables of growth seek to contrast the

secret beginnings, small and insignificant as the mustard seed and leaven, with the richness of the final harvest or the grandeur of the mighty tree." (*Biblical Theology of the Old and New Testaments*, 639.)

26. Ellisen, class handout.
27. Ibid.
28. Ibid.
29. From a dispensational point of view, the parables do *not* teach the doctrines of justification by faith, forgiveness, the Church, or the millennial reign of Christ. They do teach the reason for Messiah's rejection at His first coming; the fruitfulness of the Word in receptive hearts; the postponement of the Davidic kingdom during the absence of the King; the role of the King now as Shepherd leading His own out of the fold of Israel; the kingdom of darkness; the responsibility and rewards of those faithful in the stewardship of the King's business, etc. For an alternate view of the parables, see Simon Kistemaker, *The Parables of Jesus* (Grand Rapids: Baker, 1980).
30. Ellisen, "Lesson 6: Guidelines for Preaching the Parables" (class handout, 1976), 3.
31. Much of the material under this heading was adapted from unpublished class notes taken from James Devine, a teaching assistant at Western Conservative Baptist Seminary in the area of Homiletics, 1976-1977. See Appendix for a sample Gospel sermon.
32. Compare Paul's approach to evangelism in Athens, in Acts 17, to his testimony before the Jews in Acts 22, and before King Agrippa, in Acts 26.
33. For a Sample Sermon on a type, see page 120. For a good discussion of "The Expositor and Scriptural Typology," see Unger, *Principles of Expository Preaching*, 201-16.
34. Zuck, *Basic Bible Interpretation*, 176.
35. Ellisen, class handout. Also, see Zuck, *Basic Bible Interpretation*, 177-182.
36. Of James Barr, Childs states: "Barr was at pains to demonstrate that in terms of method there was no basic difference between allegory and typology. Both derive from a 'resultant system' in which the text is construed from the perspective of an outside system brought to bear upon it, and that the difference between allegory and typology depends largely on the resultant system being applied ... In sum, Barr characterized the New Testament's use of the Old as a different sort of operation from exegesis, and no modern approach such as typology could bridge the discrepancy." (*Biblical Theology of the Old and New Testaments*, 14) Barr's opinion seems to ignore distinctions between *types and allegories* (such as their physicality) and, more importantly, the unity of Scripture itself.
37. Compare the list of symbols in Zuck, *Basic Bible Imerpretation*, 187-93.
38. Historical schools of excessive typology include the Rabbinic (pre-Christian) Period; the Middle Ages (Dark Age) (500-1400), in which the allegorism of

Origen won over the literalism of Antioch; the school of Johannes Cocceius (1603-69), though he made an attempt to study types systematically, dividing them into "innate" and "inferred" classifications; and the school of John Hutchinson (1784), who reacted to the extreme rationalism of his day by finding typical significance in virtually everything in the Old Testament. (Ellisen, class handout)

39. Historical schools of neglect include Reformers Luther and Calvin, whose reaction to the long-entrenched allegorism of the dark ages, and desire to return to the literalism of the Antiochan school, led them to dismiss the validity of typology. The Rationalistic school denied the supernatural and assumes that New Testament writers simply accommodated their material to Old Testament material for pedagogical purposes. The school of Bishop Marsh (1757-1839), recognized only those types "declared to be so by the New Testament." (Ellisen, class handout.)
40. Patrick Fairbairn, *The Typology of Scripture or the Doctrine of Types*, 2 vols. (Philadelphia: Daniels and Smith, 1852). "The most exhaustive and definite work on the history and principles of the interpretation of Bible types. Old and laborious, but still unsurpassed." (Ellisen, class handout)
41. St. Augustine, as cited by Mears, *What the Bible Is All About*, 23.
42. Ellisen, class handout.
43. Also helpful are Zuck's nine principles for interpreting symbols, which recognize the elements of object (the symbol), referent (what the symbol refers to) and the meaning (the resemblance between the symbol and the referent). Zuck, *Basic Bible Interpretation*, 185-86.
44. Ellisen, class handout.
45. Childs refers to the observation of Stanley Walters, that key words in Genesis 22 have "peculiar resonance within the larger canonical collection." The words *ram, burnt-offering* and *appear*, found in the same cluster only in Leviticus 8-9 and 16, link "Abraham's uniquely private experience to Israel's public worship, and conversely Israel's sacrifice is drawn into the theological orbit of Abraham's offering: 'God will provide his own sacrifice.'" (*Biblical Theology of the Old and New Testaments*, 327-28.)
46. Childs complains about the typological interpretation of Genesis 22, referring to "an uncritical Christian tendency to fasten on to an external similarity between such features as Isaac's carrying the wood and Jesus' carrying the cross which obscured the true witness of the text itself. Again, the attempt to relate each biblical witness mimetically badly blurs the radical discontinuities of the text. It belongs to the basic theological task to pursue exegetically how the uniqueness of each text is preserved along with a frequently broadened theological application for ongoing Christian faith." (Ibid., 335-36.)
47. Ellisen. class handout.
48. Ibid.
49. Ibid.

Chapter 7

1. Note the similar list of attributes given by Charles Koller: "In order to be well received, the sermon must have unity, structure, aim and progression; it must be sustained by Biblical authority, and must be intelligently presented. There is no doubt that expository preaching would be far more popular than it is, if it were more generally well done." (Charles W. Koller, *Expository Preaching Without Notes* [Grand Rapids: Baker, 1962], 28.) For "six sermonic characteristics" thought essential to effective communication, see Macleod, *The Problem of Preaching*, 75-88. His suggestions are: be personal, be pictorial, be propulsive, be pastoral, be persuasive, and be prophetic.
2. John Gray, *I and II Kings: A Commentary* (Old Testament Library) (Philadelphia: Westminster. 1970), 522. Josephus, however, relates that during the Roman siege of Jerusalem, people ate dung. (Antiquities, 9.4.4)
3. M. G. Easton, *Easton's Bible Dictionary* (Oak Harbor. WA: Logos Research Systems, Inc., 1996, c1897).
4. Kaiser, *Toward an Exegetical Theology*, 113.
5. Richards and Bredfeldt, *Creative Bible Teaching*, 115.
6. Illustrations should not introduce extraneous milterial or a new subject. They should be related to the audience and limited to the facts that are needed.
7. Sue Nichols, *Words on Target* (Richmond: John Knox Press, 1973), 17.
8. White, *A Guide to Preaching*, 219.
9. Hendricks, *Teaching to Change Lives*, 15.
10. Ibid., 17-36.
11. Koller, *Expository Preaching Without Notes*, 35, quoting Blackwood, *The Fine Art of Preaching*, 159.
12. "There are as there always have been, ministers who preach effectively from manuscript or copious notes in the pulpit, as well as some who read their sermons in full: but the same preachers would be even more effective if they could stand note free in the pulpit. This seems clearly to be the verdict of history." (Koller, *Expository Preaching Without Notes*, 24. Also see Blackwood, *The Fine Art of Preaching*, 153.)

Chapter 8

1. Donald E. Demaray, *Pulpit Giants* (Chicago: Moody, 1973), 57-58.
2. Ibid.,166.
3. In 1 Corinthians 15:9-10. Paul states, "I am the least of the apostles, who am not worthy to be called an apostle, because I persecuted the church of God. But by the grace of God I am what I am, and His grace toward me was not in vain; but I labored more abundantly than they all, yet not I, but the grace of God which was with me" (NKJV).
4. Richards and Bredfeldt, *Creative Bible Teaching*, 213-14.

5. Ibid., 222.
6. Learn to adapt the manner of a sermon's delivery to the culture of the audience being addressed. This may call for radical adjustment of what seems most natural to you, but it communicates sensitivity to, and acceptance of, the audience. This is essential to good communication.
7. Some speakers conclude their messages by taking questions from the listeners. Others offer their personal e-mail addresses for follow-up discussions with those who have questions or comments.
8. Source unknown.
9. Hendricks, *Teaching to Change Lives*, 72.
10. Lynn R. Wessell, "Great Awakening: The First American Revolution," *Christianity Today* 17 (August 1973): 23.

Chapter 9

1. The books of Moses are referred to as the *Pentateuch* because they were originally written on five scrolls (*penta*), or books (*teuchos*). These same books are often referred to as the Law because they contain the revelation of God's moral and civil code. They are also called the *Torah*, a term that has the idea of giving direction for a right relationship with God and which is sometimes used of the entire Hebrew Bible.
2. Gleason Archer, *A Survey of Old Testament Introduction* (Chicago: Moody, 1964), 17.
3. Ibid.
4. Ellisen, "Part I: The Pentateuch," in *Western Baptist Seminary Bible Workbook* (Portland: Western, ca. 1973), 2.
5. Ellisen, *3 Worlds in Conflict*, 16.
6. Ellisen, "Part I: The Pentateuch," *Western Baptist Seminary Bible Workbook*, 3.
7. Ibid.
8. Welhausen's Documentary Hypothesis (1866) was based on the assumption that Israel was first a pastoral people; then more organized; then obsessed with holy living; then had a highly developed priesthood. JEDP: Jehovahistic, Elohistic, Deuteronomic, Priestly. For an evaluation of the JEDP Theory, see Umberto Cassuto, *The Documentary Hypothesis* (Jerusalem: Magnes, 1961).
9. Bruce Wilkinson and Kenneth Boa, *Talk Thru the Old Testament* (Nashville: Thomas Nelson, 1983), 3.
10. David Dorsey, *The Literary Structure of the Old Testament* (Grand Rapids: Baker, 1999), 30.
11. Gary Derickson (lecture, Faith Evangelical Seminary, Tacoma, WA, 2004).
12. Ibid.
13. Adapted from Ellisen, *Western Baptist Seminary Bible Workbook*, 4.

14. For a more complete treatment of the biblical covenants and how they are related, see Ellisen, *3 Worlds in Conflict*, 31-44.
15. Derickson (handout, Faith Evangelical Seminary).
16. Ellisen, *Western Baptist Seminary Bible Workbook.*
17. Von Rad observes another unifying feature in his comments "Over all this multitude of commands, regulations and ordinances, stands the authority of the First Commandment," and "We must study the first commandment at considerable length, because it is the head and chief of all the commandments." (Gerhard von Rad, Moses [London: Lutterworth Press, 1960), 49, 39.)
18. For more on the chiasmus and other literary devices, see Dorsey, *The Literary Structure of the Old Testament*; and Kaiser, *Toward an Exegetical Theology*.
19. The following observations may be made of the Ten Commandments: (1) Man's relations with God are balanced by man's relations with man. (2) Man's relations with God come first in priority. (3) God's Law deals with *how we think* in our hearts, as well as how we act. (4) The theme of God's Law is *holiness.* (5) The Law is addressed to *individuals.* (6) The Law is a *whole.* (7) The Law was *verbally dictated* by God Himself. (8) Eight of the Ten Commands are *negative.* (9) God's Law was meant to be *kept*, not worshipped. (10) The Law *never justified sinners.* (11) The Law provided God's covenant people with the conditions for enjoying His *blessings* in the land. (12) As God's standard of right behavior, the Law *continue*s to serve its purpose of convicting sinners (1 Tim. 1:8).
20. Archetypes include: (1) *hero stories* such as that of Joseph; (2) the *journey*, as in the case of Jacob; (3) the *comedy*, which begins happily and ends happily after encountering a degree of sorrow or loss; (4) the *tragedy*, in which the sequence of events led from prosperity to disaster; (5) the *revelation*, as with Abraham, who was taken from ignorance to hope of a glorious future. See Mathewson, *The Art of Preaching Old Testament Narrative*; and Ryken, *How to Read the Bible as Literature.*
21. *Apodictic* refers to law that necessarily follows from grounds. (Clarence L. Barnhard and Robert K. Barnhard [eds.], *The World Book Dictionary* [Chicago: Doubleday,1984] ,97.)
22. Ibid., 323.
23. K. A. Kitchen, *Ancient Orient and Old Testament* (Chicago: IVP, 1966), 90-102.
24. Ibid.
25. Ibid.
26. Earl D. Radmacher, Ronald B. Allen, and H. Wayne House, eds., *The Nelson Study Bible*, New King James Version (Nashville: Thomas Nelson, 1997), 134.

Chapter 10

1. Mathewson, *The Art of Preaching Old Testament Narrative*, 21-23.
2. Ibid., 26.

3. Wilkinson and Boa, *Talk Thru the Old Testament*, 47.
4. Ibid., 47-48.
5. Derickson, class handout.
6. Notice that the books of Samuel, the Kings, and the Chronicles are summarized without reference to the fact that they were each written on two scrolls due to their length, resulting in 1 and 2 Samuel, etc.
7. According to Thompson, "the separation of Ezra-Nehemiah into two books, Ezra and Nehemiah, can only be viewed as artificial." (*Introducing Biblical Literature*, 135.)
8. Kaiser designates as the syntactical-theological method of exegesis the "pointing out of the abiding meanings and continuing significance for all believers of all times," (*Toward all Exegetical Theology*, 197.)
9. Kaiser calls the emphasis on historical facts for their own sake, leaving the lessons in the past, *Ebionite*, since Ebionism viewed Jesus as a merely historical human being, and not as divine also. (Ibid., 203 [footnote]).
10. Ibid., 203. Kaiser calls the emphasis on spiritual lessons without reference to their historical context a docetic approach to Bible study, because the Docetists tried to separate the nature of Christ from the historicity of His life.
11. Ibid., 209.
12. Ibid., 78.
13. Ibid. In light of Kaiser's observations about narrative, Thompson's comments are worth noting: "In the Bible nothing is described which does not contribute to the action. Description of character, scenery, inner feelings, and objects extraneous to the action never distracts the narrator from bringing his story to a rapid climax ... The suppression of description, rather than giving an effect of incompleteness, gives to biblical stories an air of mystery. The emptiness and silence in the narrative become 'fraught with background' (Auerbach) like a Japanese painting." (*Introducing Biblical Literature*, 32-33.)
14. Mathewson, *The Art of Preaching Old Testament Narrative*, 47.
15. Ibid.
16. Ryken, *How to Read the Bible as Literature*, 75.
17. Ibid.
18. Ibid., 77.
19. It is also true that Old Testament characters are not to be judged on the basis of revelation they didn't have.
20. Ryken, *How to Read the Bible as Literature*, 79-81.
21. Ibid.
22. Ibid., 83.
23. Ibid., 84.
24. Ibid.
25. Ibid.

26. Ibid, 82.
27. Ibid.
28. Ibid, 83.
29. Ibid.
30. Mathewson, *The Art of Preaching Old Testament Narrative*, 43.
31. Ibid.
32. Thompson, *Introducing Biblical Literature*, 42.
33. Ibid.
34. Mathewson, *The Art of Preaching Old Testament Narrative*, 44.
35. Ibid.
36. Ibid.
37. Ibid., 45.
38. Ibid.
39. Stanley A. Ellisen, *Interpretive Outline of the Whole Bible* (Portland: Western Baptist Seminary, c 1974).
40. Gregory Trull, Survey of Biblical Literature (class lecture, Corban College, Salem, OR, 2005).
41. Mathewson, *The Art of Preaching Old Testament Narrative*, 58-59.
42. Ibid.
43. Ibid.
44. Ronald M. Hals, *The Theology of the Book of Ruth* (Philadelphia: Fortress, 1969), 3-19.
45. Kaiser, *Toward an Exegetical Theology*, 78.
46. Hals as cited by Kaiser, *Toward an Exegetical Theology*, 79.
47. Kaiser, *Toward an Exegetical Theology*, 78-79.
48. Mathewson, *The Art of Preaching Old Testament Narrative*, 73. Thompson's reference to the "editorial point of view" is a different matter, not to be confused with focalization of the storyteller. Thompson seems to hold a low view of Scripture when he says, "The editorial point of view establishes the Christian believer as the partner superseding all others in the line of God's covenanting with man." He further states, "The placement of the Christian books after the Jewish books has stamped the Christian point of view on the whole Bible." (*Introducing Biblical Literature*, 44). While revelation was given progressively, and its narrative patterns, symbols, images, character types, etc., reflect a forward relatedness, the inspired text is not ultimately the product of editors.
49. Mathewson, *The Art of Preaching Old Testament Narrative*, 73.
50. Ibid.
51. Ibid.
52. Ibid.
53. For example, "And the LORD smelled a soothing aroma. Then the LORD said in His heart, 'I will never again curse the ground for man's sake, although the

imagination of man's heart is evil from his youth'" (Gen. 8:21 NKJV). Mathewson, *The Art of Preaching Old Testament Narrative*, 73.

54. Ibid.
55. Ibid., 74.
56. House based his analysis on Hals, *The Theology of the Book of Ruth*.

Chapter 11

1. Ryken, *The Literature of the Bible*, 243.
2. Adapted from Stanley Ellisen, *Westem Baptist Seminary Workbook*, 6ff.
3. This is based on the pattern of sacrifices offered by Job as priest of his household; his longevity (about two hundred years; sec 42:16); and the lack of reference to Israel, the miraculous Exodus, or Mosaic Law. Eliphaz the Temanite may have descended from Esau through his son Eliphaz and his son Teman (Gen. 36:15). (Ibid.)
4. Ryken, *The Literature of the Bible*, 109.
5. Ibid.
6. Ibid., 110.
7. Dorsey, *The Literary Structure of the Old Testament*, 170.
8. See Francis I. Anderson, *Job* (London: IVP, 1976).
9. Arthur B. Whiting outlined the book of Job as follows: Distress, 1-2: Discussion, 3-41; Deliverance, 42. (Ellisen, *Western Bible Workbook*, lecture, 1974)
10. "One of the tragedies of topical, eisegetical preaching is that it refers to portions of Scripture without reference to where they come in the argument of the book. Job had highs and lows in the process of having his skewed view of life corrected, as it was in the end." (Derickson, lecture)
11. Ibid.
12. Ellisen, *Western Bible Workbook*, 43; Thompson, *Introducing Biblical Literature*, 251.
13. Radmacher, Allen, and House, *Nelson Study Bible*, 1076.
14. Ellisen. *Western Bible Workbook*, 44.
15. Bruce Waltke, "Do Quoheleth and Job Contradict Proverbs?" (an unpublished syllabus).
16. Ibid.
17. Dorsey, *The Literary Structure of the Old Testament*, 187.
18. Ibid., 189.
19. See Derek Kidner, *Proverbs* (London: IVP, 1976); H. Wayne House and Kenneth M. Durham, *Living Wisely in a Foolish World* (Grand Rapids: Kregel, 1992): J. Carl Laney, *Balancing Your Act Without Losing It* (Wheaton: Tyndale, 1988); and Bob Deffinbaugh, *Wisdom Literature, Proverbs* (www. Bible.org).
20. Kidner, *Proverbs*, 31-43.
21. For further study, see House and Durham, *Living Wisely in a Foolish World*, 198-214.

22. McDowell, *Right from Wrong*.
23. This outline was adapted from Kidner's subject-study of "the Sluggard." (Kidner, *Proverbs*, 42-43.)
24. Radmacher, Allen, and House, *Nelson Study Bible*, 1082.
25. Waltke, "Do Quoheleth and Job Contradict Proverbs?," 5.
26. Ibid., 7.
27. Ellisen, *Western Bible Workbook*, 27.
28. Ibid., 30.
29. Ibid.
30. Ibid.
31. Korah rebelled against God (Num. 16:1-35) , but his sons rebelled against their father's rebellion by remaining faithful. God then used them to compose the kinds of songs that should be used in the worship of the local church.
32. Radmacher, Allen, and House, *Nelson Study Bible*, 873.
33. See Claus Westermann, *The Praise of God in the Psalms* (Richmond: John Knox, 1965); Ronald B. Allen, *Praise! A Matter of Life and Breath* (Nashville: Nelson, 1980); *When Song Is New* (Nashville: Thomas Nelson, 1983); and *Lord of Song: The Messiah Revealed in the Song* (Portland: Multnomah, 1985); and Derek Kidner, *Psalms*, 2 vols. (London: IVP, 1975).
34. Thompson refers to two human situations that determine the perspective of the psalmist when he writes in first person. Either he is *off-center* (distressed) or *atcenter* (enjoying a right relationship with God). The movement is generally "toward, not away from, the center" as man partners with God–sometimes as the Creator and sometimes as the Covenanter. (*Introducing Biblical Literature*, 72 .)
35. "The basic unit in biblical poetry consists of two, sometimes three, parallel lines. A two-line unit is called a couplet or a distich; a three-line unit, a tristich" (Ibid., 25.)
36. Radmacher, Allen, and House, *Nelson Study Bible*, 925.
37. Derickson, lecture.
38. Trull, handout.
39. Radmachcr, Allen, and House, *Nelson Study Bible*, 873.
40. Ellisen, *Western Bible Workbook*, 84 .
41. Ibid.
42. Ibid.
43. Ibid.
44. Ibid.
45. Radmacher, Allen, and House, *Nelson Study Bible*, 1097.
46. Ibid.
47. Ibid.
48. Ibid.
49. Craig S. Glickman, *A Song for Lovers* (Downers Grove, IL: IVP, 1977), 173.
50. Ibid.

51. Ibid.
52. Ellisen, *Western Bible Workbook*, 84.
53. Radmncher, Allen, and House, *Nelson Study Bible*. 1098.
54. Ibid.
55. Ibid.
56. Derickson, lecture.
57. See Glickman, *A Song for Lovers.*
58. Wilkinson and Boa, *Talk Thru the Old Testament,* 206.
59. Derickson, lecture.

Chapter 12

1. Wilkinson and Boa. *Talk Thru the Old Testament,* 185.
2. Ibid.
3. For examples of the phrase "The burden of the word of the LORD," see Zechariah 9:1; 12:1; and Malachi 1:1.
4. For an example. see Roland K. Harrison, *Introduction to the Old Testament* (Grand Rapids: Eerdmans, 1969), 757-58. In a similar vein, Von Rad regarded revelation as given to the prophet "to equip him for his office" with a special endowment of the spirit that was not normative for other people. (Von Rad, *Old Testament Theology*)" 63) However, it was the revelation itself, not the prophet, who carried divine authority.
5. See 2 Peter 2:15; Judges 1:11; and Revelation 2:14.
6. In Luke 24:27. Luke writes of Jesus: "And beginning at Moses and *all the Prophets*, He expounded to them in all the Scriptures the things concerning Himself" (NKJV, emphasis added). In Acts 10:43. Peter said, "To [Jesus] *all the prophets* witness that, through His name, whoever believes in Him will receive remission of sins" (NKJV, emphasis added).
7. For biblical references to the Eternal Covenant, see Hebrews 9:15 and 13:20.
8. Ellisen, *Three Worlds in Conflict*, 29.
9. For example, the image of Nebuchadnezzar's dream in Daniel 2.
10. "Nostradamus is the Latinized name of Michel de Nostradamus, a physician and astrologer who lived in 16th-century France ... Nostradamus has been credited with prophesying dozens of pivotal episodes in recent history, including the rise of Adolf Hitler, the assassination of John F. Kennedy and, most recently, the destruction of the World Trade Center towers ... The most compelling argument against Nostradamus' powers is that his apparent 'hits' are the result of random chance and creative interpretation. There are about a thousand quatrains, most containing more than one prediction and all but a few described in vague, obscure terms. Over the course of hundreds of years, it's certainly possible that some events would line up with some predictions, simply by coincidence."

(Tom Harris, "How Nostradamus Works," http://science.howstuffworks.com/nostradamus. htm.)

11. "One commonly held interpretation maintains that the sixty-two weeks can be added to the seven weeks of v. 25, resulting in a total of sixty-nine weeks, or 483 years. If these years are added to the date of the decree of Artaxerxes in Neh. 2, 445 B.C., with an adjustment to allow for the use of a 360-day year, the end of the sixty-nine weeks coincides with the date of the crucifixion of Jesus." (Radmacher, Allen, and House, *Nelson Study Bible*, 1437.)
12. Since the whole of Scripture is God-breathed and profitable (2 Tim. 3:16), the relevance of biblical prophecies cannot be limited to the original addressees. However, Von Rad's contention that the prophet's own understanding was "only one possible way among many of understanding an oracle" seems to confuse the single intended meaning (interpretation) of biblical texts with their many possible applications. Von Rad states, "By being referred to subsequent generations and the situations confronting them, fresh possible ways of taking the prophet's oracles were opened up, and this process continued right down to the time when, in the New Testament, the prophets' preaching was for the last time reinterpreted in the light of present events." (*Old Testament Theology*, 49).
13. Apocalyptic literature is distinguished by the facts that it usually involves an angelic interpreter; is written in prose, not poetry; looks to the conclusion of history; and is highly symbolic.
14. Rather than draw a sharp distinction between prophetic and apocalyptic literature, Robert Thomas views the Revelation as a genuinely prophetic document that has apocalyptic elements, i.e., "when the message was passed on to the prophet in the form of visions." He further states, "The literary genre of inspired writings was not the choice of the human author, but was an inevitable result of the manner in which God chose to reveal his message to the prophet." (Robert Thomas, *Revelation 1-7, All Exegetical Commentary*, vol. 1, ed. Kenneth Barker [Chicago: Moody, 1992], 29)
15. Daniel 7:9 seems to support this. In this verse Daniel describes God's throne as having wheels of "burning fire" (NKJV). Archaeological evidence indicates that ancient thrones also had wheels.
16. Fruchtenbaum, "Rabbinic Quotations of the Old Testament."
17. An *exhaustive* concordance lists every word used in a particular version of the Bible. See James Strong, *Strong's Exhaustive Concordance of the Bible* (New York: Abingdon, 1890), or search in Bible software such as Libronix.
18. Bible dictionaries, such as *Harpers Bible Dictionary, Easton's Bible Dictionary*, and *New Bible Dictionary*, show that Uzziah and Azariah are alternate names for the same individual.
19. Sidney Grcidanus, *The Modern Preacher and the Ancient Text* (Grand Rapids: IVP, 1988), 239.

20. Gene Tucker, *Form Criticism of the Old Testament* (Philadelphia: Fortress, 1971), 54.
21. Ibid., 55.
22. Ibid.. 57.
23. Ibid., 58.
24. Ibid.
25. Ibid., 59.
26. Ibid.,60-70.
27. Greidanus, *The Modern Preacher*, 239.
28. Von Rad, *Old Testament Theology*, 33.
29. Dorsey, The Literary Structure of the Old Testament, 266. (Note: Not all scholars find chiasm everywhere Dorsey does. You must analyze the literary structure of Scripture with objectivity.)
30. Greidanus, *The Modern Preacher*, 252.
31. Ibid., 256.
32. Ibid.
33. Ibid., 258.
34. C. F. Keil and F. Delitzsch, *Commentary on the Old Testament* (Grand Rapids: Eerdmans. 1973) 7:303. Also see Archer, *A Survey of Old Testamell Introduction*, 348.
35. Kaiser, *Toward all Exegetical Theology*, 188.
36. Ibid.
37. Ibid., 194.
38. Hobart Freeman, *An Introduction to the Old Testament Prophets* (Chicago: Moody, 1968), 195.
39. Ibid.
40. See Strong, *Strong's Exhaustive Concordance of the Bible, Hebrew and Chaldee Dictionary*, 62.
41. Freeman, *An Introduction to the Old Testament Prophets*, 111.
42. Ellisen, *Western Bible Workbook*, 3-4.
43. Ibid.
44. Freeman, *An Introduction to the Old Testament Prophets*, 195.
45. Ellisen, *Western Bible Workbook*. 5.
46. "The Jews abandoned the traditional Messianic interpretation of the servant due to the Christian testimony of the identification of the servant with Jesus of Nazareth, and applied the prophecies to certain ones of the prophets, or to the nation of Israel itself. Beginning with the nineteenth century, critical scholars have adopted one or another of the Jewish interpretations either categorically or with certain modifications." (Freeman, *An Introduction to the Old Testament Prophets*, 209)
47. Ellisen, *Western Bible Workbook*, 27-28.
48. See Von Rad, *Old Testament Theology*, vol 2, 196ff.

49. In a lecture given at Faith Evangelical Seminary, Gary Derickson compared New Testament believers to the Israelites during their wilderness wandering. They received the covenant before they had the land in which they could fully experience its blessings.
50. Matthew Henry, *Matthew Henry's Commentary on the Whole Bible* (Peabody, MA: Hendrickson, 1996).
51. Ellisen, *Western Bible Workbook*, 61-62.
52. Freeman, *An Introduction to the Old Testament Prophets*, 178.
53. Dorsey, *The Liteary Structure of the New Testament*, 266.
54. Compare 2 Timothy 2:13.
55. Note: Peter's reference to Joel 2:28 in Acts 2:17 meant not that Joel's prophecy was then being fulfilled, but that the coming of the Holy Spirit at the Feast of Pentecost resembled one aspect of Joel's prophecy.
56. The word used for "shepherds" in 1:1 is not the usual Hebrew word ro'eh, but the rare word noqe, suggesting instead "sheepbreeders," as seen in the New King James Version. The only other Old Testament occurrence of noqe is in 2 Kings 3:4, where Mesha, king of Moab, is said to have engaged in sheep breeding on such a scale that he was able to supply the king of Israel with one hundred thousand lambs and the wool of a hundred thousand rams. Amos evidently managed or owned large herds of sheep and goats and was in charge of other shepherds. John F. Walvoord, Roy B. Zuck, and Dallas Theological Seminary, *The Bible Knowledge Commentary* [Wheaton: Victor Books, 1983], 1425.)
57. Ellisen, *Western Bible Workbook*, 14.
58. Freeman, *An Introduction to the Old Testament Prophets*, 184.
59. Adapted from Dorsey, *The Liteary Structure of the New Testament*, 278.
60. Tucker, *Form Criticism of the Old Testament*, 73.
61. Freeman, *An Introduction to the Old Testament Prophets*, 184.
62. Ibid.
63. Ibid.
64. Keil and Delitzsch, *Commentary on the Old Testament*, 239.
65. Freeman, *An Introduction to the Old Testament Prophets*, 139.
66. Ibid,184.
67. Ellisen, *Western Bible Workbook*, 21.
68. Dorsey, *The Literary Structure of the New Testament*, 289.
69. Adapted from ibid.
70. Ellisen, *Western Bible Workbook*, 23-24.
71. Ibid.
72. Dorsey, *The Liteary Structure of the New Testament*, 290.
73. Adapted from ibid., 291.
74. Ellisen, *Western Bible Workbook*, 14ff.

75. "He spoke as a man of the people, whose sympathy was with the country folk, and he sought to protect them against the greedy rich and the nobles of the capital cities." (Charles F. Pfeiffer, *The Wycliffe Bible Commentary: Old Testament* [Chicago: Moody Press, 1962])
76. Dorsey, *The Literary Structure of the New Testament*, 296.
77. Ibid., 297.
78. John Paterson, *The Goodly Fellowship of the Prophets* (New York: Scribner's, 1948), 111.
79. Dorsey, *The Literary Structure of the New Testament*, 304.
80. Wilkinson and Boa, *Talk Thru the Old Testament*, 273.
81. Ibid.
82. Freeman, *An Introduction to the Old Testament Prophets*, 251.
83. Dorsey, *The Literary Structure of the New Testament*, 309.
84. Ibid., 306.
85. We know that Josiah reigned from 640 to 609, and his reform began in the twelfth year of his rule. Zephaniah wrote sometime after 628 B.C., when the revival began, and before Nineveh was destroyed. Thus, Zephaniah wrote sometime before 612 B.C ...
86. Dorsey, *The Literary Structure of the New Testament*, 313.
87. Ibid., 311.
88. Ellisen, *Western Bible Workbook*, 46.
89. Ibid., 59.
90. Dorsey, *The Literary Structure of the New Testament*, 32 1.
91. Ibid., 324.
92. Ibid.
93. Ellisen, *Western Bible Workbook, Part V, Minor Prophets*, 49.
94. See also Dorsey, *The Literary Structure of the New Testament*, 318.

CHAPTER 13

1. Wilkinson and Boa, *Talk Thru the Old Testament*, 301.
2. *Webster's New American Dictionary*, s.v. "Gospel."
3. "1. Paul claimed that he received this creedal material from others (1 Cor. 15:3), probably from Peter and James in Jerusalem, ca. 33 to 38 A.D. (Galatians 1:18-20; especially 1:18: historeo). 2. Paul is himself an eye-witness to a resurrection appearance of Jesus (1 Cor. 15:8; cf. 1 Cor. 9:1; Gal. 1:16). 3. Paul's message was 'checked out' by the Jerusalem apostles (Gal. 2:1-10) and specifically approved (vvs. 6-10). Paul said the apostles were preaching the same message he was concerning the resurrection appearances of Jesus (1 Cor. 15:11; cf. vs. 12, 14, 15)." (Gary R. Habermas, "Who Is the Real Jesus?" [lecture, Morning Star Church, February 25, 2006])

4. David E. Aune, *The New Testament in Its Literary Environment* (Philadelphia: Westminster Press, 1987), 46-54.
5. Ryken, *How to Read the Bible as Literature*, 136.
6. Greidanus, *The Modern Preacher*, 267.
7. Ibid, 268.
8. Ibid, 264.
9. Everett F. Harrison, Geoffrey W. Bromiley, and Carl F. H. Henry. eds., *Baker's Dictionary of Theology* (Grand Rapids: Baker, 1978), 257.
10. Habermas, "Who is the Real Jesus?"
11. Good examples of the constructive application of higher criticism are found in the works of Ryken cited in previous chapters.
12. See Donald Guthrie, *New Testament Introduction* (Downers Grove, IL: IVP, 1970), 121-236.
13. See Merrill C. Tenney, *New Testament Survey* (Grand Rapids: Eerdmans, 1961), 133.
14. Ibid., 136.
15. In John 20:30-31, John said. "Many other signs Jesus also performed ... which are not written in this book; but these have been written so that you may believe" (NASB95).
16. Greidanus, *The Modern Preacher*, 276.
17. According to Habermas, only four sources support the existence of Caesar Tiberius, and three of the four were written later than the Gospel of John. (Habermas, "Who is the Real Jesus?")
18. Ibid. Also, see 2 Peter 1:16-21 and 2 Timothy 3:16-17.
19. Greidanus, *The Modern Preacher*, 277.
20. Ibid.
21. Language users will find an indispensable tool in Aland, Synopsis Quattor Evageliorum (Stuttgart, Germany: Wrtembergische, 1967).
22. An excellent resource is R. A. Meltebeke and S. Meltebeke, *Jesus Christ, the Greatest Life Ever Lived*, a revision of *The Greatest Story* (Portland: Western Seminary, 1994), a revision of Johnston M. Cheney, *The Life of Christ in Stereo*, cds. Stanley A. Ellisen and Earl D. Radmacher (Portland: Western Seminary, 1969). Also see Alfred Edersheim, *The Life and Times of Jesus the Messiah* (Grand Rapids: Eerdmans, 1971).
23. Greidanus, *The Modern Preacher*, 298-99.
24. Ibid., 299.
25. Ibid.
26. Ibid., 285-95.
27. Wilkinson and Boa, *Talk Thru the Old Testament*, 308.
28. Guthrie, *New Testament Introduction*, 34-44.
29. Ibid.

30. Wilkinson and Boa, *Talk Thru the Old Testament*, 309.
31. Greidanus, *The Modern Preacher*, 281.
32. For a review of how to preach the parables, see chapter 6.
33. Derickson, "Preaching the Gospels and Acts" (lecture).
34. Preachers should read Matthew 28 from the standpoint of who is speaking and who is being spoken about. Jesus commanded His disciples to baptize the Gentiles in the name of the Triune God. Jews never used the word nation, of themselves. They were *ha 'am*, the people. Having gone first to the House of Israel (Matt. 10), they were now to go to the nations. This may explain the Trinitarian baptismal formula in contrast to the baptism of Jewish converts to Christianity, in the name of Jesus.
35. Tenney, *New Testament Survey*, 143.
36. Ibid.
37. Greidanus, *The Modern Preacher*, 279.
38. Wilkinson and Boa, *Talk Thru the Old Testament*, 319.
39. Ibid.
40. Ibid., 320.
41. Ibid.
42. Greidanus, *The Modern Preacher*, 279.
43. Aune, *The New Testament in Its Literary Environment*, 47.
44. Ibid.
45. Greidanus, *The Modern Preacher*, 280.
46. Wilkinson and Boa, *Talk Thru the Old Testament*, 328.
47. See the "we sections" in which the author of Acts speaks in first person, along with Paul: Acts 16:10-17, 20:5-15, 21:11-18; 27:1-28:16.
48. "The Gospel of Luke is part of a two volume work composed by the same author." (Childs, *Biblical Theology of the Old and New Testaments*, 276.)
49. Tenney, *New Testament Survey*, 175 .
50. Radmacher, Allen, and House, *Nelson Study Bible*, 134.
51. Ibid.
52. Ibid., 1682.
53. Tenney, *New Testament Survey*, 176.
54. Greidanus, The Modern Preacher, 283.
55. Aune states: "Jerome (ca. A.D. 327-420) described Luke as the Evangelist most learned in the Greek language (*Letter* 20:4)." (*The New Testament in Its Literary Environment*, 116).
56. Thompson, *Introducing Biblical Literature*, 278.
57. Greidanus, *The Modern Preacher*, 283.
58. Tenney, *New Testament Survey*, 181.
59. Leon Morris, *New Testament Theology* (Grand Rapids: Zondervan, 1986), 196.

60. The Holy Spirit is identified as the Spirit of Jesus in Romans 8:9. 61. Wilkinson and Boa, *Talk Thru the Old Testament*, 336.
61. Greidanus, *The Modern Preacher*, 284.
62. See Morris, *New Testament Theology*, 266-68.
63. Ibid.
64. Ibid.
65. In the purpose clause, ἵνα πιστεύοντες ζωὴν ἔχητε ἐν τῷ ὀνόματι αὐτοῦ, the word πιστεύοντες is the present active participle, nominative, masculine, plural of πιστεύω, "believe." John writes that those of his readers who have entered into belief that Jesus is the Christ, the Son of God, might. "by [continually] believing." "keep on having," ἔχητε. "[the quality of Iife] [that is in His name."

Chapter 14

1. Greidanus, *The Modern Preacher*, 311.
2. "The Synoptic Gospels, John and Paul share a colllmon basic theological perspective, which stands in continuity to Old Testament theology in contrast to Greek dualism ... The Synoptic Gospels picture this Old Testament hope in process of fulfillment. In the person and mission of Jesus of Nazareth, the Kingdom of God has come to men in history, bringing to them many of the blessings of God's kingly rule. The God of heaven has visited men on earth to redeem them in fulfillment of the Old Testament hope." (George Eldon Ladd, *The Pattern of New Testament Truth* [Grand Rapids: Eerdmans, 1968], 109)
3. Ryken, *The Literature of the Bible*, 317.
4. Aune states, "The 'letter' was the most popular literary form in early Christianity. It is also the most problematic since it exhibits more variety and flexibility than any other literary form." (The New Testament in Its Liteary Environment, 159.)
5. Ibid.
6. Greidanus, *The Modern Preacher*, 311.
7. Strong, Strong's Exhaustive Concordance of the Bible: Greek Dictionary of the New Testament, 32.
8. Greidanus, *The Modern Preacher*, 313.
9. Aune, *The New Testament in Its Literary Environment*, 158.
10. The use of a scribe, or *amanuensis*, to pen all but the concluding lines and signature of an epistle was apparently common, according to Romans 16:22. 1 Corinthians 16:21, Colossians 4: 18, and 2 Thessalonians 3:17, "The popular culture of the first century was, technically, a rhetorical culture ... The normal mode of writing is by dictation, and that which is written down is intended to be read aloud to a group rather than silently by the individual ... Clues to the organization of thought are, of necessity. based on sound rather than on sight." (John D. Harvey. Listeningg to the Text [Grand Rapids: Baker, 1998], xv.)
11. Ryken, *The Literature of the Bible*, 327.

12. Greidanus, *The Modern Preacher*, 311.
13. Ibid.
14. Guthrie, *New Testament Introduction*, 658.
15. Ibid., 660.
16. Ibid., 661.
17. Greidanus, *The Modern Preacher*, 319, 321.
18. Ibid., 320-2 1.
19. See 1 Corinthians 15:55 for a good example of synonymous parallelism; 1 Peter 2:22 for inverted parallelism; and Romans 4:25 for antithetic parallelism. (Greidanus, *The Modern Preacher*, 322.)
20. Adam and Christ are contrasted in Romans 5:12-21; present and future suffering are opposed to one another in Romans 8:18-39 and throughout Paul's discussion in 2 Corinthians 4:16-18. (Ibid.)
21. Examples of metaphors include the armor of God in Ephesians 6:11-17, and the tongue as a fire in James 3:6. (Ibid., 323)
22. Wilkinson and Boa, *Talk Thru the Old Testament*, 367.
23. Greidanus, *The Modern Preacher*, 316.
24. Ibid., 316-17.
25. Adapted from ibid., 315-17.
26. Tenney, *New Testament Survey*, 261.
27. Wilkinson and Boa, *Walk Thru the Old Testament*, 466.
28. Ibid., 450.
29. Radmacher, Allen, and House, *Nelson Study Bible*, 1515-16.
30. Tenney, *New Testament Survey*, 265
31. Ibid.
32. Radmacher, Allen, and House, *Nelson Study Bible*, 1514.
33. Donald H. Launstein, handout, Western Baptist Seminary, 115.
34. Tenney, *New Testament Survey*, 279.
35. Ellisen, *Western Bible Workbook*, 99.
36. Tenney, *New Testament Survey*, 279.
37. Ibid.
38. Launstein, handout, 129.
39. Guthrie, *New Testament Introduction*, 421.
40. For a good discussion of Paul's possible visits and letters to the Corinthians, see ibid., 424-38.
41. Ibid., 438.
42. See Harvey, *Listening to the Text*, 156.
43. Launstein, handout, 129.
44. Aune notes: "Romans is the only letter of Paul written to a Christian community he had neither founded nor visited" (*The New Testament in Its Literary Environment*, 219)

45. For a good discussion of the origin and composition of the church in Rome, see Guthrie, *New Testament Introduction*, 393-96.
46. Greidanus, *The Modern Preacher*, 321.
47. Ibid., 322 (emphasis added).
48. Ibid.
49. Harvey, *Listening to the Text*, 120.
50. Douglas J. Moo, *The Epistle to the Romans* (Grand Rapids: Eerdmans, 1996), 24.
51. Moo, *The Epistle to the Romans*, 24.
52. Tenney, *New Testament Survey*, 314.
53. Ellisen, *Western Bible Workbook*, 7.
54. Guthrie, *New Testament Introduction*, 635.
55. Tenney, *New Testament Survey*, 316.
56. Guthrie, *New Testament Introduction*, 642, quoting U. Wickett (ZNTW, 52, 1961), 230-38.
57. Ellisen, *Western Bible Workbook*, 165 .
58. Harvey, *Listening to the Text*, 279.
59. Tenney, *New Testament Survey*, 317.
60. Guthrie, *New Testament Introduction*. 640.
61. Tenney, *New Testament Survey*, 317.
62. Guthrie, *New Testament Introduction*, 509-14.
63. Greidanus, *The Modern Preacher*, 319-23.
64. Ellisen, *Western Bible Workbook*, 8.
65. Wilkinson and Boa, *Talk Thru the Old Testament*, 302.
66. See I. Howard Marshall, *New Testament Theology*, (Downers Grove, IL: InterVarsity Press, 2004), 389.
67. Tenney, *New Testament Survey*, 321.
68. Ibid.
69. Wilkinson and Boa, *Talk Thru the Old Testament*, 411. Sec Colossians 1:4-8 and 2:1.
70. Guthrie, *New Testament Introduction*, 549.
71. Ibid., 550.
72. See Marshall, *New Testament Theology*, 366.
73. Earl Radmacher, Ronald B, Allen, and H. Wayne House, *Nelson's New Illustrated Bible Commentary* (Nashville: Thomas Nelson, 1999), 1559.
74. Marshall, *New Testament Theology*, 367.
75. Guthrie, *New Testament Introduction*, 551.
76. Marshall, *New Testament Theology*, 344.
77. Tenney, *New Testament Survey*, 324.
78. Ibid., 323.
79. Greidanus, *The Modern Preacher*, 324.
80. Marshall, *New Testament Theology*, 345.

81. Homer A. Kent, *The Pastoral Epistles* (Chicago: Moody, 1958), 20.
82. "It was not until 1703 that D. N. Serdot, followed later by Paul Anton in 1726, who popularized it, used the term 'Pastoral' to describe them." (Donald Guthrie, *The Pastoral Epistles* [Grand Rapids: Eerdmans, 1957], 11.)
83. This does not take anything away from the relevance of these epistles to those who function as shepherds, but these men should not be cited as New Testament examples of solo or senior pastors of a church.
84. Tenney, *New Testament Survey*, 333.
85. William Hendriksen, *New Testament Commentary: Exposition of the Pastoral Epistles* (Grand Rapids: Baker, 1957), 41.
86. Tenney, *New Testament Survey*, 333.
87. Radmacher, Allen, and House, *Nelson Study Bible*, 1592.
88. Launstein, handout, 179.
89. Radmacher, Allen, and House, *Nelson Study Bible*, 1594.
90. Ibid, 1592.
91. Tenney, *New Testament Survey*, 338.
92. Marshall, *New Testament Theology*, 399.
93. Tenney lists the following doctrines addressed in the epistle to Titus: "1. The personality of God (2:11, 3:6). 2. The qualities of His love and grace (2:11, 3:4). 3. His title of Savior (2:10, 3:4). 4. The saviorhood of Christ (2:13, 3:6). 5. The Holy Spirit (3:5). 6. The implication of the triune being of God (3:5,6). 7. The essential deity of Christ (2:13). 8. The vicarious atonement of Christ (2:14). 9. The universality of salvation (2:11). 10. Salvation by grace, not by works (3:5). 11. The incoming of the Holy Spirit (3:5). 12. Justification by faith (3:7). 13. Sanctification (purification) of His own people (2:14). 14. Separation from evil (2:12). 15. Inheritance of eternal life (3:7). 16. The return of Christ (2:13)." (*New Testament Survey*, 338).
94. Marshall, *New Testament Theology*, 401.
95. Guthrie, *New Testament Introduction*, 628.
96. Launstein, handout, 179.
97. Wilkinson and Boa, *Talk Thru the Old Testament*, 435.
98. Ibid.
99. Tenney, *New Testament Survey*, 351-52.
100. Marshall, *New Testament Theology*, 642.
101. Tenney, *New Testament Survey*, 350.
102. Ibid, 349-50.
103. Ellisen, *Western Bible Workbook*, 173.
104. So Marshall states, "Peter's main concern is to rehabilitate the expectation of the future coming (parousia) of Jesus." (*New Testament Theology*, 672.)
105. Guthrie, *New Testament Introduction*, 850.
106. Tenney, *New Testament Survey*, 367.

107. Wilkinson and Boa, *Talk Thru the Old Testament*, 502.
108. George Lawrence Lawlor, *Translation and Exposition of the Epistle of Jude* (Phillipsburg, NJ: Presbyterian and Reformed Publishing Co., 1972), 14.
109. Ibid.
110. Ibid.
111. Tenney, *New Testament Survey*, 374.
112. Ibid.
113. Guthrie, *New Testament Introduction*, 869.
114. Wilkinson and Boa, *Talk Thru the Old Testament*, 485.
115. B. F. Westcott, *The Epistles of John*, (Grand Rapids: Eerdmans, 1966), xxxii.
116. Guthrie, *New Testament Introduction*, 893.
117. Ibid., 896.

Chapter 15

1. Aune notes that Revelation 1:1-2 marks "the first occurrence of the term [apocalypse] in apocalyptic literature, a sentence intended to function as a title." (*The New Testament in Its Literary Environment*, 226.)
2. Guthrie, *New Testament Introduction*, 934.
3. Dionysius charged inconsistencies of Greek grammar, vocabulary, expressions, theological content, and use of the author's name. There are, however, remarkable similarities between the Revelation and the Gospel of John. Apparent differences in style can be explained by the unusual circumstances under which it was written, including exile on the Isle of Patmos, startling visions, the nature of apocalyptic literature, and possible use of a secretary. (Radmacher, Allen, and House, *Nelson Study Bible*.)
4. Guthrie, *New Testament Introduction*, 949.
5. Ibid., 949-60.
6. Radmacher, Allen, and House, *Nelson Study Bible*, 2162.
7. Thomas, Revelation 1-7, 29.
8. Greidanus, *The Modern Preacher*, 229.
9. Ibid.
10. Ibid.. 236-38.
11. Ibid.
12. Ryken, *How to Read the Bible as Literature*, 335.
13. John Walvoord, *The Revelation of Jesus Christ* (Chicago: Moody, 1966), 16-20.
14. Childs, for example, states of the apostle John, "The whole apocalyptic scenario which he inherited has now been reinterpreted as completed action. It docs not lie in the future, but in every apocalyptic cycle described, God now rules his universe and the kingdom has come (7:10; 11; 15: 19:6). Satan has been defeated by the Lamb and cast out of heaven. The Anti·Christ has been conquered and salvation is realized." (*Biblical Theology of the Old and New Testaments*, 321.)

15. Ryken, *The Literature of the Bible*, 335.
16. Guthrie, *New Testament Introduction*, 969-74.
17. Guthrie, *New Testament Introduction*, 971. In a footnote, Guthrie states that "Farrar was the first to connect the twelve houses of Israel with the signs of the Zodiac."
18. Ryken, *The Literature of the Bible*, 335.
19. Ibid., 336.
20. Adapted from Ryken, *The Literature of the Bible*, 337.
21. See Ryken, The Literature of the Bible, 337.
22. Charted on the basis of Ryken's observations and personal comparison to Revelation 6. (Ryken, *The Literature of the Bible*, 338.)
23. Ibid.
24. Ibid.
25. Walvoord, *The Revelation of Jesus Christ*, 48.
26. Morris, *New Testament Theology*, 292.
27. Thomas, *Revelation*, 1-7, 517.
28. See Greidanus, *The Modern Preacher*, 250-62, for a fuller discussion of these and other guidelines.

Appendix

1. Currah, "Outlining from the Nestle-Aland *Novum Testamentum Graece*."
2. Mears, *What the Bible Is All About*, 23.
3. With reference to age, and to distinguish an adult man from a boy, see Matthew 14:21 and 15:38 (where ἄνδρες, γυναῖκες, and παιδία are discriminated); with the added notion also of intelligence and virtue. sec 1 Corinthians 13:11 (opposed to νήπιος); Ephesians 4: 13; and James 3:2 (in the last two passages, τέλειος, ἀνὴρ).
4. James S. Hewett, ed., *Illustrations Unlimited*, 167.

Bibliography

Adams, Jay E. *Shepherding God's Flock*. Chestnut Hill: Presbyterian and Reformed Publishing Co., 1975.

Aland, Kurt. *Synopsis Quattor Evangeliorum*. Stuttgart: Wtembergische, 1967.

Allen, Ronald B. *Praise! A Matter of Life and Breath*. Nashville: Thomas Nelson, 1980.

———. *Lord of Song*. Portland: Multnomah. 1985.

———. *When Song Is New*. Nashville: Thomas Nelson, 1983.

Ames, William. *The Marrow of Theology*. Translated by John D. Eusden, ed. Boston: Pilgrim, 1968.

Anderson, Francis I. *Job*. London: InterVarsity, 1976.

Archer, Gleason. *A Survey of Old Testament Introduction*. Chicago: Moody, 1964.

Aune, David E. *The New Testament in Its Literary Environment*. Philadelphia: Westminster. 1987.

Barclay, William. *The Letters of James and Peter*. Edinburgh: St. Andrew, 1958.

Barnhard, Clarence L., and Robert K. Barnhard. eds. *The World Book Dictionary*. Chicago: Doubleday, 1984.

Blackwood, Andrew W. *The Fine Art of Preaching*. Grand Rapids: Baker, 1976.

Brown, Colin. *The New International Dictionary of New Testament Theology*, vol I. Grand Rapids: Zondervan, 1967. Bruce. F. F. ed. *The New International Commentary on the New Testament*. Grand Rapids: Eerdmans, 1971.

Carter, Tom. *Spurgeon's Commentary on Great Chapters of the Bible*. Grand Rapids: Kregel, 1998.

Cassuto, Umberto. *The Documentary Hypothesis*. Jerusalem: Magnes, 1961.

Chafer, Lewis Sperry. *Salvation*. Grand Rapids: Zondervan. 1917.

Charnock, Stephen. *The Existence and Attributes* of God. Reprint. Minneapolis: Klock & Klock, 1977.

Childs, Brevard S. *Biblical Theology of the Old and New Testaments*. Minneapolis: Fortress Press, 1992.

Cook, W. Robert. *Systematic Theology in Outline Form*. Portland: Western Baptist Seminary Press, 1970.

Cromarty, John M. "Bullinger and the Second Helvetic Confession." *Our Banner*, June 1976.

Currah, Galen. "Outlining from the Nestle-Aland *Novum Testamentum Graece*." Portland: Western Conservative Baptist Seminary, [1973].

Deffinbaugh, Bob. *Wisdom Literatur., Proverbs*. www.Bible.org.

Demaray, Donald E. *Pulpit Giants*. Chicago: Moody, 1973.

Dorsey, David A. *The Literary Structure of the Old Testament*. Grand Rapids: Baker, 1999.

Easton, M. G. *Easton's Bible Dictionary*. 1897. Oak Harbor: Logos Research Systems. Inc., 1996.

Edersheim, Alfred. *The Life and Times of Jesus the Messiah*. Grand Rapids: Eerdmans, 1971. Ellisen, Stanley A. *3 Worlds in Conflict*. Sisters: Multnomah, 1998.

Eichrodt, Walter. "Is Typological Exegesis an Appropriate Method?" In *Essays on Old Testament Hermeneutics*. Edited by Claus Westermann. Translated by James Luther Mays. Atlanta: John Knox Press, 1960, 1979.

Fairbairn, Patrick. *The Typology of Scripture or the Doctrine of Types*. 2 vols. Philadelphia: Daniels and Smith, 1852.

Farris, Stephen. *Preaching that Matters*. Louisville: Westminster John Knox Press, 1998.

Freeman, Hobart. *An Introduction to the Old Testament Prophets*. Chicago: Moody, 1968.

Fruchtenbaum, Arnold G. "Rabbinic Quotations of the Old Testament And How It Relates To Joel 2 and Acts 2." *Ariel Ministries*. http ://www.ariel.org.

Fausti, Remo P. and Edward L. McGlone. *Understandiug Oral Communication*. Menlo Park: Cummings, 1972.

Glickman, Craig S. *A Song for Lovers*. Downers Grove: InterVarsity, 1977.

Gray, John. *I & II Kings* in "The Old Testament Library." Philadelphia: Westminster, 1970.

Greidanus, Sidney. *The Modern Preacher and The Ancient Text*. Grand Rapids: InterVarsity, 1988. Grudem, Wayne. *Evangelical Feminism & Biblical Truth*. Sisters: Multnomah, 2004.

———. "Christ Preaching Through Noah: 1 Peter 3:19-20 In The Light Of Dominant Themes In Jewish Literature," *Trinity Journal* 7, 1986.

Guthrie, Donald. *New Testament Introduction*. Downers Grove: InterVarsity, 1970.

———. *The Pastoral Epistles*. Grand Rapids: Eerdmans, 1977.

Harrison, Everett F., Geoffrey W. Bromiley, and Carl F. H. Henry, eds. *Baker's Dictionary of Theology*. Grand Rapids: Baker, 1978.

Harrison, Roland K. *Introduction to the Old Testament*. Grand Rapids: Eerdmans, 1969.

Harvey, John D. *Listening to the Text*. Grand Rapids: Baker, 1998.

Hendricks, Howard. *Teaching to Change Lives*. Sisters: Multnomah, 1989.

Hendriksen, William. *New Testament Commentary: Exposition of The Pastoral Epistles*. Grand Rapids: Baker, 1957.

Hirsch, E. D. *Validity in Interpretation*. New Haven: Yale, 1967.

Hobbs, Hershel H. *Preaching Values from the Papyri*. Grand Rapids: Baker, 1964.

House, H. Wayne. *The Role of Women in Ministry Today*. Grand Rapids: Baker, 1995.

House, H. Wayne, and Kenneth M., Durham. *Living Wisely in a Foolish World*. Grand Rapids: Kregel, 1992.

Johnson, Elliot E. *Expository Hermeneutics: An Introduction*. Grand Rapids: Zondervan, 1990.

Jones, Milton, "An Investigation and Explanation of the Whiting System of Homiletics as a Practical Approach to Preaching." Th. M. thesis, Western Conservative Baptist Seminary, 1965.

Kaiser, Walter C., Jr. *Toward an Exegetical Theology*. Grand Rapids: Baker, 1981.

Kaiser, Walter C., Jr. and Moises Silva. *An Introduction to Biblical Hermeneutics*. Grand Rapids: Zondervan, 1994.

Kantenwein, Lee L. *Diagrammatical Analysis*. Winona Lake: BMH Books, 1979.

Keil, C. F. and F. Delitzsch. *Commentary on the Old Testament*. 10 vols. Grand Rapids: Eerdmans, 1973.

Kent, Homer A. *The Pastoral Epistles*. Chicago: Moody, 1958.

Kostenberger, Andreas J. and Thomas R. Schreiner, eds. *Women In The Church*. 2nd ed. Grand Rapids: Baker Academic, 1995, 2005.

Kidner, Derek, *Proverbs*. London: InterVarsity, 1976.

———. *Psalms*, 2 vols. London: InterVarsity, 1975. Kistemaker, Simon. *The Parables of Jesus*. Grand Rapids: Baker, [1980]. Kitchen, K. A. *Ancient Orient and Old Testament*. Chicago: InterVarsity, 1966.

Koller, Charles W. *Expository Preaching Without Notes*. Grand Rapids: Baker, 1962.

Ladd, George Eldon. *The Pattern of New Testament Truth*. Grand Rapids: Eerdmans, 1968. Laney, J. Carl. *Balancing Your Act Without Losing It*. Wheaton: Tyndale, 1988.

Lawlor, George Lawrence. *Translation and Exposition of the Epistle of Jude*. Presbyterian and Reformed Publishing Co., 1972.

Liefeld, Walter L. *New Testament Exposition*. Grand Rapids: Zondervan, 1984.

Maier, Paul L. *In the Fullness of Time*. San Francisco: Harper San Francisco, 1991.

Macleod, Donald. *The Problem of Preaching*. Philadelphia: Fortress, 1987.

Marshall, I. Howard. *New Testament Theology*. Downers Grove: InterVarsily, 2004.

Mathewson, Steven D. *The Art of Preaching Old Testament Narrative*. Grand Rapids: Baker, 2002.

McQuilkin, J. Robertson. *Understanding and Applying the Bible*. Chicago: Moody, 1984.

McDowell, Josh. *Right from Wrong*. Dallas: Word, 1994.

Mayers, Ronald B. *Balanced Apologetics*. Grand Rapids: Kregel, 1984.

Mears, Henriett a C. *What the Bible Is All About*. Ventura: Regal, 1999.

Moo, Douglas J. *The Epistle to the Romans*. Grand Rapids: Eerdmans, 1996.

Morris, Leon. *New Testament Theology*. Grand Rapids: Zondervan, 1986.

Nichols, Sue. *Words on Target*. Richmond: John Knox Press, 1973.

Packer, J. I. *Knowing God*. Downers Grove: InterVarsity, 1973.

———."Puritan Evangelism." www.apuritansmind.com.

Paterson, John. *The Goodly Fellowship of the Prophets*. New York: Scribner's, 1948.

Pfeiffer, Charles F. *The Wycliffe Bible Commentary: Old Testament*. Chicago: Moody Press, 1962.

Pinnock, Clark H. *Biblical Revelation*. Chicago: Moody, 1971.

Piper, John and Wayne Grudem, eds. *Recovering Biblical Manhood and Womanhood*. Wheaton: Crossway, 1991.

Radmacher, Earl D. *The Nature of the Church*. Portland: Western Baptist Press, 1972.

———. *Salvation*. Nashville: Word, 2000.

Ramm, Bernard. *Protestant Biblical Interpretation*. Grand Rapids: Baker, 1970.

Richards, Lawrence O. and Gary J Bredfeldt. *Creative Bible Teaching*. Chicago: Moody, 1998.

Robertson. A. T. *Word Pictures in the New Testament*. 6 vols. Nashville: Broadman, 1930.

Robinson, Haddon W. *Biblical Preaching*. Grand Rapids: Baker. 1980.

Ryken, Leland. *The Literature of the Bible*. Grand Rapids: Zondervan. 1974.

———. *How to Read the Bible as Literature*. Grand Rapids: Zondervan, 1984.

———. *The Word of God in English*. Wheaton: Crossway. 2002.

Saucy, Robert L. *The Church in God's Program*. Chicago: Moody, 1972.

Stott, John R. W. *The Preacher's Portrait*. Grand Rapids: Eerdmans, 1961.

Strauch, Alexander. *Biblical Eldership*. Littleton: Lewis and Roth, 1995.

Tenney, Merrill C. *New Testament Survey*. Grand Rapids: Eerdmans, 1961.

Thomas, Robert. *Revelation 1-7, An Exegetical Commentary*. Kenneth Barker, ed. Chicago: Moody, 1992.

Thompson, Leonard L. *Introducing Biblical Literature: A More Fantastic Country*. Englewood Cliffs: Prentice-Hall, 1978.

Tozer, A. W. *The Knowledge of the Holy*. New York: Harper Collins, 1961.

Traina, Robert. *Methodological Bible Study*. Wilmore: Asbury Theological Seminary, 1952.

Tucker, Gene. *Form Criticism of the Old Testament*. Philadelphia: Fortress, 1971.

Turner, Nigel. *Grammatical Insights Into the New Testament*. Edinburgh: T & T Clark, 1965.

Unger, Merrill F. *Principles of Expository Preaching*. Grand Rapids: Zondervan, 1955.

Von Rad, Gerhard. *Moses*. London: Lutterworth Press, 1960.

———. *Old Testament Theology*. Translated by D. M. G. Stalker. New York: Harper & Row. 1960.

Walvoord, John. *The Revelation of Jesus Christ*. Chicago: Moody, 1966.

Walvoord, John F. and Roy B. Zuck. *The Bible Knowledge Commentary*. Wheaton: Victor, 1983-1985.

Ward, Ronald A. *Hidden Meaning in the New Testament*. Old Tappan: Revell, 1969.

Warfield, Benjamin B. *The Inspiration and Authority of the Bible*. Philadelphia: Presbyterian and Reformed Publishing Co., 1970.

Westcott, B. F. *The Epistles of John*. Grand Rapids: Eerdmans, 1966.

Westermann, Claus. *The Praise of God in the Psalms*. Richmond: John Knox Press, 1965.

White, R. E. O.. *A Guide to Preaching*. Grand Rapids: Eerdmans, 1973.

Wilkinson, Bruce and Boa. Kenneth. Talk Thru the Bible. Nashville: Thomas Nelson, 2004. Wiseman, D.J., ed. *Tyndale Old Testament Commentaries*. Leicester: InterVarsity, 1974.

Wood, Bryant G. "The Walls of Jericho," *Bible and Spade*. Spring, 1999.

Wuest, Kenneth. *Word Studies in the Greek New Testament*. 3 vols. Grand Rapids: Eerdmans, 1973.

Zuck, Roy B. *Basic Bible Interpretation*. Wheaton: Victor, 1991.

Index

G

H

I

J

K

L

M

N

O

P

Q

R

S

T

W

Z

QUANTUM MECHANICS OF ONE- AND TWO-ELECTRON ATOMS

HANS A. BETHE

AND

EDWIN E. SALPETER

Cornell University
Ithaca, New York

A PLENUM/ROSETTA EDITION

Library of Congress Cataloging in Publication Data

Bethe, Hans Albrecht, 1906-
Quantum mechanics of one- and two-electron atoms.

"A Plenum/Rosetta edition."
Bibliography: p.
Includes indexes.
1. Problem of many bodies. 2. Atoms. I. Salpeter, Edwin E., joint author. II. Title.
QC174.17.P7B47 1977 539.7 76-30829
ISBN 0-306-20022-8

This is the authorized paperback edition of Bethe/Salpeter,
Quantum Mechanics of One- and Two-Electron Atoms. First edition

First paperback printing 1977

A Plenum/Rosetta Edition
Published by Plenum Publishing Corporation
227 West 17th Street, New York, N.Y. 10011

Printed in the United States of America

DEDICATED TO THE MEMORY OF
ARNOLD SOMMERFELD

Preface to the Plenum/Rosetta Edition.

This book was written twenty years ago, but we are leaving it unchanged—not because little has happened to the subject, but because so much has happened that any change would require very major rewriting. On the other hand, no other book on the subject seems to have appeared and we hope this paperback edition will be of some use to a younger generation—if not for another twenty years, at least until someone else has the patience to write a new book.

Although we have added no new material we have corrected some misprints. We have added new references only where they correct actual errors. We are grateful to Drs. G. Feinberg, M. Inokuti, Y. Kim, and A. Petermann for pointing out errors.

Preface.

Nearly all of this book is taken from an article prepared in 1956 for a recent volume of the Encyclopedia of Physics. This article, in turn, is partly based on Dr. NORBERT ROSENZWEIG's translation of an older article on the same subject, written by one of us (HAB) about 25 years ago for the GEIGER-SCHEEL Handbuch der Physik. To the article written last year we have added some Addenda and Errata. These Addenda and Errata refer back to some of the 79 sections of the main text and contain some misprint corrections, additional references and some notes.

The aim of this book is two-fold. First, to act as a reference work on calculations pertaining to hydrogen-like and helium-like atoms and their comparison with experiments. However, these calculations involve a vast array of approximation methods, mathematical tricks and physical pictures, which are also useful in the application of quantum mechanics to other fields. In many sections we have given more general discussions of the methods and physical ideas than is necessary for the study of the H- and He-atom alone. We hope that this book will thus at least partly fulfill its second aim, namely to be of some use to graduate students who wish to learn "applied quantum mechanics". A basic knowledge of the principles of quantum mechanics, such as given in the early chapters of SCHIFF's or BOHM's book, is presupposed.

Like its 1932 predecessor this book mainly gives "low-brow" explicit derivations rather than using more elegant and powerful, but more difficult, formalisms. However, in dealing with angular momentum and sum rules, etc., some operator manipulations are introduced, since these are now commonplace in the treatment of complex atoms. Since it is no longer necessary to "sell quantum mechanics", less space is devoted to the experimental verification of older quantum mechanical results. A large fraction of the present book is devoted to the Dirac theory of the electron and to radiative effects, including short discussions of the relevant experiments. These topics are also treated from the "low-brow" or "practical" point of view. In particular, no formal derivations of quantum-electrodynamics are presented, but the specific application to atomic systems of general field-theoretic results is described in detail.

Numbers in square brackets, in the text, e.g. [*9*], refer to a short bibliography towards the end of the book, but most references are given as footnotes. References to "this Encyclopedia" refer to the recent Encyclopedia of Physics, edited by S. FLÜGGE and published by Springer-Verlag; "this volume" refers to Vol. XXXV. In many sections atomic units are used, which are defined in the Introduction. The particular definitions of spherical harmonics we have used, as well as useful formulae, are given in an Appendix.

We are deeply grateful to many colleagues who have made suggestions, pointed out errors, communicated unpublished results and generally helped with the preparation of the manuscript or the proofreading. We are particularly indebted to Drs. J. F. BIRD and N. ROSENZWEIG who read the proofs patiently and eradicated mistakes impatiently.

September 1957. H. A. BETHE · E. E. SALPETER.

Contents.

Quantum Mechanics of One- and Two-Electron Atoms.

Introduction. Units.

α) One of the simplest, and most completely treated, fields of application of quantum mechanics is the theory of atoms with one or two electrons. For hydrogen and the analogous ions He^+, Li^{++}, etc., the calculations can be performed exactly, both in SCHRÖDINGER's nonrelativistic wave mechanics and in DIRAC's relativistic theory of the electron. More specifically, the calculations are exact for a single electron in a fixed COULOMB potential. Hydrogen-like atoms thus furnish an excellent way of testing the validity of quantum mechanics. For such atoms the correction terms due to the motion and structure of atomic nuclei and due to quantum electrodynamic effects are small and can be calculated with high accuracy. Since the energy levels of hydrogen and similar atoms can be investigated experimentally to an astounding degree of accuracy, some accurate tests of the validity of quantum electrodynamics are also possible. Finally, the theory of such atoms in an external electric or magnetic field has also been developed in detail and compared with experiment.

For atoms and ions with two electrons, such as H^-, He, Li^+, etc., exact analytic calculations are not possible at the present time. But these atoms are still simple enough, so that various approximation methods can be used to carry out calculations to a high degree of accuracy. In fact, for the ground state of such atoms the accuracy of the theoretical calculations is of the same order of magnitude as that of spectroscopic measurements. Thus, helium-like atoms not only give further confirmation of the general validity of quantum mechanics, but provide an excellent testing ground for the various approximation methods which are commonly used in quantum mechanics. Finally, the relativistic effects for two-electron atoms (and especially for positronium) provide a simple field of application for present-day theories of the interaction between electrons.

We shall largely base our treatment on the standard wavemechanical form of quantum mechanics in the nonrelativistic theory and on the DIRAC theory for the relativistic treatment of electrons (particles of spin $\frac{1}{2}$). The fundamental principles of these theories are described in detail elsewhere, see for instance the works[1] by DIRAC [*1*], KRAMERS [*2*], PAULI [*3*] or SCHIFF [*4*]. Occasionally we shall use the more general methods of matrix manipulation, described, for instance, by CONDON and SHORTLEY [*5*]. We shall not treat quantum electrodynamics in any detail, but will refer to results obtained in this theory (see for instance, HEITLER [*6*]).

β) Units. To avoid carrying too many numerical factors, we shall in general use atomic units (a.u.), introduced by HARTREE[2]. These units are built up of various combinations of the charge e and mass m of the electron and of PLANCK's

[1] Numbers in italics, e.g., [*1*], refer to a bibliography at the end of this article.
[2] D. R. HARTREE: Proc. Cambridge Phil. Soc. **24**, 89 (1928).

constant h. In general we shall find it useful to introduce, instead of h, the "rationalized PLANCK's constant",

$$\hbar = \frac{h}{2\pi} = 1.0544_5 \times 10^{-27} \text{ erg sec}.$$

We shall also use SOMMERFELD's dimensionless "fine structure constant"

$$\alpha = \frac{e^2}{\hbar c} = \frac{1}{137.037},$$

where c is the velocity of light, $c = 299793$ km/sec. In our atomic units, $\hbar$ is also the unit of action and of angular momentum.

The atomic units are:

1. Unit of charge $= e =$ charge of the electron $= 4.8029 \times 10^{-10}$ e.s.u. $= 1.6021 \times 10^{-20}$ e.m.u.

2. Unit of mass $= m =$ mass of the electron $= 9.108_5 \times 10^{-28}$ gm.

3. Unit of length $= a =$ "radius of first BOHR orbit" (innermost circular orbit for H in the old quantum theory) $= \hbar^2/m e^2 = 5.2917 \times 10^{-9}$ cm.

4. Unit of velocity $= v_0 =$ electron velocity in the first BOHR orbit $= e^2/\hbar = \alpha c = 2.1877 \times 10^8$ cm/sec.

5. Unit of momentum $= p_0 =$ electron momentum in the first BOHR orbit $= m e^2/\hbar = m v_0 = 1.9926 \times 10^{-19}$ gm cm/sec.

6. Unit of energy $= e^2/a = m e^4/\hbar^2 = p_0^2/m =$ twice the ionization potential of hydrogen (for nuclear mass ∞) $= 4.359_0 \times 10^{-11}$ erg.

7. Unit of time $= a/v_0 = \hbar^3/m e^4 = 2.4189 \times 10^{-17}$ sec.

8. Unit of frequency $= v_0/a = m e^4/\hbar^3 = 4\pi$ Ry $= 4.1341 \times 10^{16}$ sec^{-1} (Ry $=$ RYDBERG frequency).

9. Unit of electric potential $= e/a = m e^3/\hbar^2 = 0.09076$ e.s.u. $= 27.210$ Volt.

10. Unit of electric field strength $= e/a^2 = m^2 e^5/\hbar^4 = 5.142 \times 10^9$ Volt/cm.

We have defined the "RYDBERG for infinite mass" Ry as a frequency, namely $1/4\pi$ atomic frequency units. We shall sometimes express energy in terms of "RYDBERG units", that is in units of (h Ry). This quantity is *one half* an atomic energy unit and numbers expressed in terms of it will carry the symbol "Ry" after them. In many experimental results, one obtains instead of an energy E, the equivalent wave number (E/hc), expressed in cm^{-1}, or the equivalent frequency (E/h), expressed in Mc/sec. The wave number corresponding to one "RYDBERG unit of energy" is[1]

$$R_\infty = \frac{e^2}{2ahc} = \frac{\alpha}{4\pi a} = 109737.3 \text{ cm}^{-1}.$$

The RYDBERG frequency itself, $\frac{v_0}{4\pi a} = \frac{e^2}{2ah}$, is equal to 3.28985×10^9 Mc/sec. One RYDBERG unit of energy, expressed in terms of electron volts, is 13.605_0 eV.

γ) Basis for numerical values used. The numerical values quoted above for the atomic units expressed in ordinary (C.G.S.) units were taken from DUMOND and COHEN's[2] Tables of the Physical Constants. DUMOND and COHEN's best numerical values of the physical constants are based on a large number of experiments, which measure different combinations of the fundamental constants. More experiments than unknown constants were available and the "best values" were derived by a method-of-least-squares analysis. Some of the most accurate

[1] This quantity R_∞ is often referred to simply as "the RYDBERG for infinite nuclear mass" in the literature.

[2] J. W. M. DUMOND and E. R. COHEN: Rev. Mod. Phys. **25**, 691 (1953); also first article in this volume.

experiments, used in this analysis, require for their interpretation a knowledge (and the validity) of the quantum theory of atomic energy levels. This theory, to be developed in the following chapters, is required in particular (a) to derive the "RYDBERG", R_∞, from the spectroscopic measurement of wave numbers of the BALMER lines for hydrogen, (b) to derive the fine structure constant α from microwave measurements of the fine structure (or hyperfine structure) splitting of energy levels of hydrogen.

To be able to discuss experimental tests for the validity of atomic theory, it is useful to consider the "best" values of the atomic constants which can be derived from experiments *without* any recourse to atomic theory. Besides the accurately known value for the velocity of light, c, we need numerical values for h, e and m. Enough experiments for such a determination are now available: In particular PLANK's constant h can be derived from measurements of the short wave-length limit of the continuous X-ray spectrum without detailed knowledge of quantum theory, using only the postulate $E = h\nu$, relating energy E and frequency ν. An outline of some of the other experiments is as follows: X-ray diffraction experiments on crystals and gratings give the lattice constants of simple crystals in centimeters and hence AVOGADRO's number N. The measurement of the Faraday then gives e. Mass-spectroscopy (and N) gives M_p, the proton mass. Experiments comparing (indirectly) the "cyclotron frequencies" of the electron and proton finally give m/M_p, and hence m.

The numerical values obtained from these experiments, which do *not* involve atomic theory for h, e and m (and hence for R_∞ and α) are, of course, less accurate than DUMOND and COHEN's "best values" (using all experiments) which were quoted above. These "non-atomic" values[1] are

$$\begin{aligned}
\hbar &= (1.0542 \pm 0.0002) \times 10^{-27}\ \text{erg sec},\\
e &= (4.8026 \pm 0.0005) \times 10^{-10}\ \text{e.s.u.},\\
m &= (9.107_8 \pm 0.001_0) \times 10^{-28}\ \text{gm},\\
1/\alpha &= 137.02 \pm 0.02,\\
R_\infty &= (109773 \pm 35)\ \text{cm}^{-1}.
\end{aligned}$$

These non-atomic values agree with the more accurate ones, quoted above, to within (approximately) the experimental error (the discrepancy is less than 1.5 times the standard deviation in all cases)[2].

I. The hydrogen atom without external fields.

a) Nonrelativistic theory.

1. Separation of SCHRÖDINGER's equation in spherical polar coordinates. Angularly dependent eigenfunctions and the angular momentum matrix. SCHRÖDINGER's equation[3] in c.g.s. units for an electron in the field of a nucleus of charge Ze and of infinite mass is

$$\varDelta u + \frac{2m}{\hbar^2}\left(E + \frac{Ze^2}{r}\right) u = 0, \tag{1.1}$$

[1] J. W. DUMOND and E. R. COHEN: In this volume and private communication.

[2] Numerical values, found in older theoretical references (including ref. [*10*] of our bibliography), which are based on the atomic constants, should be treated with great caution: The older values of some atomic constants were in error by much more than the statistical errors in the older experiments (due to systematic errors not expected at the time).

[3] We shall use throughout the symbol $\varDelta$ for the LAPLACE operator $\left(\frac{\partial^2}{\partial x^2} + \frac{\partial^2}{\partial y^2} + \frac{\partial^2}{\partial z^2}\right)$, instead of the symbol ∇^2 which is more commonly used in English and American texts.

and in HARTREE's atomic units (see Introductory Remarks) is

$$\Delta u + 2\left(E + \frac{Z}{r}\right) u = 0. \tag{1.1'}$$

This equation can be separated in spherical polar coordinates. We choose the nucleus as origin of a polar coordinate system with some arbitrary z direction as polar axis. Let $r\vartheta\varphi$ be the coordinates of the electron. The LAPLACian operator Δ is given by

$$\Delta u = \frac{\partial^2 u}{\partial r^2} + \frac{2}{r}\frac{\partial u}{\partial r} + \frac{1}{r^2 \sin\vartheta}\frac{\partial}{\partial\vartheta}\left(\sin\vartheta\frac{\partial u}{\partial\vartheta}\right) + \frac{1}{r^2\sin^2\vartheta}\frac{\partial^2 u}{\partial\varphi^2}. \tag{1.2}$$

We try as solution

$$u = R(r)\, Y(\vartheta, \varphi) \tag{1.3}$$

and obtain

$$\frac{r^2}{R}\left[\frac{d^2R}{dr^2} + \frac{2}{r}\frac{dR}{dr} + 2\left(E + \frac{Z}{r}\right)R\right] = \lambda = -\frac{1}{Y}\cdot\left[\frac{1}{\sin\vartheta}\frac{\partial}{\partial\vartheta}\left(\sin\vartheta\frac{\partial Y}{\partial\vartheta}\right) + \frac{1}{\sin^2\vartheta}\frac{\partial^2 Y}{\partial\varphi^2}\right]. \tag{1.4}$$

The left side is a function of r only, the right side a function of ϑ and φ only. Therefore, λ is a constant. The equation on the right in (1.4), namely

$$\frac{1}{\sin\vartheta}\frac{\partial}{\partial\vartheta}\left(\sin\vartheta\frac{\partial Y}{\partial\vartheta}\right) + \frac{1}{\sin^2\vartheta}\frac{\partial^2 Y}{\partial\varphi^2} + \lambda Y = 0 \tag{1.5}$$

can be solved only if

$$\lambda = l(l+1). \quad l = 0, 1, 2, \ldots \tag{1.6}$$

In this event there are the following $2l+1$ solutions:

$$Y_{lm} = \frac{1}{\sqrt{2\pi}}\mathcal{P}_{lm}(\vartheta)\, e^{im\varphi} = \sqrt{\frac{(l-m)!}{(l+m)!}\cdot\frac{2l+1}{4\pi}}\cdot P_l^m(\cos\vartheta)\, e^{im\varphi}; \quad m = -l, \ldots, l-1, l \tag{1.7}$$

Y_{lm} is a spherical harmonic, P_l^m the unnormalized associated LEGENDRE function (cf. Appendix).

The first few spherical harmonics are given explicitly:

$$\left.\begin{aligned}
&Y_{00} = \frac{1}{\sqrt{4\pi}}, \\
&Y_{10} = \sqrt{\frac{3}{4\pi}}\cos\vartheta, && Y_{11} = \sqrt{\frac{3}{8\pi}}\sin\vartheta\, e^{i\varphi}, \\
&Y_{20} = \sqrt{\frac{5}{4\pi}}\left(\frac{3}{2}\cos^2\vartheta - \frac{1}{2}\right), && Y_{21} = \sqrt{\frac{15}{8\pi}}\sin\vartheta\cos\vartheta\, e^{i\varphi}, \\
&Y_{22} = \frac{1}{4}\sqrt{\frac{15}{2\pi}}\sin^2\vartheta\, e^{2i\varphi}, \\
&Y_{30} = \sqrt{\frac{7}{4\pi}}\left(\frac{5}{2}\cos^3\vartheta - \frac{3}{2}\cos\vartheta\right), && Y_{31} = \frac{1}{4}\sqrt{\frac{21}{4\pi}}\sin\vartheta\,(5\cos^2\vartheta - 1)\, e^{i\varphi}, \\
&Y_{32} = \frac{1}{4}\sqrt{\frac{105}{2\pi}}\sin^2\vartheta\cos\vartheta\, e^{2i\varphi}, && Y_{33} = \frac{1}{4}\sqrt{\frac{35}{4\pi}}\sin^3\vartheta\, e^{3i\varphi}, \\
&Y_{40} = \sqrt{\frac{9}{4\pi}}\left(\frac{35}{8}\cos^4\vartheta - \frac{15}{4}\cos^2\vartheta + \frac{3}{8}\right), && Y_{41} = \frac{3}{4}\sqrt{\frac{5}{4\pi}}(7\cos^3\vartheta - 3\cos\vartheta)\sin\vartheta\, e^{i\varphi}, \\
&Y_{42} = \frac{3}{4}\sqrt{\frac{5}{8\pi}}\sin^2\vartheta\,(7\cos^2\vartheta - 1)\, e^{2i\varphi}, && Y_{43} = \frac{3}{4}\sqrt{\frac{35}{4\pi}}\sin^3\vartheta\cos\vartheta\, e^{3i\varphi}, \\
&Y_{44} = \frac{3}{8}\sqrt{\frac{35}{8\pi}}\sin^4\vartheta\, e^{4i\varphi}.
\end{aligned}\right\} \tag{1.8}$$

The normalized associated LEGENDRE functions $\mathcal{P}_{lm}$ for $l=1$ to 3 are graphed in Fig. 1 (i.e., the parts of the spherical harmonics depending on geographic latitude ϑ). As one can see, the associated LEGENDRE functions P_{lm} have $l-|m|$ zeros between the poles of the sphere. Thus, the spherical harmonic Y_{lm} has $l-|m|$ "parallels of latitude" as nodal lines. Furthermore, the real part of the spherical harmonic

$$\sqrt{\frac{1}{\pi}}\,\mathcal{P}_{lm}(\vartheta)\,\frac{\cos}{\sin}\,m\varphi$$

has $|m|$ meridians as nodal lines, resulting in a total of l nodal lines.

The eigenfunctions

$$u=R(r)\,Y_{lm}(\vartheta,\varphi)$$

are closely related to the angular momentum of the atom—it turns out that both the total angular momentum and the angular momentum about the z-axis are diagonal matrices. They are quantized; i.e., if the appropriate operators are applied to the eigenfunction u,

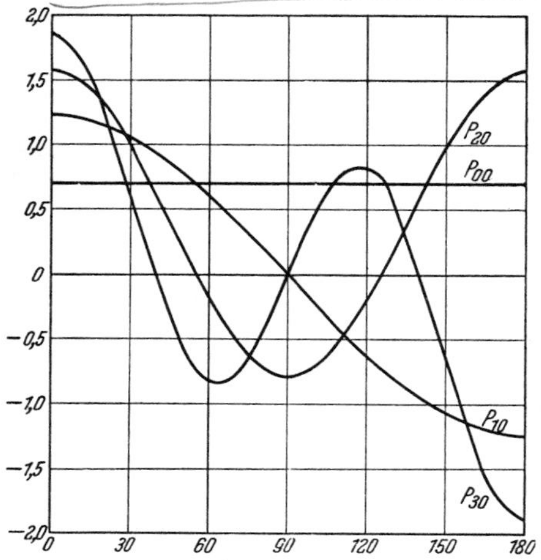

(a): $m=0$.

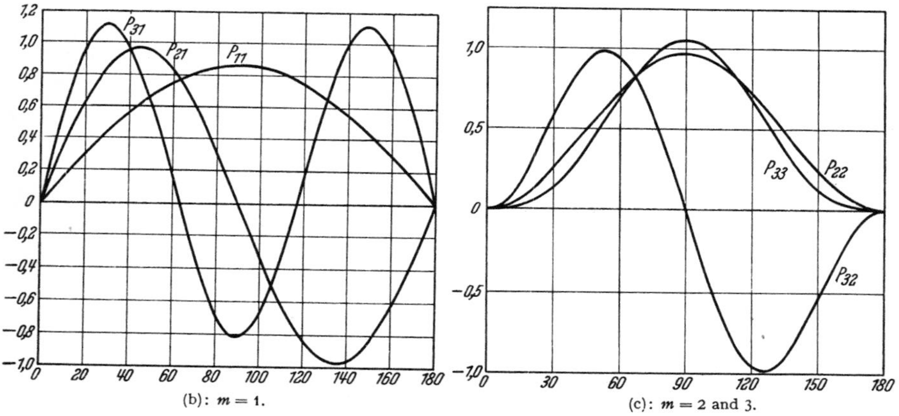

(b): $m=1$. (c): $m=2$ and 3.

Fig. 1 a—c. The normalized associated LEGENDRE function $\mathcal{P}_{lm}(\vartheta)$ plotted against ϑ (in degrees).

the result is the eigenfunction u multiplied by a constant. The operator belonging to the angular momentum about the z-axis is given by[1]

$$k_z=-i\left(x\frac{\partial}{\partial y}-y\frac{\partial}{\partial x}\right)=-i\frac{\partial}{\partial\varphi}. \tag{1.9}$$

Operating on u, one obtains

$$k_z u=-i\frac{\partial}{\partial\varphi}\left[R(r)\,\mathcal{P}_{lm}(\vartheta)\frac{1}{\sqrt{2\pi}}e^{im\varphi}\right]=m u, \tag{1.10}$$

m is a measure of the angular momentum in the z direction and is called the magnetic quantum number[2].

---

[1] k_z, x, and y are measured in atomic units.

[2] Cf. Theory of the ZEEMAN effect, Sect. 45.

The operator representing the total angular momentum is given by

$$k^2 u = -\left(x\frac{\partial}{\partial y} - y\frac{\partial}{\partial x}\right)^2 u - \left(y\frac{\partial}{\partial z} - z\frac{\partial}{\partial y}\right)^2 u - \left(z\frac{\partial}{\partial x} - x\frac{\partial}{\partial z}\right)^2 u$$
$$= r^2\left(\frac{\partial^2 u}{\partial r^2} + \frac{2}{r}\frac{\partial u}{\partial r} - \Delta u\right),$$

resulting from an elementary transformation. In view of (1.2) through (1.6) it follows that

$$k^2 u = r^2\left(\frac{\partial^2 u}{\partial r^2} + \frac{2}{r}\frac{\partial u}{\partial r} - \Delta u\right) = l(l+1)\,u. \tag{1.11}$$

We could have saved ourselves the trouble of calculating the angularly dependent eigenfunctions explicitly, by making use of some general theorems about the angular momentum. These theorems state: 1. The components and the absolute value of the total angular momentum of an electron in any central force field are constants of the motion. 2. The eigenvalues belonging to the square of the total angular momentum are equal to $l(l+1)$, where l is an integer. 3. The eigenvalues of the components in a fixed direction are equal to m, where m can assume all integral values from $-l$ to $+l$. 4. A quantum state is defined by specifying the magnitude and one of the components of the total angular momentum, i.e., by specifying l and m. Thus, by means of the generally valid formula (1.11) one can arrive at once at the differential equation for the radially dependent eigenfunction

$$\frac{d^2 R}{dr^2} + \frac{2}{r}\frac{dR}{dr} + 2\left(E + \frac{Z}{r}\right)R - \frac{l(l+1)}{r^2}R = 0, \tag{1.12}$$

which is identical with the left side of (1.4).

Before solving this equation, we shall calculate the matrix elements of the angular momenta k_x and k_y about the directions perendicular to the z-axis. By definition

$$\left.\begin{aligned} k_x &= -i\left(y\frac{\partial}{\partial z} - z\frac{\partial}{\partial y}\right) = i\sin\varphi\frac{\partial}{\partial\vartheta} + i\cot\vartheta\cos\varphi\frac{\partial}{\partial\varphi},\\ k_y &= -i\left(z\frac{\partial}{\partial x} - x\frac{\partial}{\partial z}\right) = -i\cos\varphi\frac{\partial}{\partial\vartheta} + i\cot\vartheta\sin\varphi\frac{\partial}{\partial\varphi}.\end{aligned}\right\} \tag{1.13}$$

Thus, in view of formulas (A. 25) and (A. 26) of our appendix,

$$\begin{aligned}(k_x + i k_y)\,Y_{lm}(\vartheta,\varphi) &= e^{i\varphi}\left(\frac{\partial}{\partial\vartheta} + i\cot\vartheta\frac{\partial}{\partial\varphi}\right)Y_{lm}(\vartheta,\varphi)\\ &= -\sqrt{(l-m)\,(l+m+1)}\;Y_{l,m+1}(\vartheta,\varphi),\\ (k_x - i k_y)\,Y_{lm}(\vartheta,\varphi) &= -\,e^{-i\varphi}\left(\frac{\partial}{\partial\vartheta} - i\cot\vartheta\frac{\partial}{\partial\varphi}\right)Y_{lm}(\vartheta,\varphi)\\ &= -\sqrt{(l+m)\,(l-m+1)}\;Y_{l,m-1}(\vartheta,\varphi),\end{aligned}$$

and the matrix elements of the components of the angular monentum become

$$\left.\begin{aligned}(m\,|\,k_x + i k_y\,|\,m-1) &= \int Y^*_{lm}(\vartheta,\varphi)\,(k_x + i k_y)\,Y_{l,m-1}(\vartheta,\varphi)\sin\vartheta\,d\vartheta\,d\varphi\\ &= -\sqrt{(l+m)\,(l-m+1)} = (m-1\,|\,k_x - i k_y\,|\,m).\end{aligned}\right\} \tag{1.14}$$

The matrix elements which correspond to transitions between states of different orbital quantum numbers or of different radially dependent eigenfunctions are zero. As is well known, the formulas (1.14), except for an indeterminancy in the sign of the square root, can be obtained from the general theory (ref. [3] of the bibliography).

We discuss finally the *parity* of our wave functions: For a one-electron atom the parity operation consists simply in the replacement of the position vector $\boldsymbol{r}$ of the electron by $-\boldsymbol{r}$. In spherical polar coordinates this means replacing (ϑ, φ) by $(\pi-\vartheta, \pi+\varphi)$. It follows from the properties of spherical harmonics, given in our appendix, that

$$Y_{lm}(\pi-\vartheta, \pi+\varphi) = (-1)^l Y_{lm}(\vartheta, \varphi). \tag{1.15}$$

For even l, then, our wave functions are unaffected by the parity operation and we say "the parity is even". For odd l, the wave functions change sign under the parity operation and "the parity is odd".

2. Derivation of BALMER's formula[1]. We shall now treat the differential equation satisfied by the radially dependent part of the eigenfunction

$$\frac{d^2R}{dr^2} + \frac{2}{r}\frac{dR}{dr} + \left[2E + \frac{2Z}{r} - \frac{l(l+1)}{r^2}\right] R = 0. \tag{2.1}$$

The last term in the above equation corresponds classically to the centrifugal force of the electron and increases with increasing angular momentum.

Let us begin by assuming that the energy E is negative. Since the potential energy vanishes at infinity, a negative energy corresponds to a bound electron which possesses a positive kinetic energy only by virtue of the nuclear attraction.

First, we study the asymptotic behavior by neglecting the terms in r which are of lower power compared to the ones that are kept, then

$$\frac{d^2R}{dr^2} + 2ER = 0, \qquad R = e^{\pm\sqrt{-2E}\,r}. \tag{2.2}$$

If $R(\infty)$ is to remain finite, we must select the minus sign. We introduce the notation

$$\varepsilon = +\sqrt{-2E} \tag{2.3}$$

and extend the asymptotic solution (2.2) to a solution valid for all r by putting

$$R = e^{-\varepsilon r} f(r), \tag{2.4}$$

where $f(r)$ is a function which varies slowly at infinity. Substitution of (2.4) into (2.1) results in a differential equation in f

$$f'' + 2\left(\frac{1}{r} - \varepsilon\right) f' + \left[2\left(\frac{Z-\varepsilon}{r}\right) - \frac{l(l+1)}{r^2}\right] f = 0. \tag{2.5}$$

Let us expand f in a power series,

$$f = r^\lambda \sum_{\nu=0}^{\infty} a_\nu r^\nu. \tag{2.6}$$

Substitution of (2.6) into (2.5) results in

$$\sum_{\nu=0}^{\infty} a_\nu \left[((\lambda+\nu)(\lambda+\nu+1) - l(l+1))\, r^{\lambda+\nu-2} - 2(\varepsilon(\lambda+\nu+1) - Z)\, r^{\lambda+\nu-1}\right] = 0. \tag{2.7}$$

The coefficient of each power of r must vanish in the above equation. Setting the coefficient or $r^{\lambda-2}$ (the term of lowest power in r) equal to zero, one obtains an equation which determines λ:

$$\lambda(\lambda+1) = l(l+1),$$

---

[1] Compare, for example, ref. [7], A. SOMMERFELD, Wellenmechanischer Ergänzungsband, p. 70 and the original work of E. SCHRÖDINGER, Abhandlungen zur Wellenmechanik, p. 1.

from which

$$\lambda = \begin{cases} +l \\ -l-1. \end{cases} \tag{2.8}$$

The condition that f remain finite at $r=0$ forces one to the choice $\lambda = l$. Setting the coefficient of $r^{\lambda+\nu-2}$ equal to zero one obtains the recursion formula

$$a_\nu = 2a_{\nu-1}\frac{\varepsilon(l+\nu)-Z}{(l+\nu)(l+\nu+1)-l(l+1)}. \tag{2.9}$$

Next, we require that f be a polynomial in r, i.e., that the power series terminate, $a_{n-l-1}r^{n-1}$, say, being the last term. Then

$$a_{n-l} = 0.$$

This condition will be fulfilled if

$$\varepsilon = \frac{Z}{n}, \tag{2.10}$$

$$E = -\frac{1}{2}\frac{Z^2}{n^2}. \tag{2.11}$$

If the above requirement were not made, then for large values of ν:

$$a_\nu \approx \frac{2a_{\nu-1}\varepsilon}{l+\nu+1} \approx c\frac{(2\varepsilon)^{l+\nu+1}}{(l+\nu+1)!},$$

where c is a constant; $f(r)$ would behave as $e^{2\varepsilon r}$ for large r and $R = e^{-\varepsilon r} f(r)$ would increase as $e^{+\varepsilon r}$. Therefore, the breaking off of the series is necessary to assure that the eigenfunction be bounded at infinity.

(2.11) is the well-known BALMER formula for the discrete energy levels of hydrogen ($Z=1$) and for the ions having a single electron, such as He^+, Li^{++} etc. n is the principal quantum number. The energy does not depend on the other two quantum numbers m and l. The independence of the magnetic quantum number m has its origin in the fact that all directions in space enter on equal terms. This holds for all atoms in the absence of an external field and is called directional degeneracy. On the other hand, the fact that the energy is independent of the quantum number l is a special property of the hydrogen atom which must be attributed to the presence of the exact COULOMB potential Z/r. This degeneracy has the consequence that the hydrogen atom is particularly strongly influenced by external fields (first-order STARK effect instead of the usual second-order effect[1]).

The energy formula (2.11) has been verified to an extraordinary degree by spectroscopic measurements. The spectral line emitted in a transition of the atom from quantum state n to state n' has a frequency

$$\nu = \frac{1}{2\pi}(E_n - E_{n'}) = \frac{Z^2}{4\pi}\left(\frac{1}{n'^2} - \frac{1}{n^2}\right) \tag{2.12}$$

in atomic units[2], and is equal to

$$Z^2\left(\frac{1}{n'^2} - \frac{1}{n^2}\right)\text{Ry}, \tag{2.13}$$

[1] The alkali atoms which are more closely related to hydrogen than any other atoms do not show this degeneracy. To be sure, the discrete energy levels of the alkali atoms can be calculated to a good approximation by considering only the motion of the valence electron in the field arising from a charge distribution of closed shells, but this field is a non-Coulomb central field and levels of like n and different l have entirely different energies.

[2] It should be noted that the atomic unit of action is $\hbar = h/2\pi$ and not h. The frequency of the spectral line may be obtained in c.g.s. units by dividing the energy difference (in c.g.s. units) between the initial and final states by h; or, if the energy difference is expressed in atomic units, by dividing by 2π.

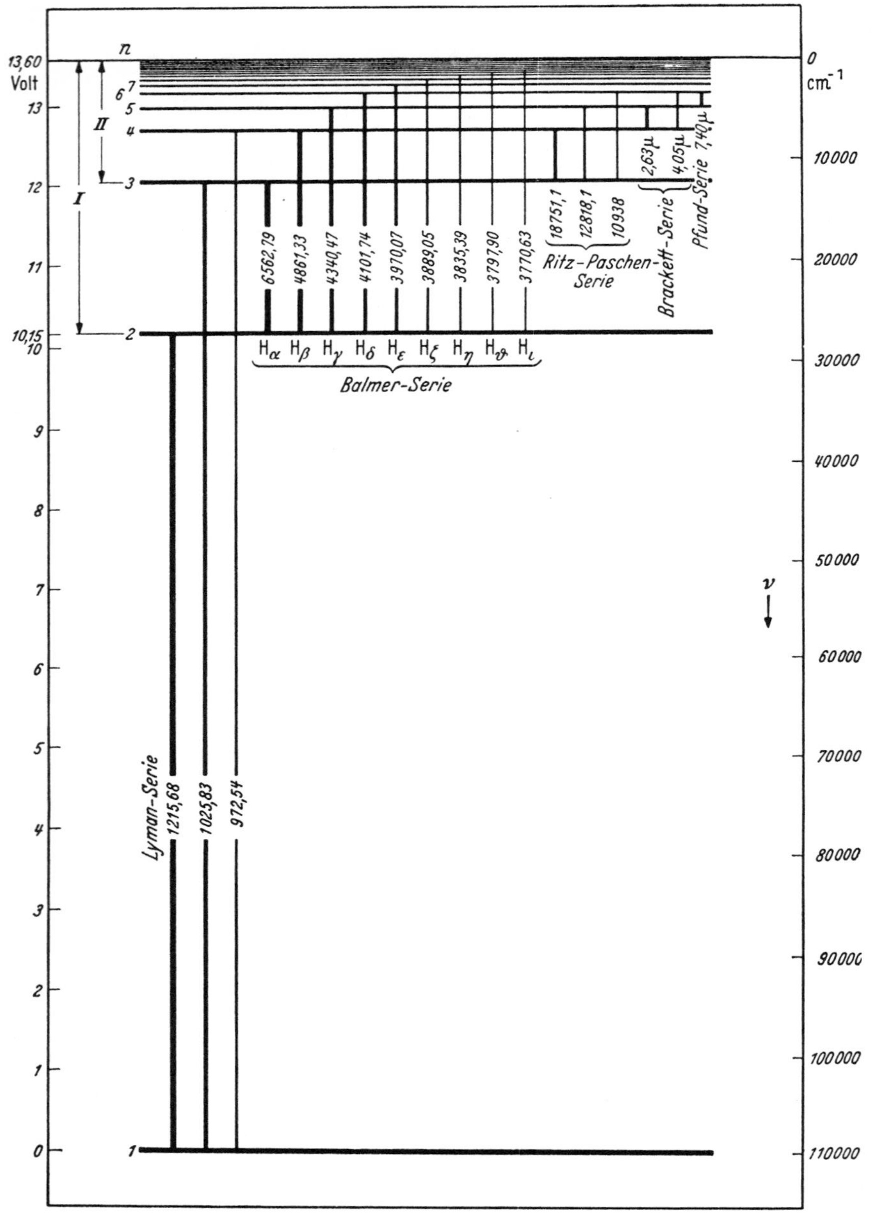

Fig. 2. The energy level scheme of hydrogen (both the energies in electron volts and the corresponding wave numbers in cm^{-1} are given).

where the RYDBERG frequency Ry was defined in the Introduction. The term scheme of hydrogen is shown in Fig. 2. The LYMAN, BALMER, PASCHEN, and BRACKET series, which have lowest levels corresponding respectively to the quantum numbers $n' = 1, 2, 3, 4$, are shown in Fig. 3. Figs. 2 and 3 are taken from

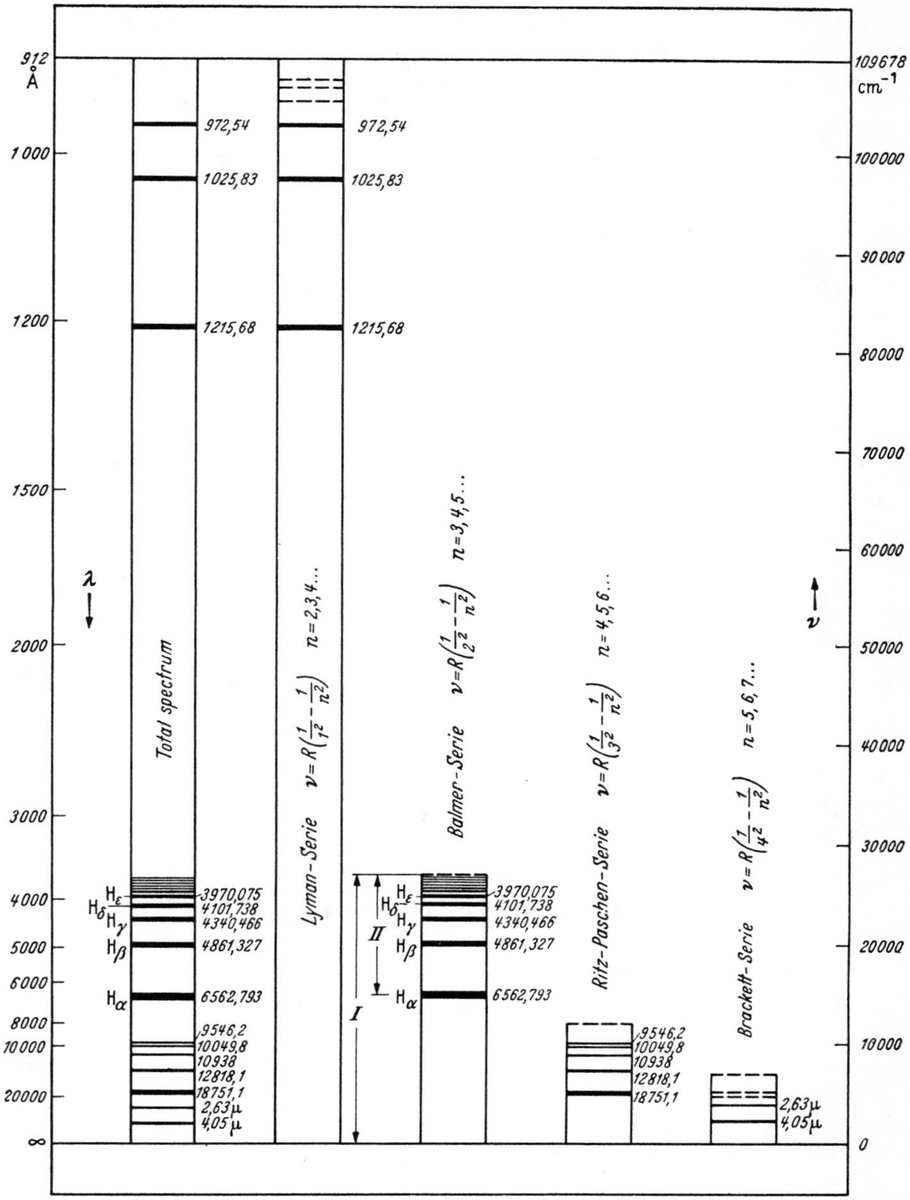

Fig. 3. The spectral lines of the hydrogen spectrum (the height of a line is proportional to its frequency, the number written next to a line is its wave length in ÅNGSTRÖM units).

GROTRIAN's book "Graphische Darstellung der Spektren von Atomen und Ionen". It is apparent that the lines in the LYMAN series are more densely spaced than the lines in the higher series.

Usually, instead of its frequency ν, the wave number (inverse of the wave-length) of a spectral line is measured, which is simply (ν/c), where c is the velocity of light, 299793 km/sec. The wave numbers of many lines of the spectrum of the hydrogen atom can be measured to an accuracy of better than one part in a million. The H_α lines in the hydrogen and deuterium spectrum, in particular, have been measured and analyzed very carefully. The exact theoretical expression for the frequency of the H_α line in an actual atom differs slightly from that obtained from (2.13). This difference is due to correction terms allowing for the finite mass of the nucleus, the relativistic fine structure (and hyperfine structure) splitting of the energy levels and quantum electrodynamic level shifts (all to be discussed later). These correction terms are small and well known. COHEN[1] has analyzed the experimental information on the H_α lines in H and D and applied the appropriate correction terms to (2.13) to obtain an extremely accurate value or the "RYDBERG constant for infinite nuclear mass". The present value is[2]

$$R_\infty = \frac{\mathrm{Ry}}{c} = \frac{m\,e^4}{4\pi\hbar^3 c} = (109737.31 \pm 0.01_2)\ \mathrm{cm}^{-1}. \tag{2.14}$$

Using this value for Ry, (2.14), obtained from the H_α line, the measured wave numbers of other spectral lines in hydrogen can be compared with the theoretical values, (2.13). After applying corrections for fine structure, etc., the agreement for a large number of spectral lines is excellent, to better than one part in a million for the H_β line, for instance. As pointed out in the Introduction, the atomic constants e, m and h, entering into the definition for Ry could also be obtained from experiments which do not require atomic theory for their analysis. Such a "non-spectroscopic" value for Ry would only be accurate to about one part in three thousand, but agrees with (2.14) to this accuracy. Many spectral lines have also been measured for hydrogen-like ions of higher nuclear charge Z, up to seven-times ionized oxygen ($Z=8$). The agreement is again excellent[3].

3. The radial eigenfunctions of the discrete spectrum[4]. We shall now deal with the radial eigenfunctions in greater detail. Combining (2.9) with (2.10) one obtains

$$a_\nu = -2\varepsilon\, a_{\nu-1}\frac{n-l-\nu}{\nu(2l+1+\nu)}, \tag{3.1}$$

and thus

$$R = c\,(2\varepsilon)^{\frac{3}{2}}\, e^{-\frac{1}{2}\varrho}\, \varrho^l\, F(-(n-l-1),\ 2l+2,\ \varrho), \tag{3.2}$$ [5]

where by definition

$$\varrho = 2\varepsilon r = 2Z\,r/n \tag{3.3}$$

and F is the (confluent) hypergeometric function[6]

$$F(\alpha,\beta,x) = 1 + \frac{\alpha}{\beta\cdot 1!}x + \frac{\alpha(\alpha+1)}{\beta(\beta+1)\cdot 2!}x^2 + \cdots \tag{3.4}$$

c is a constant.

[1] E. R. COHEN: Phys. Rev. **88**, 353 (1952).

[2] We shall often use simply the symbol Ry for this quantity although, strictly speaking, we have defined Ry as a frequency, $c R_\infty$.

[3] For a list of observed wave numbers of spectral lines in light atoms and ions see: Atomic Energy Levels, Vol. 1, U.S. National Bureau of Standards, Circular 467, 1949.

[4] Cf. W. GORDON: Ann. d. Phys. **2**, 1031 (1929).

[5] The numerical factor $(2\varepsilon)^{\frac{3}{2}}$ is included only for the sake of convenience in later calculations.

[6] For properties of the confluent hypergeometric function see ref. [8], Chap. 16 or the article of J. MEIXNER, Vol. I of this Encyclopedia. We shall in general omit the word "confluent". We shall use the more general function $F(\alpha, \beta, \gamma, x)$ very rarely and will call it the "*general* hypergeometric function".

The radial eigenfunctions can also be expressed in terms of the associated LAGUERRE functions, which are defined by means of the relations[1]

$$L_\lambda^\mu = \frac{d^\mu}{d\varrho^\mu} L_\lambda(\varrho); \qquad L_\lambda(\varrho) = e^\varrho \frac{d^\lambda}{d\varrho^\lambda}(e^{-\varrho}\varrho^\lambda). \tag{3.5}$$

This may be seen by carrying out the indicated differentiations; then

$$L_\lambda(\varrho) = \sum_{\alpha=0}^{\lambda} (-1)^\alpha \binom{\lambda}{\alpha} \frac{\lambda!}{\alpha!} \varrho^\alpha, \tag{3.6}$$

$$L_\lambda^\mu(\varrho) = (-)^\mu \lambda! \sum_{\alpha=0}^{\lambda-\mu} \binom{\lambda}{\mu+\alpha} \frac{(-\varrho)^\alpha}{\alpha!} = (-)^\mu \lambda! \binom{\lambda}{\mu} F(-(\lambda-\mu), \mu+1, \varrho). \tag{3.7}$$

On comparison with (3.2) one finds that

$$R = -c \frac{(2\varepsilon)^{\frac{3}{2}}}{(n+l)!^2} (2l+1)!\,(n-l-1)!\, e^{-\frac{1}{2}\varrho} \varrho^l L_{n+l}^{2l+1}(\varrho). \tag{3.8}$$

Naturally, one can also prove directly that (3.8) satisfies the differential Eq. (2.1).

Next, we require that the eigenfunction be normalized according to the rule

$$\int R^2 r^2 dr = 1, \tag{3.9}$$

i.e.,

$$\frac{c^2 (2l+1)!^2 (n-l-1)!^2}{(n+l)!^4} \int e^{-\varrho} \varrho^{2l+2} \left(L_{n+l}^{2l+1}(\varrho)\right)^2 d\varrho = 1. \tag{3.10}$$

R is now the normalized eigenfunction.

α) Evaluation of integrals over LAGUERRE *functions*[2]. Instead of evaluating (3.10), we evaluate the more general integral:

$$J_{\lambda\mu}^{(\sigma)} = \frac{1}{\lambda!^2} \int_0^\infty e^{-\varrho} \varrho^{\mu+\sigma} [L_\lambda^\mu(\varrho)]^2 d\varrho. \tag{3.11}$$

For this purpose we substitute the representation (3.5) for one of the LAGUERRE functions:

$$\lambda!^2 J_{\lambda\mu}^{(\sigma)} = \int_0^\infty e^{-\varrho} \varrho^{\mu+\sigma} L_\lambda^\mu(\varrho) \frac{d^\mu}{d\varrho^\mu}\left[e^\varrho \frac{d^\lambda}{d\varrho^\lambda}(\varrho^\lambda e^{-\varrho})\right] d\varrho.$$

Integrating by parts μ times with respect to ϱ one obtains

$$\left.\begin{aligned} \lambda!^2 J_{\lambda\mu}^{(\sigma)} = \sum_{\beta=0}^{\mu-1} \left|(-1)^\beta \frac{d^{\mu-\beta-1}}{d\varrho^{\mu-\beta-1}}\left(e^\varrho \frac{d^\lambda}{d\varrho^\lambda}(\varrho^\lambda e^{-\varrho})\right) \frac{d^\beta}{d\varrho^\beta}\left(e^{-\varrho}\varrho^{\mu+\sigma} L_\lambda^\mu(\varrho)\right)\right|_0^\infty + \\ +(-1)^\mu \int_0^\infty e^\varrho \frac{d^\lambda}{d\varrho^\lambda}(\varrho^\lambda e^{-\varrho}) \frac{d^\mu}{d\varrho^\mu}\left(\varrho^{\mu+\sigma} e^{-\varrho} L_\lambda^\mu(\varrho)\right) d\varrho. \end{aligned}\right\} \tag{3.12}$$

We must now distinguish between two cases:

1. If σ is non-negative, then the integrated part goes to zero at least as fast as ϱ at the lower limit and at least as fast as $e^{-\varrho}$ at the upper limit. Thus, we are

[1] Cf., for example, A. SOMMERFELD and G. SCHUR, Ann. d. Phys. **4**, 409 (1930).

[2] Special cases treated, for example, by E. SCHRÖDINGER, Abhandlung zur Wellenmechanik, p. 133; I. WALLER, Z. Physik **38**, 635 (1926); L. PAULING, Proc. Roy. Soc. Lond., Ser. A **114**, 185 (1927).

left with the evaluation of the integral. We proceed by replacing the LAGUERRE function with its power series expansion (3.7) and then carry out the μ fold differentiation:

$$J_{\lambda\mu}^{(\sigma)} = \frac{1}{\lambda!}\int_0^\infty \frac{d^\lambda}{d\varrho^\lambda}(\varrho^\lambda e^{-\varrho}) \sum_{\alpha=0}^{\lambda-\mu}\binom{\lambda}{\mu+\alpha}\frac{(-)^\alpha}{\alpha!}\sum_{\gamma=0}^{\mu}(-)^\gamma\binom{\mu}{\gamma}\frac{(\mu+\sigma+\alpha)!}{(\gamma+\sigma+\alpha)!}\varrho^{\gamma+\sigma+\alpha}.$$

Integrating by parts λ more times results in

$$J_{\lambda\mu}^{(\sigma)} = (-)^\lambda\frac{(\mu+\sigma)!}{\lambda!}\int_0^\infty \varrho^\lambda e^{-\varrho}\,d\varrho\sum_{\alpha=0}^{\lambda-\mu}(-)^\alpha\binom{\mu+\sigma+\alpha}{\alpha}\binom{\lambda}{\mu+\alpha}\sum_{\gamma=\lambda-\sigma-\alpha}^{\mu}(-)^\gamma\frac{\varrho^{\gamma+\sigma+\alpha-\lambda}}{(\gamma+\sigma+\alpha-\lambda)!}\binom{\mu}{\gamma},$$

the factor $\varrho^\lambda e^{-\varrho}$ assuring the vanishing of the integrated parts. A final integration with respect to ϱ gives

$$J_{\lambda\mu}^{(\sigma)} = (-)^\lambda(\mu+\sigma)!\sum_{\alpha=0}^{\lambda-\mu}(-)^\alpha\binom{\mu+\sigma+\alpha}{\alpha}\binom{\lambda}{\mu+\alpha}\sum_{\gamma=\lambda-\sigma-\alpha}^{\mu}(-)^\gamma\binom{\mu}{\gamma}\binom{\gamma+\sigma+\alpha}{\lambda}.$$

The summation over γ can be accomplished by elementary means and gives

$$(-1)^\mu\binom{\sigma+\alpha}{\lambda-\mu}.$$

Introducing the notation $\beta=\alpha-\lambda+\mu+\sigma$ one finally gets

$$J_{\lambda\mu}^{(\sigma)} = (-)^\sigma\frac{\lambda!}{(\lambda-\mu)!}\sigma!\sum_{\beta=0}^{\sigma}(-)^\beta\binom{\sigma}{\beta}\binom{\lambda+\beta}{\sigma}\binom{\lambda+\beta-\mu}{\sigma}. \qquad (3.13)$$

2. For negative σ the reverse is true. The integral vanishes, as is evident from (3.13), and the integrated terms make non-zero contributions at the lower limits (the upper limits still go to zero exponentially). By means of (3.7) one obtains

$$\frac{d^{\mu-\beta-1}}{d\varrho^{\mu-\beta-1}}\left(e^\varrho\frac{d^\lambda}{d\varrho^\lambda}(\varrho^\lambda e^{-\varrho})\right)_{\varrho=0} = L_\lambda^{\mu-\beta-1}(0) = (-)^{\mu-\beta-1}\lambda!\binom{\lambda}{\mu-\beta-1},$$

$$\frac{d^\beta}{d\varrho^\beta}(e^{-\varrho}\varrho^{\mu+\sigma}L_\lambda^\mu)_{\varrho=0} = \lambda!(-)^{\beta-\sigma}\sum_{\alpha=0}^{\lambda-\mu}\binom{\beta}{\alpha+\mu+\sigma}\binom{\lambda}{\mu+\alpha}\frac{(\alpha+\mu+\sigma)!}{\alpha!}.$$

Substitution into (3.12) gives

$$J_{\lambda\mu}^{(\sigma)} = \sum_{\alpha=0}^{\lambda-\mu}\binom{\lambda}{\mu+\alpha}\frac{(\alpha+\mu+\sigma)!}{\alpha!}\sum_{\beta=1}^{\mu-1}\binom{\lambda}{\mu-\beta-1}(-)^{\mu-\beta-\sigma}\binom{\beta}{\mu+\sigma+\alpha}.$$

The summation over β can be accomplished by elementary means and gives

$$(-)^\alpha\binom{\lambda-\mu-(\alpha+\sigma+1)}{-(\alpha+\sigma+1)}.$$

Putting $-(\sigma+1)=s$ and $s-\alpha=\gamma$ one finally gets

$$J_{\lambda\mu}^{(\sigma)} = \frac{\lambda!}{(\lambda-\mu)!\,(s+1)!}\sum_{\gamma=0}^{s}(-)^{s-\gamma}\frac{\binom{s}{\gamma}\binom{\lambda-\mu+\gamma}{s}}{\binom{\mu+s-\gamma}{s+1}}, \quad (\sigma=-(1+s)\leqq -1). \qquad (3.14)$$

β) Discussion of the normalized eigenfunctions. The normalization integral (3.10) can now be evaluated by setting $\lambda = n + l$, $\mu = 2l + 1$ and $\sigma = 1$ in formula (3.13):

$$J^{(1)}_{n+l,\,2l+1} = \frac{(n+l)!}{(n-l-1)!} \cdot 2n; \qquad c = \sqrt{\frac{(n+l)!}{(n-l-1)! \cdot 2n}} \cdot \frac{1}{(2l+1)!}. \tag{3.15}$$

Thus, the normalized eigenfunction [cf. (3.2), (3.8), (3.10)] becomes:

$$R_{nl}(r) = -\frac{(n-l-1)!^{\frac{1}{2}}}{(n+l)!^{\frac{3}{2}}\,(2n)^{\frac{1}{2}}} \left(\frac{2Z}{n}\right)^{\frac{3}{2}} e^{-\frac{Zr}{n}} \left(\frac{2Zr}{n}\right)^{l} L^{2l+1}_{n+l}\left(\frac{2Zr}{n}\right) \tag{3.16}$$

$$= \frac{1}{(2l+1)!} \sqrt{\frac{(n+l)!}{(n-l-1)!\,2n}} \cdot \left(\frac{2Z}{n}\right)^{\frac{3}{2}} e^{-\frac{Zr}{n}} \left(\frac{2Zr}{n}\right) F\left(-(n-l-1),\, 2l+2,\, \frac{2Zr}{n}\right). \tag{3.17}$$

We write down explicit expressions for the first few radial eigenfunctions of hydrogen ($Z = 1$):

$$\left.\begin{aligned}
R_{10} &= 2e^{-r}, \\
R_{20} &= \frac{1}{\sqrt{2}} e^{-\frac{1}{2}r}\left(1 - \frac{1}{2} r\right), \\
R_{21} &= \frac{1}{2\sqrt{6}} e^{-\frac{1}{2}r} r, \\
R_{30} &= \frac{2}{3\sqrt{3}} e^{-\frac{1}{3}r}\left(1 - \frac{2}{3} r + \frac{2}{27} r^2\right), \\
R_{31} &= \frac{8}{27\sqrt{6}} e^{-\frac{1}{3}r} r \left(1 - \frac{1}{6} r\right), \\
R_{32} &= \frac{4}{81\sqrt{30}} e^{-\frac{1}{3}r} r^2, \\
R_{40} &= \frac{1}{4} e^{-\frac{1}{4}r}\left(1 - \frac{3}{4} r + \frac{1}{8} r^2 - \frac{1}{192} r^3\right), \\
R_{41} &= \frac{1}{16}\sqrt{\frac{5}{3}}\, e^{-\frac{1}{4}r} r \left(1 - \frac{1}{4} r + \frac{1}{80} r^2\right), \\
R_{42} &= \frac{1}{64\sqrt{5}} e^{-\frac{1}{4}r} r^2 \left(1 - \frac{1}{12} r\right), \\
R_{43} &= \frac{1}{768\sqrt{35}} e^{-\frac{1}{4}r} r^3.
\end{aligned}\right\} \tag{3.18}$$

A few of the eigenfunctions are graphed as functions of ϱ in Fig. 4. Fig. 5 represents the charge distributions corresponding to these eigenfunctions. We have plotted $r^2 R^2_{nl}(r)$ as a function of r, i.e. the probability that the electron be found in the spherical shell between r and $r + dr$. It is apparent that the maximum charge density recedes from the nucleus with increasing principal quantum number n. For eigenfunctions which have the same n, the one with lowest l has the largest amplitude in the neighborhood of the nucleus. The radial eigenfunction has $n - l - 1$ zeros, and thus the complete eigenfunction

$$u = R_{nl}(r)\, \mathscr{P}_{lm}(\cos\vartheta) \begin{matrix}\cos\\ \sin\end{matrix}\, m\varphi$$

has $n - 1$ nodal surfaces of which $n - l - 1$ are concentric spheres ($r = \text{const}$), $l - m$ are cones ($\vartheta = \text{const}$) with common apex at the origin, and m are planes

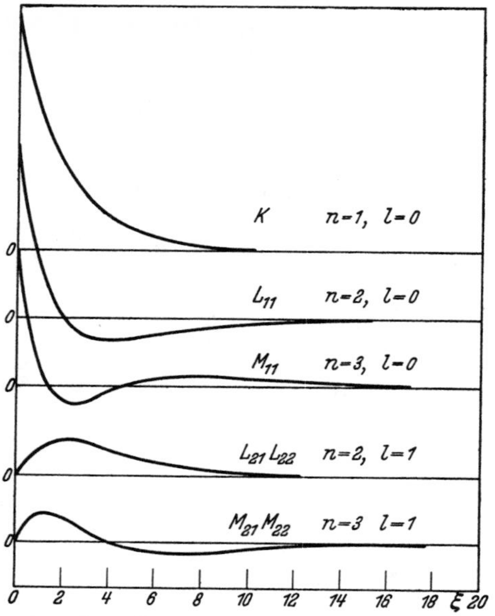

Fig. 4. The radial eigenfunctions (according to PAULING). The abscissa is $\varrho = 2r/n$, the ordinate is $n R_{nl}(r)$. The symbols K, etc. refer to the corresponding X-ray levels (in X-ray terminology the symbols L_{11}, L_{21}, L_{22} are usually replaced by L_{I}, L_{II}, L_{III}).

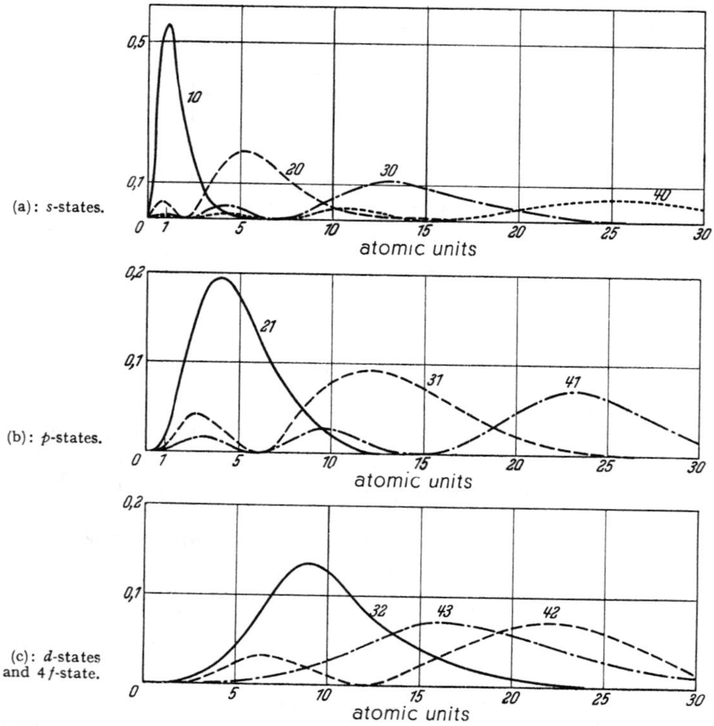

Fig. 5a—c. The charge distribution in the first few states of the hydrogen atom. The abscissa is r in atomic units, the ordinate is the charge density $r^2 R_{nl}^2(r)$. The curves are labelled with the corresponding nl values (s-states in Fig. 5a, p-states in Fig. 5b and d- and f-states in Fig. 5c).

through the origin ($\varphi = \text{const}$)[1]. A particularly beautiful pictorial representation of the charge distribution in the various states of hydrogen is afforded by the silhouettes of WHITE[2].

γ) Mean values of powers of r. The differences between the various radial eigenfunctions become particularly apparent when we form the mean value of r, the distance between electron and nucleus, raised to various powers. The mean value r^ν is given by

$$\overline{r^\nu} = \frac{\int r^\nu \psi_{nl}^2 r^2\, dr}{\int \psi_{nl}^2 r^2\, dr} = \left(\frac{n}{2Z}\right)^\nu \overline{\varrho^\nu} = \left(\frac{n}{2Z}\right)^\nu \frac{J^{(\nu+1)}_{n+l,\,2l+1}}{J^{(1)}_{n+l,\,2l+1}}, \tag{3.19}$$

in which $J^{(\sigma)}_{\lambda\mu}$ is the quantity given in (3.13) and (3.14). Assigning particular values to the indices results in the explicit formulas

$$\bar{r} = \frac{n}{2Z}\bar{\varrho} = \frac{1}{2Z}\left[3n^2 - l(l+1)\right], \tag{3.20}$$

$$\overline{r^2} = \frac{n^2}{2Z^2}\left[5n^2 + 1 - 3l(l+1)\right], \tag{3.21}$$

$$\overline{r^3} = \frac{n^2}{8Z^3}\left[35n^2(n^2-1) - 30n^2(l+2)(l-1) + 3(l+2)(l+1)\,l(l-1)\right], \tag{3.22}$$

$$\overline{r^4} = \frac{n^4}{8Z^4}\left[63n^4 - 35n^2(2l^2+2l-3) + 5l(l+1)(3l^2+3l-10) + 12\right], \tag{3.23}$$

$$\overline{r^{-1}} = \frac{Z}{n^2}, \tag{3.24}$$

$$\overline{r^{-2}} = \frac{Z^2}{n^3(l+\frac{1}{2})}, \tag{3.25}$$

$$\overline{r^{-3}} = \frac{Z^3}{n^3(l+1)(l+\frac{1}{2})\,l}, \tag{3.26}$$

$$\overline{r^{-4}} = \frac{Z^4\cdot\frac{1}{2}\cdot\left[3n^2 - l(l+1)\right]}{n^5(l+\frac{3}{2})(l+1)(l+\frac{1}{2})\,l(l-\frac{1}{2})}. \tag{3.27}$$

The mean values for the first few states of hydrogen are given in Table 1.

Table 1. *Numerical values for the expectation values of r^ν.*

	$n=1$	$n=2$		$n=3$			$n=4$			
	$l=0$	$l=0$	$l=1$	$l=0$	$l=1$	$l=2$	$l=0$	$l=1$	$l=2$	$l=3$
$\nu=1$	$1\frac{1}{2}$	6	5	$13\frac{1}{2}$	$12\frac{1}{2}$	$10\frac{1}{2}$	24	23	21	18
2	3	42	30	207	180	126	648	600	504	360
3	$7\frac{1}{2}$	330	210	$3442\frac{1}{2}$	2835	1701	18720	16800	13104	7920
4	$22\frac{1}{2}$	2880	1680	$61357\frac{1}{2}$	49005	25515	570240	497280	362880	190080
-1	1	$\frac{1}{4}$		$\frac{1}{9}$			$\frac{1}{16}$			
-2	2	$\frac{1}{4}$	$\frac{1}{12}$	$\frac{2}{27}$	$\frac{2}{81}$	$\frac{2}{135}$	$\frac{1}{32}$	$\frac{1}{96}$	$\frac{1}{160}$	$\frac{1}{224}$
-3	∞	∞	$\frac{1}{24}$	∞	$\frac{1}{81}$	$\frac{1}{405}$	∞	$\frac{1}{192}$	$\frac{1}{960}$	$\frac{1}{2688}$
-4	∞	∞	$\frac{1}{24}$	∞	$\frac{10}{729}$	$\frac{2}{3645}$	∞	$\frac{23}{3840}$	$\frac{1}{3840}$	$\frac{1}{26880}$

[1] Cf. Sect. 1.

[2] H. E. WHITE: Phys. Rev. 37, 1416 (1931).

The mean values of r raised to positive powers ν are determined essentially by the principal quantum number n, while for the mean values of r raised to negative powers ν (for $\nu < -1$) the orbital quantum number l becomes decisive. This is readily explained. For positive powers the important contributions to the integral come from the large values of r for which the eigenfunction behaves like $\varrho^{n-1} e^{-\frac{1}{2}\varrho}$; for small r, important for negative powers, the eigenfunction behaves like ϱ^l. In terms of a picture this means that the probability of finding the electron at a large distance from the nucleus is essentially the same for both the circular $(l = n-1)$ and the eccentric elliptical (small l) BOHR orbits. For fixed n the electron will be found more frequently in the immediate vicinity of the nucleus if its quantum state corresponds to an eccentric orbit than if its quantum state corresponds to a circular orbit. (It is even possible for $\overline{r^\nu}$ to diverge, as indeed happens if $\nu < -2l-2$; the mean value then becomes meaningless.)

The quantum mechanical analogue to BOHR orbits of large eccentricity (small l) is a large mean square deviation of the nucleus-electron separation:

$$\overline{(r-\bar{r})^2} = \overline{r^2} - \bar{r}^2 = \frac{n^2(n^2+2) - l^2(l+1)^2}{4Z^2}. \tag{3.28}$$

For example

$$\overline{r^2} - \bar{r}^2 = \begin{cases} \dfrac{n^2(n^2+2)}{4Z^2} & \text{for} \quad l = 0, \\[2ex] \dfrac{n^2(2n+1)}{4Z^2} & \text{for} \quad l = n-1. \end{cases}$$

As can be seen from (3.24) the expression for the mean value of r^{-1} is particularly simple. By means of it we can readily verify the well-known virial theorem[1] which states that the mean value of the potential energy $V = -\frac{Z}{r}$ is equal to twice the total energy. Thus,

$$\bar{V} = -Z\overline{r^{-1}} = -\frac{Z^2}{n^2} = 2E \qquad \text{[cf. (2.11)]}. \tag{3.29}$$

δ) Behavior of the eigenfunctions for large principal quantum number. WENTZEL-KRAMERS-BRILLOUIN *(WKB) method.* Aside from normalization, all eigenfunctions of a fixed orbital quantum number l and different principal quantum number n behave alike near the nucleus, provided $n \gg l$. This may be seen by neglecting l relative to n in formula (3.17), thus,

$$\left.\begin{aligned} R_{nl} &\approx \frac{n^l}{(2l+1)!\sqrt{2}}\left(\frac{2Z}{n}\right)^{\frac{3}{2}}\left(\frac{2Zr}{n}\right)^l e^{-\frac{Zr}{n}}\left[1 - \frac{n-l-1}{2l+2}\cdot\frac{2rZ}{n} + \frac{(n-l-1)(n-l-2)}{(2l+2)(2l+3)\,2!}\left(\frac{2rZ}{n}\right)^2 + \cdots\right] \\ &\approx 2\left(\frac{Z}{n}\right)^{\frac{3}{2}}\frac{(2Zr)^l}{(2l+1)!}\left[1 - \frac{2rZ}{2l+2} + \frac{(2rZ)^2}{(2l+2)(2l+3)\cdot 2!} - \cdots\right], \end{aligned}\right\} \tag{3.30}$$

or it can be seen, even more simply, directly from SCHRÖDINGER'S Eq. (2.1). If n is very large and r is of order 1 (more precisely, if $r \ll n^2/Z$), the energy $1/2n^2$ can obviously be neglected compared to $1/r$ and $l(l+1)/r^2$. Then (2.1) goes over into

$$\frac{d^2R}{dr^2} + \frac{2}{r}\frac{dR}{dr} + \left(\frac{2Z}{r} - \frac{l(l+1)}{r^2}\right)R = 0. \tag{3.31}$$

Since the differential Eq. (3.31) no longer contains n, its solution will also be independent of n. Its solution is

$$R_{\infty l} = \frac{c}{\sqrt{2Zr}} J_{2l+1}\left(\sqrt{8Zr}\right), \tag{3.32}$$

[1] Cf. A. SOMMERFELD: Wellenmechanischer Ergänzungsband, p. 292, ref. [7]; see also our Sect. 36ε.

where J_{2l+1} is the BESSEL function[1] of order $2l+1$ and c is a constant. If the power series expansion for J is used in (3.32), then the expansion (3.30) for R is again obtained. Using the asymptotic formula for the BESSEL function one obtains a solution valid for large r

$$R_{\infty l} = \frac{c}{(2Zr)^{\frac{3}{4}}\sqrt{\pi}} \cdot \cos\left(\sqrt{8Zr} - \frac{\pi}{4} - \frac{2l+1}{2}\pi\right). \tag{3.33}$$

One must be sure, however, that $r \ll n^2/Z$ (but $8Zr \gg 1$).

A useful approximate formula for the radial eigenfunction may be obtained by means of the WKB method when r becomes comparable to n^2/Z (cf. Sect. 53). First, we must get rid of the first derivative in Eq. (2.1). For this purpose we introduce $v = Rr$ in place of R. v satisfies the equation

$$\frac{d^2 v}{dr^2} + \left[-\frac{Z^2}{n^2} + \frac{2Z}{r} - \frac{l(l+1)}{r^2}\right] v = 0. \tag{3.34}$$

The coefficient of v represents the kinetic energy of the electron and is positive for $r_1 < r < r_2$, where

$$r_{1,2} = \frac{n^2}{Z} \pm \frac{n}{Z}\sqrt{n^2 - l(l+1)} \tag{3.35}$$

r_1 and r_2 are respectively the perihelion and aphelion of the classical electron orbit. In the region of the classical orbit $r_1 < r < r_2$ the eigenfunction may be represented according to (53.3) to a good approximation by[2]:

$$\left.\begin{aligned} v &= a\left(\frac{2Z}{r} - \frac{Z^2}{n^2} - \frac{(l+\frac{1}{2})^2}{r^2}\right)^{-\frac{1}{4}} \cos\left[\int_{r_1}^{r} \sqrt{\frac{2Z}{\varrho} - \frac{Z^2}{n^2} - \frac{(l+\frac{1}{2})^2}{\varrho^2}}\, d\varrho - \frac{\pi}{4}\right] \\ &= a\left(\frac{2Z}{r} - \frac{Z^2}{n^2} - \frac{(l+\frac{1}{2})^2}{r^2}\right)^{-\frac{1}{4}} \cos\left[\sqrt{2Zr - \frac{Z^2 r^2}{n^2} - (l+\tfrac{1}{2})^2} + \right. \\ &\left. + n \arcsin\frac{Zr - n^2}{n\sqrt{n^2 - (l+\frac{1}{2})^2}} - (l+\tfrac{1}{2}) \arcsin\frac{n}{Zr} \cdot \frac{Zr - (l+\frac{1}{2})^2}{\sqrt{n^2 - (l+\frac{1}{2})^2}} + (n-l-1)\frac{\pi}{2}\right]. \end{aligned}\right\} \tag{3.36}$$

Although (3.36) looks rather complicated it turns out to be a useful formula in practice. For $(l+\frac{1}{2})^2 \ll Zr \ll n^2$, (3.36) becomes

$$v = a\left(\frac{r}{2Z}\right)^{\frac{1}{4}} \cdot \cos\left(\sqrt{8Zr} - (2l+1)\frac{\pi}{2} - \frac{\pi}{4}\right). \tag{3.37}$$

The radial eigenfunction $R = v/r$ thus becomes identical with (3.33), as must happen[3], and the constants are related through

$$c = \sqrt{2\pi Z}\, a. \tag{3.38}$$

v decays exponentially outside of the region of the classical orbit [see (53.4)]. Thus, if we wish to evaluate the normalizing integral

$$\int_0^\infty R_{nl}^2 r^2 \, dr = \int_0^\infty v^2 \, dr = 1,$$

[1] Cf. JAHNKE-EMDE: Tables of Functions, especially p. 166 (differential equation), p. 98 (asymptotic formula), p. 90 (series expansion).

[2] See Sect. 53.

[3] The asymptotic formula for the BESSEL function can thus be looked upon as a special case of the WKB procedure.

we only need to consider the region $r_1 < r < r_2$. In addition, we can make use of the fact that the cosine in (3.36) is a rapidly varying function compared to the other factor, and replace $\cos^2$ by its mean value $\frac{1}{2}$. Then

$$\int_0^\infty v^2\,dr = \frac{1}{2}a^2 \int_{r_1}^{r^2} \frac{dr}{\sqrt{\frac{2Z}{r} - \frac{Z^2}{n^2} - \frac{(l+\frac{1}{2})^2}{r^2}}} = \frac{1}{2}a^2 \pi Z^{-2} n^3,$$

$$a = 2^{\frac{1}{2}} \pi^{-\frac{1}{2}} Z\, n^{-\frac{3}{2}}, \qquad c = 2 Z^{\frac{3}{2}} n^{-\frac{3}{2}}. \tag{3.39}$$

The eigenfunction is thus proportional to $1/n^{\frac{3}{2}}$ for $r \ll n^2/Z$ and, furthermore, this is the only factor through which u depends on n. For large n the normalization (3.39) is, of course, identical with the one previously derived. If the value for c is substituted into (3.32) and the series expansion for the BESSEL function (as given, for example, in JAHNKE-EMDE) is used, then exactly (3.30) is obtained.

ε) Generating function for LAGUERRE *functions*[1]. Occassionally a representation of the LAGUERRE polynomials different from (3.5) is preferable, particularly when we are dealing with a calculation of transition probabilities[2]. It turns out that the LAGUERRE polynomials can be defined by means of the generating function

$$e^{-\frac{xt}{1-t}} \cdot \frac{1}{1-t} = \sum_k L_k(x) \frac{t^k}{k!}. \tag{3.40}$$

Proof: Differentiating (3.40) with respect to t and setting the coefficient of t^k equal to zero gives

$$L_{k+1} - (2k+1-x)\,L_k + k^2 L_{k-1} = 0. \tag{3.41}$$

Differentiating (3.40) with respect to x, one obtains

$$L'_k = k\,(L'_{k-1} - L_{k-1}). \tag{3.42}$$

By means of a short calculation the differential equation

$$x L''_k + (1-x)\,L'_k + k L_k = 0 \tag{3.43}$$

follows from (3.41), (3.42). If we set $k = n + l$ and differentiate $2l+1$ times with respect to x, we arrive at the equation

$$x\,(L^{2l+1}_{n+l})'' + (2l+2-x)\,(L^{2l+1}_{n+l})' + (n-l-1)\,L^{2l+1}_{n+l} = 0. \tag{3.44}$$

Putting $x = \varrho = 2\varepsilon r$ and $f = r^l L^{2l+1}_{n+l}$, the differential equation (2.5) follows without difficulty in view of (2.10).

(3.40) agrees with (3.5) also with respect to normalization as can be shown by calculating the constant term in L_k, i.e., the term which is free of x, thus

$$L_k(x) = \frac{d^k}{dt^k}\left(e^{-\frac{xt}{1-t}} \cdot \frac{1}{1-t}\right)_{t=0} = \left(\frac{k!}{(1-t)^{k+1}} + x \ldots\right)_{t=0} = k! + \cdots$$

which is in agreement with (3.6). The associated LAGUERRE functions can also be represented by a generating function. Differentiating (3.40) r times with respect to x we obtain

$$\frac{(-1)^r}{(1-t)^{r+1}}\, e^{-\frac{xt}{1-t}} = \sum L^r_k(x) \frac{t^{k-r}}{k!}. \tag{3.45}$$

[1] See, for example, E. SCHRÖDINGER, Ann. d. Phys. **80**, 131 (1926).
[2] Cf. Sec. 63 and particularly W. GORDON, Ann. d. Phys. **2**, 1031 (1929).

We finally quote the value at the origin of the squares of the normalized radial and total wave functions for $l=0$ and any principal quantum number n. From (1.8) and (3.2) to (3.4) we have

$$R_{n0}^2(0)=\frac{4Z^3}{n^3},\qquad u_{n00}^2(0)=\frac{Z^3}{\pi n^3}. \tag{3.46}$$

4. The eigenfunctions of the continuous spectrum[1]. α) We shall now treat the case $E>0$. The quantity ε, defined in (2.3), is now purely imaginary

$$\varepsilon=i\sqrt{2E}=ik. \tag{4.1}$$

In every other respect there is no change in the derivation of Sect. 2 up to the recursion formula (2.9). The ratio $a_\nu/a_{\nu-1}$ becomes complex, and it is no longer possible to terminate the series (2.6) through a particular choice of ε. On the other hand, there is no need for that now because both $e^{+\varepsilon r}$ and $e^{-\varepsilon r}$ remain finite for $r=\infty$. Thus, there is a solution for every positive E, and a continuous spectrum of positive eigenvalues adjoins the discrete levels of negative energy.

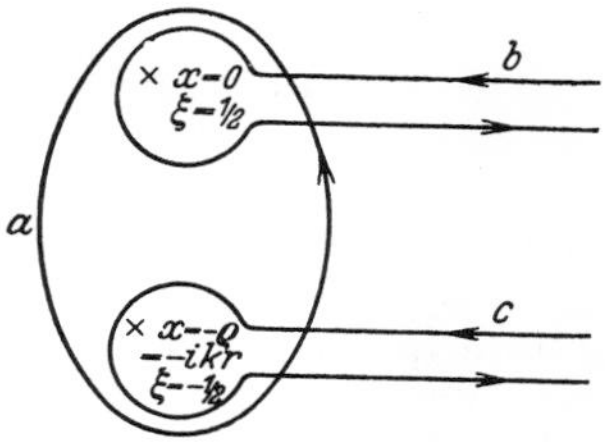

Fig. 6. Integration contour for the continuous eigenfunctions. The path a encloses both branch points $\xi=+\frac{1}{2}$ ($x=0$) and $\xi=-\frac{1}{2}$ ($x=-\varrho$) of the integrand. Integration along the path b gives (for large r) the asymptotic incoming wave $R^{(2)}$, the path c gives the outgoing wave $R^{(1)}$.

The eigenfunctions belonging to the states of the continuous spectrum are, in accordance with (3.2) and (3.4), expressible in terms of hypergeometric functions since the recursion formula (2.9) is still valid. However,

$$n=\frac{Z}{\varepsilon}=-i\frac{Z}{\sqrt{2E}}=-i\frac{Z}{k} \tag{4.2}$$

is imaginary.

Accordingly, the definition (3.5) of the LAGUERRE polynomials has no longer any apparent meaning. However, it is possible, using CAUCHY'S theorem,

$$\frac{d^\lambda f(x)}{dx^\lambda}=\frac{\Gamma(\lambda+1)}{2\pi i}\int\frac{f(z)}{(z-x)^{\lambda+1}}\,dz, \tag{4.3}$$

to obtain a representation of the LAGUERRE polynomials,

$$L_\lambda(\varrho)=\frac{\Gamma(\lambda+1)}{2\pi i}e^\varrho\int\frac{e^{-z}z^\lambda}{(z-\varrho)^{\lambda+1}}\,dz=\frac{\Gamma(\lambda+1)}{2\pi i}\int e^{-x}(x+\varrho)^\lambda x^{-(\lambda+1)}\,dx, \tag{4.4}$$

which is valid for all λ. In the second of the above representations the variable of integration z has been replaced by $x+\varrho$. The path of integration consists of the simple loop a (Fig. 6) around the two branch points $x=-\varrho$ and $x=0$ of the integrand. μ-fold differentiation of (4.4) results in the integral representation of the associated LAGUERRE functions (μ is integral and positive):

$$L_\lambda^\mu(\varrho)=\frac{(\Gamma(\lambda+1))^2}{2\pi i\,\Gamma(\lambda-\mu+1)}\int e^{-x}(x+\varrho)^{\lambda-\mu}x^{-(\lambda+1)}\,dx. \tag{4.5}$$

Finally, the radial eigenfunction is obtained by setting $\lambda=n+l$, $\mu=2l+1$, multiplying by $e^{-\varrho/2}r^l$, and including all constant factors in the constant c:

$$R=c(-i\varrho)^l e^{-\varrho/2}\cdot\frac{1}{2\pi i}\int(x+\varrho)^{n-l-1}x^{-n-l-1}e^{-x}dx, \tag{4.6}$$

$$=c\frac{(i\varrho)^{-l-1}}{2\pi}\cdot\int e^{-\varrho\xi}\left(\xi+\frac{1}{2}\right)^{n-l-1}\left(\xi-\frac{1}{2}\right)^{-n-l-1}d\xi. \tag{4.7}$$

[1] We shall follow the treatment of A. SOMMERFELD and G. SCHUR, Ann. d. Phys. **4**, 409 (1930); see also E. FUES, Ann. d. Phys. **87**, 281 (1926), W. GORDON, Ann. d. Phys. **2**, 1031 (1929), and other authors.

The representation (4.7) is obtained from (4.6) by substituting $x=\varrho(\xi-\frac{1}{2})$, the path of integration going around the branch points $\xi=\pm\frac{1}{2}$ in the positive sense. From (4.7) it is at once apparent that the radial eigenfunctions will be real if ϱ and n are pure imaginaries.

Expanding (4.6) in powers of ϱ and carrying out the integrations by means of CAUCHY's theorem, the representation (3.2) for the radial eigenfunction is again obtained (within a numerical factor):

$$\left.\begin{aligned} R_{nl}(\varrho) &= c\,\frac{(-i\varrho)^l e^{-\varrho/2}}{2\pi i}\sum_{\alpha=0}^{\infty}\binom{n-l-1}{\alpha}\varrho^\alpha \int \frac{e^{-x}}{x^{2l+2+\alpha}}\,dx \\ &= (-i\varrho)^l\cdot\frac{c}{(2l+1)!}\,e^{-\varrho/2}\cdot F(-(n-l-1),\,2l+2,\,\varrho)\,. \end{aligned}\right\} \tag{4.8}$$

The series for the hypergeometric function F [cf. (3.4)] converges for all ϱ, but the convergence is very slow for large ϱ. Therefore, it is necessary to look for an asymptotic series in descending powers of ϱ, which will be useful for large ϱ. For this purpose we deform path a (Fig. 6) into two loops b and c coming from infinity and each going around one of the branch points in the positive sense. Along path b we expand $(x+\varrho)^{n-l-1}$ in decreasing powers of ϱ:

$$(x+\varrho)^{n-l-1}=\sum_{\alpha}\binom{n-l-1}{\alpha}\varrho^{n-l-1-\alpha}\,x^\alpha\,.$$

This expansion diverges for the remote portions ($|x|>|\varrho|$) of the path of integration; the resulting asymptotic expansion for R_{nl} is, therefore, only semiconvergent. For the actual integrations we refer the reader to the work of SOMMERFELD and SCHUR and simply state here the results: The contribution of path b to the asymptotic representation of the eigenfunction is

$$R^{(2)}=c\,\frac{e^{-\frac{1}{2}\varrho-i\pi(n+\frac{3}{2}l)+n\log\varrho}}{\Gamma(n+l+1)\cdot\varrho}\,G\left(n+l,\,l+1-n,\,\frac{1}{\varrho}\right), \tag{4.9}$$

where

$$G(\alpha,\beta,x)=1+\frac{\alpha\beta}{1!}\,x+\frac{\alpha(\alpha+1)\,\beta(\beta+1)}{2!}\,x^2+\cdots$$

is a hypergeometric function[1]. Along path c it is convenient to replace x by z [cf. (4.4)]. The contribution to the asymptotic representation of the eigenfunction turns out to be exactly the complex conjugate of $R^{(2)}$.

Collecting the contributions and substituting the values of ϱ and n from (3.3), (4.1) and (4.2), the asymptotic expression for the wave-function is obtained:

$$R=\frac{c\,e^{-\frac{\pi}{2}\frac{Z}{k}}}{|\Gamma(l+1-iZ/k)|\,k r}\cos\left[k r+\frac{Z}{k}\log 2kr-\frac{\pi}{2}(l-1)-\sigma_l\right], \tag{4.10}$$

where

$$\sigma_l=\arg\Gamma\left(l+1-i\,\frac{Z}{k}\right)$$

is the complex phase of the Γ-function. Thus, asymptotically, the eigenfunctions go over into spherical waves.

We must now normalize the eigenfunction R. The well-known rule for the normalization of eigenfunctions belonging to the continuous spectrum is

$$\int_0^\infty r^2\,dr\,R_{Tl}(r)\int_{T-\Delta T}^{T+\Delta T} R_{T'l}(r)\,dT'=1\,. \tag{4.11}$$

[1] See also M. STOBBE: Ann. d. Phys. 7, 661 (1930).

In the above, T is any function of the wave number k, e.g. the energy $W=\frac{1}{2}k^2$ or k itself. ΔT is a small interval. If condition (4.11) is fulfilled and the eigenfunctions belonging to the discrete spectrum are normalized in the usual fashion,

$$\int R_{nl}^2(r)\, r^2\, dr = 1,$$

then an arbitrary function of the space coordinates $f(r, \vartheta, \varphi)$ can be expanded in terms of our eigenfunctions as follows:

$$\left.\begin{aligned} f(r,\vartheta,\varphi) &= \sum_{l=0}^{\infty}\sum_{m=-l}^{+l} Y_{lm}(\vartheta,\varphi)\left(\sum_{n=l+1}^{\infty} a_{nlm} R_{nl}(r) + \int_{k=0}^{\infty} dT(k)\, a_{Tlm} R_{Tl}(x)\right)\\ &= \sum_{nlm} a_{nlm} u_{nlm}(r,\vartheta,\varphi) + \int dT \sum_{lm} a_{Tlm} u_{Tlm}\end{aligned}\right\} \quad (4.12)$$

and the coefficients in the expansion are given by

$$\left.\begin{aligned} a_{nlm} &= \int_0^\infty r^2\, dr \int_0^\pi \sin\vartheta\, d\vartheta \int_0^{2\pi} d\varphi\, f(r,\vartheta,\varphi)\, R_{nl}(r)\, Y_{lm}^*(\vartheta,\varphi) = \int d\tau\, f\, u_{nlm}^*,\\ a_{Tlm} &= \int_0^\infty r^2\, dr \int_0^\pi \sin\vartheta\, d\vartheta \int_0^{2\pi} d\varphi\, f(r,\vartheta,\varphi)\, R_{Tl}(r)\, Y_{lm}^*(\vartheta,\varphi).\end{aligned}\right\} \quad (4.13)$$

The eigenfunctions R_{Tl} are said to be normalized in the T-scale. The eigenfunctions normalized in the T-scale and k-scale respectively are related through

$$R_T = \left(\frac{dT}{dk}\right)^{-\frac{1}{2}} R_k, \quad (4.14)$$

as follows directly from (4.11).

We calculate the normalizing factor in the k-scale by putting

$$R = \frac{b}{r}\cdot\cos\left(kr + \frac{Z}{k}\log 2kr - \delta_l\right), \quad (4.15)$$

in accordance with (4.10); b is the normalizing constant to be determined, and δ_l is independent of r. If we neglect quantities of order $1/kr$ and $\Delta k/k$ we obtain

$$\int_{k-\Delta k}^{k+\Delta k} dk' \cos\left(k'r + \frac{Z}{k'}\log 2k'r - \delta\right) = 2\cos\left(kr + \frac{Z}{k}\log 2kr - \delta\right)\frac{\sin \Delta k r}{r}. \quad (4.16)$$

Substitution of (4.15) and (4.16) into (4.11), setting $T=k$, and replacing the rapidly oscillating $\cos^2$ by its mean value $\frac{1}{2}$ results in

$$2b^2\int_0^\infty \frac{\sin\Delta k r}{r}\, dr\cos^2\left(kr + \frac{Z}{k}\log 2kr - \delta\right) = b^2\cdot\frac{\pi}{2} = 1. \quad (4.17)$$

Thus, in the k-scale

$$b = \sqrt{\frac{2}{\pi}}, \quad R_k = \sqrt{\frac{2}{\pi}}\cdot\frac{1}{r}\cdot\cos\left[kr + \frac{Z}{k}\log 2kr - \frac{\pi}{2}(l-1) - \sigma_l\right]. \quad (4.18)$$

Normalizing in the energy-scale we get, correspondingly,

$$\left.\begin{aligned} W &= \frac{1}{2}k^2, \quad \frac{dW}{dk} = k,\\ R_W &= \sqrt{\frac{2}{\pi k}}\cdot\frac{1}{r}\cdot\cos\left[kr + \frac{Z}{k}\log 2kr - \frac{\pi}{2}(l-1) - \sigma_l\right].\end{aligned}\right\} \quad (4.19)$$

Comparing the normalized eigenfunction (4.18) with the asymptotic representation (4.10) for the unnormalized eigenfunction we find that

$$c_k = \sqrt{\frac{2}{\pi}}\, k \left|\Gamma\left(l + 1 - i\frac{Z}{k}\right)\right| e^{\frac{\pi}{2}\frac{Z}{k}}, \qquad c_W = \frac{c_k}{\sqrt{k}}. \tag{4.20}$$

At this point we can find both the integral and, for small r, the series representations of the normalized eigenfunction, the former by going back to (4.6) and (4.7) and the latter by substituting (4.20) into (4.8). In doing this it is practical to write the Γ-function in terms of elementary functions by means of the well known recursion relation

$$\Gamma(x+1) = x\,\Gamma(x)$$

and the formula

$$\Gamma(x)\,\Gamma(1-x) = \frac{\pi}{\sin \pi x};$$

then[1]

$$|\Gamma(l+1-i n')| = \sqrt{\pi n'} \prod_{s=1}^{l} \sqrt{s^2 + n'^2}\,(\mathrm{Sin}\,\pi n')^{-\frac{1}{2}} \quad \text{with} \quad n' = \frac{Z}{k}. \tag{4.21}$$

We thus obtain our final integral (4.22) and series (4.23) representations:

$$\left.\begin{aligned} R_W = (-)^{l+1} \frac{2\sqrt{Z}}{\sqrt{1-e^{-2\pi n'}}} \prod_{s=1}^{l} \sqrt{s^2+n'^2}\cdot (2kr)^{-(l+1)} \times \\ \times \frac{1}{2\pi} \int e^{-\varrho\xi}\cdot \left(\xi + \frac{1}{2}\right)^{-in'-l-1} \left(\xi - \frac{1}{2}\right)^{+in'-l-1} d\xi. \end{aligned}\right\} \tag{4.22}$$

$$R_W = \frac{2\sqrt{Z}}{\sqrt{1-e^{-2\pi n'}}} \prod_{s=1}^{l} \sqrt{s^2+n'^2}\, \frac{(2kr)^l}{(2l+1)!}\, e^{-ikr} F(i n' + l + 1,\, 2l+2,\, 2ikr). \tag{4.23}$$

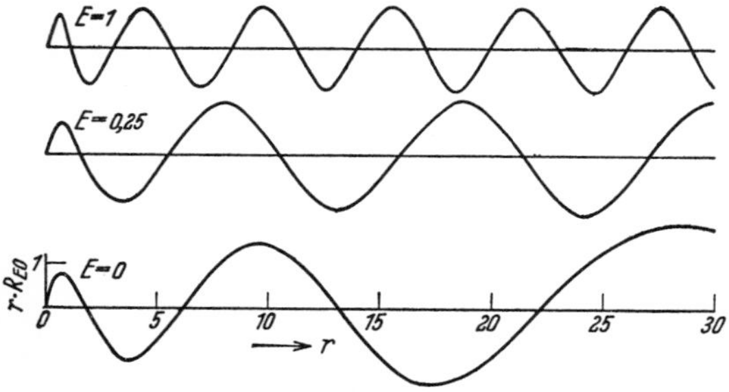

Fig. 7. The continuous eigenfunction of hydrogen for s-states ($l=0$) for three different energies E (in Ry units). Abscissa is r in atomic units, ordinate is $r R_{E0}$. Note that the "wave length" and amplitude increase rapidly with increasing r for $E=0$, but are almost constant for $E=1$.

Fig. 7 shows the eigenfunctions belonging to the continuous spectrum for $E=0$, 0.25 and 1 (in Ry units).

β) The irregular functions. In this section we have discussed wave functions for the continuous spectrum in the form of a radial wave function $R(r)$ multiplied by a spherical harmonic Y_{lm}. For *any* central potential (function of the radial distance r only) the SCHRÖDINGER equation can be separated in spherical polar coordinates and wave functions of the form $R_l(r)\, Y_{lm}$ exist. We have only calculated the radial wave functions for the special case of the COULOMB potential Zr^{-1}. Further, we have only treated radial wave functions which are finite at the origin, the "regular COULOMB functions". There exists another set of solutions forthe radial wave functions which diverge at the origin. These "irregular COULOMB functions" have an asymptotic form representing spherical standing waves, similar to that of the regular functions (4.10), but with *cosine* replaced by *sine*. These irregular functions do not arise in physical problems involving only *pure* COULOMB potentials, since physical

[1] We use the symbol Sin instead of sinh for the hyperbolic function.

wave functions must remain finite at the origin. They are of use, however, in problems involving central potentials which approximate a COULOMB potential at large distances, but deviate from it for small distances. These irregular functions occur[1], for instance, in nuclear problems but *not* in atomic theory and we shall not consider them further.

5. Motion of the nucleus. So far we have pretended (see Sect. 1) that the atomic nucleus has infinite mass and, therefore, remains at rest We shall now correct for this. Calculating to begin with, in c.g.s. units, let M be the mass and $\xi_1 \eta_1 \zeta_1$ the coordinates of the nucleus, the quantities with index 2 referring to the electron of mass m. The HAMILTONian of the system is

$$H = \frac{p_1^2}{2M} + \frac{p_2^2}{2m} - \frac{Z e^2}{\varrho}$$

and SCHRÖDINGER's equation is

$$\frac{\hbar^2}{2M} \Delta_1 u' + \frac{\hbar^2}{2m} \Delta_2 u' + \left(E' + \frac{Z e^2}{\varrho}\right) u' = 0. \tag{5.1}$$

$\Delta_1 = \frac{\partial^2}{\partial \xi_1^2} + \frac{\partial^2}{\partial \eta_1^2} + \frac{\partial^2}{\partial \zeta_1^2}$ is the LAPLACian in the configuration space of the electron. u' depends on the six coordinates of nucleus and electron. Introducing the coordinates of the center of mass

$$X = \frac{M \xi_1 + m \xi_2}{M + m} \qquad \text{(and similarly for } Y \text{ and } Z)$$

and the relative coordinates

$$x = \xi_2 - \xi_1 \quad \left(\text{and similarly for } y \text{ and } z,\ \varrho = \sqrt{x^2 + y^2 + z^2}\right)$$

we have

$$\frac{\partial^2 u'}{\partial \xi_1^2} = \left(\frac{M}{M+m}\right)^2 \frac{\partial^2 u'}{\partial X^2} - 2 \frac{M}{M+m} \frac{\partial^2 u'}{\partial X \partial x} + \frac{\partial^2 u'}{\partial x^2},$$

$$\frac{1}{M} \Delta_1 u' + \frac{1}{m} \Delta_2 u' = \frac{1}{M+m} \left(\frac{\partial^2}{\partial X^2} + \frac{\partial^2}{\partial Y^2} + \frac{\partial^2}{\partial Z^2}\right) u' + \frac{1}{\mu} \left(\frac{\partial^2}{\partial x^2} + \frac{\partial^2}{\partial y^2} + \frac{\partial^2}{\partial z^2}\right) u',$$

where

$$\mu = \frac{M m}{M + m} \tag{5.2}$$

is the reduced mass. (5.1) can be separated by means of a solution of the form

$$u' = u(x, y, z)\, u''(X, Y, Z), \qquad E' = E + E'', \tag{5.3}$$

The motion of the center of mass of the atom is governed by the equation

$$\Delta u'' + \frac{2(M+m)}{\hbar^2} E'' u'' = 0, \tag{5.4}$$

while for the relative motion of the electron the following equation holds:

$$\Delta u + \frac{2\mu}{\hbar^2} \left(E + \frac{Z e^2}{\varrho}\right) u = 0 \tag{5.5}$$

(5.5) differs from (1.1') only in that μ appears in the place of m. Thus, we need only to alter the atomic units defined in the Introduction in order to take into account the motion of the nucleus. Adopting μ as the new atomic unit of mass,

[1] For details, see the work by MOTT and MASSEY, ref. [7] of the bibliography. For tables of COULOMB wave functions see N.B.S. Appl. Math. Circ. No. 17, Vol. 1, Washington, D.C. 1952.

the previously used unit of energy becomes multiplied by

$$\frac{\mu}{m} = \frac{M}{M+m} = \left(1 + \frac{1}{1{,}836A}\right)^{-1}, \tag{5.6}$$

where A is the atomic weight of the nucleus. In terms of the new atomic units SCHRÖDINGER's equation again assumes the old form (1.1). In terms of the new units the energy of the n-th discrete state of a hydrogen-like ion is again given by BALMER's formula (2.11); in terms of the old units, which we shall retain in general, we accordingly get:

$$E_n = -\frac{Z^2}{2n^2}\frac{M}{M+m}. \tag{5.7}$$

According to (5.7) the absolute value of the energy, as a consequence of the motion of the nucleus, decreases with decreasing nuclear mass. (The unit of length a is increased by a factor of m/μ, i.e. the electrons are on the average more distant from a light nucleus than from a heavy nucleus of the same charge.)

This effect of nuclear motion has been of importance historically both for the detection of isotopes, in particular of deuterium[1], and for the "spectroscopic determination of the atomic mass of the electron". Consider, for instance, the various fine structure components of the H_α line in hydrogen and in deuterium ($Z=1$, atomic mass about 2). After applying small corrections for hyperfine structure and relativistic effects, the wave numbers of each line for hydrogen and for deuterium differ from the wave number for infinite nuclear mass only by a multiplicative factor of form (5.6). In (5.6), M is replaced by the proton and deuteron mass, respectively, for hydrogen and deuterium. The difference in wave numbers ν_H and ν_D for the two isotopes is then given by

$$\frac{\nu_D - \nu_H}{\nu_H} = \frac{m(M_D - M_H)}{(M_H - m)\,M_D} \tag{5.8}$$

where M_H, M_D are the mass of a *neutral* hydrogen and deuterium atom, respectively (including the electron mass).

The difference in wave number (5.8), has been measured by various authors[2] to an accuracy of about 1 in 5000. To get a feeling for the order of magnitude of the effect, the difference in wavelength of the H_α line in hydrogen ($\lambda = 6560$ Å) and in deuterium is about 1.75 Å, or about one-third the doublet separation of the D-lines in sodium. The values of M_H and M_D are known very accurately from mass spectroscopy and from data on nuclear reactions. In physical atomic mass units (referred to O^{16}) they are $M_H = 1.00814_2$ a.m.u., $M_D = 2.01473_7$ a.m.u. From (5.8) and the experimental values for $(\nu_D - \nu_H)$ one can then calculate the atomic mass of the electron to an accuracy of about 1 in 5000. Actually the electron's atomic mass is known more accurately from other types of experiments, in particular measurements of the "cyclotron frequency" of an electron and a proton in a constant magnetic field, giving directly the proton-electron mass ratio. The best "non-spectroscopic" value[3] for the electron mass is

$$M_H/m = 1837.13 \pm 0.05, \qquad m = (548.76 \pm 0.01_5) \times 10^{-6} \text{ a.m.u.} \tag{5.9}$$

The "spectroscopic" value for m, obtained by COHEN, is larger than the more accurate one given in (5.9) by about 1 part in 2500, i.e., by slightly more than its experimental error.

[1] UREY, BRICKWEDDE and MURPHY: Phys. Rev. **40**, 1, 464 (1932).

[2] For a detailed analysis see E. R. COHEN, Phys. Rev. **88**, 353 (1952).

[3] J. W. DUMOND and E. R. COHEN: Rev. Mod. Phys. **25**, 691 (1953). — Cf. the preceding article in this volume.

The relation between the RYDBERG constant R_{H} for an actual hydrogen (or deuterium) atom and R_∞, Eq. (2.14), is

$$\left.\begin{aligned} R_{\mathrm{H}} = R_\infty (M_{\mathrm{H}} - m)/M_{\mathrm{H}} &= (109677.58 \pm 0.01_2)\,\mathrm{cm}^{-1}, \\ R_{\mathrm{D}} &= (109707.42 \pm 0.01_2)\,\mathrm{cm}^{-1}. \end{aligned}\right\} \tag{5.10}$$

Of course, R_{H} and R_{D} are the quantities which are measured directly and R_∞ is derived from them with the help of (5.9).

6. Separation of SCHRÖDINGER's equation in parabolic coordinates[1]. SCHRÖDINGER's equation for an electron moving in any central force field can always be separated in spherical polar coordinates. If the central field is of the COULOMB type, then a separation can also be carried out in parabolic coordinates. This alternative is connected with the degeneracy of the eigenvalues belonging to like principal and different orbital quantum numbers (cf. Sect. 2). A separation in parabolic coordinates turns out to be useful in the treatment of all kinds of perturbation problems in which a particular direction in space is distinguished by some external force, e.g., STARK effect, photo-electric effect, COMPTON effect, and collision of electrons.

α) Discrete spectrum. The parabolic coordinates ξ, η, φ are defined through the relations[2]

$$\left.\begin{aligned} x &= \sqrt{\xi\eta}\cos\varphi, & \xi &= r + z, \\ y &= \sqrt{\xi\eta}\sin\varphi, & \eta &= r - z, \\ z &= \tfrac{1}{2}(\xi - \eta), & \varphi &= \arctan\frac{y}{x}, \\ r &= \tfrac{1}{2}(\xi + \eta). \end{aligned}\right\} \tag{6.1}$$

The surfaces $\xi = \text{const}$ and $\eta = \text{const}$ are paraboloids of revolution about the z-axis having the nucleus at the origin ($x = y = z = 0$) as focus. The coordinate system is orthogonal. The element of arc is given by

$$ds^2 = \frac{\eta + \xi}{4\xi}\,d\xi^2 + \frac{\eta + \xi}{4\eta}\,d\eta^2 + \xi\eta\,d\varphi^2, \tag{6.2}$$

and the volume element by

$$d\tau = \tfrac{1}{4}(\xi + \eta)\,d\xi\,d\eta\,d\varphi. \tag{6.3}$$

From (6.2) follows the expression for the LAPLACian operator, viz.

$$\Delta = \frac{4}{\xi + \eta}\frac{d}{d\xi}\left(\xi\frac{d}{d\xi}\right) + \frac{4}{\xi + \eta}\frac{d}{d\eta}\left(\eta\frac{d}{d\eta}\right) + \frac{1}{\xi\eta}\frac{d^2}{d\varphi^2}. \tag{6.4}$$

We deal with SCHRÖDINGER's equation by setting

$$u = u_1(\xi)\,u_2(\eta)\,e^{\pm i m\varphi}, \qquad Z = Z_1 + Z_2 \quad (m \geqq 0). \tag{6.5}$$

Multiplying the differential equation by $\frac{1}{4}(\xi + \eta)$ and carrying out the separation we obtain

$$\frac{d}{d\xi}\left(\xi\frac{du_1}{d\xi}\right) + \left(\frac{1}{2}E\xi + Z_1 - \frac{m^2}{4\xi}\right)u_1 = 0 \tag{6.6}$$

and also an exactly equivalent equation for $u_2(\eta)$. A procedure analogous to that in Sect. 4 leads us to conclude that u_1 behaves as $e^{-\frac{1}{2}\varepsilon\xi}$ for large ξ and as $\xi^{\frac{1}{2}m}$ for small ξ. We put

$$u_1 = e^{-\frac{1}{2}\varepsilon\xi}\,\xi^{\frac{1}{2}m}\,f_1(\xi) \quad \text{and} \quad x = \varepsilon\xi, \tag{6.7}$$

---

[1] Cf. E. SCHRÖDINGER, Abhandlungen III, p. 85.

[2] Cf., e.g., E. SCHRÖDINGER, Abhandlungen, p. 105.

so that

$$x\frac{d^2 f_1}{dx^2} + (m+1-x)\frac{df_1}{dx} + \left(\frac{Z_1}{\varepsilon} - \frac{m+1}{2}\right) f_1 = 0.$$

On comparison with (3.45) it becomes apparent that the solutions of this equation are

$$f_1 = L^m_{n_1+m}(x),$$

where

$$n_1 = Z_1/\varepsilon - \tfrac{1}{2}(m+1) \tag{6.8}$$

must be a non-negative integer (in the case of real ε) if f_1 is to remain finite for large ξ. A corresponding result may be obtained for f_2. Finally, putting

$$n = n_1 + n_2 + m + 1 \tag{6.9}$$

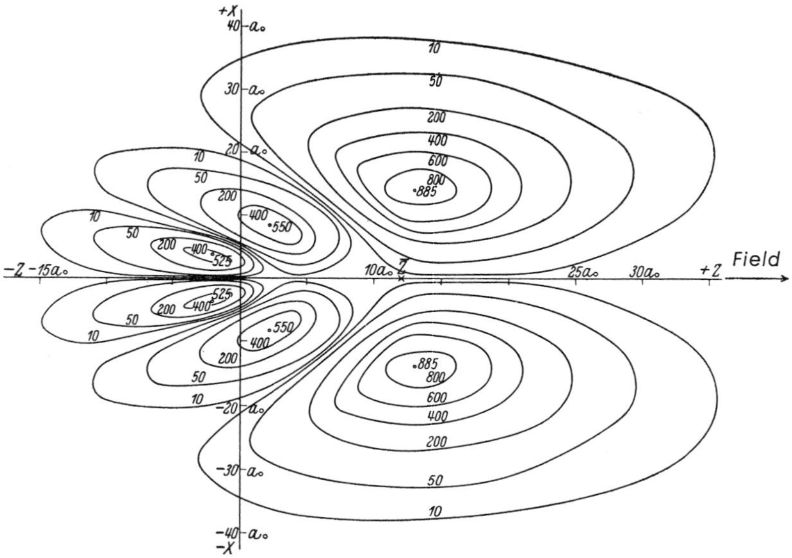

Fig. 8. Charge distribution of the state $n_1=2$, $n_2=0$, $m=1$ in parabolic quantization (according to F. G. SLACK): The figure shows a cross-section through the atom, the nucleus being at the center of the coordinate system The curves are lines of constant charge density, where charge density means the charge in a circular ring with the quantization direction (z-axis) as axis. Note the strong concentration of charge towards positive values of z

and solving (6.8) for ε, we obtain our previous energy formula (2.10), viz.,

$$E = -\frac{1}{2}\varepsilon^2 = -\frac{1}{2}\frac{Z^2}{n^2}. \tag{6.10}$$

The degree of degeneracy of the n-th eigenvalue is, as it must be, the same as in our previous calculation in polar coordinates. If m is fixed, n_1 can assume the $n-m$ values $0, 1, \ldots, n-m-1$. m itself can go from 0 to $n-1$, the non-zero values having to be counted twice because one can choose either the plus of the minus sign in $e^{\pm im\varphi}$ of (6.5). Thus, one arrives again at exactly n^2 different eigenfunctions.

We must also normalize the eigenfunctions. Since the volume element is given by (6.3), we require

$$\tfrac{1}{4}c^2\int_0^\infty d\xi\int_0^\infty d\eta\int_0^{2\pi} d\varphi\, u_1^2(\xi)\, u_2^2(\eta)\cdot(\xi+\eta) = 1. \tag{6.11}$$

The value of the integral can be taken from (3.16). The normalized eigenfunction becomes

$$u_{n_1 n_2 m} = \frac{e^{\pm i m \varphi}}{\sqrt{\pi n}} \cdot \frac{n_1!^{\frac{1}{2}}\, n_2!^{\frac{1}{2}}\, \varepsilon^{m+\frac{3}{2}}}{(n_1+m)!^{\frac{3}{2}}\,(n_2+m)!^{\frac{3}{2}}}\, e^{-\frac{1}{2}\varepsilon(\xi+\eta)} (\xi\eta)^{\frac{1}{2}m} L^m_{n_1+m}(\varepsilon\xi)\, L^m_{n_2+m}(\varepsilon\eta). \quad (6.12)$$

These eigenfunctions, contrary to the eigenfunctions in polar coordinates, are asymmetrical with respect to the plane $z=0$. For $n_1 > n_2$, the larger portion of the charge distribution of the electron lies on the positive side of z; for $n_1 < n_2$, on the negative side of z. This is best seen by examining the eigenfunctions for very large distances from the nucleus, i.e., for large arguments of the LAGUERRE functions. For large x, $L^{\mu}_{\lambda}(x)$ behaves [cf. (3.7)] as $x^{\lambda-\mu}$, and in view of the definitions (6.1) of parabolic coordinates we have

$$u_{n_1 n_2 m} \sim e^{i m \varphi}\, \xi^{n_1+\frac{1}{2}m}\, \eta^{n_2+\frac{1}{2}m}\, e^{-\frac{1}{2}\varepsilon(\xi+\eta)};$$

$$|u_{n_1 n_2 m}|^2 \sim r^{n-1} e^{-\varepsilon r} (1+\cos\vartheta)^{n_1+\frac{1}{2}m} (1-\cos\vartheta)^{n_2+\frac{1}{2}m}.$$

Fig. 8 gives contours of constant charge density for the state $n=3$, $n_1=2$, $n_2=m=0$. The large eccentricity in the charge distribution is quite evident.

The parabolic eigenfunctions can, naturally, be built up from the eigenfunctions in polar coordinates; e.g., for $n=2$, $n_1=1$, $n_2=m=0$ we have

$$u = \frac{1}{\sqrt{2\pi}} \cdot \left(\frac{1}{2} Z\right)^{\frac{3}{2}} \left[-1 + \frac{1}{2} Z r (1+\cos\vartheta)\right] e^{-\frac{1}{2}Zr}$$

$$= -\frac{1}{\sqrt{2}} R_{20}(r)\, Y_{00}(\vartheta,\varphi) + \frac{1}{\sqrt{2}} R_{21}(r)\, Y_{10}(\vartheta,\varphi),$$

in view of (3.7), (3.21), (1.8) and (6.1).

Generally, any of the $(n-m)$ wave functions in parabolic coordinates for a fixed value of n and m (and fixed sign in $e^{\pm i m \varphi}$) is a linear superposition of the $(n-m)$ spherical harmonics wave functions for the same values of n and m (and sign). For the non-degenerate ground state with $n=1$ $(n_1=n_2=m=0)$ the "parabolic" and spherical harmonics wave functions are identical.

β) Continuous spectrum. For the continuous spectrum, with positive energy E, we find that

$$n = -i n' = -i Z/k, \qquad (k^2 = +2E) \quad (6.13)$$

is again a pure imaginary and

$$n_1 = -\tfrac{1}{2}(m+1) - \tfrac{1}{2} i (n'+\lambda); \qquad n_2 = -\tfrac{1}{2}(m+1) - \tfrac{1}{2} i (n'-\lambda) \quad (6.14)$$

are complex. λ can assume continuously all values from $-\infty$ to $+\infty$. The LAGUERRE functions with the complex indices n_1+m and n_2+m can again be represented by the integrals (4.6) and (4.7), from which a series expansion corresponding to (4.8) and an asymptotic representation corresponding to (4.10) may be derived. If the normalization is performed in the k and λ scales one obtains[1]:

$$u_{k\lambda m} = \frac{k}{\sqrt{\pi}} f_{k\lambda m}(k\xi)\, f_{k,-\lambda,m}(k\eta)\, e^{\pm i m \varphi} \quad (6.15)$$

where

$$f_{k\lambda m}(x) = C_{k\lambda} \frac{x^{\frac{1}{2}m}}{2\pi i} \int d\zeta\, e^{i x \zeta} \left(\zeta - \frac{1}{2}\right)^{-\frac{1}{2}+\frac{m}{2}-\frac{1}{2} i (n'+\lambda)} \left(\zeta + \frac{1}{2}\right)^{-\frac{1}{2}+\frac{m}{2}+\frac{1}{2} i (n'+\lambda)},$$

$$C_{k\lambda} = \prod_{\varrho=\frac{1}{2},\frac{3}{2},\ldots,\frac{m-1}{2}} \frac{1}{\sqrt{\varrho^2 + \frac{1}{4}(n'+\lambda)^2}} \cdot \frac{1}{\sqrt{1+e^{-\pi(n'+\lambda)}}},$$

---

[1] Cf. J. FISCHER, Ann. d. Phys. **8**, 821 (1931) paragraph 1; G. WENTZEL, Z. Physik **58**, 348 (1929).

when m is even,

$$C_{k\lambda} = \frac{1}{\sqrt{1+e^{-\pi(n'+\lambda)}}} \cdot \sqrt{\frac{2}{n'+\lambda}} \prod_{\varrho=1,2,\dots,\frac{m-1}{2}} \frac{1}{\sqrt{\varrho^2+\frac{1}{4}(n'+\lambda)^2}},$$

when m is odd.

The path of integration in f consists, exactly as in (4.7), of a simple loop around the two branch points $\xi = \pm\frac{1}{2}$ (cf. Fig. 6). At large distances from the atom u behaves like a spherical wave, i.e., u falls off[1] as $1/r$.

γ) Eigenfunctions which behave asymptotically like plane waves. RUTHERFORD'S *scattering formula*[2]. In the theory of scattering of electrons and of other charged particles by bare nuclei it is convenient to construct a wave function which behaves asymptotically like an incident plane wave, with amplitude independent of r, plus an outgoing spherical wave. Such a wave function was first discussed by GORDON.

We try a wave function[3] of the form

$$u = e^{ikz} F(\eta) = e^{\frac{1}{2}ik\xi}\left[e^{-\frac{1}{2}ik\eta} F(\eta)\right], \tag{6.16}$$

where $k = +\sqrt{2E}$. We shall see that such a wave function has the required asymptotic behavior. Substituting (6.16) into the wave equation, we find that $F(\eta)$ is indeed a function of η only and satisfies the equation

$$\eta\frac{d^2F}{d\eta^2} + (1 - ik\eta)\frac{dF}{d\eta} + ZF = 0. \tag{6.17}$$

Comparison of (6.17) with (3.43) shows that $F(\eta)$ is, except for a normalization factor c, a LAGUERRE function

$$F(\eta) = c\,L_{-in'}(ik\eta); \qquad n' = Z/k. \tag{6.18}$$

The solution u, (6.16) with (6.18), is mathematically similar to (6.15), but for a *complex* value of λ,

$$m = 0,\ \lambda = -(n'+i); \qquad n_1 = 1,\ n_2 = -in'.$$

$F(\eta)$ can also be expressed in terms of a (confluent) hypergeometric function. Apart from a normalization constant it is

$$F(\eta) = F(in', 1, ik\eta) \tag{6.19}$$

where $n' = Z/k$.

Normalizing the wave function to unit charge density at large distance from the nucleus, we obtain the integral representation for u,

$$u = \sqrt{\frac{2\pi n'}{1-e^{-2\pi n'}}} \cdot e^{\frac{1}{2}ik\xi} \cdot \frac{1}{2\pi i}\int d\zeta\, e^{-ik\eta\zeta}\left(\zeta+\frac{1}{2}\right)^{-in'}\left(\zeta-\frac{1}{2}\right)^{in'-1}, \tag{6.20}$$

in which the path of integration, as before and exactly as in (4.7), consists of a simple loop going around the branch points $\xi = \pm\frac{1}{2}$. In view of (6.1), u is

---

[1] Cf. e. g., G. WENTZEL, Z. Physik **58**, 348 (1929), Eq. (22). More precisely, u falls off as $(r^2 - z^2)^{-\frac{1}{2}}$.

[2] W. GORDON: Z. Physik **48**, 180 (1928), cf. also G. TEMPLE, Proc. Roy. Soc. Lond., Ser. A **121**, 673 (1928); A. SOMMERFELD, Ann. d. Phys. **11**, 257 (1931), paragraph 6. See also p. 47 of ref. [*9*].

[3] See also ref. [*9*], p. 47.

represented asymptotically by

$$u = e^{i(kz - n'\log k(r-z) + \sigma_{n'})} + \frac{Z}{k^2(r-z)} e^{i(kr + n'\log k(r-z) - \sigma_{n'})}, \tag{6.21}$$

where $\sigma_{n'} = \arg \Gamma(1+in')$ is the complex phase of the Γ-function.

The first term in (6.21) represents a plane wave incident in the z direction which is slightly modified by the COULOMB potential of the nucleus. Its amplitude does not depend on the separation r between electron and nucleus. The amplitude of the second term, on the other hand, is inversely proportional to r and thus represents a spherical wave; that the spherical wave is outgoing may be seen by including in (6.21) the time factor e^{-iEt}. The spherical wave is necessarily linked to the plane wave and represents the scattering of the electron by the nucleus.

Since the amplitude of the incident wave is unity and the velocity of each electron is k (atomic units), it is clear that k electrons per unit time enter the region of interaction with the nucleus through unit area of a surface which is perpendicular to the z-axis and is located at a great distance from the nucleus. The number of electrons scattered into the solid angle $d\Omega$ per unit time, i.e., the number leaving the field of force of the nucleus through an element of area $r^2\, d\Omega$ of a distant spherical surface per unit time, is given, in view of (6.21), by

$$k\, r^2\, d\Omega \cdot \left[\frac{Z}{k^2(r-z)}\right]^2 = k \cdot \frac{Z^2\, d\Omega}{k^4(1-\cos\vartheta)^2}.$$

In the above, $\vartheta = \arc\cos\frac{z}{r}$ is the angle of deviation of the electrons caused by scattering. The coefficient for scattering at the angle ϑ thus becomes:

$$\left.\begin{aligned} S^2(\vartheta) &= \frac{\text{number of particles scattered into the solid angle } d\Omega \text{ per unit time}}{\text{number of particles incident per unit area per unit time}} \\ &= \frac{Z^2\, d\Omega}{k^4(1-\cos\vartheta)^2} \text{ at. un.} \end{aligned}\right\} \tag{6.22}$$

S^2 has the dimensions of an area and is measured in atomic units (a^2). To change to c.g.s. units we must put

$$k^2 = E/\mathrm{Ry} \tag{6.23}$$

where E is the energy of the incident particles in c.g.s. units and thus (cf. Introduction):

$$S^2(\vartheta) = \frac{Z^2 \sin\vartheta\, d\vartheta\, d\varphi}{E^2(1-\cos\vartheta)^2} \cdot \mathrm{Ry}^2 a^2 = \frac{e^4 Z^2 \sin\vartheta\, d\vartheta\, d\varphi}{16 E^2 \sin^4 \frac{1}{2}\vartheta}. \tag{6.24}$$

This is the well-known scattering formula of RUTHERFORD.

It is often useful to normalize (6.20) and (6.21) in some particular one of a number of different ways. Most frequently the normalization is such that one particle is incident on unit area per unit time; this requires multiplication of (6.20) and (6.21) by $\frac{1}{\sqrt{v}}$, where v is the velocity (k atomic units).

SOMMERFELD employs as eigenfunctions the system of functions

$$u_{\boldsymbol{k}} = e^{\frac{1}{2}i(kr + \boldsymbol{k}\cdot\boldsymbol{r})} \sqrt{\frac{n'}{1-e^{-2\pi n'}}} \cdot \frac{1}{(2\pi)^2 i} \cdot \int d\zeta \cdot \left(\zeta + \frac{1}{2}\right)^{-in'} \left(\zeta - \frac{1}{2}\right)^{in'-1} e^{-i(kr - \boldsymbol{k}\cdot\boldsymbol{r})\zeta} \tag{6.25}$$

in his theory of the continuous X-ray spectrum. $\boldsymbol{k}$ is a vector of variable direction and magnitude. The asymptotic formula for large r is

$$u_{\boldsymbol{k}} = (2\pi)^{-\frac{3}{2}} \left\{ e^{i[\boldsymbol{k}\cdot\boldsymbol{r} - n'\log(kr - \boldsymbol{k}\cdot\boldsymbol{r}) + \sigma_{n'}]} - \frac{n'}{kr - \boldsymbol{k}\cdot\boldsymbol{r}} \cdot e^{i[kr + n'\log(kr - \boldsymbol{k}\cdot\boldsymbol{r}) - \sigma_{n'}]} \right\}. \tag{6.26}$$

The system $u_{\boldsymbol{k}}$ makes the intuitive meaning of the eigenfunctions particularly clear. $u_{\boldsymbol{k}}$ is a simple plane wave incident in the $\boldsymbol{k}$ direction plus an associated scattered wave. The eigenfunction (6.26) is normalized in the k scale. Expanding an arbitrary function of the spatial coordinates in terms of the system (6.26)[1] one has

$$f(\boldsymbol{r}) = \int d k_x\, d k_y\, d k_z\, a_{\boldsymbol{k}}\, u_{\boldsymbol{k}}(\boldsymbol{r}) + \sum_{n_1 n_2 m} a_{n_1 n_2 m}\, u_{n_1 n_2 m}(\boldsymbol{r}), \tag{6.27}$$

and the coefficients in the expansion are given by

$$a_{\boldsymbol{k}} = \int u_{\boldsymbol{k}}^*(\boldsymbol{r})\, f(\boldsymbol{r})\, d\tau. \tag{6.28}$$

Finally, $u_{\boldsymbol{k}}$ can be normalized also per energy interval E and element of solid angle $d\Omega$. $d\Omega$ is the element of solid angle into which the vector $\boldsymbol{k}$ points and $E = \frac{1}{2} k^2$ atomic units. Thus, $d k_x\, d k_y\, d k_z = \sqrt{2E}\, dE\, d\Omega$. This change in normalization requires a division of (6.25) and (6.26) by $\sqrt[4]{2E} = \sqrt{k}$.

We have only discussed wave functions in the continuum which behave asymptotically like a plane wave plus spherically *outgoing* waves. For a physical problem involving *only* scattering by a pure COULOMB field, only these wave functions will occur. But in problems where the matrix element of some operator is required between an arbitrary initial state of the electron and a *final* state in the continuum, another set of wave functions is useful[2]. These other wave functions behave asymptotically like a plane wave plus spherical *incoming* waves. They can be obtained in an analogous manner, but the substitution (6.16) is replaced by

$$u = e^{ikz}\, G(\xi) = e^{-\frac{1}{2} i k \eta} \left[e^{\frac{1}{2} i k \xi}\, G(\xi)\right]. \tag{6.29}$$

An *alternative* complete set of eigenfunctions, analogous to (6.26), can be formed from wave functions of type (6.29).

The wave function (6.20), separated in parabolic coordinates, for positive energy E can also be expressed as a superposition of all the wave functions, separated in spherical polar coordinates, for the same energy E. This expansion for u, defined in (6.20) is[3]

$$u = \sqrt{\frac{\pi}{2k}} \sum_{l=0}^{\infty} (2l+1)\, i^l\, e^{-i\sigma_l} R_{Wl}(r)\, P_l(\cos\vartheta), \tag{6.30}$$

where $R_{Wl}(r)$ is the radial wave function for a particular value of l, given by (4.22) or (4.23), and $\sigma_l = \arg \Gamma(l+1+in')$. Expansions of form similar to (6.30), but for a general central potential, will be discussed in Sect. 7.

7. Methods for the continuous spectrum for a general central potential. *α) General.* The separation of the SCHRÖDINGER wave equation in spherical polar coordinates (cf. Sect. 1) is possible for *any central* potential $V(r)$ (the potential V a function of the radial distance r only). The radial wave function $R_{nl}(r)$ satisfies a one-dimensional differential equation analogous to (2.1) (with $-Z/r$ replaced by V). For the continuous spectrum the radial wave function R_{El}, which is regular at the origin, is characterized by a positive value E of the total energy and by the orbital quantum number l. It has the asymptotic behavior of a standing spherical wave. The asymptotic form is similar to (4.10), but the logarithmic term is missing for a potential which falls off more rapidly than the COULOMB potential at large distances. For such a potential the asymptotic form of R

[1] To make the system $u_{\boldsymbol{k}}$ complete, the eigenfunctions of the discrete spectrum must, of course, be included.

[2] G. BREIT and H. A. BETHE: Phys. Rev. **93**, 888 (1954).

[3] W. GORDON: Z. Physik **48**, 180 (1928).

([9], p. 22) is

$$R_{El}(r) \sim (kr)^{-1} \sin (kr - \tfrac{1}{2}\pi l + \delta_l) \tag{7.1}$$

where $k = \sqrt{2E}$ and δ_l is a dimensionless constant, the "phase-shift for the partial wave l". The phase-shift δ_l depends on the energy E and is determined uniquely by the differential equation for R_{El} and the requirement that R be regular at the origin. For a few potential shapes (square well, exponential, MORSE potentials, etc.) the wave function R, and hence δ_l, can be obtained in analytic form, but for most potential shapes approximation methods have to be used.

The separation of the wave equation in parabolic coordinates, on the other hand, is possible *only* for the special case of the COULOMB potential (Sect. 6). Nevertheless, for *any* central potential $V(r)$ and for positive energy E, a superposition of the "spherical harmonic (partial wave) wave functions" can be found, which behaves asymptotically like a plane wave plus scattered spherical outgoing waves. This wave function is[1] ([9], p. 24)

$$u(r, \vartheta, \varphi) = \sum_{l=0}^{\infty} (2l+1)\, i^l e^{i\delta_l} R_{El}(r)\, P_l(\cos\vartheta) \tag{7.2}$$

where R_{El} is a radial wave function, normalized so that its asymptotic expression is given by (7.1), and δ_l is the phase-shift defined by (7.1). The asymptotic form of the wave function (7.2) is

$$u \sim e^{ikz} + r^{-1} e^{ikr} f(\vartheta), \tag{7.3}$$

where

$$f(\vartheta) = \frac{1}{2ik} \sum_{l=0}^{\infty} (2l+1)\,(e^{2i\delta_l} - 1)\, P_l(\cos\vartheta). \tag{7.4}$$

The quantity $|f(\vartheta)|^2$ has the dimension of an area and is called the "differential cross section", in complete analogy with the $S^2(\vartheta)$ of (6.22). The quantity $f(\vartheta)$ is called the scattering amplitude.

Some crude "order of magnitude" observations on the behavior of the infinite sum (7.4) can be made for potentials which have a certain "range" R_0, i.e. for potentials which are negligibly small for radial distances much larger than R_0: If $kR_0 \ll 1$, then all the higher phase shifts are small compared with δ_0 (the S-state phase-shift). In this case only the first (constant) term in (7.4) is important and $f(\vartheta)$ is approximately independent of ϑ (isotropic angular distribution). If, on the other hand, $kR_0 \gg 1$, then all the phase-shifts δ_l for $l \lesssim kR_0$ may be appreciable, but the terms in (7.4) with $l \gg kR_0$ can still be neglected. Now, for $l \neq 0$, $P_l(\cos\vartheta)$ is approximately equal to unity for $\vartheta < l^{-1}$, but oscillates rapidly for $\vartheta > l^{-1}$ if $l \gg 1$. If we cut the series (7.4) off at $l \sim kR_0$, then $f(\vartheta)$ will be approximately constant (and *finite*) for $\vartheta < (kR_0)^{-1}$. For $\vartheta \gg (kR_0)^{-1}$ there will be strong cancellations in (7.4), due to the oscillatory nature of the LEGENDRE functions with $\vartheta^{-1} < l < kR_0$. Thus $|f(\vartheta)|^2$ will decrease with increasing angle ϑ.

β) COULOMB potential. For the special case of a COULOMB potential the wave function[2] (7.2) represents a modified plane plus scattered wave. The asymptotic form of both the plane and scattered wave is modified by the presence of the logarithmic term and is given by (6.21) instead of (7.3). It was shown by GORDON[3] that for a COULOMB potential the sum (7.2) or (6.30) is identical with (6.20)

[1] For a potential falling off more rapidly than r^{-1} at large distances.

[2] With δ_l replaced by $-\sigma_l$, where σ_l is defined in (4.10). With this substitution (7.2) and (6.30) are identical except for a change in sign [see normalization of R_W, Eq. (4.19)].

[3] W. GORDON: Z. Physik **48**, 180 (1928).

and the square of the sum (7.4) for $f(\vartheta)$ identical with (6.22). Although we have already derived the expression (6.22) in closed form, it is instructive to consider the qualitative behavior of the sum (7.4) for a COULOMB potential. This sum is of importance for potentials which deviate only slightly from a COULOMB potential.

For a potential differing from a COULOMB potential only at small distances (e.g. electrostatic potential of a small, but finite, charged sphere) the radial wave functions have an asymptotic form similar to (4.10), including the logarithmic term. Only for the lowest few values of l do the values of σ_l differ appreciably from those given in (4.10). Consider next a potential which differs from (and is smaller than) a COULOMB potential only at *large* distances, e.g. the atomic HARTREE potential which falls off more rapidly than r^{-1} for r large compared with some screening radius R_0 (due to the screening by the atomic electrons). In this case the radial wave function has the asymptotic ($kr \gg 1$ *and* $r \gg R_0$) form (7.1), without any logarithmic term. But, if $kR_0 \gg 1$, the phase shifts δ_l for all but very large values of l are nearly equal to $(C - \sigma_l)$, where σ_l is given by (4.10) and C is a *constant* of the order of magnitude of $n' \log(2kR_0)$. Only for $l \gg kR_0$ do the phase shifts δ_l differ appreciably from $(C - \sigma_l)$. For these large values of l, δ_l decreases with increasing l without changing sign (see also Sect. 7γ).

In the relativistic DIRAC theory, finally, even for a *pure* COULOMB field separation of the wave equation in parabolic coordinates is impossible and infinite series analogous to (7.4) have to be summed (the equivalent phase-shifts in the relativistic case resemble the nonrelativistic σ_l for large values of l) (see Sect. 15).

We consider a general infinite series of form (7.4),

$$k f(\vartheta) = -\tfrac{1}{2} i \sum_{l=0}^{\infty} (2l+1)\, a_l\, P_l(\cos\vartheta)\,. \tag{7.5}$$

For the special case of a COULOMB potential in the nonrelativistic theory we have, using (4.10),

$$a_l = e^{-2i\sigma_l} - 1 = \frac{\Gamma(l+1-in')}{\Gamma(l+1+in')} - 1\,, \tag{7.6}$$

where $n' = Z/k = Ze^2/\hbar v$. In this case we also have a closed analytic expression for $f(\vartheta)$, namely

$$k f(\vartheta) = \frac{n'}{(1-\cos\vartheta)} \exp\left[i n' \log(1-\cos\vartheta) - 2i\sigma_0\right]. \tag{7.7}$$

The function $f(\vartheta)$ has a singularity at $\vartheta = 0$ and the corresponding series (7.5) converges very poorly for small ϑ. Unlike the case of potentials with a finite range, for an unscreened COULOMB potential the phase-shifts σ_l, and hence a_l, do *not* decrease rapidly with increasing l for large l. For instance, if we restrict ourselves for the moment to the case of $n' \ll 1$ (energy E large compared with ground state binding energy), (7.6) reduces approximately to

$$a_l \approx -2i n' \psi(l+1)\,, \qquad \psi(z) = \frac{d}{dz} \log \Gamma(z)\,. \tag{7.8}$$

For large l, (7.8) reduces further to the approximate expression

$$a_l \approx -2i n' \log\left(l + \tfrac{1}{2}\right), \tag{7.9}$$

which actually *increases* (in absolute magnitude) with l.

A convenient method for dealing with poorly convergent series of the type (7.5) was proposed recently[1]: For the COULOMB field and similar cases the poor

[1] YENNIE, RAVENHALL and WILSON: Phys. Rev. 95, 500 (1954).

convergence is due to a singularity of $f(\vartheta)$ at $\vartheta=0$. Much more rapidly convergent series can be obtained by multiplying the left and right sides of (7.5) by positive powers of $(1-\cos\vartheta)$, which removes (or at least lessens) the singularity of the left side. For instance, multiplying merely by the first power of $(1-\cos\vartheta)$ and rearranging the right hand side of (7.5) with the help of Eq. (A.22) of the appendix, we get

$$\left.\begin{aligned} k(1-\cos\vartheta)\, f(\vartheta) &= -\tfrac{1}{2} i \sum_{l=0}^{\infty} (2l+1)\, a_l' P_l(\cos\vartheta); \\ (2l+1)\, a_l' &= (2l+1)\, a_l - (l+1)\, a_{l+1} - l\, a_{l-1}. \end{aligned}\right\} \tag{7.10}$$

For large l and for coefficients a_l of similar form to (7.6), one usually finds that a_l' is smaller than a_l by a factor of the order of l^2. For the special case where the coefficients a_l are given by the approximation (7.8), the coefficients a_l', defined by (7.10), vanish exactly for all l except for $l=0$. In this case we would have

$$k(1-\cos\vartheta)\, f(\vartheta) = n', \tag{7.7a}$$

which is just the first term in an expansion of (7.7) in powers of n'. If the exact expression (7.6) is used, a_l' decreases only as l^{-2} for large l. This is due to the fact that the *argument* of the exponential in the expression (7.7) for $(1-\cos\vartheta)\, f(\vartheta)$ still has a singularity at $\vartheta=0$, and it is convenient to apply the transformation (7.10) once more (or even twice).

γ) Born *approximation*[1]. Although no closed exact expression exists for $f(\vartheta)$ for a general central potential $V(r)$, an approximate expression for $f(\vartheta)$ in closed form can be derived, the "Born approximation". This approximation is valid only when the potential is "weak enough". Consider the Schrödinger wave Eq. (1.1) with Z/r replaced by $-V(r)$, the potential energy in atomic units of energy. We consider the potential as a small perturbation and take as our unperturbed wave function a single plane wave with momentum $\boldsymbol{k}_0$, where $k_0^2/2=E$, the total energy. We then apply first order perturbation theory to (1.1), obtaining the first order wave function as a superposition of eigenstates of the unperturbed Hamiltonian. These eigenstates are plane waves with momentum $\boldsymbol{k}$ for arbitrary direction of $\boldsymbol{k}$ but with $k^2=k_0^2=2E$. The coefficient in this superposition for a particular value of $\boldsymbol{k}\neq\boldsymbol{k}_0$ then represents the probability amplitude for scattering in the direction of $\boldsymbol{k}$. Finally, one obtains the Born approximation expression for $f(\vartheta)$, Eq. (7.3), in the form

$$\left.\begin{aligned} f(\vartheta) &= -\frac{1}{2\pi}\int d\tau\, e^{i(\boldsymbol{k}_0-\boldsymbol{k})\cdot\boldsymbol{r}}\, V(r) = -2\int_0^\infty dr\, r^2 \frac{\sin Kr}{Kr}\, V(r), \\ K &= 2k\sin\left(\tfrac{1}{2}\vartheta\right), \end{aligned}\right\} \tag{7.11}$$

where ϑ is the angle between the incident and scattered directions, $\boldsymbol{k}_0$ and $\boldsymbol{k}$.

An equivalent Born approximation expression can be obtained for the radial wave function $R_{El}(r)$ and the phase shift for the "partial wave" eigenstate for any value of the quantum number l. This is accomplished by solving the differential equation for R, analogous to (2.1), by first order perturbation theory. The Born approximation for the phase-shift ([9], p. 28) is

$$\delta_l^{(B)} = -\pi\int_0^\infty dr\, r\, [J_{l+\frac{1}{2}}(kr)]^2\, V(r), \tag{7.12}$$

---

[1] See Sect. 9 and 70, also ref. [9], pp. 116—119.

where J is a BESSEL function. This expression is a good approximation if δ_l is small compared with $\pi/2$. It can be shown that the substitution of the approximation (7.12) for δ_l into (7.4) gives (after replacing $e^{2i\delta_l}$ by $1+2i\,\delta_l$) exactly the BORN approximation (7.11) for $f(\vartheta)$. (7.11) is thus a good approximation only if *each* δ_l is small. For potentials of short range usually all the δ_l are small except for the lowest few values of l. In such cases one can obtain a good and fairly simple approximation by evaluating δ_l exactly for the lowest few values of l and using the BORN approximation for all larger values of l. Making use of the relation between (7.11) and (7.12) one then obtains for $f(\vartheta)$ the expression (7.11) plus a series of a few terms, which involve $(e^{2i\delta_l}-1-2i\,\delta_l^{(B)})$.

For the special case of a COULOMB potential, the BORN approximation formula (7.11) for the scattering amplitude $f(\vartheta)$ gives the expression (7.7a). This expression differs from the exact one, (7.7), only by a phase factor which is small at high enough energies and reasonably large angles $\left(k\gg Z\,|\log(1-\cos\vartheta)|\right)$. On the other hand, the BORN approximation (7.12) for the partial wave phase shift δ_l is *not* useful for a COULOMB potential. In view of the logarithmic term in the asymptotic expression (4.10), the concept of a phase shift is somewhat ambiguous: Consider a screened COULOMB potential, e.g. $V(r)=-Z/r$ for $r<R_0$, $V=0$ for $r>R_0$, where $kR_0\gg 1$. The phase shift is then given approximately by $\delta_l=(n'\log 2kR_0-\sigma_l)$ for $l<kR_0$. Even for small $n'=Z/k$, the first term in this expression is large compared with σ_l. It should be noted that for a weak attractive potential of short range the scattering amplitude $f(\vartheta)$ and the S-state phase shift δ_0 are positive and that δ_l decreases with increasing l. This is still true for a screened COULOMB potential for large k/Z, even though $(-\sigma_l)$, Eq. (4.10), is *negative* (σ_l is positive and increases with increasing l, $\delta_l=C-\sigma_l$ is positive and decreases with increasing l for $l<kR_0$. For $l>kR_0$, the phase shift δ_l depends on the details of the screening).

8. Wave functions in momentum space. Discrete spectrum. The wave function in momentum space, $\psi(\boldsymbol{p})$, is defined as the FOURIER transform of the ordinary "position space" wave function, $u(\boldsymbol{r})$. We shall use atomic units for momentum (see Introduction), the unit being the BOHR momentum, $p_0=mv_0=\hbar/a$. Explicitly, we have

$$\left.\begin{aligned}\psi(\boldsymbol{p}) &= (2\pi)^{-\frac{3}{2}}\int d^3r\,e^{-i\boldsymbol{r}\cdot\boldsymbol{p}}\,u(\boldsymbol{r})\,,\\ u(\boldsymbol{r}) &= (2\pi)^{-\frac{3}{2}}\int d^3r\,e^{i\boldsymbol{r}\cdot\boldsymbol{p}}\,\psi(\boldsymbol{p})\,.\end{aligned}\right\}\tag{8.1}$$

The wave function $\psi(\boldsymbol{p})$ satisfies the normalization condition

$$\int d^3p\,|\psi(\boldsymbol{p})|^2=1\,,\tag{8.2}$$

if $u(\boldsymbol{r})$ is normalized to unity.

Instead of first solving the SCHRÖDINGER equation in position space for $u(\boldsymbol{r})$ and then evaluating the FOURIER transform (8.1), it is often more convenient to rewrite the SCHRÖDINGER equation as an equation involving $\psi(\boldsymbol{p})$ directly. One possible method would be to use a representation of the quantum mechanical operators in which x is replaced by $i\,\partial/\partial p_x$, etc. The SCHRÖDINGER equation would then take the form of a differential equation in momentum space. Since one usually deals with potentials which depend on $\boldsymbol{r}$, but not on $\boldsymbol{p}$, such an equation usually is not easy to handle[1]. A more convenient approach[2] involves rewriting the SCHRÖDINGER equation in the form of an *integral* equation in momentum space.

[1] This method has, however, been used to obtain the momentum space wave functions for the discrete spectrum of hydrogen, E. A. HYLLERAAS, Z. Physik **74**, 216 (1932).

[2] H. WEYL: Z. Physik **46**, 1 (1928). — V. FOCK: Z. Physik **98**, 145 (1935).

Let $V(\boldsymbol{r})$ be an arbitrary potential in position space and $V'(\boldsymbol{p})$ its FOURIER transform [multiplied by $(2\pi)^{-\frac{3}{2}}$],

$$V'(\boldsymbol{p}) = (2\pi)^{-3} \int d^3r\, e^{-i\boldsymbol{r}\cdot\boldsymbol{p}}\, V(\boldsymbol{r}),$$
$$V(\boldsymbol{r}) = \int d^3p\, e^{i\boldsymbol{r}\cdot\boldsymbol{p}}\, V'(\boldsymbol{p}).$$

Let $u(\boldsymbol{r})$ and $\psi(\boldsymbol{p})$ be the wave function in position space and the momentum space, respectively, for an electron in this potential in a (bound) state of the discrete spectrum. By taking the FOURIER transform of the ordinary SCHRÖDINGER wave equation for $u(\boldsymbol{r})$ in position space, one obtains an integral equation for $\psi(\boldsymbol{p})$. For a state of negative energy E this equation is (in atomic units)

$$(p^2 - 2E)\,\psi(\boldsymbol{p}) = -2 \int d^3p'\, \psi(\boldsymbol{p}')\, V'(\boldsymbol{p}-\boldsymbol{p}'). \tag{8.3}$$

We are restricting ourselves to the case of "ordinary spatial potentials", which are represented in position space by a "local operator" $V(\boldsymbol{r})$, which simply multiplies the wave function $u(\boldsymbol{r})$ at each point $\boldsymbol{r}$ by a number $V(\boldsymbol{r})$. For such potentials the kernel of the integral equation (8.3), $V'(p-p')$, is a function of a *single* vector variable $(\boldsymbol{p}-\boldsymbol{p}')$. In some problems, such as in meson field theory and in the calculation of radiative corrections (see Sect. 19 and 28), more general types of "potentials" occur. These "velocity dependent" or "non-local" potentials are represented in position space by integral and/or differential operators. In many cases, however, these generalized potentials still lead to integral equations in momentum space for $\psi(\boldsymbol{p})$ of form (8.3), but $V'(\boldsymbol{p}-\boldsymbol{p}')$ is replaced by a kernel $K(\boldsymbol{p},\boldsymbol{p}')$ which depends on *two* vector variables, $\boldsymbol{p}$ and $\boldsymbol{p}'$. We shall not consider such velocity dependent potentials further.

The potential operator ordinarily is HERMITian and $V(\boldsymbol{r})$ is real. In this case one can show[1] that $V'(\boldsymbol{q}) = V'^*(-\boldsymbol{q})$. If, further, the potential $V(\boldsymbol{r})$ is a central one (function of the radial distance r only), then the "momentum space potential" $V'(\boldsymbol{p})$ is a function of the absolute value of $\boldsymbol{p}$ only and is real.

For a central potential $V'(p)$, the "wave equation" (8.3) is separable in spherical polar coordinates. If (p, ϑ, φ) are the polar coordinates of the momentum $\boldsymbol{p}$, solutions exist of the form

$$\psi_{lm}(\boldsymbol{p}) = F_l(p)\, Y_{lm}(\vartheta,\varphi). \tag{8.4}$$

In this case (8.3) can be reduced, at least in principle, to a one-dimensional integral equation for $F_l(p)$ of form

$$\left.\begin{aligned}
(p^2 - 2E)\,F_l(p) &= -\lambda \int_0^\infty dp'\, p'^2\, K_l(p,p')\, F_l(p');\\
\lambda K_l(p,p') &= 4\pi \int_{-1}^{1} dx\, V'\!\left(\sqrt{p^2+p'^2-2pp'x}\right) P_l(x).
\end{aligned}\right\} \tag{8.5}$$

The kernel K_l is symmetric in p and p' and depends on the value of l and on the *shape* of the potential $V(r)$. For convenience, the *strength* of the potential is contained in the multiplying factor λ. For mathematical purposes it is often convenient to consider the energy E as given and λ, the "potential strength parameter", as the eigenvalue to be determined. The integral equation (8.5) can be solved exactly only for a few specially simple potential shapes. For other potential shapes some approximation methods, notably iteration and variational methods,

[1] More generally, let $f(\boldsymbol{r})$ and $g(\boldsymbol{r})$ be two functions, which are complex conjugates of each other, $f^*(\boldsymbol{r}) = g(\boldsymbol{r})$. If $F(\boldsymbol{p})$ and $G(\boldsymbol{p})$ are the FOURIER transforms of f and g, respectively, one finds that $F^*(\boldsymbol{p}) = G(-\boldsymbol{p})$.

are available, but these procedures usually give good results only for the ground state and, possibly, for low excited states[1].

The expression $|p F_l(p)|^2$ is called the momentum distribution function. The probability for the absolute value of the momentum of the electron (irrespective of direction) to lie between p and $p+dp$ is $|p F_l(p)|^2\, dp$.

We return now to the special case of a COULOMB potential, $V(r) = -Z/r$. The momentum space potential is then

$$V'(p) = -\frac{Z}{2\pi^2 p^2}\,. \tag{8.6a}$$

The singularity of $V'(p)$ at $p=0$ is a characteristic of the "infinite range" of the COULOMB potential. Consider, for instance, a "screened COULOMB potential" $V(r)$ which deviates appreciably from the COULOMB potential only at *large* distances and falls off more rapidly for $r \gg R_0$, say. $V'(p)$ for such a potential deviates from the COULOMB expression only for *small* momenta and remains finite and practically constant for $p R_0 \ll 1$. For a potential of YUKAWA shape, for instance, we have

$$V(r) = -\frac{Z}{r}\, e^{-r/R_0}, \qquad V'(p) = -\frac{Z}{2\pi^2 (p^2 + R_0^{-2})}\,. \tag{8.6b}$$

To avoid ambiguities arising from the singularity of (8.6a) it is sometimes convenient to consider it as the limiting case of (8.6b) and to proceed to the limit only after integrations, etc., have been carried out.

Substituting the unscreened COULOMB potential (8.6a) into (8.3), this three-dimensional integral equation then is

$$(p^2 - 2E)\, \psi(\boldsymbol{p}) = \frac{Z}{\pi^2} \int d^3 p\, \frac{\psi(\boldsymbol{p}')}{|\boldsymbol{p} - \boldsymbol{p}'|^2}\,. \tag{8.6}$$

(8.6) has "partial wave" solutions of form (8.4) and the radial wave function $F_l(p)$ satisfies a one-dimensional integral equation of form (8.5). Using the addition theorem of the spherical harmonics and the orthogonality properties of the LEGENDRE polynomials, the kernel K_l in (8.5) can be evaluated explicity. (8.5) then reduces to

$$(p^2 - 2E)\, F_l(p) = \frac{2Z}{\pi p} \int_0^\infty dp'\, p'\, Q_l\!\left(\frac{p^2 + p'^2}{2 p p'}\right) F_l(p') \tag{8.7}$$

where Q_l is a LEGENDRE function of the second kind[2], related to the unnormalized LEGENDRE function of the first kind, P_l, by

$$Q_l(z) = \frac{1}{2} \int_{-1}^{1} dt\, \frac{P_l(t)}{z - t}\,.$$

For negative values of E, (8.7) has solutions, $F_{nl}(p)$, for a discrete spectrum of energy eigenvalues E_n. The spectrum E_n is, of course, identical with that obtained by solving (Sect. 2) the SCHRÖDINGER differential wave equation in position space (n is again the principal quantum number). The radial momentum space wave function $F_{nl}(p)$ depends on n and the orbital quantum number

[1] N. SVARTHOLM: Thesis, Lund 1945. — R. MCWEENY and C. A. COULSON: Proc. Phys. Soc. Lond. A **62**, 509 (1949). — M. LÉVY: Proc. Roy. Soc. Lond. **204**, 145 (1950). — E. E. SALPETER: Phys. Rev. **84**, 1226 (1951).

[2] See, for instance, JAHNKE and EMDE, Funktionentafeln, 4th Ed., p. 109. Berlin: Springer 1945.

$l\,(l \lesseqgtr n-1)$ but not on the magnetic quantum number m. The Eq. (8.7) has been solved directly by FOCK[1]. The wave functions $F_{nl}(p)\,Y_{lm}$ had been obtained previously[2] by carrying out the FOURIER transformation on the position space wave functions (Sect. 3).

The explicit expressions for the radial momentum space wave functions $F_{nl}(p)$ for a COULOMB potential follow. We give the wave functions for hydrogen $(Z=1)$, normalized such that

$$\int_0^\infty dp\, p^2\, |F_{nl}(p)|^2 = 1$$

and p is expressed in atomic units[3] $(p_0 = \hbar/a)$

$$F_{nl}(p) = \left[\frac{2}{\pi}\,\frac{(n-l-1)!}{(n+l)!}\right]^{\frac{1}{2}} n^2\, 2^{2(l+1)}\, l!\, \frac{n^l p^l}{(n^2p^2+1)^{l+2}}\, C_{n-l-1}^{l+1}\left(\frac{n^2p^2-1}{n^2p^2+1}\right), \tag{8.8}$$

where $C_N^\nu(x)$ is the GEGENBAUER function, defined as the coefficient of h^N in the expansion of $(1-2hx+h^2)^{-\nu}$ in powers of h. Recurrence formulae for C_N^ν will be found in [8], p. 329. The explicit expressions for C_N^ν for a few values of N are

$$\left.\begin{aligned} &C_0^\nu(x) = 1, \quad C_1^\nu(x) = 2\nu x, \\ &C_2^\nu(x) = 2\nu(\nu+1)\,x^2 - \nu. \end{aligned}\right\} \tag{8.9}$$

The first three radial wave functions $F_{nl}(p)$ are

$$\left.\begin{aligned} F_{10} &= 4\sqrt{\frac{2}{\pi}}\,\frac{1}{(p^2+1)^2}, \\ F_{20} &= \frac{32}{\sqrt{\pi}}\,\frac{4p^2-1}{(4p^2+1)^3}, \\ F_{21} &= \frac{128}{\sqrt{3\pi}}\,\frac{p}{(4p^2+1)^3}. \end{aligned}\right\} \tag{8.10}$$

The expressions (8.8) simplify if $np \ll 1$ or $np \gg 1$: For $np=0$, the argument of the GEGENBAUER function C is -1, for $np=\infty$ the argument is $+1$, and

$$C_N^\nu(1) = (-1)^N\, C_N^\nu(-1) = \frac{(2\nu+N-1)!}{(2\nu-1)!\,N!}.$$

For $l=0$ and 1, for instance, the radial functions approach the following values as $np \to \infty$

$$F_{n0}(p) = \sqrt{\frac{2}{n^3\pi}}\,\frac{4}{p^4}, \qquad F_{n1}(p) = \sqrt{\frac{2(n^2-1)}{n^5\pi}}\,\frac{8}{3p^5}. \tag{8.11}$$

More generally we have, as $np \to \infty$,

$$F_{nl}(p) \to 4\,\frac{2^{2l}\,l!}{(2l+1)!}\sqrt{\frac{2}{n^3\pi}}\left(\prod_{s=0}^{l}\sqrt{1-\frac{s^2}{n^2}}\right)\frac{1}{p^{4+l}}. \tag{8.12}$$

The ratio of two radial functions with the same value of l, but different values of n, is thus independent of p for large values of p. As np approaches zero, the radial function F_{nl} approaches zero for all non-zero values of l. For $l=0$ (S-states) it approaches

$$F_{n0}(0) = (-1)^{n-1}\,4n^3\sqrt{\frac{2}{n\pi}}. \tag{8.13}$$

---

[1] V. FOCK: Z. Physik **98**, 145 (1935).

[2] B. PODOLANSKI and L. PAULING: Phys. Rev. **34**, 109 (1929).

[3] The expressions for arbitrary nuclear charge Z are *identical* with those for hydrogen if p is expressed in units of (Zp_0).

The momentum space wave function at $p=0$ is $(2\pi)^{-\frac{3}{2}}$ times the volume integral of the position space wave function $u(\boldsymbol{r})$.

Using the known properties of the GEGENBAUER functions, one can evaluate the expectation value of the square of the momentum. It is

$$\overline{p^2} = \int_0^\infty dp\, p^2\, |F_{nl}(p)|^2\, p^2 = (Z\, p_0/n)^2, \tag{8.14}$$

where p_0 is the BOHR momentum for hydrogen ($\overline{p^2}$ for general nuclear charge Z). This relation could also have been derived from the virial theorem, (3.29), from which it follows that the expectation value of the kinetic energy $(p^2/2m)$ equals minus the total energy E.

9. Wave functions in momentum space. Continuous spectrum[1]. *α) General theory.* For positive total energy E the treatment of the integral equation (8.3) for the wave function in momentum space has to be modified. This is due to the fact that the left hand side of (8.3) vanishes if $|\boldsymbol{p}| = \sqrt{2E}$ and remains unchanged if any function is added to $\psi(\boldsymbol{p})$ on the left side, which is non-zero only for $p=\sqrt{2E}$. Before discussing (8.3), an equation in the explicit momentum space representation, we shall note some more general results.

We consider the equation of state for an eigenstate ψ of a HAMILTONian H which consists of two parts. Written in symbolic operator notation this equation is

$$(E-H)\,\psi = 0, \qquad H = H_0 + V,$$

where both H_0 and V are HERMITian. We assume that H_0 has a continuous spectrum of eigenstates, which we consider as known, and that E coincides with one of the eigenvalues in this spectrum. Let u_0 be *any* eigenstate of H_0 with energy eigenvalue E. We can then write ψ in the form

$$\psi = u_0 + \chi, \qquad (E - H_0)\, u_0 = 0,$$

where χ satisfies the equation

$$(E - H_0 - V)\,\chi - V\, u_0 = 0. \tag{9.1}$$

If we want to multiply Eq. (9.1) by the inverse operator of either $(E - H_0)$ or $(E-H)$ the resulting equations would not be well-determined unless we give an explicit prescription for handling the singularity of the "energy denominator". Two possible prescriptions are to add a positive or negative infinitesimally small quantity $\pm i\,\varepsilon$ to E in (9.1). We denote the eigenstates ψ, defined by these prescriptions, by $\psi_\pm = u_0 + \chi_\pm$. The modified Eq. (9.1) can then be rewritten in either of two forms,

$$\chi_\pm = \frac{1}{(E - H \pm i\,\varepsilon)}\, V u_0 \tag{9.2}$$

or

$$\chi_\pm = \frac{1}{(E - H_0 \pm i\,\varepsilon)}\, V(u_0 + \chi_\pm)\,. \tag{9.3$^\pm$}$$

We can now show that there is one unique state ψ_+ (and ψ_-) corresponding to *each* eigenstate u_0 of H_0: Consider $(V u_0)$ expanded in terms of some complete set of eigenstates of the *total* HAMILTONian H. Since H is HERMITian, all its eigenvalues are real and hence the energy denominator in (9.2) can never vanish and $\chi_\pm$ is, therefore, determined uniquely. For many practical problems Eq. (9.2)

---

[1] B. A. LIPPMANN and J. SCHWINGER: Phys. Rev. **79**, 469 (1950). — M. L. GOLDBERGER: Phys. Rev. **82**, 757; **84**, 929 (1951). — E. E. SALPETER: Phys. Rev. **84**, 1226 (1951).

is not a suitable starting point, since the denominator contains H, the *total* HAMILTONian[1]. We shall use, instead, Eq. (9.3) and expand $\chi_\pm$ as well as $V(u_0+\chi_\pm)$ in terms of a complete set of eigenstates of H_0. Since H_0 is HERMITian, its eigenvalues are real and the denominator in (9.3) also cannot vanish. (9.3) can then be reduced to an explicit inhomogeneous integral equation for the expansion coefficient of $\chi_\pm$, with the expansion coefficient of Vu_0 providing the inhomogeneous term. In Sects. 9β and 9γ we shall consider the special case of $H_0=p^2/2m$, the kinetic energy operator, with V standing for an ordinary potential. In Sect. 9β we shall further specialize the complete set of eigenfunctions of H_0 to the set of all "plane wave" states of a free electron. The expansion coefficients of $\chi_\pm$ then reduce to the momentum space wave functions.

The prescriptions used in (9.3) are, of course, not the only possible ones for handling the singularity of $(E-H_0)^{-1}$. One other prescription is to use the principal value $\mathscr{P}$ of this denominator. To show the connection between the various prescriptions we first define two functions by

$$\mathscr{P}\left(\frac{1}{y}\right)=\frac{y}{y^2+\varepsilon^2}, \qquad \delta(y)=\frac{1}{\pi}\,\frac{\varepsilon}{y^2+\varepsilon^2} \tag{9.4}$$

where ε is an infinitesimally small real and positive quantity. We then have the relations

$$\left.\begin{aligned}\mathscr{P}\left(\frac{1}{y}\right)&=\frac{1}{2}\left(\frac{1}{y-i\varepsilon}+\frac{1}{y+i\varepsilon}\right),\\ \delta(y)&=\frac{1}{2\pi i}\left(\frac{1}{y-i\varepsilon}-\frac{1}{y+i\varepsilon}\right).\end{aligned}\right\} \tag{9.5}$$

The functions defined in (9.4) represent the principal value of y^{-1} and the DIRAC delta-function, respectively, in the following sense: If y is finite, then $\mathscr{P}(1/y)$ and $\delta(y)$ tend to y^{-1} and zero, respectively, as ε tends to zero. Further, if $f(y)$ is a function which is continuous at the origin but otherwise arbitrary and a and b are positive constants, we have

$$\int_{-a}^{b} dy\,\mathscr{P}\left(\frac{1}{y}\right)f(y)\rightarrow\mathscr{P}\int_{-a}^{b}\frac{dy}{y}f(y), \qquad \int_{-a}^{b} dy\,\delta(y)\,f(y)\rightarrow f(0)$$

where the arrows indicate the limiting expressions as ε tends to zero. For any particular eigenstate u_0 of H_0 we can then define a unique eigenstate $\psi_{(1)}$ of H by the following equation [instead of (9.3$^\pm$)]

$$\psi_{(1)}=u_0+\chi_{(1)}; \qquad \chi_{(1)}=\mathscr{P}\left(\frac{1}{E-H_0}\right)V\psi_{(1)}. \tag{9.3a}$$

This principal value prescription is particularly useful in discussing the "partial wave" solutions. As will be shown in Sect. 9γ, it results in wave functions which behave asymptotically like *standing* spherical waves.

We have now given three different prescriptions for defining particular eigenstates ψ_+, ψ_- and $\psi_{(1)}$ of H, which correspond to a *particular* eigenstate u_0 of H_0. The states ψ_+, ψ_- and $\psi_{(1)}$, corresponding to the *same* state u_0, differ from each other in general. It should be noted, however, that the set of states ψ_+, which corresponds to a complete set of eigenstates u_0 of H_0, is by itself a complete[2] set of eigenstates of H. An example of such a set of states was discussed in Sect. 6γ with $H_0=p^2/2m$ and V equal to the COULOMB potential. There each u_0 represented

[1] Eq. (9.2) has been used recently, however, as the starting point of calculations in meson field theory. See, e.g., G. F. CHEW and F. E. LOW, Phys. Rev. **101**, 1570 (1956).

[2] Actually, the bound states must be included to complete the set.

a plane wave and the corresponding ψ_+ that plane wave plus outgoing spherical waves, scattered by the potential. (6.25) is the position space wave function for such a state and its momentum space wave function will be discussed in Sect. 9β, (9.12). Quite generally, *each* of the sets of states ψ_+, ψ_-, and $\psi_{(1)}$, corresponding to a set u_0, forms an *alternative* complete set of eigenstates of H.

Further, definite relations exist between the various states ψ_+, ψ_- and $\psi_{(1)}$, all belonging to the *same* energy eigenvalue E. First, any state ψ_+ of energy E can be written as a linear superposition of states ψ_- (or $\psi_{(1)}$), all of the same energy E. Second, for any eigenstate u of H_0 we can find another eigenstate u' of H_0 with the *same* energy eigenvalue, such that ψ_+ corresponding to u is *identical* with $\psi_{(1)}$ (or ψ_-) corresponding to u'. This can be seen as follows. Let $\psi_+[u]$ be a particular solution of (9.3$^\pm$),

$$\psi_+[u] = u + \frac{1}{E - H_0 + i\varepsilon} V \psi_+[u].$$

With the help of (9.5) we can rewrite this equation in the form

$$\psi_+[u] = u' + \mathscr{P}\left(\frac{1}{E - H_0}\right) V \psi_+[u],$$

where

$$u' = u - \pi i \, \delta(E - H_0) \, V \psi_+[u].$$

Consider $V\psi_+[u]$ expanded in terms of eigenstates of H_0. The presence of the delta-function $\delta(E - H_0)$ then ensures that u' is some eigenstate of H_0 which belongs to the same energy eigenvalue E. We see then that the solution $\psi_+[u]$ of (9.3$^\pm$) corresponding to u is identical with the solution $\psi_{(1)}[u']$ of (9.3a) corresponding to the eigenstate u' of H_0. Similarly one finds that $\psi_+[u]$ is identical with $\psi_-[u'']$, where

$$u'' = u - 2\pi i \, \delta(E - H_0) \, V \psi_+[u],$$

and so on.

β) Plane wave solutions. We return now to our explicit momentum space representation for a single particle moving in an "ordinary" potential $V(\boldsymbol{r})$ with FOURIER transform $V'(\boldsymbol{p})$. We can obtain from the general theory of Sect. 9α an integral equation analogous to (8.3) in the following manner. We take for H_0 the kinetic energy operator $p^2/2m$. The "plane wave" states of the particle form a complete set of eigenstates of the momentum operator, and hence also of H_0. We can then consider the momentum space wave function $\psi(\boldsymbol{p})$ of an eigenstate of the total HAMILTONian H as the expansion coefficient of this state in terms of the plane wave states. To define a definite eigenstate ψ of the total HAMILTONian, we must still choose one of the prescriptions (9.3$^\pm$) or (9.3a) and a particular eigenstate u_0 of H_0 with positive energy eigenvalue E. We discuss first the equation for a state ψ_+ obtained from (9.3$^+$) with u_0 chosen as a *single* plane wave with momentum $\boldsymbol{k}$.

We use again atomic units and consider a definite momentum $\boldsymbol{k}$ with $k^2 = 2E$. Except for a normalization factor, the momentum space wave function of a plane wave state of this momentum is the three-dimensional DIRAC delta-function $\delta^{(3)}(\boldsymbol{p} - \boldsymbol{k})$. Expanding both sides of the Eq. (9.3$^+$) in terms of plane waves and considering the expansion coefficient for momentum $\boldsymbol{p}$, we obtain the equation

$$\left.\begin{aligned} \psi_+(\boldsymbol{p}) &= \delta^{(3)}(\boldsymbol{p} - \boldsymbol{k}) + \chi_+(\boldsymbol{p}), \\ \chi_+(\boldsymbol{p}) &= \frac{2}{(k + i\varepsilon)^2 - p^2} \int d^3p' \, \psi_+(\boldsymbol{p}') \, V'(\boldsymbol{p} - \boldsymbol{p}'). \end{aligned}\right\} \tag{9.6}$$

(9.6) is an integral equation for the momentum space wave function $\psi_+(\boldsymbol{p})$ in analogy with (8.3) for the discrete spectrum, but differs from it in the presence of the delta-function as an inhomogeneous term and in the presence of the infinitesimal positive imaginary part $i\varepsilon$. The prescription (9.3⁻) with the same plane wave for u_0 leads to a similar equation for $\psi_-(\boldsymbol{p})$, the momentum space wave function for the state ψ_-. This equation for $\psi_-(\boldsymbol{p})$ or $\chi_-(\boldsymbol{p})$ is identical with (9.6) except that $(k+i\varepsilon)$ is replaced by $(k-i\varepsilon)$. For a central potential, $V'(\boldsymbol{p})$ is a real function and hence $\psi_-(\boldsymbol{p})$ is the complex conjugate of $\psi_+(\boldsymbol{p})$, $\chi_-(\boldsymbol{p})$ that of $\chi_+(\boldsymbol{p})$. Finally, the prescription (9.3a) gives an equation for $\psi_{(1)}(\boldsymbol{p})$ which is again identical with (9.6) except that $[(k+i\varepsilon)^2-p^2]^{-1}$ is replaced by the principal value of $(k^2-p^2)^{-1}$.

(9.6) can also be rewritten in terms of a function $f_+(\boldsymbol{p})$ as follows

$$\left.\begin{aligned} \psi_\pm(\boldsymbol{p}) - \delta^{(3)}(\boldsymbol{p}-\boldsymbol{k}) \equiv \chi_\pm(\boldsymbol{p}) &= -\frac{f_\pm(\boldsymbol{p})}{2\pi^2(k\pm i\varepsilon-p)(k+p)}, \\ f_\pm(\boldsymbol{p}) &= -(2\pi)^2\left[V'(\boldsymbol{p}-\boldsymbol{k}) + \int d^3p'\,\chi_\pm(\boldsymbol{p}')\,V'(\boldsymbol{p}-\boldsymbol{p}')\right]. \end{aligned}\right\} \tag{9.7}$$

In (9.7) the positive subscripts refer to (9.6), the negative subscripts to the analogous equation for ψ_-. The function $f_+(\boldsymbol{p})$ [and $f_-(\boldsymbol{p})$], unlike $\psi_+(\boldsymbol{p})$ and $\chi_+(\boldsymbol{p})$, in general[1] has *no* singularity for $|\boldsymbol{p}|=k$. We shall see, in fact, that the values of $f_+(\boldsymbol{p})$ for $|\boldsymbol{p}|=k$ ("on the energy shell") are related to the scattering amplitude $f(\vartheta)$, discussed in Sect. 7. To show this we consider next the asymptotic forms of the (position) spatial wave functions corresponding to $\psi_+(\boldsymbol{p})$ and $\psi_-(\boldsymbol{p})$.

For the moment we consider (9.6) or (9.7) as solved (we discuss methods of solution later) and hence $f_+(\boldsymbol{p})$ and $f_-(\boldsymbol{p})$ as known. We shall assume further that $f_\pm(\boldsymbol{p})$ is a smoothly varying function without singularities. To obtain the spatial wave function we have to evaluate the Fourier transform of $\psi_\pm(\boldsymbol{p})$. We shall need the integral

$$\mathcal{J}_\pm(\boldsymbol{r}) = \int \frac{d^3p\, e^{i\boldsymbol{r}\cdot\boldsymbol{p}}\, f_\pm(\boldsymbol{p})}{(k\pm i\varepsilon-p)(k+p)} = \int_0^\infty \frac{dp\,p^2}{(k\pm i\varepsilon-p)(k+p)} \int_0^{2\pi} d\varphi \int_{-1}^{1} dx\, e^{irpx} f_\pm(p,x,\varphi), \tag{9.8}$$

where we have used spherical polar coordinates for $\boldsymbol{p}$ with the vector $\boldsymbol{r}$ as axis and x is the cosine of the angle between $\boldsymbol{r}$ and $\boldsymbol{p}$. We are mainly interested in the asymptotic form of $\mathcal{J}_\pm(\boldsymbol{r})$, i.e. the limit as $kr\to\infty$. We can then carry out the integration over x first, using the relation

$$\int_{-1}^{1} dx\, e^{irpx} f(x) \approx \frac{1}{irp}\left[e^{irp} f(1) - e^{-irp} f(-1)\right].$$

This relation, obtained by integrating by parts, is true for any $f(x)$ without singularities in the limit of $pr\to\infty$ and is also exact for all pr if $f(x)$ is a constant. We substitute this relation into (9.8) and carry out the integration over φ by noting that, if a function $f(\boldsymbol{p}) = f(p,x,\varphi)$ is single-valued and well-behaved, then $f(p,\pm 1,\varphi)$ is independent of φ. Denoting this function by $f(p,\pm 1)$, the asymptotic expression for $\mathcal{J}_\pm(\boldsymbol{r})$ reduces to a one-dimensional integral,

$$\mathcal{J}_\pm(\boldsymbol{r}) = \frac{2\pi}{ir}\int_0^\infty \frac{dp\,p}{(k\pm i\varepsilon-p)(k+p)}\left[e^{irp} f_\pm(p,1) - e^{-irp} f_\pm(p,-1)\right].$$

Next we change the variable of integration from p to $-p$ in the second term in this integral. The function f occuring in either part of the transformed integral

[1] For a Coulomb potential, f_+ still has a singularity at $\boldsymbol{p}=\boldsymbol{k}$.

is then of form $f(\boldsymbol{r}p/r)$, the value of the function $f(\boldsymbol{p})$ for a vector $\boldsymbol{p}$ which has absolute magnitude $|\boldsymbol{p}|$ and the direction of $\boldsymbol{r}$ if p is positive, of $-\boldsymbol{r}$ if p is negative. Finally we can convert this integral into a contour integral by adding a "semi-circle at infinity" in the upper-half complex plane, which gives a vanishingly small contribution to the integral. The position of the poles, which are different for $\mathscr{I}_+$ and $\mathscr{I}_-$, as well as the contour C are shown in Fig. 9. Evaluating this contour integral, we find

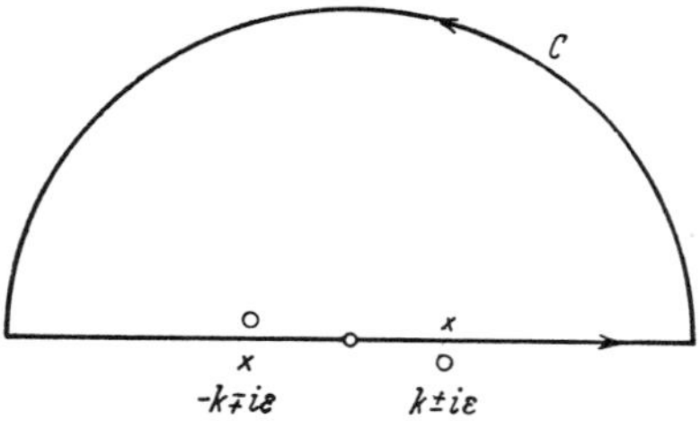

Fig. 9. The integration contour C for the integral occuring in Eq. (9.9). The first order poles for the integral $\mathscr{I}_+$ are marked by crosses, those for $\mathscr{I}_-$ by circles.

$$\left.\begin{aligned}\mathscr{I}_\pm(\boldsymbol{r}) &= \frac{2\pi}{i\,r}\oint_C \frac{dp\,p\,f_\pm(\boldsymbol{r}p/r)\,e^{irp}}{(k^2-p^2)}\\ &= -\,2\pi^2 f_\pm\left(\pm\frac{\boldsymbol{r}k}{r}\right)\frac{e^{\pm irk}}{r}.\end{aligned}\right\} \quad (9.9)$$

The expression (9.9) holds only asymptotically as $kr\to\infty$ in general, but is exact if $f_\pm$ is a constant.

Using (9.9) we obtain the asymptotic forms of the spatial wave functions $u_\pm(\boldsymbol{r})$, which are the Fourier-transforms [multiplied by $(2\pi)^{\frac{3}{2}}$] of $\psi_+(\boldsymbol{p})$ and $\psi_-(\boldsymbol{p})$,

$$\left.\begin{aligned}u_+(\boldsymbol{r}) &\equiv \int d^3p\, e^{i\boldsymbol{r}\cdot\boldsymbol{p}}\,\psi_+(\boldsymbol{p}) = e^{i\boldsymbol{k}\cdot\boldsymbol{r}} + f_+\left(\frac{\boldsymbol{r}k}{r}\right)\frac{e^{ikr}}{r},\\ u_-(\boldsymbol{r}) &= e^{i\boldsymbol{k}\cdot\boldsymbol{r}} + f_-\left(-\frac{\boldsymbol{r}k}{r}\right)\frac{e^{-ikr}}{r}.\end{aligned}\right\} \quad (9.10)$$

The first part of the asymptotic expression (9.10) for both $u_+(\boldsymbol{r})$ and $u_-(\boldsymbol{r})$ represents an unperturbed plane wave with momentum $\boldsymbol{k}$. The second part of u_+ represents a spherical outgoing wave, the effect of the scattering by the potential of the incident plane wave. The angular distribution of the scattering is determined by $f_+(\boldsymbol{r}k/r)$, called the scattering amplitude. Note that the amplitude for scattering into any direction is determined completely by the value of the function $f_+(\boldsymbol{p})$, Eq. (9.7), "on the energy-shell" i.e. for a vector $\boldsymbol{p}$ pointing in this direction, but of absolute magnitude k. For the special case of a central potential, the scattering amplitude $f_+(\boldsymbol{r}k/r)$ depends only on the angle ϑ between the scattering direction ($\boldsymbol{r}$) and $\boldsymbol{k}$. In this case $f_+(\boldsymbol{r}k/r)$ is identical with the function $f(\vartheta)$, Eq. (7.3).

The wave function $u_-(\boldsymbol{r})$, on the other hand, represents a state in which spherically incoming waves are incident on the potential with phase and amplitude relations such that the result of the scattering is a single plane wave of momentum $\boldsymbol{k}$. For the special case of a central potential, $f_-(\boldsymbol{p}) = f_+^*(\boldsymbol{p})$. In this case the spatial wave function u_+ corresponding to an incident plane wave with momentum $\boldsymbol{k}$ is the complex conjugate of the function u_- corresponding to an emergent plane wave with momentum *minus* $\boldsymbol{k}$. Our third prescription, involving the "principal value" Eq. (9.3a), is not of general use in connection with "plane wave" solutions.

For most forms of the potential function V', no exact solutions of the integral Eq. (9.6) or (9.7) are available at present. (9.7) differs from (8.3), the equation for negative energy E, by being an inhomogeneous integral equation. There is no eigenvalue to be determined but, once the inhomogeneous term $V'(\boldsymbol{p}-\boldsymbol{k})$ is given, the solution of (9.7) gives uniquely not only the shape of the function $\chi_+(\boldsymbol{p})$, but also its absolute value for all $\boldsymbol{p}$. For a weak enough potential one can use the following simple perturbation method, equivalent to the Born approximation which was discussed in Sect. 7: If V' contains a *small* multiplicative factor λ, then χ_+ and f_+ will be approximately linear in λ and the integral on the right side of (9.7) approximately quadratic in λ. First order BORN approximation consists in simply omitting the integral on the right side of (9.7),

$$f_{\pm}^{(B)}(\boldsymbol{p}) = -(2\pi)^2 V'(\boldsymbol{p}-\boldsymbol{k}). \tag{9.11}$$

As discussed before, the differential scattering cross section $|f(\vartheta)|^2$ is determined completely by the value of $f_+(\boldsymbol{p})$ "on the energy shell", i.e. for $|\boldsymbol{p}|=k$. For a central potential, the expression (9.11) on the energy shell, $-(2\pi)^2 V'(2k\sin\frac{1}{2}\vartheta)$, is identical with our previous BORN approximation expression (7.11) (ϑ is the angle between $\boldsymbol{p}$ and $\boldsymbol{k}$). (9.11) and the first line of (9.7) also give $\chi_+^{(B)}(\boldsymbol{p})$ "off the energy shell" (for general $\boldsymbol{p}$) and one could obtain second order BORN approximation (accurate to order λ^2) by substituting $\chi_+^{(B)}(\boldsymbol{p})$ into the integral on the right side of (9.7).

For the special case of the COULOMB potential an exact FOURIER transform of (6.20), the spatial COULOMB wave function representing a plane wave plus scattered outgoing waves, has been obtained by GUTH and MULLIN[1]. This momentum space wave function, analogous to $\psi_+(\boldsymbol{p})$ defined above, is

$$\psi_+(\boldsymbol{p}) = -\frac{1}{2\pi^2}\lim_{\varepsilon\to 0}\frac{d}{d\varepsilon}\left\{\frac{[p^2-(k+i\varepsilon)^2]^{-in'}}{[(\boldsymbol{p}-\boldsymbol{k})^2+\varepsilon^2]^{1-in'}}\right\}, \tag{9.12}$$

where $n' = +Z/k = Ze^2/\hbar v$ and ε is real and positive. This expression takes on an even simpler form if we carry out the differentiation of the numerator and denominator of (9.12) and, in each of these two terms, retain only the leading term in an expansion in powers of n'. Using the relation

$$\delta^{(3)}(\boldsymbol{y}) = \frac{1}{\pi^2}\lim_{\varepsilon\to 0}\frac{\varepsilon}{(y^2+\varepsilon^2)^2},$$

this approximation to (9.12), for $n' \ll 1$, is

$$\psi_+(\boldsymbol{p}) \approx \delta^{(3)}(\boldsymbol{p}-\boldsymbol{k}) - \frac{1}{\pi^2}\frac{1}{(k+i\varepsilon-p)(k+p)}\frac{Z}{(\boldsymbol{p}-\boldsymbol{k})^2}. \tag{9.13}$$

(9.13) is identical with the BORN approximation expression for $\psi_+(\boldsymbol{p})$ for a COULOMB potential as obtained from (9.11), (8.6a) and (9.7).

γ) Partial wave solutions. In Sect. 9α we have discussed general prescriptions for defining an eigenstate of the total HAMILTONian which is related to a particular eigenstate u_0 of the kinetic energy operator. In Sect. 9β we treated the special case of u_0 representing one single plane wave. For a central potential, wave functions exist which are separable in spherical polar coordinates, both in position and momentum space. These "partial wave" solutions are obtained from our general prescription by choosing for u_0 the simultaneous eigenstate of the kinetic energy operator (with eigenvalue $E=k^2/2$) and of the z-component and absolute square of the angular momentum operator, Eqs. (1.9) and (1.11) (with orbital and magnetic quantum numbers l and m). The momentum space wave function for u_0 is simply $\delta(p-k)\,Y_{lm}(\vartheta,\varphi)$. We use, for the moment, the principal value prescription (9.3a) to obtain an equation for $\psi_{lm}(\boldsymbol{p})$, the momentum space wave function of the required eigenstate of the total HAMILTONian. This equation, analogous to (8.5), is

$$\left.\begin{aligned}\psi_{lm}(\boldsymbol{p}) &= F_l(p)\,Y_{lm}(\vartheta,\varphi), \qquad F_l(p) = \delta(p-k)+\chi_l(p)\\ \chi_l(p) &= \lambda\,\mathscr{P}\left(\frac{1}{k^2-p^2}\right)\int_0^\infty dp'\,p'^2 K_l(p,p')\,F_l(p')\end{aligned}\right\} \tag{9.14}$$

[1] E. GUTH and C. J. MULLIN: Phys. Rev. **83**, 667 (1951).

where the kernel K_l is defined in (8.5). This integral equation for χ_l is an inhomogeneous one, like (9.7), but one-dimensional. Once the potential (and hence λK_l) and k are given, χ_l is determined uniquely by this equation.

In Sect. 9α we had discussed the relation between the three prescriptions ($9.3^\pm$) and (9.3a). For our present case of the partial wave solutions, for fixed values of l, m and E there exists only *one* eigenstate of H_0, and hence only one eigenstate of the total HAMILTONian. In this case then the three prescriptions ($9.3^\pm$) and (9.3a) should lead to physically *identical* wave functions. We can show this explicitly as follows. Using (9.3^+) instead of (9.3a) we obtain instead of (9.14) the equation

$$\left.\begin{aligned} F_l^{(+)}(p) &= \delta(p-k) + \frac{1}{(k+i\varepsilon)^2 - p^2} f_l^{(+)}(p), \\ f_l^{(+)}(p) &= \lambda \int_0^\infty dp'\, p'^2 K_l(p,p')\, F_l^{(+)}(p'). \end{aligned}\right\} \tag{9.14$^+$}$$

Using (9.5) we can rewrite the first line of (9.14^+) as

$$F_l^{(+)}(p) = \left[1 - \frac{\pi i}{2k} f_l^{(+)}(k)\right] \delta(p-k) + \mathscr{P}\left(\frac{1}{k^2-p^2}\right) f_l^{(+)}(p).$$

Comparison with (9.14) shows that $F_l^{(+)}(p)$ is simply $F_l(p)$ times the *constant* factor in square brackets above. We can restrict ourselves to (9.14) then without loss of generality.

We evaluate next the asymptotic behavior of the spatial wave function $u_{lm}(\boldsymbol{r})$, the FOURIER transform of $\psi_{lm}(\boldsymbol{p})$, Eq. (9.14). Using (9.5), (9.9) and the relation $Y_{lm}(\vartheta,\varphi) = (-1)^l Y_{lm}(\pi-\vartheta, \pi+\varphi)$, we find the following asymptotic expressions (for $kr \to \infty$),

$$\left.\begin{aligned} \int d^3p\, e^{i\boldsymbol{r}\cdot\boldsymbol{p}} f(p)\, Y_{lm}(\vartheta_p,\varphi_p)\, \mathscr{P}\left(\frac{1}{k^2-p^2}\right) &= -2\pi^2 \frac{f(k)}{r} Y_{lm}(\vartheta,\varphi) \begin{cases} \cos kr, & \text{if } l \text{ even} \\ i\sin kr, & \text{if } l \text{ odd}, \end{cases} \\ \int d^3p\, e^{i\boldsymbol{r}\cdot\boldsymbol{p}} f(p)\, Y_{lm}(\vartheta_p,\varphi_p)\, \delta(p-k) &= -4\pi \frac{k f(k)}{r} Y_{lm}(\vartheta,\varphi) \begin{cases} -\sin kr, & \text{if } l \text{ even} \\ i\cos kr, & \text{if } l \text{ odd}. \end{cases} \end{aligned}\right\} \tag{9.15}$$

In (9.15), $f(p)$ is any continuous function, (ϑ_p, φ_p) are the spherical polar coordinates of $\boldsymbol{p}$ and (ϑ, φ) those of $\boldsymbol{r}$. With the help of (9.15) we then get for the asymptotic behavior of $u_{lm}(r)$ (except for a normalization constant)

$$\left.\begin{aligned} u_{lm}(r) &\sim r^{-1} \sin\left(kr + \tfrac{1}{2}\pi l + \delta_l\right) Y_{lm}(\vartheta) \\ \tan\delta_l &= -\frac{\pi\lambda}{2k} \int_0^\infty dp'\, p'^2 K_l(p,p')\, F_l(p'). \end{aligned}\right\} \tag{9.16}$$

The first line of (9.16) shows that the constant δ_l is the phase shift, defined in (7.1). The second line of (9.16) shows that δ_l is determined by the value of $\chi_l(p)$ on the energy shell[1]. The exact spatial wave function $u_{lm}(\boldsymbol{r})$ has the same angular dependence as the asymptotic form (9.16).

---

[1] The same physical wave function and the *same* phase shift δ_l would, of course, be obtained from Eq. (9.14^+) in place of (9.14). With $F_l^{(+)}$ defined by (9.14^+), the phase shift δ_l is given by the expression

$$e^{i\delta_l} \sin\delta_l = -\frac{\pi\lambda}{2k} \int_0^\infty dp'\, p'^2 K_l(p,p')\, F_l^{(+)}(p').$$

For most potential shapes even the one-dimensional integral Eq. (9.14) cannot be solved exactly, but iteration and variational methods are available[1] for approximate solutions even when the potential is not very weak. If the potential is very weak, BORN approximation can again be applied, i.e. F_l is replaced by $\delta(p-k)$ in the integral on the right side of (9.14). The BORN approximation for the phase shift is then[2]

$$\delta_l^{(B)} = -2\pi^2 k \int_{-1}^{1} dx\, V'\left(k\sqrt{2-2x}\right) P_l(x). \tag{9.17}$$

As discussed in Sect. 7, the BORN approximation breaks down completely for the special case of a pure COULOMB potential. For this case the integral (9.17) diverges logarithmically at $x=1$.

b) DIRAC theory.

10. General properties of the DIRAC theory[3]. *α) Non-covariant notation.* The energy levels of an actual hydrogen atom exhibit the well known fine structure splitting which is not contained in the nonrelativistic SCHRÖDINGER theory of the previous sections. This fine structure is partly due to the relativistic variation of mass with velocity, partly due to the spin of the electron. The variation of the mass alone would be predicted by the relativistic SCHRÖDINGER equation for spin-less particles (the KLEIN-GORDON equation, see Sect. 45), but would not give correct results for the fine structure, the ZEEMAN effect and other phenomena which depend on the spin of the electron. The DIRAC wave equation, on the other hand, forms the basis of a fully relativistic theory for particles "of spin $\frac{1}{2}$". We shall now apply the DIRAC theory to an electron placed in a given electromagnetic field. In the next few sections, we shall use absolute (C.G.S.) units, instead of atomic units.

Let $\varphi(\boldsymbol{r})$, $\boldsymbol{A}(\boldsymbol{r})$ be the scalar and vector potentials of the given external electromagnetic field and $(-e)$ the charge of an electron. The DIRAC wave equation for a stationary state of *total* energy E is then

$$\left.\begin{aligned} H u &= +i\hbar \frac{\partial}{\partial t} u = E u, \\ H &= -e\varphi + \beta E_0 + \boldsymbol{\alpha}\cdot(c\boldsymbol{p} + e\boldsymbol{A}), \end{aligned}\right\} \tag{10.1}$$

where E_0 and $\boldsymbol{p}$ are the rest-mass energy and the momentum operator, respectively, of the electron,

$$\boldsymbol{p} = -i\hbar\,\mathrm{grad}, \qquad E_0 = m c^2. \tag{10.2}$$

The vector $\boldsymbol{\alpha}$ is a vector operator, whose CARTESian components $(\alpha_1, \alpha_2, \alpha_3)$, together with the operator $\beta \equiv \alpha_4$, satisfy the commutation relations

$$\alpha_i \alpha_k + \alpha_k \alpha_i = 2\delta_{ik} \quad (i, k = 1, 2, 3, 4). \tag{10.3}$$

The DIRAC operators α_i operate on the wave function u, but do not depend on the spatial coordinates $\boldsymbol{r}$ of the electron.

Most properties[4] of the DIRAC operators could be derived directly from the commutation rules (10.3), but for our purposes it will be more convenient to use

---

[1] See references at the beginning of Sect. 9.

[2] A necessary, but not sufficient, condition for the validity of BORN approximation is $\tan\delta_l \approx \delta_l \ll 1$.

[3] See references [*1*], [*2*], [*3*] and [*12*] of the bibliography.

[4] A detailed discussion of the properties of the DIRAC operators is given by R. H. GOOD, Rev. Mod. Phys. **27**, 187 (1955).

an explicit representation for them. The usual representation is one in terms of four-by-four matrices with the matrices for α_1, α_2 and $\beta=\alpha_4$ being diagonal. We shall write these DIRAC matrices in the following "split notation" (see [2], Chap. 6).

$$\boldsymbol{\alpha}=\begin{pmatrix}0 & \sigma^P\\ \sigma^P & 0\end{pmatrix},\qquad \beta=\begin{pmatrix}I & 0\\ 0 & -I\end{pmatrix}, \tag{10.4}$$

where the three CARTESian components of σ^P are two-by-two matrices, called the PAULI spin matrices, and I is the unit two-by-two matrix. The PAULI matrices satisfy the following operator relations

$$(\sigma_i^P)^2 = I,\qquad \sigma_i^P\sigma_k^P = -\sigma_k^P\sigma_i^P = i\,\sigma_l^P, \tag{10.5}$$

where (i, k, l) are cyclic permutations of the Cartesian coordinates (1, 2, 3). Our explicit representation for the PAULI matrices is

$$\sigma_1^P=\begin{pmatrix}0 & 1\\ 1 & 0\end{pmatrix},\quad \sigma_2^P=\begin{pmatrix}0 & -i\\ i & 0\end{pmatrix},\quad \sigma_3^P=\begin{pmatrix}1 & 0\\ 0 & -1\end{pmatrix};\quad I=\begin{pmatrix}1 & 0\\ 0 & 1\end{pmatrix}. \tag{10.6}$$

We shall also need later on the DIRAC spin operator $\boldsymbol{\sigma}$, whose Cartesian components are defined by

$$\sigma_i \equiv -i\,\alpha_k\alpha_l\quad (i, k, l = \text{cycl. perm. } 1, 2, 3). \tag{10.7}$$

The DIRAC spin matrices σ_i satisfy exactly the same operator relations (10.5) as the PAULI matrices and in our "split notation"

$$\boldsymbol{\sigma}=\begin{pmatrix}\sigma^P & 0\\ 0 & \sigma^P\end{pmatrix}. \tag{10.8}$$

Written out in full, our explicit representation for the DIRAC operators is one in terms of four-by-four matrices with the matrix for σ_3 and that for β diagonal. Some examples of these matrices are

$$\alpha_3=\begin{pmatrix}0 & 0 & 1 & 0\\ 0 & 0 & 0 & -1\\ 1 & 0 & 0 & 0\\ 0 & -1 & 0 & 0\end{pmatrix},\quad \sigma_3=\begin{pmatrix}1 & 0 & 0 & 0\\ 0 & -1 & 0 & 0\\ 0 & 0 & 1 & 0\\ 0 & 0 & 0 & -1\end{pmatrix},\quad \beta=\begin{pmatrix}1 & 0 & 0 & 0\\ 0 & 1 & 0 & 0\\ 0 & 0 & -1 & 0\\ 0 & 0 & 0 & -1\end{pmatrix}. \tag{10.8a}$$

From (10.7) and (10.3) also follow the relations

$$\sigma_i\alpha_i = \alpha_i\sigma_i,\qquad \sigma_i\alpha_k - \alpha_k\sigma_i = 2i\,\alpha_l. \tag{10.7a}$$

The wave function u is then not merely a single function of position $\boldsymbol{r}$, but a "matrix" with one column and 4 rows (a spinor), on which the DIRAC matrices act. The four components $u_\sigma (\sigma = 1, 2, 3, 4)$ of u are themselves functions of position (unlike the matrices α_i and β). The multiplication of u by a DIRAC operator follows the usual rules of matrix multiplication. The result is again a 1 column—4 row matrix, just like u:

$$(\alpha_i u)_\varrho = \sum_{\sigma=1}^{4} (\alpha_i)_{\varrho\sigma} u_\sigma.$$

For instance, if

$$u=\begin{pmatrix}u_1\\ u_2\\ u_3\\ u_4\end{pmatrix},\quad \text{then}\quad \alpha_2 u = i\begin{pmatrix}-u_4\\ u_3\\ -u_2\\ u_1\end{pmatrix}.$$

The differential equation (10.1) holds, of course, for each of the four rows of the eigenfunction separately and gives four simultaneous coupled equations for the four functions u_σ. For instance

$$\left.\begin{aligned}\frac{1}{c}(E+E_0+e\,\varphi)\,u_3-\left[\hbar\left(\frac{1}{i}\frac{\partial}{\partial x}-\frac{\partial}{\partial y}\right)+\frac{e}{c}(A_x-i\,A_y)\right]u_2-\\-\left(\frac{\hbar}{i}\frac{\partial}{\partial z}+\frac{e}{c}A_z\right)u_1=0\end{aligned}\right\}\qquad(10.9)$$

plus three similar equations.

The inner product of two DIRAC wave functions u and v is defined as the scalar quantity

$$\langle v^* u\rangle=\sum_{\varrho=1}^{4}\int d^3r\,v_\varrho^*(\boldsymbol{r})\,u_\varrho(\boldsymbol{r}),$$

and the wave functions are usually normalized so that $\langle u^* u\rangle$ equals unity. Perturbation theory can be developed in a manner analogous to the nonrelativistic theory, except that matrix elements now also contain sums over spinor indices. Consider a HAMILTONian $H=(H_0+H')$, where both H_0 and H' are built up of DIRAC matrices and of the four-by-four unit matrix, and let u be an eigenfunction of the operator H_0 alone. Following the rules of perturbation theory and matrix multiplication, the first order perturbation, $\Delta E^{(1)}$, to the energy eigenvalue is then given by

$$\Delta E^{(1)}=\langle u^* H' u\rangle=\sum_{\varrho,\sigma=1}^{4}\int d^3r\,u_\varrho^*\,H_{\varrho\sigma}\,u_\sigma.\qquad(10.10)$$

Eq. (10.1) is the exact wave equation for an electron in a given external classical electromagnetic field, according to DIRAC's *original* theory. This theory is fully LORENTZ-invariant ([*3*], Part B), although (10.1) is not written in a fully covariant form. It was shown by PAULI [*3*] that the original DIRAC theory can be extended by adding certain terms to the wave equation, without violating the gauge invariance and LORENTZ invariance of the theory. For this purpose it will be convenient to rewrite the DIRAC equation in a covariant form.

β) Covariant notation[1]. We introduce relativistic four-vectors for the electromagnetic potentials, the space-time coordinates of the electron and its momentum plus energy:

$$\left.\begin{aligned}A_\mu&=(\boldsymbol{A},i\,\varphi),\quad x_\mu=(\boldsymbol{r},i\,c\,t),\quad(\mu=1,2,3,4),\\p_\mu&=-i\,\hbar\frac{\partial}{\partial x_\mu}=\left(-i\,\hbar\,\mathrm{grad},\,-\frac{\hbar}{c}\frac{\partial}{\partial t}\right)=\left(\boldsymbol{p},\frac{i}{c}E\right).\end{aligned}\right\}\qquad(10.11)$$

We further define a four-vector γ_μ built up of DIRAC matrices, whose components satisfy a commutation relation equivalent to (10.3),

$$\left.\begin{aligned}\gamma_\mu&=(-i\,\beta\,\boldsymbol{\alpha},\beta),\quad(\mu=1,2,3,4),\\\gamma_\mu\gamma_\nu+\gamma_\nu\gamma_\mu&=2\,\delta_{\mu\nu}.\end{aligned}\right\}\qquad(10.12)$$

In this notation the DIRAC equation (10.1), multiplied by $i\beta/c$ takes the form [*using* (10.2), (10.3), (10.11) and (10.12)],

$$\left.\begin{aligned}\left[\sum_{\mu=1}^{4}\pi_\mu\gamma_\mu-i\,m\,c\right]u=0,\\\pi_\mu=p_\mu+\left(\frac{e}{c}\right)A_\mu.\end{aligned}\right\}\qquad(10.13)$$

---

[1] See ref. [*3*], [*12*], and [*13*] of the bibliography.

It will be convenient to derive from (10.13) a second order differential equation which contains the DIRAC matrices only in terms which vanish in the absence of an electromagnetic field. This is accomplished by multiplying both sides of Eq. (10.13) by the operator $(\sum \pi_\mu \gamma_\mu + imc)$.

We first rewrite the electric and magnetic fields, $\mathcal{E}$ and $\mathcal{H}$, in terms of the antisymmetric tensor[1]

$$F_{\mu\nu} = \frac{\partial A_\nu}{\partial x_\mu} - \frac{\partial A_\mu}{\partial x_\nu}$$

$$\mathcal{H}_i = F_{kl}, \qquad \mathcal{E}_i = i\,F_{i4}.$$

We further note that the electromagnetic potentials satisfy the LORENTZ gauge condition

$$\sum_{\mu=1}^{4} \frac{\partial A_\mu}{\partial x_\mu} = 0$$

and the following commutation rule, which follows from the definition (10.11) of p_μ in terms of differentiation operators,

$$[\pi_\mu, \pi_\nu] \equiv \pi_\mu \pi_\nu - \pi_\nu \pi_\mu = \frac{\hbar e}{i c} F_{\mu\nu}.$$

Using this last relation and the commutation relations (10.12) for γ_μ, one finally obtains the desired second order differential equation.

This equation is

$$\left\{\left[\sum_{\mu=1}^{4} \pi_\mu^2 + m^2 c^2\right] + \frac{\hbar e}{2ic} \sum_{\mu,\nu} \gamma_\mu \gamma_\nu F_{\mu\nu}\right\} u = 0. \tag{10.14}$$

In (10.14) the expression in square brackets is the operator which appears in the KLEIN-GORDON equation, the relativistic theory for spin-less particles. The last term in (10.14) is characteristic of the DIRAC theory, appropriate for particles of "spin ½". We shall see later that this term represents the interaction of the electromagnetic field with an electric and a magnetic dipole moment, collectively called the "DIRAC moment of the electron". This "DIRAC moment" term is the only term in (10.14) which involves DIRAC matrices. If the electromagnetic field is sufficiently weak, the effect of this term on the energy eigenvalue is small and can be calculated by approximation methods which involve first order perturbation theory and an expansion in inverse powers of c, the velocity of light. Such evaluations will be carried out in Sect. 12 and 13. Eq. (10.14) will be written out in full in terms of the less elegant and less symmetric but conventional notation in (12.9). Of course, (12.9) can also be derived directly from (10.1) in conventional notation.

γ) Modified DIRAC *equation.* We now consider possible modifications of the DIRAC theory, which still give a LORENTZ- and gauge invariant theory. This can be achieved by adding some LORENTZ-invariant (scalar) combinations of the DIRAC operator γ_μ and of derivatives of the electromagnetic potentials to the operators occurring in (10.13). We consider, in particular, two such combinations which give the following modified DIRAC equation

$$\left(\sum_\mu \pi_\mu \gamma_\mu - imc\right) u = \left[g_1 \left(\frac{\hbar e}{4mc^2}\right) \sum_{\mu,\nu} \gamma_\mu \gamma_\nu F_{\mu\nu} - g_2 \frac{e}{c} \left(\frac{\hbar}{mc}\right)^2 \sum_\mu \gamma_\mu \Box^2 A_\mu\right] u, \tag{10.15}$$

[1] The indices (i, k, l) are cyclic permutations of the first three ("space-like") values of the index μ, and 4 denotes the "time-like" value of μ.

where

$$\Box^2 A_\mu \equiv \sum_{\nu=1}^{4} \frac{\partial^2}{\partial x_\nu^2} A_\mu = -\frac{4\pi}{c} j_\mu$$

and j_μ is the current-charge four-vector for the *source* of the given electromagnetic field. The parameters g_1, and g_2 on the right side of (10.15) are dimensionless.

The unmodified DIRAC Eq. (10.1) represents the interaction of an electron with an external field only if we treat all electromagnetic fields *classically*. If we use quantum electrodynamics, even the interaction of the electron with a given field (i.e. even in the absence of the emission or absorption of "real" radiation) is modified. To a good approximation, these modifications can be accounted for by adding so-called "radiative correction" terms to the DIRAC equation (see Sect. 18 and 19), resulting in an equation of the form (10.15). The dimensionless constants g_1 and g_2 derived from quantum electrodynamics are small, of the order of the fine structure constant α, and we shall treat the effect of these extra terms on the energy eigenvalue only by first order perturbation theory (see Sect. 20). We shall also see that the right side of (10.15) is a good approximation to the radiative corrections only for nonrelativistic energies.

The term involving g_1, in (10.15),

$$G_1 = g_1 \left(\frac{\hbar e}{4 m c^2}\right) \sum_{\mu,\nu} \gamma_\mu \gamma_\nu F_{\mu\nu}, \tag{10.16}$$

is of very similar form as the "DIRAC moment" term in (10.14) and G_1 is often called a "PAULI moment" term. In fact, if both these terms are treated by first order perturbation theory, and to lowest order in $1/c$, their effects on the energy eigenvalue in a magnetic field are in the ratio $g_1:1$, except for terms of order g_1^2.

It should be noted, however, that this correspondence between the PAULI and DIRAC moments is *not* exact. This can be seen, for instance, by deriving an exact second order differential equation from (10.15) (with $g_2 = 0$) in analogy with the derivation of (10.14) from (10.13). The result is

$$\left\{\left[\sum_{\mu=1}^{4} \pi_\mu^2 + m^2 c^2\right] + (1+g_1)\frac{\hbar e}{2ic}\sum_{\mu,\nu}\gamma_\mu\gamma_\nu F_{\mu\nu}\right\} u = \left\{G_1^2 + \left[\sum_\mu \gamma_\mu \pi_\mu, G_1\right]\right\} u, \tag{10.17}$$

where $[A, B] = +AB - BA$. The terms on the right side involve only the PAULI, but not the DIRAC moment. They contain higher powers of $1/c$ than the term involving g_1 on the left side and one might expect them to be small in an essentially nonrelativistic case (see also Sect. 12γ). However these terms on the right side contain higher derivatives of the electromagnetic potentials and can give rise to divergence difficulties not encountered with the DIRAC moment alone, if the potentials are singular and if the expansion in $1/c$ is carried to higher terms. These difficulties again show that (10.15) cannot be an exact self-consistent equation for very high energies (or momenta).

The addition of the term involving g_2 on the right side of (10.15) can be considered as equivalent to a modification of the external potential A_μ. In fact, (10.15) with $g_1 = 0$ reduces to (10.13) if, in the definition of π_μ in (10.13), A_μ is replaced by

$$A'_\mu = A_\mu + g_2 \left(\frac{\hbar}{m c}\right)^2 \Box^2 A_\mu. \tag{10.18}$$

11. Angular momentum[1]. *α) Definitions.* According to the DIRAC theory, the electron is endowed with an intrinsic magnetic moment. We shall show that the electron is also endowed with an intrinsic angular momentum, the so-called spin, which is represented by the operator $\frac{1}{2}\hbar\sigma$, Eq. (10.7). First we review briefly some general properties of angular momentum operators.

[1] See ref. [1], Ch. VI; ref. [5], Ch. III and G. PAKE and E. FEENBERG, Quantum Theory of Angular Momentum. Cambridge: Addison-Wesley Co. 1953.

We shall call any vector operator $\boldsymbol{J}$ an "angular momentum operator" if its three CARTESian components J_i are HERMITian operators and satisfy the fundamental commutation relation

$$[J_i, J_i] = 0, \quad [J_i, J_k] = i\hbar J_l, \tag{11.1}$$

where (i, k, l) are cyclic permutations of the indices $(1, 2, 3)$ and $[a, b] = (ab - ba)$ is the commutator of a and b. We denote the operator for the square of the angular momentum by $\boldsymbol{J}^2 = \sum_{i=1}^{3} J_i^2$. It follows from (11.1) that $\boldsymbol{J}^2$ commutes with each of the three components J_i and that simultaneous eigenstates u of $\boldsymbol{J}^2$ and, say, J_z $(i=3)$ can be found. Using only (11.1) and the HERMITian nature of J_i, one can show by general operator manipulation[1] that the simultaneous eigenvalues must be of the form

$$\left.\begin{array}{ll} \boldsymbol{J}^2 u = j(j+1)\hbar^2 u, & J_z u = m\hbar u, \\ j = 0, \tfrac{1}{2}, 1, \tfrac{3}{2}, 2, \ldots; & m = -j, -j+1, \ldots, +j. \end{array}\right\} \tag{11.2}$$

The CARTESian components of the quantum mechanical operators for position and momentum, $\boldsymbol{r}$ and $\boldsymbol{p}$, satisfy the commutation rules

$$[r_i, r_k] = [p_i, p_k] = 0, \quad [r_i, p_k] = i\hbar\,\delta_{ik}. \tag{11.3}$$

The explicit definition for the *orbital* angular momentum operator [see (1.9)], is

$$\boldsymbol{J}_{\text{orb}} \equiv \hbar\boldsymbol{k} = \boldsymbol{r} \times \boldsymbol{p}, \quad ([\boldsymbol{r}\times\boldsymbol{p}]_i = r_k p_l - r_l p_k). \tag{11.4}$$

$\hbar\boldsymbol{k}$ satisfies the commutation rule (11.1) and it follows [see (1.11)] from the special form of (11.4) that the eigenvalues of $\boldsymbol{k}^2$ are $l(l+1)$, where l can only be an integer or zero (*not* half-integral). From (11.3) and (11.4) we can also derive

$$[p_i, k_i] = 0, \quad [p_i, k_k] = i\,p_l, \quad \boldsymbol{p}\times\boldsymbol{k} + \boldsymbol{k}\times\boldsymbol{p} = 2i\,\boldsymbol{p}. \tag{11.5}$$

Further, using the identity

$$[a, b^2] = [a, b]\,b + b\,[a, b], \tag{11.6}$$

we also have

$$[\boldsymbol{p}, \boldsymbol{k}^2] = i(\boldsymbol{k}\times\boldsymbol{p} - \boldsymbol{p}\times\boldsymbol{k}). \tag{11.7}$$

One can also derive relations, identical with (11.5) and (11.7) except that $\boldsymbol{p}$ is replaced by $\boldsymbol{r}$ throughout.

In (10.7) we have defined, in terms of the DIRAC matrix $\boldsymbol{\alpha}$, a vector operator σ, whose CARTESian components satisfy the operator relations (10.5). If we write

$$\boldsymbol{J}_{\text{spin}} = \hbar\boldsymbol{s}, \quad \boldsymbol{s} = \tfrac{1}{2}\sigma, \tag{11.8}$$

it follows from (10.5) that $\boldsymbol{J}_{\text{spin}}$ satisfies (11.1) and we call it the spin angular momentum operator. It follows further from (10.5) that the square of each component s_i of $\boldsymbol{s}$ equals $\frac{1}{4}$ times the unit operator. Hence

$$\boldsymbol{s}^2 u = \sum_{i=1}^{3} s_i^2 u = s(s+1)\,u, \quad s = \tfrac{1}{2} \tag{11.9}$$

for *any* state u and the 2 possible eigenvalues of s_i are $\pm\frac{1}{2}$. Since the DIRAC matrices commute with $\boldsymbol{r}$ and $\boldsymbol{p}$, any component of $\boldsymbol{s}$ also commutes with every component of $\boldsymbol{k}$. We finally define as the operator for the "total angular mo-

[1] Ref. [*1*], p. 144 or ref. [*5*], p. 46.

mentum" the sum of the orbital and spin operators,

$$\boldsymbol{J}_{\text{tot}} = \hbar \boldsymbol{M}, \qquad \boldsymbol{M} = \boldsymbol{k} + \boldsymbol{s}. \tag{11.10}$$

$\boldsymbol{J}_{\text{tot}}$ also satisfies (11.1) and further, since $\boldsymbol{k}$ commutes with $\boldsymbol{s}$,

$$[k_i, M_k] = i\, k_l, \qquad [s_i, M_k] = i\, s_l. \tag{11.11}$$

It also follows [e.g. from (11.6) and (11.11)] that each component of $\boldsymbol{M}$ (and therefore also $\boldsymbol{M}^2$) commutes with both $\boldsymbol{k}^2$ and $\boldsymbol{s}^2$. The three types of angular momentum operators, expressed in atomic (instead of C.G.S.) units are simply $\boldsymbol{k}$, $\boldsymbol{s}$ and $\boldsymbol{M}$. It should be noted that the commutation rules of the DIRAC and PAULI spin operators are the same and the general discussion of the present section holds for either type of operator.

β) Central fields. The physical significance of the spin operator $\boldsymbol{s}$ can be seen as follows. Consider an electron in any central field with scalar potential $\varphi(r)$ and zero vector potential $\boldsymbol{A}(\boldsymbol{r})$. In the nonrelativistic SCHRÖDINGER theory every component of $\boldsymbol{k}$, as well as $\boldsymbol{k}^2$, commutes with the total HAMILTONian H (or "is a constant of the motion") and simultaneous eigenstates of H, $\boldsymbol{k}^2$, and k_z exist with eigenvalues E, $l(l+1)$ and m_l, respectively. In the DIRAC theory, however, *none* of the components of $\boldsymbol{k}$ or $\boldsymbol{s}$ individually, nor $\boldsymbol{k}^2$, commute with the HAMILTONian H, Eq. (10.1). In fact, one can show that

$$[\boldsymbol{k}, H] = -[\boldsymbol{s}, H] = i\, c\, \boldsymbol{\alpha} \times \boldsymbol{p}. \tag{11.12}$$

The first part of (11.12) represents the commutator of $\boldsymbol{k}$ with the term in $\boldsymbol{\alpha} \cdot \boldsymbol{p}$ in (10.1), rewritten with the help of (11.5). The second part represents the commutator of $\frac{1}{2}\sigma$ with the $\boldsymbol{\alpha} \cdot \boldsymbol{p}$ term, rewritten with the help of (10.7a). (11.12) shows that every component of $\boldsymbol{M}$, the *total* angular momentum, commutes with the HAMILTONian H. Using (11.6) we then see that $\boldsymbol{M}^2$ also commutes with H.

Since the orbital angular momentum $\boldsymbol{k}$ is no longer a constant of the motion in the DIRAC theory, no eigenstates of the HAMILTONian exist which are also eigenstates of $\boldsymbol{k}^2$ and k_z, i.e. l and m_l (eigenvalue of k_z) are no longer "good quantum numbers". In the DIRAC theory the total angular momentum $\boldsymbol{M}$ takes the place of $\boldsymbol{k}$, i.e. we can find simultaneous eigenstates of the HAMILTONian, of $\boldsymbol{M}^2$ and of M. We denote the eigenvalue of $\boldsymbol{M}^2$ by $j(j+1)$, that of M_z by m, where m is related to j by (11.2). j, which we shall call the "inner quantum number", takes the place of the orbital quantum number l in the DIRAC theory. It can be shown that j (and hence m) only takes on half-integral values and we shall also verify this explicitly in Sect. 13β. It follows from (11.9) that *any* state is an eigenstate of $\boldsymbol{s}^2$ with eigenvalue $\frac{3}{4}$ and that $s = \frac{1}{2}$, the "absolute value" of the spin, is always a good quantum number. On the other hand, the "direction" of the spin is not quantized, e.g. any eigenstate of the DIRAC HAMILTONian is a linear superposition of *two* eigenstates of s_z with eigenvalues $m_z = \frac{1}{2}$ and $-\frac{1}{2}$.

Although $\boldsymbol{k}^2$ is not strictly a constant of the motion in the DIRAC theory, for an electron in a weak central field, l is "almost a good quantum number". This means that we can find stationary states u, for which

$$\boldsymbol{k}^2 u = l(l+1)\, u + w \tag{11.13}$$

where l is a positive integer and w is a spinor whose "large components" w_1 and w_2 are zero. The "small components" (see Sect. 12α) both of u and of w are of order $\bar{v}/c$, where $\bar{v}$ is some average velocity of the electron Thus u and w are "almost orthogonal": w is of order $\bar{v}/c$, but the expectation value of the operator $\boldsymbol{k}^2$, taken over the eigenfunction u, differs from $l(l+1)$ only by a term of order $(\bar{v}/c)^2$. The properties of $\boldsymbol{k}^2$ are discussed further in Sects. 12 and 13.

12. PAULI theory of the spin-electron. *α) "Large" and "small" components.* Let $\bar{v}$ and $\bar{p} = m\bar{v}$ be the order of magnitude of the velocity and momentum of an electron in a particular stationary state (for instance, take for $\bar{p}$ the square root of the expectation value of the operator p^2). For an electron in a reasonably weak potential ($e\varphi \ll mc^2$), stationary states exist for which the average velocity $\bar{v}$ is nonrelativistic and the total energy E is close to the rest-mass energy $E_0 = mc^2$ of the electron. I.e.

$$\bar{v} \ll c, \quad \bar{p} \ll mc, \quad |E - E_0| \sim \bar{p}^2/m \ll \bar{p}\,c \ll E_0.$$

For such states the DIRAC theory can be simplified considerably, as follows.

We have seen that the DIRAC equation (10.1) can be written in the form of four simultaneous differential equations for the four components u_σ of the spinor wave function u and have given one of these equations in (10.9). For a weak potential and a state with $E \approx E_0$, the factors multiplying the spinor components u_3 and u_4 are larger than those multiplying u_1 and u_2 by factors of order $c/\bar{v}$, in each of these equations. For instance, in (10.9) the factor of u_3 is of order $2mc$, those of u_1 and u_2 of order $\bar{p}$; in another equation the factor of u_1 is of order $(E - E_0)/c \sim \bar{p}^2/mc$, the factors of u_3 and u_4 of order $\bar{p}$, etc. It then follows that u_3 and u_4 are *smaller*[1] than u_1 and u_2 by factors of the order of $\bar{v}/c$. This conclusion forms the basis of our approximation method.

We can obtain a first approximation for u_3, one of the two "small" components, in terms of the two "large" components u_1 and u_2 from (10.9) by putting E equal to E_0 and by neglecting the potentials φ and $\boldsymbol{A}$ altogether. This approximate equation (and a similar one for u_4) reads

$$u_3 = -i\frac{\hbar}{2mc}\left(\frac{\partial u_2}{\partial x} - i\frac{\partial u_2}{\partial y} + \frac{\partial u_1}{\partial z}\right), \tag{12.1}$$

$$u_4 = -i\frac{\hbar}{2mc}\left(\frac{\partial u_1}{\partial x} + i\frac{\partial u_1}{\partial y} - \frac{\partial u_2}{\partial z}\right). \tag{12.2}$$

These two equations appear combined in a more compact form, if we use the split notation, discussed in Sect. 10, also for the wave function u. We write

$$u = \begin{pmatrix} U_A \\ U_B \end{pmatrix}; \quad U_A = \begin{pmatrix} u_1 \\ u_2 \end{pmatrix}, \quad U_B = \begin{pmatrix} u_3 \\ u_4 \end{pmatrix}. \tag{12.3}$$

Using (10.4), the exact DIRAC equation (10.1) takes the form

$$\left.\begin{aligned} (E - E_0 + e\varphi)\, U_A &= \boldsymbol{\sigma}^P \cdot (c\,\boldsymbol{p} + e\boldsymbol{A})\, U_B, \\ (E + E_0 + e\varphi)\, U_B &= \boldsymbol{\sigma}^P \cdot (c\,\boldsymbol{p} + e\boldsymbol{A})\, U_A. \end{aligned}\right\} \tag{12.4}$$

Replacing E by E_0 and neglecting φ in the second line of (12.4), we again obtain an approximate expression for the small components U_B in terms of the large components U_A. This expression, identical with (12.1) and (12.2) if $\boldsymbol{A} = 0$, is

$$U_B = (2mc)^{-1}\left[\boldsymbol{\sigma}^P \cdot (\boldsymbol{p} + e\boldsymbol{A}/c)\right] U_A. \tag{12.5}$$

If we substitute the approximation (12.5) into the first line of (12.4), we obtain an approximate equation involving only the large components U_A. This equation (of the same form as the nonrelativistic SCHRÖDINGER equation) is

$$\left[E - E_0 + e\varphi - \frac{1}{2m}\left(\boldsymbol{p} + \frac{e}{c}\boldsymbol{A}\right)^2\right] U_A = 0. \tag{12.6}$$

---

[1] In older books and in ref. [9] the large components are labelled 3, 4 and the small components 1, 2. In these references the term in the HAMILTONian which involves β differs from ours by a change in sign.

With the help of (12.5) and (12.6) one can then derive a more accurate expression for U_B in terms of U_A from (12.4) and finally a more accurate (but still not exact) equation[1] involving only U_A. We shall derive this more accurate equation for U_A by a slightly different method.

It will be seen from the explicit representation of the DIRAC operators in our split notation, (10.4) and (10.8), that β and σ only couple the large components u_1 and $u_2 (U_A)$ with each other and the small components u_3 and $u_4 (U_B)$ with each other (operators diagonal in the split notation). The CARTESian components of $\boldsymbol{\alpha}$, on the other hand, couple the components U_A with the components U_B. For a wave function u satisfying the DIRAC equation (10.1) or (12.4) we can get an approximate relation involving $\boldsymbol{\alpha}\, u$, by using (10.4) and the approximation (12.5),

$$(\boldsymbol{\alpha}\, u)_A = \sigma^P U_B \approx \frac{1}{2mc}\left[\boldsymbol{p} + i(\boldsymbol{p}\times\sigma^P)\right] U_A, \tag{12.7}$$

(12.7) holds, even approximately[2], only for the first components $(\boldsymbol{\alpha}\, u)_1$ and $(\boldsymbol{\alpha}\, u)_2$ of $(\boldsymbol{\alpha}\, u)$. For the last two components $(\boldsymbol{\alpha}\, u)_3$ and $(\boldsymbol{\alpha}\, u)_4$, the right side of (12.7) would be of a completely wrong order of magnitude, the correct expression being

$$(\boldsymbol{\alpha}\, u)_B = \sigma^P U_A \gg U_B.$$

The extent of the error made in the approximation (12.7) can best be seen by deriving an exact relation involving $\boldsymbol{\alpha}\, u$, as follows. We multiply the DIRAC equation (10.1) on the left by $\boldsymbol{\alpha}$,

$$\boldsymbol{\alpha}\,(E + e\varphi - \beta\, m c^2 - c\,\boldsymbol{\alpha}\cdot\boldsymbol{\pi})\, u = 0, \qquad \boldsymbol{\pi} = \boldsymbol{p} + e\boldsymbol{A}/c.$$

Using the relations (10.3) and the definition (10.7) of σ, we can rewrite this equation in the form

$$(E + e\varphi)\,\boldsymbol{\alpha}\, u = (-m c^2 \beta\,\boldsymbol{\alpha} + c\,\boldsymbol{\pi} + i\, c\,\boldsymbol{\pi}\times\sigma)\, u.$$

Adding $mc^2 \boldsymbol{\alpha} u$ to both sides and dividing by the factor appearing on the left side, we obtain the required *exact* relation

$$\boldsymbol{\alpha}\, u = \frac{c}{m c^2 + E + e\varphi}\left[\boldsymbol{\pi} + i\,\boldsymbol{\pi}\times\sigma + m c\,(1-\beta)\,\boldsymbol{\alpha}\right] u. \tag{12.8}$$

The first two components of the term involving $(\beta - 1)$, $[(1-\beta)\,\boldsymbol{\alpha}\, u]_A$ vanish exactly (whereas the last two components are large). If E is replaced by mc^2, $e\varphi$ neglected compared with mc^2 and $(e/c)\boldsymbol{A}$ compared with $\boldsymbol{p}$, the first two components of the Eq. (12.8) reduce to (12.7). In many problems the non-relativistic energy, $W = E - E_0$, and $e\varphi$ are of the order of magnitude of $(\bar{v}/c)^2 \times mc^2 \ll mc^2$ and the vector potential eA is either zero or at least very small compared with $c\,p$.

β) Quadratic equation. We return now to the exact quadratic equation (10.14), which we had derived from the DIRAC equation using covariant notation. We rewrite (10.14) in terms of the conventional non-covariant notation, noting in particular that

$$\gamma_k \gamma_l = +i\,\sigma_i, \qquad \gamma_k \gamma_4 = i\,\alpha_k,$$

[1] See ref. [2], Sect. 65.

[2] It should also be remembered that (12.7) only holds for a wave function u, which satisfies the DIRAC equation. Consider, for instance, the expression $(\boldsymbol{\alpha} f(\boldsymbol{r})\, u)_A$ where $f(\boldsymbol{r})$ is an arbitrary function of position, not involving DIRAC operators. Although $\boldsymbol{\alpha}$ commutes with f, $\boldsymbol{p}$ does *not*, and a valid approximation for $(\boldsymbol{\alpha}\, f\, u)_A$ is obtained from (12.7) only if we write $f(r)$ *to the left* of $\boldsymbol{p}$.

where (i, k, l) are cyclic permutations of the three "space-like" indices $(1, 2, 3)$. Dividing (10.14) through by $-2m$, we obtain

$$\left.\begin{aligned}\Big[W + e\varphi + \frac{\hbar^2}{2m}\Delta + \frac{1}{2mc^2}(W + e\varphi)^2 + i\frac{e\hbar}{mc}(\boldsymbol{A}\cdot\text{grad}) - \frac{e^2}{2mc^2}A^2 - \\ - \frac{e\hbar}{2mc}(\boldsymbol{\sigma}\cdot\mathcal{H}) + i\frac{e\hbar}{2mc}(\boldsymbol{\alpha}\cdot\mathcal{E})\Big]u = 0.\end{aligned}\right\} \tag{12.9}$$

If we disregard all but the first three members of this equation we obtain the ordinary SCHRÖDINGER equation. The next three terms are peculiar to the relativistic SCHRÖDINGER theory. This may be inferred from the fact that these terms, while containing the velocity of light, do not contain the operators $\boldsymbol{\sigma}$ and $\boldsymbol{\alpha}$. The fourth term represents the relativistic correction due to the change in mass with velocity. The fifth and sixth terms describe the effect of the external vector potential on the electron (cf. Sects. 45 and 47). Finally, the last two members are characteristic of the DIRAC theory. The seventh term may be interpreted as an interaction between the magnetic field and a magnetic moment

$$\mu_s = -\mu_0\boldsymbol{\sigma}, \qquad \mu_0 = \frac{e\hbar}{2mc}. \tag{12.10}$$

The last term represents an interaction between the electric field and an electric moment $-i\frac{e\hbar}{2mc}\boldsymbol{\alpha}$.

The exact quadratic equation (12.9) looks less elegant than the linear DIRAC equation, but is more useful for our present aim of deriving an approximate, but fairly accurate, equation which involves only the large components U_A of the wave function. This is due to the fact that $\boldsymbol{\sigma}$ is diagonal in our split (U_A, U_B) notation and only $\boldsymbol{\alpha}$ couples U_A with U_B. Now the factor multiplying $\boldsymbol{\alpha}$ in (10.1) is of order $c\bar{p}$ or $W(c/\bar{v})$, but the factor in (12.9) only of order $(e\hbar\mathcal{E}/mc)$ which is much smaller (in many problems $e\hbar\mathcal{E}$ is of order $\bar{p}\,e\varphi$, $e\varphi$ of order W, the nonrelativistic energy, and hence $e\hbar\mathcal{E}/mc$ of order $W\bar{v}/c$). Hence, the replacement of $(\boldsymbol{\alpha}u)_A$ by the approximation (12.7) results in a much smaller error in Eq. (12.9) than in (10.1). If we make this substitution we get an equation, involving only the large components U_A, which forms the basis of the approximate PAULI theory for the spin-electron[1],

$$\left.\begin{aligned}\Big[W + e\varphi + \frac{\hbar^2}{2m}\Delta + \frac{1}{2mc^2}(W + e\varphi)^2 + i\frac{e\hbar}{mc}\boldsymbol{A}\cdot\text{grad} - \frac{e^2}{2mc^2}A^2 + \\ + i\frac{\mu_0}{2mc}\mathcal{E}\cdot\boldsymbol{p} - \frac{\mu_0}{2mc}\sigma^P\cdot(\mathcal{E}\times\boldsymbol{p}) - \mu_0\sigma^P\cdot\mathcal{H}\Big]U_A = 0,\end{aligned}\right\} \tag{12.11}$$

where

$$\mu_0 = \frac{e\hbar}{2mc}$$

is the "BOHR magneton", a measure of the spin magnetic moment of the electron.

Note that (12.11) is now an equation for a two-row, one-column wave function U_A (the "PAULI spinor wave function") with components u_1 and u_2, and that the DIRAC spin-matrix $\boldsymbol{\sigma}$, (10.8), has been replaced by the PAULI spin-matrix $\boldsymbol{\sigma}^P$, Eq. (10.6). We define, in analogy with (11.8), $\boldsymbol{s}^P = \frac{1}{2}\boldsymbol{\sigma}^P$ and (11.9) holds for $\boldsymbol{s}^P$ as well as for $\boldsymbol{s}$. We can see the physical significance of u_1 and u_2 by noting that the two ortho-normal PAULI spinors α and β,

$$\alpha(s_z) = \begin{pmatrix}1\\0\end{pmatrix}, \qquad \beta(s_z) = \begin{pmatrix}0\\1\end{pmatrix}, \tag{12.12}$$

[1] W. PAULI: Z. Physik **43**, 601 (1927).

are eigenstates of the z-component of the spin-operator $\boldsymbol{s}^P$ with eigenvalues $+\frac{1}{2}$ and $-\frac{1}{2}$, respectively. In the PAULI theory a state of the electron is thus specified by a two-component wave function, $u_\sigma(\boldsymbol{r})$, where $\sigma=1, 2$ plays the role of a coordinate additional to $\boldsymbol{r}$ which specifies if the spin (in the z-direction) is "up" or "dcwn". Instead of writing wave functions explicitly as spinors, we shall sometimes write wave functions as linear superpositions of products of a spatial and a spin wave function, $u=f(\boldsymbol{r})\,\alpha+g(\boldsymbol{r})\,\beta$, where f and g are ordinary spatial functions.

γ) *Interpretation.* We have discussed the physical significance of all the terms occuring in (12.11) [see Eq. (12.9)], except for the two terms involving the electric field $\mathscr{E}$, which were derived from (12.7). The term involving $\mathscr{E}\times\boldsymbol{p}$ is connected with the fact that, for a *moving* electron, an electric field $\mathscr{E}$ is equivalent with an extra magnetic field

$$\mathscr{H}_0=\frac{1}{c}\,\mathscr{E}\times\boldsymbol{v}=\frac{1}{m\,c}\,\mathscr{E}\times\boldsymbol{p}.$$

If we add $\mathscr{H}_0$ to the external magnetic field $\mathscr{H}$ [last term in (12.11)] we get exactly *twice*[1] the second-last term in (12.11). The term involving $(\mathscr{E}\cdot\boldsymbol{p})$ has no classical analcgue.

We consider next how (12.11) would be modified if we modify the DIRAC equation by the addition of a "PAULI-moment" term: In Sect. 19 we show that, according to quantum electrodynamics, the electron behaves (to a good approximation) as though its magnetic moment were not simply given by (12.10), but by $(1+g_1)$ times that quantity, where g_1 (the anomalous moment factor) is a small constant. We have seen in Sect. 10β that such a modification can be achieved, without destroying relativistic invariance, by adding a term (10.16) involving g_1 to the linear DIRAC equation [see (10.15)].

We outline briefly how to evaluate the change in the energy eigenvalue due to the PAULI moment term, considering this term as a small perturbation. In conventional notation the inclusion of the term in g_1 in (10.15) means that we add to the HAMILTONian operator H in the linear DIRAC Eq. (10.1) a small operator

$$H'=g_1\mu_0\,[\beta\,\boldsymbol{\sigma}\cdot\mathscr{H}-i\,\beta\,\boldsymbol{\alpha}\cdot\mathscr{E}]. \tag{12.13}$$

The term involving the magnetic field $\mathscr{H}$ is simply $-g_1\beta\,\boldsymbol{\mu}_s\cdot\mathscr{H}$, where $\boldsymbol{\mu}_s$ is defined in (12.10). The interaction energy between the spin magnetic moment of the electron and the magnetic field is simply $(1+g_1)$ times the value in the unmodified DIRAC theory. We evaluate next the approximate expectation value E'_{el} of the second term in (12.13) over the DIRAC wave function u, using the approximation (12.7). We find

$$\begin{aligned}\langle u^*\,\beta\,\boldsymbol{\alpha}\cdot\mathscr{E}\,u\rangle &=\langle U_A^*\,\mathscr{E}\cdot\boldsymbol{\sigma}^P\,U_B\rangle-\langle U_B^*\,\boldsymbol{\sigma}^P\cdot\mathscr{E}\,U_A\rangle\\ &=\frac{1}{2m\,c}\,\langle U_A^*\,(\mathscr{E}\cdot\boldsymbol{p}-\boldsymbol{p}\cdot\mathscr{E}+2i\,\mathscr{E}\cdot[\boldsymbol{p}\times\boldsymbol{\sigma}^P])\,U_A\rangle,\end{aligned}$$

where we have used the fact that $\operatorname{curl}\mathscr{E}=0$ and $p_x=-i\hbar\,\partial/\partial x$. We finally get

$$E'_{\mathrm{el}}=g_1\,\frac{\mu_0}{2m\,c}\,\langle U_A^*\,(\hbar\operatorname{div}\mathscr{E}+2\mathscr{E}\cdot[\boldsymbol{p}\times\boldsymbol{\sigma}^P])\,U_A\rangle. \tag{12.14}$$

One can show that (to within the accuracy of the PAULI approximation) the expression (12.14) is $2g_1$ times the expectation value of the sum of the two

[1] Regarding this factor of two, see L. H. THOMAS, Nature, Lond. **107**, 514 (1926).

terms involving $\mathcal{E}$ in (12.11). In establishing this identity the following relation is useful:

$$\langle U^* (\mathcal{E} \cdot \boldsymbol{p} + \boldsymbol{p} \cdot \mathcal{E})\, U \rangle = 0, \tag{12.15}$$

if U is an eigenstate of $(p^2/2m + V)$ and $\mathcal{E} = -\operatorname{grad} V$. (12.15) can be proved by writing $i\hbar\,\mathcal{E} = \boldsymbol{p} V - V \boldsymbol{p}$ and showing that $\langle U^* p^2 V U \rangle = \langle U^* V p^2 U \rangle$.

One can also derive an approximate equation involving only PAULI spinors and operators from the covariant quadratic Eq. (10.17). The derivation is somewhat similar to that of (12.11), but is very lengthy and involves dropping terms whose expectation values may diverge. The final result is the same as (12.11) [dropping terms in g_1^2 and terms which involve the operator occuring in (12.15)], except that the term involving $\mathcal{H}$ is multiplied by $(1 + g_1)$ and the two terms involving $\mathcal{E}$ by $(1 + 2g_1)$.

13. PAULI theory for a central potential. We consider now the PAULI approximation (12.11) for the special case of an electron in a central electric field. We put the magnetic field $\mathcal{H}$ and vector potential $\boldsymbol{A}$ equal to zero and consider φ a function of the radial distance r only, so that

$$\mathcal{E} = -\frac{\boldsymbol{r}}{r}\frac{d\varphi}{dr}. \tag{13.1}$$

Making use of the definition (11.4) for the orbital angular momentum $\boldsymbol{k}$ and writing simply $\boldsymbol{s}$ for $\frac{1}{2}\sigma^P$, the spin, and u for the PAULI-spinor wave function, we obtain from (12.11)

$$W u = \left\{ -\left(e\varphi + \frac{\hbar^2}{2m}\Delta\right) - \frac{1}{2mc^2}(W + e\varphi)^2 + \frac{\mu_0 \hbar}{2mc}\frac{d\varphi}{dr}\left[\frac{\partial}{\partial r} - \frac{2}{r}\boldsymbol{k}\cdot\boldsymbol{s}\right]\right\} u, \tag{13.2}$$

where

$$\mu_0 = e\hbar/2mc$$

is the BOHR magnetic moment, (or magneton).

α) Energy eigenvalue. We do not consider, at the moment, the explicit dependence of the wave function u on the spin-coordinate (index $\sigma = 1, 2$) or on the angle variables ϑ, φ. We reduce, first, the differential equation (13.2) to a differential equation in the radial distance r alone, using general operator methods.

We can consider (13.2) as a generalized HAMILTONian equation with W, the nonrelativistic energy, as eigenvalue and the operator[1] on the right side as the HAMILTONian H. H depends on the angle variables and on the spin through the LAPLACE operator Δ and through $\boldsymbol{k}\cdot\boldsymbol{s}$, the "spin-orbit coupling" term. The Δ-operator we have already rewritten in (1.11) in terms of the operator $\partial/\partial r$ and the orbital angular momentum operator $\boldsymbol{k}$,

$$\Delta u = \left(\frac{\partial^2}{\partial r^2} + \frac{2}{r}\frac{\partial}{\partial r} - \frac{\boldsymbol{k}^2}{r^2}\right) u. \tag{13.3}$$

It further follows from the definition (11.10) for the operator $\boldsymbol{M}$ for the total angular momentum that

$$2\boldsymbol{k}\cdot\boldsymbol{s} = \boldsymbol{M}^2 - \boldsymbol{k}^2 - \boldsymbol{s}^2. \tag{13.4}$$

We see, therefore, that our approximate HAMILTONian operator H, Eq. (13.2), not only commutes with $\boldsymbol{M}^2$ and $\boldsymbol{s}^2$ (as does the exact DIRAC HAMILTONian), but *also* with $\boldsymbol{k}^2$ [with which the exact DIRAC HAMILTONian does *not* commute,

[1] Unlike the HAMILTONian in the nonrelativistic SCHRÖDINGER theory, H not only involves the spin operator, but also depends explicitly on the eigenvalue. We shall only consider cases where $|W| \ll mc^2$ and shall not encounter any difficulty from the dependence of H on W.

see (11.13)]. Since $\boldsymbol{M}^2$, $\mathbf{s}^2$ and $\boldsymbol{k}^2$ (and M_z) also commute with each other, we can find stationary states u which are simultaneous eigenstates of $\boldsymbol{M}^2$, $\boldsymbol{k}^2$, and $\mathbf{s}^2$ (and M_z) and hence also of $\boldsymbol{k}\cdot\mathbf{s}$, Eq. (13.4). For such a stationary state we can replace the angular momentum operators in (13.2) by their eigenvalues,

$$\left.\begin{aligned}&\boldsymbol{k}^2 \to l(l+1), \quad \boldsymbol{M}^2 \to j(j+1), \quad \mathbf{s}^2 \to s(s+1), \quad s=\tfrac{1}{2}; \\ &2\boldsymbol{k}\cdot\mathbf{s} \to X, \quad X \equiv j(j+1) - l(l+1) - s(s+1).\end{aligned}\right\} \tag{13.5}$$

We know that $s=\frac{1}{2}$ and that l is an integer or zero. We cannot yet specify j further, but we shall see later that $j=l+\frac{1}{2}$ or $j=l-\frac{1}{2}$.

On substituting (13.5) into (13.2) only the operator $\partial/\partial r$ remains, besides the quantum numbers j, l and s ,and we solve only for the radial wave function R (function of r only, not of ϑ, φ and the spin-index σ),

$$\left.\begin{aligned}&\Big\{W + e\varphi + \frac{\hbar^2}{2m}\left[\frac{d^2}{dr^2} + \frac{2}{r}\frac{d}{dr} - \frac{l(l+1)}{r^2}\right] + \\ &\qquad + \frac{1}{2mc^2}(W+e\varphi)^2 - \frac{\hbar\mu_0}{2mc}\frac{d\varphi}{dr}\left(\frac{d}{dr} - \frac{X}{r}\right)\Big\} R = 0\end{aligned}\right\} \tag{13.6}$$

where the constant X was defined in (13.5) and $\mu_0 = e\hbar/2mc$. If $\bar{v}$ is the order of magnitude of the electron velocity ($\bar{v} \ll c$), then the expectation values of the operators in the second line of (13.6) are of order $(\bar{v}/c)^2\, W$. If we neglect the operators in the second line completely, (13.6) reduces to the radial part of the non-relativistic SCHRÖDINGER equation (12.6)

$$\left[\frac{2m}{\hbar^2}(W_0 + e\varphi) + \frac{d^2}{dr^2} + \frac{2}{r}\frac{d}{dr} - \frac{l(l+1)}{r^2}\right] R_0 = 0. \tag{13.7}$$

If we solve (13.7) for W_0 and R_0, then W_0 differs from the correct W, and R_0 from the correct R, by terms of relative order $(\bar{v}/c)^2$. From a comparison of (12.7) and the exact (12.8) it follows that the approximate PAULI Eq. (13.2) or (13.6) is itself accurate up to (and including) terms of relative order $(\bar{v}/c)^2$. Thus even an exact solution of (13.6) for W would differ from the correct value given by the exact DIRAC equation (which we shall derive in Sect. 14) by terms[1] of relative order $(\bar{v}/c)^4$. For this reason we shall only calculate the eigenvalue W of (13.6) to relative order $(\bar{v}/c)^2$ by first order perturbation theory.

We consider the zero order equation (13.7) as solved for W_0 and R_0. The first order perturbation correction W_1, to be added to W_0, is then the expectation value of the operators in the second line of (13.6), using the zero order wave function R_0. To this approximation we can also replace W by W_0 in the second line of (13.6) and obtain

$$\left.\begin{aligned}W_1 &= W_a + W_b; \\ W_a &= -\frac{1}{2mc^2}\int dr\, r^2 R_0^2 (W_0 + e\varphi)^2, \\ W_b &= \frac{\mu_0\hbar}{2mc}\int dr\, r^2 R_0\left(\frac{dR_0}{dr} - X\frac{R_0}{r}\right)\frac{d\varphi}{dr}.\end{aligned}\right\} \tag{13.8}$$

We return now to atomic units, introduce the fine structure constant

$$\alpha = \frac{e^2}{\hbar c},$$

[1] The expansion parameter in the PAULI approximation scheme, roughly speaking, is $(\bar{v}/c)^2$, not $\bar{v}/c$.

write V for the electrostatic potential[1] in atomic units and note that $\mu_0 = e\hbar/2mc$ is equal to $\alpha/2$ in atomic units. In atomic units (13.8) then reduces to (dropping the subscript 0 from R_0)

$$\left.\begin{aligned} W_a &= -\tfrac{1}{2}\alpha^2 \overline{(W_0+V)^2}, \\ W_b &= \frac{\alpha^2}{4}\int dr\, r^2 R\left(\frac{dR}{dr} - X\frac{R}{r}\right)\frac{dV}{dr}, \end{aligned}\right\} \tag{13.8a}$$

where the bar in the expression for W_a denotes the average over the zero-order wave function R. W_a represents the relativity correction due to the "variation of mass with velocity" and would also be obtained from the relativistic SCHRÖDINGER equation for spin-less particles. W_b, on the other hand, is characteristic of a particle with spin and its associated electromagnetic moment.

We return now to the special case of a COULOMB-potential,

$$V = \frac{Z}{r}.$$

Substituting the BALMER formula (2.11) for the zero-order energy W_0 and using (3.24), (3.25) for the expectation values of r^{-1} and r^{-2} in a hydrogen-like atom with principal quantum number n, the first term in (13.8a) reduces to

$$W_a = -\frac{\alpha^2}{2}\left(\frac{Z^4}{4n^4} - \frac{Z^3}{n^2}\overline{r^{-1}} + Z^2\overline{r^{-2}}\right) = -\frac{\alpha^2 Z^4}{2n^3}\left(\frac{1}{l+\frac{1}{2}} - \frac{3}{4n}\right). \tag{13.9}$$

In the first term in the expression for W_b we have $r^2\, dV/dr = -Z$. Integrating by parts, we get

$$W_b = \tfrac{1}{8}\alpha^2 Z\left[R^2(0) - R^2(\infty)\right] + \tfrac{1}{4}\alpha^2 X Z\,\overline{r^{-3}}. \tag{13.10}$$

For states of non-zero orbital angular momentum ($l \neq 0$), the wave function at the origin (and hence the term in square brackets) vanishes. Using (3.26) for the expectation value of r^{-3} and writing out the explicit form of the constant X, (13.5), we get, for $l \neq 0$,

$$W_b = +\frac{\alpha^2 Z^4}{4n^3}\,\frac{j(j+1) - l(l+1) - s(s+1)}{l(l+\frac{1}{2})(l+1)}. \tag{13.11}$$

For $l=0$ (S-states) the term in square brackets in (13.10) is non-zero and finite, but $X\overline{r^{-3}}$ is indeterminate: For $l=0$, j must equal s and X is zero, but the expectation value of r^{-3} diverges. This difficulty can be overcome as follows: The term involving $\overline{r^{-3}}$ was derived by using the approximation (12.7) instead of the exact expression (12.8), in particular we have replaced $(mc^2 + E + e\varphi)$ simply by $2mc^2$. For distances r of the order of the BOHR radius a/Z for nuclear charge Z, the error made in this neglect of $E - mc^2$ and of $e\varphi(r)$ is only of relative order $(Z\alpha)^2$. In all integrals used in the evaluation of the expectation values W_a and W_b, *except* in the integral leading to $\overline{r^{-3}}$, the important range of integration comes from r of the order of a/Z and the error made in our approximations is of relative order $(Z\alpha)^2$. For the $\overline{r^{-3}}$ term for $l=0$, the wave function is finite at the origin, where the COULOMB potential diverges and the neglect of $e\varphi$ compared with mc^2 is no longer justified for $r \lesssim e^2 Z/mc^2$. For this term then we use $(2mc^2 + e\varphi)$ instead of $2mc^2$ and instead of $\overline{r^{-3}}$ we get, in atomic units, the integral $\int dr\, r^2 R^2 [r^3(1 + Z\alpha^2/2r)]^{-1}$. This integral is finite, even for $l=0$, but X vanishes *exactly* for $l=0$, so the last term in (13.10) vanishes for $l=0$. Using (3.46) for the value of $R(0)$, we then get, for $l=0$, instead of (13.11) the expression

$$W_b = \alpha^2 Z^4/2n^3. \tag{13.12}$$

[1] *Not* the potential energy of the electron, i.e. $V = Z/r$, not $-Z/r$ for a nucleus of charge Z.

We shall prove soon that, for each value of l, there are two possible values of j, the inner quantum number, namely $l+\frac{1}{2}$ or $l-\frac{1}{2}$ (except for $l=0$, when $j=\frac{1}{2}$). (13.11) can then be written in the form

$$W_b = +\frac{\alpha^2 Z^4}{2n^3}\frac{1}{2l+1}\left\{\begin{array}{ll}(l+1)^{-1} & \text{if } j=l+\frac{1}{2}\\ -l^{-1} & \text{if } j=l-\frac{1}{2}.\end{array}\right\} \tag{13.13}$$

(13.13) also reduces to the correct expression (13.12) if $l=0$, $j=\frac{1}{2}$. Combining (13.9) and (13.13) we then get our final result for $W_1=W_a+W_b$, the PAULI approximation for the shift in the energy eigenvalue,

$$W_1 = -\frac{\alpha^2 Z^4}{2n^3}\left(\frac{1}{j+\frac{1}{2}}-\frac{3}{4n}\right). \tag{13.14}$$

Eq. (13.14) is valid for all l and j and we note the important fact that W_1 depends only on j and n, but *not* on l. The two states with the same value of j and n and with $l=j+\frac{1}{2}$ and $l=j-\frac{1}{2}$ are thus *completely degenerate.*

β) PAULI *eigenfunctions and values of the inner quantum number* j. We now return to the wave equation (13.2) in the PAULI approximation and investigate the angle and spin dependence of the wave function u, which is a two-component spinor. In (13.2) we again consider $H_0=-(e\varphi+\hbar^2\Delta/2m)$ as the unperturbed HAMILTONian. For fixed values of n and l, the most general eigenfunction of H_0 is

$$u_{nl} = R_{nl}(r)\begin{pmatrix} a\,Y_{lm_l}(\vartheta,\varphi)\\ b\,Y_{lm_l'}(\vartheta,\varphi)\end{pmatrix}, \tag{13.15}$$

where ϑ, φ are the spherical polar angle coordinates of the electron, a and b are *arbitrary* constants and m_l, m_l' are independent of each other (chosen from the integers $-l, -l+1, \ldots, +l$). Only the ratio a/b is of physical significance and, if u is to be normalized, we take $|a|^2+|b|^2=1$. The total HAMILTONian, as well as H_0, commutes with $M_z=k_z+s_z$, the component in the z-direction of the *total* angular momentum. We therefore restrict ourselves to wave functions u of type (13.15) which are also eigenstates of M_z with eigenvalue m. Using (1.10) and the explicit representation (10.6) for $\sigma_3^P=2s_z$, we have, for u of form (13.15),

$$M_z\begin{pmatrix}u_1\\u_2\end{pmatrix}=\begin{pmatrix}(m_l+\frac{1}{2})\,u_1\\(m_l'-\frac{1}{2})\,u_2\end{pmatrix}.$$

u is thus an eigenstate of M_z if

$$m_l+\tfrac{1}{2}=m_l'-\tfrac{1}{2}=m \tag{13.16}$$

or if either of the coefficients a and b in (13.15) is zero.

So far the ratio a/b is arbitrary, any value leading to an eigenstate of H_0, $\boldsymbol{k}^2$ and M_z. The full HAMILTONian of (13.2), however, also contains the operator $\boldsymbol{k}\cdot\boldsymbol{s}$ and we now have to find the values of a/b for which u is also an eigenstate of $\boldsymbol{k}\cdot\boldsymbol{s}$. It further follows from (13.4) that an eigenstate of $2\boldsymbol{k}\cdot\boldsymbol{s}$ with eigenvalue X [defined in (13.5)] is also an eigenstate of $\boldsymbol{M}^2$ with eigenvalue $j(j+1)$. Using (1.10), (1.14) and (10.6) for the matrix elements of k_i and s_i and choosing u of form (13.15) with (13.16), we have

$$2\boldsymbol{k}\cdot\boldsymbol{s}\,u = X\,u = \begin{pmatrix}\left[a\,(m-\frac{1}{2})-b\sqrt{(l+\frac{1}{2})^2-m^2}\right]Y_{l,m-\frac{1}{2}}\\ \left[-a\sqrt{(l+\frac{1}{2})^2-m^2}-b\,(m+\frac{1}{2})\right]Y_{l,m+\frac{1}{2}}\end{pmatrix}R_{nl}(r).$$

This equation is fulfilled for two possible values of the ratio a/b,

$$\frac{a_+}{b_+} = -\sqrt{\frac{l+m+\frac{1}{2}}{l-m+\frac{1}{2}}}, \quad \frac{a_-}{b_-} = \sqrt{\frac{l-m+\frac{1}{2}}{l+m+\frac{1}{2}}}. \tag{13.17}$$

The values[1] of the quantum number j and the eigenvalue X, (13.5), of $2\boldsymbol{k}\cdot\boldsymbol{s}$ for the two solutions labelled $+$ and $-$ are

$$\left.\begin{aligned} X_+ &= l, & j_+ &= l+\tfrac{1}{2}, \\ X_- &= -(l+1), & j_- &= l-\tfrac{1}{2}, \end{aligned}\right\} \tag{13.18}$$

except for $l=0$, when $X_+ = X_- = 0$ and $j_+ = j_- = \frac{1}{2}$. The two normalized eigenfunctions are then

$$\left.\begin{aligned} u_{nl,j=l+\frac{1}{2},m} &= \frac{1}{\sqrt{2l+1}} R_{nl}(r) \begin{pmatrix} \sqrt{l+m+\frac{1}{2}}\, Y_{l,m-\frac{1}{2}}(\vartheta,\varphi) \\ -\sqrt{l-m+\frac{1}{2}}\, Y_{l,m+\frac{1}{2}}(\vartheta,\varphi) \end{pmatrix}, \\ u_{nl,j=l-\frac{1}{2},m} &= \frac{1}{\sqrt{2l+1}} R_{nl}(r) \begin{pmatrix} \sqrt{l-m+\frac{1}{2}}\, Y_{l,m-\frac{1}{2}}(\vartheta,\varphi) \\ \sqrt{l+m+\frac{1}{2}}\, Y_{l,m+\frac{1}{2}}(\vartheta,\varphi) \end{pmatrix}. \end{aligned}\right\} \tag{13.19}$$

It is interesting to note that the ratios a/b in (13.17) do not depend on the value of the fine structure constant α and that neither a nor b is zero (except if $j=l+\frac{1}{2}$ and $m=\pm j$). Hence, even if α were allowed to approach zero (extreme nonrelativistic limit), the wave functions (13.19) would *not* be eigenstates of the operator k_z (nor of s_z). This is due to the fact that the eigenvalues of the "zero-order" nonrelativistic HAMILTONian H_0 are exactly the same for the $+$ and $-$ solutions in (13.19). Thus, even an infinitesimally small coefficient multiplying $(\boldsymbol{k}\cdot\boldsymbol{s})$ in (13.2) is sufficient to remove the degeneracy[2].

Any of the total wave functions u given by (13.19) are not eigenstates of s_z nor of the component of the spin $\boldsymbol{s}$ in any other direction (i.e. the spin-direction is not quantized). Nevertheless, for any such wave function and for a *specific* position (r, ϑ, φ) of the electron we can ask for the "direction of the spin". By this statement we mean the following: We are considering the wave function (13.19) of a particular eigenstate of M_z, consisting of the two spinor components $u_1(r,\vartheta,\varphi)$ and $u_2(r,\vartheta,\varphi)$. For a fixed value of (ϑ,φ) (the electron's polar angle coordinates with z as polar axis and with $\varphi=0$ in the zx-plane), the ratio u_1/u_2 is a constant. The constant spinor (u_1, u_2) must then be an eigenstate of the components s_ξ of the spin $\boldsymbol{s}$ in some particular direction $\boldsymbol{\xi}$ with polar coordinates (Θ, Φ). It can be shown, both by general invariance arguments[3] and by explicitly evaluating[4] the matrix elements of s_ξ, that the direction ξ is given by the relation,

$$\tan\left(\frac{\Theta}{2}\right) e^{i\Phi} = \frac{u_2}{u_1}. \tag{13.20}$$

[1] The statement that $j = l \pm \frac{1}{2}$ is merely a specific case of a more general theorem on the eigenvalues $j(j+1)$ of the square of the sum of two commuting angular momentum operators, $\boldsymbol{k}_a + \boldsymbol{k}_b$: If the eigenvalues of $\boldsymbol{k}_a^2$, $\boldsymbol{k}_b^2$ are $l_a(l_a+1)$ and $l_b(l_b+1)$, then $j = |l_a - l_b|, |l_a - b_b| + 1, \ldots, l_a + l_b$. j is defined as the *positive* root of $j(j+1) = \text{const}$.

[2] We can, of course, find a linear superposition of the two solutions, $+$ and $-$, for fixed l and m, for which a or b vanishes. Such wave functions are eigenstates of k_z and s_z but *not* of the HAMILTONian (13.2), since the eigenvalues X_+ and X_- are different. If α is considered very small, the two eigenvalues of the total HAMILTONian are approximately the same and such a wave function is "almost a stationary state".

[3] Ref. [*1*], p. 151.

[4] Ref. [*10*], p. 310.

By substituting the explicit values of u_2/u_1 from (13.19) into (13.20) one then finds the coordinates (Θ, Φ) of the spin-direction ξ corresponding to each electron position (ϑ, φ) (in particular, $\Phi = \varphi$, i.e. the spin direction lies in the plane containing $\boldsymbol{r}$ and the z-axis).

In our preceding discussion we have classified the stationary states, for a fixed value of the principal quantum number n, first according to the value of l and second according to the value of m. The orbital quantum number l can take on the values $(0, 1, 2, \ldots, n-1)$. For a fixed value of l, if neither a nor b in (13.15) vanishes, (13.16) holds. It follows from (13.16) and the inequalities $|m_l| \lesssim l$, $|m_l'| \lesssim l$, that the possible values of m are $(-l+\frac{1}{2}, -l+\frac{3}{2}, \ldots, l-\frac{1}{2})$. For each of these $2l$ values of m, both sets of solutions, $+$ and $-$, in (13.17) are possible. There are only two other solutions, satisfying all the requirements, both for $j=l+\frac{1}{2}$: (i) $a=0$ and $m=-(l+\frac{1}{2})$ and (ii) $b=0$ and $m=+(l+\frac{1}{2})$. We thus have $2(2l+1)$ linearly independent wave functions for a fixed value of n and l. The total number of wave functions for fixed n and any possible value of l is $2n^2$, *twice* as many as in the nonrelativistic SCHRÖDINGER theory (the factor of two stems from the two possible eigenvalues of s_z).

The same set of $2n^2$ wave functions for a fixed value of n can also be classified according to the values of j and m, where $j(j+1)$ and m are the eigenvalues of $\boldsymbol{M}^2$ and of M_z. The possible values of j are $(\frac{1}{2}, \frac{3}{2}, \ldots, n-\frac{3}{2}, n-\frac{1}{2})$. For a fixed value of j, the possible values of m are $(-j, -j+1, \ldots, +j)$. For each value of j, except $j=n-\frac{1}{2}$, there are two wave functions to each value of m: One (labelled $+$) with $l=j-\frac{1}{2}$, the other (labelled $-$) with $l=j+\frac{1}{2}$. For any $j \neq n-\frac{1}{2}$ we thus have $2(2j+1)$ linearly independent solutions. For $j=n-\frac{1}{2}$, only the wave functions (labelled $+$) with $l=j-\frac{1}{2}=n-1$ exist ($2n$ in number). The total number of wave functions is thus again

$$\sum_{j=\frac{1}{2}}^{n-\frac{3}{2}} 2(2j+1) + 2n = 2n^2.$$

14. The exact solution of the DIRAC equation[1]. *α) The angular dependence of the eigenfunctions.* Next, we shall obtain the exact solution to the DIRAC differential equation for an electron in a COULOMB field, for the discrete spectrum. Accordingly, we put

$$\boldsymbol{A} = 0, \qquad \varphi = Ze/r \tag{14.1}$$

in (10.1) and write down explicitly the DIRAC equations for the four components of the wave function:

$$\left.\begin{aligned}
-\frac{i}{\hbar c}\left(E+\frac{Ze^2}{r}-E_0\right)u_1+\frac{\partial u_3}{\partial z}+\frac{\partial u_4}{\partial x}-i\frac{\partial u_4}{\partial y}&=0,\\
-\frac{i}{\hbar c}\left(E+\frac{Ze^2}{r}-E_0\right)u_2-\frac{\partial u_4}{\partial z}+\frac{\partial u_3}{\partial x}+i\frac{\partial u_3}{\partial y}&=0,\\
-\frac{i}{\hbar c}\left(E+\frac{Ze^2}{r}+E_0\right)u_3+\frac{\partial u_1}{\partial z}+\frac{\partial u_2}{\partial x}-i\frac{\partial u_2}{\partial y}&=0,\\
-\frac{i}{\hbar c}\left(E+\frac{Ze^2}{r}+E_0\right)u_4-\frac{\partial u_2}{\partial z}+\frac{\partial u_1}{\partial x}+i\frac{\partial u_1}{\partial y}&=0.
\end{aligned}\right\} \tag{14.2}$$

As a point of departure we shall make use of the fact that we already know, approximately, the components u_1 and u_2 of the wave-function [PAULI functions

[1] Cf. C. G. DARWIN: Proc. Roy. Soc. Lond., Ser. A **118**, 654 (1928). — W. GORDON: Z. Physik **48**, 11 (1928).

(13.19)]. For the case $j=l+\frac{1}{2}$ we put

$$\left.\begin{aligned} u_1 &= g(r)\sqrt{\frac{l+m+\frac{1}{2}}{2l+1}}\, Y_{l,m-\frac{1}{2}}(\vartheta,\varphi), \\ u_2 &= -g(r)\sqrt{\frac{l-m+\frac{1}{2}}{2l+1}}\, Y_{l,m+\frac{1}{2}}(\vartheta,\varphi), \end{aligned}\right\} \tag{14.3}$$

The above differs from (13.19) only in that the radially dependent eigenfunction $g(r)$ is not set equal to the SCHRÖDINGER function $R_{nl}(r)$, but is left arbitrary. Inserting (14.3) into the last two DIRAC equations (14.2), and also making use of formulas (A.37) to (A.39) one obtains

$$\begin{aligned} \frac{i}{\hbar c}\left(E+\frac{Ze^2}{r}+E_0\right)u_3 &= \frac{\partial u_1}{\partial z}+\frac{\partial u_2}{\partial x}-i\frac{\partial u_2}{\partial y} \\ &= \sqrt{\frac{l-m+\frac{3}{2}}{2l+3}}\cdot\left(\frac{dg}{dr}-l\frac{g}{r}\right)Y_{l+1,m-\frac{1}{2}}, \\ \frac{i}{\hbar c}\left(E+\frac{Ze^2}{r}+E_0\right)u_4 &= \sqrt{\frac{l+m+\frac{3}{2}}{2l+3}}\left(\frac{dg}{dr}-l\frac{g}{r}\right)Y_{l+1,m+\frac{1}{2}}. \end{aligned}$$

If we put

$$\left.\begin{aligned} u_3 &= -\sqrt{\frac{l-m+\frac{3}{2}}{2l+3}}\, i f(r)\, Y_{l+1,m-\frac{1}{2}}(\vartheta,\varphi), \\ u_4 &= -\sqrt{\frac{l+m+\frac{3}{2}}{2l+3}}\, i f(r)\, Y_{l+1,m+\frac{1}{2}}(\vartheta,\varphi), \end{aligned}\right\} \tag{14.4}$$

we find that the following relation must hold between g and f

$$\frac{1}{\hbar c}\left(E+\frac{Ze^2}{r}+E_0\right)f = \frac{dg}{dr}-l\frac{g}{r}. \tag{14.5}$$

Next, we insert (14.4) into the third and fourth equations of the set (14.2). Employing formulas (A.37) to (A.39) again, one obtains two equations which are identical and are satisfied only if the following relation holds between f and g:

$$\frac{1}{\hbar c}\left(E+\frac{Ze^2}{r}-E_0\right)g = -\frac{df}{dr}-(l+2)\frac{f}{r}. \tag{14.6}$$

For the case $j=l-\frac{1}{2}$ one obtains, in a similar manner,

$$\left.\begin{aligned} u_1 &= \sqrt{\frac{l-m+\frac{1}{2}}{2l+1}}\, g(r)\, Y_{l,m-\frac{1}{2}}, \\ u_2 &= \sqrt{\frac{l+m+\frac{1}{2}}{2l+1}}\, g(r)\, Y_{l,m+\frac{1}{2}}, \\ u_3 &= -\sqrt{\frac{l+m-\frac{1}{2}}{2l-1}}\, i f(r)\, Y_{l-1,m-\frac{1}{2}}, \\ u_4 &= \sqrt{\frac{l-m-\frac{1}{2}}{2l-1}}\, i f(r)\, Y_{l-1,m+\frac{1}{2}}, \end{aligned}\right\} \tag{14.7}$$

$$\left.\begin{aligned} \frac{1}{\hbar c}\left(E+\frac{Ze^2}{r}+E_0\right)f &= \frac{dg}{dr}+(l+1)\frac{g}{r}, \\ \frac{1}{\hbar c}\left(E+\frac{Ze^2}{r}-E_0\right)g &= -\frac{df}{dr}+(l-1)\frac{f}{r}. \end{aligned}\right\} \tag{14.8}$$

Introducing a new quantum number $\varkappa$ by setting

$$\left.\begin{aligned}\varkappa &= -(j+\tfrac{1}{2}) = -(l+1), \quad &\text{if } j = l+\tfrac{1}{2},\\ \varkappa &= +(j+\tfrac{1}{2}) = +l, &\text{if } j = l-\tfrac{1}{2},\end{aligned}\right\} \tag{14.9}$$

(14.5), (14.6) and (14.8) can be summarized as follows:

$$\left.\begin{aligned}\frac{1}{\hbar c}\left(E+\frac{Ze^2}{r}+E_0\right)f-\left(\frac{dg}{dr}+(1+\varkappa)\frac{g}{r}\right)=0,\\ \frac{1}{\hbar c}\left(E+\frac{Ze^2}{r}-E_0\right)g+\left(\frac{df}{dr}+(1-\varkappa)\frac{f}{r}\right)=0.\end{aligned}\right\} \tag{14.10}$$

Thus, $\varkappa$ is a positive or negative integer. $\varkappa=0$ is not possible, for were we to put $l=0$ and $m=\frac{1}{2}$ in (14.7), then the only non-vanishing spherical harmonic would be the one contained in u_1. However, the factor $l-m+\frac{1}{2}$ contained in u_1 vanishes. Thus, the eigenfunction would vanish identically. For $\varkappa\neq 0$ it is readily seen from (14.3), (14.5) and (14.7) that there are $2|\varkappa|$ eigenfunctions, for each $\varkappa$, having the magnetic quantum-numbers $m=-(|\varkappa|-\frac{1}{2}), -(|\varkappa|-\frac{3}{2}) \ldots |\varkappa|-\frac{3}{2}, |\varkappa|-\frac{1}{2}$.

This completes the demonstration that the functions (14.3) which were postulated for the large components of the DIRAC wave-function will indeed lead to the goal. This is not completely obvious from the beginning. It might have happened that insertion of (14.4) into the first and second DIRAC equations would require an angular dependence different from the one postulated in (14.3), or we might have been led to a contradiction in the two equations for g (see also [4], Chap. 44).

β) Solution of the radial differential equation. Next, we shall solve the radial differential equation (14.10), and we shall do this by following the treatment of GORDON[1]. First of all, we introduce the functions χ_1 and χ_2 in place of f and g as follows

$$\chi_1 = r f, \quad \chi_2 = r g. \tag{14.11}$$

Setting E_0 equal to its value mc^2, we obtain

$$\left.\begin{aligned}\frac{d\chi_1}{dr}-\varkappa\frac{\chi_1}{r}=\left[\frac{mc}{\hbar}\left(1-\frac{E}{E_0}\right)-\alpha\frac{Z}{r}\right]\chi_2,\\ \frac{d\chi_2}{dr}+\varkappa\frac{\chi_2}{r}=\left[\frac{mc}{\hbar}\left(1+\frac{E}{E_0}\right)+\alpha\frac{Z}{r}\right]\chi_1.\end{aligned}\right\} \tag{14.12}$$

In the above, $\alpha=\dfrac{e^2}{\hbar c}=1/137.037$ is SOMMERFELD's fine-structure constant. For large values of r, (14.12) has the asymptotic solution

$$\left.\begin{aligned}\chi_1 = a_1 e^{-\lambda r}, \quad \chi_2 = a_2 e^{-\lambda r}, \quad \lambda = \frac{mc}{\hbar}\sqrt{1-\frac{E^2}{E_0^2}},\\ a_1 = -a\sqrt{1-\frac{E}{E_0}}, \quad a_2 = +a\sqrt{1+\frac{E}{E_0}}.\end{aligned}\right\} \tag{14.13}$$

In passing we note that the quantity $2\pi\hbar/mc = 2.43\times 10^{-10}$ cm is the COMPTON wavelength. The COMPTON wavelength equals the radius of the first BOHR orbit multiplied by $2\pi\alpha$. Thus, in atomic units

$$\lambda = \frac{1}{\alpha}\sqrt{1-\left(\frac{E}{E_0}\right)^2} = \frac{1}{\alpha}\sqrt{1-\alpha^4 E^2}. \tag{14.14}$$

---

[1] W. GORDON: Z. Physik **48**, 11 (1928).

Use has been made of the fact that the rest energy of the electron mc^2 equals $2/\alpha^2$ in atomic units, i.e., approximately equal to 37560 times the ionization potential of hydrogen.

The next step consists of writing down a functional form which is valid for all values of r. To this end one might be tempted to replace the constant a by a function of r (cf. Sect. 2). However, this would amount to the assumption, surely unjustified, that χ_1 and χ_2 have a constant ratio for all values of r. Instead, we must have at our disposal two functions of r, and we therefore put

$$\chi_1 = \sqrt{1-\varepsilon}\, e^{-\lambda r}(\varphi_1 - \varphi_2), \qquad \chi_2 = \sqrt{1+\varepsilon}\, e^{-\lambda r}(\varphi_1 + \varphi_2), \tag{14.15}$$

$$\varepsilon = E/E_0. \tag{14.16}$$

In view of (14.13) it is clear that for large values of r, φ_2 is much greater than φ_1. Let us introduce the new independent variable

$$\varrho = 2\lambda r. \tag{14.17}$$

Then (14.12) becomes

$$\left.\begin{aligned} \frac{1}{\sqrt{1-\varepsilon}}\left(\frac{d\chi_1}{d\varrho} - \frac{\varkappa}{\varrho}\chi_1\right) &= \left(\frac{1}{2} - \sqrt{\frac{1+\varepsilon}{1-\varepsilon}}\,\alpha\frac{Z}{\varrho}\right)\frac{\chi_2}{\sqrt{1+\varepsilon}},\\ \frac{1}{\sqrt{1+\varepsilon}}\left(\frac{d\chi_2}{d\varrho} + \frac{\varkappa}{\varrho}\chi_2\right) &= \left(\frac{1}{2} + \sqrt{\frac{1-\varepsilon}{1+\varepsilon}}\,\alpha\frac{Z}{\varrho}\right)\frac{\chi_1}{\sqrt{1-\varepsilon}}. \end{aligned}\right\} \tag{14.18}$$

Inserting (14.15) into (14.18) we obtain

$$\left.\begin{aligned} \frac{d\varphi_1}{d\varrho} &= \left(1 - \frac{\alpha\varepsilon}{\sqrt{1-\varepsilon^2}}\frac{Z}{\varrho}\right)\varphi_1 + \left(-\frac{\varkappa}{\varrho} - \frac{\alpha}{\sqrt{1-\varepsilon^2}}\frac{Z}{\varrho}\right)\varphi_2,\\ \frac{d\varphi_2}{d\varrho} &= \left(-\frac{\varkappa}{\varrho} + \frac{\alpha}{\sqrt{1-\varepsilon^2}}\frac{Z}{\varrho}\right)\varphi_1 + \frac{\alpha\varepsilon}{\sqrt{1-\varepsilon^2}}\frac{Z}{\varrho}\varphi_2. \end{aligned}\right\} \tag{14.19}$$

Next, we expand φ_1 and φ_2 as power series in ϱ

$$\varphi_1 = \varrho^\gamma \sum_{\nu=0}^{\infty} a_\nu \varrho^\nu, \quad \varphi_2 = \varrho^\gamma \sum_{\nu=0}^{\infty} b_\nu \varrho^\nu. \tag{14.20}$$

Inserting the power series expansions into (14.19) and equating like powers of ϱ we obtain

$$\left.\begin{aligned} a_\nu(\nu+\gamma) &= a_{\nu-1} - \frac{\alpha\varepsilon Z}{\sqrt{1-\varepsilon^2}}a_\nu - \left(\varkappa + \frac{\alpha Z}{\sqrt{1-\varepsilon^2}}\right)b_\nu,\\ b_\nu(\nu+\gamma) &= \left(-\varkappa + \frac{\alpha Z}{\sqrt{1-\varepsilon^2}}\right)a_\nu + \frac{\alpha\varepsilon Z}{\sqrt{1-\varepsilon^2}}b_\nu. \end{aligned}\right\} \tag{14.21}$$ [1]

In particular, let us put $\nu = 0$. This gives two homogeneous equations in the two unknowns a_0 and b_0 ($a_{-1} = 0$). In order that a solution exist it is necessary that

$$\begin{vmatrix} \gamma + \dfrac{\alpha\varepsilon Z}{\sqrt{1-\varepsilon^2}} & \varkappa + \dfrac{\alpha Z}{\sqrt{1-\varepsilon^2}} \\ \varkappa - \dfrac{\alpha Z}{\sqrt{1-\varepsilon^2}} & \gamma - \dfrac{\alpha\varepsilon Z}{\sqrt{1-\varepsilon^2}} \end{vmatrix} = 0$$

[1] At this point we can readily see the advantage which (14.15) has over a function of the form $\chi_i = e^{-\lambda r} f_i(r)$. As a result of the fact that the function φ_2 approaches a power for large values of r $\left(\frac{d\varphi_2}{d\varrho} \sim \frac{\varphi_2}{\varrho}\right)$, the second Eq. (14.21) contains only a_ν and b_ν; it does not contain $a_{\nu-1}$ or $b_{\nu-1}$, so that b_ν can be expressed in terms of a_ν only.

i.e., that

$$\gamma = \pm \sqrt{\varkappa^2 - \alpha^2 Z^2}. \tag{14.22}$$

In order that φ_1 and φ_2 be acceptable eigenfunctions, they must be quadratically integrable. More precisely, the integral

$$\int (|f|^2 + |g|^2)\, r^2\, dr = \int (\chi_1^2 + \chi_2^2)\, dr = \int e^{-\varrho} (\varphi_1^2 + 2\varepsilon\, \varphi_1 \varphi_2 + \varphi_2^2)\, dr$$

must exist. That will be the case only if we choose the positive square root in (14.22). The ratio of the coefficients a_ν/b_ν can now be obtained from the second Eq. (14.21),

$$\frac{b_\nu}{a_\nu} = - \frac{-\varkappa + \alpha Z/\sqrt{1-\varepsilon^2}}{n' - \nu}. \tag{14.23}$$

In the above, we have abbreviated

$$n' = \frac{\alpha Z \varepsilon}{\sqrt{1-\varepsilon^2}} - \gamma = \frac{\alpha Z \varepsilon}{\sqrt{1-\varepsilon^2}} - \sqrt{\varkappa^2 - \alpha^2 Z^2}. \tag{14.24}$$

Inserting (14.23) into the first of the Eq. (14.21) we obtain the following recursion formula for the coefficients a_ν:

$$a_\nu = - \frac{n' - \nu}{\nu(2\gamma + \nu)} a_{\nu-1} = (-)^\nu \frac{(n'-1)\ldots(n'-\nu)}{\nu!\,(2\gamma+1)\ldots(2\gamma+\nu)} a_0, \tag{14.25}$$

and, since (14.23) gives

$$\frac{b_\nu}{a_\nu} = \frac{b_0}{a_0} \frac{n'}{n' - \nu},$$

we obtain

$$b_\nu = (-)^\nu \frac{n' \ldots (n' - \nu + 1)}{\nu!\,(2\gamma+1)\ldots(2\gamma+\nu)} b_0. \tag{14.26}$$

As in the nonrelativistic case of Sect. 3, we must require that the power series for φ_1 and φ_2 terminate for real values of λ, i.e., for $\varepsilon < 1$ and $E < E_0$ (discrete spectrum), otherwise the eigenfunctions χ_1 and χ_2 increase as $e^{+\lambda r}$ with increasing values of r. The series terminate only if n' is a non-negative integer. In this case the series for φ_2 goes up to the power $r^{n'}$, and the series for φ_1 up to $r^{n'-1}$.

The case $n' = 0$ requires special consideration. It is readily seen from (14.25) that, unless $a_0 = 0$, the coefficients of all higher powers will not vanish. It should be noted, however, that according to (14.23)

$$\frac{a_0}{b_0} = - \frac{n'}{-\varkappa + \alpha Z/\sqrt{1-\varepsilon^2}}. \tag{14.27}$$

This vanishes provided the denominator is different from zero. However, for the case $n' = 0$, (14.24) gives

$$\gamma^2 = \varkappa^2 - \alpha^2 Z^2 = \alpha^2 Z^2 \frac{\varepsilon^2}{1-\varepsilon^2}, \text{ hence } \varkappa = \pm \frac{\alpha Z}{\sqrt{1-\varepsilon^2}}.$$

Thus, the denominator in (14.27) differs from zero only for negative values of $\varkappa\,(j = l + \frac{1}{2})$ and $\varkappa = -(l+1)$. In this case $a_0 = 0$, b_0 is non-vanishing, and we have arrived at a solution to the problem. On the other hand, if $\varkappa$ is positive, the denominator goes to zero as n', the ratio a_0/b_0 has a non-vanishing value and the series for φ_1 does not terminate. The case $n' = 0$, $\varkappa = l$ must thus be excluded. On the other hand, $n' = 0$, $\varkappa = -(l+1)$ is permissible. n' replaces the radial quantum number $n_r = n - l - 1$ of the SCHRÖDINGER theory.

We finally introduce the principal quantum-number

$$n = n' + k, \qquad k = |\varkappa| = j + \tfrac{1}{2} \tag{14.28}$$

and solve (14.24) for the desired eigenvalue ε

$$\varepsilon = \frac{E}{E_0} = \frac{1}{\sqrt{1 + \frac{\alpha^2 Z^2}{(n' + \gamma)^2}}} = \frac{1}{\sqrt{1 + \left(\frac{\alpha Z}{n - k + \sqrt{k^2 - \alpha^2 Z^2}}\right)^2}}. \tag{14.29}$$

(14.29) is our final formula for the energy E of the hydrogen atom. The energy depends only on k, i.e., only on j; the energy is independent of the sign of $\varkappa$, [i.e., independent of l, cf. (13.14)]. For light atoms (small values of Z) the energy is only slightly less than the rest energy E_0 of the electron because of the small magnitude of the fine-structure constant α. A more detailed discussion of the energy formula is postponed until Sect. 17.

γ) Discussion and normalization of the radial eigenfunctions of the KEPLER *problem.* The functions φ_1 and φ_2 are essentially confluent hypergeometric functions as can be seen directly from the recursion formulas (14.25) and (14.26), namely

$$\left.\begin{aligned} \varphi_1 &= -c \frac{n'}{\sqrt{-\varkappa + \alpha Z/\sqrt{1-\varepsilon^2}}} \varrho^\gamma F(-n'+1,\ 2\gamma+1,\ \varrho), \\ \varphi_2 &= c\sqrt{-\varkappa + \alpha Z/\sqrt{1-\varepsilon^2}}\, \varrho^\gamma F(-n',\ 2\gamma+1,\ \varrho). \end{aligned}\right\} \tag{14.30}$$

The constant c is as yet undetermined, and we shall use it to normalize the eigenfunction u. The condition of normalization for the DIRAC eigenfunctions is as follows:

$$\int |u|^2 d\tau = \int (|u_1|^2 + |u_2|^2 + |u_3|^2 + |u_4|^2)\, d\tau = 1. \tag{14.31}$$

Since the spherical harmonics Y_{lm} are already normalized, the integration over angles in view of (14.3), (14.4) and (14.7), simply gives

$$\int |u|^2 d\tau = \int (|f|^2 + |g|^2)\, r^2 dr = \int (\chi_1^2 + \chi_2^2)\, dr = 1. \tag{14.32}$$

The above holds both for $j = l + \frac{1}{2}$ and $j = l - \frac{1}{2}$. The somewhat tedious integration has been carried out by BECHERT[1] giving the following value for the constant c which occurs in (14.30),

$$c = \frac{\sqrt{\Gamma(2\gamma + n' + 1)}}{\Gamma(2\gamma + 1)\sqrt{n'!}} \sqrt{\frac{\lambda\sqrt{1-\varepsilon^2}}{2\alpha Z}}. \tag{14.33}$$

The formulas can be further simplified by inserting the explicit value of the energy (14.29):

$$1 - \varepsilon^2 = \frac{(\alpha Z)^2}{(n'+\gamma)^2 + (\alpha Z)^2} = \frac{(\alpha Z)^2}{n^2 - 2n'\left(k - \sqrt{k^2 - \alpha^2 Z^2}\right)}. \tag{14.34}$$

Next, we define the "apparent principal quantum-number" N

$$N = \sqrt{n^2 - 2n'\left(k - \sqrt{k^2 - \alpha^2 Z^2}\right)}, \tag{14.35}$$

which clearly becomes equal to the actual principal quantum-number n if we neglect the relativistic correction, that is, if we set $\alpha = 0$ and thus [cf. (14.22)] $\gamma = k$. Then according to (14.13) and (14.14)

$$\lambda = \frac{mc}{\hbar}\frac{\alpha Z}{N} = \frac{1}{a_0}\frac{Z}{N}, \tag{14.36}$$

in which a_0 is the atomic unit of length. Introducing the above into (14.11), (14.15), (14.30), and (14.33), we obtain the following explicit expressions for the

[1] K. BECHERT: Ann. d. Phys. 6, 700 (1930).

normalized radial DIRAC eigenfunctions:

$$\left.\begin{aligned}
f &= -\frac{\sqrt{\Gamma(2\gamma+n'+1)}}{\Gamma(2\gamma+1)\sqrt{n'!}}\sqrt{\frac{1-\varepsilon}{4N(N-\varkappa)}}\left(\frac{2Z}{Na_0}\right)^{\frac{3}{2}} e^{-\frac{Zr}{Na_0}}\left(\frac{2Zr}{Na_0}\right)^{\gamma-1}\times\\
&\quad\times\left[n'F\left(-n'+1,2\gamma+1,\frac{2Zr}{Na_0}\right)+(N-\varkappa)F\left(-n',2\gamma+1,\frac{2Zr}{Na_0}\right)\right],\\
g &= -\frac{\sqrt{\Gamma(2\gamma+n'+1)}}{\Gamma(2\gamma+1)\sqrt{n'!}}\sqrt{\frac{1+\varepsilon}{4N(N-\varkappa)}}\left(\frac{2Z}{Na_0}\right)^{\frac{3}{2}} e^{-\frac{Zr}{Na_0}}\left(\frac{2Zr}{Na_0}\right)^{\gamma-1}\times\\
&\quad\times\left[-n'F\left(-n'+1,2\gamma+1,\frac{2Zr}{Na_0}\right)+(N-\varkappa)F\left(-n',2\gamma+1,\frac{2Zr}{Na_0}\right)\right].
\end{aligned}\right\}\quad(14.37)$$

The various quantities occurring in (14.37) were previously defined: for $\varkappa$ see (14.9), γ (14.22), ε (14.16) and (14.29), n' (14.24) and (14.28), N (14.35), and $k=|\varkappa|$.

The functions (14.37) have an appearance which is quite similar to the SCHRÖDINGER eigenfunction (3.20). They differ only in the argument in that N replaces the actual principal quantum-number n, and either $\varkappa$ or k appears in the place of l. If the fine-structure constant α is neglected compared to unity throughout (14.37), this amounts to setting $l=k$, $N=n$ and $\varepsilon=1$ [cf. (14.22), (14.28), (14.34) and (14.35)]. Then f vanishes on account of the factor $1-\varepsilon$, and g becomes precisely, as it must, the normalized SCHRÖDINGER eigenfunction (3.17), provided we express $\varkappa$ in terms of l by means of (14.9) and use the recurrence relation

$$xF(a+1,b+1,x)=bF(a+1,b,x)-bF(a,b,x).$$

We give below the explicit forms[1] of the radial wave functions (14.37) for the K and L shells ($n=1$ and 2). We define

$$\left.\begin{aligned}
&\gamma_1=\sqrt{1-\alpha^2Z^2},\qquad \gamma_2=\sqrt{4-\alpha^2Z^2};\\
&N_1=1,\quad N_2=\sqrt{2(1+\gamma_1)},\quad N_3=2;\quad \varrho_i=\frac{2Zr}{N_ia_0};\\
&\varepsilon_1=\left[1+\left(\frac{\alpha Z}{\gamma_1}\right)^2\right]^{-\frac{1}{2}},\quad \varepsilon_2=\left[1+\left(\frac{\alpha Z}{1+\gamma_1}\right)^2\right]^{-\frac{1}{2}},\quad \varepsilon_3=\left[1+\left(\frac{\alpha Z}{\gamma_2}\right)^2\right]^{-\frac{1}{2}}.
\end{aligned}\right\}\quad(14.38)$$

We then get from (14.37):

(i) $1S_{\frac{1}{2}}$-state ($n=1$, $l=0$, $j=\frac{1}{2}$):

$$\left.\begin{aligned}
g&=\left(\frac{2Z}{a_0}\right)^{\frac{3}{2}}\sqrt{\frac{1+\varepsilon_1}{2\Gamma(2\gamma_1+1)}}\,e^{-\frac{1}{2}\varrho_1}\varrho_1^{\gamma_1-1},\\
f&=-\sqrt{\frac{1-\varepsilon_1}{1+\varepsilon_1}}\,g.
\end{aligned}\right\}\quad(14.39)$$

(ii) $2S_{\frac{1}{2}}$-state ($n=2$, $l=0$, $j=\frac{1}{2}$):

$$\left.\begin{aligned}
g&=\left(\frac{2Z}{N_2a_0}\right)^{\frac{3}{2}}\sqrt{\frac{2\gamma_1+1}{\Gamma(2\gamma_1+1)}}\sqrt{\frac{1+\varepsilon_2}{4N_2(N_2+1)}}\,e^{-\frac{1}{2}\varrho_2}\left[N_2\varrho_2^{\gamma_1-1}-\frac{N_2+1}{2\gamma_1+1}\varrho_2^{\gamma_1}\right],\\
f&=-\sqrt{\frac{1-\varepsilon_2}{1+\varepsilon_2}}\,\frac{(2\gamma_1+1)(N_2+2)-(N_2+1)\varrho_2}{(2\gamma_1+1)N_2-(N_2+1)\varrho_2}\,g.
\end{aligned}\right\}\quad(14.40)$$

[1] These expressions are taken from W. B. PAYNE, Ph. D. Thesis, Louisiana State University 1955 (unpublished). Payne has also tabulated the radial wave functions for the M and N shells. See also E. H. BURHOP and H. S. MASSEY, Proc. Roy. Soc. Lond., Ser. A **153**, 661 (1935). Graphs of the DIRAC wave functions are given by H. E. WHITE, Phys. Rev. **38**, 513 (1931). Expressions for the DIRAC wave functions in terms of generalized LAGUERRE polynomials are given by L. DAVIS, Phys. Rev. **56**, 186 (1939).

(iii) $2P_{\frac{1}{2}}$-state ($n=2,\ l=1,\ j=\frac{1}{2}$):

$$\left.\begin{aligned} g &= \left(\frac{2Z}{N_2 a_0}\right)^{\frac{3}{2}} \sqrt{\frac{2\gamma_1+1}{\Gamma(2\gamma_1+1)}} \sqrt{\frac{1+\varepsilon_2}{4N_2(N_2-1)}}\, e^{-\frac{1}{2}\varrho_2} \left[(N_2-2)\,\varrho_2^{\gamma_1-1} - \frac{N_2-1}{2\gamma_1+1}\,\varrho_2^{\gamma_1}\right]. \\ f &= -\sqrt{\frac{1-\varepsilon_2}{1+\varepsilon_2}}\, \frac{(2\gamma_1+1)\,N_2-(N_2-1)\,\varrho_2}{(2\gamma_1+1)(N_2-2)-(N_2-1)\,\varrho_2}\, g. \end{aligned}\right\} \quad (14.41)$$

(iv) $2P_{\frac{3}{2}}$-state ($n=2,\ l=1,\ j=\frac{3}{2}$):

$$\left.\begin{aligned} g &= \left(\frac{Z}{a_0}\right)^{\frac{3}{2}} \sqrt{\frac{1+\varepsilon_3}{2\Gamma(2\gamma_2+1)}}\, e^{-\frac{1}{2}\varrho_3}\, \varrho_3^{\gamma_2-1}, \\ f &= -\sqrt{\frac{1-\varepsilon_3}{1+\varepsilon_3}}\, g. \end{aligned}\right\} \quad (14.42)$$

δ) Comparison with SCHRÖDINGER *wave functions.* Some general remarks can be made about the order of magnitude of the deviation of the DIRAC radial wave functions (14.37) from the equivalent nonrelativistic wave function R. We restrict ourselves, at first, to relatively small values of the principal quantum number n and to reasonably small values of the nuclear charge, $Z \ll 137$: For $\varrho = (2Zr/Na_0)$ of order of magnitude unity (r of the order of the BOHR radius for charge Z, the important range in most integrals over r), the ratios $(g-R)/R$ and $(f/g)^2$ are of order $(Z\alpha)^2$. For the states with $j=l-\frac{1}{2}$ and for $\varrho \ll 1$, the ratios $(g-R)/R$ and $(f/g)^2$ are of order $(Z\alpha)^2\varrho^{-1}$. For $j=l+\frac{1}{2}$ these ratios increase much less rapidly with decreasing ϱ. Note that for r as small as the COMPTON wavelength of the electron, ϱ is of order $(Z\alpha)$ and $(f/g)^2$ and $(g-R)/R$ are still only of order $Z\alpha$ or smaller.

The DIRAC wave functions with $j=\frac{1}{2}$ ($l=0$ or 1), unlike the other DIRAC functions and all SCHRÖDINGER wave functions, are *singular* at the origin for all principal quantum numbers n. If $Z\alpha \approx Z/137$ is small, however, this singularity is a very weak one. Consider, for instance, the states with $j=\frac{1}{2}$ and $l=0$ (for any value of n). For small distances, $\varrho \ll 1$, the SCHRÖDINGER function $R(\varrho)$ is approximately equal to a constant $R(0)$, but the DIRAC function $g(\varrho)$ is given by

$$g(\varrho) \sim R(0)\,\varrho^{\gamma-1} \sim R(0)\exp\left[\frac{1}{2}(Z\alpha)^2\log\frac{1}{\varrho}\right].$$

Thus $g(\varrho)$ is infinite at the origin but, at finite distances ϱ larger than $\exp(-1/Z^2\alpha^2)$, $(g-R)/R$ is still only of order $\frac{1}{2}(Z\alpha)^2\log\varrho$. Only for exceedingly small distances, ϱ of the order of $\exp[-2(137/Z)^2]$, does $(g-R)/R$ become of order unity or greater. For all but very large Z, this distance is well inside the nucleus. For the $j=\frac{1}{2}$, $l=1$ states, the singular term is smaller by a factor of order $(Z\alpha)^2$ than for the $l=0$ states. Since $R(\varrho)$ is proportional to ϱ for small ϱ if $l=1$, in this case $(g-R)/R$ is of order $(Z\alpha)^2/\varrho$.

We have thus seen that, for all but extremely small values of the radial distance r, the large components of the radial DIRAC wave functions approximate the nonrelativistic ones closely if $Z\alpha \approx Z/137$ is small. For heavy atoms the parameter $Z\alpha$ is by no means negligible and the deviations between the relativistic and SCHRÖDINGER wave functions are important, at least for low values of j. These deviations (and the singularity of the DIRAC functions, in particular) are especially important for the hyperfine structure and other effects for the states with $j=\frac{1}{2}$ and low n in heavy atoms. Quite generally the deviations between the DIRAC and SCHRÖDINGER functions become less marked as the values of n and especially of j increase.

We finally discuss, in the light of the preceding remarks, the accuracy of the terms, obtained in the PAULI approximation (13.10), which involve the wave function at the origin, $u(0)$. In Sect. 13 we had replaced the DIRAC wave function $u(0)$ by the nonrelativistic expression $R_0(0)$ and have to justify this procedure for states with $j=\frac{1}{2}$ ($l=0$ or 1), for which the DIRAC wave function at the origin diverges. As in the discussion preceding (13.12) we note that we have replaced $(mc^2+E+e\varphi)$ by $2mc^2$ in the derivation of (13.10). Using again the more accurate expression $(2mc^2+e\varphi)$, we get in (13.10), instead of $u^2(0)$, the integral

$$\int_0^\infty d\varrho \left(1+\frac{Z\alpha^2}{2\varrho}\right)^{-1} \frac{d}{d\varrho}\, u^2(\varrho) \tag{14.43}$$

with ϱ the radial distance in atomic units. If $Z\alpha \ll 1$ and $u(\varrho)$ is not singular, $u^2(0)$ is an excellent approximation for the integral (14.42). If $u(\varrho)$ has the weak singularity $\varrho^{-\frac{1}{2}(Z\alpha)^2}$ of the DIRAC functions for $j=\frac{1}{2}$ (and $Z\alpha\ll 1$), the integral (14.42) is still finite and equal, say, to $u^2(\varrho_0)$ where ϱ_0 is some characteristic length of order $(Z\alpha)^2$ atomic units ($\sim Z^2 r_0$ in ordinary units, where $r_0=e^2/mc^2\sim 10^{-13}$ cm is the "classical radius of the electron"). We have discussed above the relation between the radial DIRAC functions (f and g) and the SCHRÖDINGER function R for small distances ϱ. Using these relations one can show that replacing $u^2(\varrho_0)$ by $R^2(0)$ in (13.10) gives an approximation to W_b which is in error at most by terms of relative order $(Z\alpha)^2 \log Z\alpha$, both for the $S_{\frac{1}{2}}$ and the $P_{\frac{1}{2}}$ states.

15. DIRAC equation. Continuous spectrum. For a DIRAC electron in the COULOMB field of a positively charged nucleus, we found a discrete spectrum of bound states for values E of the total energy (including the rest mass $E_0=mc^2$) in the range $0<E<mc^2$. For $E>mc^2$, the effective quantum number n', Eq. (14.24), is complex. In analogy with the nonrelativistic theory, Sect. 4, one finds a continuous spectrum of stationary states in the range $E>mc^2$ and the corresponding wave functions have oscillating forms at large distances from the nucleus. As in the nonrelativistic case, the wave equation can be separated in spherical polar coordinates. From the phase shifts for these partial wave solutions one can again calculate the differential cross sections for scattering (cf. Sect. 7). We shall not carry out such calculations in detail, but merely quote the main results. We shall also discuss briefly solutions of the DIRAC equation with negative total energy E, which have no nonrelativistic analogue.

α) Partial wave solutions. For $E>mc^2$, as well as for $E<mc^2$, and for any central potential, stationary states can be found which are also eigenstates of the total angular momentum operators $\boldsymbol{M}^2$ and M_z with corresponding quantum numbers j and m. For fixed values of E, j and m we still get two linearly independent solutions. The angular and spin dependence of the one solution, denoted by $j=l+\frac{1}{2}$, is still given by (14.3) and (14.4); that of the other solution, denoted by $j=l-\frac{1}{2}$, is given by (14.7). The radial wave functions g and f again satisfy the differential Eq. (14.10), but asymptotically have the oscillating behavior of spherical waves. Exact analytic expressions for these radial wave functions (for a COULOMB potential) in terms of hypergeometric functions were derived first by DARWIN[1]. Extensive discussions of these wave functions and of alternative forms are given elsewhere[2] and we shall only quote DARWIN's result for the "large component" $g(r)$ for the case $j=l-\frac{1}{2}$.

[1] C. G. DARWIN: Proc. Roy. Soc. Lond., Ser. A **118**, 654 (1928).

[2] L. K. ACHESON: Phys. Rev. **82**, 488 (1951). — L. R. ELTON: Proc. Phys. Soc. Lond. A **66**, 806 (1953). — YENNIE, RAVENHALL and WILSON: Phys. Rev. **95**, 500 (1954). See also ref. [9], p. 79.

According to the theory of relativity the momentum $\hbar k$ and velocity v of a free electron is related to its total energy E by the relations

$$\varepsilon \equiv \frac{E}{m c^2} = \sqrt{1 + \left(\frac{\hbar k}{m c}\right)^2} = \left(1 - \frac{v^2}{c^2}\right)^{-\frac{1}{2}}. \tag{15.1}$$

We define three further dimensionless parameters

$$\left.\begin{aligned} \gamma_l &= \sqrt{l^2 - \alpha^2 Z^2}, & &(\alpha = e^2/\hbar c), \\ \eta &= \frac{Z e^2}{\hbar v} = \frac{Z \alpha \varepsilon}{\sqrt{\varepsilon^2 - 1}}, & \eta' &= \frac{Z e^2}{\hbar v}\sqrt{1 - \frac{v^2}{c^2}} = \frac{Z\alpha}{\sqrt{\varepsilon^2 - 1}}. \end{aligned}\right\} \tag{15.2}$$

We denote the "large" radial function g for the $j = l - \frac{1}{2}$ solution, Eq. (14.7), by g_{-l-1}. DARWIN's result is

$$\left.\begin{aligned} g_{-l-1} = {} & N_{-l-1} (2 k r)^{\gamma_l} r^{-1} e^{-i k r} \times \\ & \times \{(\gamma_l - i\eta) F(\gamma_l + i\eta, 2\gamma_l + 1, 2 i k r) - \\ & - (l - i\eta') F(\gamma_l + 1 + i\eta, 2\gamma_l + 1, 2 i k r)\}. \end{aligned}\right\} \tag{15.3}$$

If we choose for the normalization factor N

$$N = \frac{1}{2} \frac{|\Gamma(\gamma_l + 1 + i\eta)|}{\Gamma(2\gamma_l + 1)} \frac{\exp(\frac{1}{2}\pi\eta)}{\sqrt{(i\eta' - l)(\gamma_l - i\eta)}},$$

then the asymptotic form of g is

$$g_{-l-1} = r^{-1} \sin(k r + \eta \log 2 k r - \tfrac{1}{2}\pi l - \sigma_{-l-1}). \tag{15.4}$$

The phase-shift σ in (15.4) is given by

$$\exp(-2 i \sigma_{-l-1}) = \frac{l - i\eta'}{\gamma_l - i\eta} \frac{\Gamma(\gamma_l + 1 - i\eta)}{\Gamma(\gamma_l + 1 + i\eta)} \exp[\pi i (l - \gamma_l)]. \tag{15.5}$$

A similar expression is obtained for g_l, the "large" radial function g for the case $j = l + \frac{1}{2}$. g_l has the same asymptotic form as (15.4), except that σ_{-l-1} is replaced by σ_l, where

$$\exp(-2 i \sigma_l) = \frac{l + 1 + i\eta'}{\gamma_{l+1} + i\eta} \frac{\Gamma(\gamma_{l+1} - i\eta)}{\Gamma(\gamma_{l+1} + i\eta)} \exp[\pi i (l + 1 - \gamma_{l+1})]. \tag{15.6}$$

The expressions above are exact and valid for all positive values of $(E - mc^2)$ and of $Z\alpha$. In the fully nonrelativistic limit ($Z\alpha \ll 1$ and $\varepsilon - 1 \ll 1$), the parameter [see (15.2)] γ_l approaches l and η' approaches η (in atomic units η approaches Z/k). In this nonrelativistic limit the small radial functions f are negligible compared with g and each of the two solutions $j = l \pm \frac{1}{2}$ for a fixed value of l approaches the nonrelativistic solution for the same l. In particular, the two phase shifts σ_l and σ_{-l-1}, defined in (15.5) and (15.6), both tend to the nonrelativistic expression (4.10).

The expressions for the radial wave functions also simplify somewhat in the "extreme relativistic" limit of very high energy, $\varepsilon \gg 1$. Unlike the nonrelativistic parameter Z/k, the parameter $\eta = Z e^2/\hbar v$ tends to a non-zero limit $Z\alpha$ as the energy E approaches infinity while the velocity v approaches the velocity of light c. The parameter η', on the other hand, approaches zero in this limit. It then follows from (15.5) and (15.6) that σ_{-l-1} and σ_{l-1} (for $l \geq 1$), the phase shifts for the two states of equal j ($j = (l-1) + \frac{1}{2} = l - \frac{1}{2}$), approach each other as $\varepsilon \to \infty$ for *any* value of $Z\alpha$. In this limit the radial wave functions themselves for these two states are closely related: The "large" and "small" radial wave functions g and f are of the same order of magnitude for relativistic energies. Further, if we can neglect $E_0 = mc^2$ compared with the total energy E in (14.10) it follows that

$$g_{l-1} = f_{-l-1}, \quad f_{l-1} = -g_{-l-1} \qquad (\text{as} \quad \varepsilon \to \infty). \tag{15.7}$$

β) Plane wave solutions and scattering amplitude. We discuss first plane wave solutions of the DIRAC equation for a *free* electron. We start from (12.4), the DIRAC equation written in split notation, for the field-free case $\varphi = \boldsymbol{A} = 0$. In this case (12.4) has solutions which are eigenstates of the momentum $\boldsymbol{p}$ with eigenvalues $\hbar \boldsymbol{k}$. We can write such a solution in the following form

$$\left.\begin{aligned} u &= e^{i\boldsymbol{k}\cdot\boldsymbol{r}} \begin{pmatrix} U_A \\ U_B \end{pmatrix}, & U_B &= \frac{c\hbar}{E+E_0} (\boldsymbol{k}\cdot\boldsymbol{\sigma}^P)\, U_A, \\ E^2 &= E_0^2 + (\hbar k c)^2, & E_0 &= m c^2. \end{aligned}\right\} \tag{15.8}$$

For a fixed value of $\boldsymbol{k}$, the two components u_1 and u_2 of the PAULI spinor U_A are two arbitrary constants, but the two components u_3 and u_4 of the other PAULI spinor U_B are completely determined by U_A and $\boldsymbol{k}$. The energy E is determined, except for sign, by the absolute value of the vector $\boldsymbol{k}$. We restrict ourselves, at present, to the positive value of E.

The normalization of the DIRAC four-component spinor is determined by the normalization of the two-component U_A and the absolute value of $\boldsymbol{k}$: we write

$$\langle u^* u\rangle = \langle U_A^* U_A\rangle + \langle U_B^* U_B\rangle, \quad \langle U_A^* U_A\rangle = |u_1|^2 + |u_2|^2, \quad \langle U_B^* U_B\rangle = |u_3|^2 + |u_4|^2.$$

It then follows from the properties of the spin-matrices $\boldsymbol{\sigma}$, (10.5), that

$$(E + E_0)^2\, U_B^* U_B = (c\hbar k)^2\, U_A^* U_A. \tag{15.9}$$

The relation (15.9) also holds for any more general wave function made up by superposition of "plane wave" functions of type (15.8) with different directions, but the same absolute value, of the vector $\boldsymbol{k}$. For a fixed direction of $\boldsymbol{k}$, it is often convenient to write an arbitrary two-component spinor U_A as a superposition of the two linearly independent spinors which are eigenstates of the operator[1] $(\boldsymbol{k}\cdot\boldsymbol{\sigma}^P)$. Using (13.20), we can write these two spinors as

$$U_{A\uparrow} = \begin{pmatrix} \cos\frac{1}{2}\vartheta \\ \sin\frac{1}{2}\vartheta\, e^{i\varphi} \end{pmatrix}, \qquad U_{A\downarrow} = \begin{pmatrix} -\sin\frac{1}{2}\vartheta\, e^{-i\varphi} \\ \cos\frac{1}{2}\vartheta \end{pmatrix}, \tag{15.10}$$

where (ϑ, φ) are the angle coordinates of the vector $\boldsymbol{k}$ in a spherical polar coordinate system with polar axis in the z-direction and $\varphi = 0$ in the zx-plane. A wave function of type (15.8) with U_A given by $U_{A\uparrow}$ (or $U_{A\downarrow}$) then represents an electron with momentum $\hbar\boldsymbol{k}$ and with its spin directed parallel (or antiparallel) to $\boldsymbol{k}$. If $U = a_\uparrow U_{A\uparrow} + a_\downarrow U_{A\downarrow}$, then $|a_\uparrow|^2$, $|a_\downarrow|^2$ represent the relative probabilities for "spin up" and "spin down", respectively.

We return now to the problem of the scattering of an electron by a central potential $\varphi(r)$. As in the nonrelativistic case, solutions of the DIRAC equation exist which behave asymptotically like an incident plane wave plus scattered spherically outgoing waves. In the DIRAC case, however, we have to specify not only the directions and value of the momentum of the incident electron, but also the state of polarization of the incident electron. Consider the specific case of an electron incident in the z-direction with momentum $\hbar\boldsymbol{k}$ and with "spin up". Using (15.10), we then find for the asymptotic behavior of the first

[1] In this section $\boldsymbol{k}$ is linear momentum, *not* angular momentum.

two components of the total wave function

$$\left.\begin{aligned} u_1(\mathbf{r}) &\sim e^{ikz} + r^{-1} e^{ikr} g_1(\vartheta, \varphi), \\ u_2(\mathbf{r}) &\sim r^{-1} e^{ikr} g_2(\vartheta, \varphi), \end{aligned}\right\} \tag{15.11}$$

if the potential falls off rapidly enough for large radial distances r. Note that, in the asymptotic region, the potential is negligible and the total wave function can be considered as a superposition of plane waves all with the same absolute value of momentum $\hbar k$. Using (15.8), the asymptotic expressions for the other two components of the wave function u_3 and u_4 can then be obtained directly from (15.11). It further follows from (15.9) that, in the asymptotic region, the ratio of $|u_3|^2+|u_4|^2$ to $|u_1|^2+|u_2|^2$ is a constant independent of ϑ and φ. The scattering of the incident electron is then described completely by the two functions g_1 and g_2. The differential scattering cross section, in particular, is given by

$$|f(\vartheta, \varphi)|^2 \, d\Omega = \left[|g_1(\vartheta, \varphi)|^2 + |g_2(\vartheta, \varphi)|^2\right] d\Omega. \tag{15.12}$$

(15.12) determines only the total probability for the incident electron being scattered into the solid angle $d\Omega$ around the direction (ϑ, φ). The ratio g_1/g_2 for a particular ϑ and φ also determines, with the help of (15.10), the state of polarization of the electron scattered into this particular direction.

As in the nonrelativistic case, the exact wave function which has the asymptotic form (15.11) cannot be obtained in closed analytic form for most potentials. In the present relativistic problem this is the case even for a COULOMB potential. Nevertheless, such an exact wave function can be obtained in the form of an infinite series involving all the partial wave solutions discussed in Sect. 15α. For a potential which falls off rapidly enough with r the asymptotic form of the "large" radial functions for the two partial waves with $j=l-\frac{1}{2}$ and $j=l+\frac{1}{2}$ are [cf. Eq. (15.4)]

$$g_{-l-1} = r^{-1} \sin\left(k r - \tfrac{1}{2}\pi l + \delta_{-l-1}\right), \qquad g_l = r^{-1} \sin\left(k r - \tfrac{1}{2}\pi l + \delta_l\right).$$

The infinite series[1] for the wave function of asymptotic form (15.11) involves all the partial wave states with m, the total angular momentum in the z-direction, equal to $+\frac{1}{2}$. The functions g_1 and g_2, Eq. (15.11), are then given in terms of the phase shifts δ_l and δ_{-l-1} by

$$\left.\begin{aligned} g_1(\vartheta, \varphi) &= g_1(\vartheta), \qquad g_2(\vartheta, \varphi) = e^{i\varphi} g_2(\vartheta); \\ 2ik\, g_1(\vartheta) &= \sum_{l=0}^{\infty} \left[(l+1)\left(e^{2i\delta_l} - 1\right) + l\left(e^{2i\delta_{-l-1}} - 1\right)\right] P_l(\cos\vartheta), \\ 2ik\, g_2(\vartheta) &= \sum_{l=0}^{\infty} \left[e^{2i\delta_{-l-1}} - e^{2i\delta_l}\right] P_l^1(\cos\vartheta). \end{aligned}\right\} \tag{15.13}$$

On substituting (15.13) into (15.12) we find that the differential cross section $|f(\vartheta, \varphi)|^2$ is independent of the azimuthal angle φ, as might be expected from symmetry. In the nonrelativistic limit ($E - mc^2$ and the potential energy both small compared with mc^2), δ_l and δ_{-l-1} both approach the nonrelativistic phase shift (7.1), $g_1(\vartheta)$ approaches the nonrelativistic scattering amplitude $f(\vartheta)$, Eq. (7.4), and $g_2(\vartheta)$ approaches zero. Thus, in the nonrelativistic limit the spin of the scattered electron "points in the positive z-direction" ($g_2=0$), if the spin of the incident electron does so.

[1] For the explicit form of this series and for further details on scattering and polarization see ref. [9], pp. 74 to 82.

We have so far discussed only the scattering of an incident electron with "spin up", Eq. (15.11). The asymptotic form for an incident electron with "spin down" is, instead of (15.11),

$$u_1' \sim r^{-1} e^{ikr} g_2'; \quad u_2' \sim e^{ikz} + r^{-1} e^{ikr} g_1'. \tag{15.11a}$$

The corresponding exact wave function can again be built up out of the partial wave solutions, this time with $m=-\frac{1}{2}$. The function g_1' is identical with $g_1(\vartheta)$, Eq. (15.13) and $g_2' = -e^{-i\varphi} g_2(\vartheta)$, in contrast to $g_2 = +e^{i\varphi} g_2(\vartheta)$. The differential scattering cross section for an incident electron with "spin down" [see (15.12)] is then identical with that for an electron with "spin up". This again is expected from symmetry.

Consider now an incident electron in a more general spin-state, characterized by

$$u_1 = a\, e^{ikz}, \quad u_2 = b\, e^{ikz}; \quad |a|^2 + |b|^2 = 1.$$

This incident electron beam is still "fully polarized", i.e. it has a definite spin direction for given values of a and b [see Eq. (13.20)]. The scattered wave is given simply by a linear superposition of the scattering *amplitudes* (15.11) and (15.11a) with coefficients a and b, respectively. The differential scattering cross section is then given by

$$\begin{aligned} |f(\vartheta,\varphi)|^2 &= |a\, g_1(\vartheta) - b\, g_2(\vartheta)\, e^{-i\varphi}|^2 + |b\, g_1(\vartheta) + a\, g_2(\vartheta)\, e^{i\varphi}|^2 \\ &= |g_1(\vartheta)|^2 + |g_2(\vartheta)|^2 + 4\,\mathrm{Im}\,(a\, b^*\, e^{i\varphi})\, \mathrm{Im}\,[g_1(\vartheta)\, g_2^*(\vartheta)]. \end{aligned}$$

This expression differs from (15.12) by the last term which depends on a/b and is *not* independent of the azimuthal angle φ. If, for instance, $a=b$, the spin of the incident electron points in the direction ($\Theta=\frac{1}{2}\pi$, $\Phi=0$) and the scattered intensity has maxima and minima at $\varphi=\pm\frac{1}{2}\pi$.

However, under most experimental conditions one is dealing with an "unpolarized" beam of incident electrons. This means that each electron in the beam may have a non-zero value for a and b, but that the phase relation between a and b varies in a random fashion from one electron to the next in the beam. One then finds that the *average* scattering cross-section of all the electrons in the beam is again given by (15.12) and independent of φ. However, the electrons scattered into a particular direction will in general be "partially polarized", even if the incident beam was unpolarized. This is due to the fact that the scattering amplitude depends on the spin-state of the incident electrons and there will be some average phase relation between a and b in the scattered beam. Thus, if the scattered beam is scattered once more, there will, in general, be some dependence on φ in the scattering cross-section[1].

For the special case of a COULOMB potential, the asymptotic form of each partial wave solution is known analytically. The expression (15.13) is modified only slightly by the presence of the logarithmic phase factor and the functions g_1 and g_2 are given in the form of an infinite series of LEGENDRE polynomials $P_l(\cos\vartheta)$ with known coefficients. These series cannot be obtained in closed analytic form for general values of $Z\alpha$ and E, but numerical calculations are now available for various values of these parameters[2]. The labor involved in such numerical calculations can be reduced[3] by modifying the series to be summed,

[1] For a discussion of double scattering and expressions for the "assymetry factor" see ref. [9], p. 78 and 82.

[2] J. H. BARTLETT and R. E. WATSON: Phys. Rev. **56**, 612 (1939). — H. FESHBACH: Phys. Rev. **84**, 1206 (1951); **88**, 295 (1953). — G. PARZEN and T. WAINWRIGHT: Phys. Rev. **96**, 188 (1954). — J. DOGGETT and L. SPENCER: Phys. Rev. **103**, 1597 (1956). — N. SHERMAN: Phys. Rev. **103**, 1601 (1956).

[3] YENNIE, RAVENHALL and WILSON: Phys. Rev. **95**, 500 (1954).

as outlined in Sect. 7β [see (7.10)]. However, if $Z\alpha$ is fairly small, and each term in the infinite series (15.13) is expanded in powers of $Z\alpha$, then the series for the coefficients of the first few powers of $Z\alpha$ can be summed analytically. The first two terms in this expansion in powers of $Z\alpha$ for the scattering cross-section of an unpolarized electron beam are[1]

$$|f(\vartheta)|^2\,d\Omega = \frac{e^4 Z^2\,d\Omega}{4\,(p\,v)^2 \sin^4(\frac{1}{2}\vartheta)} \left\{\left[1-\left(\frac{v}{c}\sin\frac{\vartheta}{2}\right)^2\right] + \pi Z\alpha\frac{v}{c}\sin\frac{\vartheta}{2}\left(1-\sin\frac{\vartheta}{2}\right)\right\} \quad (15.14)$$

where the momentum p and velocity v are related to the energy E by (15.1). The expression (15.14) can also be obtained directly, without summing the partial wave series (15.13), by higher order BORN approximation if a limiting procedure is adopted (the scattering is calculated for a screened COULOMB potential and the screening radius allowed to tend to infinity[2]).

If the factor in curly brackets in (15.14) is replaced by unity and if pv is replaced by twice the kinetic energy, the nonrelativistic expression (6.24) is obtained. However, for $E \gg mc^2$, v approaches c and pv approaches E. (15.14) is valid, if $Z\alpha$ is small, for all values of the energy. Note that the second term in curly brackets in (15.14) is linear in $Z\alpha$ and the scattering cross section is thus less for negative $Z\alpha$ (i.e. for scattering of positrons from nuclei). Note also that the term in $Z\alpha$ (as well as all higher terms) contains positive powers of v/c, since in the nonrelativistic limit, $v/c \to 0$, Eq. (6.24) must be exact.

γ) *Negative energy states.* We have so far discussed only eigenstates of the DIRAC equation for which E, the total energy *including* the rest-mass energy mc^2, is positive. However, there also exist solutions of the DIRAC equation with negative total energy E, even if the potentials are weak and the characteristic momentum of the electron is small. In the field-free case, in particular, for a given momentum $\hbar k$ we have so far dealt with two linearly independent solutions of (15.8), with "spin up" and with "spin down", both with positive energy $E_+ = \sqrt{(mc^2)^2 + (\hbar k c)^2}$. (15.8) has two other linearly independent solutions with negative energy $E_- = -E_+$ with the roles of U_A and U_B reversed compared with the positive energy solutions. Loosely speaking, the DIRAC spinor wave functions have four components, compared with the one-component SCHRÖDINGER wave functions, and we should expect the DIRAC equation to have four times as many eigenstates as the SCHRÖDINGER equation. Physically, the extra degrees of freedom correspond to the possible signs of the total energy E and of the component of the spin in the z-direction.

Negative energy solutions of the DIRAC equation exist for an electron in any time-independent electromagnetic field, characterized by scalar and vector potentials φ and $\boldsymbol{A}$. Further, each negative energy solution can be related, mathematically, to a positive energy solution (in a different potential) by the following prescription: Let (U_A, U_B) be the components of a solution of the DIRAC Eq. (12.4) with negative energy $-|E|$ for a given φ and $\boldsymbol{A}$. Change the sign of the energy to $+|E|$, also the sign of the momentum operator $\boldsymbol{p}$ and of $e\varphi$ and $e\boldsymbol{A}$, and interchange U_A and U_B. The resulting wave function is then identical with a solution of (12.4) for a particle, of same mass and *opposite* sign of the charge, in the same field with positive energy $+|E|$. DIRAC[3] used this mathe-

[1] Such an expression was first derived by N. F. MOTT, Proc. Roy. Soc. Lond., Ser. A **124**, 425 (1929) but his term in $Z\alpha$ was incorrect. The expression quoted in ref. [9] is also wrong. The correct expression was obtained by W. A. MCKINLEY and H. FESHBACH, Phys. Rev. **74**, 1759 (1948).

[2] R. H. DALITZ: Proc. Roy. Soc. Lond., Ser. A **206**, 509 (1951).

[3] P. A. M. DIRAC: Proc. Roy. Soc. Lond., Ser. A **133**, 80 (1931).

matical relation to overcome the following physical difficulty in his theory for a single electron: Even if an electron is initially in a state of positive energy, according to the form of DIRAC's theory we have discussed so far ("single-electron theory"), the electron could make a transition to a state of negative energy and give up energy, by emitting radiation, in a collision with another particle, etc. No such transitions, nor any electrons with negative energy, have ever been observed. However, if we assume that electrons satisfy the PAULI exclusion principle, we can introduce a new postulate, namely that the physically observed vacuum consists of an infinite sea of electrons filling all the possible negative energy states. Transitions of a "real" electron from a state of positive to one of negative energy is then forbidden by the exclusion principle. Further, if an electron is missing from the sea of negative energy states, it follows from the relation discussed above that this "hole" has the physical properties of a particle of electronic mass, positive charge $+|e|$ and positive energy, called a positron.

We have only given a physical picture of DIRAC's "hole theory" (or "pair theory") of the electron. To put this theory on a rigorous footing, the electron has to be treated by the formalism of "second quantization" or quantum field theory. Field theoretic treatments of pair theory have been developed in great detail by many authors, using different mathematical formalisms but with the same physical content. For a discussion of these treatments the reader is referred to the standard works, including references [*1*], [*3*], [*6*], [*11*], [*12*] and [*13*]. The most direct experimental tests of the "hole theory" are furnished by high energy phenomena, such as electron-positron pair-creation. We shall merely state briefly (without proof) the differences in predictions of single-electron theory and pair theory, which are relevant to atomic theory.

Consider first a single electron of positive total energy in a time-independent electromagnetic field. If the field is considered as a classical and *given* field, then the results of single-electron and hole theory are *identical*. In practice, however, small differences do arise, as follows: (1) If an external field is introduced into a vacuum then, according to hole theory, the "sea of filled electron states" readjusts itself so that all the negative-energy states for electrons in *this* field are filled. This readjustment in general produces some change in the charge density of the "sea" and the resulting "vacuum polarization" acts on a real electron introduced into the vacuum like a small additional potential. (2) If virtual interactions of a real electron with the quantized electromagnetic field are taken into account, the electron's interaction with an external classical field is also modified. This modification, the so-called "radiative corrections", partly involves intermediate states for which the electron is in a negative energy state and the quantitative expression for these corrections is different on single electron and hole theory[1].

Consider next a process in which a single electron makes a transition between two states of positive total energy (in an arbitrary external field) with the emission or absorption of any number of real photons. If such a process is calculated by the lowest non-zero order of perturbation theory, single electron and hole theory again give identical results. The use of higher order perturbation theory (involving integrations over the momenta of virtual photons in intermediate states) again results in radiative corrections, which are different on single-electron and hole theory. For processes involving more than one real electron the two theories already give slightly different results even if radiative corrections are not considered (see Sect. 38).

[1] In fact, these corrections can be calculated in a consistent manner *only* according to hole theory.

The following general rule applies to a system with any numbers of electrons (*no* real positrons): If the potentials are fairly weak and the characteristic momenta fairly small, calculations up to (and including) the order of accuracy of the PAULI approximation (Sect. 12) are identical in single-electron and pair theory. For systems containing both electrons and positrons, single-electron theory leads to larger errors or fails completely (see Sect. 23).

16. The DIRAC equation in momentum space. We consider now the DIRAC equation (10.1) for an electron in an external time-independent electromagnetic field, transformed into an integral equation in momentum space. As in the nonrelativistic case, Sects. 8 and 9, this is accomplished simply by taking the FOURIER transform of (10.1). We put $\hbar=1$, as in atomic units, but carry the symbols for e, m, c, etc. at for the moment[1]. The DIRAC equation in momentum space then reads

$$(E - mc^2\beta - c\boldsymbol{\alpha}\cdot\boldsymbol{p})\,\psi(\boldsymbol{p}) = -e\int d^3k\,[\varphi(-\boldsymbol{k}) - \boldsymbol{\alpha}\cdot\boldsymbol{A}(-\boldsymbol{k})]\,\psi(\boldsymbol{p}+\boldsymbol{k}). \qquad (16.1)$$

In (16.1), $\psi(\boldsymbol{p})$, the DIRAC wave function in momentum space, is a four-component column matrix (or spinor) on which the DIRAC matrices $\boldsymbol{\alpha}$ and β operate. $\varphi(\boldsymbol{k})$ and $\boldsymbol{A}(\boldsymbol{k})$ are the FOURIER transforms of the scalar and vector potentials of the electromagnetic field [times $(2\pi)^{-\frac{3}{2}}$]. For the special case of the COULOMB potential of a nucleus of atomic number Z,

$$A = 0, \qquad \varphi(\boldsymbol{k}) = +\frac{Ze}{2\pi^2}\frac{1}{k^2}. \qquad (16.2)$$

For the special case of a COULOMB potential (16.2), RUBINOWITZ has[2] obtained the exact DIRAC wave function in momentum space $\psi(\boldsymbol{p})$ for the discrete spectrum by taking the FOURIER transform of the position wave function, Eq. (14.37). LÉVY[3] has obtained the same $\psi(\boldsymbol{p})$ by solving (16.1) directly. LÉVY has also given prescriptions, for a general central potential, for reducing (16.1) to two uncoupled one-dimensional integral equations and has discussed various approximation methods for solving (16.1). We shall only discuss approximation methods suitable for any "weak" electromagnetic field and for a total energy E of the electron close to $+mc^2$.

α) Mixed representation. In the split notation, discussed in Sect. 10 and 12, the DIRAC equation (16.1) reads (with $E_0 = mc^2$)

$$\left.\begin{aligned}(E-E_0)\,\psi_A(\boldsymbol{p}) &= c\,\sigma^P\cdot\boldsymbol{p}\,\psi_B(\boldsymbol{p}) - e\int d^3k\,[\varphi(-\boldsymbol{k})\,\psi_A(\boldsymbol{p}+\boldsymbol{k}) - \sigma^P\cdot\boldsymbol{A}(-\boldsymbol{k})\,\psi_B(\boldsymbol{p}+\boldsymbol{k})],\\ (E+E_0)\,\psi_B(\boldsymbol{p}) &= c\,\sigma^P\cdot\boldsymbol{p}\,\psi_A(\boldsymbol{p}) - e\int d^3k\,[\varphi(-\boldsymbol{k})\,\psi_B(\boldsymbol{p}+\boldsymbol{k}) - \sigma^P\cdot\boldsymbol{A}(-\boldsymbol{k})\,\psi_A(\boldsymbol{p}+\boldsymbol{k})].\end{aligned}\right\} \qquad (16.3)$$

ψ_A and ψ_B are two PAULI two-component spinors, the FOURIER transforms of the "large" and "small" components U_A and U_B of the PAULI reduction (Sect. 12), and (16.3) is the FOURIER transform of (12.4). If, as a first approximation, we replaced E by E_0 and omitted φ and $\boldsymbol{A}$ in the second line of (16.3), we could eliminate ψ_B and obtain an equation in ψ_A alone which is the FOURIER transform of the nonrelativistic SCHRÖDINGER Eq. (12.6) and is equivalent to (8.3). On substituting the first approximation for ψ_B on the right hand side of the second line of (16.3) (without dropping φ and $\boldsymbol{A}$) one could then obtain a better approximation for ψ_B. Substituting this approximation for ψ_B into the first line of (16.3) gives a more accurate equation for ψ_A alone, the FOURIER transform of the approximate PAULI Eq. (12.11), etc. If the potentials are weak and if

[1] e is positive.
[2] A. RUBINOWITZ: Phys. Rev. **73**, 1330 (1948).
[3] M. LÉVY: Proc. Roy. Soc. Lond., Ser. A **204**, 145 (1950).

$\gamma^2/2m \equiv E - E_0 \ll E_0$, then the important values of the momentum p will be of order $\gamma \ll mc$. The ratio $\psi_B(\boldsymbol{p})/\psi_A(\boldsymbol{p})$ is of order p/mc, which is small, but only by one power of v/c. Instead of pursuing this method further, we shall outline an alternative method of successive approximation which involves, instead of ψ_A and ψ_B, two other PAULI spinors ψ_+ and ψ_-, for which the ratio ψ_-/ψ_+ is of order $(p/mc)^3$. Since $\psi_-/\psi_+ \ll \psi_B/\psi_A$, this alternative method is more convenient than the one outlined above (especially if the external magnetic field is weaker than the electric one).

We consider first "plane-wave" solutions of (16.3) for the field-free case, $\varphi = \boldsymbol{A} = 0$. We define

$$E(p) = +\sqrt{E_0^2 + (cp)^2}, \qquad \Gamma(\boldsymbol{p}) = \frac{c\,\boldsymbol{p}\cdot\boldsymbol{\sigma}^P}{E_0 + E(p)}, \tag{16.4}$$

where $\boldsymbol{\sigma}^P$ is the 2-by-2 PAULI spin matrix ($\hbar = 1$ in our units). In analogy with the position space solution (15.8) we have two types of eigenstates of the HAMILTONian corresponding to a plane wave of momentum $\boldsymbol{q}$ with positive and negative energy eigenvalue respectively. In our split notation the two types of DIRAC wave function $\psi_q^{(+)}$ and $\psi_q^{(-)}$ are of the form

$$\left.\begin{aligned} &(E_0\beta + c\boldsymbol{\alpha}\cdot\boldsymbol{p})\,\psi_q^{(\pm)}(\boldsymbol{p}) = \pm E(q)\,\psi_q^{(\pm)}(\boldsymbol{p});\\ &\psi_q^{(+)}(\boldsymbol{p}) = \begin{pmatrix}\psi_+\\ \Gamma(\boldsymbol{p})\,\psi_+\end{pmatrix}\delta^{(3)}(\boldsymbol{p}-\boldsymbol{q}), \quad \psi_q^{(-)}(\boldsymbol{p}) = \begin{pmatrix}-\Gamma(\boldsymbol{p})\,\psi_-\\ \psi_-\end{pmatrix}\delta^3(\boldsymbol{p}-\boldsymbol{q}).\end{aligned}\right\} \tag{16.5}$$

In (16.5) ψ_+ and ψ_- are any two constant (but otherwise arbitrary), two-component PAULI-spinors on which the PAULI matrix $\Gamma(\boldsymbol{p})$ operates.

We define next the CASIMIR projection operators Λ_+ and Λ_- by

$$\Lambda_\pm(\boldsymbol{p}) = \frac{1}{2E(p)}\left[E(p) \pm (E_0\beta + c\boldsymbol{\alpha}\cdot\boldsymbol{p})\right], \quad \Lambda_+ + \Lambda_- = 1. \tag{16.6}$$

These projection operators have the property that

$$\Lambda_\pm(\boldsymbol{p})\,\psi_q^{(\pm)}(\boldsymbol{p}) = \psi_q^{(\pm)}(\boldsymbol{p}), \qquad \Lambda_\pm(\boldsymbol{p})\,\psi_q^{(\mp)}(\boldsymbol{p}) = 0. \tag{16.7}$$

We further see that *any* arbitrary DIRAC wave function $\psi(\boldsymbol{p})$ can be written in the form

$$\psi(\boldsymbol{p}) = \begin{pmatrix}1\\ \Gamma(\boldsymbol{p})\end{pmatrix}\psi_+(\boldsymbol{p}) + \begin{pmatrix}-\Gamma(\boldsymbol{p})\\ 1\end{pmatrix}\psi_-(\boldsymbol{p}). \tag{16.8}$$

where $\psi_\pm(\boldsymbol{p})$ are two-component PAULI-spinors (with arbitrary dependence on $\boldsymbol{p}$ for each of the components) on which $\Gamma(\boldsymbol{p})$, Eq. (16.4), operates[1]. Any DIRAC wave function is then specified by these two PAULI spinors $\psi_\pm(\boldsymbol{p})$ and we derive next two coupled integral equations for ψ_+ and ψ_- from the DIRAC equation (16.1).

We first define four PAULI operators $I_{++}(\boldsymbol{p}_1, \boldsymbol{p}_2)$, which are functions of two momentum variables $\boldsymbol{p}_1$ and $\boldsymbol{p}_2$, by

$$\Lambda_+(\boldsymbol{p}_1)\begin{pmatrix}1\\ \Gamma(\boldsymbol{p}_2)\end{pmatrix} = \begin{pmatrix}1\\ \Gamma(\boldsymbol{p}_1)\end{pmatrix} I_{++}(\boldsymbol{p}_1, \boldsymbol{p}_2), \quad \Lambda_-(\boldsymbol{p}_1)\begin{pmatrix}1\\ \Gamma(\boldsymbol{p}_2)\end{pmatrix} = \begin{pmatrix}-\Gamma(\boldsymbol{p}_1)\\ 1\end{pmatrix} I_{-+}(\boldsymbol{p}_1, \boldsymbol{p}_2), \tag{16.9}$$

plus two similar relations for I_{+-} and I_{--}. We similarly define four vector PAULI operators $\boldsymbol{\alpha}_{\pm\pm}$ by

$$\left.\begin{aligned} &\Lambda_+(\boldsymbol{p}_1)\,\boldsymbol{\alpha}\begin{pmatrix}1\\ \Gamma(\boldsymbol{p}_2)\end{pmatrix} \equiv \Lambda_+(\boldsymbol{p}_1)\begin{pmatrix}\boldsymbol{\sigma}^P\Gamma(\boldsymbol{p}_2)\\ \boldsymbol{\sigma}^P\end{pmatrix} = \begin{pmatrix}1\\ \Gamma(\boldsymbol{p}_1)\end{pmatrix}\boldsymbol{\alpha}_{++}(p_1, p_2);\\ &\Lambda_-(\boldsymbol{p}_1)\,\boldsymbol{\alpha}\begin{pmatrix}1\\ \Gamma(\boldsymbol{p}_2)\end{pmatrix} = \begin{pmatrix}-\Gamma(\boldsymbol{p}_1)\\ 1\end{pmatrix}\boldsymbol{\alpha}_{-+}(\boldsymbol{p}_1, \boldsymbol{p}_2);\end{aligned}\right\} \tag{16.10}$$

---

[1] Note that $E_0\beta + c\boldsymbol{\alpha}\cdot\boldsymbol{p}$ operating on the first part of (16.8) results in a multiplying factor of $+E(p)$, and a factor of $-E(p)$ for the second part.

plus two similar relations for $\boldsymbol{\alpha}_{+-}$ and $\boldsymbol{\alpha}_{--}$. (16.9) and (16.10) are to be considered as operator equations: This means that each of the equations is satisfied if the left and right hand operate on the same PAULI spinor (otherwise arbitrary). Writing the projection operators (16.6) in the split notation given in (10.4) and using the usual rules of matrix multiplication one can obtain explicit expressions for $I_{\pm\pm}$ and $\boldsymbol{\alpha}_{\pm\pm}$ involving only the PAULI operator σ^P. These expressions can be simplified further by using the following operator identities[1] which can be derived from (10.5),

$$\left.\begin{aligned} (\boldsymbol{\sigma}\cdot\boldsymbol{p})\,\boldsymbol{\sigma}+i\,\boldsymbol{p}\times\boldsymbol{\sigma}&=\boldsymbol{\sigma}(\boldsymbol{\sigma}\cdot\boldsymbol{p})-i\,\boldsymbol{p}\times\boldsymbol{\sigma}=\boldsymbol{p},\\ (\boldsymbol{\sigma}\cdot\boldsymbol{p}_1)\,(\boldsymbol{\sigma}\cdot\boldsymbol{p}_2)&=\boldsymbol{p}_1\cdot\boldsymbol{p}_2+i\,\boldsymbol{\sigma}\cdot(\boldsymbol{p}_1\times\boldsymbol{p}_2).\end{aligned}\right\}\tag{16.11}$$

Writing E_1 for $E(p_1)$, E_2 for $E(p_2)$ and $\boldsymbol{k}$ for $\boldsymbol{p}_2-\boldsymbol{p}_1$, we finally get

$$\left.\begin{aligned} I_{++}(\boldsymbol{p}_1,\boldsymbol{p}_2)&=I_{--}=\left\{1+\frac{c^2(\boldsymbol{\sigma}\cdot\boldsymbol{p}_1)\,(\boldsymbol{\sigma}\cdot\boldsymbol{k})+(E_1-E_0)\,(E_1-E_2)}{2E_1(E_0+E_2)}\right\},\\ I_{+-}(\boldsymbol{p}_1,\boldsymbol{p}_2)&=-I_{-+}=\frac{c}{2E_1}\left\{\boldsymbol{\sigma}\cdot\boldsymbol{p}_1-\frac{E_0+E_1}{E_0+E_2}\,\boldsymbol{\sigma}\cdot\boldsymbol{p}_2,\right\},\\ \boldsymbol{\alpha}_{++}(\boldsymbol{p}_1,\boldsymbol{p}_2)&=-\boldsymbol{\alpha}_{--}=\frac{c}{2E_1}\left\{\boldsymbol{p}_1-i\,\boldsymbol{p}_1\times\boldsymbol{\sigma}+\frac{E_0+E_1}{E_0+E_2}\,(\boldsymbol{p}_2+i\,\boldsymbol{p}_2\times\boldsymbol{\sigma})\right\},\\ \boldsymbol{\alpha}_{+-}(\boldsymbol{p}_1,\boldsymbol{p}_2)&=\boldsymbol{\alpha}_{-+}=\frac{1}{2E_1}\left\{(E_0+E_1)\,\boldsymbol{\sigma}-c^2\frac{(\boldsymbol{\sigma}\cdot\boldsymbol{p}_1)\,\boldsymbol{\sigma}\,(\boldsymbol{\sigma}\cdot\boldsymbol{p}_2)}{E_0+E_2}\right\}.\end{aligned}\right\}\tag{16.12}$$

We now write $\psi(\boldsymbol{p})$, the solution of the DIRAC equation (16.1), in the form (16.8) and derive two equations involving ψ_+ and ψ_- from (16.1) in the following way[2]. We operate on both sides of the Eq. (16.1) with the projection operator $\Lambda_+(\boldsymbol{p})$, then rewrite the right side in terms of $I_{\pm\pm}$ and $\boldsymbol{\alpha}_{\pm\pm}$, using the definitions (16.9) and (16.10). We then repeat the procedure, using $\Lambda_-(\boldsymbol{p})$ instead of Λ_+ to obtain a second equation. This gives

$$\left.\begin{aligned} \big(E-E(p)\big)\,\psi_+(\boldsymbol{p})&=-e\int d^3k\sum_{j=+,-}\big[\varphi(-\boldsymbol{k})\,I_{+j}(\boldsymbol{p},\boldsymbol{p}+\boldsymbol{k})-\\ &\qquad-\boldsymbol{A}(-\boldsymbol{k})\cdot\boldsymbol{\alpha}_{+j}(\boldsymbol{p},\boldsymbol{p}+\boldsymbol{k})\big]\,\psi_j(\boldsymbol{p}+\boldsymbol{k}),\\ \big(E+E(p)\big)\,\psi_-(\boldsymbol{p})&=-e\int d^3k\sum_{j=+,-}\big[\varphi(-\boldsymbol{k})\,I_{-j}(\boldsymbol{p},\boldsymbol{p}+\boldsymbol{k})-\\ &\qquad-\boldsymbol{A}(-\boldsymbol{k})\cdot\boldsymbol{\alpha}_{-j}(\boldsymbol{p},\boldsymbol{p}+\boldsymbol{k})\big]\,\psi_j(\boldsymbol{p}+\boldsymbol{k}),\end{aligned}\right\}\tag{16.13}$$

where the suffix j stands for $+$ or $-$.

The Eqs. (16.13) for ψ_+, ψ_- have a somewhat similar form to the Eqs. (16.3) for ψ_A, ψ_B. (16.3) is the DIRAC equation written in our previous "split notation", i.e. in a representation in terms of the two possible eigenvalues of β, in which the operator $\boldsymbol{\alpha}$ is represented by the square matrix (10.4) and the wave function by the column matrix (ψ_A, ψ_B). Similarly we can consider (16.13) as the DIRAC equation in a new "mixed representation" in terms of the two possible eigenvalues of the operator $E_0\beta+c\boldsymbol{\alpha}\cdot\boldsymbol{p}$, in which the wave function is represented by the column matrix (ψ_+, ψ_-). Since the operator defining the representation, $E_0\beta+c\boldsymbol{\alpha}\cdot\boldsymbol{p}$, depends on the momentum $\boldsymbol{p}$, the unit operator is represented by the matrix with components $I_{\pm\pm}(\boldsymbol{p}_1, \boldsymbol{p}_2)$, *not* simply by the unit 2-by-2 matrix. Similarly the operator $\boldsymbol{\alpha}$ is represented by the matrix $\boldsymbol{\alpha}_{\pm\pm}(\boldsymbol{p}_1, \boldsymbol{p}_2)$. Our new representation looks more complicated than the old and (16.13) seems longer than (16.3), but is nevertheless advantageous for weak enough fields, as we shall see.

[1] We shall simply write $\boldsymbol{\sigma}$ for $\boldsymbol{\sigma}^P$.

[2] H. A. BETHE: Z. Naturforsch. **3**a, 470 (1948). — E. E. SALPETER: Phys. Rev. **87**, 328 (1952).

β) The PAULI *approximation.* We consider first the simplest approximation to (16.13), involving only $\psi_+(\boldsymbol{p})$, obtained by simply putting ψ_- equal to zero in the first equation in (16.13) and omitting the second equation altogether. We can further simplify the exact expressions (16.12) by expanding in powers of p_1/mc and p_2/mc. These expansions, up to second order for I_{++} and first order for the other components, are

$$\left.\begin{aligned} I_{++} &= I_{--} = 1 + \frac{(\boldsymbol{\sigma}\cdot\boldsymbol{p}_1)(\boldsymbol{\sigma}\cdot\boldsymbol{k})}{(2mc)^2}, \qquad I_{+-} = -I_{-+} = -\frac{\boldsymbol{\sigma}\cdot\boldsymbol{k}}{2mc};\\ \boldsymbol{\alpha}_{++} &= -\boldsymbol{\alpha}_{--} = \frac{2\boldsymbol{p}_1+\boldsymbol{k}+i\,\boldsymbol{k}\times\boldsymbol{\sigma}}{2mc}, \qquad \boldsymbol{\alpha}_{-+} = \boldsymbol{\alpha}_{+-} = \boldsymbol{\sigma}. \end{aligned}\right\} \tag{16.14}$$

Substituting the approximations (16.14) for I_{++} and $\boldsymbol{\alpha}_{++}$ into the Eq. (16.13) for ψ_+ (with ψ_- neglected) and replacing $E(p)$ by the first three terms in an expansion in powers of p/mc, we get

$$\left.\begin{aligned} &\left(W - \frac{p^2}{2m} + \frac{p^4}{8m^3c^2}\right)\psi_+(\boldsymbol{p})\\ &= -e\int d^3k\left\{\left[1+\frac{(\boldsymbol{\sigma}\cdot\boldsymbol{p})(\boldsymbol{\sigma}\cdot\boldsymbol{k})}{(2mc)^2}\right]\varphi(-\boldsymbol{k}) - \left[\frac{2\boldsymbol{p}+\boldsymbol{k}+i\,\boldsymbol{k}\times\boldsymbol{\sigma}}{2mc}\right]\cdot\boldsymbol{A}(-\boldsymbol{k})\right\}\psi_+(\boldsymbol{p}+\boldsymbol{k}) \end{aligned}\right\} \tag{16.15}$$

where $W = E - E_0$.

We compare next the Eq. (16.15) for the PAULI 2-component spinor ψ_+ with the FOURIER transform of (12.11), the position space equation in the PAULI approximation. We shall see that they agree to the required order of accuracy if the magnetic field is considered small compared with the electric field: Consider first the case of no magnetic field, $\boldsymbol{A} = 0$. We make use of the approximate relation

$$(W + e\varphi)\,u(\boldsymbol{r}) \approx (p^2/2m)\,u(\boldsymbol{r}), \quad \boldsymbol{p} = -i\,\text{grad}$$

to find

$$\left[(W+e\varphi)^2 - \left(\frac{p^2}{2m}\right)^2\right]u \approx \frac{e}{2m}(\varphi p^2 - p^2\varphi)\,u = -\frac{ie}{2m}(\boldsymbol{p}\cdot\mathcal{E} + \mathcal{E}\cdot\boldsymbol{p})\,u \tag{16.16}$$

where $\mathcal{E} = -\,\text{grad}\,\varphi$ is the electric field[1]. In (12.11) we can then, to within the accuracy of the equation itself, rewrite the term in $(W+e\varphi)^2$ with the help of (16.16). Using (16.11) and the fact that curl $\mathcal{E} = 0$, (12.11) then reduces to (with $\boldsymbol{A} = \mathcal{H} = 0$)

$$\left[W + e\varphi - \frac{p^2}{2m} + \frac{p^4}{8m^3c^2} - \frac{ie}{4m^2c^2}(\boldsymbol{\sigma}\cdot\boldsymbol{p})(\boldsymbol{\sigma}\cdot\mathcal{E})\right]u = 0. \tag{16.17}$$

(16.17) is exactly the FOURIER transform of (16.15) (with $\boldsymbol{A} = 0$). Similarly the terms involving $\boldsymbol{A}(\boldsymbol{k})$ in (16.15) are the FOURIER transforms[2] of the terms involving ($\boldsymbol{A}\cdot$ grad) and $\boldsymbol{\sigma}\cdot\mathcal{H}$ in (12.11). Only the term in (12.11) involving A^2 is missing in (16.15).

γ) Improvements. The approximate Eq. (16.15) was obtained from (16.13) by omitting $\psi_-(\boldsymbol{p})$ altogether and by approximating the operators I_{++} and $\boldsymbol{\alpha}_{++}$. A simple approximation for ψ^- in terms of ψ_+ could be obtained from the second line of (16.13). On substituting this expression for ψ_- into the first line of (16.13)

[1] Although the operator $\boldsymbol{p}\cdot\mathcal{E} + \mathcal{E}\cdot\boldsymbol{p}$ is not zero itself, its expectation value with any real and bounded wave function u is $-i\int d\tau\,\text{div}(\mathcal{E}u^2) = 0$. It then also follows that the expectation value of $2\mathcal{E}\cdot\boldsymbol{p}$ equals that of $\mathcal{E}\cdot\boldsymbol{p} - \boldsymbol{p}\cdot\mathcal{E} = i\,\text{div}\,\mathcal{E}$.

[2] In carrying out the FOURIER transforms it is useful to write $\mathcal{E} = -\,\text{grad}\,\varphi = -i(\boldsymbol{p}\varphi - \varphi\boldsymbol{p})$ and $\mathcal{H} = \text{curl}\,\boldsymbol{A} = i(\boldsymbol{p}\times\boldsymbol{A} + \boldsymbol{A}\times\boldsymbol{p})$. Note also that, for time-independent potentials satisfying the LORENTZ gauge condition, div $\boldsymbol{A}(\boldsymbol{r}) = \boldsymbol{k}\cdot\boldsymbol{A}(\boldsymbol{k}) = 0$.

and keeping more accurate expressions for I_{++} and $\boldsymbol{\alpha}_{++}$, one could obtain an equation more accurate than (16.15), but again involving only ψ_+. This equation would contain terms quadratic in $\boldsymbol{A}$, as does (12.11), and would be more accurate than the PAULI approximation (12.11) if $\boldsymbol{A}$ is less important than φ. We shall not discuss this equation further, but only the behavior of the wave functions $\psi_\pm(\boldsymbol{p})$ for large $\boldsymbol{p}$.

In discussing the PAULI approximation (13.2) for a central potential we used an approximate wave function in the form of a PAULI spinor, whose radial dependence was the same as that of the nonrelativistic SCHRÖDINGER wave function. Only the spin and angle dependence was chosen so that the wave function represented an eigenstate of $\boldsymbol{M}^2$ and of M_z. Let $\psi_0(\boldsymbol{p})$ be the FOURIER transform of this PAULI spinor wave function. We consider a state of the electron with total energy E fairly close to E_0 in a fairly weak potential φ (with $\boldsymbol{A}=0$). The PAULI approximation then gives a very good approximation for the binding energy (or the scattering amplitudes for $E > E_0$), but $\psi_0(\boldsymbol{p})$ is a *poor* approximation in the region $p \gtrsim mc$. However, an approximation for the wave function, which is fairly accurate for *all* values of p, can be obtained from (16.13), essentially by an iteration method, using $\psi_0(\boldsymbol{p})$ as starting point. On the right side of (16.13) we replace $\psi_+(\boldsymbol{p})$ by $\psi_0(\boldsymbol{p})$ and ψ_- by zero and replace E by the PAULI approximation to the energy. We then get for ψ_+ and ψ_- the better approximation

$$\psi_\pm(\boldsymbol{p}) = \frac{-e}{E \mp E(p)} \int d^3q\, \varphi(-\boldsymbol{q}+\boldsymbol{p})\, I_{\pm+}(\boldsymbol{p},\boldsymbol{q})\, \psi_0(\boldsymbol{q}), \tag{16.18}$$

where $I_{\pm+}$ is given in (16.12).

Consider the special case of (16.18) for $\psi_0(\boldsymbol{p})$ corresponding to an S-state ($l=0$) in a central potential $\varphi(k)$. Comparison with (13.19) then shows that $\psi_0(\boldsymbol{p})$ is a constant PAULI spinor times a function of $|\boldsymbol{p}|$ only. In general, $\psi_0(p)$ will be extremely small if p is large compared with some characteristic momentum $p_0 \ll mc$ (for the special case of the hydrogen atom p_0 is of order αmc, the BOHR momentum). For $p \gg p_0$ we then get a very simple approximation for $\psi_\pm$ by simply replacing $\varphi(|\boldsymbol{p}-\boldsymbol{q}|)$ by $\varphi(p)$ and $I(\boldsymbol{p},\boldsymbol{q})$ by $I(\boldsymbol{p},0)$. Also replacing E by E_0 we get, using (16.12),

$$\psi_+(p) = \frac{e\,\varphi(p)\,[E(p)+E_0]}{2E(p)\,[E(p)-E_0]}\, u_0(0), \qquad \psi_-(p) = \frac{e\,\varphi(p)\, c\,\boldsymbol{\sigma}\cdot\boldsymbol{p}}{2E(p)\,[E(p)+E_0]}\, u_0(0), \tag{16.19}$$

where

$$u_0(0) = \int d^3q\, \psi_0(q)$$

is the nonrelativistic position space wave function [times $(2\pi)^{\frac{3}{2}}$] evaluated at the origin. (16.19) is just the first term of (16.18) expanded in powers of p_0/p.

For a state of non-zero l value, the expression $u_0(0)$ and hence (16.19) vanishes. For such states, $\psi_\pm(\boldsymbol{p})$ does in fact decrease more rapidly with increasing p than for $l=0$. For $l\neq 0$ and $p\gg p_0$ a better approximation for $\psi_\pm(\boldsymbol{p})$ can be obtained from (16.18) by expanding $\varphi(\boldsymbol{p}-\boldsymbol{q})$ and $I(\boldsymbol{p},\boldsymbol{q})$ in positive powers of q/p. For $p \gtrsim p_0$, another approximation for $\psi_-(\boldsymbol{p})$ can be got from (16.18), using the approximation (16.14).

In Table 2 we give the orders of magnitude of ψ_+ $p)$ and $\psi_-(p)$ for the special case of an S-state with low principal quantum number n in hydrogen, $\varphi(p) = e/2\pi^2 p^2$. Also given is the order of $\psi_+(p) - \psi_0(p)$, normalized to the same value for $p=0$. It will be seen that $\psi_-(p)$ is only of order α^3 for $p \sim p_0$, whereas $\psi_B(p)$, the "small" component of the PAULI reduction (16.3), is of order α. In the extreme relativistic region, $p \gg mc$, ψ_+ and ψ_- are of the same order of magnitude and are larger than the nonrelativistic approximation ψ_0 by about p/mc.

We finally mention a method introduced by FOLDY and WOUTHUYSEN[1], which is related to the above representation of the DIRAC wave function in terms of ψ_+ and ψ_- but is more general and elegant. They start from the DIRAC Eq. (10.1) with $\boldsymbol{\alpha}$, σ and β in the "split" representation (10.4), (10.8) but keep the representation of the momentum and position operators $\boldsymbol{p}$ and $\boldsymbol{r}$ general. In the split representation, DIRAC operators like β and σ are "even", i.e. diagonal, and $\boldsymbol{\alpha}$ is "odd", i.e. has only non-diagonal matrix elements connecting U_A with U_B. They then perform successive contact transformations, which transform the DIRAC spinor wave function u and all operators, including the HAMILTONian H, to a new representation. For a contact transformation, defined by a transformation operator S, the new representation of any operator O and the wave function u is given by the primed quantities

Table 2. *Orders of magnitude of ψ_+, ψ_- and ψ_0 for an S-state. $p_0 = \alpha m c$, where $\alpha = e^2/\hbar c$.*

	$p < p_0$	$p_0 < p < mc$	$mc < p$
$\psi_+(p)$	1	$(p_0/p)^4$	$\alpha^4 (mc/p)^3$
$\psi_-(p)$	α^3	$\alpha^3 (p_0/p)$	$\alpha^4 (mc/p)^3$
$\psi_0(p)$	$\psi_+(p)\,[1+O(p^2/m^2c^2)]$		$\alpha^4 (mc/p)^4$

$$u' = e^{iS} u, \qquad O' = e^{iS} O e^{-iS}; \qquad H' u' = E u'. \tag{16.20}$$

The aim of these successive transformations is to eliminate odd operators from the HAMILTONian, i.e. each step reduces the off-diagonal elements of H by some power of $1/m$.

For the field-free HAMILTONian ($\varphi = \boldsymbol{A} = 0$) the complete transformation, diagonalizing H, is given by the transformation operator

$$S = -\frac{1}{2} i \beta \frac{\boldsymbol{\alpha}\cdot\boldsymbol{p}}{p} \arctan\left(\frac{p}{mc}\right). \tag{16.21}$$

This transformation is exactly equivalent to our change of representation from (ψ_A, ψ_B) to (ψ_+, ψ_-), carried out explicitly in momentum space. In particular the HAMILTONian is transformed to the operator

$$H' = \beta \sqrt{(mc^2)^2 + (cp)^2}.$$

When the contact transformation (16.21) is applied to the general HAMILTONian (10.1), the DIRAC equation in the new representation is equivalent to (16.13). If the vector potential $\boldsymbol{A}$ is appreciable it is more convenient to start with a contact transformation, defined by an operator linear in $1/mc$,

$$S_1 = -\frac{i}{2mc} \beta \boldsymbol{\alpha}\cdot\left(\boldsymbol{p} + \frac{e}{c}\boldsymbol{A}\right). \tag{16.22}$$

If $\boldsymbol{A}$ were zero, (16.22) would be just the first term in an expansion of (16.21) in powers of (p/mc). The DIRAC equation, transformed by (16.22), contains all the even operators contained in the PAULI approximation (12.11) but is still exact and contains some odd operators involving the first or higher powers of $1/m$. These odd operators can be reduced further by additional contact transformations.

17. The fine structure formula. *α) Hydrogen.* We write again $W = E - E_0$ for the binding energy of an electron in a hydrogen-like atom. (14.29) then gives the exact DIRAC formula

$$\frac{W}{mc^2} = \left[1 + \left(\frac{\alpha Z}{n - k + \sqrt{k^2 - \alpha^2 Z^2}}\right)^2\right]^{-\frac{1}{2}} - 1. \tag{17.1}$$

[1] L. FOLDY and S. WOUTHUYSEN: Phys. Rev. **78**, 29 (1950).

In (17.1), n is the principal quantum number and $k=j+\frac{1}{2}$ is a quantum number which has as possible values $(1, 2, \ldots, n)$. To each value of k or j, except $k=n$, correspond two possible values of the orbital quantum number $l=j+\frac{1}{2}$ and $l=j-\frac{1}{2}$ (for $k=n$, only $l=j-\frac{1}{2}=n-1$). In the nonrelativistic SCHRÖDINGER theory for each value of n we have n^2 linearly independent eigenstates, all having the same energy. In the DIRAC theory we have $2n^2$ independent states, the factor 2 stemming from the two possible eigenvalues of a component of the electron spin. Here the degeneracy is partially removed and the SCHRÖDINGER level splits into n components, one for each value of k. Nevertheless, in the DIRAC theory the pairs of levels with $l=j\pm\frac{1}{2}$ still have *exactly* the same energy. We shall see in the following sections that radiative corrections (LAMB shift) remove this degeneracy of the $l=j\pm\frac{1}{2}$ levels, but the splitting is small and we neglect it at the moment. Remarkably enough, (17.1) had already been derived by SOMMERFELD from the "*old*" BOHR quantum theory, although the interpretation of the quantum numbers, statistical weights, etc. was different (and wrong) in the old theory[1].

Since the fine structure constant, $\alpha=e^2/\hbar c=1/137.037$, is small, the parameter $Z\alpha$ in (17.1) will be small compared with unity, except for very heavy atoms (large nuclear charge Z). If we expand (17.1) in ascending powers of $(Z\alpha)^2$, the first two terms in this expansion are

$$W=-\frac{Z^2\,\mathrm{Ry}}{n^2}\left[1+\frac{(\alpha Z)^2}{n}\left(\frac{1}{k}-\frac{3}{4n}\right)\right], \tag{17.2}$$

where $\mathrm{Ry}=e^4 m/2\hbar^2=\frac{1}{2}\alpha^2 mc^2$ is the RYDBERG energy unit. The first term in this expansion is W_0, the energy eigenvalue in the nonrelativistic SCHRÖDINGER theory. The second term is exactly equal to W_1, the correction obtained for the energy on the PAULI approximation, Eq. (13.14). Note that the expansion parameter in (17.2) is $(Z\alpha)^2$, *not* $Z\alpha$. The difference between the exact expression (17.1) and the PAULI approximation (17.2) is thus of order $(Z\alpha)^2 W_1 \sim (Z\alpha)^4 W_0$. Radiative corrections, which are not contained in the DIRAC theory, on the other hand, are of order $\alpha(\log\alpha)W_1$. For fairly small values of the nuclear charge Z, to which hydrogen-like atoms are restricted in practice, $(Z\alpha)^2 \ll \alpha\log\alpha$. The radiative corrections then are more important than the difference of (17.1) and (17.2), although both are small compared even with W_1. We therefore discuss at the moment only the PAULI approximation W_1.

To get an idea of the order of magnitude of the fine structure splitting, consider the levels with $n=2$ for hydrogen ($Z=1$). Let ΔW be the energy difference between the level with $k=1$ (both the $2S_{\frac{1}{2}}$- and $2P_{\frac{1}{2}}$- state) and with $k=2$ $(2P_{\frac{3}{2}})$. In various energy units, ΔW is approximately

$$\Delta W=\alpha^2 W_0/2n=1.33\times 10^{-5} W_0=0.365\ \mathrm{cm}^{-1}=1.10\times 10^4\ \mathrm{Mc/sec}. \tag{17.3}$$

For any Z and n the energy separation between the two extreme components of the fine structure multiplet, i.e. between $k=1$ and $k=n$, is given by

$$\Delta W=W_0(Z\alpha)^2(n-1)/n^2, \tag{17.4}$$

where W_0 is the nonrelativistic energy for the level. Thus, even the ratio of the fine structure splitting ΔW to W_0 increases with increasing Z and decreases[2] with increasing n, just as $|W_0|$ itself does. This stems from the fact that the fine

[1] For a historical survey see ref. [*10*], p. 317, and A. SOMMERFELD, Naturwiss. **28**, 417 (1940).

[2] Except that there is no splitting for $n=1$ ($j=\frac{1}{2}$ only). Nevertheless the energy *shift* W_1 is larger for $n=1$ than for any other level.

structure increases sharply with the electron's velocity (for large l, at least, a large part of W_1 is due to relativistic variation of mass with velocity): These effects are large when the average kinetic energy is large which, in turn equals $-W_0$. For fixed values of Z and n the fine structure energy shift $|W_1|$ decreases with increasing l (i.e. with k), even though W_0 is independent of l. This is due to the fact that W_1 contains the expectation value of the *square* of the kinetic energy operator [see (16.16)], which is largest when the electron penetrates closest to the nucleus, i.e. for small l.

The absolute value of the fine structure splitting ΔW, Eq. (17.4), decreases rapidly with increasing n (except for $n=1$). The splitting of a spectral line due to the transition between two states of different n is mainly due to the splitting of the lower state, with finer fine structure due to the upper state. Thus each BALMER line (lower state $n=2$) essentially consists of a doublet with separation approximately given by (17.3). Each component of this doublet is again composite (splitting of the upper state) but with splitting smaller than (17.3). Each RITZ-PASCHEN line (lower state $n=3$) essentially consists of a triplet, etc.

Detailed investigations have been carried out on the fine structure of many spectral lines of hydrogen and ionized helium, by optical spectroscopy. All the experimental results are in good *semi*-quantitative agreement[1] with (17.2). Optical observations on fine structure components are rather complicated and their quantitative accuracy is not very great. Nevertheless some small deviations from (17.2) have been observed. In particular, careful observation on the H_α-line indicates that the energy difference of the $2S_{\frac{1}{2}}$- and $2P_{\frac{1}{2}}$-levels is not exactly zero, as predicted by (17.1) or (17.2), but is about 10% of the fine structure, Eq. (17.3). The theoretical explanation of this effect, and more accurate microwave experiments, will be discussed later.

β) Alkali atoms and screening. Before discussing the fine structure of alkali and X-ray spectra, we digress a moment to consider the various "central field approximations" in the nonrelativistic treatment of many-electron atoms[2].

If we are prepared to neglect correlations between the various electrons (polarization) in a complex atom, we can write the atomic wave function in the form of an antisymmetrized product of "single-particle" wave functions. If we further neglect exchange effects, the wave function is a single product of Z functions $u_i(\boldsymbol{r}_i)$, where $\boldsymbol{r}_i$ is the position of the i-th electron. The best form $u_i(\boldsymbol{r}_i)$ is then the solution of the SCHRÖDINGER equation for a single electron in an effective potential $V_i(\boldsymbol{r}_i)$. This effective potential V_i is the sum of the COULOMB potentials due to the nuclear charge at the origin and due to the charge cloud of all the electrons, except the i-th, averaged over their respective wave functions. For the valence electron in an alkali atom (a single electron outside closed shells) $V_i(\boldsymbol{r}_i)$ is automatically a central potential, i.e. a function of the radial distance r_i only. For fairly heavy atoms in general, most of the electrons are in closed shells and we can approximate V_i by a central potential $V_i(r_i)$.

Various approximation methods are available for finding $V_i(r_i)$, the effective central potential in which the i-th electron moves. The most accurate of these is HARTREE's self-consistent field method[3]. This method requires numerical evaluation of the wave function of each electron in any particular atom and $V_i(r_i)$ is finally given in numerical form, separately for each atom. HARTREE solutions are available for a number of atoms up to Hg. Another, less accurate, method for

[1] See ref. [*10*], p. 319 and W. E. LAMB, Rep. Progr. Physics **14**, 19 (1951).

[2] For details on this voluminous subject see ref. [*5*] or A. SOMMERFELD, Atombau und Spektrallinien, 5th Ed.; or ref. [*4*], Ch. 6; or Vol. XXXVI of this Encyclopedia.

[3] D. R. HARTREE: Proc. Cambridge Phil. Soc. **24**, 111 (1928).

evaluating $V_i(r_i)$ is the THOMAS-FERMI statistical model[1]. This method treats the charge distribution of the electrons in a semi-classical manner and only gives $V(r)$, the total electrostatic potential at radial distance r due to *all* the electrons (including the i-th). This method gives good results only for medium and heavy atoms (large Z), for light atoms it overestimates the potential and charge density of the electrons at small radial distances. It has the advantage, however, of giving $V(r)$ simultaneously for all values of the nuclear charge Z. The potential due to all the electrons alone, $V(r)$, approaches a finite limit $V(0)$ at $r=0$. $V(0)$ is equal to $\int\limits_0^\infty dr\, r\, \varrho(r)$, where ϱ is the charge density due to all the electrons. According to the THOMAS-FERMI theory this limit is $3.59 Z^{\frac{4}{3}}$ Ry.

$V_i(r_i)$ is in general not of COULOMB form and the SCHRÖDINGER equation for an electron in such a potential can usually not be solved analytically. For an electron with small principal quantum number n (and generally for small $n-l$) its wave function is concentrated over a reasonably small range of radial distances near some value r_0. If we do not require very high accuracy we can replace $V_i(r_i)$ by a simple analytic function, which is a good approximation for r near r_0. The most convenient form to choose is

$$V_i(r) = -\frac{(Z-s_i)}{r} + V_{0i}. \tag{17.5}$$

Roughly speaking, the "inner screening constant" s_i represents the total charge of the part of the electronic charge cloud which lies inside r_0. The "outer screening constant" V_{0i} represents the constant potential produced at small radial distances by the electronic charge cloud which lies outside r_0. The form (17.5) has the great advantage that the wave function of the i-th electron reduces to a hydrogen-like wave function with charge $(Z-s_i)$. The nonrelativistic ionization potential of the i-th electron is then, in our approximation [see (2.11)],

$$I_i = \left[\left(\frac{Z-s_i}{n_i}\right)^2 - 2V_{0i}\right] \text{Ry}. \tag{17.6}$$

The distance r_0, at which the charge distribution of the i-th electron has its maximum, increases strongly with the principal quantum number n_i. Hence the inner screening constant s_i (electronic charge inside r_0) also increases strongly with n_i. For an atom containing N electrons in closed shells and only very few electrons outside the closed shells, s_i for the outermost electrons is about equal to N, which is almost as big as Z, and the screening is very strong. For such an outer electron with fixed principal quantum number n_i, its wave function penetrates inside the closed shells (where the screening is much weaker) more if its orbital quantum number l_i is low. Thus, for fixed n_i, the effective screening constant increases with increasing l_i. For inner electrons the dependence of s_i on l_i is weaker.

For an electron in any shell, the inner screening comes mainly from electrons in the same shell and in shells of smaller principal quantum number. The screening constant s_i for an electron in a closed shell then is almost independent of the nuclear charge Z or the number of electrons outside this particular shell. SLATER[2] and others have obtained values of s_i for electrons in a closed shell by semi-

[1] E. FERMI: Z. Physik **48**, 73 (1928). — L. H. THOMAS: Proc. Cambridge Phil. Soc. **23**, 542 (1927). See also P. GOMBÁS, Statistische Theorie des Atoms, Vienna: Springer 1949, and Vol. XXXVI of this Encyclopedia.

[2] L. PAULING: Proc. Roy. Soc. Lond., Ser. A **114** (1927). — J. C. SLATER: Phys. Rev. **36**, 57 (1930).

empirical means: For an electron in the helium atom in its ground state, $s_i = \frac{5}{16}$ (see Sect. 26 and 32). For a 1 s electron in all atoms heavier than helium, $s_1 \approx 0.3$ is still a good approximation. For a $2s$ or $2p$ electron in neon and heavier atoms, SLATER finds $s_2 \approx 4.15$ (although s_2 should be slightly lower for $2s$ than $2p$), etc.

For light atoms, especially for the outer electrons, the outer screening constant V_{0i} is unimportant. For medium-heavy and heavy atoms, especially for inner electrons, V_{0i} is quite large. However, V_{0i} only acts as an additive constant to the energy eigenvalue, but does not affect the wave function. For a 1 s electron in a medium or heavy atom a crude, but simple, approximation for the central potential $V_i(r)$ can be obtained as follows: The effect of the second 1 s electron is accounted for by choosing $s_1 = 0.3$. The potential due to all the other (outer) electrons is approximately constant over the region in which the 1 s wave function is large. We therefore take for V_{0i} the THOMAS-FERMI electrostatic potential at the origin due to all the electrons, $1.79 Z^{\frac{4}{3}}$ a.u., minus the potential at the origin due to the two 1 s electrons, which is about $2Z$ a.u. [see Eq. (3.29)]. We then have

$$V_1(r) = -\frac{(Z-0.3)}{r} + (1.79 Z^{\frac{4}{3}} - 2Z) \tag{17.7}$$

in atomic units. In this approximation the ionization potential of a 1 s electron, (17.6), becomes roughly

$$I_1 = (Z^2 - 3.59 Z^{\frac{4}{3}} + 3.4 Z) \text{ Ry}. \tag{17.8}$$

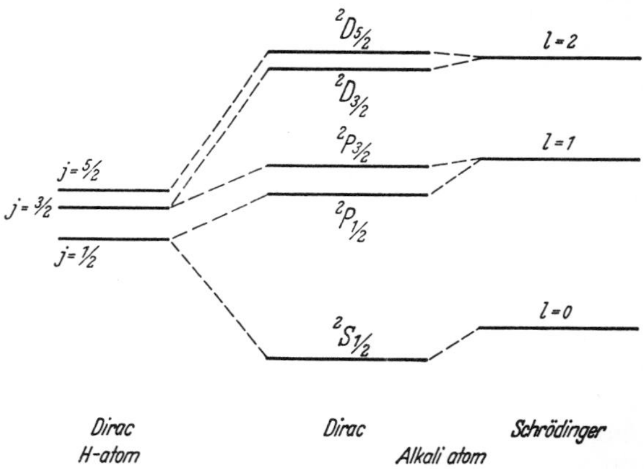

Fig. 10. Schematic level scheme for the states with $n=3$ of a DIRAC electron in an alkali atom. To the left is the level scheme for a DIRAC electron in a COULOMB potential, to the right the nonrelativistic levels in the alkali atom.

We finally return to the fine structure of energy levels in alkali atoms, containing one single electron outside closed shells. The central field approximation is then excellent for this valence electron. But, as discussed above, the shape of the effective potential $V_i(r)$ is far from the COULOMB form and, for fixed principal quantum number n, the binding energy decreases with increasing l. Thus unlike in hydrogen, there is no degeneracy between levels of different l in the nonrelativistic theory of alkali atoms. In addition, the relativistic fine structure corrections (13.8) have to be added to the nonrelativistic energy. These will result in a further splitting of any l-level (except $l=0$) into a doublet with $j = l \pm \frac{1}{2}$. The fine structure splitting of these familiar alkali doublets, being a relativistic effect, is very small compared with the (nonrelativistic) energy separation of levels of different l. The level scheme for a valence electron with $n=3$ in Li or Na is given schematically in Fig. 10.

γ) X-ray levels. For hydrogen-like atoms of reasonably low nuclear charge Z we have seen that the relativistic fine structure shifts W_1 are of order $(Z\alpha)^2 W_0$, where W_0 is the nonrelativistic energy of the level, and hence very small. Further, the difference between the exact DIRAC expression for W_1 and the PAULI approximation for it is of order $(Z\alpha)^2 W_1$, which is smaller even than the radiative corrections of order $W_1 \alpha \log \alpha$. For the heaviest atoms, however, $(Z\alpha)^2$ is not very much smaller than unity (about 0.45 for U) and the relativistic effects become very marked. For very large Z even the difference between the DIRAC and PAULI expressions is large compared with the radiative corrections and the experimental errors in the measurement of energy levels. In practice, of course, one-electron ions of heavy atoms are not available and we have to turn to the innermost electrons of neutral heavy atoms.

The relativistic effects are largest for electrons of low principal quantum number n, for which the inner screening is also weakest. We restrict ourselves therefore to the ionization potentials of electrons in the K and L shells of very heavy atoms (the K-shell contains the $1s$-electrons, the L_{I} subshell the $2s$-electrons, L_{II} and L_{III} the $2p_{\frac{1}{2}}$- and $2p_{\frac{3}{2}}$-electrons respectively; the M and N shells correspond to $n=3$ and 4, etc.). The ionization potentials of the various subshells are known experimentally to quite good accuracy from an analysis of the frequency measurements of X-ray spectra[1]. The energy differences of nearby shells and subshells are known even more accurately for most heavy atoms.

Consider, for example, the three L subshells of Uranium ($Z=92$). The experimental ionization potential of the L_{III} electrons is 1264 Ry. The energy difference between L_{II} and L_{III} is 278.4 Ry. This difference represents the relativistic fine structure splitting of the $2P$-states into $j=\frac{3}{2}$ and $\frac{1}{2}$, which would be exactly zero in the nonrelativistic SCHRÖDINGER theory, and is an appreciable fraction of the ionization potential. On the other hand, the energy difference between L_{I} and L_{II} is only 59.7 Ry. This splitting between the S and P levels of $j=\frac{1}{2}$ is essentially a nonrelativistic effect, due to the slight deviation from COULOMB shape of the effective central potential at small radial distances. A rough, but very simple, theoretical calculation of the $L_{\mathrm{II}}-L_{\mathrm{III}}$ difference can be carried out as follows. Since the nonrelativistic wave functions of $2P_{\frac{1}{2}}$ and $2P_{\frac{3}{2}}$ are identical we can use the *same* effective potential (17.5) for both states. The outer screening, the additive constant V_{0i}, then does not enter in the energy difference, which is simply obtained from the relativistic expressions for hydrogen-like ions with the same effective charge ($Z-s_2$). With SLATER's value of $s_2=4.15$, the energy difference for U obtained from the PAULI approximation (17.2) is 198 Ry, from the exact DIRAC expression (17.1) one gets 269 Ry, compared with the experimental value of 278 Ry. Note that the PAULI approximation would give too low a value (238 Ry) even with *no* screening ($s_2=0$).

In reality we should use a slightly lower value for s_2 for fine structure calculations than SLATER's nonrelativistic value of 4.15: The "expectation value" integrals for the fine structure splitting weight small distances more heavily than the integrals for the nonrelativistic energy and the screening is smaller at smaller radial distances. SOMMERFELD has shown that, with an empirical value of $s_2=3.5$, the exact DIRAC expression (17.1) gives good agreement with the experimental $L_{\mathrm{II}}-L_{\mathrm{III}}$ splitting for all elements up to the heaviest. The PAULI approximation (17.2) gives good agreement only for small nuclear charge Z, for all elements of large Z (e.g. for 92 in U) it deviates appreciably from experiment (for *any* value of s_2). More accurate calculations for the $L_{\mathrm{II}}-L_{\mathrm{III}}$ splitting on the DIRAC theory have been carried out[2], including an explicit calculation of the effect of the other electrons (instead of SOMMERFELD's empirical screening). The agreement with experiment is again good[3].

[1] LANDOLT and BÖRNSTEIN: Zahlenwerte und Funktionen, 6. Ed., Vol. I/1 Berlin: Springer 1950.

[2] R. CHRISTY and J. KELLER: Phys. Rev. **61**, 147 (1942).

[3] Small remaining discrepancies, due to the finite nuclear size, are discussed by A. SCHAWLOW and C. TOWNES, Science, Lancaster, Pa. **115**, 284 (1952) and Phys. Rev. **100**, 1273 (1955).

We consider next the ionization potential of the K-shell (1 S-electrons) in heavy atoms. For $Z=92$ (Uranium) for instance, the nonrelativistic BALMER formula for a hydrogen-like ion (91-times ionized U!) would give $|W_0|=Z^2$ Ry $=$ 8464 Ry, the PAULI approximation (17.2) would increase this value by $0.113|W_0|$, the exact DIRAC expression (17.1) by $0.150|W_0|$. For neutral U let us use the rough, but simple, approximation (17.7) for the effective potential $V_i(r)$. The nonrelativistic ionization potential, given by (17.8), is then about 7290 Ry. With this effective potential the PAULI approximation gives about 8230 Ry, the DIRAC expression 8530 Ry, compared with the experimental value of 8515 Ry. This simple calculation, based on an effective potential derived from the nonrelativistic THOMAS-FERMI model, is of course very crude, but already favors the DIRAC over the PAULI expression[1]. BRENNER and BROWN[2] have carried out similar, but more accurate, calculations for the K-shell ionization potential of a number of heavy atoms up to Hg. They take an effective potential, due to all but K-electrons, of similar form to (17.7), but calculate the best outer screening constant V_{0i} from the more accurate HARTREE potentials, corrected for relativistic effects. Further, they calculate the interaction energy between the two 1 S-electrons using more accurate relativistic expressions (see Sect. 43). Their results, using the DIRAC theory, agree with the experimental ionization potentials to within better than 20 Ry for all elements[3].

The most accurate calculation available is one by COHEN[4] on the $K-L_{\text{I}}$ energy difference ($1S-2S$) in Hg ($Z=80$). Calculating this energy *difference* has the advantage that the contribution of electrons outside the K- and L-shells is fairly small. The tabulated nonrelativistic HARTREE potentials are used merely to calculate accurate relativistic wave functions for each of the atomic electrons. The interaction energy between the 1 S- or 2 S-electron with all the other electrons is then calculated numerically, using relativistic expressions. This calculation, based on the exact DIRAC theory, gives for the $K-L_{\text{I}}$ energy difference 5025.2 Ry and the experimental value[5] is about 5022 Ry. The purely numerical errors in the calculation are about ± 0.5 Ry. The remaining small discrepancy of about 3 Ry is probably due to radiative corrections (e.g. LAMB shift) not included in the DIRAC theory. If the PAULI approximation (17.2) had been used, the discrepancy would have been of the order of 100 Ry. Even if the DIRAC expression (17.1) had been expanded in powers of $(Z\alpha)^2$ and terms up to $(Z\alpha)^8 mc^2 \sim Z^8\alpha^6$ Ry (one order *higher* than the PAULI approximation) kept, the discrepancy would still be about 20 Ry.

c) Radiative and other corrections.

18. Radiative corrections. S-matrix theory. We discuss next the modifications to the DIRAC theory of an electron, which are introduced by the quantization of the electromagnetic radiation field, the so-called "radiative corrections". We shall not attempt to describe the techniques of modern quantum electrodynamics[6], but merely how its results affect atomic theory.

---

[1] The almost exact agreement of this crude calculation for U with experiment is fortuitous.

[2] S. BRENNER and G. E. BROWN: Proc. Roy. Soc. Lond., Ser. A **218**, 422 (1953).

[3] For a more detailed comparison of theory with the latest experimental data see D. SAXON Ph. D. Thesis, Univ. of Wisconsin and J. E. MACK, Phys. Rev. **87**, 225 (1952).

[4] S. COHEN: Ph. D. Thesis, Cornell 1955.

[5] Recent experimental work by D. SAXON indicates a slightly smaller value for the $K-L_{\text{I}}$ difference, which would increase the discrepancy by a few Ry.

[6] For treatments of quantum electrodynamics see, for instance, refs. [*3*], [*6*] and [*11*] to [*14*] of the bibliography.

α) Expansion of the S-matrix. We consider a DIRAC electron under the influence of two interactions. One with an external, given, electromagnetic field, described by a four-vector potential $A_\mu(\boldsymbol{r}, t)$; the other with the electron's own (virtual) radiation field. It is this second interaction which is missing in the DIRAC theory, treated in the preceding sections. For the time being we treat both interactions as small perturbations, but later on we shall discuss the case of an arbitrarily large external potential A_μ. Further, we consider for the moment an unbound electron. First of all, the electron can be scattered any number of times by the potential A_μ. The interaction of the electron with the general radiation field then represents the possibility of the emission or absorption of any number of transverse electromagnetic quanta (photons) by the electron, one at a time. Any physical process is then described by the total transition amplitude for transitions between two "real" states A and B of the system, $S(A, B)$. Each "real" state consists of a free electron and some number of free ("real") quanta (and some number of electron-positron pairs). The states A and B have the same total energy and $S(A, B)$ is called the S-matrix. We shall only consider radiationless scattering, i.e. transitions between states A and B which contain *no* real quanta (and no pairs). For such transitions we can say that the electron interacts only with "its own virtual radiation field" (apart from its interaction with the potential).

We take, as initial and final states A and B, plane wave solutions, (15.8), with positive energy, of the field-free DIRAC equation. Let the momenta of the electron in the two states be $\boldsymbol{p}$ and $(\boldsymbol{p}+\boldsymbol{q})$, respectively, with $|\boldsymbol{p}| = |\boldsymbol{p}+\boldsymbol{q}|$ and energy $E = \sqrt{(m c^2)^2 + (p c)^2}$. The transition amplitude $S(A, B)$ is given as an infinite sum of terms, according to the rules of general perturbation theory. A general term in this perturbation expansion involves a number of intermediate states, each representing the electron in some plane wave state plus some number of virtual quanta. The total energy in the intermediate states is in general not equal to E. The overall matrix element for such a term contains the product of a number of energy denominators and of matrix elements involving the potential A_μ or the emission-absorption operators for virtual quanta. Each scattering with momentum change $\boldsymbol{k}$ by the potential introduces a factor $A_\mu(\boldsymbol{k})$, the FOURIER transform of the potential. Each emission or absorption of a quantum involves the coupling constant between the electron and field. The square of this coupling constant (itself proportional to e) is a simple multiple of α, the fine structure constant. Any quantum emitted by the electron must be subsequently reabsorbed (since A and B contain no quanta) and the number of interactions with virtual quanta is even. Thus the perturbation theory expression for the transition amplitude $S(A, B)$ consists of a double expansion in ascending powers both of α (number of virtual quanta) and of A_μ (number of scatterings by the external potential). Even though the formalism of perturbation theory is used, if one could sum the expansion for $S(A, B)$, the resulting expression would be exact (if the expansion converges).

The terms in this expansion which are of zero order in α (no virtual quanta) give simply the ordinary scattering amplitudes according to the unmodified DIRAC equation alone. Of the terms of first order in α (a single virtual quantum) we consider first the term linear in A_μ (one scattering by the potential). This term, of order α times smaller than the ordinary scattering amplitude, consists of the sum of three expressions. These expressions are described symbolically by "FEYNMAN diagrams[1]", shown in Fig. 11, diagrams 1,1a; 1,1b and 1,1c. The

[1] R. P. FEYNMAN: Phys. Rev. 76, 749, 769 (1949).

"self-energy diagram", (1,1 a), represents one scattering by the potential followed (or preceded) by the emission and reabsorption of a photon by the electron itself. The "LAMB shift diagram proper", (1,1 b), represents one potential scattering *between* the emission and reabsorption of the photon. The "vacuum polarization diagram", (1,1 c), refers to the emission of a virtual electron-positron pair by the external potential, followed by the annihilation of the pair under emission of a quantum which is absorbed by the electron (or a COULOMB interaction taking the place of the quantum exchange). Vacuum polarization terms are a feature of electron pair (or hole) theory and would be absent entirely if DIRAC single electron theory were used. A matrix element of a higher order in α and/or A_μ also consists of a sum of individual expressions, which can be described by FEYNMAN diagrams. The number and complexity of these expressions increases rapidly with the order of the matrix element. Some examples of the FEYNMAN diagrams of order $\alpha^2 A_\mu$ (2,1 a and 2,1 b) and of order αA_μ^2 (1,2 a) are given in Fig. 11.

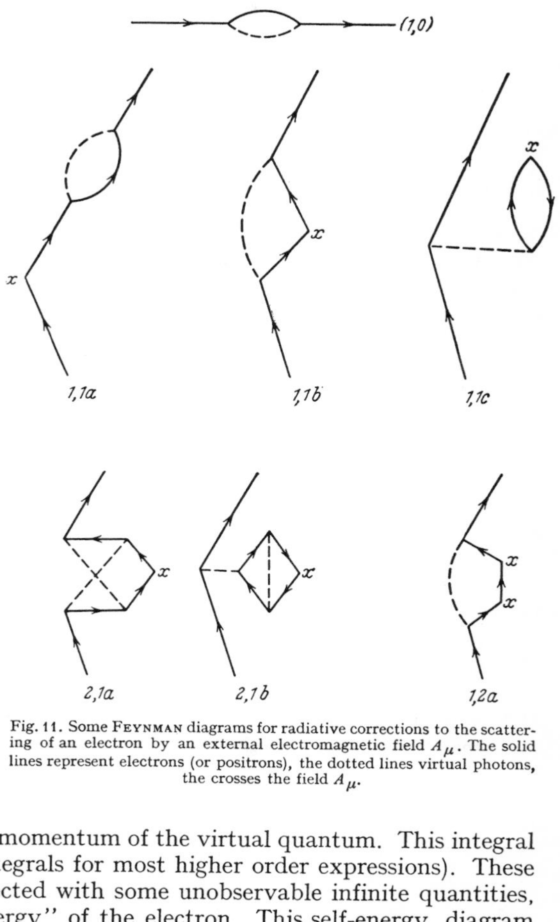

Fig. 11. Some FEYNMAN diagrams for radiative corrections to the scattering of an electron by an external electromagnetic field A_μ. The solid lines represent electrons (or positrons), the dotted lines virtual photons, the crosses the field A_μ.

β) Covariant calculation. Consider, for example, the mathematical expression for the term in the expansion which corresponds to diagram (1,1 b). For a fixed momentum change $\boldsymbol{q}$ from the initial to the final state of the electron [involving the FOURIER transform $A_\mu(\boldsymbol{q})$ of the potential] this expression contains an integral over all values of $\boldsymbol{k}$, the momentum of the virtual quantum. This integral diverges as $k \to \infty$ (as do the integrals for most higher order expressions). These divergence difficulties are connected with some unobservable infinite quantities, such as the "transverse self-energy" of the electron. This self-energy, diagram (1, 0), stems from the term in the perturbation expansion of first order in α and zero order in A_μ, the simple emission and reabsorption of a quantum by the electron. Such a term does not contribute directly to the scattering of the electron, but it adds a "constant" self-energy to the "bare" rest mass energy of the electron and the observed electron mass corresponds to the sum of these terms. This "constant" self-energy also involves an integral over $\boldsymbol{k}$, which also diverges as $\boldsymbol{k} \to \infty$. To calculate correctly the total transition amplitude of order αA_μ one has to subtract from the infinite expressions for diagrams (1,1 a, 1,1 b and 1,1 c) a multiple of $A_\mu(q)$ which is proportional to the infinite self energy.

If these subtraction procedures, called renormalizations[1], are carried out consistently the resulting transition amplitudes are finite.

Since the renormalizations involve the difference between two divergent integrals, great care must be taken to carry out the subtractions in an unambiguous manner. This can be achieved most elegantly by the use of modern, fully LORENTZ-covariant, techniques which were developed by DYSON, FEYNMAN and SCHWINGER[2]. These new covariant techniques are equivalent to "old-fashioned" perturbation theory, but are much more powerful. In principle, at least, they enable one to calculate the terms of any order in α and A_μ in the perturbation expansion for the transition amplitude. In practice, the calculation of any but the first few terms is very cumbersome even with this improved method. Both the idea of renormalization and the covariant formulations of quantum electrodynamics were developed in about 1947 to 1949, stimulated to a large extent by experiments on the LAMB shift in hydrogen and the anomalous moment of the electron.

Some of the integrals over the photon momentum $\boldsymbol{k}$, which occur in these relativistic S-matrix calculations, encounter some difficulties as $k \to 0$. These difficulties at the low-frequency end of the quantum spectrum (the infrared catastrophe) are purely nonrelativistic effects. They are not connected with the divergence difficulties at the high-frequency end which are removed by covariant renormalization. It is convenient to introduce a constant lower cut-off λ into the integrals over k in the covariant calculations, where $\lambda \ll m c$. This cut-off is equivalent to the omission of the influence of virtual quanta of momentum less than λ. The treatment of this low-frequency part of the quantum spectrum will be discussed later. With such a cut-off the covariant calculations give finite expressions for the transition amplitudes.

We merely quote the results of some calculations on the transition amplitude $S(A, B)$ for radiationless scattering of an electron in a potential A_μ for a fixed change $q_\nu = (\boldsymbol{q}, i\, q_0)$ in the momentum energy four-vector. Let $A_\mu(q_\nu)$ be the four-dimensional FOURIER transform of the potential (for a time-independent potential, $A_\mu(q_\nu)$ is non-zero only for the energy-change $q_0 = 0$, i.e. for elastic scattering). It follows from the DIRAC equation (10.13) that the first term in the perturbation expansion for $S(A, B)$ is simply proportional to $(e/c) \sum A_\mu(q_\nu)\, \gamma_\mu$. The second term in this expansion, linear in both α and $(e/c)\, A_\mu$, has been evaluated by various authors[3]. The result of these calculations, using a lower cut-off λ on the photon momentum, is to replace the first order term $\sum A_\mu \gamma_\mu$ by[4]

$$\sum_\mu \left[1 - g_2 \frac{\sum\limits_\nu q_\nu^2}{(m c)^2}\right] A_\mu(q_\nu)\, \gamma_\mu - g_1 \frac{i}{4 m c} \sum_{\mu, \sigma} \left[A_\sigma(q_\nu)\, q_\mu - A_\mu(q_\nu)\, q_\sigma\right] \gamma_\mu \gamma_\sigma. \tag{18.1}$$

In (18.1), $\sum q_\nu^2$ denotes $|\boldsymbol{q}|^2 - q_0^2$, and g_1 and g_2 are dimensionless constants given by

$$g_1 = \frac{\alpha}{2\pi}, \qquad g_2 = \frac{\alpha}{3\pi} \left[\left(\log \frac{m c}{\lambda} - \log 2 - \frac{3}{8} + \frac{5}{6}\right) - \frac{1}{5}\right]. \tag{18.2}$$

---

[1] H. A. BETHE: Phys. Rev. **72**, 339 (1947). See also our Sect. 19β.

[2] For a list of the classic papers of these authors on quantum electrodynamics see refs. [*6*], [*12*], [*13*] and [*14*].

[3] N. KROLL and W. LAMB: Phys. Rev. **75**, 388 (1949). — J. FRENCH and V. WEISSKOPF: Phys. Rev. **75**, 1240 (1949). — J. SCHWINGER: Phys. Rev. **76**, 790 (1949). — R. P. FEYNMAN: Phys. Rev. **76**, 769 (1949).

[4] The expression (18.1) holds only for a nonrelativistic change in momentum, $q_\nu^2 \ll (m c)^2$, but expressions have been evaluated which hold for all values of q_ν^2.

The term in g_2 involving $\frac{1}{5}$ comes from the vacuum polarization diagram (1, 1c), all other parts of g_2, and g_1 come from the FEYNMAN diagram (1, 1a) and (1, 1b) and the mass renormalization term.

The expression (18.1) can also be described in position space as follows: The scattering amplitude, including the effect of radiative corrections of order αA_μ, is obtained by: (i) Replacing A_μ in the DIRAC equation (10.13) by the expression

$$\left[1 + g_2\left(\frac{\hbar}{m c}\right)^2 \Box^2\right] A_\mu - g_1\left(\frac{\hbar}{4 m c}\right) \sum_\nu F_{\mu\nu}\gamma_\nu. \tag{18.3}$$

(ii) Treating the part of (18.3) which involves g_1 or g_2 as a small perturbation in (10.13) and evaluating the transition amplitude (matrix element) between two plane wave states of the electron by *first* order perturbation theory. The modified DIRAC equation is then exactly of form (10.15). The physical significance of such a modification was discussed in Sect. 10γ. When the equation is treated by lowest order perturbation theory the effect is: (i) To multiply the electromagnetic moment of the electron, given by the DIRAC theory, by the factor $(1 + g_1)$. (ii) For a time-independent electrostatic potential φ, for instance, $(\boldsymbol{A} = 0, A_4 = i\varphi)$ the potential φ is replaced by

$$\varphi + g_2\left(\frac{\hbar}{m c}\right)^2 \Delta\varphi = \varphi - 4\pi g_2\left(\frac{\hbar}{m c}\right)^2 \varrho, \tag{18.4}$$

where ϱ is the charge density of the *external* charge distribution which gives rise to the potential φ.

Calculations of all radiative corrections of second order in α and first in A_μ, as well as of second order in A_μ and first in α, have been carried out by now. We shall give some of these results in Sect. 21. We merely quote here the result[1] of the terms of order $\alpha^2 A_\mu$ on the anomalous moment of the electron. The effective total magnetic moment is again $(1 + g_1)$ times the DIRAC moment, but g_1 is now not simply given by (18.2) but includes a term in α^2,

$$1 + g_1 = 1 + \frac{\alpha}{2\pi} - 2.973\,\frac{\alpha^2}{\pi^2} = 1.0011453. \tag{18.5}$$

Consider (18.1) for radiationless scattering of an electron from initial momentum $\boldsymbol{p}$ to final momentum $(\boldsymbol{p} + \boldsymbol{q})$ in a time-independent field (initial and final energies the same). The expression (18.2) for the factors g_1 and g_2 were obtained by evaluating integrals over the momentum $\boldsymbol{k}$ of the virtual photon, with a lower cut-off λ on k, where $\lambda \ll q \ll mc$. Even for such low values of λ, some of the integrals depend on λ and, in fact, g_2 diverges logarithmically as λ tends to zero. The numerical factor multiplying this divergence is small, e.g. if λ is decreased from λ_1 to λ_2, then the transition amplitude S is decreased by a multiplicative factor given approximately by

$$1 - b\log\frac{\lambda_1}{\lambda_2}, \qquad b = \frac{\alpha}{3\pi}\left(\frac{q}{m c}\right)^2 \ll \alpha \ll 1. \tag{18.6}$$

This infrared catastrophe is connected with the fact that, besides the elastic radiationless scattering considered so far, the electron can also undergo inelastic scattering with the emission of one or more *real* photons (Bremsstrahlung, see Sect. 76 to 79). For very low photon momenta $k \ll q$, the total probability for scattering with the emission of one photon with k between λ_1 and λ_2 is given approximately by

$$P_1 = |S|^2\, 2b\log\frac{\lambda_1}{\lambda_2}, \tag{18.7}$$

[1] R. KARPLUS and N. KROLL: Phys. Rev. **77**, 536 (1950).

where S and $|S|^2$ are the transition amplitude and probability for radiationless scattering and b is given in (18.6). Hence, without any lower cut-off on the photon momentum the total number of real photons emitted in a physical scattering process will be infinite. But the momenta of most of these photons will be extremely small ("soft" quanta). Thus, on the average, only one photon will be emitted in the enormous range of momenta q to $q\,e^{-1/2b}$, another one in the range $q\,e^{-1/2b}$ to $q\,e^{-1/b}$, etc. (where $2b$ is a very small number). Further, for low photon momenta, the decrease in the probability $|S|^2$ for radiationless scattering due to radiative corrections involving virtual photons in a certain momentum range is almost exactly cancelled by the additional probability of scattering with the emission of a real photon in this range. Mathematically, if we decrease the cut-off from λ_1 to λ_2 the total probability for scattering with or without emission of a real photon changes from $|S|^2$ to [see Eqs. (18.6) and (18.7)]

$$P_{\text{tot}} = \left|S\left(1 - b\log\frac{\lambda_1}{\lambda_2}\right)\right|^2 + |S|^2\, 2b\log\frac{\lambda_1}{\lambda_2} \approx |S|^2; \tag{18.8}$$

i.e., if we neglect terms quadratic in b, the total probability is unchanged.

For a consistent treatment of the fact that the most probable number of "soft" photons emitted is *not* small, the formalism of perturbation theory has to be modified somewhat. In particular, terms in our perturbation expansion for S which involve more than one virtual photon cannot be neglected, nor processes involving the emission of more than one real photon. These formal difficulties were overcome some time ago[1] in the framework of "oldfashioned" quantum electrodynamics and, more recently[2], also for the modern, covariant formalism. The results are roughly as follows. The *total* probability P_{tot} of scattering, irrespective of the number of real photons emitted and including radiative corrections of all orders, remains finite even when the lower cut-off λ tends to zero. However, if λ is very small, the probability for all scattering processes in which *no* real photon of momentum greater than λ is emitted (but any number of photons of smaller momentum) is given, approximately, by

$$P_\lambda = P_{\text{tot}} \exp\left(-2b\log\frac{q}{\lambda}\right). \tag{18.9}$$

This expression tends to zero as λ does, which merely indicates that any scattering process is accompanied by the emission of at least some very soft photons. If in (18.2) we choose the cut-off λ such that $q\,e^{-1/2b} \ll \lambda \ll q$, then (18.1) is still a good approximation in the following sense. It furnishes the probability for an "almost elastic" scattering, i.e. for a process in which no real photons of momentum larger than λ are emitted. Although the total number of soft photons emitted is still infinite, their total energy (and hence the electron's energy loss) is finite and small.

19. Radiative corrections. Bound states. In Sect. 18 we have only discussed the perturbation expansion for the S-matrix for the scattering of *free* electrons. We are mainly interested in the effect of radiative corrections on the energy levels of an electron *bound* in a central potential, in particular in the fine structure of hydrogen-like atoms. We discuss next the extent to which the covariant formalism can be adapted to bound electrons and how the results are joined on to nonrelativistic calculations.

---

[1] F. BLOCH and A. NORDSIECK: Phys. Rev. **52**, 54 (1937). — W. PAULI and M. FIERZ: Nuovo Cim. **15**, 167 (1938).

[2] J. JAUCH and F. ROHRLICH: Phys. Rev. **98**, 181 (1955) and Helv. phys. Acta **27**, 613 (1954). — E. L. LOMON: Nuclear Physics **1**, 101 (1956).

α) Covariant calculation. The terms involving g_1 and g_2 in (18.1) hold strictly only for transitions between plane wave states of a free electron. If $p_\mu = (\boldsymbol{p}, i E_p/c)$ is the energy-momentum four-vector of the electron in its initial state then $\sum_\mu p_\mu^2 = (mc)^2$, i.e. the energy is

$$E(p) = \sqrt{(m c^2)^2 + (p c)^2}\ .$$

Similarly if $(p_\mu + q_\mu)$ is the final energy-momentum, $\sum_\mu (p_\mu + q_\mu)^2 = (mc)^2$. If these conditions are satisfied, (18.1) depends only on the momentum transfer q_μ, but not explicitly on p_μ. The wave function of a bound electron can be written as the superposition of plane wave eigenfunctions and the probability amplitude for a momentum $\boldsymbol{p}$ is simply $\psi(\boldsymbol{p})$, the momentum space wave function (see Sects. 8 and 16). However, the energy of each plane wave function of momentum $\boldsymbol{p}$ is E, the total energy of the electron's bound state (including the restmass energy mc^2), and *not* E_p, the free particle value. Hence $\sum p_\mu^2$ is not exactly $(mc)^2$ for such "bound plane waves" and (18.1) is not applicable rigorously.

The covariant formalism can, at least in principle, be modified to be applicable to such bound plane waves. It will be remembered that the calculations leading to the terms in g_1 and g_2 in (18.1) involve an integration over $\boldsymbol{k}$, the momentum of the virtual photon. Consider the transition amplitude for a transition between two "bound plane waves" of momentum $\boldsymbol{p}$ and $(\boldsymbol{p}+\boldsymbol{q})$, both with energy E. One then finds that the integrand in the integral over $\boldsymbol{k}$ has very nearly its free particle value for $q_\mu = (\boldsymbol{q}, 0)$, as long as both $E(p) - E$ and $E(|\boldsymbol{p}+\boldsymbol{q}|) - E$ are small compared with kc (the energy of the virtual photon). For an electron bound in a sufficiently weak potential the momentum space wave function $\psi(\boldsymbol{p})$ will be appreciable only for $p \ll mc$. For a hydrogen-like atom of low nuclear charge Z, for instance, only momenta of the order of $Z p_0 \sim Z \alpha m c$ are important, where p_0 is the Bohr momentum. For such an atom the important values of $E(p) - E$ are of the order of magnitude $Z^2\,\mathrm{Ry} \sim Z^2\alpha^2 mc^2 \ll mc^2$. The free particle integrands will then be a good approximation as long as $k \gg (Z\alpha)^2\, mc$.

In the integrals leading to all the terms in (18.1), (18.2) (except possibly the term in $\log\lambda$) the important values of k are of order mc. For these terms then, if $Z\alpha \ll 1$ $(Z \ll 137)$, the modification due to the plane waves being bound is small. In the integral leading to the term in $\log\lambda$ in (18.2), however, all values of k down to the cut-off λ are important. If $Z\alpha \ll 1$, it is convenient to choose λ such that $(Z\alpha)^2 mc \ll \lambda \ll mc$. The contribution of virtual photons of $k > \lambda$ is then obtained from the covariant expressions neglecting the effect of the plane waves being bound (i.e. neglecting $Z^2\alpha^2 mc/\lambda$). The contribution of photons of $k < \lambda$ is then evaluated by a different, nonrelativistic, calculation which we discuss later. For the high-frequency part $k > \lambda$ we then simply use (18.1) with $q_4 = 0$ for the transition amplitude between any two Fourier transforms of the spatial wave function of the bound state of the electron. In (18.1) the term involving unity in the first bracket is exactly the Fourier transform of the position space potential [compare Eqs. (10.1), (10.13) and (16.1)]. The remaining terms in (18.1) involve g_1 and g_2 and are thus small. We can then treat these extra terms by first order perturbation theory. The perturbation to the energy eigenvalue is then

$$\Delta E_> = \int d^3q \int d^3p\, \psi^*(\boldsymbol{p})\, \Gamma(\boldsymbol{q})\, \psi(\boldsymbol{p}+\boldsymbol{q}), \tag{19.1}$$

where ψ is the momentum space wave function and $\Gamma(\boldsymbol{q})$ is $ie\beta$ times the part of (18.1) which involves g_1 or g_2. For any part of $\Gamma(q)$ which is a constant Γ, for instance, the double integral (19.1) reduces to Γ times the absolute square of $\int d^3p\, \psi(\boldsymbol{p})$.

Instead of evaluating (19.1) directly in momentum space it is often more convenient to work in position space. As in Sect. 18 we simply replace $A_\mu(x_\mu)$ in the DIRAC equation (10.13) by the expression (18.3) and again use perturbation theory. For a time-independent potential this furnishes for $\Delta E_>$ the expression

$$\Delta E_> = \int d^3r\, u_0^*(\boldsymbol{r})\, \Gamma(\boldsymbol{r})\, u_0(\boldsymbol{r}) \equiv \langle \Gamma(\boldsymbol{r}) \rangle_{00}, \tag{19.2}$$

where $u_0(\boldsymbol{r})$ is the position space wave function and $\Gamma(\boldsymbol{r})$ is $i e \beta \sum_\mu \gamma_\mu$ times the part of (18.3) which involves g_1 or g_2. The expression (19.2) is exactly equivalent to (19.1). If the vector potential $\boldsymbol{A}$ is zero, $\Gamma(\boldsymbol{r})$ reduces to

$$\Gamma(\boldsymbol{r}) = -g_2\left(\frac{\hbar}{mc}\right)^2 e\, \Delta\varphi(\boldsymbol{r}) - g_1 \frac{ie\hbar}{2mc}\, \beta\, \boldsymbol{\alpha}\cdot\mathcal{E}(\boldsymbol{r}), \tag{19.3}$$

where φ and $\mathcal{E}$ are the electrostatic potential and field.

In Sect. 21 we shall evaluate explicitly the first order perturbation $\Delta E_>$ to the energy eigenvalue for a COULOMB potential, given by the integrals (19.1) or (19.2). We shall do this by PAULI's method of "reduction to the large components". I.e. we use for the wave function $u(\boldsymbol{r})$ or $\psi(\boldsymbol{p})$ the approximate PAULI wave functions, whose radial parts are identical with the nonrelativistic SCHRÖDINGER expressions, *not* with the exact DIRAC expressions. We shall consider only the case of $Z\alpha \ll 1$, so the error due to this replacement should be small in general. For a COULOMB potential, however, some parts of the operator $\Gamma(\boldsymbol{q})$ to be substituted into (19.1) are equal to a constant Γ_c, independent of $\boldsymbol{q}$. The equivalent part of $\Gamma(\boldsymbol{r})$ in (19.3) is then a multiple of a DIRAC[1] delta-function, $\Gamma_c\,\delta^{(3)}(\boldsymbol{r})$. The corresponding contribution to the energy shift $\Delta E_>$ is then given by

$$\Delta E_{>,c} = \frac{\Gamma_c}{(2\pi)^3}\left|\int d^3p\, \psi(\boldsymbol{p})\right|^2 = \Gamma_c\, |u(0)|^2, \tag{19.4}$$

where $u(0)$ is the position space wave function at the origin.

We have already seen in Sect. 14 that, even for small $Z\alpha$, the PAULI and DIRAC wave functions at the origin are quite different, in fact the DIRAC wave function diverges. This apparent difficulty is resolved as follows. The expressions involving g_1 and g_2 in (18.1) are only valid if $q^2 \ll (mc)^2$ and further the expression (19.1) is strictly valid only if p and $|\boldsymbol{p}+\boldsymbol{q}|$ are small compared with mc. For p and/or $|\boldsymbol{p}+\boldsymbol{q}|$ large compared with mc one finds that the operator $\Gamma(\boldsymbol{q})$ in (19.1) is replaced by a more complicated operator which falls off much more rapidly with increasing momentum. Thus the integral in (19.1) should effectively be cut off for $p, q > mc$. A comparison with Table 2 (Sect. 16) shows that, if the nonrelativistic wave functions are used, the contribution from very large momenta is small even if the integrals are allowed to run to infinity with the unmodified operator $\Gamma(\boldsymbol{q})$. Further, the main contribution to the integral comes from values of p and q of the order of Zp_0 where the SCHRÖDINGER and DIRAC radial functions are nearly the same. We therefore get a good approximation to $\Delta E_>$ by using the integral (19.1) without modifying Γ as long as we use the PAULI wave functions and *not* the DIRAC ones (which are much larger for very large momenta).

For the position space integral (19.2) the equivalent argument runs as follows. The operator $\Gamma(\boldsymbol{r})$, Eq. (19.3), is a good approximation for all but very small radial distances r. For very small r, however, $\Gamma(\boldsymbol{r})$ has to be replaced by a complicated non-local operator. The part involving $\Gamma_c\,\delta^{(3)}(\boldsymbol{r})$ should then be replaced

[1] In (18.4), for instance, the term in g_2 is proportional to the charge distribution producing the field, which is a point charge $Ze\,\delta^{(3)}(\boldsymbol{r})$ for a COULOMB potential.

by an operator extending over small, but finite, distances and $\Gamma_c|u(0)|^2$ in (19.4) should be replaced by some complicated average of $\Gamma_c|u(\boldsymbol{r})|^2$ over small distances. As discussed in Sect. 14δ, a good approximation to $\Delta E_>$ is then obtained by using the integral (19.2) without modifying $\Gamma(\boldsymbol{r})$ but using the PAULI wave function $u(r)$.

We have discussed so far only the application to bound states of the terms in the perturbation expansion for the S-matrix which are linear both in the potential and in α (one virtual photon). All terms of higher order in α (two or more virtual photons), but still linear in the potential, can be applied to bound states in exactly the same manner. The radiative correction terms involving higher powers of the potential present more difficulties. The contribution of terms, quadratic in the potential and linear in α, to the energy eigenvalues of hydrogen-like atoms have nevertheless been calculated[1]. The vacuum polarization terms, which are linear in α, have even been calculated recently[2] for an arbitrarily strong potential (all powers of A_μ). At the present time, however, no methods are available for treating the radiative corrections in general for an arbitrarily strong potential. For the very heavy atoms, where $Z\alpha$ is not very small, the LAMB shift cannot yet be calculated with good accuracy.

β) Nonrelativistic calculations. The expression (19.1) or (19.2) gives the contribution to the lowest order radiative correction to the energy eigenvalue from virtual photons of momentum k larger than a certain cut-off value λ. We chose λ to be large compared with $(Z\alpha)^2 mc$, small compared with mc ($Z\alpha$ is considered as small). The contribution from virtual photons of momentum k less than λ is best treated by a nonrelativistic method, proposed by BETHE[3]. An outline of this method is as follows.

We treat the electron nonrelativistically throughout and first solve (at least in principle) the SCHRÖDINGER equation for an electron in the external electrostatic potential $\varphi(\boldsymbol{r})$. Unlike the covariant *S-matrix* method, the electron's interaction with the potential is thus treated *exactly*. The electron's interaction with the virtual radiation field, on the other hand, is treated as a small perturbation. The perturbation HAMILTONIAN H', to be added to the SCHRÖDINGER HAMILTONIAN is obtained from "old fashioned" nonrelativistic quantum electrodynamics. H' can be written in the form

$$H' = N\frac{e}{m}\boldsymbol{p}\cdot\sum_\sigma\left[\boldsymbol{\pi}_\sigma e^{i\boldsymbol{k}_\sigma\cdot\boldsymbol{r}/\hbar}q_\sigma + \boldsymbol{\pi}_\sigma e^{-i\boldsymbol{k}_\sigma\cdot\boldsymbol{r}/\hbar}q_\sigma^*\right]. \tag{19.5}$$

In (19.5) e, m are the electronic charge and mass, $\boldsymbol{p}$ and $\boldsymbol{r}$ the momentum and position of the electron; the summation index σ denotes the direction of polarization $\boldsymbol{\pi}_\sigma$ and the momentum $\boldsymbol{k}_\sigma$ of the virtual photon and q_σ, q_σ^* are the absorption, emission operators for the photon (numerical constants have been absorbed into the symbol N). q_σ (and q_σ^*) have matrix elements proportional to $k_\sigma^{-\frac{1}{2}}$ for transitions involving the absorption (and emission, respectively) of one σ-photon.

We use as zero-order state-vectors those representing an electron in a particular atomic state, given by the SCHRÖDINGER (or rather PAULI) wave function for a potential φ, plus any number of photons. We label a general atomic state by n and are interested in the change in the energy eigenvalue for a particular atomic state, labeled 0, in the absence of any real photons. The contribution to this energy shift of lowest order in e (i.e. in $\sqrt{\alpha}$) is given by using second order

[1] R. KARPLUS, A. KLEIN and J. SCHWINGER: Phys. Rev. **86**, 288 (1952). — M. BARANGER, H. BETHE and R. FEYNMAN: Phys. Rev. **92**, 482 (1953).
[2] E. WICHMAN and N. M. KROLL: Phys. Rev. **101**, 843 (1956).
[3] H. A. BETHE: Phys. Rev. **72**, 339 (1947).

perturbation theory on H', Eq. (19.5). The first virtual transition in the two-stage process involves q_σ^*, the emission operator for a particular photon σ, the second step involves the absorption operator q_σ for the *same* photon. The perturbation of the energy then involves a double sum over intermediate states involving any atomic state n and a single (virtual) photon of any momentum $\boldsymbol{k}$ (with $k \lessgtr \lambda$) and one of two directions of polarization perpendicular to $\boldsymbol{k}$. We shall neglect retardation at the moment (see Sect. 19γ for justification), i.e. we replace the exponential factors in (19.5) by unity. The sum over photon-momentum $\boldsymbol{k}$ can be converted into an integral and the integration over the direction of $\boldsymbol{k}$ and the sum over the polarization direction carried out. We use units in which $\hbar$ is unity (but carry the symbols for e, m and c). The energy change, i.e. the "self-energy of the electron in the bound state 0", is then given by ($\alpha = e^2/\hbar c$)

$$\Delta W = -\frac{2}{3\pi}\alpha\frac{1}{m^2}\int\limits_0^\lambda dk\,k\sum_n \frac{\boldsymbol{p}_{0n}\cdot\boldsymbol{p}_{n0}}{(E_n - E_0 + k\,c)}\,. \tag{19.6}$$

E_0 and E_n are the SCHRÖDINGER energy eigenvalues for the two atomic states and $\boldsymbol{p}_{0n}$ is the matrix element of the momentum operator for transitions between them. The sum over n includes all states of the electron in the potential φ, both in the discrete and the continuous spectrum.

It is convenient to split the expression (19.6) into two parts, one of which does not involve $(E_n - E_0)$. For this term the sum over n can be eliminated by a simple sum rule and we have

$$\Delta W = -\frac{2}{3\pi}\alpha\frac{1}{m^2}\int\limits_0^\lambda dk\,k\left[\frac{\langle p^2\rangle_{00}}{k\,c} + \sum_n \frac{\boldsymbol{p}_{0n}\cdot\boldsymbol{p}_{n0}(E_0 - E_n)}{k\,c\,(k\,c + E_n - E_0)}\right]. \tag{19.7}$$

We shall show next that the *observable* change $\Delta E_<$ in the energy eigenvalue is given *not* by the whole expression for ΔW, but only by the second term in (19.7). The first term is cancelled by a mass renormalization term, which can be evaluated as follows.

Consider, for a moment, a *free* electron (*no* external potential φ). Its experimentally observed mass m consists partly of the unobservable "bare" mass m_0 and partly of a correction δm, arising from the self energy. We consider δm as small (it involves α) and expand in powers of it. The HAMILTONian for the free electron is then

$$H_{\text{free}} = \frac{p^2}{2m_0} + H' = \frac{p^2}{2m} + \left(\frac{\delta m}{m}\frac{p^2}{2m} + H'\right), \tag{19.8}$$

where H' is given by (19.5). The operator H' leads, in second order perturbation theory, to a change in energy of the *free* electron. If retardation is neglected, this energy change is found to be identical[1] with the expectation value of the first term in (19.7). By definition, the experimental mass m is such that the total energy of a free electron of momentum p is exactly $p^2/2m$. The mass correction δm must then be chosen so that the expectation value of the term involving δm in (19.8) cancels the energy change due to H' for a free electron. Thus

$$\delta m = +\frac{4}{3\pi c}\alpha\int\limits_0^\lambda dk\,.$$

[1] This follows from (19.7) as a special case. For a free electron, the momentum changes by $\boldsymbol{k}$ upon emission or absorption of a quantum. If retardation is neglected, this means that $\boldsymbol{k}$ is negligible compared with $\boldsymbol{p}$, and therefore the energy E_n after emission of the quantum, is the same as that before, E_0. Then the second term in (19.7) vanishes, q.e.d.

When we now consider an electron in a potential φ, the term in δm in (19.8) also has to be added to the HAMILTONian. The expectation value of this operator exactly cancels the first term in (19.7). The observable energy change $\Delta E_<$ is then given by the second term alone, which is, after carrying out the integration,

$$\Delta E_< = -\frac{2}{3\pi}\alpha\frac{1}{(mc)^2}\sum_n \boldsymbol{p}_{0n}\cdot\boldsymbol{p}_{n0}(E_0-E_n)\log\left(\frac{\lambda c+E_n-E_0}{|E_n-E_0|}\right). \qquad (19.9)$$

The important values of $|E_n-E_0|$ will be of the order of the ground state binding energy or Z^2 Ry for a hydrogenic atom. This energy is thus very small compared with λc, so the logarithm in (19.9) is very large and not very sensitive to the exact value of E_n-E_0. In the numerator of this logarithm we neglect (E_n-E_0) altogether and in the denominator replace it by an average energy K_0. K_0 will be of order Z^2 Ry and it is defined exactly by the relation

$$\log\left(\frac{K_0}{Z^2\,\mathrm{Ry}}\right)\sum_n \boldsymbol{p}_{0n}\cdot\boldsymbol{p}_{n0}(E_n-E_0) = \sum_n \boldsymbol{p}_{0n}\cdot\boldsymbol{p}_{n0}(E_n-E_0)\log\left|\frac{E_n-E_0}{Z^2\,\mathrm{Ry}}\right|. \qquad (19.10)$$

The evaluation of K_0 will be discussed in Sect. 21 and 74γ.

With the logarithm in (19.9) replaced by the constant $\log(\lambda c/K_0)$, the remaining sum over states can be rewritten in the form

$$\sum_n \boldsymbol{p}_{0n}\cdot\boldsymbol{p}_{n0}(E_0-E_n) = \sum_n [(H\boldsymbol{p})_{0n}\cdot\boldsymbol{p}_{n0}-(\boldsymbol{p}H)_{0n}\cdot\boldsymbol{p}_{n0}] = \langle[H,\boldsymbol{p}]\cdot\boldsymbol{p}\rangle_{00}. \qquad (19.11)$$

In the first line of (19.11), H is the HAMILTONian for the electron, excluding the interaction H' with the radiation field,

$$H = \frac{p^2}{2m} - e\varphi(\boldsymbol{r}), \qquad (19.12)$$

which gives E_0 and E_n, respectively, when operating on the wave functions for the states 0 and n. The last member of (19.11) involving the commutator of H and $\boldsymbol{p}$, is obtained from the middle member by a simple sum rule. An equivalent expression to (19.11), but with $[H,\boldsymbol{p}]\cdot\boldsymbol{p}$ replaced by $\boldsymbol{p}\cdot[\boldsymbol{p},H]$, also holds. Adding these expressions we finally obtain (putting $\hbar=1$)

$$\sum_n \boldsymbol{p}_{0n}\cdot\boldsymbol{p}_{n0}(E_0-E_n) = \tfrac{1}{2}\langle[[H,\boldsymbol{p}]\cdot,\boldsymbol{p}]\rangle_{00} = +\tfrac{1}{2}e\langle\Delta\varphi(\boldsymbol{r})\rangle_{00}, \qquad (19.13)$$

where we have used the relation

$$[p_x, f(r)] = -i\frac{\partial f}{\partial x}. \qquad (19.14)$$

Hence (19.9) reduces to

$$\Delta E_< = -\frac{\alpha}{3\pi}\frac{1}{(mc)^2}\log\left(\frac{\lambda c}{K_0}\right)\langle e\Delta\varphi(\boldsymbol{r})\rangle_{00}. \qquad (19.15)$$

We can now add the expression (19.15) for $\Delta E_<$ to the expression (19.2) [with Eqs. (18.2) and (19.3)] for $\Delta E_>$ to get the total energy shift ΔE irrespective of the frequency of the virtual photon. This shift is given by

$$\left.\begin{aligned}\Delta E = &-\frac{\alpha}{3\pi}\left(\frac{\hbar}{mc}\right)^2\left[\log\frac{mc^2}{K_0}-\log 2-\frac{3}{8}+\frac{5}{6}-\frac{1}{5}\right]\langle e\Delta\varphi(\boldsymbol{r})\rangle_{00}-\\ &-\frac{\alpha}{2\pi}i\left(\frac{e\hbar}{2mc}\right)\langle\beta\boldsymbol{\alpha}\cdot\mathcal{E}(\boldsymbol{r})\rangle_{00},\end{aligned}\right\} \qquad (19.16)$$

where K_0 is defined in (19.10). Note that, after adding $\Delta E_>$ to $\Delta E_<$, the dependence on the arbitrary cut-off λ has dropped out[1] of the expression (19.16).

[1] In the covariant evaluation of $\Delta E_>$, great care must be taken that the definition of λ is equivalent to that in the nonrelativistic calculation of $\Delta E_<$; see footnote 13 of R. P. FEYNMAN, Phys. Rev. **76**, 769 (1949).

γ) Retardation. We finally outline briefly how the neglect of retardation, used above, can be justified: If retardation is not to be neglected, the exponential terms in (19.5) must be carried. If, for instance, we consider a photon of momentum $\boldsymbol{k}$ in the z-direction, polarized in the x-direction, then in (19.6) and (19.7) the operator p_x occurring twice is replaced by $p_x e^{ikz/\hbar}$ in one factor and by $p_x e^{-ikz/\hbar}$ in the other. Now we are considering an essentially nonrelativistic system in which the order of magnitude of momentum (p_0), of atomic radius (a_0) and of the energy difference $E_0 - E_n (K_0)$, satisfy the following inequalities

$$K_0 \ll p_0 c \sim \hbar c/a_0 \ll m c^2.$$

Now retardation will certainly be negligible unless the photon momentum k is of order p_0 or bigger. Although the upper limit λ of k is small compared with mc it is not necessarily smaller than p_0. In the region of $p_0 < k < \lambda$ we should then consider retardation and keep the exponential factors in (19.7), but in this region $E_n - E_0 \sim K_0 \ll kc$ and in the denominator of the second term in (19.7) we can neglect $E_n - E_0$. Using sum rules similar to those leading to (19.13), the integrand of the modified expression (19.7) in this region reduces to (except for some factors, and before summing over polarization directions)

$$\frac{\langle p_x^2 \rangle_{00}}{k c} + \frac{1}{2 (k c)^2} \langle [[H, p_x e^{ikz/\hbar}], p_x e^{-ikz/\hbar}] \rangle_{00}, \tag{19.17}$$

where H is given by (19.12).

Now retardation also affects the mass-renormalization term [see (19.8)] which has to be subtracted from (19.17). This term involves, as a denominator, the "energy of the intermediate state" which is $(kc + k^2/2m)$, the photon energy plus recoil energy of the electron. Since $k \ll mc$ we can expand in powers of k/mc and keep only the first *two* terms (with retardation neglected the *second* term would be missing). With this approximation one finds, again using some sum rules, for the term to be subtracted from (19.17)

$$\frac{\langle p_x^2 \rangle_{00}}{k c} \left[1 - \frac{k^2/2m}{k c}\right] = \frac{\langle p_x^2 \rangle_{00}}{k c} + \frac{1}{2 (k c)^2} \langle [[H_0, p_x e^{ikz/\hbar}], p_x e^{-ikz/\hbar}] \rangle, \tag{19.18}$$

where $H_0 = p^2/2m$. The difference of (19.17) and (19.18) is then

$$- \frac{e}{2 (k c)^2} \langle [[\varphi(\boldsymbol{r}), p_x e^{ikz/\hbar}], p_x e^{-ikz/\hbar}] \rangle_{00} = \frac{e}{2 (k c)^2} \left\langle \frac{\partial^2 \varphi(\boldsymbol{r})}{\partial x^2} \right\rangle_{00}$$

which finally leads again to (19.15), the result with retardation neglected.

20. Corrections for nuclear motion and structure. In Sects. 18 and 19 we have discussed radiative corrections to the atomic energy levels given by the DIRAC theory, but have still assumed that the atomic nucleus is a stationary and structureless point charge. In reality the electron's mass m is not negligibly small compared with the nuclear mass M and we have to consider the effect of nuclear motion on the energy levels. Actual nuclei also possess some internal structure, such as a finite (although small) size and a magnetic moment, which also affect the energy levels slightly.

We first summarize, for comparison, some orders of magnitude of energies. We shall express energies in terms of the equivalent frequency (see Introduction) in units of megacycles per second (Mc). In these units

$$1\ \text{Ry} = 3.2898 \times 10^9\ \text{Mc}, \qquad 1\ \text{cm}^{-1} = 29979\ \text{Mc}. \tag{20.1}$$

The fine structure separation (FS) is of order $(Z\alpha)^2$ Ry. The radiative corrections to lowest order (LS), the LAMB shift given by (19.16), are of order

$$\alpha \log \alpha \, (Z\alpha)^2 \,\mathrm{Ry} \sim \alpha \log \alpha \,(\mathrm{FS}).$$

Radiative corrections of the next order, i.e. of order α (LS) and $Z\alpha$ (LS) have also been calculated. For the levels with $n=2$ in hydrogen, for instance, (FS) is about 10^4 Mc, (LS) about 10^3 Mc and the higher order radiative corrections about 5 Mc.

α) *Nuclear motion.* In the nonrelativistic SCHRÖDINGER theory for a hydrogen-like atom the effect of the finite value M of the nuclear mass is accounted for exactly by replacing the electron's mass m by the reduced mass $\mathcal{M} = mM/(m+M)$ in all formulae evaluated for a fixed COULOMB potential (Sect. 5). For the energy of any atomic level this is achieved by replacing Ry_∞ by R_M, i.e. multiplying the energy for a fixed COULOMB potential by the factor

$$\frac{M}{M+m} = 1 - \frac{m}{M} + \left(\frac{m}{M}\right)^2 \cdots.$$

We consider next the effect of nuclear motion on the PAULI approximation to the energies of the fine structure components for a fixed principal quantum number n. This effect is discussed in Sect. 42 by an approximation method which is accurate up to (and including) energies of order (m/M) (FS). To this approximation it is shown that any nucleus can be treated as a nonrelativistic particle of mass M with a (phenomenological) magnetic moment μ. The correction terms involving m/M consist of the sum of one term involving μ (discussed in Sects. 20β and 22) and one independent of μ. This second term is quite independent of the internal structure of the nucleus. As shown in Sect. 42β, this term has the following two effects. 1. The PAULI approximation to the energy splitting of the fine structure components for any n (for a fixed nucleus) is multiplied by the factor $(1-m/M)$, i.e. the RYDBERG constant is again replaced by R_M (the reduced mass RYDBERG) in the PAULI approximation. 2. In addition, the energy of *all* fine structure components for fixed principal quantum number n are shifted by the *same* amount, given by (42.7). This shift is about -25 Mc for the hydrogen ground state (less for $n>1$), which is beyond the accuracy of optical spectroscopy, and does not contribute to the fine structure *splitting*. Correction terms of order $(m/M)^2$ (FS) have not been calculated yet, but should be extremely small ($\lesssim 0.01$ Mc).

We consider next the various correction terms to the energy of order

$$\alpha \,(m/M)\,(\mathrm{FS}) \sim (m/M)\,(\mathrm{LS}),$$

which have all been calculated. Some terms of this order come from the effect of nuclear motion on the quantum electrodynamic effects which lead to the LAMB shift, Eq. (19.16). The main part of this effect is due to a change of distance scale in the atomic wave functions which are used in the expectation value (19.16). The "atomic radius" is changed by a factor $(m/\mathcal{M})$. This can be shown[1] to result in a multiplicative factor of $(\mathcal{M}/m)^3 \approx (1-3m/M)$ to (19.16), at least for S-states[2]. An additional correction term stems from the fact that, in the logarithmic term in (19.16), K_0 is proportional to the reduced mass $\mathcal{M}$, whereas mc^2 refers to the real mass of the electron.

[1] E. E. SALPETER: Phys. Rev. **89**, 92 (1953).

[2] For P-states a term in (19.16), connected with the electron's anomalous magnetic moment, is multiplied by $(1-2m/M)$; see W. BARKER and F. GLOVER, Phys. Rev. **99**, 317 (1955).

Some additional corrections, also of order $\alpha(m/M)$ (FS), were calculated by SALPETER[1]. These corrections are first calculated for the electron-proton system, using the covariant two-body wave equation discussed in Sect. 42γ, under the assumption that the proton is a DIRAC particle. Complex nuclei are composed of protons and neutrons (each a DIRAC particle) interacting with each other. It is then shown that the proton calculations are also valid (to a good approximation, based on the fact that mc is smaller than the relative momenta of the neutrons and protons inside the nucleus) for complex nuclei. The main parts of these corrections, which are of order $\alpha \log \alpha (m/M)$ (FS), can also be obtained from conventional perturbation theory. One such term is essentially an addition to the operator used in Sect. 42 for the BREIT interaction between electron and proton, which corrects for the fact that in deriving this operator the energy denominator in (38.5) was replaced by kc or the expression (38.17) by unity. Another such term is connected with the exchange of *two* virtual photons between the electron and proton.

The terms of order $\alpha(m/M)$ (FS) have expectation values which depend on the quantum numbers l and j (as well as on n) and hence contribute to the fine structure splitting and LAMB shift. All terms of this order combined contribute -1.27 Mc to the energy difference $2\,{}^2S_{\frac{1}{2}} - 2\,{}^2P_{\frac{1}{2}}$ in hydrogen and half this amount in deuterium. Correction terms of order $\alpha^2(m/M)$ (FS) have not been calculated yet, but are expected to be less than ± 0.05 Mc for $n=2$ in hydrogen.

β) Nuclear structure. Complex nuclei, besides having a finite mass, are not point particles but show some structure. In particular they have a finite size (radii of the order of $A^{\frac{1}{3}} \times 10^{-13}$ cm, where A is the atomic mass number), an internal angular momentum or "spin" and a magnetic dipole moment and small electric quadrupole moment[2] associated with the spin.

The finite size of the nucleus affects the atomic energy levels in a very simple way. Inside the charge distribution of the nucleus its electrostatic potential deviates from (and is less than) a COULOMB potential of charge Z. Nuclear radii are much smaller than atomic radii and (if Z is not too large and nonrelativistic atomic wave functions are justified) the following approximate expression holds for the change ΔV of the energy of an atomic state.

$$\Delta V = \frac{2\pi Z e^2}{3} |u(0)|^2 \langle r^2 \rangle, \tag{20.2}$$

where $u(0)$ is the value of the atomic wave function at the origin and $\langle r^2 \rangle$ is the mean squared radius of the nuclear charge distribution around its center of mass. In this approximation ΔV is zero for atomic states of non-zero l, whose wave function vanishes at the origin. For S-states, (20.2) gives a small upward shift of the energy. For the $2S$-state of deuterium[3], for instance, this shift is about $+0.73$ Mc. The ratio of ΔV to the binding energy of the atomic state (for $l=0$) is of the order of $\langle r^2 \rangle / a_n^2$, where a_n is the "radius" of the atomic wave function. As Z (and hence the atomic weight of the nucleus) increases, $\langle r^2 \rangle$ increases and a_n decreases. The effect of nuclear size thus increases with increasing Z. In fact, for very large Z the nonrelativistic approximation (20.2) is not very accurate and ΔV is appreciable not only for S-states but also for $P_{\frac{1}{2}}$-states, whose wave functions are reasonably large near the origin[4].

---

[1] E. E. SALPETER: Phys. Rev. **87**, 328 (1952). A small term in this paper, called ΔE_{cc}, should be doubled.

[2] No nuclei are known which have a finite electric dipole moment, see ref. [*16*], Chap. 2.

[3] E. E. SALPETER: Phys. Rev. **89**, 92 (1953).

[4] A. SCHAWLOW and C. TOWNES: Science, Lancaster, Pa. **115**, 284 (1952) and Phys. Rev. **100**, 1273 (1955).

Nuclei with non-zero "spin" usually have a non-zero magnetic moment parallel to its spin. The energy of the electron's interaction with this nuclear moment is quite large (compared with the other corrections discussed in this section) and leads to the hyperfine structure of each atomic fine structure component (discussed in Sect. 22). This hyperfine structure energy depends on the direction of the nuclear spin in a known manner and experimental results on the hyperfine structure components of a particular fine structure level can be analyzed to give the energy the level would have in the absence of hyperfine structure.

If we were to consider a nucleus as a DIRAC particle with an anomalous magnetic moment of PAULI type [see (10.16)], this moment would contribute (besides the relatively large spin-dependent hyperfine structure) a small spin-*in*dependent shift in the atom's energy[1]. For ordinary hydrogen (with a single proton as nucleus) this shift would be $+0.02$ Mc for the $2S$-state and zero for states of $l\neq 0$. This term, however, is only of the same order of magnitude as other terms which depend on the detailed internal structure of a proton, which is not yet fully understood. For instance, although a proton is a single fundamental particle and does not have a "nuclear radius" in the strict sense, its interaction with the virtual meson field is likely to spread its charge over finite distances (but distances much smaller than the radius of any complex nucleus).

21. Fine structure and the LAMB shift. *α) Lowest order* LAMB *shift.* We now evaluate explicitly the expression (19.16) for the radiative correction (to lowest order) ΔE to the energy of a state (n, l, j) in a hydrogenlike atom. For an S-state $(n, 0, \frac{1}{2})$ we have

$$(e\,\Delta\varphi)_{nn} = -4\pi e^2 Z\left(\delta^{(3)}(\boldsymbol{r})\right)_{nn} = -4\pi e^2 Z\, u_{n0}^2(0) = -\frac{4Z^4}{n^3}\ \text{at. un.}, \tag{21.1}$$

where $u_{n0}(0)$ is the nonrelativistic SCHRÖDINGER wave function at the origin. The last term in (19.16) arises from the anomalous moment of the electron and corresponds to (12.13) with $g_1=\alpha/2\pi$. To within the accuracy of the PAULI approximation this term is [see Sect. 12γ and (12.14)] simply $2g_1=\alpha/\pi$ times the expression (13.13) for any value of the orbital quantum number l. Writing mc^2 as $2\,\text{Ry}/\alpha^2$ and using (21.1) and (13.13), expression (19.16) for S-states reduces to

$$\Delta E(n,0) = \frac{8Z^4}{n^3}\frac{\alpha^3}{3\pi}\,\text{Ry}\left[2\log\frac{1}{Z\alpha} + \log\frac{Z^2\,\text{Ry}}{K_0(n,0)} + \frac{19}{30}\right], \tag{21.2}$$

where K_0 is defined by (19.10).

For states with non-zero l, the last part of (19.16) is again α/π times (13.13). The nonrelativistic wave function at the origin, and hence $(\Delta\varphi)_{nn}$, vanishes for $l\neq 0$ and we would expect the first part of (19.16) to vanish. In fact this term is finite, although extremely small, since K_0, as defined by (19.10), diverges for $l\neq 0$. To remove this difficulty[2] one can modify the definition of K_0 for $l\neq 0$ by replacing the initial state in the sum on the left hand side of (19.10) by the S-state with the same principal quantum number. One then obtains, instead of (21.2),

$$\Delta E(n,l) = \frac{8Z^4}{n^3}\frac{\alpha^3}{3\pi}\,\text{Ry}\left[\log\frac{Z^2\,\text{Ry}}{K_0(n,l)} + \frac{3}{8}\frac{c_{lj}}{2l+1}\right], \tag{21.3}$$

where

$$c_{lj} = \begin{cases} (l+1)^{-1} & \text{for} \quad j = l+\frac{1}{2} \\ -l^{-1} & \text{for} \quad j = l-\frac{1}{2}. \end{cases}$$

[1] L. L. FOLDY: Phys. Rev. **83**, 688 (1951).
[2] BETHE, BROWN and STEHN: Phys. Rev. **77**, 370 (1950)

The numerical evaluation of the dimensionless ratio $K_0(n, l)/Z^2\,\text{Ry}$ is discussed in Sect. 74γ. This ratio is independent of Z and varies rather slowly with n. For S-states, for instance, this ratio is about 19.8 for $n=1$, 15.7 for $n=4$, and not much smaller for $n=\infty$. For $l \neq 0$, this ratio is very close to unity for all n, e.g. for P-states it is about 0.97 for $n=2$ and 0.96 for $n=4$.

According to the DIRAC theory, the energy of any fine structure level for fixed n depends only on j, not l. In the PAULI approximation the energy is given by (17.2) and the only part depending on j is

$$\Delta W = -\frac{Z^4}{n^3}\frac{\alpha^2}{(j+\frac{1}{2})}\,\text{Ry}. \tag{21.4}$$

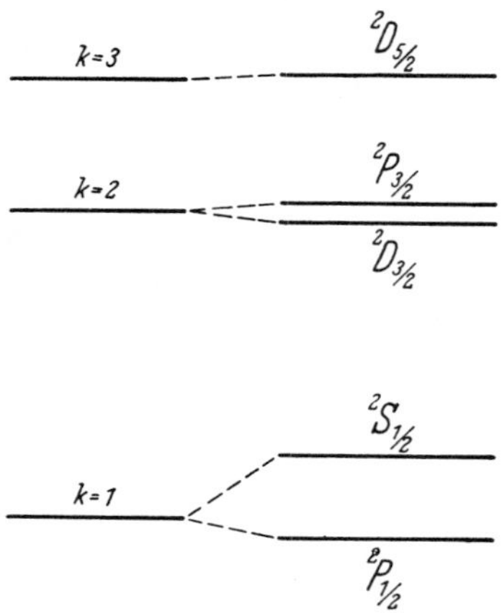

Fig. 12. Schematic energy level diagram for the states with $n=3$ in hydrogen. The levels on the left are according to the DIRAC theory without LAMB shift. The levels on the right show the level splitting due to radiative corrections (not accurately to scale, the actual $P_{\frac{3}{2}}-D_{\frac{3}{2}}$ splitting is much smaller than that on the diagram).

To this we now have to add the radiative correction ΔE, given by (21.2) or (21.3). Note that ΔW and ΔE have almost the same dependence on Z and on n [the logarithms in (21.2) and (21.3) vary slowly with Z and n]. A schematic picture of the energy level splitting is given in Fig. 12 for $n=3$.

For a fixed value of n, by far the largest radiative correction is the positive shift of the energy of the $S_{\frac{1}{2}}$-state, which is given by (21.2) and stems largely from the term in $\log \alpha$. This LAMB shift of the S-state is about 10% of the fine structure separation between the levels of $j=\frac{1}{2}$ and $\frac{3}{2}$ (for reasonably low Z and any n). For states with $l \neq 0$, the logarithmic term in (21.3) is extremely small. The last term in (21.3), which stems from the electron's anomalous moment, is sufficient to split the two levels of equal j (degenerate on the DIRAC theory), but the splitting is very small. The energy splitting of the two levels for any $j>\frac{1}{2}$ is only about 0.2% of the fine structure separation between the levels of j and $(j+1)$. Excited energy levels have a finite lifetime and hence a finite energy spread (natural line width). For $j=\frac{1}{2}$ this line width is always smaller than the LAMB shift, but for $j \geq \frac{3}{2}$ it is larger than the energy splitting given by (21.3).

For the splitting of the $n=2$, $j=\frac{1}{2}$ levels very accurate microwave experiments are available and will be discussed below. But there is also (less accurate) confirmation for the level shift (21.2) of the S-states for various n from optical spectroscopy. In deuterium, for instance, the experimental shift[1] of the $1\,S$-state is $(0.26 \pm 0.03)\ \text{cm}^{-1}$ and of[2] the $3\,S$-state $(0.008 \pm 0.003)\ \text{cm}^{-1}$. The corresponding theoretical shifts from (21.2) are $0.271\ \text{cm}^{-1}$ and $0.0103\ \text{cm}^{-1} = 309$ Mc/sec, respectively.

β) The LAMB *experiments.* Very accurate, careful and beautiful experimental work has been done by LAMB[3] and coworkers on the structure of the levels with $n=2$ in hydrogen, deuterium and singly ionized helium. This work is based on the fact that, even in hydrogen-like atoms, direct radiative (electric dipole) transitions are possible from any $n\,S_{\frac{1}{2}}$-state to both the $P_{\frac{1}{2}}$ and $P_{\frac{3}{2}}$-states with the *same* principal quantum number n. Since the energy differences are very

[1] G. HERZBERG: Proc. Roy. Soc. Lond., Ser. A **234**, 516 (1956).

[2] G. W. SERIES: Proc. Roy. Soc. Lond., Ser. A **208**, 277 (1951).

[3] For a description of the method see W. E. LAMB and R. C. RETHERFORD, Phys. Rev. **79**, 549 (1950); **81**, 222 (1951); **86**, 1014 (1951). A general review is given by W. E. LAMB, Rep. Progr. Phys. **14**, 19 (1951).

small, the probability for spontaneous transitions is negligibly small, but induced transitions can occur if a rotating (or oscillating) magnetic field of the appropriate frequency is applied to the atom (see Sect. 64γ). This frequency (of the order of 10^3 or 10^4 Mc/sec) can be measured very accurately and is simply the energy difference of the two levels divided by h. Now, the extremely accurate determinations of the RYDBERG by optical spectroscopy essentially measure a wave number which is (c/h) times the RYDBERG energy unit ($\frac{1}{2}$ a.u.), where c is the accurately known velocity of light. A measurement of the frequency of rotation in the LAMB experiment thus gives the energy separation of two levels with the *same* principal quantum number in terms of the RYDBERG (without requiring any knowledge of PLANCK's constant h).

In practice, the natural line width of the P-states and the hyperfine structure (for H and D) are very much larger than the error of measurement of the frequency of the inducing field. The line shape for each transitions is therefore measured very accurately and in great detail and compared with the theory of line shape and hyperfine structure[1]. The agreement is excellent and the energy separation of the S and P-states (as it would be in the absence of line width and hyperfine structure) can be inferred to within an error very much smaller than the line width.

The LAMB experiments can be most easily performed for the levels with $n=2$, for the following reason: The $2S$-state in hydrogen-like atoms is metastable and, in the absence of perturbations, has an extremely long lifetime compared with all other excited states (see Sect. 67α). An atomic beam apparatus can thus be designed, in which atoms in the beam in the $2S$-state can reach the detector, but atoms which initially were in other excited states (e.g. $2P_{\frac{1}{2}}$ or $2P_{\frac{3}{2}}$) make radiative transitions to the ground state long before reaching the detector. In turn, detectors can be devised which are sensitive to excited atoms in the $2S$-state, but not to atoms in the ground state. One can thus measure the depletion of a beam of $2S$-atoms, due to induced transitions to $2P_{\frac{1}{2}}$ or $2P_{\frac{3}{2}}$ in a rotating magnetic field, as a function of the applied frequency.

The experimental values for the $2S_{\frac{1}{2}}-2P_{\frac{1}{2}}$ separations are compared with the theoretical values for the LAMB shift in Sect. 21γ. But this experimental value, combined with the measurement of the $2S_{\frac{1}{2}}-2P_{\frac{3}{2}}$ separation, also gives a very accurate experimental value for the fine structure separation $2P_{\frac{1}{2}}-2P_{\frac{3}{2}}$. For deuterium[2] this separation F is (10971.59 ± 0.20) Mc/sec. The best theoretical expression for this separation is

$$F=\frac{c\,R_{\mathrm{D}}}{16}\alpha^2\left[1+\frac{5}{8}\alpha^2+\left(1-\frac{m}{M_{\mathrm{D}}}\right)\frac{\alpha}{\pi}-\frac{5.946}{\pi^2}\alpha^2\right], \tag{21.5}$$

where R_{D} is the "reduced mass RYDBERG" for deuterium and M_{D} is the deuteron's mass. The first two terms in (21.5) come from an expansion in powers of α of the DIRAC fine structure formula (17.1). The last two terms represent radiative corrections [cf. Eq. (21.3)], stemming from the anomalous magnetic moment of the electron (18.5). Terms of order α^5 Ry and $\alpha^4(m/M_{\mathrm{D}})$ Ry, effects of nuclear size, etc. have not yet been calculated. However, all these terms are expected to be very small (much smaller than for the $2S$-state) and introduce an error smaller than the present experimental one. The experimental value for F and (21.5) thus give a very accurate value for the fine structure constant,

$$\frac{1}{\alpha}=137.0371\pm 0.0012, \tag{21.6}$$

[1] W. E. LAMB: Phys. Rev. **85**, 259 (1952).

[2] E. DAYHOFF, S. TRIEBWASSER and W. LAMB: Phys. Rev. **89**, 106 (1953).

if we use a value of

$$c = (299792.9 \pm 0.8)\ \text{km/sec} \tag{21.7}$$

for the velocity of light[1]. The value of (21.6) for α agrees well[1] with values obtained from other precision measurements.

γ) Comparison with theory[2]. We summarize now the various terms contributing to the theoretical value for the LAMB shift in hydrogen, i.e., the energy by which the $2\,S_{\frac{1}{2}}$-state lies higher than the $2\,P_{\frac{1}{2}}$. The main term, of order α^3 Ry, comes from (21.2) and (21.3) for the lowest order shift of the S- and P-states, respectively. Using the values (2.14), (21.6) and (21.7) for Ry (the RYDBERG for *infinite* nuclear mass), α and c we have the following value for the "LAMB constant" L,

$$L \equiv \frac{\alpha^3}{3\pi}\,\text{Ry}\,c = (135.641 \pm 0.004)\ \text{Mc/sec}. \tag{21.8}$$

The excitation energies K_0 in (21.2) and (21.3) have been evaluated very accurately[3] (see Sect. 74γ),

$$K_0(2, 0) = 16.6398\,Z^2\,\text{Ry}, \quad K_0(2, 1) = 0.970430\,Z^2\,\text{Ry}.$$

Substituting into (21.2) and (21.3), one finds a value of $7.75703\,L$ for the LAMB shift to lowest order for $Z=1$ and a fixed nucleus, i.e.

$$S_\infty^{(1)} = (1052.17 \pm 0.04)\ \text{Mc/sec}.$$

As discussed in Sect. 18, the expression (21.2) or (21.3) is only the first term in an expansion in powers of $Z\alpha$ and of α. Numerically the largest of the higher terms in the expansion for the LAMB shift is the term of order $Z\alpha\,S_\infty^{(1)}$ (even for $Z=1$). This term[4] contributes $+7.14$ Mc/sec to the LAMB shift for hydrogen. All the various terms[5] of order $\alpha\,S_\infty^{(1)}$ have been calculated and together contribute (-0.94 ± 0.10) Mc/sec. The various corrections to the LAMB shift due to nuclear motion and structure have already been discussed in Sect. 20.

In Table 3 we compare the present theoretical values with the experimental[6] ones for H and D and those[7] for He^+. The probable errors quoted for the theoretical results do *not* include any allowance for higher order radiative corrections, which have not been calculated yet. The leading terms of these corrections are of order $\alpha^2\,S_\infty^{(1)}$ for hydrogen and might be expected to be of order ± 0.10 Mc/sec or less, but the possibility of large numerical coefficients making these terms bigger cannot be ruled out. Table 3 shows that the experimental values for H and D (but, possibly, not for He^+) are about $\frac{1}{2}$ Mc/sec larger than the theoretical ones, a discrepancy of a few times the experimental error. It is not yet known whether this small discrepancy is due to some of the $\alpha^2\,S_\infty^{(1)}$ terms or due to some other cause.

We thus see that the theoretical prediction for the energy splitting of the $2\,S_{\frac{1}{2}}$ and $2\,P_{\frac{1}{2}}$ levels in H and D is confirmed experimentally to an accuracy of about one part in 2000. The LAMB shift is thus an excellent confirmation of

---

[1] J. DUMOND and E. COHEN: This volume. — J. BEARDEN and J. THOMSEN: Atomic Constants. Baltimore: Johns Hopkins University 1955.

[2] E. E. SALPETER: Phys. Rev. **89**, 92 (1953). In this paper the notation used in this section is explained more fully.

[3] J. M. HARRIMAN: Phys. Rev. **101**, 594 (1956).

[4] M. BARANGER, H. BETHE and R. FEYNMAN: Phys. Rev. **92**, 482 (1953). — KARPLUS, KLEIN and SCHWINGER: Phys. Rev. **86**, 288 (1952).

[5] R. KARPLUS and N. KROLL: Phys. Rev. **77**, 536 (1950). — M. BARANGER, F. DYSON and E. SALPETER: Phys. Rev. **88**, 680 (1952). — BERSOHN, WENESER and KROLL: Phys. Rev. **91**, 1257 (1953).

[6] S. TRIEBWASSER, E. DAYHOFF and W. LAMB: Phys. Rev. **89**, 98 (1953).

[7] R. NOVICK, E. LIPWORTH and P. YERGIN: Phys. Rev. **100**, 1153 (1955).

Table 3. *The* Lamb *shift for hydrogen, deuterium and ionized helium (in Mc/sec).*

	H	D	He^+
Theoretical	1057.13 ± 0.13	1058.47 ± 0.13	14043 ± 3
Experimental	1057.77 ± 0.10	1059.00 ± 0.10	14043 ± 13

present day quantum electrodynamics and of the relativistic theory of the electron. For instance, some time ago there was some doubt whether vacuum polarization effects should be included in quantum electrodynamic calculations. These effects contribute the term involving $-\frac{1}{5}$ to the expression (18.2) which gives a contribution of about -27 Mc/sec to the Lamb shift in H and D. The necessity of including this term is demonstrated by the excellent agreement in Table 3.

It should also be remembered that the Lamb shift itself is a very small fraction of the total binding energy of an electron in a $2S$ or $2P$-state and has been verified to an accuracy of better than 10^{-9} times this total binding energy: If, for instance, the Coulomb law Ze/r were modified by a multiplicative factor of form $(r/a_0)^\gamma$, a value for γ of more than about 10^{-9} would contribute to the $2S-2P$ splitting an amount larger than the present limit of error.

22. Hyperfine structure splitting. So far we have only considered electrons moving in a purely central electric field. In this case the energy of the atomic levels may depend on the absolute value of the total angular momentum j of the electrons, but *not* on its component in any direction. This degeneracy is removed not only by an external non-central field but also if the atomic nucleus has a magnetic moment. Many nuclei do, in fact, have non-zero magnetic moments which are roughly of order $e\hbar/M_p c$, where M_p is the proton mass. This is smaller than the magnetic moment of the electron by a factor of order one thousand. Consequently the level splitting due to the electron's interaction with the nuclear moment should be smaller than the ordinary fine structure splitting by a factor of the same order. We shall also find that this hyperfine structure splitting is largest if the distance between electron and nucleus is smallest.

α) Derivation of operators. We consider a hydrogen-like atom with a nucleus of charge $Z \ll 137$ and a magnetic moment $\boldsymbol{\mu}$. For such small values of Z one can consider the atom as nonrelativistic to lowest order, the ordinary fine structure as a perturbation and the hyperfine structure as an even smaller perturbation. In Sect. 42 we shall derive an approximate equation for a hydrogen-like atom which takes the motion and magnetic moment of the nucleus into account. The Hamiltonian Eq. (42.2), derived from the Breit equation, contains a Hamiltonian which consists of three parts. The first part H_a is identical with the Hamiltonian of the Pauli equation (13.2) for an electron in a *fixed* Coulomb potential. The second part H_b only contributes a small level shift, which does not depend on the nuclear moment and is due merely to the nuclear recoil. The third part H_c, finally, takes account of the magnetic moment of the nucleus. We consider later the relation between the vector $\boldsymbol{\mu}$, which represents the nuclear magnetic moment, and the nuclear angular momentum. The part H_c in (42.2), which we consider as a small perturbation, reads[1]

$$H_c = -2\mu_0 \left[-\frac{8\pi}{3} (\boldsymbol{s}_1 \cdot \boldsymbol{\mu})\, \delta^{(3)}(\boldsymbol{r}) + \frac{1}{r^3} (\boldsymbol{s}_1 \cdot \boldsymbol{\mu} - 3 s_{1r} \mu_r) - \frac{1}{r^3} (\boldsymbol{k} \cdot \boldsymbol{\mu}) \right], \quad (22.1)$$

[1] In evaluating expectation values of H_c the following prescription must be used: In the expression (22.1) replace $1/r^3$ by zero for $r < \varepsilon$, evaluate all integrals, and *then* take the limit of ε tending to zero.

where $\mu_0 = e\hbar/2mc$ is the BOHR magneton (electron's magnetic moment), $\mathbf{s}_1 = \frac{1}{2}\sigma_1^P$ is the PAULI spin operator for the electron, s_{1r} the component of $\mathbf{s}_1$ in the direction $\boldsymbol{r}$, and $\boldsymbol{k}$ is the orbital angular momentum $(\boldsymbol{r}\times\boldsymbol{p})/\hbar$.

The expectation value of the operator H_c only gives the lowest order contribution to the hyperfine structure in an expansion in powers of α and of (m/M), where M is the nuclear mass. To calculate higher order terms one must start from the BREIT equation, as in Sect. 42, or some other relativistic theory for two interacting particles. The lowest order operator (22.1), however, can also be obtained in a semi-classical manner from the PAULI equation (12.11) for a single electron in a *fixed* external field, as follows.

We consider (12.11) for an electron in a fixed COULOMB potential plus a fixed external magnetic field, which we consider as weak. Neglecting terms quadratic in the vector potential $\boldsymbol{A}$, the interaction with the magnetic field is given by the perturbation HAMILTONian

$$H' = +2\mu_0\left[(\boldsymbol{A}\cdot\boldsymbol{p})\frac{1}{\hbar} + \mathbf{s}\cdot\mathcal{H}\right], \tag{22.2}$$

where $\mathbf{s}$ is the electron's spin operator (dropping the suffix 1) and $\mathcal{H} = \operatorname{curl}\boldsymbol{A}$ is the magnetic field. We now attribute to the nucleus a fixed classical magnetic dipole moment $\boldsymbol{\mu}$, which produces a magnetic field characterized by the vector potential

$$\left.\begin{aligned}\boldsymbol{A} &= \frac{\boldsymbol{\mu}\times\boldsymbol{r}}{r^3} = -\boldsymbol{\mu}\times\left(\operatorname{grad}\frac{1}{r}\right),\\ \mathcal{H} &= \operatorname{curl}\boldsymbol{A}.\end{aligned}\right\} \tag{22.3}$$

Substituting (22.3) into (22.2), using some simple vector identities and writing $\boldsymbol{k} = \boldsymbol{r}\times\boldsymbol{p}$ (using again units such that $\hbar = 1$) we get for $r \neq 0$ the same result as from (22.1),

$$H' = -\frac{2\mu_0}{r^3}\left[(\mathbf{s}\cdot\boldsymbol{\mu}) - 3 s_r\mu_r - \boldsymbol{k}\cdot\boldsymbol{\mu}\right]. \tag{22.4}$$

At $r=0$, however, the operator $(\mathbf{s}\cdot\mathcal{H})$ has a strong singularity and care must be taken not to miss a part of the operator, which contains a delta function at the origin.

One simple way to isolate this delta-function singularity of $-2\mu_0\mathbf{s}\cdot\mathcal{H}$ is to consider the FOURIER transform of this expression, which is [using (22.3), (39.6) and some vector identities]

$$\frac{\mu_0}{\pi^2}\left\{\left[\frac{(\mathbf{s}\cdot\boldsymbol{q})(\boldsymbol{\mu}\cdot\boldsymbol{q})}{q^2} - \frac{1}{3}\mathbf{s}\cdot\boldsymbol{\mu}\right] - \frac{2}{3}\mathbf{s}\cdot\boldsymbol{\mu}\right\} \tag{22.5}$$

where $\boldsymbol{q}$ denotes the momentum change. We now use some arguments, to be given in Sect. 39, leading to (39.13): The expectation value of the term in square brackets in (22.5) is zero for any spherically symmetric wave function (S-state) and this term corresponds to the second term in round brackets in (22.1) with the prescription, explained in the footnote to (22.1), of excluding an infinitesimal sphere around the origin in position space. The last term in (22.5) corresponds to the first term in (22.1) and thus (22.2) plus (22.3) again leads[1] to (22.1).

[1] A more rigorous derivation of (22.1) could be obtained as follows: From the exact Eq. (16.13) an approximate integral equation for $\psi_+(\boldsymbol{p})$ could be derived which is more accurate than the PAULI equation in momentum space for an electron in an external field, Eq. (16.15). The integrand in this equation would differ appreciably from that of (16.15) only for q (called k in Sect. 16) and p of order $mc/\hbar$ or larger. The more accurate expression replacing (22.5) would be almost identical with (22.5) except that it decreases with increasing q for $q \gtrsim mc/\hbar$. In position space one would then get an operator almost identical with (22.1) except at very small distances, i.e. $1/r^3$ would be replaced by a function somewhat like $1/r^2(r+\varepsilon)$ and $\delta^{(3)}(\boldsymbol{r})$ by a function which is appreciable only for $r \lesssim \varepsilon$ and whose volume integral is unity, where ε is some length much smaller than one atomic radius.

For a different derivation of (22.1) see ref. [*10*], p. 385.

β) Expectation values. We evaluate next the expectation value of the operator H_c, Eq. (22.1), for a particular state of an electron in a central potential and interacting with the magnetic moment of the nucleus. We make use of the fact that the magnetic moment of the nucleus is much smaller than that of the electron, and, consequently, the hyperfine structure smaller than the fine structure. We use the PAULI approximation, so that $\boldsymbol{k}^2$ is a constant of the motion and l is a good quantum number. In the absence of H_c, $\boldsymbol{M}^2=(\boldsymbol{k}+\boldsymbol{s})^2$ is also a constant of the motion and the spin-orbit coupling operator results in the dependence of the energy on the inner quantum number j (fine structure). Although the operator H_c does *not* commute with $\boldsymbol{M}^2$, $\boldsymbol{M}^2$ is still a constant of the motion to a good approximation since H_c is small compared with the spin-orbit coupling operator. On the other hand, M_z is *not* even approximately a constant of the motion, since the energy is exactly degenerate with respect to M_z in the absence of H_c and H_c does not commute with M_z.

The magnetic moment $\boldsymbol{\mu}$ of a nucleus is connected with its internal intrinsic angular momentum (or "spin") $\boldsymbol{i}$ by the relation

$$\boldsymbol{\mu}=+\mu_N g\,\boldsymbol{i} \tag{22.6}$$

where

$$\mu_N=\frac{|e|\hbar}{2M_p c}=\mu_0\frac{m}{M_p}=\frac{\mu_0}{1836.1_3} \tag{22.7}$$

is the "nuclear magneton" (M_p is the proton mass). In (22.6), g is a dimensionless constant characteristic of a particular nucleus which is positive for some nuclei and negative for others. For each nucleus the quantum number I [$I(I+1)$ is the eigenvalue of $\boldsymbol{i}^2$] is fixed. The quantity gI is sometimes called the "nuclear moment" for short and lies between -3 and $+5$ for most nuclei[1]. For a proton, $I=\frac{1}{2}$ and gI would be unity if the proton were a pure DIRAC particle. The actual value of gI is about 2.8 for a proton (and about -1.9 for a neutron). If we call $\boldsymbol{f}=(\boldsymbol{i}+\boldsymbol{j})$ the total angular momentum operator for the whole atom, then f_z and $\boldsymbol{f}^2$ [with eigenvalue $f(f+1)$] are constants of the motion, as well as $\boldsymbol{s}^2$, $\boldsymbol{k}^2$, and $\boldsymbol{M}^2$.

We consider first a state with $l\neq 0$, whose wave function at the origin vanishes. The expectation value of the first term in (22.1) then vanishes. Using the relation (A.33) of the appendix, the expectation value of H_c then equals that of the operator

$$H_c'=\frac{2\mu_0}{r^3}\left[\frac{2k^2\,\boldsymbol{s}\cdot\boldsymbol{\mu}-3(\boldsymbol{s}\cdot\boldsymbol{k})(\boldsymbol{\mu}\cdot\boldsymbol{k})-3(\boldsymbol{\mu}\cdot\boldsymbol{k})(\boldsymbol{s}\cdot\boldsymbol{k})}{(2l+3)(2l-1)}+\boldsymbol{k}\cdot\boldsymbol{\mu}\right].$$

For the expectation value over a state with fixed quantum numbers $s=\frac{1}{2}$, l and j, the operators $\boldsymbol{k}^2$ and $(\boldsymbol{s}\cdot\boldsymbol{k})$ are simply replaced by their eigenvalues $l(l+1)$ and $\frac{1}{2}X$, Eq. (13.5), respectively. For the remaining operators $(\boldsymbol{s}\cdot\boldsymbol{\mu})$ and $(\boldsymbol{k}\cdot\boldsymbol{\mu})$ we use the following relation [discussed in Sect. 46, see Eq. (46.3)]: For transitions between (or expectation values for) states of the *same* s, l and j, the operators $\boldsymbol{s}$ and $\boldsymbol{k}$ can be replaced by constant multiples of the operator $\boldsymbol{M}$,

$$\boldsymbol{s}\to\boldsymbol{M}\frac{\overline{(\boldsymbol{s}\cdot\boldsymbol{M})}}{\overline{\boldsymbol{M}^2}},\qquad \boldsymbol{k}\to\boldsymbol{M}\frac{\overline{(\boldsymbol{k}\cdot\boldsymbol{M})}}{\overline{\boldsymbol{M}^2}}, \tag{22.8}$$

where the bars denote eigenvalues[2]. Using this relation, the fact that $s=\frac{1}{2}$ and $\boldsymbol{M}=\boldsymbol{k}+\boldsymbol{s}$, and explicit expressions for the eigenvalues of $(\boldsymbol{s}\cdot\boldsymbol{M})$, $(\boldsymbol{k}\cdot\boldsymbol{M})$,

[1] See ref. [*16*], Chap. 4.

[2] Classically speaking, $\boldsymbol{s}$ and $\boldsymbol{k}$ precess rapidly about the direction of $\boldsymbol{M}$. In turn, $\boldsymbol{M}$ precesses about the direction of $\boldsymbol{f}$, but much more slowly, and only the components of $\boldsymbol{s}$ and $\boldsymbol{k}$ parallel to $\boldsymbol{M}$ are important.

etc., one finds that the expectation value of H_c equals that of

$$H'_c = +2\mu_0 \frac{l(l+1)}{j(j+1)} \boldsymbol{\mu}\cdot\boldsymbol{M}\frac{1}{r^3}. \tag{22.9a}$$

Using (22.6) and the fact that $\boldsymbol{f}=\boldsymbol{i}+\boldsymbol{M}$, we finally get for this expectation value

$$E_c = \mu_0\mu_N g\frac{l(l+1)}{j(j+1)}[f(f+1)-I(I+1)-j(j+1)]\overline{\frac{1}{r^3}}. \tag{22.9}$$

For an S-state, the expression (22.9) vanishes, since l is zero and the expectation value of $1/r^3$ is to be evaluated by excluding a small sphere around the origin, which gives a finite (although large) result. The first term in (22.1), however, gives a non-vanishing contribution. Its expectation value is[1] [using Eq. (22.6)]

$$E_{c0} = \tfrac{4}{3}\mu_0\mu_N g\,\boldsymbol{i}\cdot\boldsymbol{s}\,R^2_{n0}(0), \tag{22.10}$$

where $R_{n0}(0)$ is the normalized radial wave function at the origin. Since $l=0$, $j=s=\frac{1}{2}$ and the only possible values of f are $I+\frac{1}{2}$ and $I-\frac{1}{2}$. Thus

$$2\boldsymbol{i}\cdot\boldsymbol{s}=f(f+1)-I(I+1)-s(s+1)=\begin{cases} I & \text{for } f=I+\frac{1}{2}, \\ -(I+1) & \text{for } f=I-\frac{1}{2}. \end{cases} \tag{22.11}$$

The expressions (22.9) for $l\neq 0$ and (22.10) with (22.11) for $l=0$ hold for single-electron atoms with any central atomic potential. For the special case of hydrogen-like atoms (COULOMB potential) we have the expression (5.12) for $\overline{r^{-3}}$ and [see Eq. (3.46)]

$$R^2_{n0}(0) = \frac{4Z^3}{n^3}\ \text{at. un}.$$

In this case *both* (22.9) and (22.10) reduce to the following expression for any l (with $\mu_0=\frac{1}{2}\alpha$ and $\text{Ry}=\frac{1}{2}$ in atomic units),

$$E_c = \frac{Z^3\alpha^2 g}{n^3}\frac{m}{M_p}\frac{f(f+1)-I(I+1)-j(j+1)}{j(j+1)(2l+1)}\,\text{Ry}. \tag{22.12}$$

A fine structure level with fixed l and j is thus split further into hyperfine structure components with the possible values of f being $(j+I)$, $(j+I-1)$, ..., $|j-I|$. The multiplicity of such a level is the smaller of the two numbers $(2j+1)$ and $(2I+1)$. From (22.12) the energy separation between the two outermost components ($f=j+I$ and $|j-I|$) is

$$\Delta E = \frac{m}{M_p}\frac{4Z^3\alpha^2 g}{n^3(2l+1)(j+1)}\,\text{Ry}\begin{cases} I+\frac{1}{2} & \text{if } j\gtrless I, \\ \frac{I(j+\frac{1}{2})}{j} & \text{if } j\lessgtr I. \end{cases} \tag{22.13}$$

For a given atom the hyperfine splitting ΔE decreases very rapidly with increasing n and fairly rapidly with increasing l and j. For ordinary hydrogen, for instance, ($Z=1$, $I=\frac{1}{2}$, $g\approx 5.56$) we have

	$1S_{\frac{1}{2}}$	$2S_{\frac{1}{2}}$	$2P_{\frac{1}{2}}$	$2P_{\frac{3}{2}}$
$\frac{\Delta E}{1420\ \text{Mc/sec}}$	1	$\frac{1}{8}$	$\frac{1}{24}$	$\frac{1}{60}$

A schematic diagram of the level splitting for $n=2$ for ordinary hydrogen and for deuterium ($Z=1$, $I=1$, $g\approx 0.86$) is given in Fig. 13.

[1] This expression was first derived by E. FERMI, Z. Physik **60**, 320 (1930).

The expression (22.13) and the hyperfine splitting, as observed by optical spectroscopy, can be used to determine the spin I and magnetic moment of the nucleus (gI): The maximum multiplicity of levels with large j gives $(2I+1)$ and the amount of splitting gives the factor g. Nuclear moments of many atoms have been measured in this manner[1] [using a generalization of Eq. (22.13) for complex atoms], but with rather poor accuracy since the hyperfine splittings are very small for optical spectroscopy. More recently, accurate microwave techniques have been developed for investigating hyperfine structure. For excited atomic states accurate analyses of experiments are hampered somewhat by the fact that the natural line width of a level is usually not much less than the hyperfine splitting, but very accurate comparison of theory and experiment is possible for the ground states of hydrogen-like atoms.

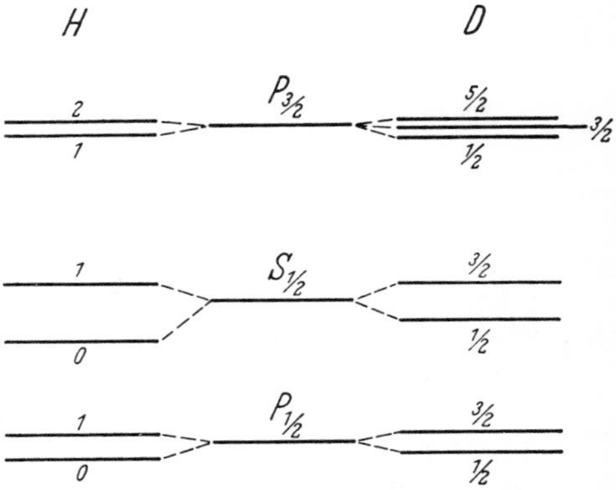

Fig. 13. Schematic energy level diagram for the hyperfine structure splitting of the states with $n=2$ in hydrogen (H) and deuterium (D). In the middle column are the levels without hyperfine structure. The number labeling each line is the value of the quantum number f.

γ) Higher order corrections for the ground state. For the ground state ($1\,S_{\frac{1}{2}}$) of hydrogen (with a proton of "spin" $\frac{1}{2}$ as nucleus), the simple FERMI formula (20.21) leads to the following expression [see (22.13)] for the hyperfine structure splitting

$$\Delta E = \frac{16}{3}\alpha^2\left(\frac{g_P\,\mu_N}{2\mu_0}\right)\text{Ry}, \qquad (22.14)$$

where g_P is the g-factor for a proton in (22.6). For comparison with very accurate experiments we discuss various theoretical corrections to this formula.

We first consider the proton as a fixed structureless point charge with a given magnetic moment. The FERMI formula (22.14) was derived from the PAULI approximation to the DIRAC theory. From a more accurate treatment of the relativistic DIRAC theory (but *without* radiative corrections) BREIT[2] derived a small correction to (22.14) in the form of a multiplying factor $(1+\frac{3}{2}\alpha^2)$. However, much larger effects[3] come from radiative corrections, largely from the electron's anomalous magnetic moment g_s [discussed in Sect. 18β, Eq. (18.5) and in Sect. 49]. Besides the effect of this anomalous moment, other radiative corrections of relative order α^2, specific to hyperfine structure in a bound S-state, have also been calculated[4].

The result for the frequency $\nu_\infty = \Delta E/h$, assuming a fixed structureless proton, is

$$\left.\begin{aligned} \nu_\infty &= \frac{16}{3}\alpha^2\left(\frac{g_P\,\mu_N}{2\mu_0}\right)c\,R_\infty\left(1+\frac{3}{2}\alpha^2\right)\left[\frac{g_s}{2}+\alpha^2\left(\frac{5}{2}-\log 2\right)\right],\\ \frac{g_s}{2} &= 1+\frac{\alpha}{2\pi}-\frac{2.973}{\pi^2}\alpha^2, \end{aligned}\right\} \qquad (22.15)$$

where R_∞ is the "RYDBERG for infinite mass" in wave numbers.

[1] S. TOLANSKI: Fine Structure In Line Spectra. London: Methuen & Co. 1935.
[2] G. BREIT: Phys. Rev. **35**, 1447 (1930).
[3] In fact, the anomalous magnetic moment of the electron was first inferred from a discrepancy between (22.14) and experiment. G. BREIT: Phys. Rev. **72**, 984 (1947).
[4] R. KARPLUS and A. KLEIN: Phys. Rev. **85**, 972 (1952). — N. M. KROLL and F. POLLOCK: Phys. Rev. **86**, 876 (1952).

We consider next the effect of nuclear motion and structure on hyperfine structure in the ground state. The largest and simplest of these effects depends only on the mass, but on no structural details, of the nucleus: The FERMI formula (22.10) is proportional to $R_{n0}^2(0)$, where $R_{n0}(r)$ is the normalized nonrelativistic radial atomic wave function. If the nucleus has a finite mass M, the distance scale of the wave function is altered by a factor $m/\mathcal{M}$, where $\mathcal{M}=mM/(m+M)$ is the reduced mass (see Sect. 5). Now the square of the normalized wave function is proportional to the minus third power of this scale factor. Thus $R_{n0}^2(0)$ and hence the FERMI formula (for a fixed nucleus) have to be multiplied[1] by a factor

$$\left(\frac{\mathcal{M}}{m}\right)^3 \approx 1 - 3\frac{m}{M}. \tag{22.16}$$

There are also corrections to the hyperfine structure of hydrogen of order $\alpha m/M$ times the FERMI formula. If the proton were simply a DIRAC particle with spin $\frac{1}{2}$ and *only* the DIRAC magnetic moment [$g=2$ in Eq. (22.6)], these corrections could be (and have been) evaluated unambiguously[2] using a relativistic two-body equation or other relativistic treatments of the quantum electrodynamic interaction of two DIRAC particles. These corrections are similar to those of order $\alpha m/M$ times the fine structure, discussed in Sect. 20α, but are of course one order of m/M smaller in absolute value. Some of these terms are actually of order $\alpha(m/M)\log(M/m)$ times the FERMI formula and can also be calculated by a conventional perturbation treatment of quantum electrodynamics (one term, for instance, representing the emission of two virtual photons by the electron and their reabsorption by the magnetic moment of the nucleus).

In reality, the proton's magnetic moment differs appreciably from the DIRAC value ($g=5.6$ instead of 2) although its spin is $\frac{1}{2}$. If the "extra" or anomalous moment $(g_P-2)\,\mu_N$ is treated as a point dipole moment of the PAULI type [see Eq. (10.16)], the corrections of relative order $\alpha m/M$ can again be calculated, in principle. In practice, in some of the terms referring to the PAULI moment, integrals over the momentum of a virtual photon diverge logarithmically at the high momentum side (see also end of Sect. 10γ). This divergence is due to the fact that a *point* magnetic moment was assumed. In reality, the proton's interaction with its virtual meson cloud, which is responsible for the proton's anomalous magnetic moment, also contributes a spatial spread and structure to this moment. If a consistent meson theory were available the equivalent integrals over photon momentum would presumably have convergence factors in them, but at the moment a completely unambiguous separation of correction terms due to nuclear motion and to nuclear structure is impossible. If, in the expressions of ARNOWITT, NEWCOMB and SALPETER, we simply omit all integrals proportional to $\int_{Mc}^{\infty} dp/p$ then the total nuclear motion corrections are only -0.2×10^{-5} times the FERMI formula for the hydrogen ground state. This very small number is due to some fortuitous cancellation; the corresponding number for individual terms is of relative order $\alpha(m/M)\log(M/m)=3.0\times 10^{-5}$.

The effects of the internal structure of a proton cannot be calculated quantitatively at present, but presumably would contribute to the hyperfine structure (besides cancelling the divergent integrals mentioned above) a finite amount, say δ times the FERMI formula. On a naive picture of such structure effects, the

[1] G. BREIT and R. MEYEROTT: Phys. Rev. **72**, 1023 (1947).

[2] R. ARNOWITT: Phys. Rev. **92**, 1002 (1953). — W. NEWCOMB and E. SALPETER: Phys. Rev. **97**, 1146 (1955).

interaction of the proton's moment with a virtual photon of momentum k is modified if k is larger than some value K, which may lie between $m_\pi c$ and $M_p c$, where $m_\pi \approx 275\, m$ and $M_p = 1836\, m$ are the masses of a π-meson and a proton. Such effects would change the hyperfine structure by a term of relative order $\alpha(mc/K)$. If we simply omit all contributions from photon momenta $k > K$, then the structure correction δ is -5.6×10^{-5} and -0.7×10^{-5}, respectively, for $K = m_\pi c$ and $M_p c$. However, our present knowledge of meson theory is insufficient even to predict the *sign* of the correct value of δ.

Collecting all the correction terms, the theoretical expression for the frequency $\nu_{\mathrm{H}} = \Delta E/h$ (for the hyperfine splitting of the hydrogen ground state) can be written in the form

$$\frac{\nu_{\mathrm{H}}}{c R_\infty} = \frac{16}{3}\alpha^2 \left(\frac{M_p}{M_p + m}\right)^3 \left(\frac{g_p \mu_N}{g_s \mu_0}\right) \frac{g_s}{2}\left[\frac{g_s}{2} + \alpha^2 (4 - \log 2) - 0.2\times 10^{-5} + \delta\right], \quad (22.17)$$

where g_s is the expression defined in (22.15). Experimentally this frequency ν_{H} has been measured very accurately and directly by atomic beam and by microwave resonance absorption techniques, by which direct magnetic dipole transitions are induced between the two hyperfine structure components of the hydrogen ground state (see Sect. 49α). The experimental value[1] is

$$\nu_{\mathrm{H}} = (1420.4057 \pm 0.0001)\ \mathrm{Mc/sec}. \quad (22.18)$$

The ratio $(g_p \mu_N / g_s \mu_0)$ in (22.17) is simply the ratio of the magnetic moments of the proton and electron. This ratio has also been measured very accurately by microwave techniques (see Sect. 49γ) and is[2]

$$\frac{g_s \mu_0}{g_p \mu_N} = 658.2293 \pm 0.0006. \quad (22.19)$$

Using this value, the expression (21.7) for c and the accurately known value for R_∞, the theoretical and experimental expressions (22.17) and (22.18) give a relation between the fine structure constant α and the nuclear structure correction δ,

$$\frac{1}{\alpha} = 137.0368\left(1 + \frac{1}{2}\delta \pm 2\times 10^{-6}\right). \quad (22.20)$$

The good agreement between (21.6) and (22.20) indicate that δ is rather small[3].

Another quantity of interest is the ratio of the hyperfine structure splitting in the ground states of ordinary hydrogen and of deuterium. The nucleus of deuterium, the deuteron, consists of a proton and neutron, rather loosely bound, with their spins "parallel" so that the "spin" I of the deuteron is unity. The g-factor in (22.6) for the deuteron is accurately known and is about 0.86 (compared with 2×2.79 for the proton and -2×1.91 for the neutron). The theoretical expression for ν_{D} is similar to (22.17) and radiative corrections drop out in the

---

[1] A. Prodell and P. Kusch: Phys. Rev. **88**, 184 (1952) and **100**, 1183 (1955). — J. Witke and R. Dicke: Phys. Rev. **96**, 530 (1954).

[2] S. Koenig, A. Prodell and P. Kusch: Phys. Rev. **88**, 191 (1952). — R. Beringer and M. Heald: Phys. Rev. **95**, 1474 (1954).

[3] The internal structure of the proton also contributes (unknown) corrections to the fine structure separation energy of the same *absolute* order of magnitude as to hyperfine structure. But, since the fine structure itself is very much larger than hyperfine structure, these corrections have a negligible effect on (21.6), but an appreciable one on (22.20). On the other hand, the purely experimental errors are larger in the experiments leading to (21.6) than in those leading to (22.20).

ratio ν_D/ν_H. Theoretically this ratio is

$$\frac{\nu_D}{\nu_H} = \frac{3}{4}\left(\frac{\mathcal{M}_D}{\mathcal{M}_H}\right)^3 \frac{2g_D}{g_p}(1+\Delta), \tag{22.21}$$

where $\mathcal{M}$ is the reduced mass and Δ is the effect of nuclear structure plus "relativistic recoil" corrections of order $\alpha m/M$. The loose structure of the deuteron, as built up from a proton and neutron, is reasonably well understood and contributes a rather large amount[1] to Δ. The $\alpha m/M$-corrections can be calculated[2] with similar limitations as for hydrogen. The present theoretical value for Δ is about 28×10^{-5}, compared with an experimental value of $(17.0\pm 0.1)\times 10^{-5}$. The poor agreement may be due to the rather large uncertainties in the calculation for deuterium.

23. The fine structure of positronium[3]. In Sect. 15γ we have discussed briefly the positron, the electron's antiparticle with the same mass m and spin $\frac{1}{2}$ as the electron, but equal and opposite charge. Since the electron and positron have opposite charge, a bound system can be formed which contains only one electron and one positron. This system, called positronium, is thus a hydrogen-like atom in which the positron takes the place of the nucleus. Experimentally positronium can be formed by radiative capture (recombination, see Sect. 75), if positrons are slowed down in a gas containing hydrogen.

Positronium differs radically from other hydrogen-like atoms in two respects: 1. Instead of having a nucleus much heavier than the electron, the two particles forming the "atom" have *equal* masses. The reduced mass of the system, $\mathcal{M}=m_1 m_2/(m_1+m_2)$ is thus $\frac{1}{2}m$, instead of being close to m. In nonrelativistic atomic theory this merely results in energy levels of exactly half the energy of levels in a hydrogen-like atom with $Z=1$ and a fixed nucleus, as well as a doubling of the distance scale in all wave functions (see Sect. 5). The equality of the two masses has a much more profound effect on the fine and hyperfine structure of positronium, which will be discussed below.

2. According to the DIRAC pair theory, an electron and a positron can annihilate each other, in which case the total rest mass energy, $2mc^2$, of the positronium atom is converted into photons. For states with non-zero orbital quantum number l the wave function at the origin is zero in nonrelativistic approximation, so that the electron and positron never overlap. In such states the probability for annihilation is very small and ordinary radiative transitions to lower atomic states are more probable. In S-states, however, the wave function at the origin is finite and the probability for annihilation may be greater than that for radiative transitions. Annihilation can also take place from the ground state of positronium, from which spontaneous radiative transitions are impossible.

From the requirement of conservation of energy and momentum, at least two photons must be produced when an electron-positron pair annihilates. For S-states of positronium in which the spins $\mathbf{s}_1$ and $\mathbf{s}_2$ of the two particles are "anti-parallel" (singlet states), two-quantum annihilations are possible. The probability for such processes is of order α^3 atomic units of frequency. For S-states with parallel spin (triplet states) some general symmetry arguments show that two-quantum annihilations are forbidden. Thus triplet states annihilate mainly with

---

[1] A. BOHR: Phys. Rev. **73**, 1109 (1948). — F. E. LOW: Phys. Rev. **77**, 361 (1950). — F. LOW and E. SALPETER: Phys. Rev. **83**, 478 (1951).

[2] C. GREIFINGER: Ph. D. Thesis, Cornell 1954.

[3] For a more detailed account and a bibliography see a review article by S. DEBENEDETTI and H. C. CORBEN, Ann. Rev. Nuc. Sci. **4**, 191 (1954). Cf. also L. SIMONS in Vol. XXXIV of this Encyclopedia.

the emission of three photons with a probability of order α^4 atomic units of frequency. These probabilities can be calculated explicitly[1], using DIRAC pair theory and quantum electrodynamics. The mean lifetimes for annihilation of a singlet and a triplet S-state of positronium are

$$\tau_{\text{sing}} = 1.25\times 10^{-10}\, n^3\,\text{sec}, \qquad \tau_{\text{trip}} = 1.4\times 10^{-7}\, n^3\,\text{sec}. \tag{23.1}$$

α) The PAULI *approximation.* We consider now relativistic corrections to the energy levels of the positronium atom to the same accuracy as the PAULI approximation for hydrogen, i.e. to order α^2 Ry. In hydrogen the proton's mass is much larger, and its magnetic moment much smaller, than that of the electron. Thus the electron's spin-orbit coupling is much larger than the magnetic interaction between the spins of electron and nucleus and the fine structure much larger than the hyperfine structure. In positronium, however, the magnetic moments of the particles are equal (and opposite) and the hyperfine structure is of the *same* order as the fine structure, i.e. of order α^2 Ry.

We first omit any effects of the possibility of virtual pair annihilation on the energy levels. To the required accuracy (α^2 Ry) we can proceed from an approximately relativistic Eq. (42.1) for two DIRAC particles interacting with each other, to be derived in Sect. 42. In this approximate equation the wave function contains one PAULI spinor each for the electron and positron, on which the respective spin operators $\mathbf{s}_1$ and $\mathbf{s}_2$ operate. In this equation we merely substitute $m_1 = m_2 = m$,

$$e_1 = -e_2 = e \quad \text{and} \quad \mu_1 = -\mu_2 = \mu_0.$$

The HAMILTONian H of this wave equation consists of the sum of six terms. Each term, and hence H, commutes with the operator $\boldsymbol{k}^2$, where $\boldsymbol{k}$ is the orbital angular momentum, and l is thus a good quantum number. The first term of the HAMILTONian, $H_0 = p^2/m - e^2/r$, is simply the nonrelativistic HAMILTONian for a fixed COULOMB potential and a reduced mass of $\frac{1}{2}m$. The other terms H_1 to H_5 are all smaller than H_0 by two powers of α and will be treated by first order perturbation theory. The terms H_2 and H_4 do not contain any spin-operators and their expectation values over a nonrelativistic eigenfunction of M_0 can be evaluated and depend only on the principal and orbital quantum numbers n and l.

The operator H_3 can be written in the form

$$H_4 = 3\,\frac{\mu_0 e}{m c}\,\frac{\hbar}{r^3}\,\boldsymbol{k}\cdot\boldsymbol{S}, \quad \boldsymbol{S} = \mathbf{s}_1 + \mathbf{s}_2, \tag{23.2}$$

where $\boldsymbol{S}$ is the operator for the total spin of the atom. We are only interested in the expectation values of the operators H_1 to H_5 over wave functions for which l is a good quantum number. For this purpose we can replace H_5 by another operator H_5', using the relation (A.33) of the appendix. Using the relation (40.8), to be derived in Sect. 40, this operator can be further simplified to read

$$\left.\begin{aligned} H_5' = 4\mu_0^2 \Big\{ &\frac{8\pi}{3}\,\mathbf{s}_1\cdot\mathbf{s}_2\,\delta^{(3)}(\boldsymbol{r}) + \\ &+ \frac{1}{r^3(2l+3)(2l-1)}\left[\left(2\mathbf{s}_1\cdot\mathbf{s}_2 + \frac{3}{2}\right)\boldsymbol{k}^2 - \frac{3}{2}\,\boldsymbol{S}\cdot\boldsymbol{k} - \frac{3}{2}\,(\boldsymbol{S}\cdot\boldsymbol{k})^2\right]\Big\}, \end{aligned}\right\} \tag{23.3}$$

where $1/r^3$ is again to be replaced by zero for $r < \varepsilon$ (and $\varepsilon \to 0$ after evaluating expectation values).

---

[1] A. ORE and J. POWELL: Phys. Rev. **75**, 1696, 1963 (1953).

The constants of the motion for the positronium atom are thus similar to those of the helium atom, discussed in Sect. 40: Since $\mathbf{s}_1^2$ and $\mathbf{s}_2^2$ are just numbers ($\frac{1}{2}\times\frac{3}{2}$ each), the spin-spin interaction operator $\mathbf{s}_1\cdot\mathbf{s}_2$ commutes with $\boldsymbol{S}^2$. Since any component of $\boldsymbol{S}$ also commutes with $\boldsymbol{S}^2$, H_3 and H_5 also commute with $\boldsymbol{S}^2$, which is then a constant of the motion. The possible eigenvalues of $\boldsymbol{S}^2$ are $S(S+1)$ with either $S=0$ (singlet state) or $S=1$ (triplet state). Let us call $\boldsymbol{M}=(\boldsymbol{k}+\boldsymbol{S})$ the total angular momentum operator. Then both M_z and $\boldsymbol{M}^2$ (but *not* S_z or k_z) commute with H_3 and H_5. The eigenvalues of $\boldsymbol{M}^2$ are $J(J+1)$ with $J=|l-S)|$, $|l-S|+1,\ldots,l+S$ and J is a good quantum number. The expectation values of H_3 and H_5 will depend on the quantum numbers S and J, as well as on n and l.

For an S-state, $l=0$ and hence S equals J and is either zero or one, and the eigenvalue of $\mathbf{s}_1\cdot\mathbf{s}_2$ is $-\frac{3}{4}$ or $+\frac{1}{4}$, respectively. With $\overline{\boldsymbol{k}^2}=\overline{\boldsymbol{k}}=l=0$, the expectation value of H_3 and of the term involving $1/r^3$ in H_5' is zero. From the δ-function term in (23.3) we then get for the expectation value W of H_3+H_5',

$$W=\frac{8}{3}\mu_0^2\,\mathbf{s}_1\cdot\mathbf{s}_2\,R_{n0}^2(0)=\frac{\alpha^2}{6n^3}\,\mathrm{Ry}\left\{\begin{array}{rl}-3 & \text{for}\quad S=0\\ 1 & \text{for}\quad S=1,\end{array}\right\} \tag{23.4}$$

where $R_{n0}(r)$ is the normalized nonrelativistic radial wave function (for reduced mass $\frac{1}{2}m$). The expectation values of H_3 and H_5' can also be evaluated for states with $l\neq 0$, following the procedures given in Sect. 40.

We have to consider next a term H_{pair} to be added to the HAMILTONian, which has no analogue in the theory of other hydrogen-like atoms, nor of helium. This term, specific to positronium (and DIRAC pair theory coupled with quantum electrodynamics), arises from the possibility of *virtual* pair annihilation. One finds a non-zero matrix element for a transition (which does *not* necessarily conserve energy) in which an electron-positron pair of total momentum $\boldsymbol{P}$ is converted into a *single* photon of the same momentum (or vice versa), if the pair is in a triplet state ($S=1$). Using second order perturbation theory one gets an additional matrix element for the scattering of an electron from a positron: In the first step the initial pair is converted into a virtual photon and this photon is then converted into another pair (with the same total, but not the same relative, momentum). The energy denominator in this matrix element is of order $2mc^2$ and if the kinetic energies are all small compared with mc^2 the additional matrix element for a real scattering between electron and positron with momentum transfer $\boldsymbol{q}$ is almost independent of $\boldsymbol{q}$ and is of order $e^2/(mc)^2$, compared with e^2/q^2 for scattering by a COULOMB potential. The FOURIER transform of this scattering matrix element corresponds to a spatial interaction potential H_{pair}. To lowest order in α one finds

$$H_{\text{pair}}=2\pi\left(\frac{e\hbar}{mc}\right)^2\delta_{S1}\,\delta^{(3)}(\boldsymbol{r}),\qquad \overline{H}_{\text{pair}}=\frac{\alpha^2}{2n^3}\,\mathrm{Ry}\,\delta_{S1}\,\delta_{l0}, \tag{23.5}$$

where $\overline{H}$ is the expectation value for a positronium state with quantum numbers n, l, S and J.

The expectation value $\overline{H}_{\text{pair}}$, which is non-zero only for triplet S-states ($l=0$, $S=J=1$), has to be added to the expectation values of H_1 to H_5, defined in (42.1). The total energy separation between the triplet and singlet S-states with the same value of n is, from (23.4) and (23.5),

$$\Delta W=\frac{7}{6}\,\frac{\alpha^2}{n^3}\,\mathrm{Ry}=\frac{1}{n^3}\,2.044\times 10^5\ \mathrm{Mc/sec}. \tag{23.6}$$

For a positronium state with arbitrary n, l, S and J the deviation (to order α^2 Ry) from the nonrelativistic value $-$ Ry$/2n^2$ is[1]

$$\left.\begin{aligned} W_{nlSJ} &= \left[\frac{11}{32n^4} + \left(\varepsilon_{lSJ} - \frac{1}{2l+1}\right)\frac{1}{n^3}\right]\alpha^2\,\mathrm{Ry};\\ \varepsilon_{l,S=0,J} = 0,\quad \varepsilon_{l,S=1,J} &= \frac{7}{6}\delta_{l0} + \frac{1-\delta_{l0}}{2(2l+1)}\begin{cases} \dfrac{3l+4}{(l+1)(2l+3)} & \text{if } J = l+1\\ -\dfrac{1}{l(l+1)} & \text{if } J = l\\ -\dfrac{3l-1}{l(2l-1)} & \text{if } J = l-1. \end{cases}\end{aligned}\right\} \qquad (23.7)$$

The relativistic splitting of the energy level for any value of n, given by (23.7), is different from that either of hydrogen or helium. Unlike hydrogen, no degeneracy with respect to J remains to order α^2 Ry. The "good quantum numbers" are the same as for helium, but in *non*relativistic approximation the l- and S-degeneracy is not yet removed. A picture of the level splitting for $n=2$ is given in Fig. 14 (to be compared with that of H in Fig. 13). The level splitting of excited states in positronium has not yet been investigated experimentally, but we discuss very accurate experiments for the ground state below.

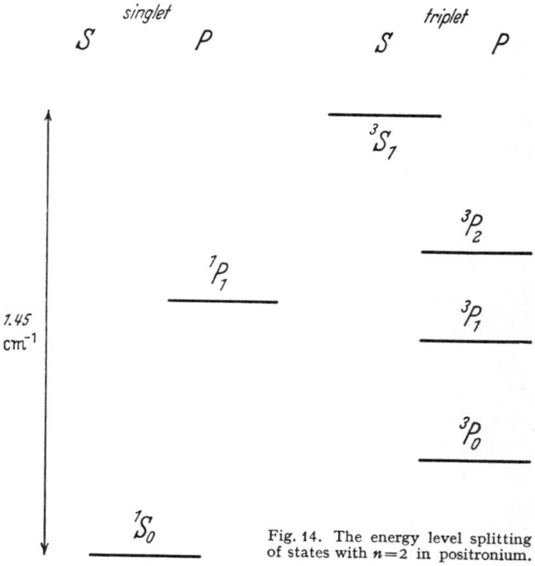

Fig. 14. The energy level splitting of states with $n=2$ in positronium.

β) The ground state. The ground state of positronium ($n=1, l=0$) is split into a singlet ($S=0$) and a triplet ($S=1$) state. The splitting energy ΔW to lowest order (α^2 Ry) is given by (23.6), but there are a number of radiative correction terms of order α^3 Ry. In addition to the (lowest order) Lamb shift and vacuum polarization terms (see Sect. 18), there are some additional terms of order α^3 Ry, which are either absent in hydrogen or contribute corrections of smaller order there. Some of these terms, for instance those representing the interchange of *two* virtual photons between electron and positron, are equivalent to the correction to hyperfine structure in hydrogen of order $\alpha^3(m/M)^2$ Ry. Other terms are specific to positronium, for instance one which represents the virtual annihilation of the pair with the emission of *two* virtual photons (followed by the creation of another pair). This particular term is present only in the singlet state. Most of these terms of order α^3 Ry cannot be calculated from the Breit equation, but have all been evaluated using a more fully relativistic treatment of the two-body problem.

[1] All terms of order α^2 Ry were first calculated by J. Pirenne, Arch. Sci. phys. nat. **29**, 121, 207, 265 (1947); V. Berestetski and L. Landau, J. exp. theor. Phys. USSR. **19**, 673, 1130 (1949). Some errors in these papers were corrected by R. A. Ferrell, Phys. Rev. **84**, 858 (1951).

The total theoretical result[1] for these corrections of order α^3 Ry to the hyperfine splitting ΔW of the positronium ground state is

$$\Delta W^{(2)} = \alpha^3 \left[-\frac{1}{\pi}\left(\frac{16}{9} + \log 2\right) + \frac{1}{2} i \right] \text{Ry}. \tag{23.8}$$

The imaginary term in (23.8) represents a "line width" of the singlet level, *not* an energy shift, i.e. its inverse (times $\frac{1}{2}\hbar$) gives the mean lifetime (23.1) of the singlet state against *real* two-quantum annihilation of the pair. The real part of $\Delta W^{(2)}$ is about 10^3 Mc/sec and, added to the expression (23.6) with $n=1$, gives a total theoretical value of

$$\Delta W_{\text{th}} = 2.0337 \times 10^5 \text{ Mc/sec}. \tag{23.9}$$

The splitting energy (in frequency units) between the singlet and triplet components of the positronium ground state has been measured very accurately in a series of experiments using a combination of microwave and counter techniques, largely by M. DEUTSCH and collaborators. In principle the experiment proceeds as follows: If positronium atoms are placed in an oscillating magnetic field of frequency corresponding to the energy splitting ΔW, transitions are induced from the longlived triplet state to the shortlived singlet states. The quenching of the slower three-quantum decay of the singlet state is then observed by counter techniques. In practice, an additional constant magnetic field is present and the theory of the ZEEMAN effect is used to analyse the experiment. The latest experimental value[2] for ΔW is

$$\Delta W_{\text{exp}} = (2.0338 \pm 0.0004) \times 10^5 \text{ Mc/sec}, \tag{23.10}$$

in excellent agreement with the theoretical result (23.9).

This agreement to such a high accuracy is not only a major achievement of experimental techniques in a difficult field, but a remarkable verification of the DIRAC pair theory and relativistic quantum electrodynamics. Unlike any other atom, a major contribution already to the terms of order α^2 Ry comes from the annihilation term, which is specific to the pair theory[3] and has no analogue in single-electron theory. But the experimental error is even 20 times smaller than the terms of order α^3 Ry, which (for positronium) also test the modern fully relativistic formulations of the two-body problem.

II. The helium atom without external fields.

a) Nonrelativistic theory.

24. The SCHRÖDINGER equation for helium (symmetry). SCHRÖDINGER'S equation for atoms having two electrons is

$$\Delta_1 u + \Delta_2 u + 2\left(E + \frac{Z}{r_1} + \frac{Z}{r_2} - \frac{1}{r_{12}}\right) u = 0. \tag{24.1}$$

r_1 and r_2 are the distances of the first and second electrons from the nucleus, r_{12} their mutual separation; $\Delta_1 = \frac{\partial^2}{\partial x_1^2} + \frac{\partial^2}{\partial y_1^2} + \frac{\partial^2}{\partial z_1^2}$ is the LAPLACian operator in

[1] R. KARPLUS and A. KLEIN: Phys. Rev. **87**, 848 (1952). Terms of the same order for excited states have been calculated by T. FULTON and P. MARTIN, Phys. Rev. **95**, 811 (1954).

[2] R. WEINSTEIN, M. DEUTSCH and S. BROWN: Phys. Rev. **98**, 223 (1955).

[3] A few years ago some doubts existed as to whether the virtual effects of pair creation (or annihilation) should be included in the theory. Since about 40% of the theoretical splitting energy (23.9) is due to the annihilation term, the experimental value (23.10) confirms its presence beyond any doubt.

the space of the first electron; u is a function of the six coordinates x_1, y_1, z_1, x_2, y_2 and z_2.

The differential equation remains unchanged when the coordinates of the first electron are interchanged with those of the second electron. Thus, $u(\boldsymbol{r}_1, \boldsymbol{r}_2)$ and $u(\boldsymbol{r}_2, \boldsymbol{r}_1)$ satisfy the same differential equation. [$u(\boldsymbol{r}_2, \boldsymbol{r}_1)$ is obtained from $u(\boldsymbol{r}_1, \boldsymbol{r}_2)$ by replacing $x_1\, y_1\, z_1$ with $x_2\, y_2\, z_2$ and vice versa.] $u(\boldsymbol{r}_2, \boldsymbol{r}_1)$ is, of course, subject to the same requirements as $u(\boldsymbol{r}_1, \boldsymbol{r}_2)$, it must be a bounded, continuous and single valued function. Therefore[1],

$$u(\boldsymbol{r}_2\, \boldsymbol{r}_1) = \varkappa\, u(\boldsymbol{r}_1\, \boldsymbol{r}_2), \tag{24.2}$$

where $\varkappa$ is a constant. Interchanging $\boldsymbol{r}_1$ and $\boldsymbol{r}_2$ once more in $u(\boldsymbol{r}_2\, \boldsymbol{r}_1)$ we obviously get $u(\boldsymbol{r}_1\, \boldsymbol{r}_2)$ again, so that

$$u(\boldsymbol{r}_1\, \boldsymbol{r}_2) = \varkappa^2 u(\boldsymbol{r}_1\, \boldsymbol{r}_2); \quad \varkappa = \pm 1; \quad u(\boldsymbol{r}_2\, \boldsymbol{r}_1) = \pm\, u(\boldsymbol{r}_1\, \boldsymbol{r}_2). \tag{24.3}$$

Thus, the eigenfunctions of an atom with two electrons either remain unchanged or change sign on interchange of the coordinates of the two electrons, i.e., the eigenfunctions are either symmetric or antisymmetric. States of symmetric eigenfunctions are called para-, those of antisymmetric eigenfunctions ortho-states.

The above does not constitute a complete theory of atoms with two electrons because, as we know, electrons possess spin. As a good approximation for light atoms we may at first neglect both the spin-orbit interaction and the relativistic change in mass (cf. Sect. 12). Then the energy does not depend on the orientation of spin relative to orbital angular momentum, and we only need to specify the components of the spins in a fixed direction z (in addition to specifying the spatial eigenfunction) in order to describe the atom completely. The complete eigenfunction is a product of the spatial eigenfunction satisfying (24.1) and a function depending on the spin coordinates [cf. (12.12)].

The spin wave function is of a particularly simple nature. Let $\mathbf{s}_1$ and $\mathbf{s}_2$ be the spin operators for the two electrons, s_{1z} and s_{2z} the components of these vector operators in a fixed z-direction. The only possible eigenvalues of s_{1z} (or s_{2z}) are $+\frac{1}{2}$ and $-\frac{1}{2}$. We then have four independent spin states, which could be represented as the product of two 2-component spinors. In the notation of (12.12) we write the state with $s_{1z} = s_{2z} = +\frac{1}{2}$ as $\alpha(1)\,\alpha(2)$, the state with $s_{1z} = +\frac{1}{2}$, $s_{2z} = -\frac{1}{2}$ as $\alpha(1)\,\beta(2)$, and so on.

Combining these four spin states with the spatial eigenfunctions, we would expect four times as many eigenstates for an atom with two spin-electrons than for two spin-less particles. In reality the number of possible states is reduced by the requirements of the PAULI exclusion principle. This requires that the *total* wave function change sign if *all* the coordinates (spatial as well as spin coordinates) of the two electrons are interchanged. Hence the spin wave function must change sign if the spatial wave function remains the same after interchanging the two electrons, and vice versa.

Of the four spin wave functions discussed above neither $\alpha(1)\,\beta(2)$ nor $\beta(1)\,\alpha(2)$ is symmetric or antisymmetric, but two simple linear combinations of them have this property. Consider the following four mutually orthogonal spin wave functions

$$\left.\begin{aligned} S_+ &= \alpha(1)\,\alpha(2), \quad S_- = \beta(1)\,\beta(2), \\ S_0 &= \frac{1}{\sqrt{2}}\left[\alpha(1)\,\beta(2) + \beta(1)\,\alpha(2)\right] \end{aligned}\right\} \tag{24.4}$$

[1] Except for degenerate eigenvalues, but in that case the eigenfunctions can always be chosen so that (24.2) holds.

and

$$S_P = \frac{1}{\sqrt{2}} \left[\alpha(1)\,\beta(2) - \beta(1)\,\alpha(2)\right]. \tag{24.5}$$

Each of these wave functions is normalized to unity. The first three, (24.4), are symmetric (remain unchanged) for an interchange of the two electrons, the last one, (24.5), is antisymmetric (changes sign). Let $\boldsymbol{S} = \boldsymbol{s}_1 + \boldsymbol{s}_2$ be the operator for the total spin, $S_z = s_{1z} + s_{2z}$ its component in the z-direction, $\boldsymbol{S}^2$ its square.

The three symmetric states S_+, S_0, S_- are eigenstates of S_z with eigenvalues 1, 0, -1 respectively. Using the explicit representation of the PAULI spin matrices, Sect. 10, one also finds that each of these states is an eigenstate of $\boldsymbol{S}^2$ with eigenvalue $1(1+1)=2$. For these states, then, the quantum number for the "absolute value of the total spin" is $S=1$. Similarly the state S_P is a simultaneous eigenstate of $\boldsymbol{S}^2$ and S_z with quantum numbers $S_z = S = 0$.

According to the PAULI principle, an antisymmetric spatial wave function (ortho-state) *must be* multiplied by one of the three symmetric spin wave functions S_+, S_0, S_-. Let $\boldsymbol{j} = \boldsymbol{k} + \boldsymbol{S}$ be the total angular momentum operator, where $\boldsymbol{k} = \boldsymbol{k}_1 + \boldsymbol{k}_2$ is the sum of the two orbital angular momentum operators. The nonrelativistic spatial wave functions can be characterized by a quantum number l (besides other quantum numbers), which corresponds to the "absolute value of $\boldsymbol{k}$". According to the rules of Sect. 11, one can find linear superpositions of the various ortho-states, with a fixed value of l and with $S=1$, which are eigenstates of $\boldsymbol{j}^2$ with quantum number

$$j = l+1, \quad l \;\text{ or }\; l-1. \tag{24.6}$$

In a purely nonrelativistic theory, the energy eigenvalues of all the ortho-states (with *fixed* values of l and of other spatial quantum numbers) are degenerate. If the relativistic interaction between spin and orbital angular momentum is taken into account, however, this degeneracy is partially removed. As we shall see later, each nonrelativistic (ortho) level is split into a triplet, the energy being slightly different for the three values (24.6) of the quantum number j.

A symmetric spatial wave function (para-state), on the other hand, *must* be multiplied by the single antisymmetric spin wave function S_P. For a fixed value of l the quantum number j must then be equal to l, since $S_z = S = 0$. Thus, even if the spin-orbit interaction is included, each nonrelativistic energy level of the para-system remains unsplit (singlet system). We shall see, however, that the energy eigenvalues for states of para-helium are quite different from those for ortho-helium (for the same l-value), *even* in the purely nonrelativistic theory.

Until Sect. 38 we shall neglect the spin-orbit interaction entirely and use the nonrelativistic SCHRÖDINGER Eq. (24.1). The errors due to this approximation (for the energy eigenvalue, etc.) are of relative order of magnitude α^2, where α is the fine structure constant. In this approximation one finds that transitions from a triplet to a singlet state (or vice versa) of helium with the emission of light are forbidden. This is due to the fact that the operator for the electric dipole moment $(x_1 + x_2)$ and the spatial wave function for a para-state are unchanged if the two electrons are interchanged, whereas the spatial wave function for an ortho-state changes sign. Now the transition matrix element involves an integral over the spatial coordinates of both electrons (see Sect. 59). This integral then vanishes[1] from these symmetry considerations.

[1] Even if the integral were finite, the singlet and triplet spin wave functions are orthogonal and the sum over the spin coordinates would make the matrix element vanish.

To summarize:

The level scheme of helium and of ions with two electrons consists of two system of levels, one containing triplet levels (orthohelium) and the other singlet levels (parahelium), which do not combine optically with each other.

25. Discussion of variation and perturbation methods. The differential equation (24.1) for the two-electron system is not separable. Unlike the solutions for the hydrogen atom, the solutions for the eigenfunctions u and energy eigenvalues E of (24.1) cannot be expressed in closed analytic form. We shall have to use various approximation methods, including the Ritz variational method, the perturbation method and some modifications of these methods. We first give a general discussion of these methods without explicit reference to (24.1). To apply the variational method we merely note that (24.1) is a Hamiltonian equation of form

$$H u = E u, \tag{25.1}$$

where the Hamiltonian H is a differential operator which does not involve the energy eigenvalue E explicitly. To apply the perturbation method we split this Hamiltonian into two parts $(H_0 + \lambda H_1)$ where

$$\left.\begin{aligned} H_0 &= -\tfrac{1}{2}(\Delta_1 + \Delta_2) + V_0(\boldsymbol{r}_1, \boldsymbol{r}_2),\\ \lambda H_1 &= -\frac{Z}{r_1} - \frac{Z}{r_2} + \frac{1}{r_{12}} - V_0. \end{aligned}\right\} \tag{25.2}$$

In later sections we discuss various choices of V_0 which attempt to keep H_0 a simple enough operator, yet make the contribution of λH_1 relatively small.

α) Ritz variation method. Consider an equation of type (25.1) which has a discrete spectrum of eigenvalues E of H. Let U be an *arbitrary* function (of the same number of dimensions as the eigenfunctions of H) and consider the expression

$$E[U] = \frac{\int d\tau\, U^* H U}{\int d\tau\, U^* U}. \tag{25.3}$$

If the function U is identical with any one of the exact eigenfunctions u, then $E[U]$ is identical with the corresponding exact eigenvalue E. Further, if U differs from any of the eigenfunctions u by an infinitesimally small function of first order, then $E[U]$ differs from the exact E by a quantity which is small of second order. In other words, Schrödinger's variational principle states that any function U for which the functional $E[U]$ has a stationary value is a solution of (25.1).

Now consider the special case of a function U which is fairly close to the eigenfunction u_g belonging to the *lowest* eigenvalue E_g of H. We can consider U written in the form

$$U = N_g u_g + \sum_{n \neq g} \delta_n u_n,$$

where u_n is any normalized eigenfunction of H and δ_n is a small expansion coefficient. (25.3) then becomes

$$E[U] = E_g + \frac{\sum_n |\delta_n|^2 (E_n - E_g)}{|N_g|^2 + \sum_n |\delta_n|^2} \geq E_g. \tag{25.4}$$

Thus any function U other than the exact u_g will give a value for $E[U]$ *larger* than E_g, the discrepancy being smaller the smaller the difference between U and u_g is. The Ritz variation method then starts by choosing some suitable analytic form for U, involving some arbitrary parameters. The expression $E[U]$ of (25.3) is then evaluated as a function of these parameters and the minimum value with respect to all parameters found. This *minimum* value of $E[U]$ then gives an *upper* limit for E_g. If a large enough number of suitable parameters is used and minimized against, then this upper bound for E_g should be very close to the exact value.

This variation method does *not*, without modification, give good approximations for the higher eigenvalues. However, consider trial wave functions U which are orthogonal to all eigenstates of H which belong to eigenvalues lower than a certain eigenvalue E_e. For such functions U, N_g and δ_n in (25.4) will be zero for all states for which $(E_n - E_g)$ is negative. In this case $E[U]$ will again be an upper limit for E_e.

β) Variation perturbation theory. Consider a general HAMILTONian equation

$$(H_0 + \lambda H_1 - E)\, u = 0, \tag{25.5}$$

where H_0 and H_1 are any two HERMITian operators and λ is considered as a small parameter. We consider the eigenfunction u and eigenvalue E expanded in powers of this parameter,

$$E = \sum_{n=0}^{\infty} \lambda^n E_n, \qquad u = \sum_{n=0}^{\infty} \lambda^n U_n. \tag{25.6}$$

If we substitute these expansions into (25.5) and equate the coefficient of each power of λ to zero, we get an infinite set of coupled linear equations,

$$H_0 U_0 - E_0 U_0 = 0, \tag{25.7}$$

$$H_0 U_1 + H_1 U_0 - E_0 U_1 - E_1 U_0 = 0, \tag{25.8}$$

$$H_0 U_2 + H_1 U_1 - E_0 U_2 - E_1 U_1 - E_2 U_0 = 0, \tag{25.9}$$

$$\cdots\cdots\cdots\cdots\cdots\cdots\cdots\cdots$$

$$H_0 U_n + H_1 U_{n-1} - \sum_{m=0}^{n} E_m U_{n-m} = 0.$$

We call (25.7) the unperturbed (or zero order) HAMILTONian equation. This equation, like the full Eq. (25.5), has a whole spectrum of solutions. We consider one *particular* solution and consider U_0 and E_0 as known completely and U_0 normalized. Multiply (25.7) by U_1, (25.8) by U_0, substract the two equations and integrate over all space[1]. One then obtains the well-known expression for E_1, the first order perturbation energy,

$$E_1 = \int U_0 H_1 U_0\, d\tau. \tag{25.10}$$

A knowledge of the zero-order wave function U_0, for one particular state alone, thus yields both E_0 and E_1 for this state.

In Eq. (25.8) for the particular state we are considering, the constants E_0 and E_1 and the function U_0 are now known. (25.8) is then an inhomogeneous differential equation for U_1, which does not contain any unknown eigenvalue. Since U_1 must satisfy some definite boundary conditions (conditions of "good behavior"), the Eq. (25.8) determines the function U_1 for the particular state *uniquely*[2], at least *in principle*. We shall discuss practical methods of solving for

---

[1] We restrict ourselves to the case of real functions U_0, U_1, U_2, etc. for the sake of simplicity.

[2] Except for an additive multiple of U_0. The normalization, etc., can be so arranged that U_1 (and U_2, etc.) is orthogonal to U_0.

U_1 in a moment. Once U_1 has been found, both E_2 and E_3 can be evaluated as follows. Multiplying (25.7) by U_2, (25.9) by U_0, subtracting the equations and integrating, we get

$$E_2 = \int U_0 H_1 U_1 d\tau, \tag{25.11}$$

where we have assumed the normalization such that U_0 and U_1 are orthogonal. Next multiply (25.7) by $-U_3$, (25.8) by $-U_2$, (25.9) by $+U_1$ and the next equation by $+U_0$. Adding these equations and integrating gives

$$E_3 = \int (U_1 H_1 U_1 - E_1 U_1^2)\, d\tau. \tag{25.12}$$

After E_2 and U_1 have been found, the Eq. (25.9) determines the function U_2 (in principle), and so on. In general, after each additional wave function (e.g. U_2) has been found, *two* additional eigenvalues (e.g. E_4 and E_5) can be evaluated.

We turn now to possible methods of solving (25.8) for the function U_1 (given U_0, E_0 and E_1). Solving this inhomogeneous differential equation *directly* is usually impractical, (but there are situations where this is not only possible but in fact the simplest method). The conventional SCHRÖDINGER perturbation method proceeds as follows. The zero order Eq. (25.7) is first solved for *all* the possible eigenfunctions and eigenvalues. After this complete set of eigenfunctions of H_0 has been found, the matrix elements of H_1 are evaluated between *any* function of this set and the eigenfunction U_0 which corresponds to the *particular* state we are considering. The unknown function U_1 is considered expanded in terms of the complete set of eigenfunctions of H_0. The expansion coefficients of U_1, and also the eigenvalue E_2, are then given in terms of the matrix elements of H_1. These expressions for U_1 and E_2 do not involve any explicit solution of the differential equation (25.8). But in many practical cases the evaluation of all the required matrix elements of H_1 is much too involved. In such cases one can still find *approximations* for U_1 and E_2 by the following method.

Consider U_0, E_0 and E_1 to be known exactly, for one *particular* state only, and let U_1 be an arbitrary trial wave function. We start from the following expression

$$E_2[U_1'] = \int (2U_1' H_1 U_0 + U_1' H_0 U_1' - E_0 U_1'^2 - 2E_1 U_0 U_1')\, d\tau. \tag{25.13}$$

The condition that this expression have a stationary value with respect to any variation of U_1' reduces exactly to the Eq. (25.8). Comparison of (25.8), (25.11) and (25.13) shows further that $E_2[U_1']$ equals the correct value of E_2, if U_1' equals the unique solution U_1 of (25.8). Let us consider now that particular state for which E_0 is the *lowest* of all the eigenvalues of H_0. For this state one can easily show that $E_2[U_1']$ is *larger* than E_2, unless U_1' equals U_1. We can then proceed as in the usual RITZ variation method. We again choose for the trial wave function U_1' a suitable analytic function with some parameters left arbitrary. We form the expression (25.13) and minimize it with respect to all the parameters. This minimum value of $E_2[U_1']$ then gives directly an *upper* limit for E_2. If enough suitable parameters are included, this bound should give a good approximation for E_2 and the corresponding function U_1' should be close to the correct U_1 .This method can be extended to give approximations for E_3, U_2, E_4, etc.

γ) Unsymmetric perturbation theory. We finally discuss another modification of first order perturbation theory, which we shall find useful in the next few sections. Consider a HAMILTONian H which can be split into a zero order HAMILTONian and a small perturbation part in two different ways,

$$H = H_{0a} + \lambda H_{1a} = H_{0b} + \lambda H_{1b}. \tag{25.14}$$

All four HAMILTONians are HERMITian, λ is a small parameter and hence the two zero order HAMILTONians H_{0a} and H_{0b} differ from each other only by a term of first order in λ. Let U_{0a} and U_{0b} be particular normalized eigenfunctions of H_{0a} and H_{0b}, respectively,

$$(H_{0a} - E_{0a})\, U_{0a} = (H_{0b} - E_{0b})\, U_{0b} = 0. \tag{25.15}$$

We restrict ourselves to cases where $E_{0a} = E_{0b} \equiv E_0$, say. Further, let U_{0a} and U_{0b} be orthogonal to each other to *zero* order in λ (since H_{0a} and H_{0b} are identical to zero order in λ, their eigenfunction spectrum is identical to the same order[1]). We are interested in that eigenfunction u of the total HAMILTONian which reduces to ($2^{-\frac{1}{2}}$ times) the sum of U_{0a} and U_{0b} in zero order. We put

$$(H - E)\, u = 0, \quad E = E_0 + \lambda E_1, \quad u = \frac{1}{\sqrt{2}}\,(U_{0a} + U_{0b}) + \lambda U_1. \tag{25.16}$$

From (25.14), (25.15) and (25.16) we find

$$\sqrt{2}\,(H - E)\, U_1 + (H_{1a} U_{0a} + H_{1b} U_{0b}) - E_1 (U_{0a} + U_{0b}) = 0. \tag{25.17}$$

We next multiply (25.17) by $(U_{0a} + U_{0b})$ and integrate over all space. We only wish to keep terms of zero order in λ in the resulting equation. To this order, $(H - E)$ $(U_{0a} + U_{0b})$ is zero and U_{0a} orthogonal to U_{0b}. We then get the following approximation for E_1,

$$E_1 = \tfrac{1}{2} \int (U_{0a} + U_{0b})\,(H_{1a} U_{0a} + H_{1b} U_{0b})\, d\tau. \tag{25.18}$$

(25.18) is the required generalization of expression (25.10) for the first order perturbation energy. Since U_{0a} and U_{0b} are only approximately orthogonal, it would however be difficult to extend the present scheme to include the higher order approximations in a systematic and simple way.

26. Level scheme of helium. As mentioned before, the SCHRÖDINGER equation for helium-like atoms cannot be solved exactly. Before discussing approximation methods in detail, we give a qualitative survey of the eigenvalue spectrum and eigenfunctions.

Consider the exact HAMILTONian (24.1) split into two parts as in (25.2). We take the zero order HAMILTONian H_0 of form

$$\left.\begin{aligned} H_0 &= -\frac{1}{2}\,(\Delta_1 + \Delta_2) + V(r_1) + V(r_2), \\ W \equiv \lambda H_1 &= -\frac{Z_1}{r_1} - V(r_1) - \frac{Z}{r_2} - V(r_2) + \frac{1}{r_{12}}, \end{aligned}\right\} \tag{26.1}$$

where V is a central potential (arbitrary, as yet). The zero-order wave equation

$$(H_0 - E_0)\, U_0 = 0 \tag{26.2}$$

is then separable with this choice for H_0. Let u_1 and u_2 be any two of the solutions u_n of the single-particle wave equation

$$\left[\tfrac{1}{2}\Delta + \varepsilon_n - V(r)\right] u_n(\mathbf{r}) = 0. \tag{26.3}$$

(26.2) is then solved by the substitution

$$E_0 = \varepsilon_1 + \varepsilon_2, \qquad U_0 = u_1(r_1)\, u_2(r_2). \tag{26.4}$$

---

[1] We assume the system has a degenerate eigenvalue spectrum, so that two orthogonal states U_{0a} and U_{0b} of the same energy exist.

Since the potential $V(r)$ is central, the single-particle Eq. (26.3) is separable in spherical polar coordinates. A solution of (26.3) can then be characterized by three quantum numbers[1] n, l, and m,

$$u_{n l m}(\boldsymbol{r}) = R_{n l}(r) \cdot Y_{l m}(\vartheta, \varphi).$$

We shall not specify the potential $V(r)$ any further in this section, but consider it chosen so that the effect of the perturbation potential W in (26.1) is fairly small. If we choose a simple COULOMB form for V, the energy eigenvalue ε_n of (26.3) would be given by

$$V(r) = -\frac{(Z-s)}{r}, \qquad \varepsilon_n = -\frac{1}{2}\frac{(Z-s)^2}{n^2} \tag{26.5}$$

and be independent of the quantum numbers l and m. We shall see later that some value between zero and one would be the best choice for the "screening constant" s (see also Sect. 17). In Sects. 27 and 31 we shall see that a better choice for $V(r)$ consists of replacing the constant s in (26.5) by a monotonically increasing function of r, which is zero at the origin and unity at infinity (HARTREE potential). For such a potential the l-degeneracy is removed and the energy eigenvalue $\varepsilon_{n l}$ of (26.3) increases (at least slightly) with increasing orbital quantum number l (for fixed n).

We return now to the spectrum of eigenstates of the zero-order, two-particle Eq. (26.2). Leaving aside for the moment the question of symmetrization, each wave function (26.4) is characterized by six quantum numbers, the values of n, l and m for each of the two electrons. For fixed values of n_1, l_1, n_2 and l_2, the states with different values of m_1 and m_2 are still degenerate. By taking linear superpositions of these degenerate eigenfunctions one can then form simultaneous eigenstates of the square and the z-component of the operator for the sum of the orbital angular momenta, $\boldsymbol{k} = \boldsymbol{k}_1 + \boldsymbol{k}_2$. The corresponding *total* orbital quantum number can take the values $l = |l_1 - l_2|, \ldots, l_1 + l_2$ and the eigenvalues of k_z are $m_l = -l, -l+1, \ldots, l$. In the zero-order approximation (26.2) these states with different l and m_l values (but same l_1 and l_2) are still degenerate. However, if the interaction $1/r_{12}$ between the two electrons (contained in the perturbation HAMILTONian W) is considered, the l-degeneracy (but not the m_l-degeneracy) is in general removed. The number and complexity of the states to be considered is reduced greatly if we restrict ourselves to states for which one of the two electrons is in the ground state, $n_1 = 1$, $l_1 = m_1 = 0$. In this case, the values of l and m_l for the atom as a whole are simply equal to the corresponding values for the second electron.

For helium the only states of practical importance are in fact those for which at least one electron is in the ground state, for the following reason. One finds that the energy of any state in He, for which both electrons are excited, is higher than the ground state energy of a He^+-ion (H-like ion with $Z = 2$) plus a *free* electron. These states then lie in the continuum and the same holds for all other He-like ions. One can show further that, for such a doubly excited state in He, dissociation into He^+ plus a free electron (AUGER effect) is much more probable than a radiative transition to a bound state of He. Spectral lines involving such doubly excited He-states are very rare in practice and we shall *not* consider them any further[2].

---

[1] For a general central potential the principal quantum number n is defined as $(l+1)$ plus the number of nodes of the radial wave function.

[2] For a discussion of doubly excited states see T. Y. WU, Phys. Rev. **66**, 291 (1944)

For the genuinely discrete states of He, to which we restrict ourselves from now on, one of the two electrons is in the ground state. These states are then characterized by merely *three* quantum numbers, n, l and m of the other electron, just as for a single-electron atom. However, besides the m-degeneracy we have also another type of degeneracy, namely the zero-order energy (26.2) is the same for the two states

$$U_0' = u_{100}(\boldsymbol{r}_1)\, u_{nlm}(\boldsymbol{r}_2), \qquad U_0'' = u_{nlm}(\boldsymbol{r}_1)\, u_{100}(\boldsymbol{r}_2). \tag{26.6}$$

As discussed in Sect. 24, the exact spatial wave function must be either symmetric or antisymmetric to the interchange of spatial coordinates of the two electrons. We shall require the same symmetry properties of our zero-order wave functions and use instead of the two functions (26.6) the two linear combinations

$$U_\pm = \frac{1}{\sqrt{2}}\, [u_{100}(1)\, u_{nlm}(2) \pm u_{nlm}(1)\, u_{100}(2)]. \tag{26.7}$$

In (26.7) the symbols (1) and (2) denote the coordinates of the first and second electron and the plus sign refers to the spatially symmetric *para*-states, the minus to *ortho*-states. We consider u_{100} and u_{nlm} orthogonal and normalized to unity. The factor $1/\sqrt{2}$ then ensures that U_+ and U_- are also normalized.

In our zero order Eq. (26.2), the two states U_+ and U_- are still degenerate of course (for *any* choice of the potential V). We shall see, however, (Sect. 28) that the "perturbation" caused by the electron-electron interaction $1/r_{12}$ removes this degeneracy and the exact energy for a para-state U_+ lies slightly higher than for the corresponding ortho-state U_-.

The ground state of helium, in which *both* electrons are in the $n=1$ state, forms an exception to (26.7). Since the two single-particle wave functions are identical, the wave function U_- for the ortho-state vanishes. We can then *only* have a para-state, whose normalized zero-order wave function is simply given by

$$U_{+g} = u_{100}(1)\, u_{100}(2). \tag{26.8}$$

The absence of an ortho-state for the He-ground state is also in line with the original formulation of the PAULI principle: "Two electrons cannot be in *exactly* the same state." If the spatial quantum numbers are the same, then the two electrons must have "opposite spin". This is the case for the spin wave function S_p, Eq. (24.5), which corresponds to para-states. The symmetric spin functions (24.4) for ortho-states represent "parallel spin" and thus at least one of the three "spatial" quantum numbers of the two electrons must be different.

We can now summarize the qualitative features of the helium spectrum (disregarding all doubly excited states): (1) As for the hydrogen spectrum, the states are characterized by three quantum numbers n, l, m and the energy is degenerate with respect to the value of m. The ground state is non-degenerate as in hydrogen. (2) The l-degeneracy is removed and the energy (for fixed n) decreases with decreasing l. (3) For each value of n, l, m (except for the ground state) we have both an ortho- and a para-state, the energy of the para-state being the higher. Thus for each hydrogen energy level with principal quantum number n we have $2n$ levels in helium ($l=0, 1, \ldots, n-1$ for ortho and para).

We finally give a preview of the quantitative positions of the various energy levels. Consider first states with fairly high values of both n and l. The wave function of the excited electron is then concentrated at appreciably larger radial distances than the inner electron. One then finds that the potential (26.5) with $s=0$ (no screening) describes the motion of the inner electron quite well; and (26.5) with $s=1$ (full screening) describes that of the outer electron. The total energy of the helium-like atom is then given approximately by

$$E_{nlm} \approx -\frac{1}{2} Z^2 - \frac{1}{2} \frac{(Z-1)^2}{n^2}. \tag{26.9}$$

For *large* n and l, then, the energies (except for the additive constant $\frac{1}{2}Z^2$) for He are very close to those for H, the energies for Li^+ close to those for He^+, and so on. For small values of n and l (especially for S-states) the wave functions of

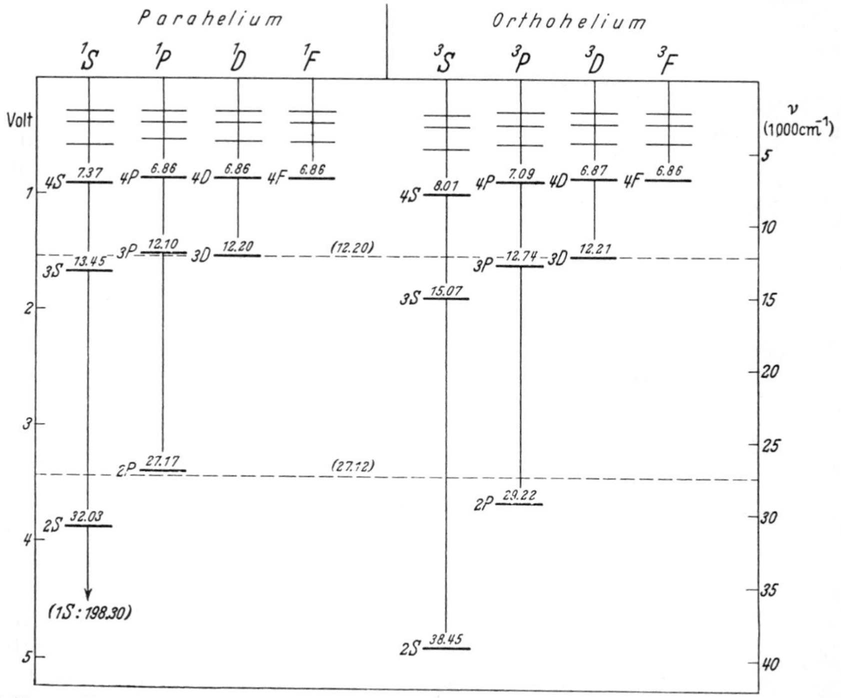

Fig. 15. The experimental energy levels of helium. The scale on the left represents ionization potential in electron volts. The numbers next to the levels are the wave numbers corresponding to the ionization potential, expressed in units of 10^3 cm^{-1}. The dotted lines represent the energy levels of hydrogen (nuclear charge $= Z-1=1$).

the two electrons overlap to an appreciable extent. The deviation of the energy eigenvalue from (26.9) is then quite considerable: it is different for ortho- and para-helium and it depends on the l-value. For He-like ions of larger charge Z (Li^+, Be^{++}, etc.) the situation is qualitatively similar, but the deviations of the correct energies from (26.9) are smaller fractions of (26.9) for larger values of Z.

In Fig. 15 we give the experimental[1] scheme of the energy levels of He.

27. Survey of approximations to be used. Approximation methods have to be used to solve the wave equation (24.1) for He-like atoms. It is convenient to use different approximation methods under different circumstances, depending on whether the quantum number n or l is large or small, whether Z is large or small, whether an accurate energy eigenvalue or a relatively simple wave function is more important, and so on. We give first a brief survey of the various approximation methods to be used in the following sections.

[1] Experimental energy levels in helium and helium-like ions (up to $Z=9$) are given by C. E. Moore, Atomic Energy Levels, Vol. 1, N.B.S. Circular 467, Washington 1949.

Most (but not all) of the approximation methods are based on perturbation theory. More specifically, one chooses the zero-order HAMILTONian H_0 of form similar to (26.1),

$$H_0 = -\tfrac{1}{2}(\Delta_1 + \Delta_2) + V_1(r_1) + V_2(r_2),$$

$$W = -\left(\frac{Z}{r_1} + V_1(r_1)\right) - \left(\frac{Z}{r_2} + V_2(r_2)\right) + \frac{1}{r_{12}}. \tag{27.1}$$

The great advantage of this choice, with V_1 and V_2 central and *single-particle* potentials, lies in the fact that the zero-order wave equation (26.2) is now separable. The zero-order wave functions and energy eigenvalues have already been discussed in Sect. 26 for cases where V_1 and V_2 are chosen identical. For the ground state of He-like atoms (where the two electrons are in identical states) we shall always make this choice. For excited states, however, the wave functions of the two electrons are radically different and it is sometimes convenient to use one potential V_1 for the inner electron and a *different* potential V_2 for the excited electron. In Sect. 25γ we have shown how perturbation theory can be carried up to *first* order even in such cases.

α) Expansion in powers of 1/Z (large Z). The simplest choice of the potentials V_1 and V_2 is obtained by simply omitting the interaction $1/r_{12}$ between the electrons altogether in H_0,

$$V_1(r) = V_2(r) = -\frac{Z}{r}, \qquad W = \frac{1}{r_{12}}. \tag{27.2}$$

The zero-order wave functions are then simply products of hydrogen-like wave functions for charge Z and the zero-order energy is

$$E_0 = -\frac{Z^2}{2} - \frac{Z^2}{2n^2}. \tag{27.3}$$

In principle one could then carry conventional perturbation theory to any desired order, with the electron interaction $1/r_{12}$ as the perturbation HAMILTONian. This method has the great advantage that the successive orders of perturbation theory form a power series in negative powers of Z. If one can carry this series far enough, one then obtains solutions for *all* the He-like ions of different charge Z simultaneously.

Unfortunately the calculations of the orders of perturbation theory after the first order get harder very rapidly. Even the rigorous calculation of the second order is extremely tedious. Only for the ground state have the first few terms in this series been calculated by HYLLERAAS[1], using the combined perturbation-variation method outlined in Sect. 25β. This method gives excellent results for the ground state of two-electıon ions of *large* Z and will be discussed in Sect. 32. It is not suitable for low Z, such as for He itself.

β) Constant screening factor (ground state). The next simplest choice of the potentials for the ground state is to take V_1 and V_2 equal and of the form of (26.5). Unlike the choice (27.2), the use of the screening constant s takes some account of the COULOMB repulsion between the two electrons. In fact one may choose the screening constant s such that the *first* order perturbation energy vanishes. This value turns out to be (see Sect. 32β) $s = \frac{5}{16}$ for the ground state, for any value of Z. The ground-state energy is then, to zero and first order [see Eq. (26.5)],

$$E_0 + E_1 = E_0 = -(Z - \tfrac{5}{16})^2. \tag{27.4}$$

[1] E. HYLLERAAS: Z. Physik **65**, 209 (1930).

The zero-order wave function is then the product of two hydrogen-like ground state wave functions of nuclear charge $(Z - \frac{5}{16})$. This very simple wave function is convenient if very high accuracy is not desired and is also a useful approximation for the two K-shell (1 s) electrons in complex atoms. This approximation is nevertheless very crude. Particularly in the ground state do the wave functions of the two electrons interpenetrate considerably. The "effective screening" thus varies appreciably as a function of radial distance and polarization is also quite important.

γ) Heisenberg's choice (excited states). If the electron 1 is in the ground state and electron 2 in a highly excited state, then most of the charge cloud of electron 1 lies appreciably closer to the nucleus than the bulk of the charge cloud of electron 2. This is the case especially when electron 2 has a large value of l (as well as n), since its wave function is then extremely small at small radial distances. Since $r_1 \ll r_2$ for the most important part of the wave function, a good approximation to the inter-electron interaction $1/r_{12}$ should be the simple function $1/r_2$. We are thus led to the *unsymmetric* choice of the potentials

$$V_1(r_1) = -\frac{Z}{r_1}, \quad V_2(r_2) = -\frac{Z-1}{r_2}, \quad W = \frac{1}{r_{12}} - \frac{1}{r_2}. \tag{27.5}$$

In other words, we consider the screening of the inner on the outer electron as "complete" (screening constant $s=1$) and neglect screening of the outer on the inner one. The zero-order wave function is again hydrogen-like for each of the two electrons, but with a *different* charge. The zero order energy is then given by (26.9).

To obtain the small, but finite, dependence of energy on l and on the symmetry of the wave function (ortho *vs.* para) we have to proceed at least to first order perturbation theory. This will be discussed in Sect. 28. As discussed in Sect. 25 γ, the lack of symmetry between V_1 and V_2 in (27.5) makes an entirely systematic treatment of perturbation theory impossible. To overcome this formal difficulty, Heisenberg[1] made the following *symmetric* choice of potentials

$$V_1(r) = V_2(r) = \begin{cases} -\dfrac{Z-1}{r} & \text{if } r > r_0, \\ -\dfrac{Z}{r} + \dfrac{1}{r_0} & \text{if } r < r_0. \end{cases} \tag{27.6}$$

r_0 is chosen to lie between the "characteristic radii" of the wave functions of the inner and outer electron. The rigorous zero-order eigenfunctions of (27.6) are very complicated, but a method, based on (27.5), can be used to justify the less systematic treatment of our Sect. 28.

It is practically impossible to carry out an *exact* second order perturbation calculation based on (27.5) or (27.6). The effect of "polarization" by the outer on the inner electron can, nevertheless be obtained in a semi-quantitative manner. This will be discussed in Sect. 29. For S-states ($l=0$ for the outer electron) the interpenetration of the two electron clouds is fairly large and Heisenberg's method does not give very satisfactory results.

δ) Hartree's[2] *method* is the most far-reaching of the attempts to approximate the true potential by means of the unperturbed potential. The potential energy acting on the first electron is taken to be the Coulomb field of the nucleus plus

[1] W. Heisenberg: Z. Physik **39**, 499 (1927).
[2] D. R. Hartree: Proc. Cambridge Phil. Soc. **26**, 89 (1928).

the potential of the charge distribution of the second electron, viz.,

$$V_1(r_1) = -\frac{Z_1}{r_1} + \int d\tau_2 u_2^2(2) \cdot \frac{1}{r_{12}}. \tag{27.7}$$

The true potential energy is thus averaged over all possible positions of the second electron. The potential energy on the second electron $V_2(r_2)$ is obtained in the same way.

HARTREE's method contrasts with the procedures described above in this sense: The eigenfunctions in zeroth, and the eigenvalues in first, approximation evidently represent very good approximations. On the other hand, a systematic perturbation treatment cannot be carried out because the potentials V_1 and V_2 differ, and consequently the eigenfunctions U do not form an orthogonal system. Thus, unlike the procedure of expanding in powers of $1/Z$, HARTREE's method does not enable one to obtain, even in principle, the exact eigenvalue by continuing the procedure to higher approximations. From the practical viewpoint HARTREE's method has the disadvantage of requiring rather lengthy numerical integrations; furthermore, eigenfunctions and potentials satisfying (26.3) and (27.7) can be obtained only through a procedure of successive approximations.

The energy of the ground state is given much more accurately by the variation method than by HARTREE's method. But for many applications it is useful to have as good a wave function as possible, which is still of the form of a product of two single-particle wave functions. HARTREE's method gives the best wave function of this type and will be discussed in Sect. 31.

ε) FOCK's method[1]. This method is similar to HARTREE's, but uses fully symmetrized wave functions of product form. FOCK's method thus takes exchange effects into account, but the numerical calculations are considerably more involved than even for HARTREE's method. This method will be discussed only for highly excited S-states (Sect. 30), where HEISENBERG's method is too crude and exchange effects are important.

ζ) The variation method[2] (cf. Sects. 32 through 34). The most exact results for eigenvalues and eigenfunctions may be obtained by means of RITZ's variation method. A plausible form for the eigenfunction is set up from simple physical considerations, in which several numerical constants such as screening constants, coefficients in power series expansions, etc., are left arbitrary. These parameters are then determined by the condition that SCHRÖDINGER's variational integral, i.e., the total energy, be a minimum. SCHRÖDINGER's variational problem is thus reduced to an ordinary minimum problem. By including a sufficient number of arbitrary constants in the general form of the eigenfunction, to be determined by the minimizing condition, one can approximate the eigenfunction and eigenvalue as closely as one pleases. An adroit choice of the form of the eigenfunction will make the procedure converge rapidly. In this connection a choice of suitable independent variables is particularly important.

The procedure, unfortunately, is applicable only to low levels because the eigenfunction of an excited state must always be orthogonal to the eigenfunctions of all lower levels. This imposes a large number of subsidiary conditions on the excited state eigenfunctions which make the variational procedure unwieldy and eventually useless (cf. Sect. 35).

---

[1] V. FOCK: Z. Physik **61**, 126 (1930).

[2] E.g., E. A. HYLLERAAS: Z. Physik **54**, 347 (1929). — G. KELLNER: Z. Physik **44**, 91 (1927).

28. First order HEISENBERG's method (excited states). We discuss now HEISENBERG's method in detail, which is especially suitable if one of the two electrons is in a fairly highly excited state of non-zero angular momentum. We now apply the method, discussed at the end of Sect. 25γ, to the choice of potentials of (27.5). In the notation of (25.14) we have

$$\left.\begin{aligned} H_{0a} &= -\frac{1}{2}(\Delta_1 + \Delta_2) - \frac{Z}{r_1} - \frac{Z-1}{r_2}, \\ W_a &\equiv \lambda H_{1a} = \frac{1}{r_{12}} - \frac{1}{r_2}. \end{aligned}\right\} \tag{28.1}$$

Let u_1 denote the normalized ground state wave function for a hydrogen-like atom of charge Z, u_{nlm} the normalized hydrogen-like wave function for an excited state with charge $(Z-1)$. Then $u_1(1)\, u_{nlm}(2)$ is an eigenstate of the zero-order HAMILTONian H_{0a} with energy eigenvalue E_0 given by (26.9). Define H_{0b} and W_b as in (28.1), but with the roles of r_1 and r_2 interchanged. Then $u_{nlm}(1)\, u_1(2)$ is an eigenstate of H_{0b} with the *same* eigenvalue E_0.

We now take as our zero-order wave functions, following (26.7),

$$U_\pm(1,2) = \frac{1}{\sqrt{2}}\left[u_1(1)\, u_{nlm}(2) \pm u_{nlm}(1)\, u_1(2)\right], \tag{28.2}$$

where the plus sign refers to para-states, the minus sign to ortho-states[1]. We now apply Eq. (25.18) for E_1, the first order perturbation energy. Putting the perturbation parameter λ equal to unity, we have

$$E_1 = \frac{1}{\sqrt{2}}\int d\tau_1\, d\tau_2\, U_\pm^* \left[\left(\frac{1}{r_{12}} - \frac{1}{r_2}\right) u_1(1)\, u_{nlm}(2) \pm \left(\frac{1}{r_{12}} - \frac{1}{r_1}\right) u_{nlm}(1)\, u_1(2)\right], \tag{28.3}$$

where $d\tau_1$, $d\tau_2$ are the volume elements for the first and second electron, respectively. Consider now the integrals involving $1/r_2$. In keeping with the philosophy of the method of Sect. 25β we *assume*[2] that u_1 and u_{nlm} are orthogonal to zero-order. We thus make the replacement

$$\int d\tau_1\, u_1(1)\, u_{nlm}^*(1) \int d\tau_2\, u_{nlm}^*(2)\, u_1(2) = 0$$

with a similar equation for some terms involving $1/r_1$. (28.3) then reduces to

$$E_1 = \frac{1}{2}\int d\tau_1\, d\tau_2 \left[2\,|U_\pm|^2 \frac{1}{r_{12}} - |u_1(1)|^2\, |u_{nlm}(2)|^2 \frac{1}{r_2} - |u_{nlm}(1)|^2 |u_1(2)|^2 \frac{1}{r_1}\right]. \tag{28.4}$$

We next expand out the expression $|U_\pm|^2$ and collect integrals which are identical. Adding E_1 to the zero-order energy E_0, Eq. (26.9), we get finally for the total energy, up to and including first order,

$$E_{(1)} \equiv E_0 + E_1 = -\frac{1}{2} Z^2 - \frac{1}{2}\frac{(Z-1)^2}{n^2} + J \pm K, \tag{28.5}$$

where

$$J = \int d\tau_1\, d\tau_2 \left(\frac{1}{r_{12}} - \frac{1}{r_2}\right) u_1^2(1)\, |u_{nlm}(2)|^2, \tag{28.6}$$

$$K = \int d\tau_1\, d\tau_2\, u_1(1)\, u_{nlm}^*(1) \frac{1}{r_{12}} u_1(2)\, u_{nlm}(2). \tag{28.7}$$

---

[1] The choice of the linear combinations U_+ and U_- is not only *convenient* for the consideration of the PAULI principle, etc., but is *necessary* from the point of view of perturbation theory. This choice, and no other, ensures that the perturbation HAMILTONian W has zero matrix element $\langle U_\pm^* W U_\mp \rangle$ between these two degenerate zero-order eigenstates.

[2] For the special case of $l=0$ these two wave functions are not exactly orthogonal, since they correspond to different nuclear charges. A more systematic derivation of (28.4) will be found in ref. [*10*], Sect. 14, based on our Eq. (27.6).

α) Physical meaning of the integrals. J and K have a very simple physical meaning: J is the COULOMB interaction between the charge distributions of the two electrons plus the interaction between the outer electron and one unit of positive charge concentrated at the nucleus.

The latter interaction appears in the perturbation theory because in zeroth approximation we regarded the outer electron to be under the influence of an effective nuclear charge $Z-1$ rather than the actual nuclear charge Z. Since the charge cloud of the inner electron lies almost entirely inside that of the outer electron, the COULOMB effect on the outer electron is almost the same as if the cloud of the inner electron were concentrated at the nucleus. Hence, the two COULOMB interactions of which J is composed almost cancel each other. This is a welcome indication of the usefulness of our unperturbed potential and zeroth order eigenfunctions. The COULOMB integral J does not vanish altogether, only because a small fraction of the charge cloud of the inner electron is farther from the nucleus than the charge cloud of the outer electron. J has a small negative value because the unscreened remainder of the nuclear charge exercises an attractive force on the outer electron.

K is the so-called exchange integral. It is a measure of the frequency with which the two electrons exchange their quantum states. To make this clear, let us assume that we *know*[1] that at time $t=0$ electron 1 is in the ground state and electron 2 is in an excited state. We may, for example, assume that electron 2 has just been bound to a He^+ ion. Then the wave function at $t=0$ would be

$$\Psi(0) = u_1(1)\, u_n(2) = \frac{1}{\sqrt{2}}\,(U_+ + U_-)\,.$$

Including the time factors in the eigenfunctions we obtain as the wave function at time t:

$$\left.\begin{aligned}\Psi(t) &= \frac{1}{\sqrt{2}}\left(\Psi_+(t) + \Psi_-(t)\right) = \frac{1}{\sqrt{2}}\left(U_+\, e^{-i(E+K)t} + U_-\, e^{-i(E-K)t}\right)\\ &= e^{-iEt}\cdot\left[u_1(1)\, u_n(2)\cos Kt - i\, u_n(1)\, u_1(2)\sin Kt\right]\end{aligned}\right\} \qquad (28.8)$$

[E is the arithmetic mean between the energies of ortho and para state as given by (28.5)]. When the time interval $\pi/2K$ has elapsed, the two electrons have interchanged their respective roles; electron 1 is now excited and electron 2 is in the ground state. At time π/K they are back in their original orbits. Time is, of course, measured in the atomic unit ($1/4\pi$ Ry) (Ry = RYDBERG frequency). In c.g.s. units the period of the exchange is $\frac{\pi}{K}\cdot\frac{1}{4\pi\,\mathrm{Ry}} = \frac{1}{4K\,\mathrm{Ry}} = \frac{0.75\times 10^{-16}\,\mathrm{sec}}{K}$.
The more the eigenfunctions of the two electrons overlap (i.e., the smaller the principal and orbital quantum numbers of the outer electron are), the larger will be K and the more frequently will the electron exchange take place. If, for example, the outer electron is in the $2p$ state then (Sect. 28γ) $K=0.00382$ and an exchange (there and back) takes 10^{-14} sec. If, on the other hand, the outer electron has quantum numbers $n=10$, $l=9$, an exchange of electrons takes place only once every 0.5×10^{11} sec $=1600$ years, although the "diameter" of the outer electron orbit amounts to only 100 atomic units (0.5×10^{-6} cm).

The separation between the ortho and the corresponding para term, when measured in units of frequency, is precisely equal to the frequency of the electron exchange. The para term lies always somewhat higher then the ortho term

[1] This assumption violates the principle of the indistinguishability of electrons and the following argument should not be taken too seriously.

because K, being the potential due to the effect of the charge distribution $u_1 u_{nlm}$ on itself, is always positive.

β) Evaluation of the direct COULOMB *interaction integral.* We would like to evaluate the integrals J and K and shall do so, considering J first. Let us recall that the eigenfunction u_{nlm} is the product of a radially dependent function and a spherical harmonic:

$$u_{nlm} = R_{nl}(r)\, Y_{lm}(\vartheta, \varphi).$$

Substituting this into (28.6) we obtain

$$J = \int_0^\infty \int_0^\infty r_1^2\, dr_1\, r_2^2\, dr_2\, R_{10}^2(r_1)\, R_{nl}^2(r_2)\, J(r_1 r_2), \tag{28.9}$$

where

$$J(r_1 r_2) = \int_0^\pi \sin\vartheta_1\, d\vartheta_1 \int_0^{2\pi} d\varphi_1 \int_0^\pi \sin\vartheta_2\, d\vartheta_2 \int_0^{2\pi} d\varphi_2 \left(\frac{1}{r_{12}} - \frac{1}{r_2}\right) Y_{00}^2(\vartheta_1, \varphi_1)\, |Y_{lm}(\vartheta_2, \varphi_2)|^2. \tag{28.10}$$

The integrations over angles in $J(r_1 r_2)$ can easily be carried out by expanding $1/r_{12}$ in terms of spherical harmonics. Paying attention to the normalization of the spherical harmonics, one obtains

$$J(r_1 r_2) = \begin{Bmatrix} 1/r_1 - 1/r_2, & \text{if } r_1 > r_2, \\ 0, & \text{if } r_1 < r_2. \end{Bmatrix} \tag{28.11}$$

$u_{10}(r_1)$ is the eigenfunction of the ground state of an atom having nuclear charge Z and a single electron [cf. Eq. (3.18)], hence,

$$R_{10}(r) = 2 Z^{\frac{3}{2}} e^{-Zr}, \tag{28.12}$$

so that

$$\left.\begin{aligned} \int_0^\infty R_{10}^2(r_1)\, J(r_1 r_2)\, r_1^2\, dr_1 &= \int_{r_2}^\infty \left(\frac{1}{r_1} - \frac{1}{r_2}\right) r_1^2\, dr_1 \cdot 4 Z^3 e^{-2Zr_1} \\ &= -\left(Z + \frac{1}{r_2}\right) e^{-2Zr_2}. \end{aligned}\right\} \tag{28.13}$$

The eigenfunction of the excited electron $R_{nl}(r_2)$, as we have seen, is also a hydrogenic eigenfunction, but the nuclear charge must be taken to be $Z-1$. Accordingly, from (3.16) we obtain:

$$\left.\begin{aligned} R_{nl}(r_2) &= \frac{(n-l-1)!^{\frac{1}{2}}}{(n+l)!^{\frac{3}{2}}\,(2n)^{\frac{1}{2}}} \cdot \left[\frac{2(Z-1)}{n}\right]^{\frac{3}{2}} \varrho^l e^{-\frac{1}{2}\varrho} L_{n+l}^{2l+1}(\varrho), \\ \varrho &= \frac{2(Z-1)}{n} r_2. \end{aligned}\right\} \tag{28.14}$$

Substituting (28.13) and (28.14) into (28.9) and replacing the integration variable r_2 by ϱ throughout, we obtain

$$J = -\frac{(n-l-1)!}{(n+l)!^3\, 2n} \cdot Z \cdot \int_0^\infty e^{-\varrho - \frac{Zn}{Z-1}\varrho}\, \varrho^{2l+2} \left(L_{n+l}^{2l+1}(\varrho)\right)^2 \left[1 + \frac{2(Z-1)}{nZ\varrho}\right] d\varrho. \tag{28.15}$$

The integration over ϱ is straightforward for the case $n = l+1$ (corresponding to the circular orbits of BOHR's theory) because the LAGUERRE function reduces to a constant, viz.,

$$L_{2l+1}^{2l+1} = -(2l+1)!,$$

as may be seen by inspection of (3.7). The COULOMB integral (28.15) can be carried out by elementary means and amounts to

$$J = -Z \cdot \frac{(Z-1)^{2n+1}}{[Z(n+1)-1]^{2n+1}} \left[1 + \frac{Z(n+1)-1}{Z n^2}\right]. \tag{28.16}$$

This formula made its first appearance in HEISENBERG's classic work on the helium spectrum[1]. The integration of (28.15) also presents no particular difficulty[2] for $n = l+2$ for which the LAGUERRE function consists of two terms. For larger n (and fixed l) however, the evaluation of, and the final formula for, J become rather complicated. For very large n, on the other hand, it is possible to obtain a relatively simple asymptotic formula which may be derived by making use of the generating function for the associated LAGUERRE function which is given at the end of Sect. 3. One obtains[3]

$$\left.\begin{aligned} J = -\frac{1}{n^3} \frac{(Z-1)^{2l+3}}{Z^{2l+2}} e^{-2\frac{Z-1}{Z}} \sum_{k=0}^{\infty} \left(\frac{Z-1}{Z}\right)^{2k} \times \\ \times \frac{1}{k!\,(2l+k+1)!} \left[1 + \frac{2l+k+2}{2}\left(1 - \frac{Z-1}{Z\cdot(2l+k+2)}\right)^2\right]. \end{aligned}\right\} \tag{28.17}$$

The summation over k introduces no complications because the sum converges extremely rapidly. The following conclusions may be drawn from (28.17) without further calculations:

1. For large principal quantum number, the COULOMB integral J is inversely proportional to $1/n^3$ and does not otherwise depend on n. It is therefore possible to sum up the unperturbed energy of the outer electron in the field of the nuclear charge $Z-1$ and the COULOMB energy J in a formula of the RYDBERG type:

$$-\frac{(Z-1)^2}{2n^2} + J = -\frac{(Z-1)^2}{2(n+\delta_C)^2}. \tag{28.18}$$

The RYDBERG correction δ_c is given by

$$\delta_c = \frac{n^3 J}{(Z-1)^2} = \frac{1}{Z} \cdot \left(\frac{Z-1}{Z}\right)^{2l+1} e^{-2\frac{Z-1}{Z}} \cdot \sum_k \ldots, \tag{28.19}$$

(28.19) is the most convenient expression for the deviation of the helium spectrum from the hydrogen spectrum since it is (for large n) independent of the principal quantum number n[4]. (The index c stands for COULOMB interaction).

2. The RYDBERG correction δ_c falls off rapidly with increasing orbital quantum number on account of both the factor $\left(\frac{Z-1}{Z}\right)^{2l+1}$ and the denominators $(2l+1+k)!$. This comes about in this way: J is the larger, the more frequently electron 2 penetrates the charge cloud of the inner electron 1. After all, according to (28.11), only the regions $r_1 > r_2$ contribute to J (see also the above discussion about the meaning of the COULOMB integral). Electrons with small orbital quantum number (moving in eccentric BOHR orbits) are more likely to penetrate than those with large l (the probability of finding an electron in the neighborhood of the nucleus is proportional to r^{2l}).

---

[1] W. HEISENBERG: Z. Physik **39**, 499 (1926).

[2] Cf. W. HEISENBERG: loc. cit. Eq. (16).

[3] E. HYLLERAAS: Z. Physik **66**, 453 (1930).

[4] For small n, δ_c, defined by (28.18) and computed by evaluating the appropriate J, e.g. (28.16), naturally differs somewhat from its value for large n. The relative difference is so very small however (cf. Table 4), that the value of δ_c for any n may be found very accurately by interpolating between its values at three values of n, such as $n = l+1, l+2, \infty$.

3. The dependence of the RYDBERG correction δ_c on the nuclear charge Z comes about from the presence of two mutually opposing effects. On the one hand, there is the factor $1/Z$ in (28.19) which has its origin in that δ_c essentially represents the ratio of the interaction J between the two electrons to the interaction between the outer electron and the nucleus (unperturbed energy of the outer electron). On the other hand, there is the factor $\left(\frac{Z-1}{Z}\right)^{2l+1} \exp\left(-2\frac{Z-1}{Z}\right)$ which increases rapidly with increasing Z. Its presence is consistent with the fact that the ratio between the radii of inner and outer electronic orbits is proportional to $Z/Z-1$. The larger Z is, the more contracted is the orbit of the outer electron relative to that of the inner electron, and, thus, the more frequently does the outer electron penetrate the K shell (cf. Sect. 2). For small nuclear charge this increase in $|\delta_c|$ with increasing Z outweighs the decrease due to $1/Z$ (cf. Table 4, He and Li^+).

γ) Evaluation of the exchange integral. The integral over the angles

$$K(r_1 r_2) = \iiiint \sin\vartheta_1\, d\vartheta_1\, d\varphi_1 \sin\vartheta_2\, d\vartheta_2\, d\varphi_2\, Y_{00}(\vartheta_1\varphi_1)\, Y_{lm}^*(\vartheta_1\varphi_1)\, Y_{00}(\vartheta_2\varphi_2)\, Y_{lm}(\vartheta_2\varphi_2)\, \frac{1}{r_{12}}$$

is most easily carried out by expanding $1/r_{12}$ again in terms of spherical harmonics. The result is

$$K(r_1 r_2) = \frac{1}{2l+1}\frac{r_1^l}{r_2^{l+1}}, \quad \text{if} \quad r_1 < r_2; \qquad \frac{1}{2l+1}\frac{r_2^l}{r_1^{l+1}}, \quad \text{if} \quad r_1 > r_2. \tag{28.20}$$

Substituting this into (28.7) gives

$$K = \frac{2}{2l+1}\int_0^\infty r_2^{l+2}\, dr_2\, R_{10}(r_2)\, R_{nl}(r_2) \int_{r_2}^\infty r_1^{-l+1}\, dr_1\, R_{10}(r_1)\, R_{nl}(r_1). \tag{28.21}$$

The factor of 2 comes from indicating an integration over the region $r_1 > r_2$ only, the region $r_1 < r_2$ contributes an exactly equal amount. Substituting the radial eigenfunctions (28.12) and (28.14) we obtain, for $n = l+1$ [1],

$$K = \frac{4Z^3(Z-1)^{2n+1}\, n^2}{[Z(n+1)-1]^{2n+3}}\, \frac{2n+3}{2n-1}. \tag{28.22}$$

We shall at once write down the RYDBERG correction for large n which must be applied to the principal quantum number of the outer electron because of electron exchange, viz.,

$$\left.\begin{aligned} \delta_A &= \frac{n^3}{(Z-1)^2} K \\ &= \frac{2}{Z(2l+1)}\left(\frac{Z-1}{Z}\right)^{2l+1} e^{-2\frac{Z-1}{Z}} \sum_{k=0}^\infty \frac{2l+k+2}{k!\,(2l+k+1)!}\left(\frac{Z-1}{Z}\right)^{2k} \Phi_{2l+k+2}\left(\frac{Z-1}{Z}\right) \end{aligned}\right\} \tag{28.23}$$

where the index A stands for exchange and

$$\begin{aligned} \Phi_\lambda(x) = {} & 2\left(1-\frac{x}{\lambda}\right)\left[1-\frac{x}{\lambda}+4x\left(2-\frac{1}{\lambda}\right)F(1,\lambda+1,-x) - 8xF(1,\lambda,-x)\right] + \\ & + (\lambda+1)\left(1-2\frac{x}{\lambda}+\frac{x^2}{\lambda(\lambda+1)}\right)\left[1+4\frac{x}{\lambda}-\frac{x^2}{\lambda(\lambda+1)}-8\frac{x}{\lambda}F(1,\lambda+1,-x)\right]. \end{aligned}$$

---

[1] Cf. W. HEISENBERG: loc. cit. There may be found the somewhat more complicated formula for $n = l+2$ (Eq. 22).

F is the confluent hypergeometric function

$$F(1, \lambda, -x) = \sum_{\varrho=0}^{\infty} \frac{(-x)^\varrho}{\lambda(\lambda+1)\cdots(\lambda+\varrho-1)} \,. \tag{28.24}$$

In spite of its complicated appearance, formula (28.23) is easily managed since all series (both over ϱ and k) converge very rapidly. They are considerably simpler than those of HYLLERAAS[1].

The qualitative behavior of the RYDBERG correction δ_A is evidently the same as that of $\delta_c \cdot \delta_A$ is constant for large n (otherwise there would be no sense to introducing it); changes very little when passing to small n (with l fixed); falls off rapidly with increasing l and contains two factors which are respectively increasing and decreasing functions of Z. The qualitative justification for this is also quite analogous to that for the COULOMB integral. It is true that K, unlike J, does not depend on the penetration of the charge cloud of the inner electron by the outer electron, but it does depend on the extent of overlap of the two charge clouds and this amounts to the same thing as far as the l and Z dependences are concerned.

δ) Result of the first approximation. The total energy in first approximation of the outer electron of an atom having two electrons thus amounts to [cf. Eq. (28.5)]

$$E_1 + \frac{1}{2} Z^2 = -\frac{1}{2} \frac{(Z-1)^2}{(n+\delta_c \pm \delta_A)^2} \,. \tag{28.25}$$

The positive sign in front of δ_A belongs to parahelium, the negative sign to orthohelium. Table 4 shows a comparison between observed and calculated values of the RYDBERG correction $\delta_c \pm \delta_A$ of the helium terms. As empirical value of δ_c we must, of course, take the arithmetic mean between the RYDBERG corrections of ortho and parahelium, as δ_A half the difference of the two RYDBERG corrections[2].

Table 4. RYDBERG *corrections for He and Li*$^+$.

δ_0, δ_P are observed ortho and para corrections; δ_c and δ_π are the theoretical first order and polarization COULOMB corrections and δ_A the exchange correction.

	$-\delta_c$	$-(\delta_c+\delta_\pi)$	$-\frac{1}{2}(\delta_0+\delta_P)$ Observed	δ_A	$-\frac{1}{2}(\delta_0-\delta_P)$ Observed
		He			
∞S	0.168	0.216	0.218	0.376	0.078
$2P$	0.0083	0.0232	0.0265	0.0305 (0.0339)	0.0358
$3P$	0.009	0.0242	0.0273	0.0332	0.0384
∞P	0.0104	0.0248	0.027_9	0.0351	0.039_8
$3D$	0.00010	0.00203	0.00198	0.00034 (0.00029)	0.00020
∞D	0.00018	0.00262	0.0025_2	0.00066	0.0003_5
$4F$	$< 10^{-5}$	0.00008	0.00013	$< 10^{-5}$	0.00008
		Li$^+$			
∞S	0.112	0.127	0.127	0.145	0.052
$2P$	0.009	0.017	0.020	0.030	0.033
∞P	0.011	0.019	0.021	0.033	0.034
$3D$	0.0002	0.0016	0.0015	0.0006	0.0005

[1] E. A. HYLLERAAS: Z. Physik **66**, 453 (1930).

[2] The experimental results are taken from C. E. MOORE, Atomic Energy Levels, Vol. I, NBS Circular No. 467. 1949.

As the Table 4 shows, both the experimental and theoretical RYDBERG corrections increase very slowly with increasing principal quantum n and decrease very rapidly with increasing orbital quantum number l. For $l \neq 0$ the theoretical exchange correction δ_A is at least in semi-quantitative agreement[1] with the ortho-para separation, $\frac{1}{2}(\delta_0 - \delta_P)$. The theoretical COULOMB correction, δ_c, on the other hand, is much too small compared with the experimental $\frac{1}{2}(\delta_0 + \delta_P)$, especially for the larger values of l. The agreement with $\frac{1}{2}(\delta_0 + \delta_P)$ is much improved if δ_π, a correction due to polarization of the inner electron by the outer, is added to δ_c. A method for calculating δ_π is outlined in Sect. 29. For S-states the present method gives unsatisfactory results for δ_A. The S-states with large n are discussed in Sect. 30, those with $n=2$ in Sect. 35.

29. Polarization for excited states. In Sect. 28 we merely treated HEISENBERG's choice of potential (28.1) in first order perturbation theory. This consisted of taking the expectation value of the HAMILTONian over the zero-order wave function, which consists of the product of two independent single-particle wave functions. In reality, the correct He wave functions cannot be exactly of this simple form, since the presence of one electron at a particular position affects the wave function of the other. The COULOMB repulsion due to one electron polarizes the charge distribution of the other such as to increase their mutual separation. Conventional second order perturbation theory would take account of the perturbation of the zero-order wave function, and hence of polarization. A rigorous second-order treatment is, however, much too tedious. We shall merely outline[2] a cruder but relatively simple approximation method, applicable to excited states.

We shall only evaluate the effect of polarization on the COULOMB correction δ_c, *not* its effect on the exchange term, δ_A. For this purpose it is sufficient to take an *unsymmetrized* wave function. We consider electron 1 to be in the ground state, electron 2 in the excited state. The zero-order energy is still given by (26.9), but the zero-order wave function U_0 and first-order energy E_1 (putting $\lambda = 1$ again) by

$$U_0 = u_1(1)\, u_{nlm}(2), \qquad E_1 = \int d\tau_1\, d\tau_2\, W\, |U_0|^2 = J. \tag{29.1}$$

In (29.1) the perturbation potential W is given by (28.1),

$$W(\boldsymbol{r}_1, \boldsymbol{r}_2) = \frac{1}{r_{12}} - \frac{1}{r_2}, \tag{29.2}$$

and J by (28.6). The first order perturbation U_1 to the wave function is then determined by the differential Eq. (25.8), which takes the form

$$\left[\frac{1}{2}(\Delta_1 + \Delta_2) + \frac{Z}{r_1} + \frac{Z-1}{r_2} - \frac{Z^2}{2} - \frac{(Z-1)^2}{2n^2}\right] U_1 = (W - J)\, U_0. \tag{29.3}$$

Once U_1 has been determined, the second order perturbation E_2 to the energy is then given by the integral (25.11),

$$E_2 = \int d\tau_1\, d\tau_2\, W(\boldsymbol{r}_1, \boldsymbol{r}_2)\, U_0\, U_1. \tag{29.4}$$

We discuss only an approximate method for solving (29.3). We make use of the fact that the "average velocity" of the outer electron 2 is small compared with that of the inner electron 1. This follows from the fact that for a state of larger principal quantum number (electron 2) the binding energy and hence (from the virial theorem) the average *kinetic energy* is smaller than for $n=1$.

[1] The values in parentheses in the δ_A-column of Table 4 (for $2P$ and $3D$) are discussed at the end of Sect. 29.

[2] A detailed account of this method will be found in ref. [*10*], Sect. 15.

We can then apply an approximation method, somewhat equivalent to the FRANCK CONDON principle used in the treatment of molecules. Physically speaking, we consider the slow-moving electron 2 as "temporarily at rest" at some position $\boldsymbol{r}_2$. The inner electron 1 then "sees", in addition to the zero order potential, the potential W, Eq. (29.2), for this *fixed* value of $\boldsymbol{r}_2$. For each value of $\boldsymbol{r}_2$ we then have a polarized wave function for the inner electron, somewhat like in the quadratic STARK effect (Sect. 52). The outer electron 2 at position $\boldsymbol{r}_2$, on the other hand, "sees" only the average charge distribution of the fast-moving inner electron 1. Electron 2 then "sees", in addition to the zero order potentials only an extra potential $\varepsilon_1(\boldsymbol{r}_2)+\varepsilon_2(\boldsymbol{r}_2)$, due to the charge cloud of the inner electron 1, but *integrated* over the coordinates of electron 1. The potential ε_1 is due to the zero order, unpolarized, distribution of electron 1 and simply leads to the first order energy $E_1=J$. The potential ε_2 is due to the polarization of electron 1. ε_1 and ε_2 are fairly small and do not affect the wave function of the outer electron greatly. The expectation value of ε_2, averaged over the unperturbed wave function of electron 2, should then give the desired approximation for the effect of polarization on the total energy.

Mathematically speaking, we write the first order wave function in the form

$$U_1 = u_{\boldsymbol{r}_2}(\boldsymbol{r}_1)\, u_{n l m}(\boldsymbol{r}_2), \tag{29.5}$$

where $u_{\boldsymbol{r}_2}$ is an (as yet arbitrary) function of $\boldsymbol{r}_1$, which also depends on $\boldsymbol{r}_2$, and u_{nlm} is the unperturbed wave function of the outer electron. By substituting (29.5) into (29.3), we can still get an exact equation for $u_{\boldsymbol{r}_2}(\boldsymbol{r}_1)$. Our physical approximation consists of dropping all derivatives with respect to $\boldsymbol{r}_2$ in this equation. In this case this six-dimensional equation reduces to an infinite uncoupled set of three-dimensional equations, one for each value of $\boldsymbol{r}_2$,

$$\left(\frac{1}{2}\Delta_1+\frac{Z}{r_1}-\frac{Z^2}{2}\right) u_{\boldsymbol{r}_2}(\boldsymbol{r}_1) = \left(\frac{1}{r_{12}}-\frac{1}{r_2}-J\right) u_{100}(\boldsymbol{r}_1), \tag{29.6}$$

where u_{100} is the zero order wave function for electron 1. After solving (29.6) for $u_{\boldsymbol{r}_2}$, we then get an approximation for the second order energy E_2 from (29.4),

$$E_2 = \int d\tau_2 |u_{nlm}(2)|^2 \varepsilon_2(\boldsymbol{r}_2), \tag{29.7}$$

where

$$\varepsilon_2(\boldsymbol{r}_2) = \int d\tau_1\, u_{\boldsymbol{r}_2}(\boldsymbol{r}_1)\left(\frac{1}{r_{12}}-\frac{1}{r_2}\right) u_{100}(r_1). \tag{29.8}$$

We approximate the Eq. (29.6) further before solving it. The term involving J is fairly small and would give an even smaller contribution to E_2 and we omit it. Next we expand $\left(\frac{1}{r_{12}}-\frac{1}{r_2}\right)$ in spherical harmonics and keep only the first nonzero term,

$$\frac{1}{r_{12}}-\frac{1}{r_2}=\frac{1}{r_1}-\frac{1}{r_<}+\frac{r_<}{r_>^2}\cos\vartheta_{12}+\cdots,$$

where ϑ_{12} is the angle between $\boldsymbol{r}_1$ and $\boldsymbol{r}_2$, $r_<$ and $r_>$ are the smaller and larger, respectively, of r_1 and r_2. Since r_2 is "mostly" much larger than r_1, the higher terms are not very important and, since $\frac{1}{r_1}-\frac{1}{r_<}$ is "mostly" zero, we drop this term also. (29.6) then reduces to the simpler equation

$$\left.\begin{aligned} u_{\boldsymbol{r}_2}(\boldsymbol{r}_1) &\equiv w_{\boldsymbol{r}_2}(r_1)\cos\vartheta_{12}, \\ \left(\frac{d^2}{dr_1^2}+\frac{2}{r_1}\frac{d}{dr_1}-\frac{2}{r_1^2}-Z^2+\frac{2Z}{r_1}\right) w_{\boldsymbol{r}_2}(r_1) &= 2\frac{r_<}{r_>^2}\, u_{100}(r_1). \end{aligned}\right\} \tag{29.9}$$

This equation, finally, can be solved fairly simply[1] for $w_{\boldsymbol{r}_2}(r_1)$, using the explicit form (3.18) for u_{100} and the fact that w must be finite for $r_1 = 0$ and ∞. The integral (29.8) can then be evaluated explicitly and the resulting expression for $\varepsilon_2(r_2)$ is an elementary but lengthy expression[2] involving exponentials and polynomials in the quantity (Zr_2).

For Zr_2 approaching infinity the "exact" expression[3] for $\varepsilon_2(r_2)$ reduces to the simple expression

$$\varepsilon_2(r_2) = -\frac{9}{4Z^4}\frac{1}{r_2^4}. \tag{29.10}$$

This *limiting* expression could have been obtained much more simply by replacing the electric field due to the very distant electron 2 by the *constant* electric field $F = 1/r_2^2$. The ordinary formula (52.3) for the STARK effect then immediately yields (29.10). Clearly, this approximation is valid only if r_2 is much larger than the BOHR radius of the inner electron, i.e. if $Zr_2 \gg 1$. For smaller values of r_2 the exact expression for ε_2 has to be used. For $Zr_2 \ll 1$, for instance, ε_2 reduces to $-\frac{2}{3}(Zr_2)^2$.

Finally, the second order correction E_2 is obtained by substituting the exact expression for $\varepsilon_2(r_2)$ into the integral (29.7), using the explicit hydrogen-like wave functions u_{nlm}. This integral can be evaluated explicitly (the rather lengthy results are given in ref. [*10*], p. 344). For large principal quantum number n, E_2 (as well as E_1) is proportional to n^{-3}. In analogy with (28.25) we define a "polarization correction" δ_π by the relation

$$E_0 + E_1 + E_2 + \frac{Z^2}{2} = -\frac{1}{2}\frac{(Z-1)^2}{n^2} + J \pm K + E_2 \equiv -\frac{1}{2}\frac{(Z-1)^2}{(n+\delta_C+\delta_\pi\pm\delta_A)^2}. \tag{29.11}$$

The term δ_π, as well as δ_c and δ_A, is then a slowly varying function of n.

For large orbital quantum number l, the wave function of the outer electron is extremely small at "small" radial distances ($Zr_2 \lesssim 1$). If the approximation (29.10) is used for ε_2 in (29.7), then E_2 is simply $-9/4Z^4$ times the expectation[4] value $\overline{r^{-4}}$ in (3.27). If, in addition, n is large, we have

$$\delta_\pi = \frac{n^3}{(Z-1)^2} E_2 \approx -\frac{27}{8}\frac{(Z-1)^2}{Z^4 l^5}\prod_{s=1}^{3}\left(1+\frac{s}{2l}\right)^{-1}. \tag{29.12}$$

For lower values of l, however, the wave function of the outer electron penetrates to an appreciable extent to radial distances smaller than the BOHR radius of the inner electron. For such small values of r_2, (29.10) is a bad overestimate for ε_2. For the $2P$, ∞P and $3D$ states in He, for instance, the ratio of the exact expression for δ_π to the approximation obtained from (29.10) is 0.32, 0.26 and 0.93, respectively. For S-states the expectation value of ε_2 as given by (29.10) would diverge altogether.

In the second column of Table 4, Sect. 28, we have added to the first order COULOMB correction δ_c the polarization correction δ_π, calculated from the "exact" expression for E_2. The table shows that δ_π decreases with increasing values of l, but not as rapidly as δ_c. For larger l, then, δ_π dominates δ_c and the theoretical expression $(\delta_c + \delta_\pi)$ is in fairly good agreement with the experimental value $\frac{1}{2}(\delta_0 + \delta_P)$, even for S-states.

---

[1] This is an example in which direct solution of a perturbation equation is simpler than expansion in a series of eigenfunctions of the unperturbed equation, cf. remarks after (25.12).

[2] The functions w and ε_2 are given explicitly in ref. [*10*], pp. 342 and 343.

[3] I.e. making no approximations *after* those leading to (29.9).

[4] In this expectation value, Z is replaced by $(Z-1)$.

The methods discussed in this section can also be extended to evaluate the effect of polarization on the exchange correction δ_A. These calculations are very tedious and the effect is small. It has nevertheless been calculated approximately by LUDWIG[1] for the $2P$ and $3D$ terms in He. The theoretical values for δ_A including LUDWIG's corrections for these two states are given in Table 4 in brackets. This correction improves the agreement with experiment slightly.

30. FOCK's method[2] (excited S-states). In Sects. 28 and 29 we have found theoretical expressions for the "average quantum defect" $\frac{1}{2}(\delta_0+\delta_P)$ (COULOMB or screening effects) and for the difference of the ortho-para defects, $\delta_0-\delta_P$ (exchange effects). For excited S-states, the theoretical expression for $\delta_0+\delta_P$ agrees reasonably well with the observed value, but the expression for $\delta_0-\delta_P$ does not agree at all. For S-states, the effect of polarization on $\delta_0+\delta_P$ is fairly small and one can show that its effect on $\delta_0-\delta_P$ is even smaller. The failure of HEISENBERG's method in calculating the exchange effect for S-states is thus due not to the use of product wave functions as such, but due to a poor choice for these wave functions.

The exchange integral K, Eq. (28.7), depends on the "overlap charge density" $\chi \equiv u_{100}(\boldsymbol{r})\, u_{nlm}(\boldsymbol{r})$. For large l, u_{nlm} is extremely small for small radial distances r and the overlap density χ has its maximum value for r appreciably larger than the BOHR radius a_0 for the inner electron. For S-states, on the other hand, u_{nlm} is appreciable even for small values of r and χ has its maximum for r of the order of a_0. Most of the contribution to the exchange integral K then comes from radial distances of the second electron which are partly *inside* the charge distribution of the inner electron. Now, HEISENBERG's method is based on the assumption that the outer electron "sees" only the COULOMB potential due to a "fully screened" effective charge $(Z-1)$. Although this is still a good approximation for the bulk of the wave function of the excited electron (at $r \sim n\, a_0 \gg a_0$), it is *not* good at the smaller distances ($r \sim a_0$) from which most of the contribution to the exchange integral comes. We shall, therefore, attempt to find a wave function which is still of product form (polarization neglected), but with correct symmetrization and of *better* form than the simple hydrogenic wave functions of HEISENBERG's method.

FOCK's method restricts itself to wave functions of this type,

$$U(\boldsymbol{r}_1, \boldsymbol{r}_2) = \frac{1}{\sqrt{2}}\left[u_1(1)\, u_2(2) \pm u_2(1)\, u_1(2)\right], \tag{30.1}$$

but finds the *most accurate* form possible for the two functions $u_1(\boldsymbol{r})$ and $u_2(\boldsymbol{r})$. One starts from the general variational principle which states that the expression (25.3) has a stationary value with respect to any infinitesimal variation of the trial wave function U, if U coincides with a correct eigenfunction of the total HAMILTONian H. We next substitute the form (30.1) for U into the expression (25.3) and require it to have a stationary value for any infinitesimal change $\delta u_1(\boldsymbol{r})$ and $\delta u_2(\boldsymbol{r})$ of the functions u_1 and u_2. Since $u_1(1)$ and $u_1(2)$ are identical functions, $\delta u_1(\boldsymbol{r}_1)$ and $\delta u_1(\boldsymbol{r}_2)$ are also identical and we have only two (not four) independent variations δu_1 and δu_2. Collecting together the terms involving δu_1 and δu_2, the variational principle takes the form

$$\sum_{i=1}^{2} \int d\tau_1\, \delta u_i(1) \left\{\int d\tau_2\, u_j(2)\, (H-E)\left[u_j(2)\, u_i(1) \pm u_i(2)\, u_j(1)\right]\right\} = 0, \tag{30.2}$$

[1] G. LUDWIG: Helv. phys. Acta 7, 273 (1934).
[2] V. FOCK: Z. Physik 61, 126 (1930).

where $j=2$ if $i=1$ and vice versa. Now $\delta u_1(1)$ and $\delta u_2(1)$ are independent of each other and arbitrary for *each* value of $\boldsymbol{r}_1$. For (30.2) to hold, the coefficients of $\delta u_1(1)$ and $\delta u_2(1)$ for each value of $\boldsymbol{r}_1$ (the two expressions in curly brackets in (30.2) with $i=1$ and 2) must vanish separately. This results in two coupled differential equations for the two unknown functions $u_1(\boldsymbol{r})$ and $u_2(\boldsymbol{r})$, which involve the eigenvalue E. These two equations, together with the boundary conditions of "good behavior", determine (in *principle*) the best approximations to the set of eigenfunctions and eigenvalues which are compatible with the restriction (30.1).

We introduce the following abbreviations (u_1 and u_2 are normalized to unity),

$$\left.\begin{aligned} H_0(r) &= -\frac{1}{2}\Delta - \frac{2}{r}, \\ I_{12} &= I_{21} = \int d\tau\, u_1 u_2, \\ H_{ik} &= H_{ki} = \int d\tau\, u_i H_0 u_k, \\ G_{ik}(r_1) &= G_{ki}(r_1) = \int d\tau_2\, u_i(2)\, u_k(2) \frac{1}{r_{12}}. \end{aligned}\right\} \qquad (30.3)$$

Using the explicit form (24.1) for the HAMILTONian for He the two equations for u_1 and u_2 become[1]

$$\left.\begin{aligned} [H_0(\boldsymbol{r})-E+H_{22}+G_{22}(\boldsymbol{r})]\,u_1(\boldsymbol{r}) &= \mp[I_{12}(H_0-E)+H_{12}+G_{12}(\boldsymbol{r})]\,u_2(\boldsymbol{r}), \\ [H_0(\boldsymbol{r})-E+H_{11}+G_{11}(\boldsymbol{r})]\,u_2(\boldsymbol{r}) &= \mp[I_{12}(H_0-E)+H_{12}+G_{12}(\boldsymbol{r})]\,u_1(\boldsymbol{r}), \end{aligned}\right\} \qquad (30.4)$$

where the minus-sign refers to para-, the plus-sign to ortho-He. The two Eqs. (30.4) have to be solved simultaneously and the "constants" I_{12} and H_{ik} and the function $G_{ik}(r)$ themselves depend on the form of the wave functions u_1 and u_2. As in HARTREE's method (see Sect. 31), these equations have to be solved by a method of successive approximation. The general solution of (30.4) would be much more laborious still than of the HARTREE equation, due to the presence of the terms on the right hand side of these equations (which stem from our requirement of symmetrization). We shall only discuss an approximate method of solving (30.4) for S-states.

We restrict ourselves to highly-excited S-states[2], i.e. outer electrons with $l=0$ and very large principal quantum number n. As n tends to infinity, $n^{\frac{3}{2}} u_2(r)$ becomes independent of n for finite values of r (see Sect. 3δ). From our previous discussion of the HEISENBERG method we know that the total energy E of the helium atom will be of form

$$E = E_1 + E_2, \qquad E_1 = -2, \qquad E_2 = -\frac{1}{2(n+\delta)^2}, \qquad (30.5)$$

where δ approaches a constant limit as n tends to infinity. We wish to determine these limits of δ and of $n^{\frac{3}{2}} u_2(\boldsymbol{r})$.

Consider the first equation in (30.4) for "finite" values of r (r of order unity, rather than n), where the wave function u_1 is appreciable (and of order unity). On the right side of this equation I_{12}, H_{12} and G_{12}, as well as u_2, are of order $n^{-\frac{3}{2}}$. The whole right hand side is then of order n^{-3} and can be dropped. On

[1] Since we are mainly interested in S-states, (30.2) to (30.4) are written for real wave functions only. The extension for complex u_1, u_2 is trivial.

[2] The ground state with $n=1$ and the states with $n=2$ are treated most accurately by the variation method (see Sects. 32 and 35). Since the RYDBERG corrections δ_0 and δ_P are slowly varying functions of n, a discussion of $n=1$, 2 and ∞ should suffice. For a separate discussion of S-states with intermediate values of n, see also E. HYLLERAAS, Z. Physik **83**, 739 (1933).

the left side H_{22}, G_{22} and $-E_2$ are of order n^{-2} and their sum can be shown to be of order n^{-3}, which we again neglect. With an error of order n^{-3} only, the differential equation for u_1 is then identical with that for the ground state wave function of He^+,

$$(H_0 - E_1)\, u_1 = 0, \qquad u_1 = 2^{\frac{5}{2}}\, e^{-2r}. \tag{30.6}$$

Physically speaking, only a fraction of order n^{-3} of the charge cloud of the outer electron penetrates inside the BOHR radius of the inner electron, whose wave function is then almost unscreened. Using (30.6), H_{11} reduces to E_1, H_{12} to $E_1 I_{12}$ and the second equation in (30.4) reduces to

$$[H_0 - E_2 + G_{11}(\boldsymbol{r})]\, u_2(\boldsymbol{r}) = \mp [E_1 I_{12} + G_{12}(\boldsymbol{r})]\, u_1(\boldsymbol{r}). \tag{30.7}$$

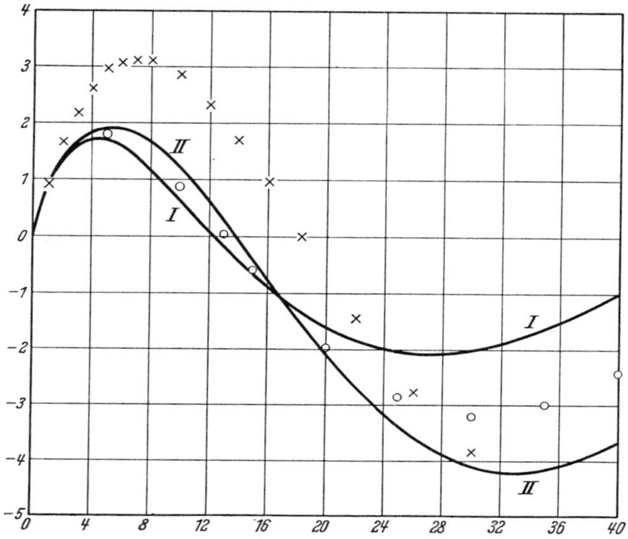

Fig. 16. The radial wave function $r\,R(r)$ for highly excited s-electrons in helium, according to FOCK's method (calculated by L. P. SMITH), plotted against radial distance r. Curve I is for orthohelium, curve II for parahelium, the circles denote the HARTREE wave function (exchange neglected) and the crosses denote the hydrogenic wave function (for zero energy).

For S-states, u_2 is spherically symmetric and (30.7) reduces to

$$\left[\frac{1}{2}\frac{d^2}{dr^2} + \frac{2}{r} - G_{11}(r) + E_2\right] v(r) = \pm [E_1 I_{12} + G_{12}(r)]\, r\, u_1(r), \tag{30.8}$$

where $v(r) = r\, u_2(r)$. Since u_1 is given by (30.6) and E_1 by (30.5), (30.8) is an nhomogeneous integral-differential equation for a single unknown function v of one variable r with one eigenvalue E_2. This equation was solved by SMITH[1], using a semi-numerical method. He treated the regions of $r < r_0$ and $r > r_0$ separately, where $1 \ll r_0 \ll n$. In the inner region both v and G_{12} are of order $n^{-\frac{3}{2}}$ and one can drop the term in E_2, which is smaller by two powers of n than the leading terms. The resulting equation, independent of n, can then be solved numerically, using the boundary condition $v(0) = 0$. This solution gives the logarithmic derivative of $v(r)$ at $r = r_0$ (which is appreciably different from that of a hydrogen wave function). In the outer region $r > r_0$ (r much larger than first BOHR radius), the term involving u_1 is very small and can be dropped and $G_{11}(r)$

[1] L. P. SMITH: Phys. Rev. 42, 176 (1932).

replaced by $1/r$. The term involving $E_2 = -\frac{1}{2}(n+\delta)^{-2}$ on the other hand, is retained. The general solution in the outer region for very large n can be found, using the WKB method (see Sects. 3 δ and 53), and is required to match the solution for the inner region at $r = r_0$. The outer solution remains regular at infinity only for values of $(n+\delta)$ which differ from an integer by a constant amount and the RYDBERG correction δ is thus found (separately for ortho- and para-helium).

The values calculated by SMITH for the RYDBERG correction δ for highly excited S-states are -0.289 and -0.160 for ortho- and para-helium, respectively, in quite good agreement with the experimental values of -0.298 and -0.140. In Fig. 16 we give the calculated $v(r)$, which is r times the wave function of the excited electron for ortho- and para-He. The HARTREE wave function, obtained by omitting the right side (the exchange effects) of (30.4), and the hydrogen wave function (used in HEISENBERG's method) are also shown.

31. HARTREE's method[1]. The HARTREE method (see Sect. 27 δ) has been very successful for the treatment of even very complex atoms. An outline of the procedure is as follows. The wave function of a particular atom is written in the form of a product of single particle wave functions $u_i(\boldsymbol{r}_i)$, one for each of the electrons. A guess is made of the wave function u_i of each electron and the electrostatic potential throughout space, $V_i(\boldsymbol{r})$, due to the charge distribution $|u_i(\boldsymbol{r}_i)|^2$ is calculated. These potentials V_i are summed over all values of i, except a particular one, k, and averaged over angles. This central potential (plus the nuclear one) is substituted into the SCHRÖDINGER equation for the k-th electron and the equation solved numerically for the wave function $u'_k(\boldsymbol{r}_k)$. This procedure is carried out for all values of k. In general the initial (guessed) wave functions u_i do not agree with the final ones u'_i. The whole procedure is then repeated, using now as *initial* wave functions u'_i (or some compromise between u_i and u'_i). New final wave functions u''_i are then calculated and used again as initial ones. This procedure is repeated until the initial and final wave functions agree to the desired accuracy. The field in which the electrons are assumed to move is then "self-consistent", i.e. identical with the field produced by the charge distribution of the electrons.

For two-electron atoms the HARTREE method is relatively simple. The wave function U of the atom is taken of the form $u_1(1)\, u_2(2)$. This is of similar form to the choice (30.1) of the FOCK method, but *without* symmetrization; hence HARTREE's method gives the same wave functions and energies for ortho- and para-states (exchange effects are neglected). Two equations for u_1 and u_2 can then be derived from the SCHRÖDINGER variational principle in analogy with the derivation of (30.4) in Sect. 30. The resulting equations are identical with (30.4), except that the right side of each equation in (30.4) is replaced by zero. Various states (including even doubly-excited ones) in He, Li^+, etc. have been investigated by HARTREE, WILSON and LINDSAY[2] and others.

We consider here only the ground state of He. Since the two electrons are in identical states we consider the two functions u_1 and u_2 as identical,

$$U = u(r_1)\, u(r_2). \tag{31.1}$$

(31.1) already has the right symmetry properties and HARTREE's and FOCK's methods are identical. The expression $E(U)$, Eq. (25.3), is then required to have

[1] D. R. HARTREE: Proc. Cambridge Phil. Soc. **24**, 89 (1928).

[2] For a list of earlier references see W. S. WILSON and R. B. LINDSAY, Phys. Rev. **47**, 681 (1935). For a discussion of K-shell electrons in heavier atoms see R. E. MEYEROTT, Phys. Rev. **95**, 72 (1954).

a stationary value with respect to a variation in the *single* function u. This requirement leads to a single differential-integral equation, instead of (30.4). This differential-integral equation can be written in the form of two coupled equations,

$$\left[\frac{1}{2}\Delta + E_1 + \frac{2}{r} - G(r)\right] u(r) = 0, \tag{31.2}$$

together with

$$G(r_1) = \int d\tau_2\, u^2(r_2)\, \frac{1}{r_{12}}, \tag{31.3}$$

and the function $u(r)$ is normalized to unity. The Eqs. (31.2) and (31.3) are then solved simultaneously, by the method of successive approximation outlined above, which yields the wave function $u(r)$ and eigenvalue E_1.

The solution of (31.2) and (31.3) yields the HARTREE wave function $u(r)$, which gives the best total wave function of form (31.1), and the corresponding eigenvalue parameter E_1 of (31.2). We now have to find the corresponding approximation for the total energy E of the actual atom, which is *not* simply twice E_1. This approximation to E is defined as the expectation value (25.3) of the total HAMILTONian H over the HARTREE wave function $u(r_1)\,u(r_2)$. Since we are considering the *ground* state of the atom, the arguments of Sect. 25α show that this value for E is an *upper* limit for the correct expression and the best (i.e. lowest) value obtainable with a wave function of product form (31.1).

To evaluate the energy expectation value we write the total HAMILTONian H in the form

$$H = H_1 + H_2 + \left[\frac{1}{r_{12}} - G(r_1) - G(r_2)\right], \qquad H_i = -\frac{1}{2}\Delta_i - \frac{2}{r_i} + G(r_i), \tag{31.4}$$

where G is defined by (31.3). The expectation value of H_1 and H_2 is simply E_1 each and the expectation value E of H is then

$$E = 2E_1 - \overline{G}, \tag{31.5}$$

where

$$\overline{G} = \int d\tau\, u^2(r)\, G(r) = \iint d\tau_1\, d\tau_2\, u^2(r_1)\, \frac{1}{r_{12}}\, u^2(r_2) \tag{31.6}$$

and $u(r)$ is the normalized HARTREE wave function. The function $G(r)$ is the potential due to the charge distribution of one electron and $\overline{G}$ is the electrostatic interaction energy between the two electrons. The physical reason for the expression (31.5) is the fact that in evaluating the energy $2E_1$ we have included this interaction *twice*, once each in the wave equation (31.2) for each electron

The ionization potential J of the helium ground state is the difference in energy of the ground states of the singly ionized helium ion He^+ (energy $E_0 = -2$ a.u.) and of the helium atom [E given by (31.5)]. Thus

$$J = E_0 - E = -2E_1 + \overline{G} + E_0. \tag{31.7}$$

The best value of J obtainable from the HARTREE wave function is given by (31.7), but one can show that J is at least fairly close to $-E_1$, as follows.

The normalized wave function u_0 of the He^+ ground state satisfies the equation

$$\left(\frac{1}{2}\Delta + E_0 + \frac{2}{r}\right) u_0(r) = 0. \tag{31.8}$$

Multiply (31.2) by u_0, (31.8) by $-u$, add the two equations and integrate over all space. In the resulting equation we call $\delta u \equiv u - u_0$, *assume* that δu is reasonably small and neglect terms quadratic in δu. In this approximation, comparison with (31.7) gives the following relation

$$J + E_1 \approx \int d\tau\, u\, \delta u\, [G(r) - \bar{G}]. \qquad (31.9)$$

Since $G(r)$ is a fairly slowly varying function of r (it is finite at the origin), the difference $G - \bar{G}$ will be fairly small. If, in addition, δu is fairly small, as we have assumed, then the right hand side of (31.9) will be quite small. These arguments can be generalized to complex atoms, where HARTREE's single-electron eigenvalue E_1 for a particular electron is often used as a simple approximation for (minus) the electron's ionization potential.

Eqs. (31.2) and (31.3) were solved first by HARTREE and, more accurately, by WILSON and LINDSAY[1]. A shortened version of their results is given in Table 5. The function $P(r)$ is r times the wave function, normalized such that

$$\int_0^\infty dr\, P^2(r) = 1,$$

with r in atomic units. Instead of $G(r)$, Eq. (31.3), a function $Z_p(r)$ is tabulated which is defined by

$$\frac{Z_p(r)}{r} = \frac{2}{r} - G(r). \qquad (31.10)$$

The total charge (including the nucleus) inside radius r is given by

$$Z_{\text{eff}}(r) = 2 - 2\int_0^r dr'\, P^2(r') = 2\int_r^\infty dr'\, P^2(r'). \qquad (31.11)$$

The calculations also give (in atomic units)

$$2E_1 = -1.836, \qquad G(0) = +1.687, \qquad \left(\frac{P}{r}\right)_{r=0} = 4.75_5. \qquad (31.12)$$

Using the tabulated values of $P(r)$ and $G(r)$, the constant $\bar{G}$, Eq. (31.6), can be evaluated by numerical integration. The result is $\bar{G} = 1.027$. Using (31.7) one finds for the ionization potential, $J = 1.726$ Ry (which is indeed not very different from $-E_1 = 1.836$ Ry as predicted above). The experimental value is $J = 1.807$ Ry. The much simpler hydrogenic wave function discussed in Sect. 27β would give [see Eq. (27.4)] $J = 1.695$ Ry. The energy eigenvalue obtained by

Table 5. *The ground state of the neutral helium atom; self-consistent field, potential and charge distribution.*

r	$P(r)$	$Z_p(r)$	$Z_{\text{eff}}(r)$	r	$P(r)$	$Z_p(r)$	$Z_{\text{eff}}(r)$
0	0.000	2.000	2.000	1.6	0.489	1.024	0.239
0.05	0.215	1.916	1.998	1.8	0.405	1.014	0.158
0.1	0.390	1.834	1.989	2.0	0.333	1.009	0.105
0.2	0.643	1.683	1.932	2.2	0.272	1.005	0.068
0.3	0.798	1.552	1.826	2.4	0.221	1.003	0.044
0.4	0.885	1.442	1.683	2.6	0.178	1.0018	0.028
0.5	0.924	1.352	1.518	2.8	0.143	1.0011	0.018
0.6	0.930	1.279	1.345	3.0	0.115	1.0006	0.012
				3.2	0.092	1.0004	0.007
0.8	0.880	1.173	1.014				
1.0	0.789	1.106	0.734	3.6	0.058	1.0001	0.0028
1.2	0.686	1.065	0.516	4.0	0.036	1.0000	0.0012
1.4	0.584	1.039	0.355	4.8	0.014	1.0000	0.0002

[1] W. S. WILSON and R. B. LINDSAY: Phys. Rev. **47**, 681 (1935).

the HARTREE method is thus not much better than the (simpler) approximation (27.4) and is much worse than the value given by the (more complicated) variation method (see Sect. 32). For helium-like atoms the main advantage of the HARTREE method lies in furnishing the most accurate wave functions obtainable in product form (31.1). For many applications the HARTREE wave function is much easier to handle than the more accurate, but much more complicated, variational one. Correlation effects between the two electrons are, of course, not included but the *overall* charge distribution of the two electron given by the HARTREE method agrees very well[1] with the variational one (see Fig. 17, Sect. 32).

32. RITZ variation method (helium ground state). Historically, an accurate quantum mechanical treatment of the ground state of He was of great interest since the "old quantum theory" had failed completely in such problems. It was therefore gratifying that even the earliest wave mechanical calculations[2] gave a reasonably good value for the ground state energy E of He. Today the wave mechanical value for this energy is one of the most accurate of all quantum mechanical results which have to be obtained by *approximation* methods. An accurate knowledge of the ground state *wave function* is also required for calculating many macroscopic quantities, such as the diamagnetic (Sect. 50) and dielectric (Sect. 58) susceptibility, VAN DER WAALS' constant, boiling point, etc. Helium is especially suitable for the comparison of the experimental and theoretical values for such constants, since it is the simplest monatomic gas.

The most suitable method for the treatment of the He ground state is the RITZ procedure which was first applied to the He problem by KELLNER[3] and then with even greater success by HYLLERAAS[4]. The starting point of the procedure is SCHRÖDINGER's variational principle

$$E[U] \equiv \frac{\int UHU\,d\tau}{\int U^2\,d\tau} = \text{Min.} \tag{32.1}$$

(H is the HAMILTONian operator). The general form of the eigenfunction U is assumed, but, to begin with, a number of parameters, such as the effective nuclear charge or the coefficients of a power series expansion, are left arbitrary. Then the integrals in (32.1) are carried out, and E is a function of the parameters which have been introduced. By finding the absolute minimum of this function, the parameters, thereby the eigenfunction, and above all, the energy of the atom are determined.

We use as our three distance coordinates the two "elliptic coordinates" plus the interparticle distance,

$$s = r_1 + r_2, \quad t = r_1 - r_2, \quad u = r_{12}. \tag{32.2}$$

The variables s and u are positive, by definition, while t can take both positive and negative values. The exact symmetry requirement (24.3) then takes the simple form that U be an even function of t for parahelium, an odd function of t for ortho-helium. Since the HAMILTONian H is an even function of t and since the integrals in (32.1) contain two factors, the contribution to the integral from $-t$ is identical with that from $+t$. We therefore restrict ourselves to positive

[1] H. A. BETHE: Z. Physik **55**, 431 (1929).
[2] For instance A. UNSÖLD, Ann. d. Phys. **82**, 355 (1927).
[3] G. W. KELLNER: Z. Physik **44**, 91 (1927).
[4] E. A. HYLLERAAS: Z. Physik **48**, 469 (1928) and particularly **54**, 347 (1929). See also E. A. HYLLERAAS, Die Grundlagen der Quantenmechanik mit Anwendungen auf atomtheoretische Ein- und Mehrelektronenprobleme, Oslo 1932 (Norske Vidensk. Akad. Skrift., Mat.-naturv. Kl. **1932**, No. 6).

values of t in the integrals and multiply the volume element by a factor of 2. Since the HAMILTONian H and also the wave function U (for S-states) do not depend on the EULER angles, we can integrate over them immediately. The resulting volume element is then found to be[1]

$$d\tau = 2\pi^2 (s^2 - t^2)\, u\, ds\, dt\, du \tag{32.3}$$

and the limits of integration are

$$0 \leq t \leq u \leq s \leq \infty. \tag{32.4}$$

We now have to rewrite the HAMILTONian H,

$$H = -\tfrac{1}{2}\Delta_1 - \tfrac{1}{2}\Delta_2 + V, \tag{32.5}$$

in terms of the variables s, t and u. The potential energy V is

$$V = -\frac{Z}{r_1} - \frac{Z}{r_2} + \frac{1}{r_{12}} = -\frac{4Zs}{s^2 - t^2} + \frac{1}{u}. \tag{32.6}$$

The integrals involving the LAPLACE operators Δ can be rewritten, using GREEN'S theorem,

$$\overline{p_1^2} \equiv -\int d\tau\, U \Delta_1 U = +\int d\tau\, (\mathrm{grad}_1 U)^2, \tag{32.7}$$

and expressing grad_1 in terms of differentiation with respect to s, t, u. The variational principle (32.1) finally takes the form

$$\left.\begin{aligned} &\frac{1}{N}\int_0^\infty ds \int_0^s du \int_0^u dt \Big\{u(s^2-t^2)\left[\left(\frac{\partial U}{\partial s}\right)^2 + \left(\frac{\partial U}{\partial t}\right)^2 + \left(\frac{\partial U}{\partial u}\right)^2\right] + 2\frac{\partial U}{\partial u}\times \\ &\times\left[s(u^2-t^2)\frac{\partial U}{\partial s} + t(s^2-u^2)\frac{\partial U}{\partial t}\right] - U^2\left[4Zsu - s^2 + t^2\right]\Big\} \equiv E = \min, \end{aligned}\right\} \tag{32.8}$$

where

$$N = \int_0^\infty ds \int_0^s du \int_0^u dt\, u(s^2 - t^2)\, U^2.$$

α) First order. In Sect 27β we have discussed a simple wave function for the ground state of form

$$U = e^{-(Z-\sigma)r_1} e^{-(Z-\sigma)r_2} = e^{-(Z-\sigma)s} \tag{32.9}$$

where the screening factor σ represents, in a crude way, the partial screening of each electron by the other. As a first step in our variation method let us choose a trial wave function U, which is an *arbitrary* function of the variable s but, like (32.9), is independent of t and u. We can then integrate (32.8) over t and u, which gives

$$\delta\int_0^\infty ds\left\{\frac{4}{15}s^5\left(\frac{dU}{ds}\right)^2 - \left(\frac{4}{3}Z - \frac{5}{12}\right)s^4 U^2 - E\cdot\frac{4}{15}s^5 U^2\right\} = 0. \tag{32.10}$$

This variational principle then reduces to the differential equation

$$\frac{d^2U}{ds^2} + \frac{5}{s}\frac{dU}{ds} + \left(E + 5\frac{Z}{s} - \frac{25}{16s}\right)U = 0. \tag{32.11}$$

The lowest eigenvalue E of this equation is $-(Z - \frac{5}{16})^2$ and the corresponding eigenfunction is *exactly* (32.9) with $\sigma = 5/16$.

[1] For a derivation see ref. [*10*], p. 354.

The experimentally measured quantity is not the *total* energy E of a helium-like atom, but its ionization potential J. J equals $E_0 - E$, where E_0 is the ground state energy of the singly ionized (hydrogen-like) atom, $E_0 = -Z^2/2$. The simple wave function (32.9) then gives the following approximation for the ionization potential[1] for nuclear charge Z

$$J_Z = \left[\left(Z - \frac{5}{16}\right)^2 - \frac{1}{2} Z^2\right] \text{a.u.} = \left(Z^2 - \frac{5}{4} Z + \frac{25}{128}\right). \tag{32.12}$$

The comparison of this expression with the experimental values in Rydberg[2] is as follows

	H^-	He	Li^+	Be^{++}
Theoretical	−0.055	+1.695	+5.445	+11.195
Experimental	+0.055	+1.807	+5.560	+11.312
Difference	0.110	0.112	0.115	0.117

The agreement is gratifying, considering the simplicity of the derivation. Note also that the difference between the approximation (32.12) and the experimental value is almost independent of Z [see also Eq. (33.12)].

The same result (32.12) could also have been obtained as follows. Following the discussion of partial screening in Sect. 27β, we choose a trial wave function of form (32.9) with σ an arbitrary parameter. Substituting this wave function into (32.8), we obtain E as a function of σ. One finds that $E(\sigma)$ has its minimum value exactly for $\sigma = \frac{5}{16}$, which leads to (32.12). The introduction of the screening constant σ into the unscreened hydrogenic wave function e^{-Zs} is equivalent to a simple change of scale of radial distance r_1 and r_2 (and hence of s). This scale factor in the wave function is important, for obtaining good values for the energy. If we had, for instance, substituted the unscreened wave function e^{-Zs} for He instead of (32.9) into (32.8), the discrepancy between the experimental and theoretical values for the energy would have been about three times larger.

β) Higher approximations. We may except, therefore, that the convergence of higher approximations will also be considerably improved if we let the "effective nuclear charge" (or unit of length) be arbitrary in the eigenfunction, i.e., let

$$U(s, t, u) = \varphi(ks, kt, ku). \tag{32.13}$$

The "effective charge" k is to be fixed by the condition that E be a minimum. Thus $\varphi(s, t, u)$ will not depend on k. In arriving at a more detailed statement about the form of φ, we are guided by the fact that the eigenfunction in first approximation (32.9) is an exponential function of s and independent of t and u. Therefore, a suitable assumption is

$$\varphi(s, t, u) = e^{-\frac{1}{2}s} P(s, t, u). \tag{32.14}$$

$P = 1$ corresponds to the first approximation. For higher approximations we expand P in a power series which may be expected to converge rapidly for medium-sized values of s, t, and u:

$$P = \sum_{l, n, m=0}^{\infty} c_{n, 2l, m} s^n t^{2l} u^m. \tag{32.15}$$

[1] 1 a.u. of energy = 2 Ry (see Introduction).

[2] Actually in terms of R_{He}, R_{Li}, etc. the RYDBERG for the appropriate reduced mass (see Sect. 5). The "experimental" value for H^- is actually an accurate theoretical one (Sect. 34).

Of course, the series contains only even powers of t [cf. remark following (32.2)]. The exponential factor in (32.14) assures convergence of the integrals (32.8). If (32.13) and (32.14) are substituted into (32.8), one obtains

$$E = \frac{k^2 M - k L}{N}, \tag{32.16}$$

with the abbreviations

$$\left.\begin{aligned}
L &= \int_0^\infty ds \int_0^s du \int_0^u dt\,(4Z s u - s^2 + t^2)\,\varphi^2(s,t,u),\\
M &= \int_0^\infty ds \int_0^s du \int_0^u dt \Big\{u(s^2 - t^2)\left[\left(\frac{\partial\varphi}{\partial s}\right)^2 + \left(\frac{\partial\varphi}{\partial t}\right)^2 + \left(\frac{\partial\varphi}{\partial u}\right)^2\right] +\\
&\qquad + 2s(u^2 - t^2)\frac{\partial\varphi}{\partial s}\frac{\partial\varphi}{\partial u} + 2t(s^2 - u^2)\frac{\partial\varphi}{\partial t}\frac{\partial\varphi}{\partial u}\Big\},\\
N &= \int_0^\infty ds \int_0^s du \int_0^u dt\, u(s^2 - t^2)\,\varphi^2.
\end{aligned}\right\} \tag{32.17}$$

The expressions L, M, and N are quadratic in the coefficients $c_{n,2l,m}$ only; however, E depends also on k, as per (32.16). We must make E a minimum as a function of the variables $c_{n,2l,m}$ and k. The coefficients c, the "effective nuclear charge" k, and E are to be determined by the minimizing conditions

$$\frac{\partial E}{\partial c_{n,2l,m}} = 0, \qquad \frac{\partial E}{\partial k} = 0. \tag{32.18}$$

In view of (32.16), the last condition can be satisfied immediately by taking

$$k = \frac{L}{2M}. \tag{32.19}$$

Thus, if the $c_{n,2l,m}$ are fixed, the minimum E has the value

$$E = -\frac{L^2}{4MN}. \tag{32.20}$$

Now (32.17) is, of course, a function of the coefficients c only. The more coefficients one has at one's disposal, i.e., the more terms of the power series expansion (32.15) of the eigenfunction are taken, the more accurate, naturally, will be the eigenvalue and eigenfunction; but the more complicated also will be the calculation.

To proceed from (32.20), in carrying out an actual calculation, is hardly the thing to do, because both L^2 and MN are fourth degree expressions in the coefficients c, and, consequently, the Eq. (32.18) would be of third degree in the c's. A better procedure is to substitute an approximate value for k in (32.16). We then obtain the system of equations

$$k^2 \frac{\partial M}{\partial c_{n,2l,m}} - k \frac{\partial L}{\partial c_{n,2l,m}} - E \frac{\partial N}{\partial c_{n,2l,m}} = 0 \quad \text{for all} \quad n, l, m. \tag{32.21}$$

The unknowns in the Eq. (32.21) are the coefficients $c_{n,2l,m}$. The equations are linear and homogeneous in these unknowns since L, M, and N are quadratic functions of the $c_{n,2l,m}$. The system of equations (32.21) will have solutions if the determinant of its coefficients vanishes:

$$\left| k^2 \frac{\partial^2 M}{\partial c_{n,2l,m}\,\partial c_{n',2l',m'}} - k \frac{\partial^2 L}{\partial c_{n,2l,m}\,\partial c_{n',2l',m'}} - E \frac{\partial^2 N}{\partial c_{n,2l,m}\,\partial c_{n',2l',m'}} \right| = 0. \tag{32.22}$$

From this, an equation determining E is obtained in the usual fashion, the degree of the equation being equal to the number of terms of the power series expansion (32.15). The lowest root of this equation is the eigenvalue E. Once it is determined (32.21) may be solved for the $c_{n,2l,m}$. If the values of the c's found in this manner are now substituted into (32.19) and (32.20), even better values for E and k are obtained. At the same time the procedure enables us to keep track of our calculations by permitting a comparison with the values previously obtained[1].

More recently KINOSHITA[2] has used variational wave functions of a more general type than the HYLLERAAS functions (32.15). Besides the terms occurring in (32.15), he also includes terms of the form

$$c_{hij}\, s^{h+1} \left(\frac{u}{s}\right)^{i} \left(\frac{t}{u}\right)^{2j}. \tag{32.23}$$

Because of the inequality (32.4), such terms have no singularity in the region of integration for h, i, j all positive (or zero).

γ) Results. For the ground state of helium itself ($Z=2$) such variational calculations have by now been carried out with wave functions containing up to thirty-eight[3,4] parameters. In Table 6 we give the parameters used and their coefficients [$c_{n,2l,m}$ in (32.15), normalized such that $c_{0,0,0}$ is unity], as well as the scale factor k, for HYLLERAAS' three and six parameter and KINOSHITA's ten parameter wave functions.

The results for the total energy E and the ionization potential J from these more accurate calculations are as follows. Writing

$$E = -(2.90 + 0.001\,x) \text{ a.u.}, \qquad J = (1.80 + 0.002\,x) \text{ Ry} \tag{32.24}$$

the results are

	HYLLERAAS		CHANDRASEKHAR *et al.*			KINOSHITA
	3	6	10	14	18	38
x	2.44	3.24_0	3.603	3.701	3.715	3.723

compared with $x = -52$ for the one-parameter expression (32.12). The thirty-eight parameter value for E,

$$E = -2.903\,722_5 \text{ a.u.} \quad (J = 1.807445 \text{ Ry}) \tag{32.25}$$

is still a *rigorous upper limit* to the exact value. The convergence of the values for E in the table above is seen to be quite good. From Table 10, Sect. 36, another expectation value, $(\overline{H^2} - E^2)/E$, can be evaluated for each wave function. From the convergence of this quantity one can estimate that the inclusion of infinitely

[1] Nowadays the minimization for a wave function with many parameters can be carried out on electronic computing machines by a method of successive approximation. In this case it may be practical to minimize directly the quartic expression (32.20) for E. After minimization, k is then given by (32.19).

[2] T. KINOSHITA: Unpublished work. See also H. M. SCHWARTZ, Phys. Rev. **103**, 110 (1956), for other wave functions.

[3] E. A. HYLLERAAS: Z. Physik **54**, 347 (1929).

[4] CHANDRASEKHAR, HERZBERG and ELBERT: Phys. Rev. **91**, 1172 (1953); **98**, 1050 (1955). Also T. KINOSHITA (unpublished) and E. A. HYLLERAAS (unpublished). KINOSHITA's thirty-eight parameter wave function is not yet fully minimized with respect to energy.

many parameters would probably[1] lower the energy E by not much more than 10^{-6} a.u. below the value in (32.25). Although the value of J in (32.25) is a lower limit to the nonrelativistic expression for an infinitely heavy nucleus, it is actually *higher* than the experimental value of $J = 1.80739\, R_{\mathrm{He}^4}$. This is due to some corrections for nuclear motion (the mass-polarization, Sect. 37) and to some relativistic and radiative corrections (Sect. 41). These corrections (see Table 12, Sect. 41) add $(-6.5_5 \pm 0.4)\ \mathrm{cm}^{-1}$ to the ionization potential J. Using the thirty-eight parameter value in (32.25) for the uncorrected J (and $R_{\mathrm{He}^4} = 109\,722.27\,\mathrm{cm}^{-1}$) to evaluate the total theoretical ionization potential, we find

$$J^{\mathrm{tot}}_{\mathrm{theor}} = 198310.4_1\ \mathrm{cm}^{-1}, \quad J_{\mathrm{exp}} = (198310.5 \pm 1)\ \mathrm{cm}^{-1}, \tag{32.26}$$

where the experimental value is taken from unpublished work by HERZBERG and ZBINDEN. The phenomenal agreement in (32.26) supports the estimate that (32.25) is not in error by much more than 10^{-6} a.u. $\approx 0.2\ \mathrm{cm}^{-1}$.

Table 6. *Variational wave functions for the helium ground state.*

Term	$10c(u)$	$10c(s)$	$100c(t^2)$	$100c(u^2)$	$100c(s^2)$	$100c(us)$	$10c\left(\frac{u^2}{s}\right)$	$10c\left(\frac{t^2}{u}\right)$	$10c\left(\frac{t^2}{s}\right)$	$100c\left(\frac{st^2}{u}\right)$	k
3 param.	0.81		1.0								3.63
6 param.	0.972	−0.277	0.97	−0.24	0.25						3.636
10 param.	1.2128	−0.5210	0.5486		0.2271	−0.3145	−0.2377	0.0575	0.0743	0.1189	3.4592

Since the war, completely analogous accurate calculations for $Z = 1, 3, 4$ and 8 have been carried out by HENRICH[2] (H^-), ERIKSSON[3] (Li^+), CHANDRASEKHAR and HERZBERG[4] (Li^+ and $O^{(6+)}$) and HYLLERAAS[5] (H^-, Li^+ and Be^{++}). The best (i.e. lowest) values for E in atomic units are: $-0.527\,72_5$ for[5] H^-, $-7.279\,90_9$ for[5] Li^+, $-13.655\,56_3$ for[5] Be^{++} and $-59.156\,59$ for[5] $O^{(6+)}$. The absolute accuracy of these values should be almost as good as that of (32.25) for He. The rapidity of convergence of E as a function of the number of parameters becomes somewhat better with increasing Z. Comparisons of these values of E for He and heavier ions with experiment are given in Sect. 33, a discussion of the H^--ion in Sect. 34.

A simple 4-parameter variational wave function of form (32.13), (32.14) for Li^+ is[6]

$$\varphi(s, t, u) = e^{-\frac{1}{2}s}\left(1 + 0.587 \times 10^{-1} u + 0.510 \times 10^{-2} t^2 - 0.103 \times 10^{-2} u^2\right). \tag{32.27}$$

with $k = 5.660$.

33. Ground state of helium-like ions with arbitrary Z. The variation procedure discussed in Sect. 32, which includes as a parameter the "effective charge" or scale parameter k, gives very accurate results but has to be carried through

[1] The value of $E_{(n)}$ must decrease monotonically as the degree n of the polynomial in the wave function increases, but cannot fall below the correct value E. $E_{(n)}$ is therefore bounded, but the question remains whether $E_{(n)}$ converges towards E or towards some higher constant. This question, first raised by J. BARTLETT, J. GIBBONS and C. DUNN: Phys. Rev. **47**, 679 (1935), has not yet been answered with complete mathematical rigor but it now seems likely that $E_{(n)}$ *does* converge towards E; see, for instance V. A. FOCK, Izv. Acad. Nauk. SSSR., Ser. Fiz. **18** (2), 161 (1954) and T. KATO, Trans. Amer. Math. Soc. **70**, 212 (1951).

[2] L. R. HENRICH: Astrophys. J. **99**, 59 (1944).

[3] H. A. ERIKSSON: Ark. Mat. Astron. Fysik, B **30**, No. 6 (1944).

[4] S. CHANDRASEKHAR and G. HERZBERG: Phys. Rev. **98**, 1050 (1955).

[5] E. A. HYLLERAAS and J. MIDTDAL: Phys. Rev. **103**, 829 (1956). These authors use 24 parameters including terms of the type of (32.23) and some terms involving log s. These are the best results to date for $Z = 1, 3, 4$ and 8.

[6] H. A. ERIKSSON: Z. Physik **109**, 762 (1938).

separately for each value of Z. For the ions with large Z it is more convenient to use a procedure which does not include the scale parameter k but gives results as a function of Z in one calculation. Such a method, based on the variation-perturbation method discussed in Sect. 25β, was devised by HYLLERAAS[1].

In our SCHRÖDINGER equation (24.1), let us change the unit of length to $(1/2Z)$ a.u. and of energy to $2Z^2$ a.u. $= 4Z^2$ Ry, i.e.

$$\varrho = 2Z\,r; \quad \sigma = 2Z\,s, \quad \tau = 2Z\,t, \quad v = 2Z\,u; \quad \varepsilon = \frac{E}{2Z^2}. \tag{33.1}$$

In these units the SCHRÖDINGER equation is then of the form of (25.5),

$$(H_0 + \lambda H_1 - \varepsilon)\,u = 0, \tag{33.2}$$

where

$$H_0 = -\left(\Delta_1 + \Delta_2 + \frac{1}{\varrho_1} + \frac{1}{\varrho_2}\right); \quad H_1 = +\frac{1}{\varrho_{12}}, \quad \lambda = \frac{1}{Z}. \tag{33.3}$$

We can then expand the energy eigenvalue ε in inverse powers of Z,

$$\varepsilon = \varepsilon_0 + \varepsilon_1 \frac{1}{Z} + \varepsilon_2 \frac{1}{Z^2} + \varepsilon_3 \frac{1}{Z^3} + \cdots, \tag{33.4}$$

with a similar expansion for the wave function u.

The zero order wave equation (25.7), with H_0 given by (33.3), has the simple and exact normalized solution

$$U_0 = \tfrac{1}{2} e^{-\frac{1}{2}\sigma}, \qquad \varepsilon_0 = -\tfrac{1}{2} \tag{33.5}$$

for the ground state. With H_1 given by (33.3), the expression (25.10) for the first order energy ε_1 can then be easily integrated, using (29.11), and the result is

$$\varepsilon_1 = 2 \times \tfrac{1}{4} \int_0^\infty d\varrho_1\, \varrho_1^2 \int_{\varrho_1}^\infty d\varrho_2\, \varrho_2\, e^{-(\varrho_1+\varrho_2)} = \tfrac{5}{16}. \tag{33.6}$$

It is interesting to compare the results so far with the results of Sect. 32β, using the simple wave function (32.9) *with* the scale parameter $(Z-\sigma)$. In our present units, (32.12) would give $-\frac{1}{2}(1-5/16Z)^2$ as an approximation for ε. The values for ε_0 and ε_1 would be the same as (33.5) and (33.6) and the value $-25/512 = -0.0488$ would be obtained as a (very crude) approximation for ε_2.

To obtain an accurate expression for ε_2 one has to minimize the expression (25.13) with respect to the first order trial wave function U_1. It is convenient to write

$$U_1 = U_0\,\varphi. \tag{33.7}$$

After using (25.7) and (33.7) and the explicit form of H_0 and H_1, carrying out an integration by parts and simplifying the expressions, one can finally rewrite (25.13) in the form

$$\varepsilon_2 = 2\int d\tau\, U_0^2 \left[(H_1 - E_1)\,\varphi + \tfrac{1}{2}(\operatorname{grad}_1 \varphi)^2 + \tfrac{1}{2}(\operatorname{grad}_2 \varphi)^2\right] = \min. \tag{33.8}$$

In analogy with (32.15), HYLLERAAS takes the trial wave function φ of form

$$\varphi = \sum c_{n l m}\, \sigma^n\, \tau^{2l}\, v^m \tag{33.9}$$

and minimizes ε_2 with respect to all the parameters which are included. Using eight parameters he found

$$\left.\begin{aligned} U_1 = e^{-\frac{1}{2}\sigma}(&0.05737\,\sigma + 0.18797\,v + 0.01539\,\tau^2 + 0.00118\,\sigma^2 - 0.01495\,v^2 \\ &+ 0.00472\,\sigma v - 0.00076\,\tau^2 v + 0.00041\,v^3). \end{aligned}\right\} \tag{33.10}$$

[1] E. A. HYLLERAAS: Z. Physik **65**, 209 (1930).

and $\varepsilon_2 = -0.07865$. The inclusion of 12 parameters gave $\varepsilon_2 = -0.07872$ and finally a more recent calculation[1], using 24 carefully selected combinations of the 50 terms up to $(n+2l+m)=6$, gave

$$\varepsilon_2 = -0.078827_8. \tag{33.11}$$

The convergence of ε_2 with the number of parameters is quite rapid and (33.11) should be an excellent approximation (and is a rigorous upper limit) to ε_2.

In principle, the same variation method could also be used to calculate the higher coefficients ε_3, ε_4, etc. Unfortunately this procedure converges extremely slowly already for ε_3 and is impractical for higher terms. Nevertheless, we now have exact values for ε_0 and ε_1, and a very accurate approximation for ε_2. One can then get an excellent semi-empirical expansion for ε by using these values of ε_0 to ε_2 and by fitting ε_3 to ε_6 to the values of ε determined *directly* for $Z=1, 2, 3$ and 8 (see Sect. 32). The actual energy E in Rydberg for any Z is $4Z^2\varepsilon$ and the ionization potential $J=E_0-E=-Z^2(4\varepsilon+1)$ Ry, where E_0 is the ground state energy of the hydrogenic atom with charge Z. The expansion for J (in Rydberg) is then

$$\left.\begin{aligned} J = Z^2 - \tfrac{5}{4} Z + 0.315\,311 - 0.01707\frac{1}{Z} + 0.00068\frac{1}{Z^2} + \\ + 0.00164\frac{1}{Z^3} + 0.00489\frac{1}{Z^4}. \end{aligned}\right\} \tag{33.12}$$

It is interesting to note how small the coefficients of negative powers in (33.12) are. The constant term in (33.12) and the individual expressions for $Z=1$ to 3 and for 8, from which this polynomial for J was derived, are all rigorous lower limits. For other values of Z the interpolation formula (33.12) is not *rigorously* a lower limit (but probably is in practice) and should be an excellent approximation. For Be^{++} ($Z=4$) this formula gives $J=11.311131$ Ry, the direct evaluation gave 11.311125 Ry.

The theoretical values for the ionization potentials J for $Z=2$ to 8 are given in Table 7. The experimental values are, of course, measured in units of cm^{-1}. We have so far restricted ourselves to the ideal case of infinitely heavy nuclei. In Sect. 37 we shall discuss in detail the effect of nuclear motion. We shall see, however, that most of this effect is accounted for if in the theoretical expressions the energy unit Ry $= R_\infty$ is replaced by R_A, the appropriate unit for a nucleus of atomic mass A (see Sect. 5). With A in physical atomic mass units, we have

$$R_A \approx R_\infty\left(1-\frac{m}{M_A}\right) = \left(109737.31 - \frac{60.22}{A}\right)\,\mathrm{cm}^{-1}. \tag{33.13}$$

In Table 7 we also give the experimental[2] ionization potentials, in units of R_A. The agreement between theory and experiment is seen to be excellent. The remaining (very small) discrepancies are largely due to further corrections for nuclear motion (see Sect. 37) and especially to relativistic effects (see Sect. 41).

A simple variational wave function U for arbitrary Z is given by Eriksson[3] as

$$\left.\begin{aligned} U(\sigma,\tau,v) = \tfrac{1}{2} e^{-\frac{1}{2}\sigma}\Big[\Big(1-\frac{1.0694}{Z}-\frac{0.174}{Z^2}\Big)+\Big(\frac{0.1220}{Z}-\frac{0.022}{Z^2}\Big)v + \\ +\Big(\frac{0.0800}{Z}+\frac{0.018}{Z^2}\Big)\sigma+\Big(\frac{0.00927}{Z}+\frac{0.0070}{Z^2}\Big)\tau^2\Big]. \end{aligned}\right\} \tag{33.14}$$

[1] E. A. Hylleraas and J. Midtdal: Phys. Rev. **103**, 829 (1956). Some terms of the type of (32.23) and logarithmic terms were also included.

[2] G. Herzberg and R. Zbinden (unpublished) for $Z=1$; C. E. Moore, Atomic Energy Levels, I, NBS Circular 467 (1949) for $Z \gtrless 2$.

[3] H. A. Eriksson: Z. Physik **109**, 762 (1938).

Table 7. *Nonrelativistic theoretical ionization potentials in Ry* ($=\frac{1}{2}$ *atomic units) and experimental values in units of* R_A.

	He	Li^+	Be^{++}	$B^{(3+)}$	$C^{(4+)}$	$N^{(5+)}$	$O^{(6+)}$
J_{obs}	1.80739	5.5599	11.3116	19.0643	28.820	40.578	54.340
J_{theor}	1.80744	5.55982	11.31113	19.06194	28.8125	40.5629	54.3132

34. The negative hydrogen ion. The H^--ion is an interesting special case of He-like ions ($Z=1$). It is "only just" stable against dissociation into a neutral hydrogen atom plus a free electron. The dissociation energy J of the H^- ground state is only about 0.75 eV and this ion possesses *no* other bound states. This ion therefore has no discrete spectrum and its continuous spectrum is difficult to observe under laboratory conditions[1] and its dissociation energy has not yet been measured directly.

The structure of the negative hydrogen ion has been of interest almost since the advent of quantum mechanics in connection with the theory of alkali hydrides. These structures can be thought of as a combination of a positive alkali ion (closed shell) and the negative H^- ion. Lithium hydride is particularly simple theoretically, since both Li^+ and H^- are helium-like ions. Some time ago already HYLLERAAS[2] succeeded in calculating the attractive COULOMB force and repulsive exchange force between these two ions. This calculation gave values for the lattice spacing and binding energy of the LiH crystal in good agreement with experiment.

More recently, the negative hydrogen ion has been found to be of great importance for the opacity of the atmosphere of the sun and of similar stars. The ionization potential of H^-, $J\approx 0.75$ eV, equals k (BOLTZMANN's constant) times about 8700 °K, which is slightly higher than the temperature in the solar atmosphere. Some free electrons are released by the ionization of the metals present in the gas and, since neutral hydrogen is the main constituent by far of the gas, many of these electrons will be captured to form H^-. Conversely, the flux of radiation coming from the sun's interior will tend to be absorbed by the H^- ions accompanied by dissociation of these ions (photoeffect, Sect. 74). The electrons released will again be captured by H-atoms with the emission of radiation (recombination, Sect. 75), and so on. This process is the main source of opacity in the solar atmosphere and the continuous absorption coefficient of H^- has been studied extensively and used in the theory of the solar atmosphere. In fact, discrepancies between early calculations and observational evidence on the sun's radiation pointed out the inaccuracies of the wave functions for H^- which were available then[3].

Calculations of the wave function and energy of H^- are also of purely methodological interest, since this most loosely bound of all He-like ions provides the most severe test of the approximation methods used in the preceding sections. The simple hydrogen-like wave function U with screening constant $\frac{5}{16}$, for instance, would give a *negative* value (32.12) for the ionization potential J, i.e. no binding at all,

$$U = e^{-0.688(r_1+r_2)}, \qquad J = -\frac{7}{128}\,\mathrm{Ry}. \tag{34.1}$$

[1] R. FUCHS: Z. Physik **130**, 69 (1951).

[2] E. A. HYLLERAAS: Z. Physik **63**, 771 (1930).

[3] For a discussion of these astrophysical topics see L. H. ALLER, Astrophysics, The Atmospheres of the Sun and Stars, New York: Ronald Press 1953 and R. WOOLLEY and D. STIBBS, The Outer Layers of A Star. Oxford: Clarendon Press 1953.

The variation method of Sect. 32 has been applied to the H^- ion by BETHE[1], HYLLERAAS[2], and HENRICH[3], using wave functions with 3, 6 and 11 parameters, respectively. The corresponding values for the ionization potential J (in Ry) were 0.0506, 0.0529 and 0.05512, respectively. Comparison with the equivalent values for He (Sect. 32) shows that the convergence of J with the number of parameters is slower for H^-. The best value is the 24-parameter result[4] of $J = 0.05545_1$.

The wave function of the negative hydrogen ion is also of interest, since it shows up many features of He-like wave functions most drastically. The three-parameter wave function of form

$$\left.\begin{aligned} U(s,u,t) &= \varphi(ks,ku,kt),\\ \varphi(s,u,t) &= e^{-\frac{1}{2}s}(1+c_1 u + c_2 t^2)\end{aligned}\right\} \quad (34.2)$$

Table 8. *Coefficients of the three-parameter wave functions for the ground states of H^-, He and Li^+.*

	c_1	c_2	k
H^-	0.20	0.05	1.535
He	0.08	0.010	3.63
Li^+	0.08	0.004	5.792

is compared with the analogous functions for He and Li^+ in Table 8. For this (as well as the more accurate) wave functions the coefficients of u, t^2, etc. are

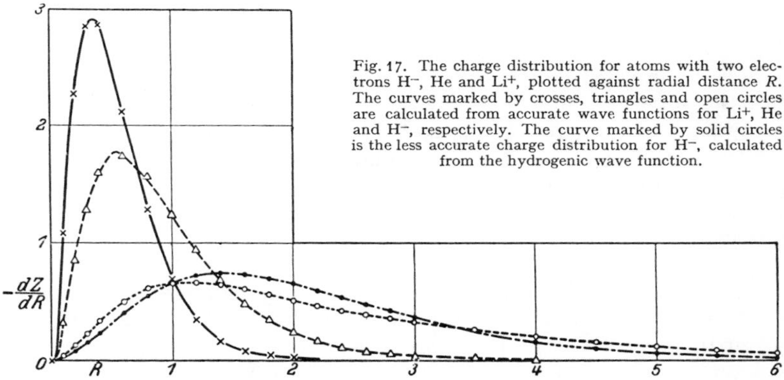

Fig. 17. The charge distribution for atoms with two electrons H^-, He and Li^+, plotted against radial distance R. The curves marked by crosses, triangles and open circles are calculated from accurate wave functions for Li^+, He and H^-, respectively. The curve marked by solid circles is the less accurate charge distribution for H^-, calculated from the hydrogenic wave function.

considerably larger for H^- than for He (and smaller still for Li^+, etc.). The smaller the nuclear charge Z, the stronger is the effect of the electrons on each other. The charge distribution, obtained by integrating the square of the variational wave function over the coordinates of one electron, is compared in Fig. 17 with that obtained from the simple hydrogen-like approximation (34.1). Note that the hydrogenic charge distribution is too small both at very small and at very large radial distances.

The behavior of the wave function for large values of r_1 is also illustrated by considering the simpler expression obtained by setting r_2 equal to zero. For the 11-parameter wave function this gives

$$U(r_1,0) = e^{-0.708\,r_1}\left[1 + 1.19\,\frac{r_1}{10} + 6.1\left(\frac{r_1}{10}\right)^2 + 4.7\left(\frac{r_1}{10}\right)^4 + 1.8\left(\frac{r_1}{10}\right)^6\right] \quad (34.3)$$

compared with the hydrogen-like one-parameter expression

$$U(r_1,0) = e^{-0.688\,r_1} = e^{-0.708\,r_1}\left[1 + 0.20\,\frac{r_1}{10} + 0.020\left(\frac{r_1}{10}\right)^2 + \cdots\right].$$

[1] H. A. BETHE: Z. Physik **57**, 815 (1929).
[2] E. A. HYLLERAAS: Z. Physik **63**, 291 (1930).
[3] L. R. HENRICH: Astrophys. J. **99**, 59 (1944).
[4] E. HYLLERAAS and J. MIDTDAL: Phys. Rev. **103**, 829 (1956).

The series (34.3) should be a fairly good approximation for $r_1 \lesssim 5$ and in this range is larger than the hydrogen-like expression above. The same qualitative features are found for He, Li^+, etc., but to a much smaller extent.

The hydrogen-like wave function is too small at small distances, since the actual screening is much smaller near the nucleus than the assumed constant $\frac{5}{16}$. The behavior at large distances can be seen as follows. The exact wave function for the negative hydrogen ion can (in principle) be written in the form

$$U(\boldsymbol{r}_1, \boldsymbol{r}_2) = \sum_{nlm} f_{nlm}(\boldsymbol{r}_1)\, u_{nlm}(\boldsymbol{r}_2). \tag{34.4}$$

In (34.4), u_{nlm} are the normalized, mutually orthogonal hydrogen wave functions for $Z=1$ (which form a complete set) and f_{nlm} are arbitrary functions (of a single coordinate) which have to be determined from the wave equation. Consider now values of r_1 very large compared with the radial distances for which $u_{nlm}(r_2)$ is appreciable. Multiply the full wave equation by $u^*_{nlm}(\boldsymbol{r}_2)$ and integrate over $\boldsymbol{r}_2$. We can then neglect the terms involving $(r_1^{-1} - r_{12}^{-1})$ and the remaining equation reduces to an asymptotic equation for f,

$$(\varDelta_1 + 2E - 2E_n)\, f_{nlm}(\boldsymbol{r}_1) = 0, \tag{34.5}$$

where E is the total energy of the two-electron atom and $E_n = -1/2n^2$ is the energy of a hydrogen atom in the state u_{nlm}.

Since the wave function must be bounded at infinity, the radial part of f must be an exponentially decreasing factor proportional to $\exp\left(-\sqrt{2E_n - 2E}\, r_1\right)$. The smallest exponent comes from $n=1$ and this term (in 34.4) will predominate at very large distances. For the spherically symmetric ground state of H^-, f_{100} will also be spherically symmetric and $E = -0.52756$ a.u. In this case we have asymptotically

$$f_{100}(r) = a_1 e^{-\sqrt{2J}\, r} = a_1 e^{-0.235\, r}, \tag{34.6}$$

where a_1 is an unknown constant. The exponent in (34.6) is much smaller[1] than that in (34.1) and the correct wave function has a much longer "tail".

A comparison of (34.3) and (34.6) shows that the variational wave function cannot have the correct asymptotic behavior for *very* large r_1, where the polynomial in square brackets in (34.3) is a poor approximation (and an *under*estimate) for $e^{+0.473\, r_1}$. This large difference in the exponents of (34.3) and (34.6) suggests the use of trial wave functions for H^- of a form slightly different from the standard HYLLERAAS wave function (32.15). CHANDRASEKHAR[2] has investigated a function of the form

$$U = \left(e^{-a r_1 - b r_2} + e^{-b r_1 - a r_2}\right)(1 + c\, r_{12}). \tag{34.7}$$

Even with the polarization term in r_{12} omitted ($c=0$), the variation method gave $a = 1.039$, $b = 0.283$ and $J = 0.027$ Ry. Although this value of J is quite poor, it is much better than the *negative* value obtained from (34.1). Note how close a is to unity and b to the exponent of (34.6); this wave function "almost" represents an unscreened hydrogen atom plus a very loosely bound outer electron. Including also the term in $c r_{12}$, CHANDRASEKHAR found $a = 1.075$, $b = 0.478$, $c = 0.312$ and $J = 0.0518$ Ry (better than the 3-parameter HYLLERAAS value, worse than the 6-parameter value).

Attempts have been made to use trial wave functions of form similar to (34.7), but with more parameters, for the H^- ground state. When the number of parameters is large, a wave function of this type does not seem to give a better energy value than the standard HYLLERAAS wave function with as many parameters.

[1] Due to the fact that the ionization potential J of H^- is so small.

[2] S. CHANDRASEKHAR: Astrophys. J. **100**, 176 (1944).

It should be remembered that, although (34.6) is the *asymptotic* form of the correct wave function, the constant a_1 may be quite small and the function may approach (34.6) only for *very* large values of r_1. For He, Li^+, etc. the variational wave functions also decrease more rapidly than the correct ones for very large radial distances, but the discrepancy is much smaller for the larger values of Z.

35. Variation method for excited states. *α) General remarks.* The calculation of excited states is rendered more difficult, compared to that of the ground state, by the appearance of the subsidiary condition that the eigenfunction of every excited state must be orthogonal to the eigenfunctions of all lower states[1]. This subsidiary condition reduces considerably the number of available trial functions which may be chosen to approximate the eigenfunction and inserted in the variation integral; as a result, the convergence of the procedure is not nearly as good as before.

However, cases do exist in which the subsidiary condition is satisfied automatically if the form of the trial function is taken as prescribed by the character of the term to be calculated. A case in point is the $2S$ term of orthohelium. Every function designed to approximate the eigenfunction of this term must, of course, be chosen to be antisymmetric in the coordinates of the two electrons, and this in itself is sufficient to assure orthogonality to the symmetric eigenfunction of the ground state. The subsidiary condition is satisfied automatically also for the two $2P$ terms. The eigenfunction of every P term has an explicit, characteristic dependence on the orientation of the atom in space, while the eigenfunctions of S terms depend only on the mutual separations of the electrons and on their distances from the nucleus. As a result, the product of an S and P eigenfunction vanishes on integration over the EULERian angles; however, S states are the only states which are lower than the two $2P$ states. Furthermore, the eigenfunctions belonging to the $2\,^1P$ and the $2\,^3P$ terms are also orthogonal to each other since they are of different symmetries in the two electrons and, thus, the subsidiary condition is satisfied for both $2P$ states. In general, the eigenfunctions belonging to two states of an atom are automatically orthogonal if either the total orbital angular momentum L or the total spin S (or both) have different values for the two states. Hence, the calculation by the RITZ method of the lowest state belonging to a given L and S is always straigtforward; it does not matter if there exist lower terms, as long as they have some other value for L or/and S. According to this rule, the $2\,^3S$, $2\,^1P$, and $2\,^3P$ (also $3\,^1D$, $3\,^3D$, etc.) states of helium can be treated by the RITZ procedure without additional complications, i.e., any function which has the appropriate symmetry and angular dependence may be adopted as trial function. In the calculation of the $2\,^1S$ term, on the other hand, one must specifically provide for the orthogonality of the eigenfunction to that of the ground state $1\,^1S$.

β) The $2\,^3S$-state. We start with the lowest state of ortho-helium, which contains a $1s$-electron and a $2s$-electron. Let us consider as a simple trial wave function the antisymmetrized product of two hydrogen-like wave functions with nuclear charge Z_i and Z_a for the inner and outer electron. This wave function is

$$\left.\begin{aligned} U &= e^{-Z_i r_1} e^{-\frac{1}{2} Z_a r_2} \left(\tfrac{1}{2} Z_a r_2 - 1\right) - e^{-Z_i r_2} e^{-\frac{1}{2} Z_a r_1} \left(\tfrac{1}{2} Z_a r_1 - 1\right) \\ &= e^{-ks}\left[\left(-\tfrac{1}{2} Z_a s + 2\right) \operatorname{Sin} ct - \tfrac{1}{2} Z_a t \operatorname{Cos} ct\right], \end{aligned}\right\} \quad (35.1)$$

[1] If the subsidiary condition is disregarded and the RITZ procedure is carried out to sufficiently high approximation, one always obtains a (bad) approximation to the ground state rather than the desired (good) approximation to the excited state. This will happen even if the initial form of the trial function is a good choice for the eigenfunction of the excited level.

where

$$2k = Z_i + \tfrac{1}{2} Z_a, \qquad 2c = Z_i - \tfrac{1}{2} Z_a. \tag{35.2}$$

One can then substitute (35.1) into the variational integral (32.8), consider k and c (i.e. Z_i and Z_a) as parameters to be varied and find the energy minimum E. Such calculations were carried out by ECKART[1] both for He and Li^+. His results are given in Table 9, where J is again the ionization potential of the state, i.e. minus the total energy E minus Z^2 Ry.

Table 9. ECKART'S *results for the $n=2$ states in He and Li^+. (Energy in Ry.)*

	He				Li^+			
	Z_i	Z_a	J_{theor}	J_{exp}	Z_i	Z_a	J_{theor}	J_{exp}
$2\,^3S$	2.01	1.53	0.334	0.350	3.03	2.56	1.21	1.21
$2\,^3P$	1.99	1.09	0.262	0.266	2.98	2.16	1.04	1.05
$2\,^1P$	2.00	0.97	0.245	0.247	3.01	1.94	0.99	1.00

It is interesting to note that, both for He and Li^+ ($Z=2$ and 3), the value of Z_a lies between the two limiting values $(Z-1)$ and $(Z-\frac{5}{16})$. The lower limit is appropriate for highly excited states, where the outer electron is totally screened by the inner one[2], and the upper limit for the ground state. Z_i is slightly larger than Z, i.e. the outer electron "pushes in" the charge cloud of the inner one towards the nucleus to a small extent.

For He, a trial wave function similar to (35.1), but containing more parameters (c_1 to c_6) has been used by HYLLERAAS and UNDHEIM[3]. This wave function, odd in t ,is

$$U = e^{-ks}\left[(c_1 + c_2 s + c_4 u + c_5 u s)\,\mathrm{Sin}\,ct + t(c_3 + c_6 u)\,\mathrm{Cos}\,ct\right]. \tag{35.3}$$

Minimizing the energy with respect to all parameters[4], they find $J=0.35044$ Ry, in excellent agreement with the experimental value of 0.35047 R_{He}. A similar calculation, but with fewer parameters, for Li^+ was carried out by BREIT and collaborators. Their value[5] for J is lower than the experimental one, $J=1.2215\,R_{\text{Li}}$, by about 0.3%.

γ) The 2P terms. In dealing with P terms there appear a number of features which distinguish them from S terms, the only type we have treated so far[6]. In the first place, the P terms are degenerate. The magnetic quantum number m, i.e., the angular momentum about a distinguished z-axis in units of $\hbar$, can assume the values 1, 0, and -1, and to each value of m belongs an eigenfunction. Secondly, the eigenfunctions depend explicitly on the orientation of the atom in space relative to a distinguished z-axis. To be specific, if ϑ_1, φ_1 are the polar coordinates of the first electron and ϑ_2, φ_2 those of the second electron (z is the

[1] C. ECKART: Phys. Rev. **36**, 878 (1930).

[2] The energy value for He obtained from the variational integral by simply substituting $Z_i=2$, $Z_a=1$ is $J=0.247$ Ry, considerably worse than ECKART's value.

[3] E. HYLLERAAS and B. UNDHEIM: Z. Physik **65**, 759 (1930). See also S. HUANG: Astrophys. J. **108**, 354 (1948).

[4] They find $k=1.32$ and $c=0.725$ and (35.2) then gives $Z_i=2.05$ and $Z_a=1.19$.

[5] G. BREIT and F. DOERMANN: Phys. Rev. **36**, 1732 (1930). More recently, a much more accurate wave function for the $2\,^3S$-state in Li^+ has been obtained by LUKE, MEYEROTT and CLENDENIN, Phys. Rev. **85**, 401 (1952). Their method is outlined in Sect. 36β and gives a value of J in almost exact agreement with experiment.

[6] Cf. G. BREIT: Phys. Rev. **35**, 569 (1930).

polar axis), the eigenfunctions may be written in the following form:

$$\left.\begin{aligned} U_1 &= \frac{\sqrt{3}}{4\pi}\left(F \sin\vartheta_1 e^{i\varphi_1} \mp \widetilde{F} \sin\vartheta_2 e^{i\varphi_2}\right) && (m=1),\\ U_0 &= \frac{\sqrt{6}}{4\pi}\left(F \cos\vartheta_1 \mp \widetilde{F} \cos\vartheta_2\right) && (m=0),\\ U_{-1} &= \frac{\sqrt{3}}{4\pi}\left(F \sin\vartheta_1 e^{-i\varphi_1} \mp \widetilde{F} \sin\vartheta_2 e^{-i\varphi_2}\right) && (m=-1). \end{aligned}\right\} \quad (35.4)$$

In the above, F depends only on the distances r_1, r_2 of the electrons from the nucleus and their mutual separation r_{12}; or, what amounts to the same thing, F depends only on r_1, r_2 and Θ, the angle between the radius vectors $\boldsymbol{r}_1$ and $\boldsymbol{r}_2$. $\widetilde{F}$ arises from F by interchanging the two electrons:

$$\widetilde{F}(r_1, r_2, \Theta) = F(r_2, r_1, \Theta). \quad (35.5)$$

In (35.4) the minus sign refers to the ortho-state $2\,^3P$, the plus sign to the para-state $2\,^1P$.

For the radial trial wave function F, Eckart again chose a product of a $1s$ and a $2p$ hydrogenlike radial function with nuclear charge Z_i and Z_a, respectively,

$$F = r_1 e^{-\frac{1}{2}Z_a r_1} e^{-Z_i r_2}. \quad (35.6)$$

Substituting the wave function (35.4) with (35.6) into the variational integral, he evaluated the energy minimum for variations of the parameters Z_i and Z_a. His results for the $2\,^3P$ and $2\,^1P$ states[1] of He and Li^+ are given in Table 9. Note that Z_a is much closer to $(Z-1)$ (complete screening) than for the $2S$ states.

One could improve the calculation by using instead of (35.6) a trial wave function with more parameters, which give an account of polarization effects. So far only a wave function with one extra parameter c has been used for the $2\,^3P$ state in He by Breit[2],

$$F = r_1 e^{-\frac{1}{2}Z_a r_1} e^{-Z_i r_2}(1 + c\cos\Theta). \quad (35.7)$$

He finds $c = -0.0089$ and almost the same values for J, Z_i and Z_a as Eckart. (35.7), unlike (35.6), gives an approximate, but simple, account of polarization (the term in c), which is seen to be small. The first order Heisenberg method of Sect. 28 ($Z_i = 2$, $Z_a = 1$) gives $J = 0.260$ Ry, the second order calculation (polarization) of Sect. 29 gives $J = 0.264$ Ry. This second value is better (but involves lengthier calculations) than Breit's and Eckart's $J = 0.262$ Ry. The experimental value is $J = 0.266$ Ry.

δ) The $2\,^1S$-state. One is tempted to treat the $2\,^1S$-state of para-helium in an analogous manner to $2\,^3S$ but with a symmetric, instead of antisymmetric, trial wave function. As mentioned before, such a wave function is not necessarily orthogonal to the wave function of the ground state (with lower energy) and the standard variation method cannot be applied. Hylleraas and Undheim[3] have, nevertheless, developed a modification of the variation method which can be used.

---

[1] He also performed similar calculations for the $3\,^3D$ and $3\,^1D$ states.

[2] G. Breit: Phys. Rev. **36**, 383 (1930).

[3] E. Hylleraas and B. Undheim: Z. Physik **65**, 759 (1930). For a similar calculation for the $3\,^3P$ and $3\,^1P$ states in He see L. Goldberger and A. Clogston, Phys. Rev. **56**, 696 (1939).

They choose a trial wave function with a number of parameters and substitute it into the variational integral, as in the conventional variation method. They require the energy integral E to be stationary for variations of the parameters and again obtain the determinantal equation (32.22). However, they solve not for the lowest root $E_{(1)}$ (which would correspond to the ground state), but for the *second* lowest root $E_{(2)}$ of this equation. The corresponding wave function $U_{(2)}$ is then at least orthogonal to the *trial* wave function $U_{(1)}$ corresponding to the lowest root. Although $U_{(1)}$ is only an approximation to the ground state wave function, they show that the second root $E_{(2)}$ is *rigorously* an *upper limit* to the total energy of the second state of the para-system (the $2\,^1S$-state). The remaining procedure is then identical with the standard variation method.

They used a trial wave function identical with (35.3), except for an interchange of the Cos and Sin terms so that the wave function is symmetric. They found $k=1.34$, $c=0.73$ [$Z_i=2.08$, $Z_a=1.21$ in (35.2)] and for the ionization potential $J=0.2898$ Ry, compared with the experimental value of $J=0.2920$ Ry. The convergence of J with the number of parameters is much slower for the $2\,^1S$ state than for $2\,^3S$ (whose trial wave function is automatically orthogonal to the ground state).

COOLIDGE and JAMES[1] have obtained a much improved theoretical value of $J=0.2916$ Ry, using essentially the same method but a better trial wave function. The improvement is due largely to the inclusion of terms with two different exponential factors for the outer electron [compare the discussion of (34.7)]. They also give an illuminating comparison of the HEISENBERG, HARTREE, FOCK and variation methods as applied to the $2\,^1S$ state.

36. Miscellaneous calculations. We have discussed in detail some of the more commonly used methods of approximation in the treatment of He-like atoms. We shall merely mention some other methods and some properties of the wave functions (mainly for the ground state).

α) The "local energy". Let U be some approximation to some exact eigenfunction of the total HAMILTONian operator H, given by (24.1) in our case. We can then define a function of position, called the "local energy", by

$$E_{\text{loc}}(\boldsymbol{r}_1, \boldsymbol{r}_2) = \frac{1}{U(\boldsymbol{r}_1, \boldsymbol{r}_2)} H\, U(\boldsymbol{r}_1, \boldsymbol{r}_2). \tag{36.1}$$

If the wave function U were the exact eigenfunction, E_{loc} would of course be a constant equal to the exact energy eigenvalue. In the first order perturbation method and in the variation method one first finds some approximate function U and uses, as an approximation to the correct energy eigenvalue, the expectation value of E_{loc} (or the HAMILTONian) over this function,

$$E \equiv \overline{H} = \int d\tau\, U^* H\, U = \int d\tau\, |U|^2 E_{\text{loc}}. \tag{36.2}$$

The variation method chooses a function U such that the error in this expectation value is minimized. The *overall* form of the function U will then be excellent (if enough parameters are used) in the regions where the wave function is appreciable. But the variational function U will *not* be good at extremely large values of r_1 or r_2 (where U is extremely small). One can also show that the second and higher derivatives of any variational wave function (with a finite number of parameters) are poor approximations if r_1, r_2 or r_{12} are very small. In fact, when these wave functions are used, E_{loc} tends to $-\infty$ as r_1 or r_2 approach zero and tends to $+\infty$ as r_{12} approaches zero.

[1] A. COOLIDGE and M. JAMES: Phys. Rev. **49**, 676 (1936).

BARTLETT[1] recently obtained an approximate wave function for the ground state of helium in numerical form. This wave function, obtained by a numerical iteration procedure on an electronic computing machine, was designed to give as small fluctuations of E_{loc} as possible. For this wave function, E_{loc} is finite even at r_1, r_2 or r_{12} equal to zero and lies between -2.88 and -2.92 (a.u.) for all values of r_1 and r_2 up to about 4 a.u. But the energy eigenvalue E cannot be determined from this wave function to very much better than $-2.90 \pm 0.01_5$. The HYLLERAAS six-parameter wave function, on the other hand, gives $E = -2.9032$ (in error by only 0.0005) but has large fluctuations of E_{loc} around this value (apart from infinite values of E_{loc} if r_1, r_2 or r_{12} is zero). Nevertheless the normalized HYLLERAAS (6-parameter) and BARTLETT wave functions do not differ by more than $\pm 3\%$ from each other for all values of r_1 and r_2 up to about 4 a.u.

A variational method can also be devised which minimizes not E itself but the fluctuations of the function E_{loc}. One again chooses a trial wave function U with some arbitrary parameters and finds the minimum with respect to the parameters of

$$\overline{(E_{\text{loc}} - E)^2} = \int d\tau \, |(H - E)\, U|^2. \tag{36.3}$$

This method has not been used extensively in practice[2].

β) Expansion in LEGENDRE *polynomials.* For S-states of helium-like atoms, the exact wave function U depends only on the shape and size of the triangle formed by the coordinates of the two electrons, $\boldsymbol{r}_1$ and $\boldsymbol{r}_2$, and the line joining them. We can choose for the three variables describing this triangle the radial distances r_1 and r_2 and the angle ϑ_{12} between the vectors $\boldsymbol{r}_1$ and $\boldsymbol{r}_2$. The full normalized wave function U can then be expressed as an expansion in the normalized LEGENDRE polynomials $\mathcal{P}_{l0}$,

$$U(\boldsymbol{r}_1, \boldsymbol{r}_2) = \sum_{l=0}^{\infty} c_l \, \Phi_l(r_1, r_2) \, \mathcal{P}_{l0}(\cos\vartheta_{12}), \tag{36.4}$$

where Φ_l is some normalized function of two variables and c_l is a constant. Substituting (36.4) into the full wave equation for U, one then obtains an infinite set of coupled differential equations in r_1 and r_2 for the functions $c_l \Phi_l$. For all S-states in He-like atoms (except possibly for H^-) the constant c_0 is almost unity and c_1, c_2, etc. are small and decrease rapidly. These equations can then be solved by an iteration method, starting from the homogeneous equation for Φ_0.

A very accurate wave function for the 2^3S state in Li^+ has been obtained by this method[3]. The constant c_1 is only about 0.014, c_2 about 0.003. This method has not yet been applied to the ground state of He, but the HYLLERAAS six-parameter wave function has been expanded[4] in the form of (36.4). The first few coefficients c_l for the He ground state are

$$c_0 = 0.998, \quad c_1 = 0.063, \quad c_2 = 0.012, \quad c_3 = 0.004. \tag{36.5}$$

Each function Φ_l could in turn be written as an infinite sum of products of single particle wave functions. Actually Φ_0 is fairly close[5] to the HARTREE wave

[1] J. H. BARTLETT: Phys. Rev. **98**, 1076 (1955).

[2] H. JAMES and F. YOST: Phys. Rev. **54**, 646 (1938).

[3] LUKE, MEYEROTT and CLENDENIN: Phys. Rev. **85**, 401 (1952).

[4] L. C. GREEN *et al.*: Phys. Rev. **91**, 35 (1953); **96**, 319 (1954).

[5] See also H. MITLER: Phys. Rev. **99**, 1835 (1955). MITLER uses the HARTREE wave function and energy as a starting point and calculates the correlation energy (the effect of the correlation between the positions of the two electrons) by a perturbation method.

function (Sect. 31) and Φ_1, is approximated (very roughly) by

$$\Phi_1(r_1, r_2) = N r_1 r_2 e^{-2.3(r_1+r_2)}, \tag{36.6}$$

where N is a normalization constant.

γ) Wave functions in momentum space. In analogy with the discussions of Sect. 8, the SCHRÖDINGER equation for a He-like atom can be written in the form of an integral equation in momentum space. The momentum space wave function $\psi(\boldsymbol{p}_1, \boldsymbol{p}_2)$ is the six-dimensional FOURIER transform of the spatial wave function $U(\boldsymbol{r}_1, \boldsymbol{r}_2)$. Taking the FOURIER transform of the SCHRÖDINGER equation (24.1) gives the desired integral equation in momentum space. Replacing for the moment the nuclear potential $-Z/r$ by a general potential $V(\boldsymbol{r})$, we get

$$\left.\begin{aligned}(E - \tfrac{1}{2}p_1^2 - \tfrac{1}{2}p_2^2)\,\psi(\boldsymbol{p}_1, \boldsymbol{p}_2) = \int d^3k\, V'(-\boldsymbol{k})\,[\psi(\boldsymbol{p}_1 + \boldsymbol{k}, \boldsymbol{p}_2) + \\ + \psi(\boldsymbol{p}_1, \boldsymbol{p}_2 + \boldsymbol{k})] + \int d^3k\, \frac{1}{2\pi^2 k^2}\,\psi(\boldsymbol{p}_1 - \boldsymbol{k}, \boldsymbol{p}_2 + \boldsymbol{k}),\end{aligned}\right\} \tag{36.7}$$

where

$$\psi(\boldsymbol{p}_1, \boldsymbol{p}_2) = \frac{1}{(2\pi)^3}\iint d^3r_1\, d^3r_2\, e^{-i(\boldsymbol{r}_1\cdot\boldsymbol{p}_1 + \boldsymbol{r}_2\cdot\boldsymbol{p}_2)}\, U(\boldsymbol{r}_1, \boldsymbol{r}_2)$$

and $V'(\boldsymbol{k})$ is $(2\pi)^{-\frac{3}{2}}$ times the FOURIER transform of $V(\boldsymbol{r})$. If $V(\boldsymbol{r})$ is the nuclear potential $-Z/r$, then $V'(\boldsymbol{k}) = -Z(2\pi^2 k^2)^{-1}$. The last term on the right side of (36.7) represents the interaction of the two electrons.

For an S-state, $\psi(\boldsymbol{p}_1, \boldsymbol{p}_2)$ only depends on the absolute values p_1 and p_2 of the two vectors $\boldsymbol{p}_1$ and $\boldsymbol{p}_2$ and on the angle ϑ_{12} between them. Another quantity of interest for S-states is the momentum distribution function $P(p)$, which gives the probability that either electron has momentum p (regardless of its direction or of the value of the momentum of the other electron). If ψ is normalized we have

$$P(p_1) = 4\pi p_1^2 \int d^3p_2\, \psi^2(p_1, p_2, \vartheta_{12}), \qquad \int_0^\infty dp\, P(p) = 1.$$

For the ground state of He-like atoms with nuclear charge Z, the simplest approximate wave function is again the hydrogen-like one with $z = Z - \frac{5}{16}$. Using (8.10) we find

$$\psi = \frac{8}{\pi^2}\,\frac{z^5}{(p_1^2 + z^2)^2\,(p_2^2 + z^2)^2}, \qquad P(p) = \frac{32 z^5 p^2}{\pi(p^2 + z^2)^4}. \tag{36.8}$$

As discussed in Sect. 8, better wave functions could be obtained by successive iterations of (36.7), using as the initial function occurring in the integrals the approximation (36.8). One such iteration has been carried out[1] and the corresponding approximation for $P(p)$ evaluated. Further iterations would be extremely tedious and no very accurate wave functions in momentum space are as yet available for helium.

δ) Some expectation values. We shall discuss now the ground state expectation values (denoted by bars) of a few operators, evaluated by using various wave functions. These expectation values will be needed in evaluating some relativistic corrections (Sect. 41) and also throw some light on the various types of wave functions.

Consider first the three-dimensional DIRAC delta-functions $\delta^{(3)}(\boldsymbol{r}_1)$ and $\delta^{(3)}(\boldsymbol{r}_{12})$. Their expectation values are

$$\left.\begin{aligned}\overline{\delta^{(3)}(\boldsymbol{r}_1)} &= \int d\tau_1\, U^2(\boldsymbol{r}_1, 0), \\ \overline{\delta^{(3)}(\boldsymbol{r}_{12})} &= \int d\tau_1\, U^2(\boldsymbol{r}_1, \boldsymbol{r}_1).\end{aligned}\right\} \tag{36.9}$$

[1] R. MCWEENEY and C. COULSON: Proc. Phys. Soc. Lond. A **62**, 509 (1949).

If we use either the HARTREE or hydrogen-like wave functions for the ground state of a He-like atom, U is of form $u(r_1)\, u(r_2)$. If $u(r)$ is normalized we then have

$$\overline{\delta^{(3)}(\boldsymbol{r}_1)} = u^2(0), \qquad \overline{\delta^{(3)}(\boldsymbol{r}_{12})} = \int d\tau\, u^4(r). \tag{36.10}$$

For the hydrogen-like wave function for nuclear charge $(Z - \frac{5}{16})$, in particular, this gives

$$\overline{\delta^{(3)}(\boldsymbol{r}_1)} = \frac{1}{\pi}\left(Z - \frac{5}{16}\right)^3, \qquad \overline{\delta^{(3)}(\boldsymbol{r}_{12})} = \frac{1}{8\pi}\left(Z - \frac{5}{16}\right)^3. \tag{36.11}$$

If the HYLLERAAS variational wave functions are used, the integrals (36.9) can be expressed in terms of the usual variables u, s, t and evaluated analytically.

We consider next the operator for (twice) the kinetic energy of one electron, $p_1^2 = -\Delta_1$. For a wave function of product form (hydrogenic or HARTREE) the single particle wave function $u(r_1)$ satisfies an equation of form

$$p^2 u = -\Delta u = 2\,[\varepsilon - V(r)]\, u(r). \tag{36.12}$$

For such a wave function the expectation value of p^2 is then

$$\overline{p^2} = 2 \int d\tau\, u^2(r)\, [\varepsilon - V(r)]. \tag{36.13}$$

For the hydrogenic wave function, $\overline{p^2}$ is simply $(Z - \frac{5}{16})^2$ a.u. For the HARTREE wave function (Sect. 31) the integral in (36.13) can be evaluated numerically. For the variational wave functions, $\overline{p_1^2}$ is simply equal to minus E, the expression for the total energy (see Sect. 36 ε).

We finally consider the square of the kinetic energy operator for electron 1, or $p_1^4 = \nabla_1^4 \equiv \Delta_1^2$. We first note that

$$\operatorname{div}_1 [U \operatorname{grad}_1 (\Delta_1 U) - (\Delta_1 U) \operatorname{grad}_1 U] = U(\Delta_1^2 U) - (\Delta_1 U)^2. \tag{36.14}$$

For any analytic function U which falls off exponentially at large distances, the integral of the left side of this equation over the *whole* $\boldsymbol{r}_1$-space must vanish (from GAUSS' theorem). We then have two alternative forms for the expectation value of p^4,

$$\overline{p_1^4} = \int d\tau_1\, d\tau_2\, U\, \Delta_1^2 U = d\tau_1\, d\tau_2\, (\Delta_1 U)^2. \tag{36.15}$$

Great care must be taken if the first form in (36.15) is used: For the exact wave function, $\Delta_1 U$ behaves like Z/r_1 or like $1/r_{12}$ if r_1 or r_{12} approaches zero, just like the potential energy in the total HAMILTONian. $\Delta_1^2 U$ then has a delta-function type of singularity at $r_1 = 0$ and $r_{12} = 0$ and a *wrong* answer would be obtained if the first integral in (36.15) were evaluated by a limiting process which excludes an infinitesimal region around the origin and around $r_{12} = 0$. The second form of (36.15) is free from these difficulties and is, in any case, easier to evaluate in practice.

For a normalized product wave function, this second form of (36.15) becomes, using (36.12),

$$\overline{p^4} = 4 \int d\tau\, u^2(r)\, [\varepsilon - V(r)]^2. \tag{36.16}$$

For the hydrogen-like wave function we find, using (3.25),

$$\overline{p^4} = 5\,(Z - \tfrac{5}{16})^4 \text{ a.u.} \tag{36.17}$$

For the HARTREE wave function, (36.16) can be integrated numerically. For the variational wave functions, $(\Delta_1 U)$ can be expressed in terms of the variables u, s and t and the analytic evaluation of the second integral in (36.15) is elementary but tedious.

Table 10. *Expectation values in atomic units of various operators for the ground state of Helium.*

Wave function[2]	H-like	HARTREE	3	6	18	38
$-E=-\overline{H}$	2.8438	2.8617	2.9024	2.90324	2.903715	2.903723
$-\overline{H^2}/\overline{H}$	3.160		2.9188	2.9091	2.90403	2.90376
$\overline{\delta^{(3)}(\boldsymbol{r}_1)}$	1.530	1.798	1.7984	1.8167	1.8102	1.8106
$\overline{\delta^{(3)}(\boldsymbol{r}_{12})}$	0.191	0.188	0.1162	0.1114	0.1072	0.1065
$\overline{p_1^4}$	40.54	52.46	53.42	54.50	54.072	54.092
$\overline{\boldsymbol{p}_1\cdot\boldsymbol{p}_2}$	0	0	0.178	0.164	0.1591	0.1591

The results[1] obtained with different wave functions for these expectation values for He ($Z=2$) are given in Table 10. The most reliable value in each case is probably (but *not* necessarily) the one for the variational wave function with the most parameters. Note that the HARTREE wave function (as well as the hydrogenic one) overestimates $\overline{\delta^{(3)}(\boldsymbol{r}_{12})}$ badly, since the polarization depresses the wave function appreciably when the two electrons are close (or coincide). For the other expectation values the HARTREE wave function gives much better results than the hydrogenic one and the polarization effects are not very strong.

It can also be seen from Table 10 that, for the variational wave functions, the fractional accuracy of the expectation value of most other operators is much poorer than that of the HAMILTONian H itself. For instance, the fractional differences between the expectation values for the 3 and 38 parameter functions are about 0.6×10^{-2} for $\delta^{(3)}(\boldsymbol{r}_1)$ and 9×10^{-2} for $\delta^{(3)}(\boldsymbol{r}_{12})$, but only 4×10^{-4} for H. Imagine a normalized variational wave function U_{var} expanded in terms of the *exact* normalized eigenfunctions U_n of the HAMILTONian H for helium,

$$U_{\text{var}}=\sqrt{1-\sum_{n=1}^{\infty}|c_n|^2}\;U_0+\sum_{n=1}^{\infty}c_n U_n, \tag{36.18}$$

where U_0, E_0 are the true wave function and energy of the ground state. We then have

$$\overline{H}-E_0=\sum_n|c_n|^2(E_n-E_0),\qquad \overline{H^2}-E_0^2=\sum_n|c_n|^2(E_n-E_0)^2. \tag{36.19}$$

If the coefficients c_n are small, then the error in the expectation value of an operator Q which does not commute with H will (in general) involve terms like $\sum c_n Q_{0n}$ which are linear in the c_n, whereas the error in $\overline{H}$ only contains terms quadratic in the c_n.

The error in $\overline{H^2}$ is also quadratic in the c_n, but with large coefficients: The quantity $(E_n+E_0)_{\text{av}}$ defined by

$$(E_n+E_0)_{\text{av}}\equiv\frac{\sum|c_n|^2(E_n^2-E_0^2)}{\sum|c_n|^2(E_n-E_0)}=\frac{\overline{H^2}-E_0^2}{\overline{H}-E_0} \tag{36.20}$$

measures, in a certain sense, the average energy of the most important higher terms in the expansion (36.18). The values of $\overline{H^2}$ and $\overline{H}$ for the three-parameter

[1] These results were obtained by T. KINOSHITA, D. BOWERS, J. F. BIRD and P. KABIR (unpublished). The expression $\overline{p_1^4}$ in the Table denotes the *second* integral in (36.15).

[2] "H-like" denotes the one-parameter hydrogenic wave function, the last four wave functions are the variational 3- and 6-parameter ones of HYLLERAAS', KINOSHITA's 38-parameter and HERZBERG and CHANDRASEKHAR's 18-parameter functions. Actually, a slightly improved version of the 18-parameter function was used, i.e. the function was minimized (for energy) more accurately by KINOSHITA by a method of successive approximation. The 38-parameter function is not yet fully minimized.

function, for instance, give a value[1] of about 30 a.u. or 60 Ry for $(E_n+E_0)_{\mathrm{av}}$, which is very large compared with the ionization potential.

ε) The virial theorem. In Sect. 32γ we have discussed variational wave functions for the ground state of a helium-like atom. The expectation value of the total kinetic energy T and of the total potential energy V is then $k^2 M/N$ and $-k\,L/N$, respectively [M, L, N defined by Eq. (32.17)]. Using (32.19) we then find that

$$\tfrac{1}{2}\overline{V} = -\overline{T} = \overline{H}, \tag{36.21}$$

where the bar denotes expectation values. This relation, which is an outcome of the virial theorem[2], can be generalized to apply to *any* bound and stationary state of an *arbitrary* atom, as follows.

Consider a nonrelativistic system of n charged particles which interact with each other only by means of Coulomb interactions. The total Hamiltonian H, kinetic energy T and potential energy V are then of the form

$$H = T + V, \qquad T = \sum_i \frac{p_i^2}{2m_i}, \qquad V = \sum_{i\neq j} \frac{a_{ij}}{r_{ij}}, \tag{36.22}$$

where m_i and a_{ij} are constants. Let φ be any bounded, quadratically integrable function of $\boldsymbol{r}_1, \boldsymbol{r}_2, \ldots, \boldsymbol{r}_n$ and call

$$L = -\int d\tau\,\varphi^* V\varphi, \qquad M = \int d\tau\,\varphi^* T\varphi, \qquad N = \int d\tau\,\varphi^*\varphi,$$

where the integral is extended over all values of the coordinates $\boldsymbol{r}_1$ to $\boldsymbol{r}_n$. Now let k be an arbitrary (as yet) parameter and form the following expectation value

$$\overline{H} = \frac{\int d\tau\, U^* H U}{\int d\tau\, U^* U} = \frac{k^2 M - k L}{N}, \tag{36.23}$$

where

$$U(\boldsymbol{r}_1, \ldots, \boldsymbol{r}_n) = \varphi(k\boldsymbol{r}_1, \ldots, k\boldsymbol{r}_n).$$

The factors k^2 and $-k$ stem from the fact that the operator T only contains second derivatives with respect to position and the operator V (for a Coulomb potential) only contains terms of the minus first power of distance.

For any correct eigenfunction of H, the expectation value (36.23) must have a stationary value with respect to any infinitesimal variation of the wave function, including a variation of the scale parameter k. We thus have, for any correct eigenfunction

$$\frac{\partial\overline{H}}{\partial k} = 0, \qquad k = \frac{L}{2M}, \qquad 2\overline{T} = -\overline{V} = -2\overline{H},$$

which is the required relation. For a more general potential of form $V = \sum_{i,j} a_{ij} r_{ij}^{\nu}$, one can similarly prove the relation

$$2\overline{T} = \nu\overline{V} = \frac{2\nu}{2+\nu}\overline{H}. \tag{36.24}$$

---

[1] The very accurate 38-parameter value of $\overline{H}$ can be used as an approximation for E_0 when evaluating the expression (36.20) for *less* accurate wave functions. The numerical value of $(E_n+E_0)_{\mathrm{av}}$ fluctuates somewhat from one variational wave function to another but, as a general trend, increases with increasing accuracy of the wave function (from about 10 a.u. for the 1-parameter to about 80 a.u. for a 14-parameter function). Rigorous upper bounds to the discrepancy between $\overline{H}$ for any function and the true energy E_0 can be calculated, if $\overline{H^2}$ is known [L. Wilets and I. Cherry, Phys. Rev. **103**, 112 (1953)]. These upper bounds grossly overestimate the actual error in $\overline{H}$ (this is connected with the fact that $(E_n+E_0)_{\mathrm{av}}$ is so large for these functions). If we *assume* that $(E_n+E_0)_{\mathrm{av}}$ is of the same order of magnitude (or larger) for 38 as for, say, 14 parameters and use the value of $(\overline{H}-\overline{H^2}/\overline{H})$ in Table 10 for the 38 parameter function, we find that the error in $\overline{H}$ for this function is only of the order of magnitude of 10^{-6} a.u.

[2] See also ref. [*4*], p. 140.

37. Motion of the nucleus. Next, we shall study the influence of the motion of the nucleus having mass M and coordinates $\xi_0 \eta_0 \zeta_0$. Let us consider an atom with n electrons having mass m and coordinates $\xi_1 \eta_1 \zeta_1 \ldots \xi_n \eta_n \zeta_n$. We introduce the coordinates of the center of mass

$$X = \frac{1}{M + n m} (M \xi_0 + m \xi_1 + \cdots + m \xi_n) \qquad \text{(similarly for } Y, Z) \qquad (37.1)$$

and the relative coordinates

$$x_i = \xi_i - \xi_0 \; (i = 1, 2, \ldots, n) \qquad \text{(similarly for } y_i, z_i). \qquad (37.2)$$

Then we obtain

$$\frac{\partial}{\partial \xi_i} = \frac{\partial}{\partial X} \cdot \frac{m}{M + n m} + \frac{\partial}{\partial x_i} \qquad (i = 1, \ldots, n),$$

$$\frac{\partial}{\partial \xi_0} = \frac{\partial}{\partial X} \cdot \frac{M}{M + n m} - \frac{\partial}{\partial x_1} - \cdots - \frac{\partial}{\partial x_n}.$$

The following expression, twice the kinetic energy, appears in the SCHRÖDINGER equation:

$$\frac{1}{M} \frac{\partial^2}{\partial \xi_0^2} + \frac{1}{m} \left(\frac{\partial^2}{\partial \xi_1^2} + \cdots + \frac{\partial^2}{\partial \xi_n^2} \right) = \frac{1}{M + n m} \frac{\partial^2}{\partial X^2} + \frac{1}{m} \sum_i \frac{\partial^2}{\partial x_i^2} + \frac{1}{M} \sum_{i k} \frac{\partial^2}{\partial x_i \partial x_k}. \quad (37.3)$$

Separating out the motion of the center of mass of the atomic system, i.e., the dependence of the eigenfunction on $X Y Z$, we obtain the SCHRÖDINGER equation in c.g.s. units:

$$\left[\frac{\hbar^2}{2m} \sum_{i=0}^{n} \Delta_i + \frac{\hbar^2}{2M} \sum_{i=1}^{n} \sum_{k=1}^{n} \left(\frac{\partial^2}{\partial x_i \partial x_k} + \frac{\partial^2}{\partial y_i \partial y_k} + \frac{\partial^2}{\partial z_i \partial z_k} \right) + E - V \right] U = 0. \quad (37.4)$$

The second term is the effect of the motion of the nucleus which we sought; it results in a correction of the eigenvalue which is proportional to the ratio of the electron mass to the nuclear mass, m/M. It is expedient to divide that term into two parts, one containing terms with $i = k$, and the other terms with $i \neq k$. Introducing the reduced mass of the electron,

$$\mu = \frac{m M}{M + m}, \qquad (37.5)$$

(37.4) becomes

$$\left[\frac{\hbar^2}{2\mu} \sum_i \Delta_i + \frac{\hbar^2}{M} \sum_{i<k} \left(\frac{\partial^2}{\partial x_i \partial x_k} + \frac{\partial^2}{\partial y_i \partial y_k} + \frac{\partial^2}{\partial z_i \partial z_k} \right) + E - V \right] U = 0. \quad (37.6)$$

Thus, the motion of the nucleus modifies the SCHRÖDINGER equation in two ways. In the first place, the effective mass of the electron μ replaces the actual mass of the electron m. Secondly, to the SCHRÖDINGER equation in which the motion of the nucleus is not considered, is added a perturbing term which changes the energy of the atom by the amount

$$\varepsilon_2 = - \frac{\hbar^2}{M} \sum_{i<k} \int U \left(\frac{\partial^2}{\partial x_i \partial x_k} + \frac{\partial^2}{\partial y_i \partial y_k} + \frac{\partial^2}{\partial z_i \partial z_k} \right) U \, d\tau.$$

Introducing atomic units and integrating by parts, the above is seen to be equal to

$$\varepsilon_2 = + \frac{m}{M} \sum_{i<k} \int (\text{grad}_i U \cdot \text{grad}_k U) \, d\tau. \qquad (37.7)$$

α) Elementary mass correction. We are familiar with the first modification of the SCHRÖDINGER equation, from the theory of the atoms which contain but a single electron. It can be dealt with simply by introducing a new atomic unit for the energy which differs from the usual energy unit by the factor

$$\frac{\mu}{M} = \frac{M}{M+m} \approx 1 - \frac{m}{M}.$$

Thus, if we solve the SCHRÖDINGER equation and express the energy of an atomic state in RYDBERG units, then, instead of taking the RYDBERG corresponding to infinite nuclear mass

$$R_\infty = \frac{m\,e^4}{2\pi\,c\,\hbar^3} = 109737.32\ \mathrm{cm}^{-1}, \tag{37.8}$$

we must take the RYDBERG corresponding to the mass of the atom in question, viz.,

$$R_M = R_\infty \frac{M}{M+m} \approx R_\infty \left(1 - \frac{m}{M}\right). \tag{37.9}$$

We may also put it this way: First, we calculate the energy levels for infinite nuclear mass, and then we apply the correction $\varepsilon_1 = -\frac{m}{M} E_\infty$ in which E_∞ is the term value for $M = \infty$. This part of the mass correction affects all the levels of the atom in the same way, and is also independent of the state of ionization of the atom. The frequencies of the spectral lines of the atom are all reduced in the same ratio $1 - \frac{m}{M}$.

β) Mass correction due to electron exchange[1]. On the other hand, the second part of the mass correction (37.7) differs for the various states of the atom. If the electrons in the atom moved entirely independently of each other, i.e., if the eigenfunction of the atom were a simple product of the eigenfunctions of the individual electrons,

$$U = \prod_{i=1}^{n} u_i(i),$$

then the second part of the mass correction would vanish, viz.,

$$\varepsilon_2 = \frac{m}{M} \sum_{i<k} \int d\tau_i\, u_i \operatorname{grad} u_i \int d\tau_k\, u_k \operatorname{grad} u_k = 0.$$

This follows from the fact that for a bound electron the expectation value of the momentum in any direction x,

$$\int u \frac{\partial u}{\partial x}\, d\tau,$$

is necessarily equal to zero. Thus the mass correction ε_2 is essentially determined by the extent to which the electrons affect one another's motion, i.e., insofar as definite phase relationships exist between the orbital motions of the electrons. The importance of these phase relationships for the mass correction is easily understood. If, for example, the electrons tend to move in the same direction, then the nucleus, in order to balance the motion of the electrons, will move about much more than if the motions of the individual electrons move independently of one another or even tend to be predominantly opposed to each other.

[1] Cf. D. S. HUGHES and C. ECKART: Phys. Rev. **36**, 694 (1930).

There are two reasons why the individual electrons affect one another's motion, the PAULI principle and the electrostatic interaction (polarization effect). We shall pursue both of these influences more closely in the example of an atom with two electrons. We consider first the exchange effects and approximate the eigenfunction by a sum of products of the eigenfunctions belonging to the two individual electrons; i.e., we neglect the polarization effect resulting from the electronic interaction:

$$U = \frac{1}{\sqrt{2}} \left(u(1)\, v(2) \pm v(1)\, u(2)\right). \tag{37.10}$$

The plus sign belongs to parahelium and the minus sign to orthohelium. Substituting (37.10) into (37.7) we obtain

$$\varepsilon_2 = \frac{m}{M} \int \operatorname{grad} u^*(1)\, v^*(2) \left[u(1) \operatorname{grad} v(2) \pm v(1) \operatorname{grad} u(2)\right] d\tau_1\, d\tau_2. \tag{37.11}$$

The first term inside the brackets yields zero, because

$$\int u \operatorname{grad} u^*\, d\tau = 0$$

vanishes, since it is the expectation value of the momentum of a bound electron. The second term yields

$$\varepsilon_2 = \pm \frac{m}{M} \left| \int \operatorname{grad} u^* \cdot v\, d\tau \right|^2. \tag{37.12}$$

The above integral is essentially the optical transition probability for going from the one occupied electronic state to the other. Thus, the mass correction (37.12) is applicable only if the two electronic states combine optically. Since, in the case of atoms with two electrons, one of the electrons is always in the ground state, which is a $1s$ state, it follows that only p states are affected by the additional mass correction. In that case, the energy of the para levels is raised, i.e., for those terms the correction acts in the same direction as the elementary mass correction; the energy of the ortho terms is lowered. Physically, this means that in para states the two electrons move mostly in the same direction, and in ortho states more frequently in opposite directions.

γ) Polarization-mass correction (He-ground state). We now consider the second type of correlation effect, produced by the electrostatic repulsion between the electrons. Due to this polarization effect, the exact wave function cannot be of the simple product form (37.10), but depends also on the distance between the electrons. Hence the integral (37.7) will not be exactly zero even for states with $l \neq 1$. But for excited states the polarization of the wave function is fairly small and decreases rapidly with increasing orbital quantum number l (see Sect. 29). For the He-ground state, however, the two electrons are close and the polarization effect is by no means negligible, especially in view of the high accuracy of the variational calculations (Sect. 32).

For the ground state of He-like atoms the variational wave functions (Sects. 32 and 33) should be accurate enough to give a good account of polarization. We again introduce the coordinates s, t and u, Eq. (32.2). The integral (37.7) then takes the form

$$\left.\begin{aligned} \varepsilon_M = \frac{m}{MN} \int_0^\infty ds \int_0^s du \int_0^u dt \Big\{ (s^2+t^2-2u^2) \left[\left(\frac{\partial U}{\partial s}\right)^2 - \left(\frac{\partial U}{\partial t}\right)^2\right] u \,- \\ -(s^2-t^2)\, u \left(\frac{\partial U}{\partial u}\right)^2 - 2\frac{\partial U}{\partial u}\left[s\frac{\partial U}{\partial s}(u^2-t^2) + t\frac{\partial U}{\partial t}(s^2-u^2)\right]\Big\}, \end{aligned}\right\} \tag{37.13}$$

where M is the nuclear mass and N a normalization factor, given in (32.8).

The expression (37.13) has now been evaluated both for HYLLERAAS' and CHANDRASEKHAR[1] *et al.*'s functions and for KINOSHITA's[2] 38-parameter wave function. The 38-parameter results for He^4 are (see Table 10, Sect. 36 for $\boldsymbol{p}_1\cdot\boldsymbol{p}_2$)

$$\varepsilon_M = +\frac{0.1591\,m}{M} = +2.18\times 10^{-5}\text{ a.u.} = +4.79\text{ cm}^{-1}. \tag{37.14}$$

HYLLERAAS' (presumably less accurate) six-parameter wave function[3] gave $+4.95\text{ cm}^{-1}$. Using CHANDRASEKHAR *et al.*'s wave functions for Li^+ and $O^{(+6)}$, WILETS and CHERRY find

$$\begin{aligned}\varepsilon_M &= +0.271\,m/M = +4.7\text{ cm}^{-1} \quad (Li^+,\ Z=3,\ A=7),\\ \varepsilon_M &= +1.00\,m/M = +7.5\text{ cm}^{-1} \quad (O^{(6+)},\ Z=8,\ A=16).\end{aligned}$$

The expression (37.13) for ε_M has also been evaluated[4] for helium-like ions of arbitrary Z, using a variational wave function similar to (33.14), but involving more terms. Results from this expression for $Z=3$ and 8 disagree with the (presumably much more accurate) ones of WILETS and CHERRY, but ε_M is at any rate less than the experimental error in J for Li^+ and all heavier ions.

The mass-polarization term ε_M is additional to the main effect ε_1 of the nuclear mass on the energy of the helium ground state. This main effect we have already taken into account by using the "reduced mass RYDBERG", Eq. (37.9), which reduces the ionization potential J of helium by Jm/M or about 27 cm^{-1} from the value obtained by using R_∞. The correction term ε_M raises the ground state energy and thus also lowers the ionization potential J.

δ) Comparison with experiment. For excited states of He-like atoms the largest mass effect (apart from the elementary one, ε_1) should be the exchange effect, which is present for P-states only. For P-states we neglect the polarization effects and use a wave function of form (37.10) which leads to (37.12). Using for u and v the simple hydrogenic wave functions of ECKART (Sect. 35γ), (37.12) reduces to

$$\varepsilon_2 = \pm\frac{128}{3}\frac{m}{M}(Z_i Z_a)^5\frac{(Z_i n - Z_a)^{2n-4}}{(Z_i n + Z_a)^{2n+4}}\,n^3(n^2-1)\text{ Ry}. \tag{37.15}$$

Using ECKART's values for the charge parameters Z_i and Z_a (Table 9, Sect. 35) we find for the $n=2$ states of He^4

$$\varepsilon_2 = -1.72\text{ cm}^{-1}\,(2\,{}^3P), \qquad \varepsilon_2 = +1.13\text{ cm}^{-1}\,(2\,{}^1P). \tag{37.16}$$

The polarization effect for the $2S$ states, calculated[5] from the variational wave functions of Sect. 35, is only $+0.22\text{ cm}^{-1}$ for 2^3S and -0.48 for 2^1S. For $n=3$ in He^4, (37.15) gives about -0.52 cm^{-1} for 3^3P and $+0.35\text{ cm}^{-1}$ for 3^1P. The polarization effects for $3\,S$ should again be smaller and the effects for $3\,D$ negligible. The total mass corrections for P-states have not yet been calculated using very accurate wave functions which also take polarization into account, but (37.15) should be a fairly good approximation.

Two isotopes of the helium atom exist with physical atomic mass units 4.0039 and 3.0170, respectively. The small frequency difference of a large number of equivalent spectral lines for these two isotopes have been measured very accurately[6].

---

[1] L. WILETS and I. CHERRY: Phys. Rev. **103**, 112 (1956).

[2] T. KINOSHITA: Phys. Rev. **105**, 1490 (1957).

[3] Previously quoted values of 5.2 cm^{-1} and 4.1 cm^{-1} for the six-parameter function are wrong.

[4] H. A. ROBINSON: Phys. Rev. **51**, 14 (1937).

[5] A. P. STONE: Proc. Phys. Soc. Lond. A **68**, 1152 (1955).

[6] FRED, TOMPKINS, BRODY and HAMERMESH: Phys. Rev. **82**, 406 (1951). — L. BRADLEY and H. KUHN: Proc. Roy. Soc. Lond., Ser. A **209**, 325 (1951).

Their spectra differ in part by the presence of hyperfine structure effects for He^3, but not for He^4. These effects have been analyzed in detail, are fairly small and reasonably well understood (Sect. 44). After applying corrections for these hyperfine structure effects to the experimental frequencies, the remaining frequency shifts between He^4 and He^3 should be largely due to the various mass effects discussed above. These mass effects are larger in He^3 than in He^4 by a factor 4.004/3.017. From these experiments one can then deduce the total mass-effect in He^4, say, for each spectral line. This, in turn, gives the difference in the mass-effects for the lower and upper states of the transition.

The experiments of FRED *et al.*, and BRADLEY and KUHN[1] certainly confirm the theoretical order of magnitude of the exchange mass effect for *P*-states and the smallness of the polarization effects for *S* and *D* states, etc. (in addition to the much larger elementary mass correction ε_1). Quantitatively, however, the agreement with theoretical predictions for ε_2 is rather poor. The cause of these discrepancies is not yet known.

b. Relativistic Theory.

38. Discussion of the BREIT equation. We consider in the next few sections relativistic corrections to the energy eigenvalues of helium-like atoms. At present the exact relativistic theory for the two-electron system cannot be written in closed form. However, methods are available for obtaining (at least in principle) energy eigenvalues to any accuracy in the form of an expansion in powers of α, the fine structure constant. We shall discuss mainly the case of small nuclear charge Z, where one can also expand in powers of $Z\alpha$. We shall carry explicitly only corrections to the nonrelativistic energy up to relative order $(Z\alpha)^2$ and only indicate possible methods for calculating higher order corrections. The $(Z\alpha)^2$ corrections give the energy to the same order of accuracy as the PAULI approximation (Sects. 12 and 13) for hydrogenic atoms. For large values of Z other approximation methods are available, which involve expansions in powers of $1/Z$ as well as of α (but not of $Z\alpha$). These will be discussed briefly in Sect. 43.

One possible starting point for such calculations, if Z is small, is the BREIT equation[2], which has been used extensively in the past. It is a differential equation for a relativistic wave function U for two electrons, interacting with each other and with an external electromagnetic field. The BREIT equation is akin to the DIRAC equation for a single electron, but—unlike the DIRAC equation—is *not* fully LORENTZ invariant and is only an approximation. It reads (for a stationary state)

$$\left(E - H_{(1)} - H_{(2)} - \frac{e^2}{r_{12}}\right) U = -\frac{e^2}{2r_{12}}\left[\boldsymbol{\alpha}_1 \cdot \boldsymbol{\alpha}_2 + \frac{(\boldsymbol{\alpha}_1 \cdot \boldsymbol{r}_{12})(\boldsymbol{\alpha}_2 \cdot \boldsymbol{r}_{12})}{r_{12}^2}\right] U, \qquad (38.1)$$

where

$$H_{(1)} = -e\varphi(\boldsymbol{r}_1) + \beta_1 mc^2 + \boldsymbol{\alpha}_1 \cdot (c\boldsymbol{p}_1 + e\boldsymbol{A}(\boldsymbol{r}_1)). \qquad (38.2)$$

The wave function U depends on the positions $\boldsymbol{r}_1$ and $\boldsymbol{r}_2$ of the two electrons and has sixteen spinor components, four each for electrons 1 and 2. The operator $H_{(1)}$ is identical with the DIRAC HAMILTONian, Eq. (10.1), and the DIRAC matrices $\boldsymbol{\alpha}_1$ and β_1 operate on the spinor components of U (for electron 1) in the usual way. The momentum operator $\boldsymbol{p}_1$ is again $-i\hbar\,\mathrm{grad}_1$, φ and $\boldsymbol{A}$ are the scalar and vector potentials of the external electromagnetic field (including the nuclear COULOMB potential), $\boldsymbol{r}_{12}$ the distance between the two electrons and E the total energy.

[1] See footnote 6, previous page.

[2] G. BREIT: Phys. Rev. **34**, 553 (1929); **36**, 383 (1930); **39** 616 (1932). See also J. R. OPPENHEIMER, Phys. Rev. **35**, 461 (1930).

The BREIT equation is based on two, essentially distinct, types of approximations. First, the term on the right side of (38.1) is only an approximation to the relativistic interaction between the two electrons (in addition to the "instantaneous" COULOMB interaction e^2/r_{12}), which is prescribed by quantum electrodynamics. But even if quantum electrodynamic effects were absent altogether, the remaining BREIT equation would still not be exact. More precisely, this equation would be compatible with DIRAC single-electron theory, but not with DIRAC pair ("hole") theory (see Sect. 15γ). In a correct field-theoretic treatment of pair theory, processes involving the creation of virtual electron-positron pairs occur, which are not treated exactly by (38.1). We shall discuss the two types of approximations separately.

α) Single-electron theory. We treat the electrons at first not according to field theory, but simple single-electron theory (negative energy states treated on the same footing as positive ones). If we were also to neglect quantum electrodynamic effects, the obvious semi-relativistic wave equation[1] for the two electrons would be (38.1) with the right hand side replaced by zero,

$$\left(E - H_{(1)} - H_{(2)} - \frac{e^2}{r_{12}}\right) U = 0. \tag{38.3}$$

The Eq. (38.3) would satisfy two requirements. First, if we take the nonrelativistic limit it would reduce to the SCHRÖDINGER equation for the two-electron system, (24.1). Second, if we neglect the COULOMB interaction e^2/r_{12}, the solutions are

$$\left.\begin{aligned} U &= U_1(\boldsymbol{r}_1)\, U_2(\boldsymbol{r}_2), \qquad & E &= E_1 + E_2; \\ (E_i - H_{(i)})\, U_i(\boldsymbol{r}_i) &= 0; & i &= 1, 2. \end{aligned}\right\} \tag{38.4}$$

U_1 and U_2 are thus solutions of the LORENTZ-invariant DIRAC equation and (38.4) would be fully relativistic. The COULOMB term in (38.3), however, is not even approximately LORENTZ invariant and relativistic corrections to the interaction between the two electrons are furnished by quantum electrodynamics. A number of methods are available for treating these interactions via the quantized transverse electromagnetic field. All these methods make use of the fact that the coupling of each electron with this field involves the small fine structure constant $\alpha = e^2/\hbar c$. We shall only consider the lowest order non-zero terms in an expansion in powers of α. We shall use "old-fashioned" perturbation theory, which is the least elegant of the various methods but, to this order, the simplest.

We assume that all the eigenstates U_n and energy eigenvalues E_n of (38.3) have been found (in principle) and let U_0, E_0 refer to a particular such eigenstate. We treat the quantized electromagnetic field just as in Sect. 19β and evaluate the energy change ΔW, due to the perturbation H', Eq. (19.5)[2], in second order perturbation theory only. Following the discussion of Sect. 19β, we find two types of terms. One type involves the emission of a virtual photon by one electron, which is then absorbed by the *other* electron. This term, which requires the presence of two electrons, is the interaction term we wish to calculate and will lead to an energy change of order $\alpha(Z\alpha)(Z^2\,\text{Ry})$. The other type involves the emission and absorption of the photon by the *same* electron. Although these terms would actually diverge individually if no cut-off were used, their sum—including mass renormalization terms—is finite and small. In fact, this sum leads to the LAMB

[1] For a formal justification see Sect. 38β.

[2] Except that the momentum $\boldsymbol{p}$ is replaced by the DIRAC matrix $mc\boldsymbol{\alpha}$. For details see refs. [5], [6] and [13] of the bibliography.

shift for a two-electron atom which is only of order $\alpha(Z\alpha)^2(Z^2\,\mathrm{Ry})$: This is smaller than the desired terms by one order[1] of $Z\alpha$ and we shall omit it (see, however, Sect. 41β).

The second order energy ΔW, due to the exchange of a photon between the two electrons, can be calculated in a similar manner to the derivation of (19.6). However, we replace the nonrelativistic expression $\boldsymbol{p}$ by $mc\boldsymbol{\alpha}$, do not neglect retardation and do not introduce a cut-off in the integration over k. We again use units such that $\hbar=1$ and $e^2=\alpha c$. Before summing over polarization directions and integrating over the directions of $\boldsymbol{k}$, we obtain

$$\Delta W = -\frac{e^2 c}{4\pi^2}\sum_{\pi}\int\frac{d^3k}{k}\sum_{n}\frac{\langle 0|\alpha_{1\pi}e^{i\boldsymbol{k}\cdot\boldsymbol{r}_1}|n\rangle\langle n|e^{-i\boldsymbol{k}\cdot\boldsymbol{r}_2}\alpha_{2\pi}|0\rangle}{kc+E_n-E_0} \tag{38.5}$$

plus a similar term with the subscripts 1 and 2 interchanged. $\alpha_{1\pi}$ is the component of the DIRAC matrix $\boldsymbol{\alpha}_1$ in the direction of polarization $\boldsymbol{\pi}$. $\boldsymbol{\pi}$ is summed over two directions perpendicular to each other and to the vector $\boldsymbol{k}$. $\langle 0|A|n\rangle$ denotes the matrix element of an operator A for a transition between the initial state 0 and another atomic state n. The n-summation extends over all eigenstates (discrete and continuous spectrum) of (38.3). The term shown in (38.5) corresponds to the photon going from electron 1 to electron 2, the other term to the inverse process.

It would be very difficult to evaluate the expression (38.5) exactly. It is simplified considerably, however, if we neglect (E_n-E_0) compared with kc in the denominator of (38.5). This approximation will lead to the BREIT interaction. It can be justified as follows, for a bound state in a "weak" external field. By "weak" we mean that the binding energies of all bound states are small compared with mc^2 and that $\bar{p}$, the "average" momentum in these states is small compared with mc. If the external field is a COULOMB potential with nuclear charge Z, then $\bar{p}$ and a^{-1} (a is the "atomic radius") are of order $(Z\alpha)mc$. The important values of k in the integral in (38.5) are of the same order of magnitude ($ka\sim 1$). One then finds that the important values of $|E_n-E_0|$ in the sum over n in (38.5) are of the order of $\bar{p}^2/m\sim k^2/m\sim Z^2\,\mathrm{Ry}\sim(Z\alpha)^2mc^2$, which is one order of $Z\alpha$ smaller than the important values of kc. Omitting E_n-E_0 in (38.5) is then a good approximation if the atomic states are essentially nonrelativistic, i.e. if $Z\alpha\ll 1$ or $Z\ll 137$. Actually, the omission is also justified (at least in some cases) if $Z\gg 1$, for a different reason. This will be discussed in Sect. 43β. For the moment we restrict ourselves to the case of weak potentials (Z small).

If E_n-E_0 is omitted in the denominator of (38.5), the summation over n can be carried out immediately by means of a sum rule. Also carrying out the summation over the two directions of polarization π, we get[2]

$$\left.\begin{aligned}\Delta W &= \langle 0|B|0\rangle,\\ B &= -\frac{e^2}{2\pi^2}\int\frac{d^3k}{k^2}e^{i\boldsymbol{k}\cdot\boldsymbol{r}_{12}}\left[\boldsymbol{\alpha}_1\cdot\boldsymbol{\alpha}_2-\frac{(\boldsymbol{\alpha}_1\cdot\boldsymbol{k})\,(\boldsymbol{\alpha}_2\cdot\boldsymbol{k})}{k^2}\right],\end{aligned}\right\} \tag{38.6}$$

where the expectation value of the operator B is to be evaluated over the wave function of the particular eigenstate of (38.3). The DIRAC matrices $\boldsymbol{\alpha}_1$ and $\boldsymbol{\alpha}_2$ commute with $\boldsymbol{k}$ and $\boldsymbol{r}_{12}$ and the integral in (38.6) can be evaluated as shown in

---

[1] The LAMB shift involves one interaction with the nuclear COULOMB potential, in addition to one virtual photon. Actually it is smaller by one order of $Z\alpha\log\alpha$.

[2] Adding the term not explicitly shown in (38.5), which is identical with (38.5) in this approximation.

Sect. 39β. Using (39.8) and (39.7) we get

$$B = -\frac{e^2}{2r_{12}}\left[\boldsymbol{\alpha}_1 \cdot \boldsymbol{\alpha}_2 + \frac{(\boldsymbol{\alpha}_1 \cdot \boldsymbol{r}_{12})\,(\boldsymbol{\alpha}_2 \cdot \boldsymbol{r}_{12})}{r_{12}^2}\right]. \tag{38.7}$$

This expression, called the BREIT operator, is identical with the operator occuring on the right hand side of (38.1).

The BREIT equation (38.1) is thus a good approximation (for a weak external field) as long as the small BREIT operator B on the right hand side is only treated by first order perturbation theory for a particular atomic state. In this case one simply evaluates its expectation value over an eigenfunction of (38.3) to obtain the perturbation energy ΔW [see Eq. (38.6)]. However, one would get quite wrong results if one solved (38.1) exactly or treated B in higher order perturbation theory. This can be seen as follows. The Eq. (38.3) also has eigenstates l in which both electrons are in negative energy states. If 0 denotes an ordinary positive energy eigenstate and l one particular such negative energy state, perturbation theory applied to (38.1) would give a matrix element $\langle 0|B|l\rangle$ for a transition between these states. If we use quantum electrodynamics, as we should, we get, instead, an expression similar to (38.5) but with $\langle n|\boldsymbol{\alpha}_2|0\rangle$ replaced by $\langle n|\boldsymbol{\alpha}_2|l\rangle$. Consider again a weak potential, so that $\bar{p} \ll mc$. The properties of the DIRAC matrix $\boldsymbol{\alpha}$ are such that the main contribution comes from terms where electron 1 is in a negative energy state in the intermediate state n. Thus $E_n - E_0$ is of order $-2mc^2$, which is *not* small, but in fact *large* compared with kc. We could replace $(kc + E_n - E_0)$ by $-2mc^2$ and again apply a sum rule. The quantum electrodynamic matrix element would then be of form $\langle 0|B'|l\rangle$, but the operator B' would be given approximately by

$$B' = +\frac{e^2}{4\pi^2 m c}\int \frac{d^3 k}{k}\, e^{i\boldsymbol{k}\cdot\boldsymbol{r}_{12}}\left[\boldsymbol{\alpha}_1 \cdot \boldsymbol{\alpha}_2 - \frac{(\boldsymbol{\alpha}_1 \cdot \boldsymbol{k})\,(\boldsymbol{\alpha}_2 \cdot \boldsymbol{k})}{k^2}\right]. \tag{38.8}$$

This operator is of quite a different order of magnitude (smaller by an order of $1/mcr_{12}$) than the BREIT operator B, Eq. (38.6).

Also, if in (38.1) we treated the BREIT operator B by second order perturbation theory, the corresponding energy change would be

$$\Delta W_2 = \sum_l \frac{\langle 0|B|l\rangle\langle l|B|0\rangle}{E_0 - E_l}. \tag{38.9}$$

The DIRAC matrices contained in B ensure that the main contribution to this sum comes from states l in which both electrons are in negative energy states. For such transitions the operator B should be replaced by B', Eq. (38.8). Thus, even for a positive energy state 0 in a weak potential, the expression (38.9) would be of quite the wrong order of magnitude (and too large).

To summarize the situation for single-electron theory in a weak external potential: The BREIT equation (38.1) gives the leading term for the relativistic corrections to the interaction between the two electrons, if the BREIT operator on the right hand side is treated by first order perturbation theory. This term is of order $\alpha(Z\alpha)(Z^2\,\mathrm{Ry})$. The BREIT equation cannot, without modification, be used consistently to evaluate higher order corrections. The higher corrections could, however, be calculated, for instance by starting from (38.3) and using higher order perturbation theory for the electron's interaction with the virtual radiation field. We merely outline how the next highest terms could be obtained (see also Sect. 41β).

Transitions involving the emission and absorption of a single virtual photon by the *same* electron, plus renormalization terms, lead to the LAMB shift. The calculation[1] proceeds in a similar manner to the discussion of Sect. 19β and the result is again of order $\alpha(Z\alpha)^2(Z^2\,\mathrm{Ry})\log\alpha$. Consider next the exchange of a single photon between the two electrons. The leading term for this process is already contained in (38.6). One can then evaluate (at least approximately) the difference between (38.6) and the exact expression (38.5). The calculation for this difference is similar to that of the LAMB shift and the result is of order $\alpha^2(Z\alpha)\log\alpha\,(Z^2\,\mathrm{Ry})$.

One would consider next terms corresponding to the exchange of *two* photons, by means of fourth order perturbation theory. The expression (38.9) with B replaced by B', Eq. (38.8), represents one such term. This term corresponds to the absorption of the first photon *before* the emission of the second one. Other terms of the same order of magnitude also occur, for instance a term representing the emission of two successive photons by one electron, followed by their absorption by the second electron. These processes would give energy shifts of order $\alpha^2(Z\alpha)(Z^2\,\mathrm{Ry})$.

β) Pair theory. For a discussion of the modifications introduced by DIRAC pair theory, it is convenient to work in momentum space. We first FOURIER transform the BREIT equation (38.1) into an integral equation in momentum space. Following the notation of (16.1), this equation is

$$\left.\begin{aligned}(E-H_{01}-H_{02})\,\psi(\boldsymbol{p}_1,\boldsymbol{p}_2) = -e\int d^3k\,\{[\varphi(-\boldsymbol{k})-\boldsymbol{\alpha}_1\cdot\boldsymbol{A}(-\boldsymbol{k})]\,\psi(\boldsymbol{p}_1+\boldsymbol{k},\boldsymbol{p}_2)\,+\\ +\,[\varphi(-\boldsymbol{k})-\boldsymbol{\alpha}_2\cdot\boldsymbol{A}(-\boldsymbol{k})]\,\psi(\boldsymbol{p}_1,\boldsymbol{p}_2+\boldsymbol{k})\}\,+\\ +\,\frac{e^2}{2\pi^2}\int\frac{d^3k}{k^2}\,(1-\mathscr{B})\,\psi(\boldsymbol{p}_1-\boldsymbol{k},\boldsymbol{p}_2+\boldsymbol{k}),\end{aligned}\right\}\tag{38.10}$$

where

$$\left.\begin{aligned}H_{01} &= mc^2\beta_1 + c\,\boldsymbol{\alpha}_1\cdot\boldsymbol{p}_1,\\ \mathscr{B} &= \boldsymbol{\alpha}_1\cdot\boldsymbol{\alpha}_2 - \frac{(\boldsymbol{\alpha}_1\cdot\boldsymbol{k})\,(\boldsymbol{\alpha}_2\cdot\boldsymbol{k})}{k^2}.\end{aligned}\right\}\tag{38.11}$$

The momentum space wave function ψ is, like U, a 16-component spinor on which the DIRAC matrices for the two electrons operate.

It is convenient to rewrite (38.10) in the mixed representation defined and discussed in Sect. 16α. There we split the DIRAC wave function (16.8) into two parts. These two parts were eigenstates of H_0 with positive and negative eigenvalues, respectively, and involved a PAULI spinor, ψ_+ and ψ_-, respectively. We were then able to write the DIRAC equation as two coupled integral equations, (16.13), involving only PAULI (not DIRAC) operators and the two PAULI spinors ψ_+ and ψ_-. Similarly we can split the 16-component two-electron wave function $\psi(\boldsymbol{p}_1,\boldsymbol{p}_2)$ into four parts. One part is a simultaneous eigenstate of $H_{01}(\boldsymbol{p}_1)$ and $H_{02}(\boldsymbol{p}_2)$ with *positive* eigenvalues $E(p_1)$ and $E(p_2)$, where

$$E(p) = +\sqrt{(mc^2)^2+(pc)^2}.\tag{38.12}$$

This part of the wave function involves known DIRAC operators and a PAULI-type spinor $\psi_{++}(\boldsymbol{p}_1,\boldsymbol{p}_2)$ which has four components ("spin up" and "spin down" for each of the two electrons). Similarly a second part is an eigenstate of H_{01} and H_{02} with eigenvalues $+E(\boldsymbol{p}_1)$ and $-E(\boldsymbol{p}_2)$, respectively, and involves a PAULI spinor ψ_{+-}, and so on. By methods analogous to those of Sect. 16α one

[1] For further discussion and references see Sect. 41β.

can then rewrite (38.10) in the form of four coupled integral equations involving only the PAULI spinors $\psi_{++}, \psi_{+-}, \psi_{-+}$ and ψ_{--}. We shall not write out this set of equations explicitly, but only discuss an approximation to them.

In Sect. 16β we discussed approximate forms for the equivalent set of Eq. (16.13), valid for an electron in a weak potential with total energy close to the rest mass energy mc^2. We showed that the fine structure effects could be obtained, to a good approximation, by merely considering the equation for ψ_+ and putting ψ_- equal to zero in this equation. We can get an equally good approximation in our present case for two electrons in a weak potential in a state of total energy close to $2mc^2$. Of the four coupled equations we consider only the one which involves ψ_{++} on the left hand side. In the integrals on the right hand side of this equation we simply replace ψ_{+-}, ψ_{-+} and ψ_{--} by zero, retaining only the term in ψ_{++}. We are then left with an equation which only involves ψ_{++},

$$\left.\begin{aligned}&[E-E(p_1)-E(p_2)]\,\psi_{++}(\boldsymbol{p}_1,\boldsymbol{p}_2)\\ &\quad=-e\int d^3k\{[\varphi(-\boldsymbol{k})I^{(1)}_{++}(\boldsymbol{p}_1,\boldsymbol{p}_1+\boldsymbol{k})-\boldsymbol{A}(-\boldsymbol{k})\cdot\boldsymbol{\alpha}^{(1)}_{++}(\boldsymbol{p}_1,\boldsymbol{p}_1+\boldsymbol{k})]\,\psi_{++}(\boldsymbol{p}_1+\boldsymbol{k},\boldsymbol{p}_2)+\\ &\quad+[\varphi(-\boldsymbol{k})\,I^{(2)}_{++}(\boldsymbol{p}_2,\boldsymbol{p}_2+\boldsymbol{k})-\boldsymbol{A}(-\boldsymbol{k})\cdot\boldsymbol{\alpha}^{(2)}_{++}(\boldsymbol{p}_2,\boldsymbol{p}_2+\boldsymbol{k})]\,\psi_{++}(\boldsymbol{p}_1,\boldsymbol{p}_2+\boldsymbol{k})\}+\\ &\quad+\frac{e^2}{2\pi^2}\int\frac{d^3k}{k^2}[I^{(1)}_{++}(\boldsymbol{p}_1,\boldsymbol{p}_1-\boldsymbol{k})\,I^{(2)}_{++}(\boldsymbol{p}_2,\boldsymbol{p}_2+\boldsymbol{k})-\mathscr{B}']\,\psi_{++}(\boldsymbol{p}_1-\boldsymbol{k},\boldsymbol{p}_2+\boldsymbol{k}),\end{aligned}\right\}\tag{38.13}$$

where

$$\mathscr{B}'=\boldsymbol{\alpha}^{(1)}_{++}(\boldsymbol{p}_1,\boldsymbol{p}_1-\boldsymbol{k})\cdot\boldsymbol{\alpha}^{(2)}_{++}(\boldsymbol{p}_2,\boldsymbol{p}_2+\boldsymbol{k})-\frac{(\boldsymbol{\alpha}^{(1)}_{++}\cdot\boldsymbol{k})\,(\boldsymbol{\alpha}^{(2)}_{++}\cdot\boldsymbol{k})}{k^2}.\tag{38.14}$$

In (38.13), $E(p)$ is the function defined in (38.12) and $I^{(1)}_{++}$, $\boldsymbol{\alpha}^{(1)}_{++}$ are the expressions defined in (16.12) with the PAULI spin matrix σ replaced by σ_1, the matrix which operates on those spin components of ψ_{++} which refer to the first electron.

The Eq. (38.13) is only an approximation to the set of four equations which is identical with the BREIT equation, but has one formal advantage. The difficulties encountered in Sect. 38α by treating the BREIT operator exactly, or at least to higher order than the first, were all connected with negative energy states. In (38.13) all reference to negative energy states has been eliminated and no inconsistencies would be encountered in an attempt to solve this equation exactly or to treat $\mathscr{B}'$, Eq. (38.14), in higher order perturbation theory. Of course, higher order corrections involving more than one virtual photon or any virtual pairs are not contained in (38.13). We shall merely outline a method for calculating higher order corrections in a manner consistent with DIRAC's pair theory which involves (38.13) as a first step.

One technique for treating the two-electron system to any required order, according to DIRAC pair (hole) theory, is the TAMM-DANCOFF method[1]. One starts from a symbolic equation of form

$$(E-H_0)\,\Psi=H'\,\Psi.\tag{38.15}$$

The symbolic operator H' represents the interaction of charged particles with photons, the COULOMB interaction between particles and the interaction of particles with external fields. If $H'=0$ (no interactions at all, e.g. if the electronic charge is replaced by zero), the eigenstates of the "unperturbed" HAMILTONian H_0 are states containing *any* number of "bare" (i.e. non-interacting) particles and photons. One considers the state function Ψ expanded as an infinite sum

[1] I. TAMM: J. Phys. USSR. **9**, 449 (1945). — S. M. DANCOFF: Phys. Rev. **78**, 382 (1950).

of eigenstates of H_0, each term corresponding to some definite number of "bare" particles and photons ("FOCK space" expansion),

$$\Psi = \Phi_0 \psi_0 + \Phi_{1,0} \psi_{1,0}(\boldsymbol{p}) + \Phi_{2,0} \psi_{2,0}(\boldsymbol{p}_1, \boldsymbol{p}_2) + \Phi_{1,1} \psi_{1,1}(\boldsymbol{p}; \boldsymbol{k}) + \cdots. \quad (38.16)$$

Φ_0 is a symbolic state vector representing no bare particles or photons at all (the "bare vacuum"), ψ_0 its probability amplitude for the actual state Ψ. Similarly $\Phi_{1,0}$ is a state vector representing one bare particle and no bare photons, $\psi_{1,0}(\boldsymbol{p})$ the probability amplitude for finding one such particle with momentum $\boldsymbol{p}$ (and a certain spin, etc.) in state Ψ. Similarly for the higher terms.

The matrix elements of H' for transitions between such states containing different numbers of bare particles and photons, $\Phi_{n,m}$ and $\Phi_{n',m'}$ are given by standard rules of field theory[1], in terms of operators which create and destroy individual "bare" particles and photons with known commutation rules for these operators. With Ψ expanded in terms of bare particle states $\Phi_{n,m}$, one can then write out $H'\Psi$ in terms of a similar expansion. One can then isolate from (38.15) the terms involving a particular number of bare particles (n) and photons (m) i.e. the terms involving $\Phi_{n,m}$. Formally this is done by operating on both sides of (38.15) with n particle and m photon absorption operators and taking the scalar product of this resulting equation with the bare vacuum state vector Φ_0. In this manner one finally obtains an infinite set of coupled integral equations in momentum space involving the various probability amplitudes $\psi_{n,m}(\boldsymbol{p}_1, \ldots)$. This set of "TAMM-DANCOFF equations" no longer involves creation or annihilation operators nor any symbolic state vector Φ.

Consider now an eigenstate Ψ of (38.15) which represents a two-electron system. The leading term in (38.16) is then $\Phi_{2,0}\psi_{2,0}(\boldsymbol{p}_1, \boldsymbol{p}_2)$. Let us omit for the moment the coupling between electrons and photons in (38.15). If, further, we were using single-electron theory, then negative energy states of an electron are treated on an equal footing with positive energy ones. In this case one finds that H' in (38.15) only has non-zero matrix elements for transitions between states of the same number of electrons (but not necessarily the same numbers in positive and negative energy states) and photons. In this case the TAMM-DANCOFF equations are uncoupled and we simply get a *single* equation for $\psi_{2,0}(\boldsymbol{p}_1, \boldsymbol{p}_2)$ for our two-electron state. This equation is identical with (38.10), with the term in $\mathscr{B}$ omitted, and is exactly the FOURIER transform of (38.3).

According to pair theory, however, no electrons are supposed to exist in negative energy states. Instead of these negative energy states we now have states involving positrons (also of positive energy). In this formalism, the operator H' also couples states which contain a *different* number of positron-electron pairs. For our two-electron state the leading term is still $\psi_{2,0}$. But only those parts of $\psi_{2,0}$ are present which correspond to both electrons in positive energy states, ψ_{++} in the notation of our mixed representation, Eq. (38.13). But other probability amplitudes, e.g. for three electrons plus one positron, also occur and we have an infinite set of coupled equations. However, as a first approximation, we can omit all probability amplitudes except $\psi_{2,0}$. Then only one equation remains, which is *identical* with (38.13), except for the absence of $\mathscr{B}'$. Thus, in the present approximation, single-electron and pair theory give identical results.

We still have to include in H' the interaction of the electrons with the radiation field. Instead of using perturbation theory on these terms, as in Sect. 38α, they can also be treated in the framework of the TAMM-DANCOFF method. $\psi_{2,0}$ is then coupled to $\psi_{2,1}$, the probability amplitude for two (positive energy)

[1] See refs. [*11*], [*12*] and [*13*].

electrons plus a photon. In the pair theory treatment, $\psi_{2,0}$ is also coupled to $\psi_{2,(1),1}$, the symbol (1) referring to one electron-positron pair. The equation for $\psi_{2,1}$, in turn, is coupled back to $\psi_{2,0}$ and also to $\psi_{2,(1),0}$, $\psi_{2,(1),2}$ and $\psi_{2,2}$; and so on. If one puts all probability amplitudes except $\psi_{2,0}$ and $\psi_{2,1}$ equal to zero, one can then express $\psi_{2,1}$ explicitly in terms of $\psi_{2,0}$ and finally get an equation involving $\psi_{2,0}$ alone. This approximate equation is found to be identical[1] with (38.13), *including* the term $\mathscr{B}'$, except that $\mathscr{B}'$ is multiplied by the factor

$$\frac{1}{2}\,\frac{k\,c}{k\,c+E(p_1)+E(|\boldsymbol{p}_2+\boldsymbol{k}|)-E}+\frac{1}{2}\,\frac{k\,c}{k\,c+E(|\boldsymbol{p}_1-\boldsymbol{k}|)+E(p_2)-E}, \tag{38.17}$$

where $E(p)$ is again given by (38.12).

For a weak potential the effect of replacing the factor (38.17) by unity is found to be small. To within the accuracy of the PAULI approximation, the TAMM-DANCOFF method (based on pair theory) gives the same results as single-electron theory [from which (38.13) was derived]. In principle at least, higher order corrections could then be calculated by successive approximation by including more and more of the terms $\psi_{2,2}$, $\psi_{2,(1),1}$, etc. of the full TAMM-DANCOFF equations.

A very similar set of equations was derived by BROWN and RAVENHALL[2] by a slightly different method (using successive contact transformations). They showed explicitly that all relativistic correction terms of order $(Z\alpha)^2(Z^2\mathrm{Ry})$ and $\alpha(Z\alpha)(Z^2\mathrm{Ry})$ are contained in (38.13). These terms will be derived from (38.13) in the next three sections. They also showed that, except for the LAMB shift and vacuum polarization terms of order $\alpha(Z\alpha)^2(Z^2\mathrm{Ry})$ which we have encountered in Sect. 38α, all terms omitted in (38.13) are of order $\alpha^2(Z\alpha)(Z^2\mathrm{Ry})$ or smaller.

Other methods for evaluating higher order corrections are also available (in principle). One example is the socalled "New TAMM-DANCOFF Method"[3]. Like the TAMM-DANCOFF method it involves an infinite set of coupled integral equations; but it also involves probability amplitudes for negative energy states. Formally these equations are obtained by operating on (38.15) with creation *and* annihilation operators and then taking the scalar product of this equation with a certain state vector Ψ_0. This state vector Ψ_0 is *not* Φ_0, the "bare vacuum" term. Instead, Ψ_0 is the eigenstate of (38.15) with the lowest eigenvalue, which represents the "real vacuum" in the presence of the external field and the electron-photon interaction. The "New TAMM-DANCOFF" equations have the conceptual advantage that negative energy states also appear and the lowest order equation is of form similar to (but not identical with) the BREIT Eq. (38.10) or (38.1). In particular, if the interaction between the electrons is neglected altogether these equations automatically reduce to the DIRAC equation for two non-interacting electrons. This method, however, has not yet been used in any explicit calculations for the two-electron system.

The methods outlined above are not formulated in a manner which exhibits the LORENTZ invariance of the theory automatically. For the simpler case of two electrons (or any two FERMI-DIRAC particles) interacting with each other in the *absence* of any external field, fully relativistic methods have been developed in detail. These methods will be discussed in Sect. 42γ. They can be[4] generalized

[1] After dropping self-energy and mass renormalization terms, which lead to the LAMB shift and are thus small.

[2] G. E. BROWN and G. RAVENHALL: Proc. Roy. Soc. Lond., Ser. A **208**, 552 (1951).

[3] F. J. DYSON: Phys. Rev. **90**, 994 (1953).

[4] G. WENTZEL: Phys. Rev. **89**, 684 (1952). — A. O. ROBINSON: Canad. J. Phys. **33**, 369, 707 (1955).

to the case of two electrons interacting with the COULOMB field of a nucleus, but no detailed calculations of higher relativistic corrections for the helium atom have yet been performed with these methods. In fact, only some but *not all* the corrections of order $\alpha^2(Z\alpha)(Z^2\,\mathrm{Ry})$ have been calculated so far (by *any* method).

39. The PAULI approximation (low Z). *α) Momentum space.* We use the approximate form (38.13) of the BREIT equation as our starting point for the treatment of the two-electron system in a weak external electromagnetic field. For the case of helium-like atoms, "weak" means low nuclear charge, $Z \ll 137$. No inconsistencies would be encountered in an attempt to solve (38.13) exactly. However, some correction terms of order $\alpha(Z\alpha)^2(Z^2\,\mathrm{Ry})$ are missing from (38.13) and we shall only use this equation to evaluate the energy eigenvalue up to (and including) order $(Z\alpha)^2(Z^2\,\mathrm{Ry})$ and $Z\alpha^2(Z^2\,\mathrm{Ry})$. To this accuracy it is sufficient to expand the integrand of (38.13) in powers of p/mc and k/mc and drop all terms higher than $1/c^2$. This treatment will be equivalent to the PAULI approximation to the DIRAC theory for a single electron, as derived in Sect. 16β.

We write for the nonrelativistic energy $W = E - 2mc^2$ and expand the expression (38.12) for $E(p)$ in powers of p/mc. For the PAULI operators I_{++} and $\boldsymbol{\alpha}_{++}$ we use, instead of the exact expressions (16.12), the approximations (16.14). We further rewrite I_{++}, using the operator identity (16.11), use the vector identity

$$(\boldsymbol{a}\times\boldsymbol{k})\cdot(\boldsymbol{b}\times\boldsymbol{k}) = k^2(\boldsymbol{a}\cdot\boldsymbol{b}) - (\boldsymbol{a}\cdot\boldsymbol{k})(\boldsymbol{b}\cdot\boldsymbol{k})$$

and note that $\boldsymbol{k}\cdot\boldsymbol{A}(\boldsymbol{k}) = 0$, since $\operatorname{div}\boldsymbol{A}(\boldsymbol{r}) = 0$. The PAULI approximation for the two-electron system is then (dropping the subscript $++$ from ψ)

$$\left.\begin{aligned}
&\left[W - \frac{1}{2m}(p_1^2+p_2^2) + \frac{1}{8m^3c^2}(p_1^4+p_2^4)\right]\psi(\boldsymbol{p}_1,\boldsymbol{p}_2) = \\
&-e\int d^3k\,\varphi(-\boldsymbol{k})\left\{\left[1+\frac{\boldsymbol{p}_1\cdot\boldsymbol{k}+i\,\boldsymbol{\sigma}_1\cdot(\boldsymbol{p}_1\times\boldsymbol{k})}{(2mc)^2}\right]\psi(\boldsymbol{p}_1+\boldsymbol{k},\boldsymbol{p}_2)+\right.\\
&\qquad\left.+\left[1+\frac{\boldsymbol{p}_2\cdot\boldsymbol{k}+i\,\boldsymbol{\sigma}_2\cdot(\boldsymbol{p}_2\times\boldsymbol{k})}{(2mc)^2}\right]\psi(\boldsymbol{p}_1,\boldsymbol{p}_2+\boldsymbol{k})\right\}+\\
&+\frac{e^2}{2\pi^2}\int\frac{d^3k}{k^2}\left\{1+\frac{(\boldsymbol{p}_2-\boldsymbol{p}_1)\cdot\boldsymbol{k}-i\,\boldsymbol{\sigma}_1\cdot(\boldsymbol{p}_1\times\boldsymbol{k})+i\,\boldsymbol{\sigma}_2\cdot(\boldsymbol{p}_2\times\boldsymbol{k})}{(2mc)^2}\right\}\psi(\boldsymbol{p}_1-\boldsymbol{k},\boldsymbol{p}_2+\boldsymbol{k})-\\
&-\frac{e^2}{2\pi^2(2mc)^2}\int\frac{d^3k}{k^2}\left\{4\left[\boldsymbol{p}_1\cdot\boldsymbol{p}_2-\frac{(\boldsymbol{p}_1\cdot\boldsymbol{k})(\boldsymbol{p}_2\cdot\boldsymbol{k})}{k^2}\right]+2i\left[\boldsymbol{\sigma}_2\cdot(\boldsymbol{p}_1\times\boldsymbol{k})-\boldsymbol{\sigma}_1\cdot(\boldsymbol{p}_2\times\boldsymbol{k})\right]+\right.\\
&\qquad\left.+\left[k^2\,\boldsymbol{\sigma}_1\cdot\boldsymbol{\sigma}_2-(\boldsymbol{\sigma}_1\cdot\boldsymbol{k})(\boldsymbol{\sigma}_2\cdot\boldsymbol{k})\right]\right\}\psi(\boldsymbol{p}_1-\boldsymbol{k},\boldsymbol{p}_2+\boldsymbol{k})+\\
&+\frac{e}{2mc}\int d^3k\,\boldsymbol{A}(-\boldsymbol{k})\cdot\{(2\boldsymbol{p}_1+i\,\boldsymbol{k}\times\boldsymbol{\sigma}_1)\,\psi(\boldsymbol{p}_1+\boldsymbol{k},\boldsymbol{p}_2)+\\
&\qquad+(2\boldsymbol{p}_2+i\,\boldsymbol{k}\times\boldsymbol{\sigma}_2)\,\psi(\boldsymbol{p}_1,\boldsymbol{p}_2+\boldsymbol{k})\}.
\end{aligned}\right\}\quad(39.1)$$

In (39.1), as in (38.13), the wave function ψ is a PAULI (*not* DIRAC) spinor with four components, two for the spin variable of the first electron on which the PAULI matrix σ_1 operates and two for electron 2. On the right hand side of (39.1), the first term in parentheses represents the interaction with the external electric field (including relativistic corrections). The second term represents the COULOMB interaction between the two electrons, the third term the interaction between the two electrons via the quantized radiation field (the BREIT operator), and the fourth term the interaction with the external magnetic field.

If we dropped all terms in (39.1) which contain negative powers of c (and hence should be small), this equation would reduce to

$$\left.\begin{aligned}\left[W_0-\frac{1}{2m}(p_1^2+p_2^2)\right]\psi_0(\boldsymbol{p}_1,\boldsymbol{p}_2)=-e\int d^3k\,\varphi(-\boldsymbol{k})\,[\psi_0(\boldsymbol{p}_1+\boldsymbol{k},\boldsymbol{p}_2)+\\ +\psi_0(\boldsymbol{p}_1,\boldsymbol{p}_2+\boldsymbol{k})]\\ +\frac{e^2}{2\pi^2}\int\frac{d^3k}{k^2}\psi_0(\boldsymbol{p}_1-\boldsymbol{k},\boldsymbol{p}_2+\boldsymbol{k})\,.\end{aligned}\right\}\qquad(39.2)$$

(39.2) is identical with the nonrelativistic SCHRÖDINGER equation (36.7) for the twoelectron system, written in momentum space. In the next two sections we shall find an approximation to the eigenvalue W of (39.1), as follows. We first solve (39.2) for the nonrelativistic energy W_0 and eigenfunction ψ_0. We then merely take the expectation values over ψ_0 of the other operators occuring in (39.1), to find a correction to the energy W_0 according to first order perturbation theory.

It should be remembered that the operators occuring in (39.1) are good approximations to those in (38.13) *only* for $p\ll mc$, $k\ll mc$. For $p\gg mc$, the operators in (39.1) are quite wrong, for instance $E(p)-mc^2$ is proportional to p for very large momenta, not to p^2 or p^4. Similarly, the eigenfunctions ψ_0 of (39.2) are good approximations to those of (38.13) only for $p\ll mc$. For $p_1, p_2\gg mc$, ψ_0 decreases more rapidly with increasing momentum than the correct eigenfunction ψ of (38.13) (cf. Table 2). For a "weak" external potential (like the COULOMB potential for low charge Z), the characteristic momenta are of order $\bar{p}\ll mc$. In momentum space, the expectation value of an operator consists of an integral over the momenta $\boldsymbol{p}_1$ and $\boldsymbol{p}_2$, which involves a wave function $\psi(\boldsymbol{p}_1,\boldsymbol{p}_2)$. One can show that the main contribution to these integrals comes from momenta of order $\bar{p}$, if (a) the operators occuring in (38.13) and the *correct* eigenfunctions ψ of (38.13) are used, or if (b) the operators occuring in (39.1) and the *nonrelativistic* eigenfunctions ψ_0 of (39.2) are used. It therefore does not matter that, for case (b), in the relativistic region $p\gg mc$, both the operators and wave functions are quite wrong (operators too large, wave functions too small). However, (39.1), unlike (38.13), is *not* a completely self-consistent equation. For instance, spurious divergences in the integrals are encountered if (39.1) is treated in higher order perturbation theory.

β) Position space. For many practical applications it is more convenient to work in ordinary position space, instead of momentum space. In particular, the FOURIER transforms of the eigenfunctions ψ_0 of (39.2) are simply the nonrelativistic wave functions in position space, which were discussed at great length in Sects. 24 to 37. We therefore carry out the FOURIER transformation of Eq. (39.1).

We shall make use of some general properties of FOURIER transforms, which can be derived as follows. Let $(2\pi)^{\frac{3}{2}}V'(\boldsymbol{p})$ and $\psi(\boldsymbol{p})$ be the FOURIER transforms of $V(\boldsymbol{r})$ and $U(\boldsymbol{r})$, respectively. We then have

$$\left.\begin{aligned}(2\pi)^{-\frac{3}{2}}\int d^3p\,e^{i\boldsymbol{r}\cdot\boldsymbol{p}}\int d^3k\;V'(\boldsymbol{k})\,\psi(\boldsymbol{p}-\boldsymbol{k})\\ =\int d^3k\,V'(\boldsymbol{k})\,e^{i\boldsymbol{r}\cdot\boldsymbol{k}}\int d^3q\,(2\pi)^{-\frac{3}{2}}\,\psi(\boldsymbol{q})\,e^{i\boldsymbol{r}\cdot\boldsymbol{q}}=V(\boldsymbol{r})\,U(\boldsymbol{r})\,.\end{aligned}\right\}\qquad(39.3)$$

We denote this relation simply by

$$V'(\boldsymbol{k})\,\psi(\boldsymbol{p}-\boldsymbol{k})\to V(\boldsymbol{r})\,U(\boldsymbol{r})\,.\qquad(39.4)$$

By differentiating the integrands of the various integrals in (39.3) with respect to $\boldsymbol{r}$, we can verify the following general relations

$$\boldsymbol{p}\,V'(\boldsymbol{k})\,\psi(\boldsymbol{p}-\boldsymbol{k})\to-i\,\mathrm{grad}\,[V(\boldsymbol{r})\;U(\boldsymbol{r})]=\boldsymbol{p}\,V\,U\,,\qquad(39.5)$$

$$\boldsymbol{k}\,V'(\boldsymbol{k})\,\psi(\boldsymbol{p}-\boldsymbol{k})\to-i\,[\mathrm{grad}\,V(\boldsymbol{r})]\;U(\boldsymbol{r})=[\boldsymbol{p}\,V-V\,\boldsymbol{p}]\,U\,.\qquad(39.6)$$

We also shall make use of the following relations $\left(\frac{\partial}{\partial \boldsymbol{r}}\right.$ stands for $\left.\text{grad}_{\boldsymbol{r}}\right)$

$$\frac{1}{2\pi^2}\int \frac{d^3k}{k^2}\, e^{i\boldsymbol{k}\cdot\boldsymbol{r}} = \frac{1}{r}, \tag{39.7}$$

$$\left.\begin{aligned}\frac{1}{2\pi^2}\int \frac{d^3k}{k^2}\, e^{i\boldsymbol{k}\cdot\boldsymbol{r}}\,\frac{(\boldsymbol{a}\cdot\boldsymbol{k})\,(\boldsymbol{b}\cdot\boldsymbol{k})}{k^2} &= \frac{i}{2}\left(\boldsymbol{a}\cdot\frac{\partial}{\partial\boldsymbol{r}}\right)\int d^3k\, e^{i\boldsymbol{k}\cdot\boldsymbol{r}}\left(\boldsymbol{b}\cdot\frac{\partial}{\partial\boldsymbol{k}}\right)\frac{1}{k^2}\\ &= \frac{1}{2}\left(\boldsymbol{a}\cdot\frac{\partial}{\partial\boldsymbol{r}}\right)\left[\boldsymbol{b}\cdot\boldsymbol{r}\,\frac{1}{r}\right] = \frac{1}{2r}\left[\boldsymbol{a}\cdot\boldsymbol{b} - \frac{(\boldsymbol{a}\cdot\boldsymbol{r})\,(\boldsymbol{b}\cdot\boldsymbol{r})}{r^2}\right],\end{aligned}\right\} \tag{39.8}$$

$$\frac{1}{2\pi^2}\int \frac{d^3k}{k^2}\, e^{i\boldsymbol{k}\cdot\boldsymbol{r}}\,\boldsymbol{k} = i\,\frac{\boldsymbol{r}}{r^3}. \tag{39.9}$$

We now have to deal with some operators which exhibit a singularity in position space of the type of a DIRAC delta-function. Generally, a momentum space potential $V'(\boldsymbol{k})$ which does not decrease with increasing k (for very large k), may lead to a position space potential $V(\boldsymbol{r})$ whose volume integral over an *infinitesimal* volume around the origin is non-zero. A constant $V'(\boldsymbol{k})$ gives simply a three-dimensional DIRAC delta-function,

$$\frac{1}{2\pi^2}\int \frac{d^3k}{k^2}\, e^{i\boldsymbol{k}\cdot\boldsymbol{r}}\, k^2 = -\Delta\left(\frac{1}{r}\right) = +4\pi\,\delta^{(3)}(\boldsymbol{r}). \tag{39.10}$$

We consider next a particular $V'(\boldsymbol{k})$ which depends on the direction but not the magnitude of $\boldsymbol{k}$, namely $(\boldsymbol{a}\cdot\boldsymbol{k})\,(\boldsymbol{b}\cdot\boldsymbol{k})/2\pi^2k^2$. Carrying out the FOURIER transformation directly, we get

$$\left.\begin{aligned}V(\boldsymbol{r}) &\equiv \frac{1}{2\pi^2}\int \frac{d^3k}{k^2}\, e^{i\boldsymbol{k}\cdot\boldsymbol{r}}\,(\boldsymbol{a}\cdot\boldsymbol{k})\,(\boldsymbol{b}\cdot\boldsymbol{k})\\ &= -\left(\boldsymbol{a}\cdot\frac{\partial}{\partial\boldsymbol{r}}\right)\left(\boldsymbol{b}\cdot\frac{\partial}{\partial\boldsymbol{r}}\right)\frac{1}{r} = \frac{1}{r^3}\left[\boldsymbol{a}\cdot\boldsymbol{b} - 3\,\frac{(\boldsymbol{a}\cdot\boldsymbol{r})\,(\boldsymbol{b}\cdot\boldsymbol{r})}{r^2}\right].\end{aligned}\right\} \tag{39.11}$$

The last expression on the right hand side of (39.11) is unique only for *non-zero* values of r and has a strong singularity at the origin. We want to consider next the volume integral of $V(\boldsymbol{r})$, multiplied by a function $f(\boldsymbol{r})$, over a sphere around the origin with infinitesimally small radius ε. We assume that $f(\boldsymbol{r})$ is finite and continuous at the origin and use for $V(\boldsymbol{r})$ the first form on the right hand side of (39.11). Keeping only terms which remain finite when ε tends to zero, we find

$$\int_\varepsilon d\tau\, V(\boldsymbol{r})\, f(\boldsymbol{r}) = -f(0)\int_\varepsilon d\tau\left(a_x b_x\frac{\partial^2}{\partial x^2} + a_y b_y\frac{\partial^2}{\partial y^2} + a_z b_z\frac{\partial^2}{\partial z^2}\right)\frac{1}{r}.$$

Now, from symmetry requirements, the value of the integral can depend only on the relative but *not* the absolute orientation in space of the two vectors $\boldsymbol{a}$ and $\boldsymbol{b}$. We can then replace $a_x b_x$ (as well as $a_y b_y$ and $a_z b_z$) by the average value $\frac{1}{3}\,\boldsymbol{a}\cdot\boldsymbol{b}$ and get, using the fact that $\Delta r^{-1} = -4\pi\delta^{(3)}(\boldsymbol{r})$,

$$\int_\varepsilon d\tau\, V(\boldsymbol{r})\, f(r) = \frac{4\pi}{3}\,(\boldsymbol{a}\cdot\boldsymbol{b})\int d\tau\,\delta^{(3)}(\boldsymbol{r})\, f(\boldsymbol{r}) = \frac{4\pi}{3}\,(\boldsymbol{a}\cdot\boldsymbol{b})\, f(0). \tag{39.12}$$

Using (39.10) and (39.12), we can express the behavior near the origin of the function $V(\boldsymbol{r})$, defined in (39.11) in the following way

$$\left.\begin{aligned}V(\boldsymbol{r}) - \frac{4\pi}{3}\,(\boldsymbol{a}\cdot\boldsymbol{b})\,\delta^{(3)}(\boldsymbol{r}) &\equiv \frac{1}{2\pi^2}\int\frac{d^3k}{k^2}\, e^{i\boldsymbol{k}\cdot\boldsymbol{r}}\left[(\boldsymbol{a}\cdot\boldsymbol{k})\,(\boldsymbol{b}\cdot\boldsymbol{k}) - \frac{1}{3}\,(\boldsymbol{a}\cdot\boldsymbol{b})\,k^2\right]\\ &= \left[\frac{\boldsymbol{a}\cdot\boldsymbol{b}}{r^3} - 3\,\frac{(\boldsymbol{a}\cdot\boldsymbol{r})\,(\boldsymbol{b}\cdot\boldsymbol{r})}{r^5}\right]'.\end{aligned}\right\} \tag{39.13}$$

The prime $[\,]'$ on the right hand side of (39.13) indicates the following prescription: When $[\,]'$ occurs in any integral over position space, replace $[\,]'$ by zero for $r<\varepsilon$, evaluate the integral and then take the limit of $\varepsilon\to 0$. With this prescription, the integral over all space of any *spherically symmetric* function $f(r)$ times the right hand side of (39.13) is zero[1].

Using the relations given above we can finally carry out the FOURIER transformation of (39.1). This gives the BREIT equation in PAULI approximation in position space. This equation takes the form of the differential equation

$$\left.\begin{aligned}
&W\,U = (H_0 + H_1 + H_2 + \cdots + H_6)\,U;\\
&H_0 = -e V + \frac{1}{2m}(p_1^2 + p_2^2),\\
&H_1 = -\frac{1}{8m^3c^2}(p_1^4 + p_2^4),\\
&H_2 = -\frac{e^2}{2(mc)^2}\frac{1}{r_{12}}\left[\boldsymbol{p}_1\cdot\boldsymbol{p}_2 + \frac{\boldsymbol{r}_{12}\cdot(\boldsymbol{r}_{12}\cdot\boldsymbol{p}_1)\,\boldsymbol{p}_2}{r_{12}^2}\right],\\
&H_3 = \frac{\mu}{mc}\left\{\left[\mathcal{E}_1\times\boldsymbol{p}_1 + \frac{2e}{r_{12}^3}\boldsymbol{r}_{12}\times\boldsymbol{p}_2\right]\cdot\boldsymbol{s}_1 + \left[\mathcal{E}_2\times\boldsymbol{p}_2 + \frac{2e}{r_{12}^3}\boldsymbol{r}_{21}\times\boldsymbol{p}_1\right]\cdot\boldsymbol{s}_2\right\},\\
&H_4 = \frac{i e\hbar}{(2mc)^2}(\boldsymbol{p}_1\cdot\mathcal{E}_1 + \boldsymbol{p}_2\cdot\mathcal{E}_2),\\
&H_5 = 4\mu^2\left\{-\frac{8\pi}{3}(\boldsymbol{s}_1\cdot\boldsymbol{s}_2)\,\delta^{(3)}(\boldsymbol{r}_{12}) + \frac{1}{r_{12}^3}\left[\boldsymbol{s}_1\cdot\boldsymbol{s}_2 - \frac{3(\boldsymbol{s}_1\cdot\boldsymbol{r}_{12})(\boldsymbol{s}_2\cdot\boldsymbol{r}_{12})}{r_{12}^2}\right]'\right\},\\
&H_6 = 2\mu\,[\mathcal{H}_1\cdot\boldsymbol{s}_1 + \mathcal{H}_2\cdot\boldsymbol{s}_2] + \frac{e}{mc}[\boldsymbol{A}_1\cdot\boldsymbol{p}_1 + \boldsymbol{A}_2\cdot\boldsymbol{p}_2],
\end{aligned}\right\}\quad(39.14)$$

where

$$V = \frac{Ze}{r_1} + \frac{Ze}{r_2} - \frac{e}{r_{12}} + \varphi(r_1) + \varphi(r_2),\qquad \mu = \frac{e\hbar}{2mc}.$$

In (39.14), V in H_0, all of H_4 and the part of H_3 which[2] involves $\mathcal{E}$ correspond to the first two curly brackets in (39.1). H_2, the part of H_3 involving r_{12} and H_5 correspond to the three parts of the third curly bracket (the BREIT operator) in (39.1). Finally, H_6 corresponds to the last curly bracket in (39.1). It should be remembered that the momentum operator $\boldsymbol{p}_1 = -i\,\mathrm{grad}_1$, does not in general commute with functions of position. Nevertheless, using the fact that curl $\mathcal{E}_1$ and div $\boldsymbol{A}$ are zero and some symmetry properties, one can shown that the order of the momentum operators and functions of position is immaterial in all terms in (39.14) *except*[3] in H_2 and H_4.

The physical significance of the various terms in (39.14) is as follows:

H_0 is the ordinary nonrelativistic HAMILTONian.

H_1 is the relativistic correction due to the "variation of mass with velocity" (which does not depend on electron spin).

---

[1] The relation (39.13) could be derived more rigorously along the following lines: Multiply the integral over $\boldsymbol{k}$ on the left hand side of (39.13) by any function $f(\boldsymbol{r})$, for which the radius of convergence of its TAYLOR expansion around the origin is non-zero. Integrate this product over a sphere of radius ε around the origin in position space, carrying out the $\boldsymbol{r}$-integration before the $\boldsymbol{k}$-integration. One can then show that this double integral tends to zero when ε approaches zero. See also J. SUCHER and H. FOLEY, Phys. Rev. **95**, 966 (1955).

[2] $\mathcal{E}_1 = -\,\mathrm{grad}_1 V$ is the COULOMB field due to the nucleus *plus* electron 2 plus any external field (potential φ).

[3] For non-commuting vector operators, $\boldsymbol{a}\cdot(\boldsymbol{a}\cdot\boldsymbol{b})\,\boldsymbol{c}$ means $\sum_{i,j=1}^{3} a_i a_j b_j c_i$.

H_2 corresponds to the classical relativistic correction to the interaction between the electrons. This correction is due to the retardation of the electromagnetic field produced by an electron.

H_3 is the interaction between the spin magnetic moment and the orbital magnetic moment of the electrons (spin-orbit coupling).

H_4 is a term characteristic of the Dirac theory, which is also present in the Hamiltonian for a single electron in an electric field (see Sect. 12).

H_5 represents the interaction between the spin magnetic dipole moments of the two electrons.

H_6 is the interaction with an external magnetic field.

It is sometimes found convenient to rewrite the terms (H_1+H_4) in a different form, as follows. As discussed earlier, we shall not solve (39.14) exactly but use eigenfunctions U_0 of

$$(W-H_0)\,U_0=0$$

to evaluate the expectation values of the operators H_1 to H_6. We then have the relation

$$\frac{1}{2m}\,(p_1^2+p_2^2)\,U_0=f\,U_0, \qquad f\equiv W+e\,V.$$

Using (16.16) we then find that

$$\frac{1}{2m}\,(p_1^2+p_2^2)^2\,U_0=f\,(p_1^2+p_2^2)\,U_0+i\,e\,[\boldsymbol{p}_1\cdot\mathcal{E}_1+\mathcal{E}_1\cdot\boldsymbol{p}_1+\boldsymbol{p}_2\cdot\mathcal{E}_2+\mathcal{E}_2\cdot\boldsymbol{p}_2]\,U_0. \tag{39.15}$$

With the help of (39.15) we can then rewrite H_1+H_4 in the form

$$\left.\begin{aligned} H_1+H_4&=H_1'+H_4',\\ H_1'&=-\frac{1}{(2mc)^2}\left[f\,(p_1^2+p_2^2)-\frac{1}{m}\,p_1^2\,p_2^2\right],\\ H_4'&=-\frac{i\,e\,\hbar}{(2mc)^2}\,[\mathcal{E}_1\cdot\boldsymbol{p}_1+\mathcal{E}_2\cdot\boldsymbol{p}_2]. \end{aligned}\right\} \tag{39.16}$$

One can then also show that the expectation value of H_1' can be rewritten as

$$\int d\tau\,U_0^*\,H_1'\,U_0=-\frac{1}{8m^3c^2}\int d\tau\,[|p_1^2\,U_0|^2+|p_2^2\,U_0|^2]. \tag{39.17}$$

As we discussed in Sect. 16β and 36δ, the expectation value $\overline{H}_1$ of H_1 equals that of H_1' *if* care is taken to extend the integrals over all of space (or if the evaluations are carried out in momentum space). However, $p_1^4\,U_0$ has a delta-function singularity at $r_1=0$ and $r_{12}=0$ and it is more convenient to use the form (39.17), where an infinitesimal region around $r_1=0$ and $r_{12}=0$ can be excluded without making an error. It should also be remembered that, in evaluating the expectation value of the second part of H_5, an infinitesimal region around $r_{12}=0$ has to be excluded from the integral.

From (39.16) and the fact that the expectation values of H_1 and H_1' are equal it also follows that the expectation values of H_4 and H_4' are equal[1]. We can then

[1] In the footnote below (16.16) we showed that the expectation value of $\boldsymbol{p}\cdot\mathcal{E}+\mathcal{E}\cdot\boldsymbol{p}$ over a *real* and bounded position space wave function is zero for *any* real vector function $\mathcal{E}(\boldsymbol{r})$. This expectation value is also zero for any wave function of form $R(r)\,Y_{lm}(\vartheta,\varphi)$, with R real, if $\mathcal{E}(\boldsymbol{r})$ is any real and *central* field. In our present discussion of the two-particle system, the wave functions U_0 and $\mathcal{E}_1$ are more complicated. The expectation values of H_4 and H_4' are equal only if $\mathcal{E}_1$ is the *special* function —grad$_1$ V, where V is the potential which occurs in the Hamiltonian H_0 of which U_0 is an eigenfunction.

write these expectation values (denoted by a bar) as

$$\left.\begin{aligned}\overline{H}_4=\overline{H}_4'&=\frac{1}{2}\frac{ie\hbar}{(2mc)^2}\left(\overline{\boldsymbol{p}_1\cdot\mathscr{E}_1}-\overline{\mathscr{E}_1\cdot\boldsymbol{p}_1}+\overline{\boldsymbol{p}_2\cdot\mathscr{E}_2}-\overline{\mathscr{E}_2\cdot\boldsymbol{p}_2}\right)\\&=\frac{1}{2}\frac{e\hbar^2}{(2mc)^2}\left(\overline{\operatorname{div}_1\mathscr{E}_1}+\overline{\operatorname{div}_2\mathscr{E}_2}\right).\end{aligned}\right\}\quad(39.18)$$

The differential equation (39.14) can also be derived directly in position space from the BREIT equation (38.1). The method[1] of derivation is very similar to that used in Sect. 12 for the case of the DIRAC equation. By this method one also gets a small term H_6' to be added to H_6 in (39.14), which is quadratic in the vector potential,

$$H_6'=\frac{e^2}{2mc^2}(A_1^2+A_2^2).\quad(39.19)$$

However, in such a position space derivation it is easy to miss some terms which involve delta-function types of singularities. In particular, the first part of H_5 was missed in older derivations[2]. Recently, another method for the reduction of equations of the BREIT form to equations of the PAULI form has been developed[3], which is a generalization of the FOLDY-WOUTHUYSEN method (see Sect. 16γ). This method can also be applied[4] to relativistic two-body equations (discussed in Sect. 42γ).

40. Fine structure splitting[5] of helium. Using the differential equation (39.14), we shall now calculate the relativistic energy levels of atoms with two electrons in the absence of external fields ($\mathscr{H}=0$). Because of the small magnitude of the fine structure constant it is sufficient to determine the eigenfunction in zeroth and the eigenvalues in first approximation[6]. The zeroth approximation is given by the solutions of the nonrelativistic SCHRÖDINGER equation

$$E_0U_0=H_0U_0$$

with which we have dealt extensively in Sects. 24 to 36. Thus, the unperturbed eigenfunctions (cf. Sect. 24) are products of a spatial and a spin eigenfunction; in the case of orthohelium the three spin eigenfunctions S_+, S_0, S_- [cf. Eqs. (24.4) and (24.5)] are possible, for parahelium only the one spin function S_p (24.6). The unperturbed eigenfunctions may be characterized by the magnetic quantum numbers of spin and orbit, i.e., by m_l and m_s[7]. The energy in zeroth approximation does not depend on these two quantum numbers, it depends only on the principal, orbital and spin quantum numbers, n, l and S[8].

[1] See ref. [*10*], Sect. 22.

[2] This term was omitted in ref. [*10*] and also by H. A. ERIKSSON, Z. Physik **109**, 762 (1938). ERIKSSON also omitted a part of the expectation value of H_1. More specifically, he evaluated the integral of $U_0^*(p_1^4U_0)$ not over all space (as one should) but over a region excluding spheres of infinitesimal radius about the points $r_1=0$ and $r_{12}=0$. The delta-function part of H_5 has been derived by V. BERESTETSKI and L. LANDAU, J. exp. theor. Phys. USSR. **19**, 673 (1949); A. SESSLER and H. FOLEY, Phys. Rev. **92**, 1321 (1953); J. SUCHER and H. FOLEY, Phys. Rev. **95**, 966 (1954).

[3] Z. V. CHRAPLYVY: Phys. Rev. **91**, 388; **92**, 1310 (1953).

[4] W. BARKER and F. GLOVER: Phys. Rev. **99**, 317 (1955).

[5] Cf. G. BREIT: Phys. Rev. **36**, 483 (1930); also W. HEISENBERG, Z. Physik **39**, 499 (1926); Y. SUGIURA, Z. Physik **44**, 190 (1927); L. GAUNT, Proc. Roy. Soc. Lond. **122**, 153 (1929); Phil. Trans. **228**, 151 (1929).

[6] The eigenvalues will then be given correctly to within order α^2. As a matter of fact, a greater accuracy is not possible in view of the manner of derivation of (39.14).

[7] $m_s=1, 0, -1$ for S_+, S_0, S_-. m_l is the second index of the spherical harmonic $Y_{lm_l}(\vartheta,\varphi)$ which specifies the angular dependence of the spatial eigenfunction.

[8] S is determined by the term system, it equals 1 for ortho and 0 for parahelium.

Of the relativistic perturbations three of them, namely H_1, H_2, H_4, do not remove the degeneracy of the eigenvalues with respect to m_l and m_s[1]. Their only effect is to shift the eigenvalue by a small amount, which is of no interest to us, since the shift is negligibly small compared to the errors committed in our previous calculation of the nonrelativistic eigenvalue[2]. On the other hand, the perturbations H_3 and H_5 split each term of orthohelium[3] into three fine structure levels having inner quantum numbers $j=l+1$, l and $l-1$, where $j(j+1)$ is equal to the square of the magnitude of the total angular momentum $\boldsymbol{M}=\boldsymbol{k}+\boldsymbol{S}$. In view of this splitting, the above mentioned products of a space and spin function are actually not the correct zeroth order eigenfunctions; instead, one must form appropriate linear combinations of them. We shall save ourselves the trouble of explicitly forming these linear combinations by using the matrix method in our calculations.

In order to obtain the greatest possible accuracy in the evaluation of the fine structure, the calculations must, of course, be based on the exact spatial eigenfunction of the level in question. BREIT has carried out an accurate calculation for the 2^3P state of He, in which he determined the eigenfunction by means of the variation method[4]. We shall discuss his results below.

In Sect. 41 we shall discuss the expectation values of all the operators occuring in (39.14) for the ground state of helium-like atoms. In this section we discuss only the fine structure *splitting*, which can only be produced by the operators H_3 and H_5. It follows from the symmetry arguments given above, that even these terms can give splitting only for states in which both l and S are non-zero, i.e. for ortho-helium states other than S-states. We shall also verify this explicitly. We shall make some general remarks about the expectation values of H_3 and H_5, which hold for any wave functions with the correct symmetry properties (and hence also for the exact one). We shall carry out explicit calculations only using simple approximate wave functions. We first of all neglect polarization effects, but should nevertheless take a product form spatial wave function,

$$U=\frac{1}{\sqrt{2}}\left[u_1(1)\,u_n(2)-u_n(1)\,u_1(2)\right],$$

of the correct symmetry for ortho-states. Actually we shall only take an unsymmetrized wave function

$$U=u_1(1)\,u_n(2). \tag{40.1}$$

One can show that the error committed in leaving out symmetrization (exchange integrals) is only of the order of the ratio of the "radius" of the orbit of the inner electron to that of the outer. Since the inner electron is in the ground state and the outer electron in an excited state of non-zero l, this ratio is reasonably small. For such states we shall also approximate u_{nlm} by the corresponding hydrogenic wave function for nuclear charge $(Z-1)$, (complete screening). The errors due to all these approximations should become smaller as n and l increase.

[1] This follows from the fact that H_1, H_2 and H_4 depend only on the spatial position of the electron and, thus, are independent of spin. Consequently, these operators commute with S_z; thus k_z is a constant of the motion and therefore S_z is also. [$M_z=k_z+S_z$ is a constant of the motion even for the total HAMILTONian function.]

[2] Except for the ground state; see Sect. 41.

[3] The terms of parahelium, of course, are not split; since there exists only one spin eigenfunction S_p, the quantum states are completely determined by the specification of m_l only. Evidently, the energy must be independent of m_l since no direction in space is distinguished.

[4] However, the eigenfunction used by BREIT does not meet the highest standards of accuracy, as the corresponding eigenvalue is rather bad.

α) *Spin-orbit interaction.* We evaluate now the spin-orbit interaction, i.e. the expectation value of the operator H_3 in (39.14). We first note that the spin-operator $\boldsymbol{s}_1$ can be written in the form

$$\boldsymbol{s}_1 = \tfrac{1}{2}\boldsymbol{S} + \tfrac{1}{2}(\boldsymbol{s}_1 - \boldsymbol{s}_2); \quad \boldsymbol{S} = \boldsymbol{s}_1 + \boldsymbol{s}_2, \tag{40.2}$$

with a similar relation for $\boldsymbol{s}_2$. For any of the four (symmetric or antisymmetric) spin wave functions, the expectation value of the odd operator $(\boldsymbol{s}_1 - \boldsymbol{s}_2)$ is identically zero. Since $\boldsymbol{s}_1$ and $\boldsymbol{s}_2$ occur linearly in H_3, the expectation value of H_3 remains unchanged if we replace $\boldsymbol{s}_1$ (as well as $\boldsymbol{s}_2$) by $\frac{1}{2}\boldsymbol{S}$. Making this replacement and substituting $\mathscr{E}_1 = (Z\boldsymbol{r}_1/r_1^3 - \boldsymbol{r}_{12}/r_{12}^3)$ we have, in atomic units,

$$H_3 = \frac{1}{4}\alpha^2\left[\frac{Z}{r_1^3}\boldsymbol{r}_1\times\boldsymbol{p}_1 + \frac{Z}{r_2^3}\boldsymbol{r}_2\times\boldsymbol{p}_2 + \frac{3}{r_{12}^3}(\boldsymbol{r}_1 - \boldsymbol{r}_2)\times(\boldsymbol{p}_2 - \boldsymbol{p}_1)\right]\cdot\boldsymbol{S}. \tag{40.3}$$

For singlet states (parahelium), the total spin $\boldsymbol{S}$ is zero and the expectation value of H_3 vanishes identically (for *any* wave function, including the exact one).

For triplet states (orthohelium) we note that $\boldsymbol{r}_1\times\boldsymbol{p}_1 = \boldsymbol{k}_1$ and $\boldsymbol{r}_2\times\boldsymbol{p}_2 = \boldsymbol{k}_2$, where $\boldsymbol{k}_1$ and $\boldsymbol{k}_2$ are the operators of orbital angular momentum for the inner and outer electron. For the inner ($1s$) electron, $\boldsymbol{k}_1 = 0$ and the first term in (40.3) vanishes[1]. If the outer electron is also in an s-state, then $\boldsymbol{k}_2$ and l are zero and the expectation values of the second and third terms in (40.3) also vanish[2]. Thus, for $l=0$, the expectation value of H_3 is exactly zero (for *any* wave function).

For $l \neq 0$ we then have, using the fact that $\boldsymbol{k}_1 = 0$,

$$H_3 = \frac{1}{4}\alpha^2\left\{\frac{Z}{r_2^3}\boldsymbol{k}_2 + \frac{3}{r_{12}^3}\left[(\boldsymbol{r}_1\times\boldsymbol{p}_2 - \boldsymbol{k}_2) + \boldsymbol{r}_2\times\boldsymbol{p}_1\right]\cdot\boldsymbol{S}.\right. \tag{40.4}$$

We now restrict ourselves to the approximate wave function (40.1) and note further that the important contributions to the wave function[3] come from $r_1 \ll r_2$ (at least if the outer electron is in a *highly* excited state). We therefore neglect r_1 compared with r_2 and replace r_{12} by r_2. For our product wave function (no polarization) the expectation value of $\boldsymbol{r}_2\times\boldsymbol{p}_1$ vanishes from symmetry arguments (with $\boldsymbol{k}_1 = 0$). With these approximations, H_3 reduces to

$$H_3 = \frac{1}{4}\alpha^2(Z-3)\frac{1}{r_2^3}\boldsymbol{S}\cdot\boldsymbol{k},$$

where $\boldsymbol{k} = \boldsymbol{k}_2$ is the total orbital angular momentum, since $\boldsymbol{k}_1 = 0$.

We now have to evaluate the expectation value of $\boldsymbol{S}\cdot\boldsymbol{k}$ for ortho-states. The nonrelativistic eigenfunctions are eigenstates of $\boldsymbol{S}^2$ with eigenvalue $S(S+1)$, where $S=1$, and of $\boldsymbol{k}^2$ with eigenvalue $l(l+1)$. In the nonrelativistic theory the eigenstates with the same $S=1$ and l, but different values of m_l and m_s,

---

[1] The expectation value of r_1^{-3} itself diverges for an s-state electron. However, the operators occuring in (39.14) are only approximations, which break down where the potentials are very large. The correct operator, to which r_1^{-3} is an approximation, is less singular for very small r_1 and its expectation value is finite (although large). Since $\boldsymbol{k}_1$ is exactly zero, dropping the first term in (40.3) is justified.

[2] The third term vanishes for the following reason: Any S-state spatial wave function is invariant to the simultaneous rotation of the vectors $\boldsymbol{r}_1$ and $\boldsymbol{r}_2$ through the same angle. The expectation value of the component of the (pseudo) vector $\boldsymbol{r}_{12}\times(\boldsymbol{p}_2 - \boldsymbol{p}_1)$ in any direction is then independent of the direction and hence zero.

[3] Actually, the expectation values of some of the terms in (40.4) diverge *individually* as r_{12} approaches zero. An inspection of the term in square brackets in (40.3) shows that the *total* operator behaves only like r_{12}^{-2} as $r_{12}\to 0$ and the contribution to the expectation value integral from small r_{12} is finite and even *small* compared with the contribution from $r_1 \ll r_{12}$, which we are retaining.

are degenerate. Rewriting $\boldsymbol{k}\cdot\boldsymbol{S}$ in terms of the total angular momentum operator $\boldsymbol{M}=\boldsymbol{k}+\boldsymbol{S}$ [with the help of (13.4)], we see that H_3 removes this degeneracy. The correct stationary states are those linear combinations of the nonrelativistic wave functions which are eigenstates of $\boldsymbol{M}^2$ with quantum number j equal to $l-1$ or l or $l+1$. If we call X the expectation value of $2\boldsymbol{k}\cdot\boldsymbol{S}$, as in (13.5), we have

$$\tfrac{1}{2}X=\tfrac{1}{2}[j(j+1)-l(l+1)-S(S+1)]=\left\{\begin{array}{ll} l & \text{for } j=l+1 \\ -1 & \text{for } j=l \\ -(l+1) & \text{for } j=l-1. \end{array}\right\} \tag{40.5}$$

We finally use a hydrogenic wave function for charge $(Z-1)$ for u_{nlm} and obtain the expectation value of r_2^{-3} from (3.26). In our approximation, then, the final expression for the expectation value E_3 of H_3 is

$$\left.\begin{aligned} E_3 &= \tfrac{1}{4}\alpha^2(Z-3)\,\overline{r_2^{-3}}\,(\tfrac{1}{2}X),\\ \overline{r_2^{-3}} &= \frac{2(Z-1)^3}{n^3(2l+1)(l+1)\,l}. \end{aligned}\right\} \tag{40.6}$$

Generally speaking, the energy level in *any* atom (with given values of S and l) will be split into the components with different j-values, running from $|l-S|$ to $l+S$. If the splitting energy of each component is proportional to the expectation value X of $2\boldsymbol{k}\cdot\boldsymbol{S}$, we speak of a "regular multiplet" (LANDÉ interval rule). This was the case in hydrogen (see Sect. 13). If H_3 were the only operator contributing to the splitting in orthohelium, according to (40.6) we would have "regular triplets". For He itself $(Z-3)$, and hence the multiplying factor of X, is negative and we speak of an "inverted regular triplet" (and for Li^+ this factor is zero). The effect of the inner electron, so to speak, overcompensates that of the nucleus. The observed level splitting in He and Li^+ is quite different, due to the spin-spin interaction, which we discuss next.

β) Spin-spin interaction. We consider next the expectation value E_5 of the operator H_5 in (39.14). This term, derived from the BREIT operator, represents the magnetic interaction between the spins of the two electrons. The expectation value of the part of H_5 involving the delta function depends on the value of S, but not on the inner quantum number j. Hence it contributes to the level shift (cf. Sect. 41), but not to the level *splitting* and we omit it. The expectation value of the second part of H_5 vanishes for S-states from symmetry considerations. For non-zero l we again approximate r_{12} by r_2 in this part of H_5 and note that $\boldsymbol{k}=\boldsymbol{k}_2\,(\boldsymbol{k}_1=0)$. We further rewrite the expectation value of this approximate operator, using the relation (A.33), derived in the Appendix,

$$\left.\begin{aligned} E_5 &\equiv \alpha^2\,\overline{\left[\frac{\boldsymbol{s}_1\cdot\boldsymbol{s}_2}{r_2^3}-3\,\frac{(\boldsymbol{s}_1\cdot\boldsymbol{r}_2)(\boldsymbol{s}_2\cdot\boldsymbol{r}_2)}{r_2^5}\right]} = -\frac{\alpha^2\,\overline{r_2^{-3}}}{(2l+3)(2l-1)}\,Y,\\ Y &= 2(\boldsymbol{s}_1\cdot\boldsymbol{s}_2)\,\boldsymbol{k}^2-3(\boldsymbol{s}_1\cdot\boldsymbol{k})(\boldsymbol{s}_2\cdot\boldsymbol{k})-3(\boldsymbol{s}_2\cdot\boldsymbol{k})(\boldsymbol{s}_1\cdot\boldsymbol{k}). \end{aligned}\right\} \tag{40.7}$$

We first rewrite

$$(\boldsymbol{s}_1\cdot\boldsymbol{k})(\boldsymbol{s}_2\cdot\boldsymbol{k})+(\boldsymbol{s}_2\cdot\boldsymbol{k})(\boldsymbol{s}_1\cdot\boldsymbol{k})=(\boldsymbol{S}\cdot\boldsymbol{k})^2-(\boldsymbol{s}_1\cdot\boldsymbol{k})^2-(\boldsymbol{s}_2\cdot\boldsymbol{k})^2.$$

Further, making use of the commutation rules of $\boldsymbol{k}$ and of the spin operator $\boldsymbol{s}$ for an individual electron (see Sect. 11),

$$\boldsymbol{k}\times\boldsymbol{k}=i\,\boldsymbol{k},\qquad \boldsymbol{s}\times\boldsymbol{s}=i\,\boldsymbol{s},\qquad s_i\,s_j+s_j\,s_i=\tfrac{1}{2}\,\delta_{ij},$$

we can write further
$$(\mathbf{s}_1 \cdot \mathbf{k})^2 = \tfrac{1}{4}\mathbf{k}^2 - \tfrac{1}{2}\mathbf{s}_1 \cdot \mathbf{k}.$$

We therefore get the following expression for the operator Y in (40.7),
$$Y = (2\mathbf{s}_1 \cdot \mathbf{s}_2 + \tfrac{3}{2})\,\mathbf{k}^2 - \tfrac{3}{2}(\mathbf{S} \cdot \mathbf{k}) - 3(\mathbf{S} \cdot \mathbf{k})^2. \tag{40.8}$$

Each term in (40.8) commutes with $\mathbf{k}^2$, $\mathbf{S}^2$ and $\mathbf{M}^2$ and hence the operator Y is diagonal in a representation in terms of the quantum numbers l, S and j. If $l=0$ (S-state), the eigenvalue of Y is zero for any value of the "total spin" quantum number S. We also have
$$2\mathbf{s}_1 \cdot \mathbf{s}_2 = S(S+1) - s_1(s_1+1) - s_2(s_2+1) = S(S+1) - \tfrac{3}{2}. \tag{40.9}$$

For para-states the quantum number S is zero and Y again vanishes, for any value of l. For ortho-states with non-zero l, we have $S=1$, $\mathbf{k}^2 = l(l+1)$, $2\mathbf{s}_1 \cdot \mathbf{s}_2 = \tfrac{1}{2}$ and $\mathbf{S} \cdot \mathbf{k}$ is given by (40.5). For ortho-states we get finally
$$Y = -\tfrac{1}{2}\begin{cases} l(2l-1) & \text{for } j = l+1, \\ -(2l+3)(2l-1) & \text{for } j = l, \\ (2l+3)(l+1) & \text{for } j = l-1. \end{cases} \tag{40.10}$$

γ) More accurate calculations. The expectation values of the operators H_3 and H_5 in (39.14) have been calculated more accurately by BREIT[1]. He used the variational wave functions for the 2^3P states of He, which were discussed in Sect. 35. These wave functions are antisymmetrized correctly and take polariza tion into account at least approximately. BREIT evaluated the expectation values of the operators for these wave functions without neglecting r_1 compared with r_2.

We have so far considered only the *expectation* values of the operators H_3 and H_5 for states of fixed quantum numbers l and S. Actually, H_3 and H_5 also have matrix elements for transitions between states of *different* values for l and S, as long as the inner quantum number j is the same for both states. For instance, in H_3 the odd operator $(\mathbf{s}_1 - \mathbf{s}_2)$ occurs, whose expectation values vanish but which has matrix elements for transitions between orthostates ($S=1$) and para-states ($S=0$). Thus, in the relativistic theory, l and S are no longer strictly "good" quantum numbers, but j is. The correct eigenfunctions of the total HAMILTONian are no longer pure ${}^3P_1$, ${}^1P_1$, etc. wave functions, but have a small admixture of wave functions belonging to other states with the same value of j. Since H_3 and H_5 are very small compared with H_0, the amount of mixing should be quite small (of order $Z^2\alpha^2$) but could become appreciable if different states with the same j value happened to have very similar energies[2].

This mixture between various wave functions has been investigated by ARAKI[3]. With these admixtures included, the fine structure splitting of the ortho-states is not simply given by the expectation values of H_3 and H_5, but also depends on the non-diagonal matrix elements of these operators. The largest mixing effect for an ortho-state comes from the para-state with the same values of n and l, since their energy difference is rather small (given by the exchange integral K, Sect. 28). Even so the effect of mixing on the fine structure separation is very small (of relative order H_3/K), less than 1% for all states in He.

ARAKI's calculation of the fine structure separations in He is similar to BREIT'S, but he used the type of wave functions mentioned in Sect. 29 (given in detail

[1] G. BREIT: Phys. Rev. **36**, 383 (1930).
[2] The case of $Z \gg 1$ is discussed in Sect. 43α.
[3] G. ARAKI: Proc. Phys. Math. Soc. Japan **19**, 128 (1937).

in [*10*], Sect. 15) instead of the variational ones. Both BREIT's and ARAKI's results should be considerably better than those of our simple approximations, (40.5) and (40.7). But they are still not very accurate, since the results depend fairly strongly on the details of the wave functions used, which in turn are not very accurate.

δ) Results. We discuss first our approximate results (40.5) with (40.6) and (40.7) with (40.10) for E_3 and E_5, respectively. E_3 alone would give rise to regular triplets for $Z \gtrsim 4$, no splitting at all for $Z=3$ (Li^+) and inverted regular triplets for $Z=2$. E_5 alone would give rise to partially inverted triplets, the $j=l-1$ level being highest and $j=l$ lowest. For Li^+ this is indeed the whole effect. For $Z>4$, E_3 becomes more important relative to E_5 with increasing Z and with increasing l. For low values of l and Z, even the qualitative features of the level splitting change from one value of l or Z to another.

For ${}^3P$ states ($l=1$) the energy separation between the states of $J=0$ and 1 (or $J=1$ and 2) is given by (in RYDBERG'S)

$$\Delta E = \frac{\alpha^2 (Z-1)^3}{6n^3} \begin{Bmatrix} 6-(Z-3) & \text{for} \quad j=0\to 1 \\ -\frac{2}{5}-2(Z-2) & \text{for} \quad j=1\to 2. \end{Bmatrix} \tag{40.11}$$

For ${}^3D$ states ($l=2$) we have

$$\Delta E = \frac{\alpha^2 (Z-1)^3}{30\, n^3} \begin{Bmatrix} 4-2(Z-3) & \text{for} \quad j=1\to 2 \\ \frac{3}{7}-3(Z-2) & \text{for} \quad j=2\to 3. \end{Bmatrix} \tag{40.12}$$

Quite generally the level splitting is independent of the principal quantum number n, according to our simple approximation, except for an overall multiplying factor of n^{-3}. For He the more accurate results of BREIT and ARAKI are only slightly different from ours. Note that, for the ${}^3P$ levels in He, the $J=1$ and $J=2$ levels happen to have almost the same energy (for all values of n). In Fig. 18 we give a schematic diagram of the level splitting of ${}^3P$ states for $Z=2$ (He), $Z=3$ (Li^+) and large Z ($Z>10$).

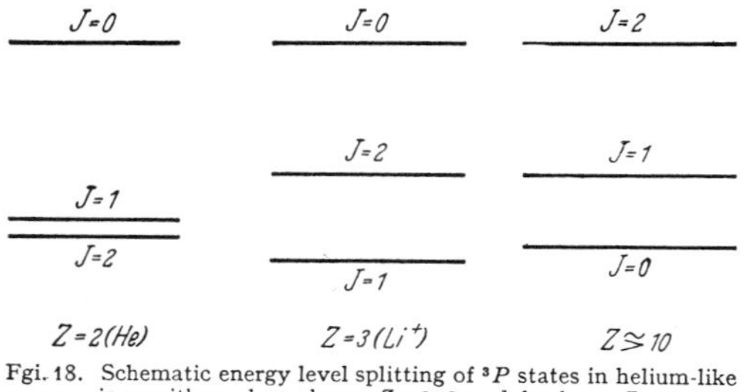

Fgi. 18. Schematic energy level splitting of ${}^3P$ states in helium-like ions with nuclear charge $Z=2$, 3 and for large Z.

Measurements of the fine structure splitting of many energy levels in helium-like atoms have been carried out by means of optical spectroscopy, but it is rather difficult to obtain an accuracy of better than ± 0.01 cm^{-1}. Only recently microwave methods have been developed for measuring the energy differences in direct transitions between the components of ${}^3P$-triplets. These methods are capable of an accuracy of much better than ± 0.001 cm^{-1}. In Table 11 we compare the theoretical results, obtained from the approximation (40.11) (labeled Appr.) and from BREIT's and ARAKI's calculations, with experimental measurements[1] of the splitting of a few ${}^3P$-states. The agreement is fairly good, but not excellent, and the discrepancies are most probably due to the inaccuracy of the wave functions used in the theoretical calculations.

[1] FRED, TOMKINS, BRODY and HAMERMESH: Phys. Rev. **82**, 406 (1951) for He 2P (optical). H. SCHÜLER: Z. Physik **42**, 487 (1927) for Li^+ 2P (optical, using the Li_6 isotope, which has no observable hyperfine structure). T. MAIMAN and W. LAMB: Phys. Rev. **98**, 1194 (1955) for He 3P (microwave).

Table 11. *Fine structure splitting of ^3P levels in* He *and* Li^+ *(in* cm^{-1}*).*

	2 *P* (He)				3 *P* (He)			2 *P* (Li^+)	
	Appr.	Breit	Araki	Expt.	Appr.	Araki	Expt.	Appr.	Expt.
$^3P_0 - {}^3P_1$	0.84	0.97	0.94	0.99	0.25	0.22	0.272	5.82	5.1_5
$^3P_1 - {}^3P_2$	−0.05	0.14	0.07	0.08	-0.01_5	0.01_8	0.0220	−2.33	-2.1_0

41. Relativistic corrections for the ground state. For the ground state ($1\,^1S$) of helium-like atoms, l, S and j are all zero and there is no fine structure splitting. Nevertheless, the operators H_1 to H_5 in (39.14) contribute relativistic corrections (or level shifts) to the nonrelativistic energy eigenvalue (Sects. 32 and 33) of relative order $(Z\alpha)^2$ and $Z\alpha^2$. These corrections, derived from the Pauli approximation, are themselves only the leading terms in an expansion in powers of α and $Z\alpha$. The accuracy of the nonrelativistic calculations on the ground state energy and of the measurements of the ionization potential of He warrants the inclusion of the Pauli approximation terms (Sect. 41 α) and even (to some extent) of the higher correction terms (of which the most important is the Lamb shift, Sect. 41 β).

α) Pauli approximations. We consider now the expectation values of the operators H_1 to H_5 in (39.14) for the ground state of a He-like atom with nuclear charge Z. Working in atomic units and denoting expectation values by bars, we get for the expectation value E_1 of H_1

$$E_1 = -\frac{\alpha^2}{8}\left(\overline{p_1^4} + \overline{p_2^4}\right) = -\frac{\alpha^2}{4}\overline{p_1^4}. \tag{41.1}$$

As discussed in Sect. 36 δ, great care must be taken in the evaluation of $\overline{p_1^4}$ and it is simplest and safest to use the last form on the right hand side of (36.15) [see also Eq. (39.17)].

It can be shown (after some algebra) that the expectation value E_2 of the operator H_2 vanishes if any wave function of product form $U = u(r_1)\,u(r_2)$ is used, i.e. both for the hydrogen-like and for the Hartree wave function. If a more accurate wave function, which includes the effects of polarization, is used, then a finite (but numerically small) value is obtained for E_2. As was shown in Sect. 40 α, the expectation value of H_3 vanishes *exactly* (for any wave function) for all S-states and hence for the ground state.

The expectation value E_4 of the operator H_4 is given by (39.18) with div $\mathcal{E}_1 = -\Delta_1 V$. Using the explicit expression (39.14a) for V (in the absence of an external field) and working in atomic units, we get (using $\Delta r^{-1} = -4\pi\,\delta^{(3)}(\boldsymbol{r})$,

$$E_4 = +\pi\alpha^2\left[Z\,\overline{\delta^{(3)}(\boldsymbol{r}_1)} - \overline{\delta^{(3)}(\boldsymbol{r}_{12})}\right]. \tag{41.2}$$

We finally come to the expectation value E_5 of the operator H_5. The expectation value of the second term in the expression for H_5 in (39.14) vanishes exactly for any S-state. From (40.9), for any singlet state ($S=0$) we have $\overline{\boldsymbol{s}_1\cdot\boldsymbol{s}_2} = -\frac{3}{4}$ and the first part of H_5 gives (in atomic units)

$$E_5 = +2\pi\alpha^2\,\overline{\delta^3(\boldsymbol{r}_{12})}. \tag{41.3}$$

The total energy shift for the ground state of the helium-like atom, in the Pauli approximation, is given by the sum of E_1, E_2, E_4 and E_5. The corresponding energy shift for the ion with one of the two electrons removed is, from (13.14), $-(Z^4\alpha^2/8)$ atomic units (in the Pauli approximation). The shift E_J in the ionization potential J of the two-electron atom is then

$$E_J = \alpha^2 \left[-\frac{Z^4}{8} + \frac{1}{4} \overline{p_1^4} - \pi Z \overline{\delta^{(3)}(\boldsymbol{r}_1)} - \pi \overline{\delta^{(3)}(\boldsymbol{r}_{12})} \right] - E_2. \tag{41.4}$$

Accurate numerical evaluations will be discussed in Sect. 41 γ. If we use as a very simple approximation to the wave function of the two-electron atom the hydrogenic form

$$\exp\left[-\tfrac{1}{2}\left(Z - \tfrac{5}{16}\right)(r_1 + r_2)\right],$$

then $E_2 = 0$ and the other expectation values are given by (36.11) and (36.17). The resulting approximation for E_J, carrying only the first three terms in an expansion in powers of $1/Z$, is

$$E_J \approx \tfrac{1}{4} \alpha^2 Z^2 (Z^2 - 6Z + 4.5) \,\text{Ry}. \tag{41.5}$$

In Sect. 41 γ we shall give a somewhat more accurate expansion in powers of $1/Z$ for E_J, Eq. (41.11).

β) *The* LAMB *shift*. We have so far considered only relativistic corrections of relative order $Z^2\alpha^2$ and $Z\alpha^2$ to the nonrelativistic energy of the two-electron atom and the corresponding one-electron ion. There are also radiative corrections (see Sects. 18 to 21) which are smaller by one more power of α. For helium, at least, these radiative corrections are not smaller than the experimental error of the ionization potential.

For the one-electron ion, the radiative corrections to the ground state energy of relative order $Z^2\alpha^3$ are simply the (lowest order) LAMB shift, (21.2), and there are no terms of order $Z\alpha^3$. From (21.2) we have for this shift

$$E_{L,1} = \frac{8\alpha^3 Z}{3} \frac{Z^3}{\pi} \left[2 \log \frac{1}{Z\alpha} - \log \frac{K_0}{Z^2 \,\text{Ry}} + 0.63 \right] \text{Ry}, \tag{41.6}$$

where $K_0 = 19.77 Z^2$ Ry is the average excitation energy defined in (19.10). For the two-electron atom, the only radiative corrections of order $Z^2\alpha^3$ are also LAMB shift terms, which correspond to the emission of a virtual photon by either electron, this electron's interaction with the nuclear COULOMB potential and reabsorption of the photon by the same electron. These terms contribute[1] a shift to the ground state energy of the two-electron atom of

$$E_L = \frac{16}{3} \alpha^3 Z \,\overline{\delta^3(\boldsymbol{r}_1)} \left[\log \frac{m c^2}{K_0} + \frac{19}{30} - \log 2 \right] \text{Ry}, \tag{41.7}$$

where the bar again denotes the expectation value in atomic units. The average excitation energy K_0 in (41.7) is defined in a manner similar to (19.10), but using the wave-functions for the two-electron atom. The evaluation of K_0 is discussed in Sect. 74 γ. K_0 approaches $19.77 Z^2$ Ry for large Z and is about 84 Ry for He ($Z = 2$).

For the two-electron atom there are a large number of terms, which contribute corrections of relative order $Z\alpha^3$. One such term corresponds to a LAMB shift type of process, as E_L above, but the electron interacts with the COULOMB potential due to the other electron (instead of that due to the nucleus). Another term comes from a correction to the BREIT operator, which corrects for the neglect of $E_n - E_0$ in the energy denominator of (38.5). A third term corresponds to the exchange of two virtual photons between the two electrons. Some of these terms involve, besides $Z\alpha^3$, also the factor $\log \alpha$ and these terms (to an accuracy

[1] H. E. HAKANSSON: Ark. Fysik 1, 555 (1950). — P. KABIR and E. SALPETER: (unpublished work).

of ± 1 as compared with $\log\alpha$) can be calculated fairly easily using quantum electrodynamics and a perturbation method[1]. The sum of the terms involving $\log\alpha$ is

$$E'_L = \tfrac{28}{3}\alpha^3 \overline{\delta^3(\boldsymbol{r}_{12})} \log\alpha \,\mathrm{Ry}. \tag{41.8}$$

The terms of order $Z\alpha^3 (Z^2 \,\mathrm{Ry})$ which do not involve $\log\alpha$ have not been calculated, but since E'_L is numerically rather small[2] compared with E_L (even for low Z), their neglect is not expected to introduce very large errors.

The radiative correction to the ionization potential J of the two-electron atom is then

$$\Delta E_J = E_{L,1} - E_L - E'_L. \tag{41.9}$$

Numerical values for ΔE_J are given in Sect. 41γ.

γ) *Numerical results.* We consider first the expression (41.4) for the relativistic correction E_J (in the Pauli approximation) to the ground state energy of He ($Z=2$). This expression involves the expectation values of various operators over the nonrelativistic ground state wave function which is not known exactly. These expectation values have been evaluated using various variational wave functions and the Hartree functions and some of the results are given in Table 10, Sect. 36. For Kinoshita's 38-parameter wave function, the values of the five terms in (41.4) are (in units of $\alpha^2\,\mathrm{Ry} = \frac{1}{2}\alpha^2$ at. un. $= 5.844\ \mathrm{cm}^{-1}$),

Term involving	ion	E_2	p^4	$\delta(r_1)$	$\delta(r_{12})$	E_J
Value[3]	-4	$+0.28$	$+27.05$	-22.75	-0.67	-0.10

The values of E_J minus the mass-polarization correction ε_M, defined in (37.13), for various wave functions is (in cm^{-1}).

Number of parameters	1	(Hartree)	3	18	38
$E_J - \varepsilon_M$	-24.0	-10.1	-7.2	-5.41	-5.35

Note that the various contributions to E_J almost cancel each other for He. As discussed in Sect. 36, the percentage errors in the various expectation values which make up E_J are very much larger than the percentage error in the variational nonrelativistic ionization potential. Nevertheless, the 38-parameter value, $E_J - \varepsilon_M = -5.35\ \mathrm{cm}^{-1}$, should not be in error by more than (plus or minus) a few times $0.1\ \mathrm{cm}^{-1}$.

We turn now to the evaluation of ΔE_J, given by (41.6) to (41.9), for He. We use the value in (74.8) for the average excitation energy K_0 and the values given in Table 10 for the expectation values of $\delta^{(3)}(\boldsymbol{r}_1)$ and $\delta^{(3)}(\boldsymbol{r}_{12})$. The result is (in cm^{-1})

$$E_{L,1} = 3.53, \quad -E_L = -4.97, \quad -E_{L'} = 0.21; \quad \Delta E_J = -(1.2_3 \pm 0.2)\ \mathrm{cm}^{-1}. \tag{41.10}$$

The probable error includes an order of magnitude estimate of the radiative correction terms which have not yet been evaluated.

---

[1] P. Kabir and E. Salpeter: (unpublished work).

[2] The smallness of these terms, even for small Z, is due to the fact that the expectation value of $\delta(\boldsymbol{r}_{12})$ is very much smaller than that of $\delta(\boldsymbol{r}_1)$ (by a factor of about 17 for He, see Table 10, Sect. 36).

[3] The numerical values are the expectation values multiplied by the coefficients occuring in (41.4).

We turn finally to an evaluation of E_J and ΔE_J for helium-like ions[1] of $Z>2$. For Li^+ ($Z=3$), we have evaluated the various expectation values which are involved in E_J, using the simple variational wave function (32.26). The result is $E_J=+14\ \text{cm}^{-1}$. This value may be in error by several cm^{-1}. For larger values of Z, the expectation values were evaluated[2], using a wave function given in ERIKSSON's paper which involves four parameters [instead of three, as in (33.14)] and an expansion in powers of $1/Z$. The result for the first few terms in this expansion is

$$E_J=\tfrac{1}{4}\alpha^2 Z^2(Z^2-4.254Z+5.57)\ \text{Ry}. \qquad (41.11)$$

The term in Z^4 is exact, but the accuracy of the other two coefficients may not be very good. Finally, we use (74.9) and substitute the expectation values from ERIKSSON's wave function into (41.9) to find the radiative corrections. The result, for the first few terms in the expansion in $1/Z$, is

$$\Delta E_J=-\frac{16Z^4\alpha^3}{3\pi}\left[(3.745-\log Z)+\frac{1}{Z}(1.44\log Z-6.46)\right]. \qquad (41.12)$$

The theoretical and experimental results for the ionization potentials of He and a few helium-like ions are summarized in Table 12: J_{NR} represents the theoretical result for the nonrelativistic ionization potential. For He we have used the value in (32.25) and for the other ions the expression (33.12). Multiplying these expressions by the appropriate values of the "reduced mass RYDBERG", (33.13), gives J_{NR} in cm^{-1}. The mass polarization corrections ε_M (which are rather unimportant for large Z) are taken from Sect. 37, E_J and ΔE_J from the discussions of this section. As Table 12 shows, the agreement between theory and experiment is excellent in all cases.

Table 12. *Experimental and theoretical ionization potentials for helium-like ions (in cm^{-1}).*

Z	2	3	4	6	8
ion	He	Li^+	Be^{++}	$C^{(4+)}$	$O^{(6+)}$
J_{NR}	198316.9_8	610072	1241177	3161660	5959980
$E_J-\varepsilon_M$	-5.3_5	$+9$	$+100$	$+840$	$+3320$
ΔE_J	-1.2_3	-6	-23	-120	-360
J_{theor}	198310.4_0	610075	1241254	3162380	5962940
J_{exp}	198310.5 ± 1	610079 ± 25	1241225 ± 100	3162450 ± 300	5963000 ± 600

42. BREIT equation without external field. We consider now the special case of the BREIT equation for two particles, which interact with each other, but in the absence of any external field. We generalize slightly from the case of two electrons to that of two (not necessarily identical) particles of mass and charge m_1, m_2 and e_1, e_2 respectively. But we still asume, for the moment, that each of the particles is a "FERMI-DIRAC particle", which has spin $\frac{1}{2}$ and obeys (if by itself) the DIRAC equation. One can easily generalize the full BREIT equation (38.1) for this case, but we consider only the PAULI approximation (39.14).

The approximate Eq. (39.14) can easily be modified for the case of unequal masses and charges of the two particles. If no external fields are present, this equation simplifies considerably. First, the terms involving $\boldsymbol{A}(\boldsymbol{r})$ are missing and eV, defined in (39.14a), is simply e_1e_2/r_{12}. Second, the total momentum $\boldsymbol{p}_1+\boldsymbol{p}_2$ is now a constant of the motion. If we work in the center of mass system

[1] J. SUCHER and H. FOLEY: Phys. Rev. **95**, 966 (1954). — M. A. ERIKSSON: Z. Physik **109**, 762 (1938).

[2] J. BIRD, D. BOWERS, and P. KABIR: Unpublished work.

$(\boldsymbol{p}_1+\boldsymbol{p}_2=0)$, the wave function U only depends on the relative displacement $(\boldsymbol{r}_1-\boldsymbol{r}_2)$, instead of on two variables. We write

$$\boldsymbol{p}=\boldsymbol{p}_1=-\boldsymbol{p}_2, \qquad \boldsymbol{r}=\boldsymbol{r}_{12}=\boldsymbol{r}_1-\boldsymbol{r}_2.$$

We then have, instead of (39.14),

$$\left.\begin{aligned}
W U &= (H_0+H_1+\cdots+H_5)\,U:\\
H_0 &= \frac{e_1 e_2}{r}+\frac{1}{2}\left(\frac{1}{m_1}+\frac{1}{m_2}\right)p^2,\\
H_1 &= -\frac{1}{8c^2}\left(\frac{1}{m_1^3}+\frac{1}{m_2^3}\right)p^4,\\
H_2 &= \frac{e_1 e_2}{2m_1 m_2 c^2}\,\frac{1}{r}\,(p^2+p_r^2),\\
H_3 &= -\frac{\boldsymbol{r}\times\boldsymbol{p}}{r^3}\cdot\left[\frac{\mu_1 e_2}{m_1 c}\,\boldsymbol{s}_1+\frac{\mu_2 e_1}{m_2 c}\,\boldsymbol{s}_2+\frac{2\mu_1 e_2}{m_2 c}\,\boldsymbol{s}_1+\frac{2\mu_2 e_1}{m_1 c}\,\boldsymbol{s}_2\right],\\
H_4 &= \frac{i e_1 e_2 \hbar}{(2c^2)}\left(\frac{1}{m_1^2}+\frac{1}{m_2^2}\right)\boldsymbol{p}\cdot\operatorname{grad}\frac{1}{r},\\
H_5 &= 4\mu_1\mu_2\left[-\frac{8\pi}{3}(\boldsymbol{s}_1\cdot\boldsymbol{s}_2)\,\delta^{(3)}(\boldsymbol{r})+\frac{1}{r^3}(\boldsymbol{s}_1\cdot\boldsymbol{s}_2-3s_{1r}s_{2r})'\right],
\end{aligned}\right\} \tag{42.1}$$

where

$$\mu_1=\frac{e_1\hbar}{2m_1 c}, \quad \mu_2=\frac{e_2\hbar}{2m_2 c}, \quad s_{1r}=\frac{\boldsymbol{s}_1\cdot\boldsymbol{r}}{r}, \quad p_r^2=\frac{1}{r^2}\,\boldsymbol{r}\cdot(\boldsymbol{r}\cdot\boldsymbol{p})\,\boldsymbol{p}.$$

α) One heavy particle. The application of Eq. (42.1) to the positronium system is discussed in Sect. 23. This equation can also be used to calculate the effect of nuclear motion and hyperfine structure on the energy levels of hydrogen-like atoms. We assume at the moment that one of the two particles is an electron and the other a nucleus which is a DIRAC particle of mass much larger than the electron's,

$$e_1=-e, \quad m_1=m, \quad e_2=Ze, \quad m_2=M\gg m.$$

We expand all the expressions in (42.1) in powers of m/M and retain only the zero and first power. We further rearrange the terms so that the largest ones involve the reduced mass $\mathcal{M}$ (called μ in Sect. 5),

$$\mathcal{M}=\frac{mM}{m+M}\approx m\left(1-\frac{m}{M}\right).$$

(42.1) then reduces to

$$W U=(H_a+H_b+H_c)\,U, \tag{42.2}$$

where

$$H_a=\left(-\frac{Ze^2}{r}+\frac{p^2}{2\mathcal{M}}\right)-\frac{p^4}{8\mathcal{M}^3c^2}+\frac{1}{r^3}\,\frac{\mu_{\mathcal{M}}Ze\hbar}{\mathcal{M}c}\,\boldsymbol{k}\cdot\boldsymbol{s}_1-\frac{iZe^2\hbar}{(2\mathcal{M}c)^2}\,\boldsymbol{p}\cdot\operatorname{grad}\frac{1}{r},$$

$$H_b=\frac{1}{Mc^2}\left[\frac{3}{8m^2}\,p^4-\frac{Ze^2}{2m}\,\frac{1}{r}\,(p^2+p_r^2)+\frac{iZe^2\hbar}{2m}\,\boldsymbol{p}\cdot\operatorname{grad}\frac{1}{r}\right],$$

$$H_c=H_5+\frac{2\mu_2}{mc}\,\frac{\hbar e}{r^3}\,\boldsymbol{k}\cdot\boldsymbol{s}_2,$$

and H_5 is given in (42.1). We have also written $\boldsymbol{k}=\boldsymbol{r}\times\boldsymbol{p}$ for the orbital angular momentum and $\mu_{\mathcal{M}}$ for $e\hbar/2\mathcal{M}c$.

So far we have derived (42.2) only under the assumption that the nucleus has spin $\frac{1}{2}$ and only a magnetic moment given by the DIRAC theory. In reality many nuclei have a spin other than $\frac{1}{2}$ and a magnetic moment which bears no simple relation to the DIRAC theory, in view of the complicated structure of nuclei. Even the simple proton, which has spin $\frac{1}{2}$, has a rather large anomalous magnetic moment (stemming from a coupling of the proton with its virtual meson charge cloud). That (42.2) can also be applied to such nuclei can be seen as follows.

Of the terms involving $1/m$ which occur in (42.1), we have only retained those in (42.2) which are linear in $1/m_2$. By referring back to (39.1), one can show that these terms come only from the nonrelativistic kinetic energy $p^2/2m_2$ and from the BREIT operator. The BREIT operator, in turn, represents the exchange of a photon between the electron and nucleus. Let λ denote the direction of polarization and $\boldsymbol{q}$ the momentum of the photon, $\boldsymbol{p}_2$ the momentum of the nucleus. In deriving the approximate form of the BREIT operator occurring in (39.1), we have used a factor

$$e_2 \alpha_{\lambda++} = \frac{e_2}{m_2 c} p_\lambda + \frac{2i}{\hbar} \mu_2 (\boldsymbol{q} \times \mathbf{s}_2)_\lambda . \tag{42.3}$$

Now, according to quantum electrodynamics, for *any* nonrelativistic particle with charge e_2 and an empirical magnetic moment $\boldsymbol{\mu}$ interacting with a photon we get a factor exactly of form (42.3), except that $2\mu_2 \mathbf{s}_2$ is replaced by $\boldsymbol{\mu}$. In other words, the nucleus has been treated in a sufficiently nonrelativistic manner in (42.2), so that no terms characteristic of the DIRAC theory (for the nucleus) remain.

In (42.2) all the terms which involve the spin of the nucleus $\mathbf{s}_2$ are contained in H_c. These terms are responsible for the hyperfine structure in hydrogen-like atoms. For these terms we have already written $e\hbar/2Mc$ in the form μ_2. For any nucleus with empirical magnetic moment $\boldsymbol{\mu}$ we simply have to replace $2\mu_2 \mathbf{s}_2$ by $\boldsymbol{\mu}$. The expectation value of H_c is evaluated and discussed in Sect. 22.

β) Nuclear motion. We discuss now the effect of the operator H_b in (42.2). The term H_c depends on the direction of the nuclear spin and is zero if the nuclear magnetic moment is zero. The term H_a is exactly the PAULI HAMILTONian for an "electron" with reduced mass $\mathcal{M}$ (not the real electron mass m), but in a *fixed* COULOMB field. If the HAMILTONian consisted solely of H_a, the effect of the nuclear motion on the fine structure would be exactly the same as the effect on the nonrelativistic energy (to first order in m/M). I.e. all energies are $(1-m/M)$ times those obtained for an infinitely heavy nucleus (fixed potential) and we merely have to replace R_∞ by R_M, the "reduced mass RYDBERG", in all terms in Sect. 13. However, the operator H_b is also of order (m/M) times the fine structure splitting. This order of magnitude is not much smaller than that of the LAMB shift. But we show now that the expectation value of H_b depends only on the principal quantum number n, *not* on l or j, and thus contributes only to a level *shift* and *not* to the fine structure *splitting*.

We evaluate only the expectation value E_b of the operator H_b using the nonrelativistic wave function U_0. Returning now to atomic units, we have

$$\tfrac{1}{2} p^2 U_0 = (W_0 + Z r^{-1}) U_0 ,$$

where W_0 is the nonrelativistic energy $(-Z^2/2n^2)$ a.u. For a state of orbital quantum number l it follows further from (1.11) that

$$\frac{1}{2} p_r^2 U_0 = \frac{1}{2}\left(p^2 - \frac{1}{r^2} k^2\right) U_0 = \left[W_0 + \frac{Z}{r} - \frac{l(l+1)}{2r^2} + \frac{1}{r}\frac{\partial}{\partial r}\right] U_0 . \tag{42.4}$$

We also use the fact (see Sect. 16) that the expectation value of $2\boldsymbol{p}\cdot(\operatorname{grad} 1/r)$ equals that of $-i\Delta r^{-1} = +4\pi i\,\delta^{(3)}(\boldsymbol{r})$. Using all these relations to evaluate E_b

from the operator H_b in (42.2), we get

$$E_b = \alpha^2 \frac{m}{M} \left\{ \frac{3}{2} \overline{\left(W_0 + \frac{Z}{r}\right)^2} - \frac{Z}{r} \overline{\left[2\left(W_0 + \frac{Z}{r}\right) - \frac{l(l+1)}{2r^2} + \frac{1}{r}\frac{\partial}{\partial r}\right]} - \pi Z \overline{\delta^{(3)}(\boldsymbol{r})} \right\}. \tag{42.5}$$

E_b is clearly independent of the quantum number j, but many of the individual terms in (42.5) depend on l. One has to evaluate all the terms explicitly to show that their sum is independent of l, if hydrogenic wave functions are used. W_0 is simply given by the BALMER formula and the expectation values of r^{-1}, r^{-2} and r^{-3} (for $l \neq 0$) by Eqs. (3.24), (3.25) and (3.26). For S-states, $\overline{r^{-3}}$ itself diverges, but the expression for which this is an approximation is finite. The term in $l(l+1)r^{-3}$ is thus zero for an S-state. On the other hand, the expectation value of $\delta^{(3)}(\boldsymbol{r})$ is simply the square of the wave function at the origin, which vanishes for $l \neq 0$ and, for an S-state, is given by [see (3.46)]

$$\pi \overline{\delta^{(3)}(\boldsymbol{r})} = \pi U_0^2(0) = Z^2/n^3. \tag{42.6}$$

Substituting these expectation values into (42.5) one finds[1], after some algebra,

$$E_b = -\frac{\alpha^2}{8}\frac{m}{M}\left(\frac{Z}{n}\right)^4 = -\left(\frac{Z\alpha}{2n}\right)^2 \frac{m}{M} |W_0|. \tag{42.7}$$

This energy shift is indeed independent of l and j and thus does not contribute to the fine structure splitting. For all states in H this shift is less than 10^{-8} of the nonrelativistic energy, which is beyond the limits of accuracy of optical spectroscopy.

γ) Fully covariant methods. The Eq. (42.1) is only an approximation to the BREIT equation (38.1) which reads, for two FERMI-DIRAC particles in the absence of external fields,

$$\left.\begin{aligned} &(E - H_1 - H_2)\, U(\boldsymbol{r}) = G_B(\boldsymbol{r})\, U(\boldsymbol{r}), \\ \text{with} \\ &H_1 = m_1 c^2 \beta_1 + c\,\boldsymbol{p}\cdot\boldsymbol{\alpha}_1, \quad H_2 = m_2 c^2 \beta_2 - c\,\boldsymbol{p}\cdot\boldsymbol{\alpha}_2, \\ &G_B(\boldsymbol{r}) = \frac{e_1 e_2}{r}\left[1 - \frac{1}{2}\boldsymbol{\alpha}_1\cdot\boldsymbol{\alpha}_2 - \frac{1}{2}\frac{(\boldsymbol{\alpha}_1\cdot\boldsymbol{r})(\boldsymbol{\alpha}_2\cdot\boldsymbol{r})}{r^2}\right], \end{aligned}\right\} \tag{42.8}$$

where $\boldsymbol{r}$ is the relative distance and $\boldsymbol{p}$ is the relative momentum. Eq. (42.8) is not only written in a non-covariant notation, but actually is not fully compatible with the special theory of relativity. This is connected with the fact (see Sect. 38α) that (42.8) is itself only an approximation. In Sect 38β some methods (e.g. the TAMM-DANCOFF and the perturbation methods) were outlined for calculating exact expressions (in principle) for the energy, etc., in the form of an expansion in powers of the fine structure constant α. These methods have the disadvantage that individual terms in the expansion are not LORENTZ invariant, although their sum is. The evaluation of a higher order term is also tedious since it involves summations over intermediate states or the solution of a set of coupled integral equations.

Other methods[2] have also been developed for treating the interaction of two FERMI-DIRAC particles with each other (according to pair theory and quantum

[1] For a more detailed derivation of (42.7) see G. BROWN and G. BREIT, Phys. Rev. **74**, 1278 (1948). This equation had also been obtained by K. BECHERT and J. MEIXNER, Ann. d. Physik **22**, 525 (1935).

[2] J. SCHWINGER: Proc. Nat. Acad. Sci. USA. **37**, 452, 455 (1951). — E. SALPETER and H. BETHE: Phys. Rev. **84**, 1232 (1951). — M. GELL-MANN and F. LOW: Phys. Rev. **84**, 350 (1951).

electrodynamics), which exhibit the LORENTZ invariance of the theory automatically. There are various (equivalent) ways of formulating such relativistic methods and we shall outline very briefly the BETHE-SALPETER formulation in terms of a fully covariant wave equation.

This wave equation for a two-body system bears some similarity to the BREIT equation, but is radically different in one respect. The wave function occurring in this covariant equation depends on one more variable than the BREIT wave function. In position space, for instance, the wave function depends on the positions of the two particles (as before), but also depends on one time-variable *each* for the two particles (instead of one common time). This puts time and position on the same footing and enables a LORENTZ-invariant formulation. In the absence of external fields and for a stationary state of the system, the momentum-energy four-vector P_μ for the motion of the center of mass can be eparated out. The covariant BETHE-SALPETER wave equation is then of the form

$$\left[\sum_\mu\left(\frac{m_1}{m_1+m_2}P_\mu+p_\mu\right)\gamma_\mu^{(1)}-i m_1 c\right]\left[\sum_\mu\left(\frac{m_2}{m_1+m_2}P_\mu-p_\mu\right)\gamma_\mu^{(2)}-i m_2 c\right]\psi(x_\nu)=i\bar{G}(x_\nu)\,\psi(x_\nu)\,. \quad (42.9)$$

The wave function ψ is a function of the four-vector $x_\nu=(\boldsymbol{r}, ict)$, where $\boldsymbol{r}=\boldsymbol{r}_1-\boldsymbol{r}_2$ is the relative distance as in (42.8) and t, the "relative time" t_1-t_2, is a variable without analogue in (42.8). In (42.9), p_μ is the operator $-i\hbar\,\partial/\partial x_\mu$ and P_μ is a constant four-vector; the invariant $E=\sqrt{-\sum_\mu P_\mu^2}$ is the total energy in the center of mass system and takes the place of the eigenvalue parameter E in (42.8). The interaction operator $\bar{G}$ consists of an infinite series of terms. *Each* term in this series is a LORENTZ-invariant operator G_n, which can be derived from the FEYNMAN formulation of quantum electrodynamics, multiplied by $(e_1 e_2/\hbar c)^n$ for the n-th term. For the first term in this series, G_1 is simply $\sum_\mu \gamma_\mu^{(1)}\gamma_\mu^{(2)}$ times a function of the invariant $\sum_\mu x_\mu^2$, the higher terms are generally integral operators. The four-dimensional FOURIER transform of (42.9) is a *single* integral equation, but the kernel consists of an infinite series of terms.

Little progress has been made so far in the application of (42.9) to *highly* relativistic systems. But for hydrogenlike atoms of low Z and for positronium the coupling constant $(-e_1 e_2/\hbar c)$ is small ($Z\alpha$ and α, respectively). For bound states of such systems the first few terms in the expansion of the energy eigenvalue E in powers of the coupling constant can be obtained from (42.9). The results of some such calculations[1] are quoted in Sects. 20α and 23β. The smallness of the coupling constant makes it possible to write the operator $\bar{G}$ as an „instantaneous" COULOMB interaction plus smaller correction terms. For an instantaneous interaction alone [a function of $\boldsymbol{r}$ times $\delta(t)$], (42.9) can be reduced to a three-dimensional wave equation for $\psi(\boldsymbol{r}, 0)$, which is somewhat similar to the BREIT equation (42.8), and the dependence of $\psi(\boldsymbol{r}, t)$ on t can be found. With this approximate solution of (42.9) as a starting point, the higher relativistic corrections to the energy are then obtained by perturbation (or iteration) methods.

43. Treatment for large Z. α) *The level scheme.* We consider now the case of helium-like atoms of large nuclear charge Z, for which $Z\alpha$ is not very much smaller than unity[2]. In this case the approximations used in the preceding few sections,

[1] E. E. SALPETER: Phys. Rev. **87**, 328 (1952). — R. KARPLUS and A. KLEIN: Phys. Rev. **87**, 848 (1952). — W. BARKER and F. GLOVER: Phys. Rev. **99**, 317 (1955).

[2] No two-electron ions of Z much larger than about 10 can be studied experimentally with good accuracy. However, the spectra of *complex* atoms with Z up to about 100 can be measured and the methods discussed in this section serve as a starting point for the theoretical treatment of the inner electrons in such atoms (see Sect. 17γ).

which considered relativistic effects as small perturbations and obtained results in the form of power series in $Z\alpha$, are no longer very good. On the other hand, we can make use of the fact that $1/Z$ is small and treat the *whole* interaction between the two electrons (including the COULOMB interaction) as a small perturbation compared with the interaction between either electron and the nucleus. Compared with the nonrelativistic energy $2Z^2$Ry, the effect of the spin-orbit interaction for an individual electron (given by the DIRAC equation for a single electron) is of relative order $(Z\alpha)^2$, whereas the interaction energy between the two electrons is of relative order $1/Z$. Thus, if $1/Z \ll (Z\alpha)^2$, i.e. if $Z \gg 27$, one can use the following approximation method, known as the j-j coupling scheme[1].

We first neglect the interaction between the electrons completely. Let $\psi_a(\boldsymbol{r}_1)$ be one of the exact DIRAC wave functions (a spinor with four components) for a stationary state of a single electron (1) in a static central potential $\varphi(r)$. Let $\boldsymbol{M}_1 = \boldsymbol{k}_1 + \boldsymbol{s}_1$ be the total angular momentum of this electron, then $\boldsymbol{M}_1^2$ and M_{1z} are constants of the motion and the state a is characterized by the principal, inner and magnetic quantum numbers n_1, j_1 and m_1, plus the "parity" π_1 of the state (corresponding to the two possibilities $l_1 = j_1 - \frac{1}{2}$ and $l_1 = j_1 + \frac{1}{2}$). In the absence of interaction, the wave function for a state of the two-electron system is of the form

$$\psi(1, 2) = \frac{1}{\sqrt{2}} \left[\psi_a(1)\, \psi_b(2) - \psi_b(1)\, \psi_a(2)\right], \tag{43.1}$$

where 1 refers to the first electron, 2 to the second. This wave function is a 16-component spinor (4 components for each electron) and is automatically antisymmetric to an interchange of all coordinates (spin as well as spatial) of the two electrons, as required by FERMI-DIRAC quantum statistics (of which the PAULI exclusion principle is a consequence).

The state (43.1) is characterized by the quantum numbers $n_1, n_2, j_1, j_2, m_1, m_2$ and the two possible values each of the parities π_1 and π_2. For any central potential $\varphi(r)$, the energy of the state depends on n_1, n_2, j_1 and j_2 but is independent of the values of m_1 and m_2. We restrict ourselves to nuclear charges $Z \gg 27 = \alpha^{-\frac{2}{3}}$. The part of the energy which depends on j_1 and j_2 is proportional to $(Z\alpha)^2$, which we do *not* assume to be small. For $\varphi(r)$ equal to the nuclear COULOMB potential Ze/r, the energy is also independent of π_1 and π_2 (i.e. independent of l_1 and l_2 for fixed j_1 and j_2).

Consider all the states of a given configuration (n_1, n_2, l_1, l_2) which have also fixed values of j_1 and j_2. In our zero-order approximation (central potential only) the energy is independent of the quantum numbers m_1 and m_2 and any linear superposition of the wave functions (43.1) with different m_1 and m_2 (but all other quantum numbers fixed) is also an eigenfunction. In particular, we can form those linear superpositions which are eigenstates of M_z (with eigenvalue M) and of $\boldsymbol{M}^2$ [with eigenvalue $J(J+1)$], where $\boldsymbol{M} = \boldsymbol{M}_1 + \boldsymbol{M}_2$ is the total angular momentum of the whole atom. The operator representing the interaction between the two electrons (discussed in Sect. 43β) commutes with $\boldsymbol{M}^2$ and M_z, but *not* with m_{1z} and m_{2z}. This operator, although small, removes the degeneracy with respect to m_{1z} and m_{2z} and the correct eigenstates are those of $\boldsymbol{M}^2$ and M_z. The possible values of the quantum numbers J and M are

$$J = |j_1 - j_2|, \ldots, j_1 + j_2; \quad M = -J, \ldots, +J. \tag{43.2}$$

The energy of these states is still independent of M (in the absence of external fields), but depends on J because of the electron-electron interaction (the splitting being of order $1/Z$ relative to Z^2Ry).

[1] For details see ref. [5], Chap. 10.

We thus see that for *all* values of the nuclear charge Z, J and M are good quantum numbers. For $Z \ll \alpha^{-\frac{2}{3}} = 27$ (discussed in Sects. 24 to 40), L and S are also (almost) good quantum numbers and the energies of the various levels of a particular configuration depend largely on L and S. For $Z \gg 27$ we have (instead of L and S) j_1 and j_2 as (almost) good quantum numbers and the energy splittings of a configuration depend largely on j_1 and j_2. We have so far considered only levels of a particular configuration (fixed n_1, n_2 and l_1, l_2). In reality these quantum numbers are *not* exact quantum numbers (for any Z) and mixing between various configurations[1] can occur (see Sect. 36β). If one of the two electrons is in the ground state, the configuration interaction is found to be rather small and we do not discuss it further. In Fig. 19 we give a schematic diagram of the level splitting of the configuration $1s\,2p$ (one electron in the ground state $l_1 = 0$, the other in a state with $l_2 = 1$) both for small Z ($5 < Z \ll 27$) and for large Z ($Z \gg 27$). The numbers above the lines denote the values of J (for this configuration $L = 1$ and $j_1 = \frac{1}{2}$ for all levels).

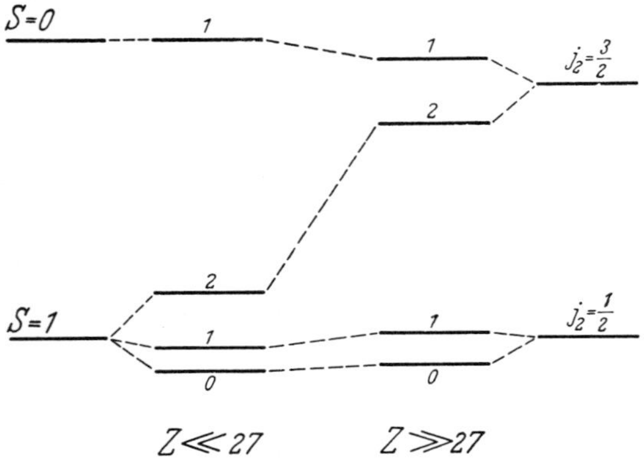

Fig. 19. Schematic energy level diagram for the configuration $1s\,2p$ in helium-like ions, both for small and large nuclear charge Z. The number against each level is the J-value. The levels at the extreme left are those without any spin-orbit coupling, those at the extreme right without any electron-electron interaction.

For very large Z it is most convenient to take as the central potential $\varphi(r)$ simply the nuclear COULOMB potential. In this case the electrostatic as well as the relativistic interaction between the two electrons is treated by a first order perturbation method (see Sect. 43β). The error in such a calculation is of order $1/Z^2$ (relative to Z^2 Ry). If $27 = \alpha^{-\frac{2}{3}} \ll Z \ll 137$ (or for inner electrons in a complex atom) higher accuracy is achieved if one takes the HARTREE potential for $\varphi(r)$ and solves for the DIRAC single-electron eigenfunctions [to be used in (43.1)] numerically[2].

β) *The interaction energy.* We outline briefly[3] how the interaction energy between the two electrons can be obtained from quantum electrodynamics by a perturbation method, if Z is large. We take as our unperturbed HAMILTONian the DIRAC HAMILTONian for two electrons in a central field, but without *any* interaction between the electrons. An unperturbed eigenstate with fixed quantum numbers J and M is given by a linear superposition of wave functions of form (43.1), all from a given configuration and given (j_a, j_b). We denote a term of this wave function of the form $\psi_a(1)\,\psi_b(2)$ by (ab) and $\psi_b(1)\,\psi_a(2)$ by (ba). The symbols a, a' etc. denote the various single-electron states (with fixed n_a, l_a and j_a, but different values of m_a, $m_{a'}$, etc.) which all have the same energy $\varepsilon_a = \varepsilon_{a'}$ etc. Similarly $\varepsilon_b = \varepsilon_{b'}$ etc. (but ε_a and ε_b are generally *not* equal). The expectation value of the operator for the interaction between the two electrons is then a linear superposition of two types of terms: The matrix elements of

---

[1] See ref. [5], Chap. 15, for details on configuration interaction.

[2] S. COHEN: Ph. D. Thesis, Cornell University, 1955.

[3] For details see G. BREIT, Phys, Rev. **34**, 553 (1929) and G. E. BROWN, Phil. Mag. **43**, 467 (1952).

this operator between wave functions (ab) and $(a'b')$ (direct term) and those between (ab) and $(b'a')$ (exchange term).

The operator for the COULOMB interaction is simply e^2/r_{12}. As discussed in Sect. 38 the two electrons also interact with each other via the quantized electromagnetic field. The lowest order term, corresponding to the exchange of a virtual photon between the electrons, is obtained by second order perturbation theory from quantum electrodynamics and is similar to (38.5). The (exchange) matrix element for a transition between the states (ab) and $(b'a')$, for instance, is given by [the notation is the same as for (38.5)]

$$\langle a\,b|B_{tr}|\,b'\,a'\rangle = -\frac{e^2\,c}{4\pi^2}\sum_{\pi}\int\frac{d^3k}{k}\sum_{n}\frac{\langle a\,b\,|\,\alpha_{1\pi}\,e^{i\boldsymbol{k}\cdot\boldsymbol{r}_1}|\,n\rangle\,\langle n\,|\,\alpha_{2\pi}\,e^{-i\boldsymbol{k}\cdot\boldsymbol{r}_2}|\,b'\,a'\rangle}{k\,c+E_n-\varepsilon_a-\varepsilon_b}, \qquad (43.3)$$

plus a similar term with 1 and 2 interchanged. For our complete set of wave functions n we can choose the set $\psi_c(1)\,\psi_d(2)$, where ψ_c,ψ_d are any of the DIRAC single-electron wave functions. Each of the two matrix elements in (43.3) is then the product of two matrix elements involving only single-electron wave functions. In particular, the first part of (43.3) contains the matrix element (for the operator unity, since no operator for electron 2 appears) $\langle b|d\rangle$ and the second part contains $\langle c|b'\rangle$. Since the single-electron wave functions form an orthogonal set, the only non-zero term in the sum over n in (43.3) is the one with $c=b'$ and $d=b$ and with energy $E_n=\varepsilon_b+\varepsilon_{b'}$. We therefore can replace the energy denominator[1] in (43.3) by $(kc+\varepsilon_{b'}-\varepsilon_a)$ and can then eliminate the summation over n by a simple sum rule. This gives

$$\langle a\,b\,|B_{tr}|\,b'\,a'\rangle = -\frac{e^2\,c}{4\pi^2}\int\frac{d^3k}{k}\sum_{\pi}\frac{\langle a\,b\,|\,\alpha_{1\pi}\,\alpha_{2\pi}\,e^{i\boldsymbol{k}\cdot\boldsymbol{r}_{12}}|\,b'\,a'\rangle}{k\,c+\varepsilon_{b'}-\varepsilon_a} \qquad (43.4)$$

plus another term with a and b interchanged and with a' and b' interchanged.

We are only considering states for which $\varepsilon_a=\varepsilon_{a'}$ and $\varepsilon_b=\varepsilon_{b'}$ and we denote $\varepsilon_a-\varepsilon_b$ by $c\Gamma$. The denominators in the term shown explicitly in (43.4) and the other term are then $c(k-\Gamma)$ and $c(k+\Gamma)$, respectively. We add these two terms and use the fact that $\sum_{\pi}$ denotes summation over two directions perpendicular to each other and to $\boldsymbol{k}$. We then find that the matrix element (43.4) is equal to that of the operator

$$B_{tr} = -\frac{e^2}{2\pi^2}\int\frac{d^3k}{(k^2-\Gamma^2)}\,e^{i\boldsymbol{k}\cdot\boldsymbol{r}_{12}}\left[\boldsymbol{\alpha}_1\cdot\boldsymbol{\alpha}_2-\frac{(\boldsymbol{\alpha}_1\cdot\boldsymbol{k})\,(\boldsymbol{\alpha}_2\cdot\boldsymbol{k})}{k^2}\right]. \qquad (43.5)$$

Note that this "operator" depends on the state (ab) on which it is operating, through the term Γ^2 in the denominator. If we were to neglect Γ^2 compared with k^2, which is justified only if $(Z\alpha)^2\ll 1$, this operator would reduce to the BREIT operator defined in (38.6). The matrix element (43.3) is an "exchange term", but "direct terms", i.e. matrix elements for transitions from (ab) to $(a'b')$, also occur. A similar analysis can be carried through for these direct terms, resulting in an operator *identical* with (38.6), i.e. with Γ replaced by zero in (43.5).

The integrand in the integral over $\boldsymbol{k}$ in (43.5) has singularities at $|\boldsymbol{k}|=|\Gamma|$. These singularities are connected with the possibility of a spontaneous radiative transition of one of the electrons from the state a to the state b' with the emission of a real photon of energy $\varepsilon_a-\varepsilon_b=\Gamma c$ if $\varepsilon_a>\varepsilon_b$ (a transition from b to a' of the other electron if $\varepsilon_b>\varepsilon_a$). A finite mean lifetime of an atomic state can be represented by a negative imaginary part in the energy of this state. In (43.5), $|\Gamma|$

[1] Note that this replacement involves no nonrelativistic approximation, unlike the replacement by kc, used in Sect. 38.

should then be replaced by $|\Gamma| - i\eta$ where η is positive and small compared with Γ. A good approximation to the integral (43.5) is then obtained by considering η as an infinitesimally small quantity, carrying out the angle integration first and evaluating the integral over k by contour integration. The imaginary part of the result represents a contribution to the "width" [$2\hbar$ times the inverse of the lifetime, see (67.1)] of the initial energy level. For finding the energy shift of a level of fixed J and M we only require the real part of (43.5), which is simply given by the principal part of the integral [see (9.5)].

The integral (43.5) can be evaluated fairly easily, but it is often more convenient to combine this term with the COULOMB interaction

$$\frac{e^2}{r_{12}} = \frac{e^2}{2\pi^2} \int \frac{d^3 k}{k^2} e^{i\boldsymbol{k}\cdot\boldsymbol{r}_{12}}.$$

The sum of this term and (43.5) can be written as

$$\left.\begin{aligned} B_{\text{tot}} &= \frac{e^2}{2\pi^2} \int \frac{d^3 k}{k^2 - \Gamma^2} \left[e^{i\boldsymbol{k}\cdot\boldsymbol{r}_{12}} (1 - \boldsymbol{\alpha}_1 \cdot \boldsymbol{\alpha}_2) + \frac{\mathscr{B}'}{k^2} \right], \\ \mathscr{B}' &= e^{i\boldsymbol{k}\cdot\boldsymbol{r}_{12}} [(\boldsymbol{\alpha}_1 \cdot \boldsymbol{k})(\boldsymbol{\alpha}_2 \cdot \boldsymbol{k}) - \Gamma^2]. \end{aligned}\right\} \tag{43.6}$$

We now show that the (exchange) matrix element $\langle a b | \mathscr{B}' | b' a' \rangle$ is zero, as follows. Let $H_1 = mc^2\beta_1 + c\boldsymbol{p}_1 \cdot \boldsymbol{\alpha}_1 - e\varphi_1$ be the single-particle HAMILTONian of which a, b, etc. are eigenstates. Using the fact that $\Gamma c = \varepsilon_a - \varepsilon_{b'}$ and that (with $\hbar = 1$) $[H_1, f(\boldsymbol{r})] = -ic\boldsymbol{\alpha}_1 \cdot \operatorname{grad}_1 f(\boldsymbol{r}_1)$, we find

$$\Gamma c \langle a | e^{i\boldsymbol{k}\cdot\boldsymbol{r}} | b' \rangle = \langle a | [H_1, e^{i\boldsymbol{k}\cdot\boldsymbol{r}}] | b' \rangle = c \langle a | \boldsymbol{\alpha}_1 \cdot \boldsymbol{k}\, e^{i\boldsymbol{k}\cdot\boldsymbol{r}_1} | b' \rangle.$$

Using a similar relation for $\langle b | e^{-i\boldsymbol{k}\cdot\boldsymbol{r}_2} | a' \rangle$ and the fact that $\boldsymbol{r}_{12} = \boldsymbol{r}_1 - \boldsymbol{r}_2$, one then finds that

$$\Gamma^2 \langle a b | e^{i\boldsymbol{k}\cdot\boldsymbol{r}_{12}} | b' a' \rangle = \langle a b | e^{i\boldsymbol{k}\cdot\boldsymbol{r}_{12}} (\boldsymbol{\alpha}_1 \cdot \boldsymbol{k})(\boldsymbol{\alpha}_2 \cdot \boldsymbol{k}) | b' a' \rangle. \tag{43.7}$$

The matrix element of $\mathscr{B}'$ in (43.6) is then zero. The operator B'_{tot}, obtained by replacing $\mathscr{B}'$ by zero in (43.6) and by evaluating only the principal part of the integral is

$$B'_{\text{tot}} = e^2 \frac{\cos(\Gamma r_{12})}{r_{12}} (1 - \boldsymbol{\alpha}_1 \cdot \boldsymbol{\alpha}_2). \tag{43.8}$$

The relations (43.7) and (43.8) can also be derived in a more elegant manner from FEYNMAN's[1] covariant formalism. FEYNMAN's papers also contain the justification for an omission we have made in our derivation of (43.4) from (43.3). We have neglected the PAULI exclusion principle in the intermediate states n which forbids, for instance, the state (b, b') if $b' = b$. FEYNMAN shows that these errors are compensated exactly by some changes in the self energy of one of the two electrons, caused by the presence of the other (and the exclusion principle).

For the "direct term" matrix element from (ab) to $(a'b')$, we have already seen that Γ is replaced by zero in the expression equivalent to (43.5). By arguments, equivalent to those leading to (43.7), one can also show that

$$\langle a b | e^{i\boldsymbol{k}\cdot\boldsymbol{r}_{12}} (\boldsymbol{\alpha}_1 \cdot \boldsymbol{k})(\boldsymbol{\alpha}_2 \cdot \boldsymbol{k}) | a' b' \rangle = 0. \tag{43.9}$$

For a "direct term", the total matrix element (including the COULOMB part) is then equal to the matrix element of the operator (43.8) with $\cos(\Gamma r_{12})$ replaced by unity[2].

---

[1] R. P. FEYNMAN: Phys. Rev. **76**, 749, 769 (1949).

[2] For explicit calculations for inner electrons in heavy atoms, see S. BRENNER and G. E. BROWN, Proc. Roy. Soc. Lond., Ser. A **218**, 422 (1953); S. COHEN, Ph. D. Thesis, Cornell University 1955.

44. Hyperfine structure. We discuss now the hyperfine structure of the energy levels of singly excited states of a helium-like atom with small nuclear charge ($Z \ll 137$). In nonrelativistic approximation the energy (for given principal quantum number $n = n_2$) depends on the orbital quantum number $l = l_2$ ($l_1 = 0$, since one electron is in the ground state) and on the total spin S ($S = 0$ for para— or singlet—states, $S = 1$ for ortho—or triplet—states). Relativistic effects then give a small (fine structure) energy splitting for triplet states (if $l \neq 0$) according to the value of the quantum number J for the total angular momentum of the two electrons, $J = l + 1$, l or $l - 1$. If the nucleus possesses[1] a "spin" I and magnetic moment, a further splitting of the energy levels results, which depends on the quantum number F for the total angular momentum of the whole atom (nucleus plus electrons), where $F = |J - I|, \ldots, J + I$. Since the magnetic moments of nuclei are much smaller than that of the electron, the hyperfine splitting is usually (but not always) small compared with the fine structure splitting and J remains an (almost) good quantum number.

α) Excited states with $l \neq 0$. If one electron is in the ground state (1) and the other in an excited state (n) with non-zero orbital quantum number l, a good approximation to the spatial wave function is (see Sect. 28)

$$U = \frac{1}{\sqrt{2}} \left[u_1(1)\, u_n(2) \pm u_n(1)\, u_1(2) \right]. \tag{44.1}$$

In (44.1) the + sign refers to singlet states, the — sign to triplet states, u_1 is the ground state hydrogenic wave function for nuclear charge Z and u_n the hydrogenic wave function for an excited state for nuclear charge ($Z - 1$). The magnetic interaction between the nucleus and the electron cloud, which leads to the hyperfine structure splitting, is represented by the sum of two operators, each of form (22.1) with $\boldsymbol{s}$, $\boldsymbol{k}$ and $\boldsymbol{r}$ referring to electron 1 and 2 respectively. If we use a spatial wave function of product form (44.1) to evaluate the expectation value of the sum of these two operators, the spatial integrations can be carried out immediately. Since each operator operates only on the wave function for one of the two electrons and since u_1 and u_n are orthogonal, no "exchange" terms are obtained. The resulting expectation value consists of the sum of two terms. The one term is similar to the hyperfine structure energy shift for a hydrogenic atom (charge Z) in the ground state (see Sect. 22β), the other to the shift for a hydrogenic atom (charge $Z - 1$) in the excited state n. The same angular momentum operators occur in these two terms as in the corresponding terms in Sect. 22β, but their expectation values are of course somewhat different for the two-electron atom.

As discussed in Sect. 22β, the hyperfine structure energy of a single electron decreases rapidly with increasing principal and orbital quantum numbers n and l. We are only considering states with $n \gtrless 2$ and $l \gtrless 1$ and can, to a good approximation, neglect the interaction of the outer electron with the nuclear moment. In this approximation we find, from (22.10), for the energy shift E due to the nuclear moment

$$E = \tfrac{4}{3} \mu_0 \mu_N g R_{10}^2(0)\, \overline{\boldsymbol{i} \cdot \boldsymbol{s}_1} \text{ at. un.}, \tag{44.2}$$

where $\boldsymbol{s}_1$ is the spin operator for one (the inner) electron and the bar denotes the expectation value [μ_N and g defined in (22.6)].

In our present approximation we neglect the direct effect on the interaction energy of the outer electron. The hyperfine structure is nevertheless radically

[1] The vector operator for the nuclear angular momentum is denoted by $\boldsymbol{i}$ and the eigenvalue of $\boldsymbol{i}^2$ is $I(I+1)$.

different for two-electron and for one-electron atoms, because the expectation values of the operator $(\boldsymbol{i}\cdot\mathbf{s}_1)$ in (44.2) are different. The energy separation between the singlet and triplet states is a nonrelativistic effect and very large compared with both the fine structure and hyperfine structure splitting. We therefore neglect any mixing between singlet and triplet states and only consider the expectation value of $\boldsymbol{i}\cdot\mathbf{s}_1$ for states of fixed total spin S. Following the discussion of (40.2) in Sect. 40α, we can then replace $\mathbf{s}_1$ by $\frac{1}{2}(\mathbf{s}_1+\mathbf{s}_2)=\frac{1}{2}\boldsymbol{S}$. The energy E, given by (44.2), is then zero for singlet states ($S=0$). For triplet states we have to evaluate the expectation value of $\frac{1}{2}(\boldsymbol{i}\cdot\boldsymbol{S})$.

In the absence of a nuclear magnetic field, the operator $\boldsymbol{M}^2$, where $\boldsymbol{M}=\boldsymbol{k}+\boldsymbol{S}$, is a constant of the motion with eigenvalue $J(J+1)$. In the presence of the nuclear magnetic field, $\boldsymbol{F}^2$, where $\boldsymbol{F}=\boldsymbol{M}+\boldsymbol{i}$, is an exact constant of the motion with eigenvalue $F(F+1)$. The operator $\boldsymbol{i}\cdot\boldsymbol{S}$ does not commute with $\boldsymbol{M}^2$, so J is no longer exactly a good quantum number. However, if the factor in (44.2) which multiplies $\boldsymbol{i}\cdot\boldsymbol{S}$ is small compared with the energy separation between states of different values of J, we can neglect the mixing of states of different J. Since the nuclear magnetic moment is much smaller than the BOHR magneton, this is usually the case (with some important exceptions, see below). For transitions between states of the *same* J we can use the following replacement [see Eq. (22.8) and also Eq. (46.3)],

$$\boldsymbol{S}\rightarrow\frac{\overline{\boldsymbol{S}\cdot\boldsymbol{M}}}{\overline{\boldsymbol{M}^2}}\boldsymbol{M}=\frac{\overline{\boldsymbol{M}^2}+\overline{\boldsymbol{S}^2}-\overline{\boldsymbol{k}^2}}{2\,\overline{\boldsymbol{M}^2}}\boldsymbol{M}, \tag{44.3}$$

if $J\neq 0$. (If J is zero, $\boldsymbol{S}$ is replaced by zero.) Finally the expectation value of the operator $\boldsymbol{i}\cdot\boldsymbol{M}$ is

$$\tfrac{1}{2}(\overline{\boldsymbol{F}^2}-\overline{\boldsymbol{i}^2}-\overline{\boldsymbol{M}^2})=\tfrac{1}{2}[F(F+1)-I(I+1)-J(J+1)].$$

We thus have for Y_F, the expectation value of $\boldsymbol{i}\cdot\mathbf{s}_1$ for a state with fixed quantum numbers $S=1$, l, $J\neq 0$ and F,

$$Y_F=\frac{1}{2}\,\frac{\overline{(\boldsymbol{S}\cdot\boldsymbol{M})}\;\overline{(\boldsymbol{i}\cdot\boldsymbol{M})}}{\overline{\boldsymbol{M}^2}}=\frac{[J(J+1)+S(S+1)-l(l+1)]\,[F(F+1)-I(I+1)-J(J+1)]}{8J(J+1)}. \tag{44.4}$$

Substituting (44.4) and the explicit expression $4Z^3$ a.u. for $R_{10}^2(0)$ into (44.2) we have for the energy shift (using $\mu_0=\frac{1}{2}\alpha$ a.u., Ry $=\frac{1}{2}$ a.u.)

$$E=\frac{8}{3}Z^3\alpha^2 g\frac{m}{M_p}Y_F\,\mathrm{Ry}, \tag{44.5}$$

if $S=1$, $J\neq 0$. The energy shift is zero for all singlet states $S=0$ and for all states with $J=0$, in the present approximation. Note also that the shift is independent of the principal quantum number n of the excited electron. Consider, for example, the P-states ($l=1$) for any value of n. The $^1P_1$ and the $^3P_0$ states are unsplit. If the nuclear spin I is $\frac{1}{2}$, the $^3P_1$ and $^3P_2$ states each split into a doublet with $F=J\pm\frac{1}{2}$ and the splitting energy ΔE, given by (44.4) and (44.5), is

$$\Delta E=\frac{1}{3}Z^3\alpha^2 g\frac{m}{M_p}\mathrm{Ry}\begin{Bmatrix}\times 5 & \text{for} & ^3P_2,\\ \times 3 & \text{for} & ^3P_1.\end{Bmatrix} \tag{44.6}$$

In Fig. 20 we give the splitting of the 2^3P_1 and 2^3P_2 levels for $Z=2$ and a hypothetical nucleus with $I=\frac{1}{2}$ and $|g|\gtrsim 1$, calculated from (44.4) and (44.5).

The expression (44.4) breaks down if the hyperfine structure is *not* small compared with the fine structure splitting. In spite of the small factor m/M_p in (44.5), this does happen in many practical cases for the following reasons. (1) The fine structure splitting decreases with increasing principal quantum number n, whereas (44.5) does not. (2) For some states of helium-like atoms with small Z (especially for $Z=2$ and to some extent for $Z=3$ and 4, see Sect. 40) fortuitous cancellations make the energy separation of some fine structure components with different J values very small. (3) For many nuclei the numerical value of the g-factor is rather large.

More exact calculations of hyperfine structure splitting have been carried out for[1] Li^+ and for[2] He without assuming this splitting to be smaller than the fine structure. In this case F is still an exact quantum number, but J is not. The exact wave functions for the various states of fixed F are then linear superpositions of the states with different J values. The matrix elements of the operator $\boldsymbol{i}\cdot\boldsymbol{S}$ for transitions between states of *different* J values are required to calculate the amount of mixing of the different states and the energy shifts. In Fig. 20 we show (schematically) the hyperfine splitting of the $2\,^3P_1$ and $2\,^3P_2$ levels for He^3 (the numbers above the lines denote the value of F). The nucleus of this atom has $Z=2$, spin $I=\frac{1}{2}$ and g about -4.26. There is only one level each with $F=\frac{1}{2}$ and $F=\frac{5}{2}$ and their exact theoretical energy shifts are close to the values given by (44.4) and (44.5) (the $^3P_0$ level also has $F=\frac{1}{2}$, but lies about 1 cm^{-1}higher and hardly affects the other $F=\frac{1}{2}$ level). However, there are two levels with $F=\frac{3}{2}$ and their exact energy shifts approximate those given by (44.4) and (44.5) only for $|g|\lesssim 1$, but *not* for the actual value of $g\approx -4.26$.

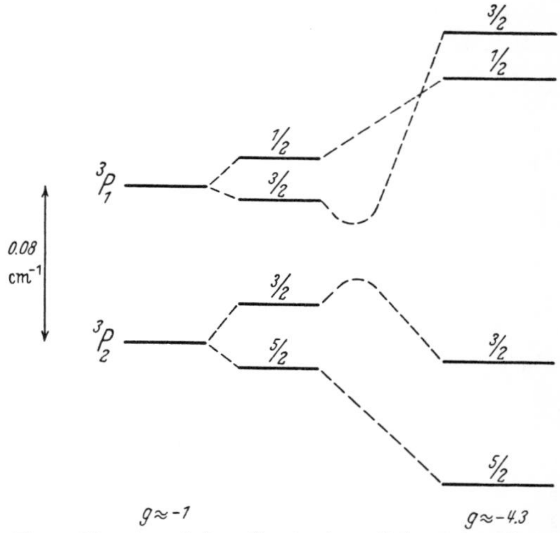

Fig. 20. The schematic hyperfine structure splitting of the $2\,^3P_1$ and $2\,^3P_2$ states in He^3, both for a (hypothetical) value of $g\approx-1$ and for the actual value of g. Each level is marked with its quantum number F.

We have neglected the direct effect of the magnetic interaction of the outer electron with the nuclear moment. For triplet states with $l\gtrless 1$ this effect is very small, especially for large n. For singlet states with $l\gtrless 1$ this interaction results in some hyperfine splitting, but the splitting energy is very small compared with that of triplet states. Singlet S-states have $S=l=J=0$ and $F=I$ and exhibit no splitting at all. The hyperfine splitting of triplet states in He^3 and in the Li^7-positive ion have been measured by optical spectroscopy. The agreement with the theory outlined above (with the interaction of the outer electron neglected) is good[3] for $l\gtrless 1$, although the experimental accuracy is not very great. The splitting of triplet S-states is discussed below.

β) The triplet S-states. Singlet S-states (including the ground state of helium-like atoms) show no fine or hyperfine structure splitting at all. Triplet S-states

[1] P. GÜTTINGER and W. PAULI: Z. Physik **67**, 743 (1931).
[2] FRED, TOMKINS, BRODY and HAMERMESH: Phys. Rev. **82**, 406 (1951).
[3] P. GÜTTINGER: Z. Physik **63**, 749 (1930). — FRED *et al.*, (loc. cit.) and ref. [*10*], p. 389.

have $l=0$ and $S=J=1$ and show no fine structure splitting. They do show hyperfine splitting however, the energy depending on the value of $F(|J-I|$ to $J+I)$. For $I=\frac{1}{2}$ the splitting results in doublets with $F=\frac{1}{2}$ and $\frac{3}{2}$, for $I \geqq 1$ triplets result with $F=I-1$, I and $I+1$. Since the hyperfine splitting energy is extremely small compared with the energy separation of a ^3S-state from states with other values of S or l (the nonrelativistic COULOMB and exchange energies), we need only the expectation value of the interaction operator for fixed $S=J=1$. For such states the expectation value Y_F of $\boldsymbol{i}\cdot\boldsymbol{s}_1$ is [see Eq. (44.4)]

$$Y_F = \tfrac{1}{2}\overline{\boldsymbol{i}\cdot\boldsymbol{S}} = \tfrac{1}{4}\,[F(F+1) - I(I+1) - S(S+1)] \tag{44.7}$$

with $S=1$.

If we use again the approximate wave function (44.1) and neglect the direct interaction of the outer electron, the energy shift E of the level component with a particular F value is again given by (44.5), but with the expression (44.7) for Y_F. In this approximation, E is independent of the principal quantum number n of the outer electron. The exact expression for E is (44.5) times a correction factor

$$1+\varepsilon = \frac{\overline{\delta^{(3)}(\boldsymbol{r}_1)} + \overline{\delta^{(3)}(\boldsymbol{r}_2)}}{Z^3/\pi}, \tag{44.8}$$

where the bar denotes the expectation value over the exact nonrelativistic spatial wave function $U(\boldsymbol{r}_1, \boldsymbol{r}_2)$ of the ^3S-state and Z^3/π is the expectation value of $\delta^{(3)}(\boldsymbol{r})$ over a hydrogenic ground state wave function for charge Z. For large n, the correction parameter ε is proportional to n^{-3} and is small. For the $2\,^3S$-states in Li^+ and in He, the expression (44.8) has been evaluated[1] and gives for $1+\varepsilon$

$$1.06191 \pm 0.00003\ (Li^+); \qquad 1.0363 \pm 0.0007\ (He). \tag{44.9}$$

We have not considered any relativistic or radiative corrections or effects of the nucleus' structure and motion so far. The two largest of these corrections are the "reduced mass" factor (22.16) and the effect of the lowest order anomalous magnetic moment $\alpha/2\pi$ of the electron (see Sect. 22γ). Including these corrections we find for the hyperfine splitting energy ΔE between the components of the doublet $F=\frac{1}{2}, \frac{3}{2}$

$$\Delta E = 2Z^3\alpha^2 \frac{g\,m}{M_p}\left(1+\varepsilon - 3\frac{m}{M} + \frac{\alpha}{2\pi}\right) R_\infty \tag{44.10}$$

for a nucleus with spin $I=\frac{1}{2}$ and mass M. The He^3 nucleus has spin $\frac{1}{2}$ and the ratio gm/M_p is very accurately known (see Sect. 49γ), $\frac{1}{2}g$ being about -2.1276. For the metastable 2^3S-state of He^3 the frequency $\Delta\nu = \Delta E/h$, corresponding to the hyperfine splitting energy, has been measured very accurately by microwave techniques[2]. This experimental value and the theoretical one, using (44.9) and (44.10), are

$$\Delta\nu_{\text{exp}} = (6739.71 \pm 0.05)\ \text{Mc/sec}, \qquad \Delta\nu_{\text{th}} = (6736 \pm 5)\ \text{Mc/sec}, \tag{44.11}$$

---

[1] For He, W. TEUTSCH and V. HUGHES, Phys. Rev. **95**, 1461 (1954) used the six-parameter wave function discussed in Sect. 35β. For Li^+, P. LUKE, R. MEYEROTT and W. CLENDENIN, Phys. Rev. **85**, 401 (1952) used a very accurate wave function expanded in terms of LEGENDRE polynomials (Sect. 36β). See also G. BREIT and F. DOERMANN, Phys. Rev. **36**, 1732 (1930).

[2] G. WEINREICH and V. HUGHES: Phys. Rev. **95**, 1451 (1954).

corresponding to about 0.225 cm^{-1}. Higher order relativistic and radiative corrections and the effect of the internal structure of the He^3 nucleus have also been calculated[1], but these corrections are smaller than the present uncertainty in $\Delta\nu_{\text{th}}$ due to the poor wave function used in evaluating ε, Eq. (44.9).

III. Atoms in external fields.

a) ZEEMAN effect.

45. ZEEMAN effect for a single-electron atom. We consider now the effect of an external magnetic field on single-electron atoms (with a *central* potential). We use, at the moment, CGS units instead of atomic units. We shall see that part of the effect of the magnetic field depends on the intrinsic spin, another part, connected with the orbital angular momentum, is independent of spin.

α) Spinless electron. We consider first the quantum theory for a spinless (KLEIN-GORDON) particle in an external electromagnetic field. The relativistic wave equation for such a spinless "electron" is not the DIRAC equation but the KLEIN-GORDON (or "relativistic SCHRÖDINGER") equation,

$$\left[\sum_{\mu=1}^{4}\left(p_\mu + \frac{e}{c}A_\mu\right)^2 + (m\,c)^2\right]\psi = 0. \tag{45.1}$$

In (45.1) we have used the covariant notation of Sect. 10,

$$p_\mu = -i\hbar\frac{\partial}{\partial x_\mu}, \qquad x_4 = i\,c\,t, \qquad A_\mu = (\boldsymbol{A}, i\,\varphi),$$

where $\boldsymbol{A}$ is the vector potential and $-iA_4 = \varphi$ the scalar potential of the external electromagnetic field (the charge of the "electron" is $-e$ and the potential energy is $V = -e\varphi$). We restrict ourselves to time-independent fields (we use the LORENTZ gauge for A_μ) and a stationary state of (nonrelativistic) energy E. The time dependence of the wave function ψ is then

$$\psi(\boldsymbol{r}, t) = e^{-\frac{i}{\hbar}(E+mc^2)t}\,u(\boldsymbol{r}),$$

where u satisfies the equation

$$\left\{\left[\frac{\hbar^2}{2m}\Delta + E - V\right] - \frac{e}{mc}\boldsymbol{A}\cdot\boldsymbol{p} + \frac{1}{2mc^2}\left[(E-V)^2 - e^2A^2\right]\right\}u = 0. \tag{45.2}$$

The last expression in square brackets is a small relativistic correction. The part quadratic in $(E-V)$ represents the relativistic "variation of mass" and is independent of the magnetic field. The part quadratic in $\boldsymbol{A}$ leads to diamagnetism (see Sect. 50) and is otherwise important only for states of large orbital angular momentum in strong magnetic fields (Sect. 47δ). We omit both these relativistic correction terms at the moment and consider only the effect of the term[2] in $\boldsymbol{A}\cdot\boldsymbol{p}$.

We restrict ourselves now to the special case of a uniform[3] magnetic field $\mathcal{H}$ and a central potential V. We can then take for the vector potential

$$\boldsymbol{A}(\boldsymbol{r}) = \frac{1}{2}\mathcal{H}\times\boldsymbol{r}. \tag{45.3}$$

---

[1] A. SESSLER and H. FOLEY: Phys. Rev. **98**, 6 (1955).

[2] This term can also be obtained from the *non*relativistic SCHRÖDINGER equation by replacing $\boldsymbol{p}$ by $(\boldsymbol{p} + e\boldsymbol{A}/c)$.

[3] If $\mathcal{H}$ is uniform over distances of the order of many atomic radii, the results are almost the same as for an exactly uniform $\mathcal{H}$.

We then have

$$\frac{1}{\hbar} \boldsymbol{A} \cdot \boldsymbol{p} = \frac{1}{2\hbar} (\mathcal{H} \times \boldsymbol{r}) \cdot \boldsymbol{p} = \frac{1}{2\hbar} \mathcal{H} \cdot (\boldsymbol{r} \times \boldsymbol{p}) = \frac{1}{2} \mathcal{H} \cdot \boldsymbol{k},$$

where $\hbar \boldsymbol{k}$ is the orbital angular momentum operator (see Sect. 11). If we take our z-axis in the direction of the field $\mathcal{H}$, we have

$$\Delta u + \frac{2m}{\hbar^2} [E - V - \hbar \omega k_z] u = 0, \tag{45.4}$$

$$\omega = \frac{e \mathcal{H}}{2mc}, \tag{45.5}$$

where ω is the *circular* frequency of the LARMOR precession. The solution of the SCHRÖDINGER equation without a magnetic field,

$$u = R_{nl}(r) P_{l m_l}(\vartheta) e^{i m_l \varphi},$$

is an eigenstate of k_z with eigenvalue m_l. This wave function is thus also a solution of the Eq. (45.4) *with* field and the energy eigenvalue is

$$E = E_0 + \hbar \omega m_l, \tag{45.6}$$

where E_0 is the energy without magnetic field.

The interaction energy $\hbar \omega m_l$ is proportional to the strength of the magnetic field and to the magnetic quantum number m_l. It does *not* depend on the quantum numbers n and l, nor on the electrostatic potential V. This result can be interpreted as follows: The orbital angular momentum of the electron gives rise to a magnetic moment $\boldsymbol{\mu}$,

$$\boldsymbol{\mu} = -\frac{e}{2mc} \boldsymbol{r} \times \boldsymbol{p} = -\mu_0 \boldsymbol{k}, \qquad \mu_0 = \frac{e\hbar}{2mc}, \tag{45.7}$$

where $\boldsymbol{r} \times \boldsymbol{p}$ and $\boldsymbol{k}$ are the orbital angular momentum in CGS and atomic units, respectively. The energy of this magnetic moment in the field $\mathcal{H}$ is

$$W_1 = -\mathcal{H} \cdot \boldsymbol{\mu} = \mathcal{H} \mu_0 k_z, \tag{45.8}$$

which agrees with (45.4) and (45.6).

The proportionality factor μ_0 in (45.7) is the well-known BOHR magneton. In atomic units μ_0 equals $\frac{1}{2}\alpha$. The equivalent proportionality factor between $\boldsymbol{\mu}$ and $\boldsymbol{r} \times \boldsymbol{p}$, expressed in CGS units, is $e/2mc$ and is thus *independent* of PLANCK'S constant h. In fact, the relation (45.7) (in CGS units) can also be derived from classical electrodynamics.

The result (45.6) which we have derived for the ZEEMAN effect of the hydrogen atom is in complete agreement with the result of the classical theory of the ZEEMAN effect and does not supersede the classical result in any way. In order to appreciate this, we must look at the splitting of the spectral lines in a magnetic field as obtained from (45.6), instead of the splitting of the eigenvalues. As is well known, the magnetic quantum number m of the atom remains unchanged in the emission of light which is linearly polarized parallel to the magnetic field. In this case the frequency of the spectral line is given by

$$\nu_{mm} = \frac{1}{h} (E - E') = \frac{1}{h} (E_0 - \hbar \omega m - E_0' + \hbar \omega m) = \nu_0,$$

i.e., it is equal to the frequency of the line without magnetic field. On the other hand, if the light is linearly polarized in a direction perpendicular to the field, then m must change by ± 1 and the line frequencies are given by

$$\nu_{m,m\pm1} = \frac{1}{h}\left[E_0 - \hbar\,\omega\,m - E_0' + \hbar\,\omega\,(m\pm1)\right] = \nu_0 \pm \frac{\omega}{2\pi},$$

i.e., the frequency is equal to the frequency of the unperturbed line plus or minus the frequency of the LARMOR precession. Thus, when the light is observed in a direction perpendicular to the magnetic field, in place of every line of the atom without field, there appears a triplet of three equidistant lines, with the two outer components of the triplet polarized in a direction perpendicular to the field and the middle component parallel to the field. On the other hand if the line is observed in a direction parallel to the field, only the outer components appear, the polarization of which is circular[1] about the axis of the magnetic field. This agrees exactly with the old LORENTZ theory. The separation between the outer components of the LORENTZ triplet amounts to

$$\frac{\omega}{\pi c} = \frac{e}{2\pi\,m\,c^2}\,\mathscr{H} = \frac{4.80\times10^{-10}}{6.28\times9.11\times10^{-28}\times8.99\times10^{20}}\,\mathscr{H} = 9.34\times10^{-5}\,\mathscr{H} = \frac{\mathscr{H}}{10710}\ \mathrm{cm}^{-1},$$

in which $\mathscr{H}$ is measured in Gauss. For magnetic field strengths which are ordinarily available, say 30000 Gauss, one obtains ZEEMAN splittings of the order of 3 wave-numbers ≈ 1 Å for visible light.

β) Electron with spin. We turn now to the theory of real electrons which possess spin and obey the DIRAC equation. In Sects. 10 and 12 we have derived from the DIRAC equation an exact quadratic Eq. (10.14) or (12.9), which is of similar form to (45.1) or (45.2) but which contains additional "DIRAC moment" terms. We thus add to (45.2) the expression

$$-\tfrac{1}{2}\,g_s\,\mu_0\,(\boldsymbol{\sigma}\cdot\boldsymbol{\mathcal{H}} - i\,\boldsymbol{\alpha}\cdot\boldsymbol{\mathcal{E}})\,u\,.$$

According to (12.9) and the DIRAC theory, the factor $\frac{1}{2}g_s$ is exactly unity, but we leave it arbitrary at the moment. The interaction energy W with the magnetic field $\boldsymbol{\mathcal{H}}$ is then not simply given by W_1, Eq. (45.8), but contains an additional term of the same order of magnitude as W_1. We again put $\frac{1}{2}\boldsymbol{\sigma} = \mathbf{s}$ for the spin-operator, $\boldsymbol{M}$ for the *total* angular momentum operator $(\boldsymbol{k}+\mathbf{s})$, in atomic units, and take our z-axis along the magnetic field. We then have

$$W = \mu_0\,\boldsymbol{\mathcal{H}}\cdot(\boldsymbol{k} + g_s\,\mathbf{s}) = \mu_0\,\mathscr{H}\left[M_z + (g_s - 1)\,s_z\right]. \tag{45.9}$$

The atomic DIRAC eigenfunctions for no magnetic field are eigenstates of M_z, but *not* eigenstates of (45.9) and the effect of this interaction energy operator W is more complicated than for spinless particles. We shall use the PAULI approximation to the exact DIRAC theory. The wave functions are then two-component PAULI spinors and in (45.9) the spin operator $\mathbf{s}$ is now represented by two-by-two PAULI matrices (not DIRAC matrices). The spin-dependent parts of the total HAMILTONian are then W, Eq. (45.9), plus the spin-orbit coupling term which is independent of the magnetic field [see the last term in (13.2)]. If the central potential is a COULOMB one, this term is

$$\Sigma = \tfrac{1}{2}\,\alpha^2 Z\,\overline{r^{-3}}\,\boldsymbol{k}\cdot\mathbf{s}\,. \tag{45.10}$$

We have to consider the operator $(W+\Sigma)$ as a perturbation on the nonrelativistic HAMILTONian and to find the perturbed eigenfunctions and eigenvalues. This will be discussed in the next section.

[1] The electric field of the light corresponding to the short wave-length component rotates in the same sense as the current which produces the magnetic field; the long wave-length component rotates in the opposite sense.

46. Dependence on magnetic field strength. Let us consider first the unperturbed nonrelativistic HAMILTONian and PAULI-type eigenfunctions, i.e., SCHRÖDINGER spatial wave functions multiplied by two-component spin wave functions. Consider all the possible eigenstates with fixed values of the quantum numbers n and l [the eigenvalue of the square $\boldsymbol{k}^2$ of the orbital angular momentum is $l(l+1)$]. There are $2(2l+1)$ such states with m_l (eigenvalue of k_z) equal to $-l, -l+1, \ldots, l$ and with m_s (eigenvalue of s_z) equal to $+\frac{1}{2}$ or $-\frac{1}{2}$. Using the unperturbed HAMILTONian, these states are all degenerate and any linear superposition of them is also an eigenstate. Our problem is now to find those superpositions which are also eigenstates of the perturbation HAMILTONian $(W+\Sigma)$, where the operators W and Σ are defined in (45.9) and (45.10).

We first note that $\boldsymbol{k}^2$, $\mathbf{s}^2$ and $M_z = k_z + s_z$ all commute both with W and with Σ. Hence l, $s=\frac{1}{2}$ [the eigenvalue of $\mathbf{s}^2$ is $s(s+1)$] and $m = m_l + m_s$ are still good quantum numbers. We therefore consider states with fixed values of n, l and also of m, the z-component of the total angular momentum (eigenvalue of M_z). On the other hand, s_z (and k_z) does not commute with Σ and $\boldsymbol{M}^2$ does not commute with W. For the HAMILTONian containing $(W+\Sigma)$, neither s_z (and k_z) nor $\boldsymbol{M}^2$ are in general constants of the motion and the eigenstates and eigenvalues of $(W+\Sigma)$ depend in a rather complicated way on the relative strength of W and Σ, i.e., on the magnetic field strength $\mathscr{H}$. Before discussing the general case, we consider two simple limiting cases: (a) "Weak" magnetic field, so that the expectation values of W are small compared with those of Σ; (b) "Strong" field, so that Σ is small compared with W.

α) *Weak magnetic field (anomalous* ZEEMAN *effect).* In this case we consider W as a small perturbation to Σ. We use as wave functions the eigenstates of Σ and merely add the expectation value of W (first order perturbation theory), for such a wave function, to the eigenvalue of Σ. For fixed values of n, l, m, the operator Σ has two eigenstates which are eigenstates of $\boldsymbol{M}^2$ with quantum number $j = l+\frac{1}{2}$ and $l-\frac{1}{2}$, respectively (see Sect. 13). The two eigenvalues Σ_j of Σ are given in (13.13). They depend on j (and are responsible for the ordinary fine structure splitting for fixed l), but do *not* depend on m.

We now evaluate the expectation value of

$$W = \mu_0 \mathscr{H}[M_z + (g_s - 1)\, s_z], \tag{46.1}$$

for a simultaneous eigenstate of $\boldsymbol{k}^2$, $\mathbf{s}^2$, $\boldsymbol{M}^2$ and M_z. We shall show in Sect. 48 that similar relations hold for a many-electron atom, with the angular momentum operators mentioned above summed over all electrons. We therefore evaluate the expectation value of W by a general method, based only on commutation rules which also hold in a many-electron atom, and keep the quantum number s [eigenvalue of $\mathbf{s}^2$ is $s(s+1)$] general. We make use of an operator identity, derived from the commutation rules in [5], p. 60,

$$\tfrac{1}{4}\left[\boldsymbol{M}^2, [\boldsymbol{M}^2, \mathbf{s}]\right] = \tfrac{1}{2}(\boldsymbol{M}^2\mathbf{s} + \mathbf{s}\boldsymbol{M}^2) - \boldsymbol{M}(\boldsymbol{M}\cdot\mathbf{s}). \tag{46.2}$$

We now take the expectation values of both sides of (46.2) over a simultaneous eigenstate of $\boldsymbol{k}^2$, $\mathbf{s}^2$ and $\boldsymbol{M}^2$. The left hand side then vanishes and on the right hand side $\boldsymbol{M}^2$ and $2\boldsymbol{M}\cdot\mathbf{s} = \boldsymbol{M}^2 + \mathbf{s}^2 - \boldsymbol{k}^2$ are replaced by their eigenvalues. Thus[1]

$$\overline{\mathbf{s}} = \left[\frac{\overline{\boldsymbol{M}\cdot\mathbf{s}}}{\boldsymbol{M}^2}\right]_{lsj} \overline{\boldsymbol{M}} = \frac{j(j+1) + s(s+1) - l(l+1)}{2j(j+1)}\, \overline{\boldsymbol{M}}. \tag{46.3}$$

[1] The classical vector model would interpret (46.3) as follows: The vector $\mathbf{s}$ precesses about the direction of $\boldsymbol{M}$. The "average of $\mathbf{s}$" then points in the same direction as $\boldsymbol{M}$, but its absolute value is smaller than $|\boldsymbol{M}|$ by the factor $(\boldsymbol{M}\cdot\mathbf{s})/M^2$.

The expectation value of $(W+\Sigma)$, to be added to the nonrelativistic energy, is then, for a state of given n, l, j, m,

$$E'_{nljm} = \Sigma_{nlj} + \mathcal{H}\mu_0 g\, m. \tag{46.4}$$

In this equation,

$$g = 1 + (g_s - 1)\frac{j(j+1)+s(s+1)-l(l+1)}{2j(j+1)} \tag{46.5}$$

is the "LANDÉ splitting factor" (with $g_s = 2$ according to DIRAC theory) and Σ_{nlj} is the eigenvalue of the operator Σ. If we multiply the orbital part of (45.9), $\mu_0\, \mathcal{H}\cdot \boldsymbol{k}$, by a factor g_l, then (46.5) is modified to

$$g = g_l \frac{j(j+1)-s(s+1)+l(l+1)}{2j(j+1)} + g_s \frac{j(j+1)+s(s+1)-l(l+1)}{2j(j+1)}. \tag{46.5a}$$

In Sect. 47β we shall see that g_l differs very slightly from unity for an atom with a nucleus of finite mass. The energy shift in the magnetic field $\mathcal{H}$ is proportional to $\mathcal{H}$ (as for a spinless "electron") and to m (*not* to m_l) and also depends on the inner quantum number j through the LANDÉ factor g. If we return now to the case of a single-electron atom, $s=\frac{1}{2}$ and $j=l\pm\frac{1}{2}$. Substituting these values and the DIRAC value $g_s=2$ into (46.5), this equation reduces to

$$g = \frac{j+\frac{1}{2}}{l+\frac{1}{2}}. \tag{46.6}$$

(46.6) could also have been obtained explicitly using the PAULI eigenfunctions (13.19).

According to (46.6) the separation of two adjacent ZEEMAN components, $m_1 = m_2 + 1$, belonging to the levels of $j=l+\frac{1}{2}$ is larger than the separation for an electron without spin ($g=1$), and is smaller for $j=l-\frac{1}{2}$. The explanation of this lies in the fact that the spin, which interacts with the magnetic field more strongly than does the orbital angular momentum, is essentially parallel to the total angular momentum for the case $j=l+\frac{1}{2}$ and antiparallel for $j=l-\frac{1}{2}$. For some special cases one obtains:

$$g = 2 \quad \tfrac{2}{3} \quad \tfrac{4}{3} \quad \tfrac{4}{5} \quad \tfrac{6}{5}$$
for $s \quad p_{\frac{1}{2}} \quad p_{\frac{3}{2}} \quad d_{\frac{3}{2}} \quad d_{\frac{5}{2}}$ terms.

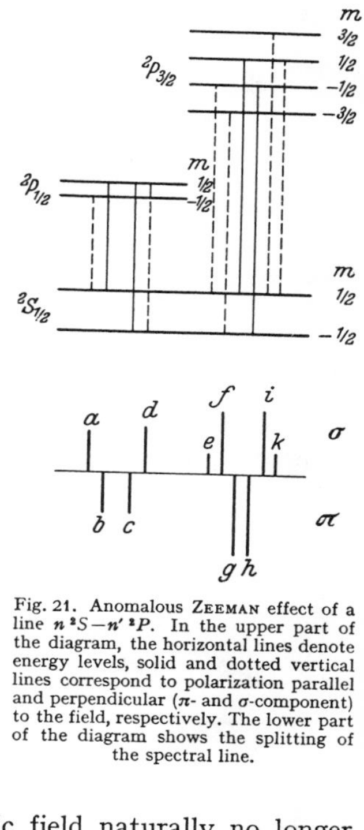

Fig. 21. Anomalous ZEEMAN effect of a line $n\,^2S - n'\,^2P$. In the upper part of the diagram, the horizontal lines denote energy levels, solid and dotted vertical lines correspond to polarization parallel and perpendicular (π- and σ-component) to the field, respectively. The lower part of the diagram shows the splitting of the spectral line.

The splitting of the spectral lines in a magnetic field naturally no longer results in the ordinary LORENTZ triplet; instead, a more complicated pattern appears which enables one to draw some conclusions about the quantum number l and j of the initial and final level corresponding to a given line. For the purpose of constructing the ZEEMAN pattern, one should note that the selection rules are the same as for an electron without spin, namely:

$\Delta m = 0$ for the line components polarized parallel to the field,

$\Delta m = \pm 1$ for the component polarized perpendicularly to the field.

In Fig. 21 the splitting of the p and s levels and the pattern of the lines $1s - 2p_{\frac{1}{2}}$ and $1s - 2p_{\frac{3}{2}}$ which results therefrom are shown. The theory of the anomalous

ZEEMAN effect which we have presented has been abundantly verified by experiment[1].

β) Strong magnetic field ("quasi-normal ZEEMAN*" or "complete* PASCHEN-BACK*" effect).* We now consider Σ as small compared with W. We first find the eigenstates and eigenvalues of W and then merely take the expectation value of Σ over the eigenfunctions of W. We put $g_s = 2$, according to the DIRAC theory.

First approximation: The eigenfunction is a product of a spatial and a spin wave function and the eigenvalue of the magnetic energy operator W is, from (46.1),

$$W = \mathscr{H}\mu_0 (m_l + 2m_s). \tag{46.7}$$

Since m_l is integral and m_s half-integral, the magnetic energy, as in the case of the electron without spin, is equal to $\mathscr{H}\mu_0$ multiplied by an integer and, thus, a normal ZEEMAN effect is simulated. This is also true for the splitting of the corresponding spectral lines: Since the spin and orbital angular momenta are no longer coupled in the eigenfunction, the spin quantum number m_s is not allowed to change in an optical transition[2] and we have the selection rule

$$\left.\begin{aligned} &\Delta m_s = 0, \\ &\Delta m_l = 0, \pm 1, \text{ depending on the polarization of the light.} \end{aligned}\right\} \tag{46.8}$$

Thus, the spectral lines have the appearance of a LORENTZ triplet, provided that both the initial and final level corresponding to the line undergo a complete PASCHEN-BACK effect[3].

In the second approximation we must consider the spin-orbit interaction. We obtain its effect in strong fields by computing the expectation value of the interaction energy (45.10) over the orbital motion. Since $\boldsymbol{k}$ and $\boldsymbol{s}$ precess independently around the magnetic field, the time average of $(\boldsymbol{k}\cdot\boldsymbol{s})$ is equal to the product of the time averages of the components of $\boldsymbol{k}$ and $\boldsymbol{s}$ along the direction of the field, namely

$$\Sigma = \tfrac{1}{2}\,\alpha^2 Z\,\overline{r^{-3}}\,m_l m_s.$$

Using for $\overline{r^{-3}}$ the value obtained from the fine structure splitting in the absence of external fields,

$$\Delta E \equiv E_{j=l+s} - E_{j=l-s} = \tfrac{1}{2}\,\alpha^2 Z\,\overline{r^{-3}} \left\{\begin{matrix} l\,(2s+1) & \text{if } l < s \\ s\,(2l+1) & \text{if } l > s, \end{matrix}\right\} \tag{46.9}$$

we obtain

$$\Sigma = m_l m_s \Delta E \left\{\begin{matrix} l^{-1}(2s+1)^{-1} & \text{if } l < s \\ s^{-1}(2l+1)^{-1} & \text{if } l > s. \end{matrix}\right\} \tag{46.10}$$

(46.10) is valid for arbitrary values of the total spin s and the orbital angular momentum l. Specializing to atoms with a single electron, $s = \frac{1}{2}$, yields

$$\Sigma = m_l m_s \frac{\Delta E}{l + \frac{1}{2}}. \tag{46.11}$$

The total energy of the atom for the state $n\,l\,s\,m_l\,m_s$ is obtained by adding (46.7) and (46.10) to the center of gravity with respect to energy of the multiplet $n\,l\,s$.

---

[1] See, for example, E. BACK, ZEEMAN-Effekt und Multiplettstruktur, Section II.

[2] The transition probability is given by

$$\sum_{s_z=-\frac{1}{2}}^{+\frac{1}{2}} \int u^*_{n'l'm'_l}(r,\vartheta,\varphi)\,\delta_{m'_s s_z}\,q\,u_{nlm_l}(r,\vartheta,\varphi)\,\delta_{m_s s_z}\,d\tau = \delta_{m'_s m_s} \int u^*_{n'l'm'_l}\,q\,u_{nlm_l}\,d\tau.$$

[3] The case in which one of the levels undergoes the PASCHEN-BACK effect, while the other level has an anomalous ZEEMAN effect is designated as a partial PASCHEN-BACK effect.

In a strong magnetic field each ZEEMAN level of the atom exhibits a splitting which is of the order of magnitude of the fine structure splitting in the absence of external fields. The same statement holds also for the spectral lines.

In Fig. 22 the splitting pattern for the transitions $1s-2p$ of an alkali atom in a strong magnetic field are shown; the term scheme is given in the upper part, the corresponding splitting of the spectral lines in the lower part.

γ) General field strength (general PASCHEN-BACK *effect).* We now derive exact expressions for the eigenfunctions and eigenvalues of the operator $(W+\Sigma)$, which are valid for arbitrary magnetic field strength, for a single-electron atom. Besides $\boldsymbol{k}^2$, M_z is still an exact constant of the motion. We consider states with fixed values of the quantum numbers n, l and m (eigenvalue of M_z). The general wave function with these quantum numbers can then be written as a superposition of two linearly independent spin wave functions. We take for these two independent states the two eigenstates of the PAULI HAMILTONian in the absence of a magnetic field, Sect. 13. These states are eigenstates of $\boldsymbol{M}^2$ with inner quantum number $j=l+\frac{1}{2}$ and $j=l-\frac{1}{2}$, respectively. We denote these states by u_+ and u_-. In this representation the unperturbed HAMILTONian H_0 and Σ are diagonal. We denote the two eigenvalues of $(H_0+\Sigma)$ by E_+ and E_- (the field-free energies of the PAULI approximation). We further define a dimensionless parameter ξ by

$$\xi=\frac{\mathscr{H}\mu_0}{\Delta E}, \qquad \Delta E\equiv E_+-E_-. \tag{46.12}$$

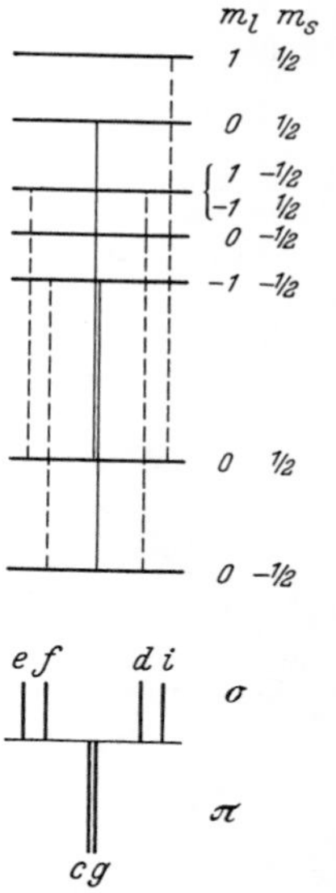

Fig. 22. Complete PASCHEN-BACK effect of a line $n\,{}^2S-n'\,{}^2P$. Energy levels in the upper, splitting of the spectral line in the lower, part of the diagrams. The letters refer back to Fig. 21. The lines a, b, h, k are suppressed in strong magnetic fields. The splitting between e and f, etc. is due to the spin-orbit coupling.

We can find the explicit matrix representation of the operator W in terms of u_+ and u_- from the PAULI eigenfunctions, Eq. (13.19). The eigenvalue and eigenfunction of the total HAMILTONian $(H_0+W+\Sigma)$ can then be written in the form

$$E=\tfrac{1}{2}(E_++E_-)+E', \qquad u=a\,u_++b\,u_-. \tag{46.13}$$

E', a and b are given by the eigenvalue equation (with $g_s=2$)

$$\begin{pmatrix} \frac{1}{2}+\xi\frac{2m(l+1)}{2l+1} & \xi\frac{\sqrt{(l+\frac{1}{2})^2-m^2}}{2l+1} \\ \xi\frac{\sqrt{(l+\frac{1}{2})^2-m^2}}{2l+1} & -\frac{1}{2}+\xi\frac{2ml}{2l+1} \end{pmatrix}\begin{pmatrix} a \\ b \end{pmatrix}=\frac{E'}{\Delta E}\begin{pmatrix} a \\ b \end{pmatrix}. \tag{46.14}$$

The two possible eigenvalues E' are obtained by solving the determinantal equation of (46.14), which gives

$$E'=\Delta E\left[\xi m\pm\frac{1}{2}\sqrt{1+\xi\frac{4m}{2l+1}+\xi^2}\right]. \tag{46.15}$$

The normalized eigenfunctions (46.13) corresponding to these two eigenvalues are then given by

$$\left.\begin{aligned} a&=\sqrt{\tfrac{1}{2}(1+\gamma)}, & b&=\sqrt{\tfrac{1}{2}(1-\gamma)} & &\text{for the higher level,} \\ a&=-\sqrt{\tfrac{1}{2}(1-\gamma)}, & b&=\sqrt{\tfrac{1}{2}(1+\gamma)} & &\text{for the lower level,} \end{aligned}\right\} \tag{46.16}$$

where

$$\gamma = \frac{1 + \xi \frac{2m}{2l+1}}{\sqrt{1 + \xi \frac{4m}{2l+1} + \xi^2}}.$$

The same eigenfunctions can also be written in the form of two-component Pauli spinors, i.e. in a representation in which s_z (and hence W) is diagonal (see Sect. 12). These spinors are

$$\left.\begin{aligned} u &= R_{nl}(r) \begin{pmatrix} \sqrt{\tfrac{1}{2}(1+\delta)}\; Y_{l,m-\frac{1}{2}} \\ -\sqrt{\tfrac{1}{2}(1-\delta)}\; Y_{l,m+\frac{1}{2}} \end{pmatrix} \quad \text{for the higher level} \\ u &= R_{nl}(r) \begin{pmatrix} \sqrt{\tfrac{1}{2}(1-\delta)}\; Y_{l,m-\frac{1}{2}} \\ \sqrt{\tfrac{1}{2}(1+\delta)}\; Y_{l,m+\frac{1}{2}} \end{pmatrix} \quad \text{for the lower level,} \end{aligned}\right\} \tag{46.17}$$

where

$$\delta = \frac{\xi + \frac{2m}{2l+1}}{\sqrt{1 + \xi \frac{4m}{2l+1} + \xi^2}}. \tag{46.18}$$

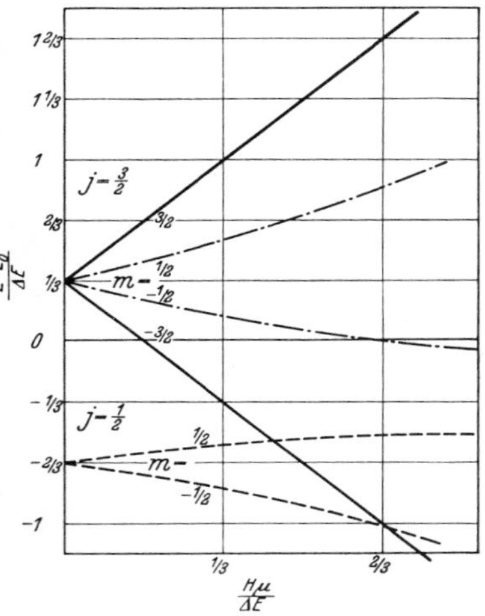

Fig. 23. Energy shift $E-E_0$ (in units of ΔE) for ${}^2P$-states plotted against $\xi = \mathcal{H}\mu_0/\Delta E$, where $\mathcal{H}$ is the magnetic field strength and ΔE is the field-free fine structure splitting.

If $\xi \ll 1$ (weak field), (46.15) can be expanded in powers of ξ and the first two terms in this expansion give the results of Sect. 46α. Similarly, if $\xi \gg 1$ (strong field), (46.15) can be expanded in powers of $1/\xi$ and the first two terms give the results of Sect. 46β. Also, as $\xi \to 0$, the factor γ in (46.16) approaches unity. Thus either a or b in (46.13) reduces to zero and the wave function to an eigenstate of $\boldsymbol{M}^2$ (and hence of Σ). As $\xi \to \infty$, the factor δ in (46.17), (46.18) reduces to unity and the wave function (46.17) to an eigenstate of s_z and k_z (and thus of W).

The dependence of the energy on the dimensionless parameter $\xi = \mu_0 \mathcal{H}/\Delta E$ is plotted[1] in Fig. 23 from weak to fairly strong field strength for np-states in hydrogen. For $n=2$, $\Delta E = 0.365\ \text{cm}^{-1}$ and ξ equals unity for a field strength of $\mathcal{H} = 7800$ Gauss. Note that the energies of some pairs of levels cross at medium field strengths, but never for two levels with the same value of m. Note also that the energy is linear in $\mathcal{H}$ for $m = \pm(l+\frac{1}{2})$, since for these values of m only *one* eigenstate of $\boldsymbol{k}^2$ is possible and this eigenstate is independent of $\mathcal{H}$.

In general, the energy E' is not linear in $\mathcal{H}$ for medium field strength (Paschen-Back region). The "moment of the atomic state" $\mu_m = \partial E'/\partial \mathcal{H}$ is then *not* independent of $\mathcal{H}$. This quantity μ_m is important in Stern-Gerlach type of experiments in which deflections of an atomic beam in an inhomogeneous magnetic field are measured. In fact, the deflection is proportional to μ_m and to the spatial gradient of $\mathcal{H}$ (see also Sect. 47γ for the "zero moment" method).

The theory presented in this section is in good semiquantitative agreement with experiment[2]. In fact, this theory, together with accurate optical measurements of Zeeman effect splittings, have been used in the past to get values of moderate accuracy for e/m for the electron. However, various corrections have

[1] See also K. Darwin, Proc. Roy. Soc. Lond., Ser. A **118**, 264 (1928).
[2] For a detailed discussion see ref. [*10*], Sect. 27 d.

to be applied to the theory outlined above. Some of these are discussed in Sect. 47. The effect of the anomalous magnetic moment of the electron and some recent precision experiments are discussed in Sect. 49.

47. Some corrections to the ZEEMAN effect. We briefly discuss some small corrections which have to be applied to the theory of Sect. 46 of the ZEEMAN effect for a single-electron atom: In Sect. 46 we have approximated the DIRAC equation by the PAULI equation and, consequently, evaluated the ZEEMAN effect only to lowest order in α^2 (see Sect. 47α). We have neglected so far the effect of the motion (Sect. 47β) and the magnetic moment (Sect. 47γ) of the atomic nucleus. The effect of the term quadratic in A in (45.2) is discussed in Sect. 47δ, That of the anomalous moment of the electron in Sect. 49.

α) *Relativistic effect.* In Sect. 10 we have written down the exact DIRAC equation (10.1) for an electron in an arbitrary external electromagnetic field. This equation can be solved exactly for a uniform magnetic field of arbitrary strength in the *absence* of any electric field[1]. The DIRAC equation cannot be solved exactly for a central electrostatic field plus a uniform magnetic field $\mathcal{H}$, but the part of the energy which is *linear* in $\mathcal{H}$ can be evaluated.

We proceed from the DIRAC equation and consider the term in $\boldsymbol{\alpha}\cdot\boldsymbol{A}$ as a small perturbation ("weak" field as in Sect. 46α). One can then evaluate[2] the expectation value of this operator using the exact DIRAC wave functions (discussed in Sect. 14) for zero magnetic field. For an arbitrary central electric potential and uniform magnetic field $\mathcal{H}$ (in the z-direction) the perturbation energy can be written in the form

$$E' = \mathcal{H}\mu_0 m \frac{j+\frac{1}{2}}{l+\frac{1}{2}}\left[1 - \frac{2\varkappa}{\varkappa-\frac{1}{2}}\int\limits_0^\infty dr\, f^2 r^2\right]. \tag{47.1}$$

The quantum number $\varkappa$ is defined in (14.9) and f is the radial wave function for the "small component" defined in (14.10) and normalized as in (14.32). If the term in square brackets in (47.1) is replaced by unity this expression reduces to the nonrelativistic weak field expression (46.4) with (46.6). For a COULOMB potential of nuclear charge Z the radial wave functions f are known. For the ground state $1\,S_{\frac{1}{2}}$, the integral in (47.1) can be evaluated easily and the correction factor in square brackets becomes

$$1 + \tfrac{2}{3}\left(\sqrt{1-Z^2\alpha^2} - 1\right). \tag{47.2}$$

If the central electric field has arbitrary shape but is "weak" and the atom is essentially nonrelativistic, the integral in (47.1) can be simplified. The correction factor is obtained up to order $(Z\alpha)^2$ if f is replaced by the approximation

$$f = \frac{\hbar}{2mc}\left[\frac{dg}{dr} + (1+\varkappa)\frac{g}{r}\right], \tag{47.3}$$

obtained from (14.10), and if g is replaced by the radial SCHRÖDINGER wave function R_{nl}. The correction factor to this order can also be obtained by a more

[1] L. D. HUFF: Phys. Rev. **38**, 501 (1931). — M. JOHNSON and B. LIPPMANN: Phys. Rev. **76**, 828 (1949); **77**, 702 (1950). See also p. 327 of ref. [*15*] of our bibliography. We shall not discuss these solutions. The motion of a free electron in a circular orbit in a uniform magnetic field under most practical conditions (e.g. in a cyclotron) corresponds to a superposition of states with extremely large values of the magnetic quantum number m. No quantum (or spin) effects are of any importance in such "large scale" motions, e.g. the revolution frequency of the electrons' orbit is the same as that given by the relativistic theory of a classical point-charge.

[2] G. BREIT: Nature, Lond. **122**, 649 (1928). — H. MARGENAU: Phys. Rev. **57**, 383 (1940). See also ref. [*9*], p. 72.

careful treatment[1] of the PAULI type of approximation: Additional terms in (12.11) involving the magnetic field are obtained if in the approximate relation (12.7) the operator $\boldsymbol{p}$ is replaced by $(\boldsymbol{p}+e\boldsymbol{A}/c)$ [see also Eq. (12.8)]. In addition, in the term in $(E+e\varphi)^2$ in (12.11) account must be taken of the shift in energy due to the magnetic field. For a COULOMB potential, the correction factor in square brackets in (47.1) can be evaluated analytically to this order for all atomic states. For the $n\,S_{\frac{1}{2}}$-state, for instance, this factor is

$$1-\frac{1}{3}\frac{(Z\alpha)^2}{n^2}. \tag{47.4}$$

For the ground state of hydrogen, this factor is $(1-1.78\times10^{-5})$ [the first two terms in an expansion of (47.2)].

β) Nuclear motion. We have so far considered the source of the nuclear COULOMB potential as fixed. For an actual nucleus of finite mass M, a small correction to the ZEEMAN effect arises from nuclear motion. This was investigated by LAMB[1] by an extension of the method discussed in Sect. 42. Working only to order m/M, he finds that the effect of nuclear motion is to multiply the orbital term $\mu_0\,\mathcal{H}\cdot\boldsymbol{k}$ in (45.9) by a factor g_l,

$$g_l=1-\frac{m}{M}. \tag{47.5}$$

The spin term $g_s\,\mu_0\,\mathcal{H}\cdot\mathbf{s}$ in (45.9) is unaffected to this order and terms of relative order $\alpha m/M$ have not been investigated yet.

These results might have been expected from the following physical arguments: A fraction $m/(M+m)$ of the orbital angular momentum $\boldsymbol{k}$ of the atom is contributed by the motion of the nucleus and the fraction $M/(M+m)$ by the electron (the momenta of the two particles are equal and opposite, their distances from the center of mass in the ratio m/M). The electron's contribution to the orbital angular momentum, and hence to the orbital term $\mu_0\,\mathcal{H}\cdot\boldsymbol{k}$, is thus reduced by the factor $M/(M+m)$ which is (approximately) (47.5). The nucleus gives a negligible orbital contribution (of order m^2/M^2), since its magnetic moment (for the *same* angular momentum) is smaller by a factor of order $\mu_N/\mu_0=m/M$ than that of the electron. The spin term $\mu_0 g_s\,\mathcal{H}\cdot\mathbf{s}$, however, is connected with the electron's *intrinsic* spin and magnetic moment and is unaffected by the nuclear motion.

γ) Effect of nuclear magnetic moment. If the atomic nucleus has a non-zero magnetic moment, the atomic ZEEMAN effect will be modified. Nuclear magnetic moments are of the order of a nuclear magneton μ_N which is about 1/1836 times the electronic BOHR magneton μ_0. In the absence of a magnetic field the hyperfine structure splitting $\Delta\varepsilon$ of energy levels (magnetic electron-nucleus interaction) is generally smaller than the fine structure splitting ΔE (electronic spin-orbit interaction) by a factor of the same order. One would then also expect the effect of the nuclear magnetic moment on the ZEEMAN effect to be small. This is indeed the case for all but *very* weak magnetic fields, where the ZEEMAN pattern is altered drastically.

In Sect. 46 we have discussed the dependence on the magnetic field strength $\mathcal{H}$ of the energy eigenvalues and eigenfunctions of states in the hydrogen atom in the absence of a nuclear moment. We found that, besides n and l, also m, the eigenvalue of $M_z=k_z+s_z$, is an exact quantum number. We dealt with two

[1] W. E. LAMB: Phys. Rev. **85**, 259 (1952).

non-commuting operators: (1) The ZEEMAN effect operator W, Eq. (45.9), which is proportional to $M_z + s_z$ and whose expectation values are of order $\mu_0 \mathcal{H}$. (2) The spin-orbit coupling operator Σ, Eq. (45.10), which is proportional to $\boldsymbol{k} \cdot \boldsymbol{s}$ and whose eigenvalues lead to the field-free fine structure separation ΔE of the levels with $j = l + \frac{1}{2}$ and $l - \frac{1}{2}$. We found that j is approximately a good quantum number ($\boldsymbol{M}^2$ conserved) if $\mu_0 \mathcal{H} \ll \Delta E$ and that m_s (and hence m_l) is almost a good quantum number if $\mu_0 \mathcal{H} \gg \Delta E$. In the presence of a nuclear magnetic moment we have extra terms in the HAMILTONian and the situation is more complicated.

As discussed in Sect. 22β, many nuclei have a non-zero and fixed value I for their "spin", where $I(I+1)$ is the eigenvalue of the square of an operator $\boldsymbol{i}$ which represents the intrinsic internal angular momentum of the nucleus. The nucleus then has a magnetic moment

$$\mu = + \mu_N g_I \boldsymbol{i},$$

where μ_N is defined in (22.7) and g_I is a constant for each nucleus. We then have two additional terms in the HAMILTONian. One represents the interaction of the nucleus with the external magnetic field $\mathcal{H}$ and is given by

$$H'' = - g_I \mu_N \mathcal{H} i_z.$$

The other operator H' is given by (22.1) and (22.6). Physically it represents the interaction of the nuclear moment with the magnetic field produced by the electron's motion and spin and does not depend explicitly on the external field $\mathcal{H}$. The operator H'' bears some analogy to the operator W and its expectation values are smaller by one order of $\mu_0/\mu_N = 1836$. The expectation values of the operator H' are smaller than those of Σ by a factor of the same order.

For external fields in the PASCHEN-BACK region, i.e., $\mu_0 \mathcal{H} \gtrsim \Delta E$, the electronic wave functions are essentially unaffected by the nuclear moment terms H' and H''. For very strong fields in particular, $\mu_0 \mathcal{H} \gg \Delta E$, one finds that the effect of H' on the energy is much smaller than that of H''. The nuclear spin is then essentially "uncoupled" from the electron's angular momenta. Each of the energy levels discussed in Sect. 46β is merely split further, according to the eigenvalue m_I of i_z (which is now a good quantum number), and the additional energy shift is given by the (small) eigenvalue $-g_I \mu_N \mathcal{H} m_I$ of the operator H''. We shall not discuss these cases further (see [*16*]), but only the case of $\mu_0 \mathcal{H} \ll \Delta E$.

If $\mu_0 \mathcal{H} \ll \Delta E$, then (see Sect. 46$\alpha$) the ZEEMAN effect operator W is small compared with the electronic spin-orbit coupling operator Σ. The hyperfine structure operator H' is small compared with Σ (by a factor of order 1836) and the nuclear ZEEMAN operator H'' is small compared with W (by a factor of the same order) and also compared with H' (by one order of $\mu_0 \mathcal{H}/\Delta E$). The stationary states are then eigenstates (to a good approximation) of Σ, and hence of $\boldsymbol{M}^2$, and j is a good quantum number. In the absence of W, H' and H'', the energy depends on j through the eigenvalue Σ_{nlj}, but is degenerate with respect to m and m_I, the eigenvalues of M_z ($\boldsymbol{M}$ is the total angular momentum of the electron) and of i_z. We consider H' and W as small perturbations which remove this degeneracy, but neglect mixing between states of different j-values. H'' is smaller than both H' and W, but H' is not necessarily smaller than W.

For transitions between states with the *same* j-value, the hyperfine structure operator H' can be written [see Eq. (22.9)] in the form

$$H' = a_{nlj} g_I \boldsymbol{i} \cdot \boldsymbol{M}, \tag{47.6}$$

where a_{nlj} is a constant for given values of n, l and j. As in Sect. 22β, we call $\boldsymbol{f}=\boldsymbol{i}+\boldsymbol{M}$ the operator for the angular momentum of the whole atom and $f(f+1)$ the eigenvalue of $\boldsymbol{f}^2$. Now $f_z=M_z+i_z$ commutes with H', W and H'' and its eigenvalue $m_f=m+m_I$ is thus an *exact* quantum number. On the other hand, H' does not commute with M_z and W does not commute with $\boldsymbol{f}^2$. Hence neither m (and therefore m_I) nor f is an exact quantum number. Calculations for arbitrary field strengths are tedious, but we discuss two simple limiting cases (neglecting H'', which is smaller than H' and W, in both cases).

Let $\Delta\varepsilon$ be the order of magnitude of the hyperfine structure splitting, i.e. of $a_{nlj}\,g_I$ in (47.6), which is of order $\Delta E/1836$. We consider first the case of extremely weak magnetic fields, $\mu_0\mathscr{H}\ll\Delta\varepsilon\ll\Delta E$ (ZEEMAN splitting less than hyperfine splitting). We then consider W as a small perturbation on H' and use the eigenfunctions of H' (for which f, *not* m, is a good quantum number) to evaluate the expectation value of W. The main splitting of a fine structure level is then the hyperfine structure splitting (eigenvalues of H') as evaluated in Sect. 22, which gives an energy depending on f, but not on m_f. Each level with given f then splits further into components with different values of m_f. This extra splitting energy is given by the expectation value of W, i.e. by $\mu_0\mathscr{H}g_j\overline{m}$, where g_j is the factor g defined in (46.5) and $\overline{m}$ is the expectation value of M_z for an eigenstate of $\boldsymbol{M}^2$, $\boldsymbol{f}^2$ and f_z (quantum numbers j, f and m_f). By arguments similar to those leading to (46.3), one can show that

$$\overline{m}=\frac{f(f+1)+j(j+1)-I(I+1)}{2f(f+1)}\,m_f, \tag{47.7}$$

if $f\neq 0$, and that $\overline{m}=0$ if $f=0$.

If, on the other hand, $\Delta\varepsilon\ll\mu_0\mathscr{H}\ll\Delta E$, we consider H', Eq. (47.6), as a small perturbation on the ZEEMAN operator W, Eq. (46.1). We then consider both j and m as good quantum numbers and a level with given j primarily splits into levels of different m values with the splitting energy given by (46.4) and (46.5). In addition, each m-level is split further with the splitting energy given by the expectation value $\overline{H}'$ of H', Eq. (47.6), for an eigenstate of $\boldsymbol{M}^2$, M_z and f_z (and hence of i_z). The expectation value of $\boldsymbol{i}\cdot\boldsymbol{M}$ equals that of $i_z M_z$ and

$$\overline{H}'=a_{nlj}\,g_I\,m_I\,m, \tag{47.8}$$

where $m_I=(-I,\ldots,I-1,I)$ is the eigenvalue of i_z. In either of the two limits discussed, the total number of levels (for fixed n, l, j) is $(2j+1)\,(2I+1)$.

Calculations for the energy levels in the intermediate region, $\Delta\varepsilon\sim\mu_0\mathscr{H}\ll\Delta E$ are somewhat lengthy and have to be carried out separately for each value of j. For $j=\frac{1}{2}$ one finds the following result[1], for any value of I: In the absence of a magnetic field, the level is split into a doublet with $f=I+\frac{1}{2}$ and $I-\frac{1}{2}$ and energy separation $\Delta\varepsilon=a_{nlj}\,g_I(I+\frac{1}{2})$. For arbitrary values of $\mu_0\mathscr{H}/\Delta\varepsilon$ and without neglecting the small operator H'', the energies $E_\pm$ of the two levels with fixed m_f are given by (relative to the mean energy of the field-free doublet)

$$E_\pm=-g_I\mu_N\mathscr{H}\pm\frac{\Delta\varepsilon}{2}\sqrt{1+\frac{4m_f}{2I+1}\,x+x^2};\qquad x=\frac{(g_j\mu_0-g_I\mu_N)\,\mathscr{H}}{\Delta\varepsilon}. \tag{47.9}$$

If we neglect μ_N/μ_0 in $E_\pm$ and proceed to the limits $x\to 0$ or $x\to\infty$, this expression reduces to our approximate ones above.

[1] G. BREIT and I. RABI: Phys. Rev. **38**, 2082 (1931). — S. MILLMAN, I. RABI and J. ZACHARIAS: Phys. Rev. **53**, 384 (1938). See also ref. [*16*], Chap. 2B.

The effect of the nuclear magnetic moment on the ZEEMAN effect is of practical importance for two reasons. (1) In many experiments on the atomic ZEEMAN effect it is convenient to work in the weak-field region of Sect. 46α (see, for nstance, Sect. 49β), where $\mu_0 \mathcal{H} \ll \Delta E$. Although the hyperfine splitting $\Delta\varepsilon$ is very small compared with ΔE, in these experiments $\Delta\varepsilon$ is not necessarily very small compared with $\mu_0 \mathcal{H}$ and the corrections discussed in this section may be important. (2) In the region where $\mu_0 \mathcal{H}$ and $\Delta\varepsilon$ are comparable ($x \sim 1$), the energy E of the atomic state is by no means linear in $\mathcal{H}$. In fact the "moment of the atomic state", $\mu_m = \partial E/\partial \mathcal{H}$, can vanish at a particular field strength which depends critically on g_I (i.e. on $\Delta\varepsilon$). An atomic beam passing through an *in*homogeneous magnetic field suffers a deflection proportional to μ_m and is undeflected when the atomic state has "zero moment". This fact is used in the "zero moment method[1]" to yield values for nuclear g_I-factors by measuring the values of $\mathcal{H}$ for which $\mu_m = 0$.

δ) *The quadratic term*[2]. We have considered so far only the perturbation term in the HAMILTONian which is linear in the magnetic field $\mathcal{H}$. Putting $g_s = 2$ in (45.9), this term is

$$W = \frac{e\hbar\mathcal{H}}{2mc}(k_z + 2s_z). \tag{47.10}$$

We have now to consider the effect of the part of the HAMILTONian which is quadratic in the vector potential $\boldsymbol{A}$ [last term in (45.2)]. This term, present both in the DIRAC and KLEIN-GORDON theories, is

$$W_Q = \frac{e^2}{2mc^2}A^2 = \frac{e^2\mathcal{H}^2}{8mc^2} r^2 \sin^2\vartheta. \tag{47.11}$$

In (47.11) we have used (45.3) for a uniform magnetic field and ϑ is the angle between $\boldsymbol{r}$ and the direction of $\mathcal{H}$ (taken as z-axis).

We first give some order of magnitude arguments to show that the effect of W_Q is much smaller than that of W, except for states of large principal quantum number n in very strong fields. Consider a state in hydrogen with a small value of n. The order of magnitude of W_Q is given by

$$W_Q = \left(\frac{e\hbar\mathcal{H}}{2mc}\right)^2 \left(\frac{r}{\hbar}\right)^3 \frac{m}{2}\sin^2\vartheta \sim \frac{W^2}{\hbar^2/r^2 m} \sim \frac{W}{\mathrm{Ry}} W, \tag{47.12}$$

where we have replaced r by one BOHR radius and $\hbar^2/2r^2m$ by one RYDBERG. Hence W_Q is smaller than W by a factor of order W/Ry. Now the ZEEMAN energy W for all practical fields is much smaller than a RYDBERG. In particular, we have seen (Sect. 46γ) that for $\mathcal{H}$ of the order of 10^4 Gauss, W is comparable with the fine structure splitting $\Delta E \sim \alpha^2$ Ry. For such fields, then, W_Q/W is of order $\alpha^2 \sim 10^{-4}$.

The ratio of the expectation value of W_Q to that of W is negligibly small for fields of the order of 10^4 Gauss or less and for states of low principal quantum number n. At larger field strengths ("strong" field case, complete PASCHEN-BACK effect) the energy shift due to W is linear in $\mathcal{H}$, that of W_Q quadratic. Further, (3.21) shows that the expectation value of r^2 is roughly proportional to n^4. Hence W_Q/W is roughly proportional to $\mathcal{H} n^4$ and can become comparable to unity for large $\mathcal{H}$ and n. Note that the energy shift due to W changes sign when both m_l and m_s change sign, whereas the expectation value of W_Q is independent of the sign of the magnetic quantum numbers. W_Q is important even

[1] R. COHEN: Phys. Rev. **46**, 713 (1934).

[2] For a detailed discussion of these effects see L. SCHIFF and H. SNYDER, Phys. Rev. **55**, 59 (1938).

for low field strengths in cases where the expectation value of W is zero and leads to diamagnetism (for the case of helium, this is calculated in Sect. 50).

The operator W commutes with $\boldsymbol{k}^2$ and we have so far considered l as a good quantum number. On the other hand, W_Q does *not* commute with $\boldsymbol{k}^2$ and also has matrix elements for transitions between states of l-values differing by ± 2. These off-diagonal matrix elements are of the same order of magnitude as the expectation values of W_Q and result in a "mixing" of wave functions of different l-values. The amount of mixing can be calculated by first order perturbation theory and is of order $\overline{W}_Q/\Delta E$, where ΔE is the fine structure energy difference for levels of different l-values. This mixing in of excited states of H is again quite small unless $\mathscr{H}$ and n are large. The mixing is still smaller for the valence electron of an alkali atom, since the energy depends on l even nonrelativistically. The mixing is completely negligible for the ground state of H, since the biggest admixture would come from the $3d$ state with ΔE almost 1 Ry (instead of α^2 Ry for the excited states).

ε) Anomalous moment of the electron. In Sect. 18 we have discussed the various corrections to the DIRAC theory introduced by quantum electrodynamics. One simple and important effect is the anomalous magnetic moment of the electron. In the PAULI equation for the motion of an electron in an external field, the terms arising from the intrinsic moment of the electron have to be multiplied by a factor differing slightly from unity. This factor is to be used for $\frac{1}{2}g_s$ in (45.9) and can be calculated from quantum electrodynamics in the form of an expansion in powers of the fine structure constant α. The term linear in α in this expansion has been calculated by FEYNMAN and by SCHWINGER in their classic papers and the term in α^2 by KARPLUS and KROLL[1]. To this order, the correction factor is given by [see Eq. (18.5)]

$$\frac{1}{2} g_s = 1 + \frac{\alpha}{2\pi} - 2.973 \frac{\alpha^2}{\pi^2} = 1.0011454. \tag{47.13}$$

Terms of order α^3 and higher have not been calculated yet, but they are expected to contribute less than $\pm 10^{-6}$ to g_s. Precision experiments by KUSCH and others, which verify (47.13), are discussed in Sect. 49.

48. Extension to many-electron atoms. *α) General theory.* In Sects. 39 to 41 we have discussed an approximately relativistic wave equation for the two-electron system. This equation, which is of the same accuracy as the PAULI approximation, can also be generalized to a many-electron atom. The HAMILTONian corresponding to this equation contains a part which depends on an external magnetic field $\mathscr{H}$. This part is in the form of sums over all electrons of terms which individually are just of the form of the field-dependent terms in the single-electron equation. We shall omit at the moment the terms quadratic in $\mathscr{H}$. We denote the sum over electrons of the orbital angular momentum, spin etc. by capital letters,

$$\boldsymbol{K} = \sum_i \boldsymbol{k}_i, \qquad \boldsymbol{S} = \sum_i \boldsymbol{s}_i, \qquad \boldsymbol{M} = \sum_i (\boldsymbol{k}_i + \boldsymbol{s}_i). \tag{48.1}$$

The eigenvalues of K_z, S_z, and M_z are m_L, m_S and m, those of $\boldsymbol{K}^2$, $\boldsymbol{S}^2$ and $\boldsymbol{M}^2$ are $L(L+1)$, $S(S+1)$ and $J(J+1)$. The term W in the HAMILTONian which is linear in $\mathscr{H}$ has then a form in complete analogy with (45.9),

$$W = \mu_0 \mathscr{H} (K_z + g_s S_z). \tag{48.2}$$

[1] R. KARPLUS and N. KROLL: Phys. Rev. **77**, 536 (1950).

We now have to consider the parts of the HAMILTONian which are independent of $\mathscr{H}$. If one takes only the nonrelativistic approximation H_0 to this HAMILTONian one finds that $\boldsymbol{K}^2$, $\boldsymbol{S}^2$, K_z and S_z all commute with H_0; and L, S, m_L and m_S are all good quantum numbers. Due to the electrostatic interaction between the electrons and exchange effects, the energy eigenvalue of H_0 depends in general on the values of both L and S, but *not* on m_L and m_S (compare Sect. 28). The relativistic part of the HAMILTONian contains various types of terms, including the BREIT interaction between electrons, and some of these terms do *not* commute with $\boldsymbol{K}^2$ or $\boldsymbol{S}^2$. We consider only the case where the electrons are essentially nonrelativistic (low effective nuclear charge) and where the nonrelativistic energies for states of different L and S do not (accidentally) lie extremely close. One can then use the following approximation, called the RUSSELL-SAUNDERS coupling scheme.

We consider the relativistic part of the HAMILTONian as a small perturbation and consider first only the part of this perturbation which is diagonal in a representation in terms of L and S. This part can usually be written[1] in the form (to a good approximation)

$$\Sigma = a\,\boldsymbol{K}\cdot\boldsymbol{S}, \tag{48.3}$$

where a may depend on L and S, but not on m_L and m_S. This term Σ is then completely analogous to the operator in (45.10). In some cases (e.g. helium) the diagonal part Σ is *not* well represented by (48.3), but even in these cases Σ commutes with $\boldsymbol{M}^2$. If (for fixed L and S) we express operators in a representation in terms of J (eigenstates of $\boldsymbol{M}^2$), then Σ is diagonal,

$$\Sigma_{JJ'} = \Sigma'_J\,\delta_{JJ'}, \tag{48.4}$$

where Σ'_J is a number independent of the quantum number m. The approximate form (48.3) is a special case of operators satisfying (48.4).

The off-diagonal parts of the relativistic HAMILTONian will cause some admixture of wave functions with different values of L and S. But since the relativistic terms are small, this admixture is small and their effect on the energy is of *second* order (counting Σ as first order). The admixture will only be of order $(Z\alpha)^2\,\mathrm{Ry}/\delta E$, where δE is the energy difference between the level considered and the nearest level with different values of L and S. In He this ratio is quite small and the method used in Sect. 40 (except for ARAKI's corrections) is in fact equivalent to the RUSSELL-SAUNDERS scheme.

In alkali atoms, the neglect of off-diagonal matrix elements is again an excellent approximation for the following reason. We normally consider only states with the single valence electron outside a closed shell and L, S are simply the quantum numbers l, s for this valence electron. Now the relativistic HAMILTONian will couple this state only to those states where one of the core electrons has been lifted to a higher shell. The energy difference δE is thus large and, further, the valence electron sees a small effective nuclear charge and is essentially nonrelativistic.

If we neglect the off-diagonal relativistic matrix elements and consider L and S as exact quantum numbers, the theory of the ZEEMAN effect of a many-electron atom is very similar to the theory worked out in Sect. 46. For the weak-field case of Sect. 46α, the results of (46.4) and (46.5) were already derived by general operator methods for *arbitrary* values of l and s. These results then apply without modification for a many-electron atom (in the RUSSELL-SAUNDERS

[1] See ref. [5], p. 194.

approximation), except that l, s are replaced by L, S and j by J [the eigenvalue of $(\boldsymbol{K}+\boldsymbol{S})^2$ is $J(J+1)$]. For weak fields, J is again (almost) a good quantum number, m_L and m_S not at all. Note that these results are based only on the assumption that (48.4) holds, but not necessarily (48.3).

For strong fields (complete PASCHEN-BACK effect) the results of Sect. 46β again apply, essentially without modification. In this case m_L and m_S are (almost) good quantum numbers, J not at all. The total energy is then

$$E = E_0 + \mu_0 H (m_L + g_S m_S) + \overline{\Sigma}_{m_L m_S}, \tag{48.5}$$

where $\overline{\Sigma}$ is the expectation value of Σ, Eq. (48.4), for an eigenstate of K_z and S_z. If Σ is given by the special form (48.3), then $\overline{\Sigma}$ reduces to

$$\overline{\Sigma} = a\, m_L\, m_S, \tag{48.6}$$

in complete analogy[1] with (46.10).

For intermediate field strengths (W and Σ comparable) the situation is more complicated. For fixed L, S and m one can, for instance, use a representation in terms of eigenstates of $\boldsymbol{M}^2$ with $J = |L-S|, \ldots, L+S$. Σ, as given by (48.4), is diagonal in this representation and the matrix elements of K_z and S_z (and hence of W) can be found. One then has to find the eigenvalues and eigenstates of the matrix $(W+\Sigma)$. This must be done separately for states of different values of L and S and the calculations are lengthy for large values of S. In the case of alkali atoms with $S=\frac{1}{2}$ the theory of Sect. 46γ still holds. We only[2] discuss briefly the case of helium with $S=0$ or 1.

β) Helium. The para-states of helium have total spin zero, $S=0$. In this case the spin-orbit coupling term (48.3) and the term involving S_z in (48.2) both vanish. We then have exactly the "normal ZEEMAN effect" described in Sect. 45α as for spinless particles. The field-free wave functions are exact eigenfunctions for all field strengths and the interaction energy $\mu_0 \mathscr{H} m_L$ is strictly linear in the field (always omitting the quadratic term of Sect. 47δ). This theory is in good agreement with experiment[3].

For orthostates of helium the total spin is given by $S=1$. For states of zero orbital angular momentum, $L=0$, the field-free wave function for each value of $m=m_s=1, 0, -1$ is an exact eigenfunction and the interaction energy is simply $\mu_0 \mathscr{H} g_s m_s$. For $L \neq 0$, the correct eigenfunctions for a particular value of m are three different superpositions of three linearly independent wave functions. For weak fields these are the three eigenstates of $\boldsymbol{M}^2$ and their energies are given by (46.4). The LANDÉ factor (46.5) reduces to (with $g_s=2$ and $S=1$)

$$g = \left\{ \begin{array}{lll} (L+2)(L+1)^{-1} & \text{if} & J = L+1, \\ 1 + L^{-1}(L+1)^{-1} & \text{if} & J = L, \\ (L-1)\, L^{-1} & \text{if} & J = L-1. \end{array} \right\} \tag{48.7}$$

By "weak" fields we mean that $\mu_0 \mathscr{H}$ is small compared with the energy difference between any two of three (field-free) fine structure components, i.e., with $\Sigma'_J - \Sigma'_{J'}$, where Σ'_J is defined in (48.4).

For strong fields ($\mu_0 \mathscr{H}$ much larger than fine structure splitting) the three eigenstates (with fixed m and L) are the eigenstates of K_z with eigenvalues

[1] The case of He, where $\boldsymbol{\Sigma}$ is not of form (48.3) and (48.6) does not apply, is discussed in Sect. 48β.

[2] See also ref. [5], Chap. 16.

[3] W. LOHMANN: Phys. Z. **7**, 809 (1906).

$m_L = m+1$, m and $m-1$. The energies of these states are given by (48.5). The term $\overline{\Sigma}_{m_L m_S}$ is independent of $\mathscr{H}$ [and much smaller than the second term in (48.5)] and can be evaluated as follows: One first calculates the three eigenvalues Σ'_J (for $J = L+1$, L and $L-1$) of the fine structure operator Σ, as discussed in Sect. 40. One can then write the eigenstate of K_z and S_z (eigenvalues m_L and m_S) as a linear superposition of the three eigenstates of $\boldsymbol{M}^2$ (with fixed $m = m_L + m_S$), with expansion coefficients $c(m_L, m_S; J\ m)$ which are given in [5], Chap. 3, Sect. 14. Making use of the diagonal property (48.4) of Σ, one finds

$$\overline{\Sigma}_{m_L m_S} = \sum_{J=L-1}^{L+1} |c\,(m_L\, m_S\, ; Jm)|^2\, \Sigma'_J\,.$$

For intermediate field strengths one has to find the exact eigenvalues and eigenstates of the submatrix for $(W+\Sigma)$, as discussed in Sect. 48α.

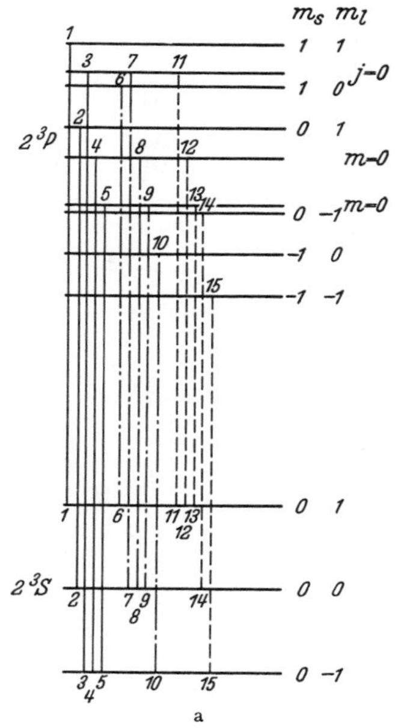

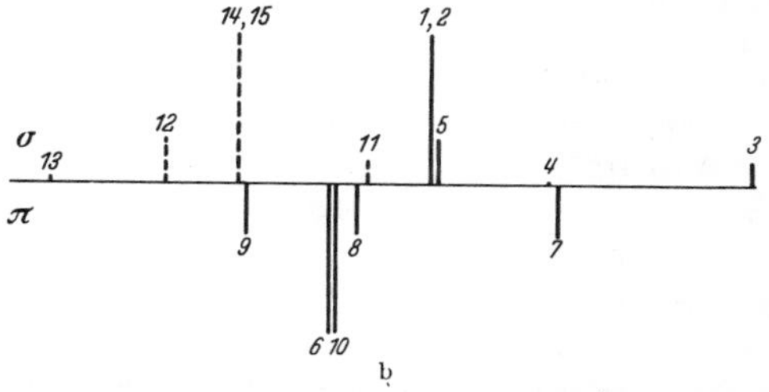

Fig. 24a and b. ZEEMAN effect for the $2^3P \to 2^3S$ line in helium for a field strength of $\mathscr{H} = 8500$ Gauss. a. The energy level scheme. The six levels with $m = \pm 1$ of the 2^3P-state exhibit the complete PASCHEN-BACK effect; for $m=0$ the uppermost level is essentially the field-free $j=0$ state, the two lower ones are combinations of $j=1$ and 2. b. The theoretical splitting diagram for the spectral line. The numbers correspond to those in Fig. 24a. Solid lines: right, broken lines: left circular polarization.

For P-states ($L=1$) and $m=0$, for instance, the operator $(W+\Sigma)$ is represented by a three-by-three matrix, the rows and columns referring to $J = 0, 1, 2$,

$$W + \Sigma = \begin{pmatrix} \Sigma'_0 & \sqrt{\tfrac{2}{3}}\,\mu_0 \mathscr{H} & 0 \\ \sqrt{\tfrac{2}{3}}\,\mu_0 \mathscr{H} & \Sigma'_1 & \sqrt{\tfrac{1}{3}}\,\mu_0 \mathscr{H} \\ 0 & \sqrt{\tfrac{1}{3}}\,\mu_0 \mathscr{H} & \Sigma'_2 \end{pmatrix}. \tag{48.8}$$

Since $m=0$, the energies Σ'_0, Σ'_1, Σ'_2 are those without field [for $m \neq 0$, the first order ZEEMAN effect, with g given by (48.7), should be added]. The eigenvalues of this matrix are discussed in [*10*], Sect. 28. For the P-states in helium (see Sect. 40) the field-free energies Σ'_1 and Σ'_2 (for $J=1$ and 2) almost coincide accidentally and there is a region of fairly low field strengths where the $J=0$ level shows the weak-field ZEEMAN effect, but the $J=1, 2$ levels show the PASCHEN-BACK effect ([*10*], p. 401). For $m = \pm 1$, (48.8) is replaced by a two-by-two matrix, involving $J=1$ and 2, for $m = \pm 2$ there is no degeneracy and the state $J=2$ has a linear ZEEMAN effect. The level splitting for 2^3P and 2^3S for He at 8500 Gauss is shown in Fig. 24.

γ) Relativistic corrections. For weak magnetic fields, the LANDÉ factor g should be given by (46.5) according to the discussion of Sect. 48α. Even when

(47.12) is substituted for g_s in (46.5) this expression is still not exact. As discussed in Sect. 48α some parts of the relativistic HAMILTONian give an admixture to the wave function from states with different values of L and S, for which the expression (46.5) for g is different from the value for the state considered. These effects cannot be calculated with any great accuracy for complex atoms, but semi-quantitative estimates have been made[1] for alkali atoms in their ground state (one electron with $l=0$ outside closed shells). The effect increases with atomic number and the deviation of the LANDÉ factor g from the expression (46.5) [with g_s given by Eq. (47.12)] should be of the order of two parts in 10^5 for potassium and up to ten parts in 10^5 in cesium. According to rough estimates, the deviations of g from (46.5) for atoms with three electrons outside closed shells should not be very much greater than for alkali atoms of comparable atomic number.

Besides the effects of configuration mixing discussed above, specific relativistic corrections occur of a type similar to the BREIT-MARGENAU corrections in hydrogen (Sect. 47α). In many-electron atoms these corrections also include contributions from the BREIT interaction between electrons. For the $n\,^3S_1$-states of ortho-helium these corrections have been calculated explicitly[2]. For the metastable $2\,^3S_1$-state, g differs from g_s [the value given by Eq. (46.5a)] by 4.1 parts in 10^5, compared with two in 10^5 for the hydrogen ground state. For alkali atoms and other complex atoms only semi-quantitative estimates of these relativistic effects are available[3]. These corrections to g should be of the order of magnitude of 10^{-5} to 10^{-4}.

In Sect. 49β precision experiments will be discussed which are capable of measuring the ratios of the LANDÉ factor g for states of various values of L, S and J in various atoms to an accuracy of about one part in 10^5. The value in (47.12) for g_s has been firmly established (see Sect. 49δ). The remaining discrepancies between the measured g-values and (46.5) should then be due to the corrections discussed in this section. The measured discrepancies are of the same order of magnitude as the rough theoretical estimates for them. For the ground states of the alkali atoms, for instance, the experimental g-values[4] agree with g_s to one part in 10^5 for Li, Na and K and $g/g_s=(1+5\times10^{-5})$ and $(1+13\times10^{-5})$, respectively, for Rb and Cs. For the $2\,^3S_1$-state in helium[5] $g/g_s=(1-4\times10^{-5})$, in good agreement with theory. Even for the ground state of Cr, which has five d-electrons and one s-electron outside closed shells, with $L=0$ and $J=S=3$, the LANDÉ factor is close[6] to g_s, namely $g/g_s=1-(35\pm5)\times10^{-5}$. Measurements of g-values have also been carried out[7] on $^2P_{\frac{1}{2}}$ and $^2P_{\frac{3}{2}}$ states of atoms with three electrons outside closed shells, such as Ga and In. The g-values differ from (46.5) by less than 20 parts in 10^5 in most cases.

49. Comparison with precision experiments. Numerous experimental investigations on the ZEEMAN effect in hydrogen-like and complex atoms have been carried out many years ago by means of optical spectroscopy. These experiments

[1] M. PHILLIPS: Phys. Rev. **88**, 202 (1952).

[2] W. PERL and V. HUGHES: Phys. Rev. **91**, 842 (1953).

[3] W. PERL: Phys. Rev. **91**, 852 (1953).

[4] P. KUSCH and H. TAUB: Phys. Rev. **75**, 1477 (1949). — P. FRANKEN and S. KOENIG: Phys. Rev. **88**, 199 (1952).

[5] HUGHES, TUCKER, RHODERICK and WEINREICH: Phys. Rev. **91**, 828 (1953).

[6] BRIX, EISINGER, LEW and WESSEL: Phys. Rev. **92**, 647 (1953).

[7] P. KUSCH and H. FOLEY: Phys. Rev. **74**, 250 (1948). — A. MANN and P. KUSCH: Phys. Rev. **77**, 435 (1950).

verified the various aspects of the theory of Sect. 46 in great detail[1], but *not* to a very high accuracy. Even with strong magnetic fields the ZEEMAN-splitting frequencies are only of the order of a few cm^{-1}, which is a small fraction of the frequency of an optical transition (order of 10^4 cm^{-1}). To within the experimental accuracy, no discrepancy with the theory of Sect. 46 (with the DIRAC value of 2 for g_s) was found. In fact, until fairly recently, the optical measurement[2] of the ZEEMAN effect together with theory provided one of the methods for measuring the ratio e/m for the electron.

Apart from confirming other details of the theory, the optical measurements confirmed the DIRAC value of 2 for g_s in (46.1) to within the experimental accuracy[3] of about one part in 500. Only recently microwave and other experimental techniques became available, which made much more accurate measurements of g_s possible. Historically, a value of g_s differing slightly from 2 (anomalous magnetic moment) was first suggested[4] by discrepancies between precision experiments and the DIRAC theory for hyperfine structure. However, the most direct measurements of g_s come from modern experiments on the ZEEMAN effect, which we shall discuss briefly.

α) Experimental techniques[5]. In optical spectra one usually deals with electric dipole transitions between two atomic states whose orbital quantum numbers L differ by unity ($\Delta L = \pm 1$). For hydrogen-like atoms the principal quantum number n also changes in an optical transition. In connection with the LAMB shift (Sect. 21) we have already considered electric dipole transitions between states in hydrogen of the *same* principal quantum number but different values of l, whose energy difference is a relativistic effect. Another type of electromagnetic transition is possible, the magnetic dipole transitions (see Sect. 66γ). For an atom in a weak (or no) external magnetic field, the selection rules for such a transition are $\Delta L = 0$, $\Delta J = 0, \pm 1$ and $\Delta m = 0, \pm 1$. We then have the possibility of a transition between two states of the *same* principal quantum number and the same L, S and J, but with $\Delta m = \pm 1$. The *whole* energy difference between two such states is then due to the interaction with the magnetic field and the frequency of the radiation emitted or absorbed in this transition gives directly the energy of the ZEEMAN splitting. In this discussion we have neglected the effects of hyperfine structure (Sect. 47γ). For atoms with a finite nuclear moment in weak magnetic fields the energy difference between two states of identical L, S and J (but different m or F) depends also on the hyperfine structure interaction energy. This complicates the measurement of the ZEEMAN effect somewhat, but also makes possible a measurement of the hyperfine structure splitting energy by observing direct transitions between states of different values of F.

The probability for such a transition with the *spontaneous* emission of radiation is negligibly small, since the frequency of the radiation is extremely small (and, further, magnetic dipole transitions generally have smaller probabilities than electric ones). On the other hand, a rotating (or oscillating) magnetic field, even

---

[1] For the dependence on field strength of many lines in the H-spectrum see K. FOERSTERLING and G. HANSEN, Z. Physik **18**, 26 (1923) and ref. [*10*], Sect. 27d. For a survey, of the ZEEMAN effect in complex atoms see E. BACK and LANDÉ, ZEEMAN Effect (Berlin: Springer 1925); also R. BACHER and S. GOUDSMIT, Atomic Energy States (New York: McGraw-Hill Co. 1932).

[2] L. KINSLER and W. HOUSTON: Phys. Rev. **45**, 104 (1934); **46**, 533 (1934).

[3] The more accurate measurements of KINSLER were for singlet states which show the normal ZEEMAN effect and do not involve g_s.

[4] G. BREIT: Phys. Rev. **72**, 984 (1947).

[5] For a much more detailed account see ref. [*16*], Chap. 3.

of modest field strength, represents an extremely large number of electromagnetic quanta of frequency ν, if the rotation frequency ν is much smaller than optical frequencies (order of 10^{16} cps). The rotation frequency ν in a typical experiment lies in the short wave radio or in the microwave region (order of 10^8 or 10^9 cps). Such a rotating magnetic field can thus cause transitions[1] by absorption or *induced* emission if $h\nu$ is just equal to the energy difference between the two states. If these states form part of the ground state of the atom in question, their lifetimes will be long and the resonances will be very sharp (only a small frequency range will induce transitions).

Transitions induced by a rotating field of the correct frequency form the basis of many experimental techniques. The various techniques differ mainly in their method of detecting the transitions. In the atomic beam resonance method a transition of state of a particle in an atomic beam affects its trajectory, which is detected. In the microwave resonance absorption method the absorption of energy from the imposed rotating field is detected. In the magnetic resonance induction method one essentially detects the magnetic field produced by the induced emission of radiation. In all cases one essentially measures a frequency which corresponds to the energy of ZEEMAN splitting in a constant magnetic field or of the hyperfine splitting.

One can also measure the magnetic moments of nuclei by similar methods. Consider a nucleus in ionic solution or in a certain kind of molecule, so that there is no net magnetic interaction between the nucleus and the electrons. If the nucleus changes the direction of its spin $\boldsymbol{i}$ in a uniform magnetic field $\mathcal{H}$, the only change in energy will be that due to the interaction between the nuclear magnetic moment and this magnetic field. A rotating field with $h\nu$ equal to this energy difference can then induce transitions between states of different $\boldsymbol{i}\cdot\mathcal{H}$. These transitions can again be detected by the resonance absorption or induction method. Such experiments will be discussed further in Sect. 49γ.

The order of magnitude of some rotational frequencies ν in typical experiments are as follows. For a transition between the two hyperfine structure components of the hydrogen ground state (with no magnetic field), ν is 1420 Mc/sec. For the transition between the two ZEEMAN components of any $S_{\frac{1}{2}}$-state in hydrogen in a uniform magnetic field of 1000 Gauss, ν is about 2800 Mc/sec. In the same magnetic field, for a "spin flip" of the magnetic moment of a free proton, ν is about 4.25 Mc/sec.

β) The ratio g_s/g_l. The experimental techniques discussed above make possible the measurement of frequencies, corresponding to the ZEEMAN effect energies in a constant magnetic field $\mathcal{H}$, with extremely high precision. Consider, for instance, an atomic state with no hyperfine structure in a "weak" field $\mathcal{H}$. The frequency ν corresponding to a transition in which the magnetic quantum number m changes by unity is then, according to (46.4),

$$\nu = \frac{\Delta E}{h} = \frac{e}{4\pi m c}\mathcal{H} g. \tag{49.1}$$

If the RUSSELL-SAUNDERS approximation holds, the LANDÉ factor g should be given by (46.5) or (46.5a). If, further, the unmodified DIRAC theory were correct, g_l and g_s in (46.5a) would be unity and two, respectively. We are mainly interested in investigating deviations of g_l and g_s from these values.

To obtain an accurate value for g in (49.1) we need, besides a precision measurement of the frequency ν, an accurate knowledge of the ratio e/m and of the magnetic

[1] For a detailed quantum mechanical theory see H. SALWEN, Phys. Rev. **99**, 1274 (1955).

field $\mathcal{H}$. Although magnetic fields of very high uniformity can be obtained relatively easily, it is very difficult and tedious to measure the *absolute* field strength (in C.G.S. units) with high accuracy. Further, no absolute measurements of e/m of very great precision were available until recently. These difficulties can be avoided if we are satisfied with a measurement of the *ratio* of the g-values for two atomic states in the same or different atoms. One simply has to measure the ratio of the two transition frequencies in the *same* magnetic fields. This idea forms the basis of the classic experiment of KUSCH and FOLEY[1], which gave the first direct indication of the anomalous moment of the electron.

KUSCH and FOLEY used the atomic beam resonance method to measure transition frequencies for the ZEEMAN effect. To obtain sharp resonances they used atoms in their ground state and compared atoms for which the RUSSELL-SAUNDERS approximation should be very good, but which have different combinations of L, S and J. If one assumes the LANDÉ factor g to be of form (46.5a), but with g_l and g_s left arbitrary, then the ratio of the g-factors in two states with different L and/or S values immediately gives the ratio g_l/g_s. KUSCH and FOLEY used the ${}^2P_{\frac{3}{2}}$ and ${}^2P_{\frac{1}{2}}$ states in Ga and In and the ${}^2S_{\frac{1}{2}}$ state in Na. Assuming (46.5a), the mean of their measurements gave

$$\frac{g_s}{g_l} = 2\,(1.00119 \pm 0.00005)\,. \tag{49.2}$$

This value clearly indicates a deviation from the DIRAC value of two. According to (47.5), the deviation of g_l from unity in the more refined theory is negligible for the reasonably heavy nuclei considered. The value of (49.2) is then in good agreement with the theoretical value given by quantum electrodynamics,

$$\frac{g_s}{g_l} \approx g_s = 2 \times 1.0011454\,. \tag{49.3}$$

Experimental techniques have improved still further since 1948 and the ratios of g-factors in various atomic states have by now been measured with errors of less than one part in 10^5. However, most of these measurements are for states in complex atoms. As discussed in Sect. 48γ, the actual g-factors in such atomic states can differ from the expression (46.5a) by about one part in 10^4 and these deviations cannot be calculated with any accuracy at the moment. Experiments of this type then determine the ratio g_l/g_s to not much better than one part in 10^4 at the moment, in spite of the high experimental accuracy. In fact, these experiments are used nowadays to investigate the purity of atomic states etc., after assuming the theoretical value in (49.3). It should also be pointed out that these experiments measure only the ratio g_l/g_s, not g_l and g_s separately. In Sect. 49δ we discuss an accurate absolute measurement of g_s.

γ) Auxiliary measurements. We have already mentioned measurements of the frequency ν_p for the "spin flip" of the magnetic moment μ_p of a free proton in a uniform magnetic field $\mathcal{H}$ by the resonance absorption or induction method. μ_p can be written in the form

$$\mu_p = \frac{1}{2}\,g'_p\,\mu_0 = \frac{1}{2}\,g_p\,\mu_{NM}\,, \qquad \mu_{NM} = \frac{e\hbar}{2M_p c}\,, \tag{49.4}$$

where μ_0 is the BOHR magneton (45.7), μ_{NM} the nuclear magneton (22.7), M_p the proton mass and the factor $\frac{1}{2}$ is the value of the spin of the proton. The frequency ν_p is then

$$\nu_p = \frac{e}{4\pi m c}\,\mathcal{H}\,g'_p = \frac{e}{4\pi M_p c}\,\mathcal{H}\,g_p\,. \tag{49.5}$$

[1] P. KUSCH and H. FOLEY: Phys. Rev. **74**, 250 (1948).

If the proton were a pure DIRAC particle, g_p would be exactly two. Actually it possesses an anomolous magnetic moment, like the electron, which largely stems from interaction with the virtual meson field (instead of the electromagnetic field). Unlike the fine structure constant α, the equivalent mesonic coupling constant is *not* small, g_p differs considerably from 2 and its value cannot be calculated with any accuracy from present-day meson theories.

One practical use of the proton resonance experiments is the accurate (but relative) calibration of magnetic fields. From (49.5), ν_p is directly proportional to the magnetic field $\mathscr{H}$ and measurements of ν_p in the two magnetic fields to be used in two different experiments immediately gives the ratio of the field strengths. μ_p has also been measured on an absolute scale (C.G.S. units) in a magnetic field calibrated by the U.S. Nat. Bur. Stand. in C.G.S. units[1], but only to an accuracy of about 3 parts in 10^5. This measurement is important for a determination of the absolute constants e, m and M_p, but will not be discussed further.

Experiments of great importance for our present discussion are measurements of the "cyclotron frequency" of charged particles, i.e. the frequency of revolution ν of a free particle moving in a large (on an atomic scale) circular orbit in a uniform magnetic field $\mathscr{H}$,

$$\nu = \frac{e}{2\pi M c} \mathscr{H} \tag{49.6}$$

where e and M are the charge and mass of the particle. Such measurements are not quite as accurate as those of the ZEEMAN splitting or proton resonance frequencies. The cyclotron frequency has been measured for the electron[2] and for the proton[3] together with a measurement of the proton resonance frequency ν_p. These two measurements then give values for the factors g_p' and g_p, respectively in (49.4).

$$\tfrac{1}{2} g_p' = 0.001\,521\,01\,(1 \pm 1.2\times 10^{-5}), \qquad \tfrac{1}{2} g_p = 2.79276 \pm 0.00006. \tag{49.7}$$

The ratio of these two factors gives the ratio of the proton and electron mass. g_p alone is of importance in connection with precision measurements of the hydrogen hyperfine structure. We shall only use the value of g_p' in connection with ZEEMAN splitting frequencies.

δ) The absolute value of g_s. The limitation in the interpretation of the experiments discussed in Sect. 49β lies not in the experimental errors, but in the theoretical uncertainties in the LANDÉ factor g of (46.5) for complex atoms. For the ground state of hydrogen these difficulties do not arise. The magnetic interaction energy in weak fields can be calculated exactly and the ratio of g to g_s (after applying corrections for hyperfine structure effects), due to relativistic effects, is given by (47.4). The frequency of the ZEEMAN transition in a uniform magnetic field has been measured with extremely high precision, both by the atomic beam resonance method[4] and the resonance absorption method[5]. The proton resonance frequency ν_p is measured in the same field in each experiment. Such an experiment then gives the ratio of g_s to g_p' [see Eqs. (49.1) and (49.5)]. The two experi-

---

[1] THOMAS, DRISCOLL and HIPPLE: Phys. Rev. **78**, 787 (1950); **80**, 901 (1950).

[2] J. GARDNER and E. PURCELL: Phys. Rev. **83**, 996 (1950).

[3] F. BLOCH and C. JEFFRIES: Phys. Rev. **80**, 305 (1950). — HIPPLE, SOMMER and THOMAS: Phys. Rev. **80**, 487 (1950).

[4] KOENIG, PRODELL and KUSCH: Phys. Rev. **88**, 191 (1952).

[5] R. BERINGER and M. HEALD: Phys. Rev. **95**, 1474 (1954).

ments are in good agreement and give[1]

$$g_s/g_p' = 658.229 \pm 0.001\,. \tag{49.8}$$

The quantity of interest is not the ratio (49.8), but g_s itself. This can be obtained by combining (49.8) with g_p', Eq. (49.7), obtained from the electron cyclotron[1] frequency, and is

$$g_s = 2\,(1.001\,147 \pm 0.000\,012)\,. \tag{49.9}$$

This value for g_s is in excellent agreement with the theoretical value, Eq. (47.12), (49.3). The term of order α^2 in (47.15) contributes about 3×10^{-5} to g_s, so the accuracy of (49.9) is sufficient to check at least the order of magnitude of even this higher order term.

It should be pointed out that, in obtaining (49.9), the proton resonance frequency was only used as a convenient intermediary. In effect, the ZEEMAN frequency of an electron in a bound state was compared with the orbital revolution frequency of an electron in the same magnetic field. The error in (49.9) comes overwhelmingly from the electron cyclotron experiment. Incidentally, a comparison of (49.9) and the values for g_s/g_l, discussed in Sect. 49β, shows that g_l for a bound state with orbital angular momentum equals unity to within the uncertainty of interpretation of about 1 part in 10^4.

50. The diamagnetism of helium[2]. The ground state of helium is a singlet state ($S=0$) and possesses no orbital angular momentum ($L=0$). The linear term W in the interaction HAMILTONian with a magnetic field is thus zero, the ground state wave function is non-degenerate and there is no ZEEMAN splitting. Nevertheless, the quadratic term (47.11) in the HAMILTONian produces a small *shift* in energy, which depends on the magnetic field. This operator is

$$W_Q = \frac{e^2}{2mc^2}\left(A_1^2 + A_2^2\right) = \frac{e^2\mathscr{H}^2}{8mc^2}\left(r_1^2\sin^2\vartheta_1 + r_2^2\sin^2\vartheta_2\right). \tag{50.1}$$

Noting that the wave function is spherically symmetric and symmetric in $\boldsymbol{r}_1$ and $\boldsymbol{r}_2$ we find for the energy change ΔE (in atomic units),

$$\Delta E = \tfrac{1}{4}\alpha^2\mathscr{H}^2\,\overline{r^2}\,\overline{\sin^2\vartheta} = \tfrac{1}{6}\alpha^2\mathscr{H}^2\,\overline{r^2}\ \text{at. un.} \tag{50.2}$$

where $\overline{r^2}$ is the expectation value of r^2 for one electron. The average value may be computed by means of HARTREE's charge distribution, Table 5, resulting in

$$\overline{r^2} = 1.19\ \text{(a. u.)}, \quad \Delta E = 1.05\times10^{-5}\mathscr{H}^2\ \text{(a. u.)}. \tag{50.3}$$

In the presence of a field strength $\mathscr{H} = 100\,000$ Gauss $= 0.006$ atomic units, the term shift amounts to approximately 4×10^{-10} at. units $= 0.8\times10^{-4}\ \text{cm}^{-1}$, and thus, surely, is far below the limits of spectroscopic observability. Nonetheless, this slight term shift is responsible for the diamagnetism of helium.

The magnetic susceptibility per mole, χ, is defined by

$$\mathscr{N}\Delta E = -\tfrac{1}{2}\chi\mathscr{H}^2, \tag{50.4}$$

where ΔE is the term shift evaluated above, and $\mathscr{N}$ is AVOGADRO's number $= 6.02\times10^{23}$. χ has the dimensions of a volume. If we insert the value of ΔE,

[1] The value quoted in (49.8) refers to g_p' for protons bound in molecules in a sample of mineral oil. Due to diamagnetic corrections this is not quite the same as for a free proton. The values quoted in (49.7) are the extrapolated ones for a free proton; the experimental value for mineral oil is $\frac{1}{2}g_p' = 0.001\,520\,97$.

[2] See J. C. SLATER: Phys. Rev. **31**, 333 (1928).

(50.3), we obtain χ in units of a^3, where a is the radius of the hydrogen atom. In terms of cm³ we obtain the value

$$\chi = -\frac{2\Delta E}{\mathcal{H}^2}\mathcal{N}a^3 = -2\times 1.05\times 10^{-5}\times 6.02\times 10^{23}\times 0.529\times 10^{-24} = -1.87\times 10^{-6}.$$

The measured[1] value of χ is equal to -1.88×10^{-6}; the agreement is excellent.

b) STARK effect in hydrogen.

51. Linear STARK effect. *α) Symmetry considerations.* We shall consider an *arbitrary* atom in a homogeneous external electric field pointing in a direction parallel to the z-axis and of field strength F. The nonrelativistic SCHRÖDINGER equation for the atom is then, in atomic units,

$$(\tfrac{1}{2}\Delta + E - V - \Phi)\,u = 0, \quad \Phi = F\sum_i z_i. \tag{51.1}$$

The perturbation HAMILTONian Φ represents the sum over all electrons i of the interaction energy eFz of the electron with the electric field.

We now show that the expectation value of the perturbation potential Φ, using an eigenfunction u_0 of the field-free atom,

$$\overline{\Phi} = \int d\tau\,|u_0|^2\,\Phi,$$

vanishes in general: Consider an inversion about the nucleus of the spatial co-ordinates of all the electrons, i.e., change $\boldsymbol{r}_1, \boldsymbol{r}_2, \ldots, \boldsymbol{r}_n$ to $-\boldsymbol{r}_1, -\boldsymbol{r}_2, \ldots, -\boldsymbol{r}_n$ (*without* altering the spin wave functions, if any). The field-free HAMILTONian remains unchanged under such an inversion. It then follows that the field-free eigenstates have definite *parity*, i.e., u_0 either remains unchanged (even parity) or merely changes sign (odd parity) under inversion. Hence $|u_0|^2$ is unchanged but *Φ changes sign* under inversion ($z_i \to -z_i$). It then follows that the integral leading to the expectation value $\overline{\Phi}$ vanishes.

It follows from a similar argument that the matrix element of Φ for a transition between two unperturbed states a and b ($|u_0|^2$ replaced by $u_a^* u_b$ in the above integral) vanishes unless the two states have *opposite* parity. For a single electron in a central potential a state with orbital and magnetic quantum numbers l and m has odd (even) parity if l is odd (even), independent of the value of m. This follows from a property of spherical harmonics under inversion,

$$Y_{lm}(\pi - \vartheta, \pi + \varphi) = (-1)^l\, Y_{lm}(\vartheta, \varphi). \tag{51.2}$$

Thus Φ has non-zero matrix elements only for a transition from a state of odd l to one of even l (or vice versa). More explicitly, on writing $z = r\cos\vartheta$ and considering the orthogonality properties of spherical harmonics [see Eq. (A.22) of the appendix], the matrix element vanishes unless the two states have the same m and values of l differing by ± 1 (see also Sect. 60).

In complex atoms, states of different parity have different field-free energies. First order perturbation theory applied to Φ then gives no energy shift, since the expectation value $\overline{\Phi}$ vanishes. For weak fields the interaction energy is then given by *second* order perturbation theory and is *quadratic* in the field strength F. However, hydrogen-like atoms form an exception to this rule: States of different l-values (for fixed principal quantum number n) are degenerate (in non-relativistic approximation). Since Φ has non-zero matrix elements for transitions

[1] A. P. WILLS and L. G. HECTOR: Phys. Rev. **23**, 209; **24**, 418 (1924).

between states of odd and even l, the perturbation Φ will remove this degeneracy. The eigenfunctions *with* field are then superpositions of the field-free functions with different l-values and first order perturbation theory gives an interaction which is *linear* in the field-strength (for weak fields).

β) Calculations. It is, of course, possible to evaluate the linear STARK effect of the hydrogen atom by constructing the perturbation matrix (51.1) by means of the usual eigenfunctions in polar coordinates and finding the eigenvalues of that matrix. Fortunately, the STARK effect can also be treated in a simpler fashion by calculating in parabolic instead of polar coordinates. As we have seen in Sect. 6, the SCHRÖDINGER equation of the hydrogen atom in the absence of external fields can also be separated in parabolic coordinates (a fact which is closely related to the degeneracy of the hydrogen levels with respect to l). We shall now show that the separability is maintained in the presence of the electric field. The perturbation potential of the electric field, Fz, may be expressed in parabolic coordinates according to (6.1):

$$F z = \tfrac{1}{2} F(\xi - \eta).$$

The SCHRÖDINGER equation

$$\left(\frac{1}{2}\Delta + E + \frac{Z}{r} - F z\right) u = 0,$$

on writing the Laplacian operator in parabolic coordinates according to (6.4) and multiplying the equation by $\frac{1}{2}(\xi + \eta)$, assumes the form

$$\frac{\partial}{\partial\xi}\left(\xi\frac{\partial u}{\partial\xi}\right) + \frac{\partial}{\partial\eta}\left(\eta\frac{\partial u}{\partial\eta}\right) + \left(\frac{1}{4\xi} + \frac{1}{4\eta}\right)\frac{\partial^2 u}{\partial\varphi^2} + \left[\frac{1}{2}E(\xi+\eta) + Z - \frac{1}{4}F(\xi^2 - \eta^2)\right] u = 0.$$

As in Sect. 6, the above differential equation is separated by the assumption (6.5):

$$u = u_1(\xi)\, u_2(\eta)\, e^{i m \varphi}, \quad Z = Z_1 + Z_2.$$

However, the functions u_1 and u_2—instead of (6.6)—now must satisfy the differential equations

$$\left.\begin{aligned} \frac{d}{d\xi}\left(\xi\frac{d u_1}{d\xi}\right) + \left(\frac{1}{2}E\xi + Z_1 - \frac{m^2}{4\xi} - \frac{1}{4}F\xi^2\right) u_1 = 0, \\ \frac{d}{d\eta}\left(\eta\frac{d u_2}{d\eta}\right) + \left(\frac{1}{2}E\eta + Z_2 - \frac{m^2}{4\eta} + \frac{1}{4}F\eta^2\right) u_2 = 0, \end{aligned}\right\} \tag{51.3}$$

which differ in the sign in front of F. The ordinary differential Eq. (51.3) may either be directly integrated—we shall do this in Sect. 53—or they may be treated by means of a perturbation procedure which has as its starting point the unperturbed eigenfunctions (6.7), (6.8) and the unperturbed eigenvalues (6.10). The perturbation procedure will be satisfactory as long as the field intensity is not too large.

The perturbation procedure differs from the usual one in that the separation parameters Z_1 and Z_2, rather than the energy E, are the eigenvalues of the problem. Solving the differential equations determines Z_1 and Z_2 as a function of E and the field intensity F. The condition that $Z = Z_1 + Z_2$ gives the relation which we are after, namely, the energy E as a function of the field intensity F.

Introducing, as in Sect. 6, the quantity

$$\varepsilon = \sqrt{-2E} \tag{51.4}$$

the "eigenvalue" Z_1, in the absence of external electric field, may be expressed in terms of the electric quantum number n_1 and the magnetic quantum number m according to the formula

$$Z_1^{(0)} = \left(n_1 + \frac{m+1}{2}\right) \varepsilon. \tag{51.5}$$

The first order perturbation of this eigenvalue, produced by the field F, is given by the integral of the perturbation potential evaluated over the unperturbed eigenfunction. Except for normalization, that eigenfunction is given by (6.7) and (6.8). Normalizing according to the condition

$$\int_0^\infty u_1^2(\xi)\, d\xi = 1,$$

we obtain [cf. Eq. (3.13)]:

$$u_1(\xi) = \frac{n_1!^{\frac{1}{2}}}{(n_1+m)!^{\frac{3}{2}}} e^{-\frac{1}{2}\varepsilon\xi} \xi^{\frac{1}{2}m} \varepsilon^{\frac{1}{2}(m+1)} L_{n_1+m}^m(\varepsilon\xi), \tag{51.6}$$

and thus [cf. Eq. (3.13)]

$$\left.\begin{aligned} Z_1^{(1)} &= \frac{1}{4} F \int_0^\infty \xi^2 u_1^2\, d\xi = \frac{1}{4} F \frac{n_1!}{(n_1+m)!^3} \int \varepsilon^{m+1} \xi^{m+2} e^{-\varepsilon\xi}\, d\xi \left(L_{n_1+m}^m(\varepsilon\xi)\right)^2 \\ &= \frac{1}{4} F \varepsilon^{-2} (6n_1^2 + 6n_1 m + m^2 + 6n_1 + 3m + 2). \end{aligned}\right\} \tag{51.7}$$

Thus, altogether we obtain to first order [cf. Eq. (51.5)]

$$Z_1 = Z_1^{(0)} + Z_1^{(1)} = \varepsilon\left(n_1 + \frac{m+1}{2}\right) + \frac{1}{4}\frac{F}{\varepsilon^2}(6n_1^2 + 6n_1 m + m^2 + 6n_1 + 3m + 2) \tag{51.8}$$

and similarly

$$Z_2 = Z_2^{(0)} + Z_2^{(1)} = \varepsilon\left(n_2 + \frac{m+1}{2}\right) - \frac{1}{4}\frac{F}{\varepsilon^2}(6n_2^2 + 6n_2 m + m^2 + 6n_2 + 3m + 2).$$

Adding the two equations and paying due regard to the definition of the principal quantum number n, (5.8) yields

$$Z = \varepsilon n + \frac{3}{2}\frac{F}{\varepsilon^2}(n_1 - n_2)\, n \tag{51.9}$$

or, solving for ε,

$$\varepsilon = \frac{Z}{n} - \frac{3}{2} F \left(\frac{n}{Z}\right)^2 (n_1 - n_2). \tag{51.10}$$

Thus, the energy is given by

$$E = -\frac{1}{2}\varepsilon^2 = -\frac{1}{2}\frac{Z^2}{n^2} + \frac{3}{2}\frac{Fn}{Z}(n_1 - n_2). \tag{51.11}$$

Formula (51.11) for the linear STARK effect was derived by SCHWARZSCHILD and EPSTEIN on the basis of the old quantum theory and from wave-mechanics by SCHRÖDINGER in his third communication. The energy of the linear STARK effect, aside from the dependence on the principal quantum number n is a function of the difference $n_1 - n_2$ only which is also designated as the "electric quantum number"; there is no dependence on the magnetic quantum number m (m first appears in the second order approximation). The energetically highest STARK component belonging to the term with principal quantum number n is obtained by setting the parabolic quantum numbers $n_1 n_2$ equal to $n-1$ and 0, respectively, the lowest STARK component corresponds to $n_1 = 0$, $n_2 = n-1$.

The separation between these two extreme term components as given by (51.11) amounts to:

$$\Delta E = 3F\frac{n(n-1)}{Z}. \tag{51.12}$$

The separation of the terms in the STARK effect thus goes as n^2. The growth of the separation with increasing principal quantum number n is quite understandable: The larger the diameter of the electron's orbit the greater is the potential difference between diametrically opposite points in that orbit.

In order to arrive at a notion of the absolute magnitude of the STARK effect, we must remember that F is measured in atomic units. The unit of electric field intensity is the field produced by a proton at a distance equal to the radius of the first BOHR orbit of hydrogen, viz.:

$$\frac{e}{a^2} = \frac{4.80\times 10^{-10}}{(5.29\times 10^{-9})^2} = 1.71\times 10^7 \text{ e.s.u.} = 5.142\times 10^9 \text{ Volt/cm}. \tag{51.13}$$

The unit of energy is equal to twice the RYDBERG energy 2.19×10^5 cm^{-1}. Thus, if the field is measured in Volt/cm and the energy in cm^{-1}, we obtain

$$E = \left[-\frac{1.097\times 10^5}{n^2}Z^2 + \frac{F}{15620}\frac{n}{Z}(n_1 - n_2)\right] \text{cm}^{-1}. \tag{51.14}$$

The STARK splitting, especially of the highly excited terms, may attain large values. For $n=5$ the separation between the outer components, $n_1=4$, $n_2=0$ and $n_2=4$, $n_1=0$, in a field of 500000 Volt/cm is as much as

$$32\times 5\times 8 = 1280 \text{ cm}^{-1},$$

i.e., almost equal to the separation of the terms $n=5$ and $n=6$ in the absence of fields (1400 cm^{-1}).

The appearance of the eigenfunctions belonging to the stationary states of the STARK effect is of interest. For the case $n_1 > n_2$, as shown in Sect. 6, the electron is predominantly on the positive side of the z-axis. Since for positive z the potential energy of the electron and the external field, eFz, is positive it is not surprising that the energy belonging to the states $n_1 > n_2$ is raised by the electric field. For a view of the asymmetry of the charge distribution, we refer the reader to Fig. 8 of Sect. 6 which gives the charge distribution of the state $n=4$, $n_1=2$, $n_2=0$ and $m=1$. Only for the case $n_1=n_2$ is there no asymmetry[1].

The experimental verification of formula (51.11) is very good[2]. Because of the dependence of the term splitting on n, the main contribution to the splitting of a spectral line comes from the upper level. The selection rule reads as usual: $\Delta m=0$ for light polarized parallel to the field, $\Delta m=\pm 1$ for perpendicular polarization. There is no selection rule with respect to the parabolic quantum numbers $n_1 n_2$, although the transitions which involve a change in the sign of $n_1 - n_2$ are mostly weak. In our approximation the STARK splitting of every term, and therefore also of every spectral line, is an integral multiple of $\frac{3}{2}F$ atomic units $= F/15620$ cm^{-1}. The most convenient designation of a line consists of giving the shift relative to the line without field in units of $F/15620$ and specifying in addition the polarization (π parallel, σ perpendicular to the electric field).

---

[1] Cf., F. G. SLACK: Ann. d. Phys. **82**, 576 (1927) Fig. 2.

[2] Quantitative verification in the work of K. SJÖGREN, Z. Physik **77**, 290 (1932).

That has been done, for example, in Fig. 25. Fig. 25a shows the splitting of the second and third levels of hydrogen and the associated transitions which are allowed. The numbers which accompany the transitions designate the shift of the corresponding spectral line in units of $F/15620\ \text{cm}^{-1}$. In Fig. 25b, the resulting splitting patterns of the BALMER line H_α is shown; the length of the line has been taken to be proportional to the intensity of the line which has been calculated from formulas (65.1) and (65.2). For the purpose of comparison, Fig. 25c shows the photometric curves observed by MARK and WIERL for light polarized in directions parallel and perpendicular to the field respectively. For the higher terms of the BALMER series, see

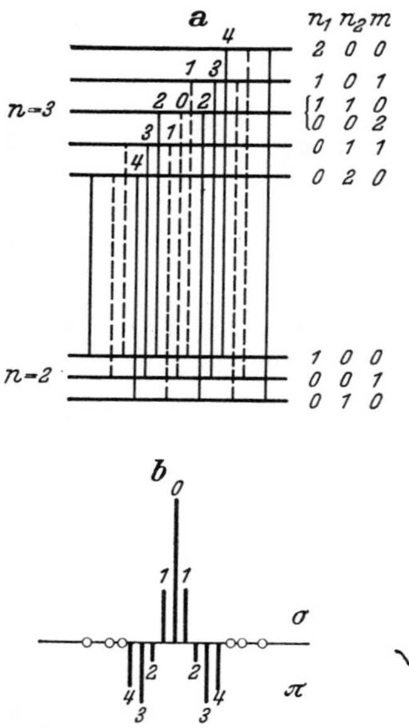

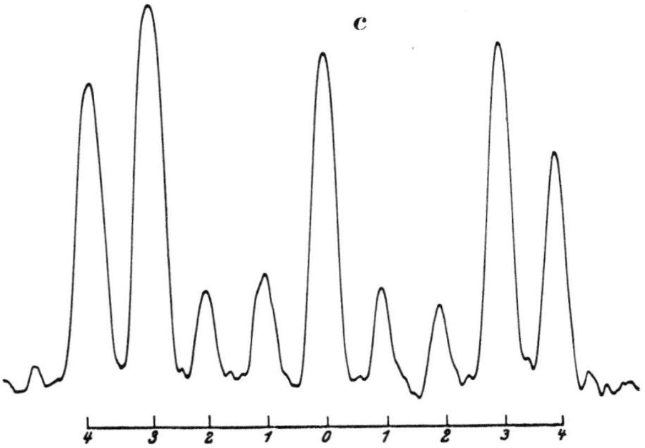

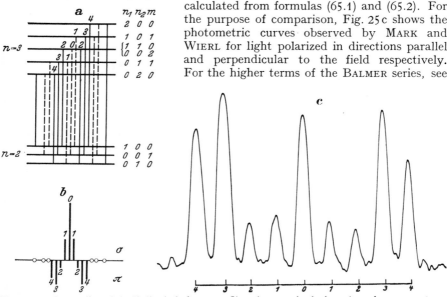

Fig. 25a—c. STARK effect of the H_α-line in hxdrogen. a. Gives the energy level scheme (π- and σ-components are solid and dotted vertical lines, respectively). b. The theoretical splitting diagram of the spectral lines: The length of a line is proportional to its intensity (circles denote lines with very small intensity). The number against each line is the shift relative to the field-free line in units of $F/15620$. c. An experimental photometric curve (MARK and WIERL), which corresponds to the theoretical Fig. 25b (with π- and σ-components on the same picture).

E. SCHRÖDINGER, Abhandlungen zur Wellenmechanik, p. 116; H. MARK and R. WIERL, Z. Physik **53**, 526; **55**, 156; **57**, 494 (1929).

52. The quadratic STARK effect. With increasing field strength a term which is quadratic in the electric field appears in addition to the linear STARK effect, and a mixing of levels having different principal quantum numbers takes place. In order to evaluate the quadratic effect we must consider the second order perturbation of the "eigenvalue" Z_1 of the first of the differential equation (51.3). According to the general SCHRÖDINGER perturbation theory the second order perturbation is given by

$$Z_1^{(2)} = \left(\frac{1}{4}F\right)^2 \sum_{n_1' \neq n_1} \frac{|(\xi^2)_{n_1 n_1'}|^2}{Z_1^{(0)}(n_1) - Z_1^{(0)}(n_1')}\,. \tag{52.1}$$

The non-diagonal elements of the matrix of ξ^2 which occur in (52.1) vanish if $n_1' > n_1 + 2$ or $n_1' < n_1 - 2$. For the non-vanishing matrix elements the following values are obtained[1]:

$$\left.\begin{aligned} (\xi^2)_{n_1, n_1-1} &= -2\varepsilon^{-2}(2n_1+m)\sqrt{n_1(n_1+m)}\,, \\ (\xi^2)_{n_1, n_1-2} &= \varepsilon^{-2}\sqrt{n_1(n_1-1)(n_1+m)(n_1+m-1)}\,. \end{aligned}\right\} \tag{52.2}$$

[1] Derivation by means of the generating function for the LAGUERRE functions (3.40).

The separation parameters Z_1 in zeroth approximation are given by (51.5), thus

$$Z_1^{(0)}(n_1) - Z_1^{(0)}(n_1') = \varepsilon(n_1 - n_1').$$

Evaluating the above we obtain

$$Z_1^{(2)} = -\tfrac{1}{32} F^2 \varepsilon^{-5} (m + 2n_1 + 1)\left[8m^2 + 34(2m n_1 + 2n_1^2 + m + 2n_1) + 36\right].$$

Adding to the above the corresponding expression for $Z_2^{(2)}$ gives $Z^{(2)}$ and in view of (51.9) one obtains:

$$\begin{aligned} Z &= Z^{(0)} + Z^{(1)} + Z^{(2)} \\ &= \varepsilon n + \tfrac{3}{2} F n \varepsilon^{-2}(n_1 - n_2) - \tfrac{1}{16} F^2 n \varepsilon^{-5}\left[17n^2 + 51(n_1 - n_2)^2 - 9m^2 + 19\right]. \end{aligned}$$

This relation between Z and ε yields the following value for the energy in second approximation:

$$\left.\begin{aligned} E_2 = -\frac{1}{2}\varepsilon^2 = -\frac{Z^2}{2n^2} + \frac{3}{2} F \frac{n}{Z}(n_1 - n_2) - \\ -\frac{1}{16} F^2 \left(\frac{n}{Z}\right)^4 \left[17n^2 - 3(n_1 - n_2)^2 - 9m^2 + 19.\right] \end{aligned}\right\} \quad (52.3)$$

According to (52.3) the quadratic STARK effect, unlike the linear STARK effect, depends not only on n, n_1 and n_2 but also on the magnetic quantum number m. On the other hand, the second order effect remains unaltered on interchange of n_1 and n_2; thus, in so far as the second order perturbation is concerned, it does not matter whether the electron is more frequently in locations of high or low potential. Next, we note that the quadratic STARK effect always results in a lowering of the levels. Since $n_1 - n_2 < n - m$, the quantity inside the parentheses of the last term of (52.3) is always greater than $8n^2$, and consequently the depression of the term value is always greater than $F^2 n^6/2Z^4$. For $n \gtrsim 3$ this is greater than $360 F^2/Z^4$. On the other hand, it also follows from (52.3) that the components of the second quantum state which are affected to the greatest extent (namely, $n=2$, $n_1=1$, $n_2=m=0$) are shifted by only $84F^2/Z^4$, i.e., to a lesser extent than any of the higher states. Thus, all the lines of the BALMER series are shifted in the direction of smaller wave numbers, i.e., toward the red end of the spectrum. For example, measuring F in Volt/cm and wave numbers in cm^{-1}, the shift for the STARK components "+4" and "−4" for the line H_α (cf., Fig. 24a) amounts to:

$$\frac{2.19\times 10^5}{16}\left(\frac{F}{5.14\times 10^9}\right)^2 (81\times 160 - 16\times 84) \approx \left(\frac{F}{400000}\right)^2 \text{cm}^{-1}.$$

For a field strength of 400000 Volt/cm, for which the separation of the outermost components of H_α amounts to as much as 200 cm^{-1}, the red shift produced by the quadratic STARK effect amounts to only 1 cm^{-1}. On the other hand, for the same field strength, the outermost of the intense components (π 18) of H_γ, (transition $n=5$, $n_1=4$, $n_2=0$, $m=0$ to $n=2$, $n_1=1$, $n_2=0$, $m=0$) which are separated by approximately 900 cm^{-1}, undergo a red shift by as much as 22 cm^{-1}.

The perturbation expansion was carried through by ISHIDA and HIYAMA[1] up to terms of third order in the field strength F. Their result is

$$E_3 = E_2 + \frac{3}{32} F^3 \left(\frac{n}{Z}\right)^7 (n_1 - n_2)\left(23n^2 - (n_1 - n_2)^2 + 11m^2 + 39\right). \quad (52.4)$$

[1] Y. ISHIDA and S. HIYAMA: Sci. Pap. Inst. phys. and chem. Res., Tokyo **1928**, Nr. 152.

For the two outermost components ($\pm\pi 18$) of the H_γ line, for instance[1], the frequency shift $\Delta\nu$ (in cm^{-1}), obtained from (52.4) is

$$\Delta\nu = \pm 1152.4\,F - 127.1\,F^2 \pm 28.3\,F^3, \tag{52.5}$$

where the field strength F is expressed in units of 10^6 Volt/cm.

The experimental dependence of the STARK effect on field strength has been investigated thoroughly by RAUSCH V. TRAUBENBERG[2]. The agreement with theory is excellent. For the $\pi 18$ components of H_γ, for instance, the experimental $\Delta\nu$ has been measured up to fields of about 10^6 Volt/cm and the presence of even the *third* order term in (52.5) has been verified at the higher field strengths. A picture of the STARK effect on some lines in the BALMER series is shown in Fig. 26. The field strength increases from the bottom of the picture towards the top (the maximum field is 1.1×10^6 Volt/cm). Note that the components on the red side (to the left) of the field-free (vertical) lines are displaced more than the violet components (quadratic STARK effect). Note also that each line ceases to exist above a critical field strength F_0. This quenching of lines will be discussed in Sect. 54.

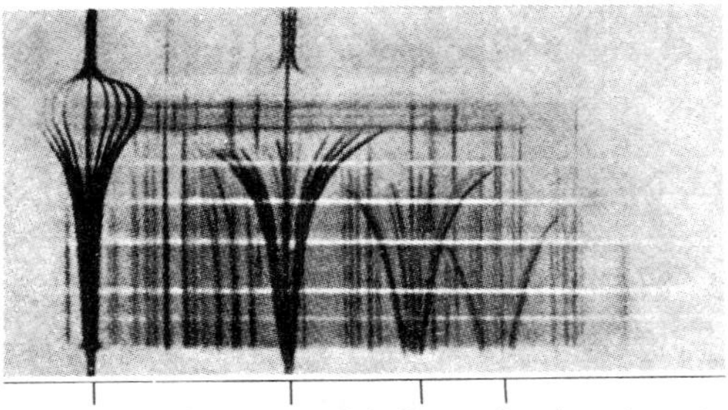

Fig. 26. STARK effect on some of the BALMER lines (experiments by RAUSCH V. TRAUBENBERG). The electric field strength increases from the bottom of the picture upwards, the maximum value (a little below the top of the picture) is 1.14 million Volt/cm, the horizontal white lines are lines of constant field strength.

53. STARK effect for strong fields[3]. The evaluation of terms of fourth order (and higher) in the field strength, according to perturbation theory, would be very tedious. For a hydrogen atom in a very strong field F, it is more convenient to solve the pair of differential equation (51.3) by an approximation method which does not involve expansions in powers of F. A suitable technique (especially for states with a reasonably large principal quantum number n) is the WENTZEL-KRAMERS-BRILLOUIN[4] (W.K.B.) method. We shall merely outline a calculation by LANCZOS[5], using this method

We eliminate first derivatives from (51.3) by substituting as new wave functions

$$\chi_1 = u_1\sqrt{\xi}, \qquad \chi_2 = u_2\sqrt{\eta}. \tag{53.1}$$

Substituting χ_1 into the first equation of (51.3) we get

$$\frac{d^2\chi_1}{d\xi_1^2} + \Phi_1(\xi)\,\chi_1 = 0, \qquad \Phi_1(\xi) = -\frac{1}{4}\,\varepsilon^2 + \frac{Z_1}{\xi} - \frac{m^2-1}{4\,\xi^2} - \frac{1}{4}F\,\xi, \tag{53.2}$$

where $\varepsilon = \sqrt{-2E}$. χ_2 obeys a similar equation. The function $\Phi_1(\xi)$ is essentially the "local kinetic energy" of the electron at position ξ. Φ_1 is plotted against ξ in Fig. 27, both for a finite field strength F and for zero field. In the region between the two classical turning points ξ_1 and ξ_2, the "kinetic energy" is positive

[1] For further details see ref. [*5*], p. 403.
[2] H. RAUSCH V. TRAUBENBERG: Z. Physik **54**, 307; **56**, 254 (1929); **62**, 289 (1930); **71**, 291 (1931). — Naturwiss. **18**, 417 (1930).
[3] For details see ref. [*10*], Sect. 32.
[4] G. WENTZEL: Z. Physik **38**, 518 (1926). — H. A. KRAMERS: Z. Physik **39**, 828 (1926). — L. BRILLOUIN: C. R. Acad. Sci., Paris **183**, 24 (1926).
[5] C. LANCZOS: Z. Physik **65**, 431 (1930).

and the wave function χ_1 is oscillatory and approximately of the form

$$\chi_1(\xi) = a\,\Phi_1^{-\frac{1}{4}}(\xi)\cos\left(\int_{\xi_1}^{\xi}\sqrt{\Phi_1(x)}\,dx - \frac{\pi}{4}\right). \tag{53.3}$$

Since the wave function must be bounded, it must decrease exponentially on either side of the two turning points ξ_1 and ξ_2. From this requirement and considerations of continuity one can obtain the essential result of the W.K.B. method for our purpose, namely the relation

$$\int_{\xi_1}^{\xi_2}\sqrt{\Phi_1(x)}\,dx = (n_1 + \tfrac{1}{2})\,\pi. \tag{53.4}$$

In (53.4), n_1 is an integer identical with the parabolic quantum number n_1 used in Sects. 6 and 51.

The relation (53.4) is only an approximation, but a fairly accurate one even for small values of n_1, and very accurate for large n_1. Using the definition (53.2) of Φ_1, the Eq. (53.4) gives a relation between the parameters ε and Z_1 for any value of F and m. From the equation for χ_2 one obtains a similar relation between ε and Z_2. These two relations, plus the condition $Z_1+Z_2=Z$, finally give a value for the energy parameter ε corresponding to any value of the field strength F.

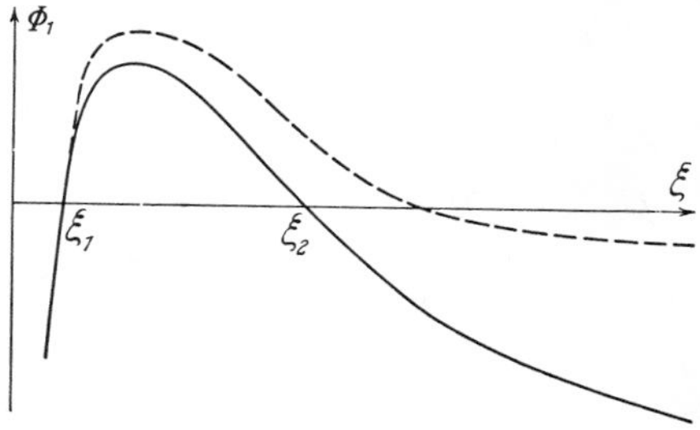

Fig. 27. The energy function $\Phi_1(\xi)$ plotted against ξ.

Such values for the energy parameter ε as a function of F were obtained numerically by LANCZOS. His results approximate those of the third order perturbation approximation (52.4) closely, except for very strong fields. For the violet component $+\pi 18$ of the H_γ line and $F=10^6$ Volt/cm, for instance, LANCZOS' calculations give a shift of about 1052 cm^{-1}, compared with 1058 cm^{-1} from the third order approximation (52.5). For still stronger fields the difference would be much larger, but the field strengths at which observations can be made are limited by the quenching effect (see Sect. 54). For fields just below the critical (quenching) value the experimental results are in even better agreement with LANCZOS' calculations than with the third order result.

54. Ionization by the electric field. Quenching of the lines in the STARK effect[1]. Our discussion of the STARK effect must be supplemented by a very important point, namely, that the electric field is capable of altogether removing an electron from the atom. Looking at the potential energy of the electron

$$-V = -\frac{Z}{r} + Fz,$$

we see that the atomic center is not the only location at which the potential is a minimum; at distances which are sufficiently far from the atom in the direction of the anode, i.e., negative z, the potential is even lower. It is well known from wave-mechanics that whenever two potential troughs exist it is always possible for the electron to pass from one trough (the atom) to the other (the anode). Evidently, once the electron has passed through the potential barrier between the two troughs it will not return to the atom but will be accelerated toward the

[1] Cf., C. LANCZOS, Z. Physik **62**, 518 (1930), and especially **68**, 204 (1931); J. R. OPPENHEIMER, Phys. Rev. **31**, 66 (1928).

anode; i.e., the atom will be left ionized. Experimentally the ionization from a given level becomes apparent in that the spectral lines initiated at that level are weakened.

Qualitatively, it is readily seen which circumstances are favorable for ionization. Above all, the radius of the electron's orbit must be large, i.e., the principal quantum number must be high. For a given principal quantum number those states are most easily ionized for which the electron's orbit is predominantly on the anode side of the atom. This is the case for the quantum states having the smallest possible n_1 and the largest possible n_2. Thus, of the terms having a given principal quantum number n, those which lie energetically the lowest are the least stable [cf. Eq. (51.11)], and, accordingly, as the field strength increases the "red" STARK components of each spectral line disappear first. This is exactly in accord with experimental observation, e.g., as in the photograph of the STARK effect by RAUSCH V. TRAUBENBERG (Fig. 26) in which the field intensity increases from bottom to top. All the lines suddenly die out at a certain field strength; the lines starting from levels of high principal quantum number n are seen to die out at lower field strengths than the lines coming from levels of lower principal quantum numbers (e.g., H_ζ before H_ε, and the latter before H_δ, etc.). Furthermore, for each line the red STARK component dies out at lower field strengths than the violet component.

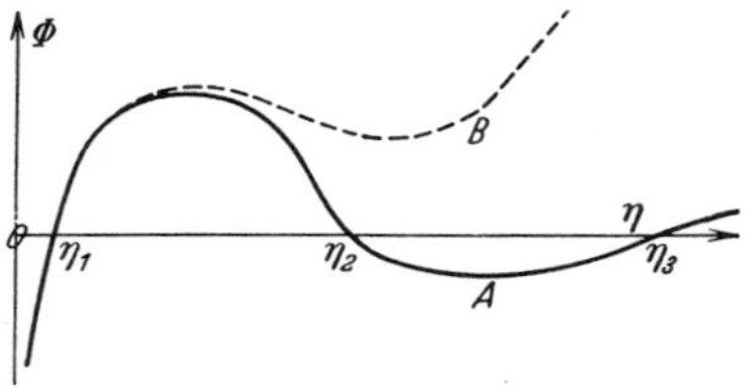

Fig. 28. The energy function $\Phi_2(\eta)$ plotted against η. Curve A is for fields of medium strength, curve B for very strong fields.

α) *Ionization limit according to classical mechanics.* For the purpose of pursuing the question of the ionization by the field quantitatively, we shall examine the differential equation for the part of the eigenfunction which depends on η. By definition the parabolic coordinate $\eta = r - z$ is large for large negative values of z, i.e., near the anode. The fact that the potential energy of the electron has a minimum near the anode is expressed in the "kinetic energy of the electron in the η direction"

$$\Phi_2(\eta) = -\frac{1}{4}\varepsilon^2 + \frac{Z_2}{\eta} - \frac{m^2-1}{4\eta^2} + \frac{1}{4}F\eta. \tag{54.1}$$

When η is large, $\Phi_2(\eta)$ is positive—contrary to the energy function $\Phi_1(\xi)$ in (53.2).

The possible types of behavior of $\Phi_2(\eta)$ are shown in Fig. 28 in which curve A corresponds to small and intermediate and B to high values of the field strength For small values of η, curve A behaves quite similarly to the curve for $\Phi_1(\xi)$ in Fig. 27; however, for large η it turns upward again and becomes positive for $\eta > \eta_3$. The "normal" motion of the electron, which we have treated so far, takes place in the "inner" region between η_1 and η_2; the ionization consists of the electron's passing into the outer region of positive kinetic energy beyond η_3. The "inner" and "outer" regions are separated by a potential barrier the height of which is of order of magnitude $|E| = \frac{1}{2}\varepsilon^2$ and the width of which is of order $|E|/F$.

As the field strength increases, the potential barrier becomes steadily lower and narrower until it finally disappears (curve B). At that stage the "inner" and "outer" regions are no longer separated by a potential barrier and ionization is possible even according to classical mechanics. The potential barrier disappears when the minimum of the function Φ_2 has the value zero, i.e., when both Φ_2 and its derivative vanish. For example, for $m=1$ one obtains

$$F_0 = \frac{E^2}{4Z_2}, \tag{54.2}$$

where F_0 is the value of F for which the expression (54.1) and its derivative is zero. According to classical mechanics, ionization would take place only if F exceeds this critical[1] value F_0. Using LANCZOS' expressions (see Sect. 53) for E and Z_2 as a function of F, one can solve (54.2) for F_0. For the "reddest component" of the level with $n=5$, which is the initial state for the H_γ-line, F_0 is about 1.1×10^6 Volt/cm. Experimentally the reddest component of H_γ is already quenched for fields of about 0.7×10^6 Volt/cm. This lowering of the critical field strength is due to the quantum mechanical effect of barrier penetration, which we shall discuss now.

β) Ionization according to wave-mechanics. We only need to deal with case *A* in which the "inner" and "outer" potential troughs are well defined and one can speak of the electron as being either in the atom or removed from it. Evidently up to the second zero the eigenfunction behaves almost exactly as previously, and beyond η_2 it must, as before, assume an exponential character. Thus, we are confronted with the same problem as in the theory of radioactivity (transmission of a potential step). Assuming that the electron is bound to the atom at time $t=0$, the calculation gives an outward current of electrons for all times $t>0$. Naturally, the current must be interpreted to mean that there exists a certain probability per second that the electron will escape from the atom.

A rigorous treatment of the problem has been carried through by LANCZOS. The treatment is based on the fact that in the presence of an infinitely extended potential trough there actually exist no discrete eigenvalues; rather, to any arbitrary eigenvalue there belongs an eigenfunction and the eigenfunctions differ only in that their amplitudes inside the atom vary in magnitude. This enables one to build up from these eigenfunctions a wave-function the amplitude of which vanishes exactly outside the atom. The time development of the wave-function automatically yields the migration of the charge from the atom.

We shall only use a less rigorous derivation involving the W.K.B. method, as used in the elementary theory of α-decay: Between the two classical turning points η_1 and η_2, the wave function $\chi_2(\eta)$ has the form of (53.3), with ξ and Φ_1 replaced by η and by Φ_2 [see Eq. (54.1)]. The normalization constant a in (53.3) is determined by the condition that the integral of χ_2^2 over the "classical region", from η_1 to η_2, be unity. In this integral the $\cos^2$-factor varies more rapidly than the rest of the integrand and we replace it by its average value of $\frac{1}{2}$. With this approximation, the normalization constant a is given by

$$\frac{1}{a^2} = \frac{1}{2}\int_{\eta_1}^{\eta_2} d\eta\, |\Phi_2(\eta)|^{-\frac{1}{2}}. \tag{54.3}$$

Inside the potential barrier ($\eta_2<\eta<\eta_3$), the wave function decreases exponentially[2]

$$\chi(\eta) = \tfrac{1}{2}\, a\, |\Phi(\eta)|^{-\frac{1}{4}} \exp\left[-\int_{\eta_2}^{\eta} \sqrt{|\Phi(x)|}\, dx\right]. \tag{54.4}$$

Outside the barrier ($\eta>\eta_3$), the kinetic energy is again positive and the wave function oscillatory, but its amplitude is decreased by a constant exponential

[1] In (54.2), E and Z_2 are the energy and charge parameter evaluated for field strength F_0.
[2] We drop the subscript 2 from χ and Φ.

(barrier penetration) factor

$$\chi(\eta) = \frac{1}{2} a \,|\Phi(\eta)|^{-\frac{1}{4}} \exp\left[-\int_{\eta_2}^{\eta_3} \sqrt{|\Phi(x)|}\, dx\right] \cos\left[\int_{\eta_3}^{\eta} \sqrt{|\Phi(x)|}\, dx + \frac{\pi}{4}\right]. \quad (54.5)$$

We are mainly interested in the current S outside the barrier ($\eta > \eta_3$). Since the "velocity" of the electron at the point η is $\sqrt{\Phi(\eta)}$, this current is simply $\chi^2 \sqrt{\Phi}$, where χ is given by (54.5). In the expression for χ^2 we again replace $\cos^2$ by its average value of $\frac{1}{2}$. In this approximation the current S is, as it should be, independent of the position η. Using (54.3), the current leaving the atom is then

$$S = \frac{\exp\left[-2\int_{\eta_2}^{\eta_3} \sqrt{|\Phi(\eta)|}\, d\eta\right]}{4\int_{\eta_1}^{\eta_2} \Phi^{-\frac{1}{2}}(\eta)\, d\eta}. \quad (54.6)$$

With Φ given in atomic units, as it is in (54.1), the expression (54.6) then represents the probability of ionization of the atom (in a particular state) during one atomic unit of time (2.4×10^{-17} sec).

Experimentally one does not observe the ionization directly, but the quenching by a field F of spectral lines due to radiative transitions from a particular initial atomic state to lower ones. Such spectral lines are suppressed if the probability for ionization of the initial state is greater than the probability for radiative transitions from this state. The latter probabilities (see Sect. 63, Table 15) are of the order of magnitude of 10^8 sec^{-1} or about 10^{-9} atomic units of frequency and the quenching of the spectral lines will be appreciable if the value (54.6) for S is also of order 10^{-9} or larger. When the field F is very near the "classical critical field strength" F_0, S is of order unity; thus S is of order 10^{-9} for an appreciably *smaller* field strength F_Q, the "quantum mechanical critical field strength". At these fields the smallness of S is due to the exponential term in (54.6), which depends critically on the height and width of the potential barrier and hence on F. Hence a small change in F away from F_Q produces a relatively large change in S (e.g., a 3% change in F changes S by a factor of two). Hence the intensity of a spectral line changes from essentially its field-free value to a very small value for quite a small increase in the field strength from below to above F_Q.

Numerical values for F_Q were calculated by LANCZOS[1] for a number of atomic states of hydrogen. His values for the initial states of the outermost components of the H_γ and H_ε lines, for instance, are

	H_γ (red)	H_γ (violet)	H_ε (red)	H_ε (violet)
F_Q	0.69	1.01	0.20	0.32

with F_Q in units of 10^6 Volt/cm. These values are appreciably lower than the corresponding classical values F_0 and agree fairly well with the experimental values. The rapidity of the change of intensity with field strength is also verified experimentally (see Sect. 52, Fig. 26).

55. STARK effect of the fine structure of hydrogen[2]. The theory of the STARK effect which we have presented so far has been based on the SCHRÖDINGER equation without considering relativistic corrections or the spin of the electron.

[1] C. LANCZOS: Z. Physik **68**, 204 (1931).
[2] Cf. V. ROJANSKY: Phys. Rev. **33**, 1 (1929). — R. SCHLAPP: Proc. Roy. Soc. Lond. **119**, 313 (1928). — G. LÜDERS: Ann. d. Phys. [6] **8**, 301 (1951).

This is certainly justified for electric field intensities which are ordinarily encountered in practice, namely, 100000 Volt/cm or greater which give rise to STARK splittings of 10 to several 1000 cm^{-1}. On the other hand, our treatment is not applicable to fields of less than about 1000 Volt/cm because then the STARK splitting is of the same order of magnitude as the fine structure.

α) STARK effect small compared to fine structure. First of all we shall deal with the case of very weak fields in which the STARK splitting is small compared to the separation of neighboring fine structure levels. In this case the quantum states have definite values of the principal quantum number n, the inner quantum number j (magnitude of the total angular momentum), and the magnetic quantum number m (component of the total angular momentum in the direction of the field, M_z). The first two quantum numbers determine the energy in the absence of field; our assumption that the STARK effect be small compared to the fine structure is equivalent to the assumption that eigenfunctions belonging to different fine structure levels are not mixed to any appreciable extent. M_z, on the other hand, is a constant of the motion for arbitrary field strengths. However, the orbital angular momentum l is a good quantum number only for vanishing field; if the field has a finite value, however small, l is not quantized[1]. Thus, in order to calculate the splitting we only need to know the matrix elements of the perturbing electric field which connect the states njm, $l=j-\frac{1}{2}$ with the states njm, $l=j+\frac{1}{2}$. The PAULI eigenfunctions of the states in question are

$$u_+ = \frac{R_{n,j+\frac{1}{2}}(r)}{\sqrt{2j+2}} \begin{pmatrix} \sqrt{j-m+1}\; Y_{j+\frac{1}{2},m-\frac{1}{2}} \\ \sqrt{j+m+1}\; Y_{j+\frac{1}{2},m+\frac{1}{2}} \end{pmatrix}, \quad u_- = \frac{R_{n,j-\frac{1}{2}}}{\sqrt{2j}} \begin{pmatrix} \sqrt{j+m}\; Y_{j-\frac{1}{2},m-\frac{1}{2}} \\ -\sqrt{j-m}\; Y_{j-\frac{1}{2},m+\frac{1}{2}} \end{pmatrix}. \tag{55.1}$$

and the corresponding matrix elements are given by

$$\left.\begin{aligned} \sum_\sigma \int u_-^* z\, u_+\, d\tau = \int_0^{+\infty} r^2 dr \cdot R_{n,j-\frac{1}{2}} R_{n,j+\frac{1}{2}}\, r \cdot \frac{1}{2\sqrt{j(j+1)}} \times \\ \times \Big[\sqrt{(j+m)(j-m+1)} \int Y^*_{j-\frac{1}{2},m-\frac{1}{2}} Y_{j+\frac{1}{2},m-\frac{1}{2}} \cos\vartheta\, d\omega - \\ - \sqrt{(j-m)(j+m+1)} \int Y^*_{j-\frac{1}{2},m+\frac{1}{2}} Y_{j+\frac{1}{2},m+\frac{1}{2}} \cos\vartheta\, d\omega\Big]. \end{aligned}\right\} \tag{55.2}$$

Using (A.21), the integration over angles can readily be carried out and the quantity in the parentheses of (55.2) becomes

$$\frac{1}{2\sqrt{j(j+1)}}\left[(j+m)(j-m+1) - (j-m)(j+m+1)\right] = \frac{m}{\sqrt{j(j+1)}}.$$

The integration over r can be carried out in exactly the same way as at the beginning of Sect. 52 and yields

$$-\tfrac{3}{2} n \sqrt{n^2 - (j+\tfrac{1}{2})^2}.$$

Since the diagonal elements of the perturbation matrix

$$\int u_+^* z\, u_+\, d\tau = \int u_-^* z\, u_-\, d\tau = 0$$

vanish, the part of the matrix belonging to the quantum numbers njm is given simply by

$$-\frac{3n}{4} \frac{\sqrt{n^2-(j+\frac{1}{2})^2}}{j(j+1)} \cdot F m \begin{pmatrix} 0 & 1 \\ 1 & 0 \end{pmatrix}. \tag{55.3}$$

[1] We neglect the LAMB shift, at the moment.

The eigenvalues of the matrix are

$$\varepsilon_m^{\pm} = \pm \frac{3}{4} \sqrt{n^2 - \left(j + \frac{1}{2}\right)^2} \frac{n\, m}{j(j+1)} F. \tag{55.4}$$

The eigenfunctions are simply the sum and the difference respectively of the eigenfunctions without field (55.1). Thus, each fine structure level is split by the electric field into $2j+1$ equidistant terms labelled by $m = -j \ldots, +j$. The separation of neighboring terms amounts to $\frac{n}{2} \frac{F}{15620} \frac{\sqrt{n^2 - (j+\frac{1}{2})^2}}{j(j+1)}$ cm^{-1}, and the splitting increases with increasing n and decreasing j. For any given n, the term belonging to the highest value of j ($j = n - \frac{1}{2}$) is not split since that term is not degenerate with respect to the orbital quantum number l (l has the fixed value $j - \frac{1}{2} = n - 1$). For example, for the ground state of the BALMER series, $n = 2$, only the fine structure level $j = \frac{1}{2}$ is split and, because $m = \pm\frac{1}{2}$, it is split into two equidistant levels separated by

$$\Delta\varepsilon \equiv \varepsilon^+ - \varepsilon^- = 2\sqrt{3}\, F. \tag{55.5}$$

The splitting is of the same order of magnitude as the splitting of the second quantum state produced by the usual linear STARK effect which, according to (51.11), amounts to $6F$.

We have so far considered the two states for a given j-value to have the same energy without a field. In reality the energies of the $l = j - \frac{1}{2}$ and $j + \frac{1}{2}$ states differ slightly due to the LAMB shift (Sect. 21). The LAMB shift for $j = \frac{1}{2}$ is a reasonably small fraction of the fine structure splitting δ, (energy difference between states of different j) and is negligible for $j \geqq \frac{3}{2}$. The approximate expression (55.4) holds only if the STARK effect is small compared with the fine structure, but large compared with the LAMB shift. We derive now an expression which also holds for extremely weak fields, where the LAMB shift cannot be neglected, at least for states with $j = \frac{1}{2}$.

Consider the states with $j = \frac{1}{2}$ and fixed value of n and of m ($+\frac{1}{2}$ or $-\frac{1}{2}$). We use a representation in terms of the field-free eigenfunctions u_s and u_p, corresponding to $l = 0$ and 1, respectively. We take the energy of the field-free P-state as our zero-point and call the energy displacement (LAMB shift) of the field-free S-state L. Our perturbation HAMILTONian H' is then (55.3) plus a diagonal matrix

$$H' = -n\sqrt{n^2 - 1}\, m F \begin{pmatrix} 0 & 1 \\ 1 & 0 \end{pmatrix} + L \begin{pmatrix} 1 & 0 \\ 0 & 0 \end{pmatrix}, \tag{55.6}$$

where the lower row refers to u_p. The two eigenfunctions and corresponding eigenvalues ε of (55.6) are given by[1]

$$u = a\, u_s + b\, u_p, \quad \frac{a}{b} = \frac{2n\sqrt{n^2 - 1}\, m F}{L \pm \sqrt{L^2 + 4(n^2 - 1)(n\, m F)^2}}, \tag{55.7}$$

$$\varepsilon = \tfrac{1}{2} L \pm \tfrac{1}{2} \sqrt{L^2 + 4(n^2 - 1)(n\, m F)^2}. \tag{55.8}$$

If the LAMB shift L is small compared with the STARK effect expression $S = n\sqrt{n^2 - 1}\, |mF|$ (for $n = 2$, the two expressions are equal for a field strength of about 475 Volt/cm) the present results essentially reduce to our previous, less accurate, ones: $a/b = \pm 1$ for the two states, and their energies are given by (55.4) plus a shift of $+\frac{1}{2} L$ for each of the two states. If S is small compared

[1] Neglecting the ratio of STARK effect to fine structure splitting, i.e., for $F \ll \delta$.

with L, the two eigenstates are almost pure u_s and u_p, respectively, and the energies differ from the field-free values only by terms *quadratic* in the field strength, namely $\pm S^2/L$. In Fig. 29b the energy splitting between the $2S_{\frac{1}{2}}$ and $2P_{\frac{1}{2}}$-states is plotted as a function of field strength. Fig. 29b is an enlargement of the low field portion of Fig. 29a, but corrected for the LAMB shift.

β) Transition region. If the field strength is such (e.g., about 3000 Volts/cm for $n=2$) that the fine structure and STARK effect are comparable, the calculations of the level splitting are quite complicated. Only n and m are good quantum numbers, but neither j and l, nor the parabolic quantum numbers, are. The secular equations have to be solved separately for each value of n and m to find

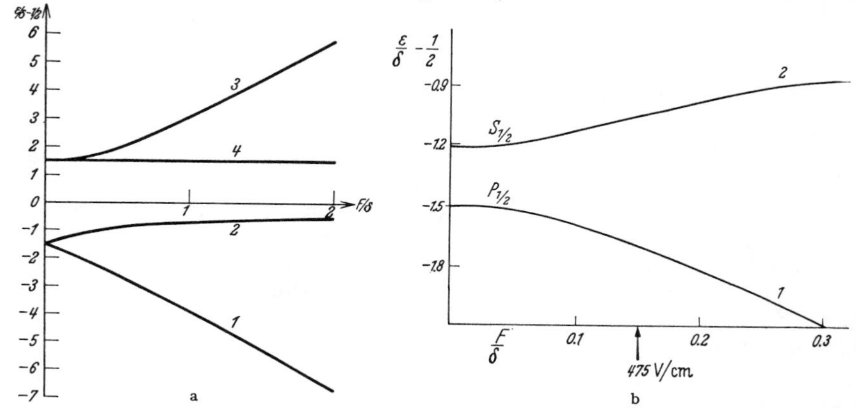

Fig. 29a and b. The STARK effect on the fine structure of the states with $n=2$ in hydrogen. Abscissa is the field strength F measured in units of $(\frac{2}{3})$ 15620 $\delta=2910$ Volt/cm, where $\delta=0.365$ cm^{-1} is the field-free fine structure splitting. Ordinate is the level energy, in units of δ, relative to the field-free mean energy. a. Level splitting (up to $F\sim 2\delta$) with the LAMB shift neglected. Note the remnant of fine structure even for strong fields in components 2 and 4. b. Level splitting for weak fields (up to $F\sim 0.3\,\delta$) of components 1 and 2, with the LAMB shift included.

the eigenvalues and eigenfunctions of each of $2(n-|m|)$ eigenstates. Such calculations were carried out by ROJANSKI[1] and, more accurately, by LÜDERS[1] for $n=2$, 3 and 4.

We reproduce in Fig. 29a the dependence on field strength F of the energies of the states with $n=2$ and positive m. We shall not discuss the results further, except for some general properties: If F (in atomic units) is small compared with the field-free fine structure splitting δ, the results essentially reduce to those of Sect. 55α. However, in addition to the energy shift (55.4) (and zero for $j=n-\frac{1}{2}$), one finds additional shifts of order F^2/δ. If F is larger than δ, one can expand the results in powers of δ/F. The leading terms are identical with the results of Sect. 51. The next term in the expansion for the energy is independent of F and is of the order of magnitude of δ.

c) STARK effect in helium.

56. The STARK effect for weak fields. In the case of helium[2], as well as for all other atoms except hydrogen, the STARK effect produced by relatively weak fields is proportional to the square of the electric field intensity. The first order perturbation in the energy vanishes since the levels are not degenerate with

[1] V. ROJANSKI: Phys. Rev. **33**, 1 (1929). — G. LÜDERS: Ann. d. Phys. [6] **8**, 301 (1951). See also ref. [*10*], Sect. 34b.

[2] Cf. J. S. FOSTER: Proc. Roy. Soc. Lond. **117**, 137 (1928.)

respect to the orbital quantum number l. Therefore, the shift of a level i produced by the electric field is given by the SCHRÖDINGER formula for the second order perturbation in the energy

$$E_i^{(2)} = \sum_k \frac{|H_{ik}|^2}{E_i - E_k}, \tag{56.1}$$

in which H_{ik} are the matrix elements of the perturbation and E_i, E_k are the energies belonging to the levels i and k of the atom in the absence of fields.

Thus, we must form the matrix elements of the perturbation energy produced by the external field,

$$H_{ik} = F \int u_i^* \, (z_1 + z_2) \, u_k \, d\tau, \tag{56.2}$$

and we shall be particularly interested in those matrix elements for which the states i and k have nearly the same unperturbed energy.

Since the perturbing potential

$$F(z_1 + z_2)$$

is symmetric with respect to the electrons, H_{ik} vanishes if the states i and k belong to different term systems, since in that case one of the eigenfunctions u_i, u_k is symmetric and the other one is antisymmetric in the electron coordinates. Furthermore, H_{ik} is non-vanishing only if the orbital angular momentum along the direction of the field, $k_z = m$, is the same for both i and k. We restrict ourselves to initial states i in which one electron is in the ground state. We use for our symmetrized (para) or antisymmetrized (ortho) spatial wave functions the approximate product form

$$U = \frac{1}{\sqrt{2}} \left[u_1(1) \, u_{nlm}(2) \pm u_{nlm}(1) \, u_1(2) \right],$$

where u_1 is the single-electron ground state wave function. Further, in the sum over k in (56.1), we shall retain only states k for which one electron is again in the ground state and the other in a state with the *same* principal quantum number, $u_{nl'm'}$. For the states we are neglecting, the energy denominator $(E_i - E_k)$ is much larger than for states differing only in their l-value[1]. Using the appendix Eq. (A.22), one can also show that the matrix element vanishes (for all n') unless the l-values in states i and k differ by ± 1. Substituting the eigenfunctions into (56.2), we obtain for (56.1), in our approximation,

$$E_{nl}^{(2)} = F^2 \left(\frac{|\int z \, u_{nlm} u_{n\,l+1\,m}^* \, d\tau|^2}{E_{nl} - E_{n,l+1}} + \frac{|\int z \, u_{nlm} u_{n\,l-1\,m}^* \, d\tau|^2}{E_{nl} - E_{n,l-1}} \right). \tag{56.3}$$

Thus, the perturbation of the energy level $n\,l$ consists of "interactions" with the levels $l+1$ and $l-1$, and is the larger the closer the "perturbing" levels are to the perturbed level $n\,l$. The integrations can be carried out if we substitute for the eigenfunctions u_{nlm} hydrogenic eigenfunctions with nuclear charge $Z-1$. The angular integrations can be carried out, using (A.22), and the radial integrations by the methods used in Sect. 52.

Thus, one finally obtains the following value for the perturbation in the energy:

$$E_{nlm}^{(2)} = F^2 \frac{9n^2}{4(Z-1)^2(2l+1)} \left[\frac{(n^2 - (l+1)^2)\,((l+1)^2 - m^2)}{(2l+3)\,(E_{nl} - E_{nl+1})} + \frac{(n^2 - l^2)\,(l^2 - m^2)}{(2l-1)\,(E_{nl} - E_{nl-1})} \right]. \tag{56.4}$$

According to the above, the STARK effect terms—in weak fields—depend on the square of the magnetic quantum number m, and, thus, terms which differ

[1] In this approximation we get no STARK effect at all for the ground state of helium.

only in the sign of m are degenerate. Formula (56.4) was first derived by UNSÖLD[1]. The magnitude and the direction of the term shift produced by the field are largely determined by the resonance denominators in (56.4), i.e., by the relative positions of the levels in the helium atom without field. However, as we have noted previously, for a given n and fixed term system the term values generally increase with increasing orbital quantum number l. The two ^1P terms which lie above the ^1D terms form an exception. Thus, except for the ^1P terms, the first term inside the parentheses of (56.4) is negative and the second term is positive. Furthermore, the energy differences of terms having successive values of l decrease with increasing l, i.e.,

$$E_{n,l+1} - E_{nl} < E_{nl} - E_{n,l-1},$$

and, accordingly, the absolute value of the first term in the parentheses is considerably larger than that of the second[2]. Accordingly, the STARK effect produces the following shift in the terms of helium:

In the first place, the STARK effect generally results in a reduction of the energy[2], and, secondly, in magnitude the shift is largest for $m=0$ and smallest for $m=l$.

For the purpose of getting a better quantitative understanding of the dependence of the STARK effect on the quantum numbers $n\,l$, let us examine the shift[3] of the STARK component $m=0$. We introduce the RYDBERG corrections in place of the unperturbed energy levels by setting in the usual fashion (cf. Sect. 28)

$$E_{nl} = -\frac{(Z-1)^2}{2(n-\delta_l)^2}.$$

Then we obtain

$$E^{(2)}_{nl0} = -\frac{9F^2 n^5}{16(Z-1)^4}\left\{\frac{4(l+1)^2}{4(l+1)^2-1}\,\frac{n^2-(l+1)^2}{\delta_l-\delta_{l+1}} - \frac{4l^2}{4l^2-1}\,\frac{n^2-l^2}{\delta_{l-1}-\delta_l}\right\}. \tag{56.5}$$

For $n \gg l$ the splitting grows enormously with increasing principal quantum number (as n^7) and grows rapidly also with increasing orbital quantum number since the RYDBERG corrections δ_l are reduced by a factor of 2 to 5 whenever l is increased by 1.

In order to obtain a convenient measure of the absolute magnitude of the effects which may be expected, let us define F_0 as that field strength for which the term shift of the level $m=0$ amounts to exactly one wave-number (cm^{-1}). Then for an arbitrary field the shift evidently is given by

$$E^{(2)}_{nl0} = (F/F_0)^2\ \text{cm}^{-1} \tag{56.6}$$

and, for $n \gg l$,

$$F_0 = \frac{(Z-1)^2}{n^{\frac{7}{2}}} \times 1.46 \times 10^7 \times \left(\frac{4(l+1)^2}{4(l+1)^2-1}\cdot\frac{1}{\delta_l-\delta_{l+1}} - \frac{4l^2}{4l^2-1}\cdot\frac{1}{\delta_{l-1}-\delta_l}\right)^{-\frac{1}{2}}. \tag{56.7}$$

Inserting the observed values for the RYDBERG corrections from Table 4, Sect. 28, we obtain for the characteristic fields F_0

for		S terms	P terms	D terms		
orthohelium	$F_0 =$	$5.95\,n^{-\frac{7}{2}}$	$4.50\,n^{-\frac{7}{2}}$	$0.66\,n^{-\frac{7}{2}}$	million	(56.8)
parahelium		$4.86\,n^{-\frac{7}{2}}$	$1.58\,n^{-\frac{7}{2}}$	$0.60\,n^{-\frac{7}{2}}$	Volt/cm.	

[1] A. UNSÖLD: Ann. d. Phys. **82**, 355 (1927).

[2] However, if $l=n-1$, the first term vanishes and the second term becomes dominant, and the energy of the terms having $l=n-1$ is increased by the electric field. Furthermore, the ^1P terms form an exception, as noted above.

[3] As noted above, this component is shifted the most.

Thus, the terms of parahelium are affected more strongly than those of orthohelium, and this is especially true of the P terms as the separation between the ^1P and the ^1D terms amounts to only about $\frac{1}{4}$ of the distance between the corresponding triplet terms. (The ^1P terms are also distinguished in that—contrary to the general rules of the STARK effect—they undergo a shift toward higher energies since they are situated above the ^1D terms to begin with; cf. above.)

In the following table we have listed the values of the characteristic fields F_0 for the individual terms of helium. The listed values (in Kilovolt/cm) of F_0 are the field strengths for which (56.4) gives a shift of 1 cm^{-1} for the component $m=0$ of states with different n and l.

n	^3S-	^1S-	^3P-	^1P-	^3D-	^1D-terms
2	735	535	735	535	—	—
3	151	115	157	42	103	45
4	52	40	42	13.8	8.3	6.5
5	23	18	17.5	6	3.3	2.6
6	12	9.5	9	3.1	1.65	1.30

A glance at the table reveals immediately the huge differences in the splittings of the individual terms. For example, a field of 10000 Volt/cm shifts the component $m=0$ of the 2^3S term by only 0.0002 cm^{-1}, whereas the corresponding component of the 6^1D term is shifted by 60 cm^{-1}. Thus, for the purpose of calculating the splittings of the lines of the helium spectrum one only needs to know the splitting of the upper level, that of the lower level is usually unobservably small. The splitting of the terms is about as large (actually somewhat smaller) as the shift of the STARK effect component $m=0$ relative to the unperturbed term, which is the quantity we have tabulated.

57. Dependence on field strength. *α) Splitting of energy levels.* For field-free states of the helium atom, we can distinguish three different orders of magnitude of energy. (i) The fine structure splitting δ, contributed by the relativistic parts of the HAMILTONian (Sect. 40). (ii) The energy differences Δ_l of states with the same principal quantum number n, but with different values of l. Δ_l is contributed by the COULOMB and exchange interaction between the electrons (Sect. 28). (iii) The energy differences Δ_n of states with principal quantum numbers n and $n+1$ (interaction with the nuclear field). These energies satisfy the inequality $\delta \ll \Delta_l < \Delta_n$ and are all approximately proportional to n^{-3}.

The calculation of the STARK effect splitting S of an energy level is very complicated if this splitting[1] is comparable with δ, Δ_l or Δ_n. We merely outline the situation for some simpler limiting cases.

Case I. $\delta \ll S \ll \Delta_l$. This is the most important case in practice and the one for which the approximations of Sect. 56 are applicable. The fine structure can be neglected, since it is even small compared with the STARK effect S, and perturbation theory can be used for S, since $S \ll \Delta_l$. The range of field strengths F for which these approximations hold depends strongly on n and l, since S increases and δ, Δ_l decrease with increasing n and l. For instance, this range of field strengths (in kilovolt/cm) is roughly 500 to 50000 for 2^3P, 2 to 200 for 4^3P and 0.1 to 20 for 4^3D. For all states of parahelium and for all S-states, there is no fine structure splitting and the equivalent ranges start from zero field strength.

[1] J. S. FOSTER: Proc. Roy. Soc. Lond. **117**, 137 (1928); ref. [10] Sect. 35.

To summarize the situation for Case I: n, l and m_l (and m_s) are good quantum numbers, the energy splitting is given, to a first approximation, by (56.3) and the splitting is quadratic in the fieldstrength F. If the electron spin and relativistic effects are also taken into account, one obtains an additional small splitting for triplet states with $l \neq 0$. m_s, and hence $m = m_l + m_s$, is also a good quantum number. For triplet states the splitting of the nonrelativistic energy levels into components with $m_s = -1, 0, 1$ is of the order of the field-free fine structure splitting (cf. Sect. 55).

Case II. $S \ll \delta$ (very weak field). This case exists only for triplet states with $l \neq 0$. n, l, j and m ($m = m_l + m_s$ is the component of total angular momentum in the direction of the field) are good quantum numbers, as in the field-free case. The STARK effect removes the m-degeneracy of the relativistic field-free energy levels. Unlike in hydrogen, the STARK effect splitting is quadratic (not linear) in F, since field-free levels of the same j and different l are not degenerate. In the transition region between Cases I and II only n, l and m are good quantum numbers and the effect is complicated.

Case III. $\Delta_l \ll S \ll \Delta_n$ (strong field[1]). Since the field-free energy dependence on l is small compared with the STARK effect splitting, the theory of Sect. 51 for hydrogen applies to a good approximation. The good quantum numbers then are n, m_l, m_s and the parabolic quantum numbers n_1 and n_2. To a first approximation the energy splitting is linear in F, as for hydrogen. In addition, each level is shifted by a small amount, indedendent of F, which is of the same order of magnitude as Δ_l.

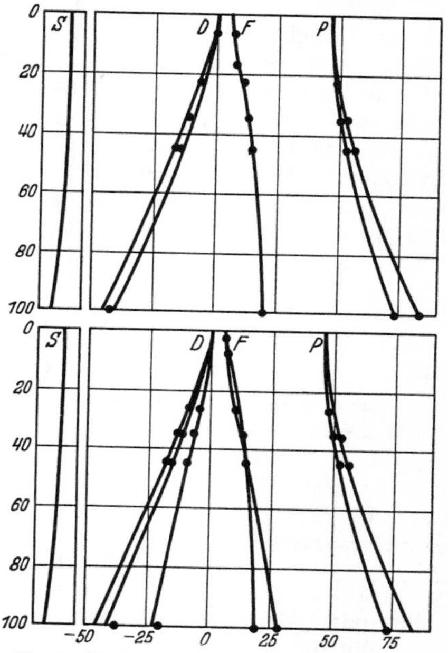

Fig. 30. The STARK effect on the lines in parahelium due to transitions from levels with $n=4$ (4 S, 4 P, 4 D, 4 F) to the $2P$-state. π-components in the upper diagram, σ-components in the lower. Abscissa is field strength in kilovolt/cm. Ordinate is the line shift, relative to the field-free 4 $^1D-2$ ^1P line, in cm^{-1}. The curves are theoretical ones, the solid circles are experimental points.

For reasonably large values of n and a considerable range of field strengths F one has a "partial transition region" between Cases I and III. I.e., the STARK effect splitting S is large compared with the field-free energy difference between adjacent states of large l, but smaller than those with small l. For $n=4$ and $F \sim 100$ Kilovolt/cm, for instance, the D- and F-states show a *linear* STARK effect (Case III) which is much larger than their field-free separation. The S-state, on the other hand, is still an almost pure state and shows a *quadratic* STARK effect (Case I). In Fig. 30 we show the theoretical dependence on field strength of the frequencies of transitions from the paralevels with $n=4$ to the 2^1P-state. The splitting is almost entirely due to that of the $n=4$ states (the STARK effect on $2P$ is negligible). The points on the theoretical curves are a few experimental ones (FOSTER, loc. cit.) and are seen to agree well.

---

[1] We shall not consider the case of extremely strong fields, where S is comparable with or larger than Δ_n. For all but very large n, $S \sim \Delta_n$ requires unreasonably large fields, e.g., a few million Volt/cm for $n=4$.

β) Weakening of the selection rules. So far we have only considered the effect of the field on the *energy* of levels (splitting and shift). The field also affects the wave functions and, hence, also the selection rules for optical transitions between two states in helium. Consider weak fields, Sect. 56 and Case I of Sect. 57α. If u_{nlm} is the field-free wave function of a particular state, the equivalent eigenfunction in a weak field contains a small admixture of the two wave functions $u_{n,l\pm 1,m}$. The amount of this admixture can be calculated by first order perturbation theory and is linear in the field strength F.

For a field-free transition the selection rule (Sect. 60β) on the change in orbital quantum number, $\Delta l = \pm 1$, applies. In an electric field this selection rule can be violated, due to the admixture of states in the field. The admixture of states (as well as the energy shifts) increases rapidly with increasing principal quantum number n. In an optical transition we can then neglect the effect of the field on the *lower* level and consider only the admixture in the *upper* level of $u_{n,l+1,m}$ and $u_{n,l-1,m}$. These wave functions combine optically with lower levels of orbital quantum number l, $l+2$ and l, $l-2$, respectively. In a weak field we then also get transitions of smaller intensity which obey the selection rule

$$\Delta l = 0, \pm 2. \tag{57.1}$$

Using first order perturbation theory one can calculate the ratio of intensities of the "forbidden" lines obeying (57.1) to those of "allowed" lines with $\Delta l = \pm 1$. For the intensity J' of a transition from an upper level $n\,l$ to a lower level $n_0\,l$, for instance, the result is[1]

$$J'^{\,n_0 l}_{nl} = \frac{9}{4}\,\frac{F^2}{(E_{n,l+1} - E_{nl})^2}\,[n^2 - (l+1)^2]\,n^2\,\frac{(l+1)^2 - m^2}{4\,(l+1)^2 - 1}\,J^{n_0 l}_{n,l+1}, \tag{57.2}$$

where $J^{n_0 l}_{n,l+1}$ is the total intensity for allowed transitions $n, l+1, m$ to $n_0\,l\,m_0$, summed over all m_0. Similar relations hold for transitions with $\Delta l = \pm 2$. In general the intensities of the "forbidden" lines are quadratic in the field strength (the matrix elements are linear) and are smaller than those of the allowed lines by about the ratio of the STARK effect energy shift of the upper level to its energy separation from a level with $l+1$ (or $l-1$).

In the helium spectrum, forbidden lines from upper states ending in the $2S$ or $2P$ states fall in the visible region and are observed. In Fig. 30, for instance, lines from $4P$ and $4F$ to $2P$ occur. At a field strength of about 15 Kilovolts/cm, the theoretical intensity of the lines from $4P$ and $4F$ are about 1 and 30%, respectively, of the intensity of the allowed line from $4D$. The theoretical intensities are also verified experimentally.

In strong fields (Case III of Sect. 57α), no selection rules on l apply. Instead, the intensities are obtained in terms of the parabolic eigenfunctions, as for hydrogen (see Sect. 65).

58. The dielectric constant of helium[2]. In order to calculate the dielectric constant ε of helium we need to know the second order STARK effect for the ground level of helium. If the perturbation of the eigenvalue in the field F is given by $E_2 F^2$, then ε may be evaluated from the relation

$$\varepsilon = 1 - 8\pi N E_2, \tag{58.1}$$

[1] Neglecting a similar term involving the state $n, l-1$ (instead of $n, l+1$) which is much smaller.

[2] Cf. H. R. HASSÉ: Proc. Cambridge Phil. Soc. **26**, 542 (1930). — J. C. SLATER and J. G. KIRKWOOD: Phys. Rev. **37**, 682 (1931). The calculations of J. V. ATANASOFF, Phys. Rev. **36**, 1232 (1930) are less satisfactory.

in which N is the number of atoms per unit volume. If E_2 and F are expressed in atomic units, it is necessary to do likewise for the volume. Thus, N is the number of atoms in the volume a^3, where a is the radius of the hydrogen atom,

$$N = \mathcal{N} a^3 \frac{\varrho}{A} = 0.089 \frac{\varrho}{A} \tag{58.2}$$

in which ϱ is the density and A is the atomic weight of the substance. For a gas at standard conditions (0° C and 760 mm of pressure) $A/\varrho = 22400$, and thus

$$\varepsilon = 1 - 1.00 \times 10^{-4} E_2. \tag{58.3}$$

The ground state of helium is the *only* state with $n=1$. The approximation used in Sect. 56 for the second order perturbation energy would thus give zero and the energy shift is in fact considerably smaller for the ground state than for any excited state. In principle one could calculate this energy shift by orthodox second order perturbation theory, but this would involve calculating matrix elements for a large number of excited P-states. We shall use instead the variation-perturbation method of Sects. 25β and 33 [see Eqs. (33.7) and (33.8)].

The unperturbed HAMILTONian (in atomic units) is

$$H_0 = -\frac{1}{2}\Delta_1 - \frac{1}{2}\Delta_2 - \frac{2}{r_1} - \frac{2}{r_2} + \frac{1}{r_{12}}. \tag{58.4}$$

The perturbation resulting from the electric field is $F(z_1 + z_2)$ in which the field strength F is regarded as the perturbation parameter. In terms of the notation of Sects. 25 and 33 we simply have

$$H_1 = z_1 + z_2. \tag{58.5}$$

The first order perturbation in the energy vanishes, and (33.8) becomes

$$E_2 = 2\int u_0^2 \left[\varphi(z_1+z_2) + \tfrac{1}{4}(\mathrm{grad}_1\varphi)^2 + \tfrac{1}{4}(\mathrm{grad}_2\varphi)^2\right] d\tau = \min. \tag{58.6}$$

(58.6) must be minimized by a variation of φ. Perhaps the simplest assumption for φ is the following[1]

$$\varphi = \alpha H_1 = \alpha(z_1 + z_2) \tag{58.7}$$

in which α is to be varied. This gives $\mathrm{grad}_1\varphi = \alpha$, and (58.6) becomes

$$E_2 = 2\int u_0^2 \left[\alpha(z_1+z_2)^2 + \tfrac{1}{2}\alpha^2\right] d\tau. \tag{58.8}$$

Inserting for u_0 the simple eigenfunction (32.9)

$$u_0 = e^{-\frac{1}{2}k(r_1+r_2)} \cdot k^3, \qquad k = \tfrac{27}{8}, \tag{58.9}$$

gives

$$E_2 = \frac{1024}{729}\alpha + \alpha^2.$$

The minimum corresponds to $\alpha = -512/729$ and has the value

$$E_2 = -\left(\frac{512}{729}\right)^2 = -0.49, \tag{58.10}$$

which is pretty far from the correct value of -0.74.

The main reason for the disagreement lies in that (58.9) represents a rather poor approximation to the true eigenfunction of the helium atom in the absence

[1] E_2 is more sensitive to small changes in u_0 than to changes in φ, since φ is always corrected to the "most favorable possible" value by the variation.

of fields. Therefore, SLATER and KIRKWOOD (loc. cit.) have substituted the HARTREE eigenfunction[1] for u_0. In addition they improved the form of the function φ by setting

$$\varphi = \alpha\, r_1^\nu r_2^\nu (z_1 + z_2), \tag{58.11}$$

in which the two parameters α and ν are disposable. The minimum corresponds to a ν of about $\frac{1}{2}$; this means that the eigenfunction is more strongly perturbed by the electric field when the electrons are far from the nucleus than when they are near the nucleus. This makes good sense. The calculation yields

$$E_2 = -0.715.$$

From this the dielectric constant is evaluated from (58.3) with the result

$$\varepsilon = 1.0000715,$$

whereas the observed value is

$$\varepsilon = 1.000074.$$

The agreement is satisfactory.

IV. Interaction with radiation.

a) Discrete spectrum.

59. General formulas. *α) The dipole approximation.* We start from the fundamental formula of radiation theory for the probability of a spontaneous transition of an atom from[2] a state n to a state n' (energies E_n and $E_{n'}$), with the emission of one photon. Let $\boldsymbol{k}$ be the propagation vector, $k = |\boldsymbol{k}|$ the wave number, $\nu_{nn'}$ and $\omega_{nn'}$ the "ordinary" and "angular" frequency of the photon. We then have the BOHR energy relation[3]

$$\omega_{nn'} \equiv 2\pi\nu_{nn'} \equiv c\,k = \frac{1}{\hbar}(E_n - E_{n'}). \tag{59.1}$$

If the photon has polarization direction x and a propagation vector $\boldsymbol{k}$ in the solid angle $d\Omega$, the fundamental transition probability per unit time is

$$W_{n'n}(\boldsymbol{k}, x)\, d\Omega = \frac{e^2\hbar\,\omega_{nn'}}{2\pi m^2 c^3}\,|D_{nn'}^{\boldsymbol{k}x}|^2\, d\Omega. \tag{59.2}$$

In (59.2), D is the following matrix element

$$D_{n'n}^{\boldsymbol{k}x} = \int u_{n'}^* \sum_i e^{i\boldsymbol{k}\cdot\boldsymbol{r}_i} \frac{\partial u_n}{\partial x_i}\, d\tau \tag{59.3}$$

where $\boldsymbol{r}_i$ is the position of the i-th atomic electron and the integral extends over the configuration space of all the electrons[4].

The fundamental expression (59.2), (59.3) is derived elsewhere[5] from quantum electrodynamics. Crudely speaking, the matrix element (59.3) is similar to that

[1] More correctly, they have used an analytic function derived by SLATER, which agrees very closely with the HARTREE eigenfunction.

[2] Here n denotes all the quantum numbers which specify the state, not merely the principal quantum number.

[3] $\hbar$ is the "rationalized" PLANCK's constant $h/2\pi$.

[4] We shall mainly discuss $W_{n'n}$, the probability for the spontaneous emission of a photon. Two other related quantities are the probabilities for absorption of a photon (transition of the atom from a lower to a higher state) and for the emission of a photon, which is induced by the exposure of the atom to radiation. These probabilities can be obtained from $W_{n'n}$ by the so-called EINSTEIN relations discussed in ref. [5], Chap. 4, Sect. 1 (see also our Sect. 69).

[5] See for instance, ref. [2], [5] and [6].

which one would obtain from (45.2) by putting $\boldsymbol{A}$ equal to the vector potential of a classical electromagnetic wave with polarization direction x and propagation vector $\boldsymbol{k}$. We merely list the approximations made in deriving (59.2), (59.3) from quantum electrodynamics. (1) The electrons have been treated nonrelativistically and the SCHRÖDINGER equation has been used instead of the DIRAC or PAULI equations (neglect of magnetic moment and of specific relativistic effects). (2) The interaction of the electron with the radiation field has been treated as a small perturbation (with the fine structure constant α as the perturbation parameter) and only the lowest order term kept in the expansion in powers of α. We are thus neglecting processes involving the simultaneous emission or absorption of two or more photons (and also small radiative corrections akin to the LAMB shift).

In most cases one can simplify (59.3) considerably by making a further approximation: The important distances r_i of the electrons from the nucleus are of the order of the BOHR radius of the atom, i.e. about 10^{-8} cm for low nuclear charge Z. For transitions in the discrete spectrum for low Z the wave number $k=2\pi/\lambda$ of the emitted light is much smaller than 10^8 cm^{-1}, e.g. for visible light k is of order 10^5 cm^{-1}. The exponent $\boldsymbol{k}\cdot\boldsymbol{r}_i$ in the exponential in (59.3) is thus small and we can replace the exponential by unity[1], i.e. we "neglect retardation" and use the "electric dipole approximation". In this approximation $D^{\boldsymbol{k}x}_{n'n}$ is the x-component of a vector $\boldsymbol{D}_{n'n}$ which does not depend on $\boldsymbol{k}$,

$$\boldsymbol{D}_{n'n} = \int u^*_{n'} \sum_i \operatorname{grad}_i u_n \, d\tau. \tag{59.4}$$

The vector $\boldsymbol{D}_{n'n}$ is simply $i/\hbar$ times the matrix element $\boldsymbol{p}_{n'n}$, for the transition $n\to n'$, of the total linear momentum operator $\boldsymbol{p}=\sum\boldsymbol{p}_i=-i\hbar\sum\operatorname{grad}_i$. It is often useful to write $\boldsymbol{D}_{n'n}$ in a different form (to be proved in Sect. 59β),

$$\boldsymbol{D}_{n'n} \equiv \frac{i}{\hbar}\,\boldsymbol{p}_{n'n} = \frac{i\,m}{\hbar}\,\boldsymbol{v}_{n'n} = \frac{m}{\hbar}\,\omega_{n n'}\,\boldsymbol{r}_{n'n}. \tag{59.5}$$

In (59.5), $\boldsymbol{v}$ and $\boldsymbol{r}$ are the sum of electron velocities and positions, respectively, $\omega_{n'n}$ is given[2] by (59.1) and $\boldsymbol{r}_{n'n}$ is the dipole matrix element

$$\boldsymbol{r}_{n'n} = \int u^*_{n'} \sum_i \boldsymbol{r}_i u_n \, d\tau. \tag{59.6}$$

Substituting (59.5) into (59.2), we obtain:

$$W(\Omega, j)\, d\Omega = \frac{e^2}{2\pi\hbar c^3}\,\omega^3_{nn'}\,(\boldsymbol{e}_j\cdot\boldsymbol{r}_{n'n})^2\, d\Omega. \tag{59.7}$$

(59.7) is the probability that an atom will undergo a transition from the state n to n' and emit light of polarization direction $\boldsymbol{e}_j$ into the solid angle $d\Omega$. The intensity of the light emitted into the solid angle $d\Omega$ in erg/sec is obtained by multiplying the probability by the energy of the light quantum $h\nu=\hbar\omega$:

$$J_j\, d\Omega = \frac{e^2}{2\pi c^3}\,\omega^4\,(\boldsymbol{e}_j\cdot\boldsymbol{r}_{n'n})^2\, d\Omega. \tag{59.8}$$

The above is precisely the classical formula for the intensity of light emitted by an oscillating dipole having dipole moment $e\,\boldsymbol{r}_{n'n}\,e^{i\nu_{nn'}t}$ and frequency $\nu_{nn'}$. For

[1] The order of magnitude of kr_i increases with Z and for very large Z this approximation is no longer very good. The approximation also fails, even for small Z, for transitions to states in the continuum of very high energy (Sects. 72 and 73). See also Sect. 66 for the effect of higher terms in the expansion of the exponential in powers of kr_i.

[2] Note that the last form of (59.5) shows that the transition probability between states of equal energy is zero ($\omega_{nn'}$, i.e. the photon frequency, is zero).

this reason the radiation obtained by neglecting the retardation [exponential factor in (59.3)] is called dipole radiation. $\boldsymbol{r}_{n'n}$ takes the place of the amplitude of the classical dipole.

If the angle between the direction of observation $\boldsymbol{k}$ and the dipole moment $\boldsymbol{r}_{n'n}$ is ϑ and the measuring device subtends a solid angle $d\Omega$ at the location of the emitting atom, the observed intensity is given by

$$J\,d\Omega = \frac{e^2}{2\pi c^3}\,\omega^4\,\mathcal{N}_n\,|\boldsymbol{r}_{n'n}|^2\sin^2\vartheta\,d\Omega \tag{59.9}$$

in which $\mathcal{N}_n$ is the number of atoms in the state n [1]. The total intensity of emitted light is obtained by integrating (59.9) over all directions of propagation of the emitted light, viz., over $d\Omega$:

$$J_{n'n} = \frac{4}{3}\,\frac{e^2\,\omega^4}{c^3}\,|\boldsymbol{r}_{n'n}|^2 \tag{59.10}$$

in erg/sec per emitting atom. The total transition probability for going from n to n' is obtained by dividing (59.10) by $h\nu$:

$$A_{n'n} = \frac{4}{3}\,\frac{e^2\,\omega^3}{\hbar\,c^3}\,|\boldsymbol{r}_{n'n}|^2. \tag{59.11}$$

If one finally sums (59.11) over all states n' which have energy less than that of the initial state n, one arrives at the total probability per unit of time that the state n is vacated through light emission

$$\beta_n = \sum_{E_{n'}<E_n} A_{n'n} \tag{59.12}$$

and, thus, the reciprocal of the mean life time of the state n is given by

$$T_n = \frac{1}{\beta_n} = \frac{1}{\sum\limits_{E_{n'}<E_n} A_{n'n}}\,. \tag{59.13}$$

T is of the order of magnitude 10^{-9} sec (cf. Table 15).

Finally, it is convenient to define the oscillator strength

$$f_{n'n} = \frac{2m}{\hbar}\,\omega_{n'n}\,|x_{n'n}|^2 \tag{59.14}$$

which we shall discuss further in Sects. 59β and 61. Altogether we have introduced five quantities which differ successively by a factor of ν as follows:

the square of the matrix element of the coordinate (dipole moment) $|\boldsymbol{r}_{n'n}|^2$,

the oscillator strength $f_{n'n}$, which is proportional to ν times the dipole moment,

the square of the matrix element of the momentum, $\boldsymbol{D}_{n'n}$ [cf. Eq. (59.5)], which is proportional to ν^2 times the dipole moment,

the transition probability $A_{n'n}$ proportional to ν^3 times the dipole moment,

and the intensity of emission $J_{n'n}$, proportional to ν^4 times the dipole moment.

Numerically, one obtains

$$A_{n'n} = 8.0\times 10^9\left(\frac{\nu}{\mathrm{Ry}}\right)^2 f_{n'n}\ \mathrm{sec}^{-1}, \tag{59.15}$$

$$J_{n'n} = 0.173\left(\frac{\nu}{\mathrm{Ry}}\right)^3 f_{n'n}\ \mathrm{erg/sec} \tag{59.16}$$

per emitting atom.

[1] The direction of polarization is perpendicular to $\boldsymbol{k}$. Therefore, if the direction of polarization is resolved into two components, one, $\boldsymbol{e}_1$, perpendicular to $\boldsymbol{r}_{n'n}$ the other one, $\boldsymbol{e}_2$, will lie in the plane determined by $\boldsymbol{k}$ and $\boldsymbol{r}_{n'n}$ at an angle of $\frac{\pi}{2}-\vartheta$ with $\boldsymbol{r}_{n'n}$. Light of polarization 1 is not emitted at all, and polarization 2 is emitted with intensity given by (59.9).

We finally give some crude order of magnitude arguments, for transitions in the discrete spectrum, which are based on the smallness of the fine structure constant α. For a hydrogen-like atom of nuclear charge Z, the following are characteristic orders of magnitude:

$$a_z = a/Z \sim \hbar/Z\alpha m c \qquad \text{for the atomic "radius"},$$

$$p_z = \hbar/a_z \sim Z\alpha m c \qquad \text{for the momentum},$$

$$W_z \sim p_z^2/m \sim Z^2\,\mathrm{Ry} \sim (Z\alpha)^2 m c^2 \qquad \text{for the level energies and}$$

$$\nu_z \sim W_z/h \sim (Z\alpha)^2 m c^2/\hbar \qquad \text{for the "revolution frequency"}.$$

The angular frequency ω of light emitted in radiative transitions is also of order ν_z, or about $Z^2 \times 10^{16}\ \mathrm{sec}^{-1}$, and its wave number k of order ν_z/c. The dipole matrix elements $r_{n'n}$ are of order a_z (but numerically usually smaller) and the factor $k r_{n'n}$ is then of order $(\nu_z/c)\, a_z$ or $Z\alpha$.

We thus see that the "dipole approximation", which consists of neglecting $k r_{n'n}$ compared with unity, is justified as long as $Z \ll 137$. The total decay probability β_n [see Eq. (59.12)] of an excited state is of order $\alpha (Z\alpha)^2 \nu_z \sim Z^4 10^9\ \mathrm{sec}^{-1}$. An excited state has a finite energy spread (radiation width, see Sect. 67) of order $\hbar A_n \sim \alpha (Z\alpha)^2 W_z$ or about α times the fine structure splitting. The oscillator strength $f_{n'n}$ is dimensionless and of order (but numerically less than) unity. In fact we shall see that

$$\sum_{n'} f_{n'n} = 1 .$$

β) Alternative forms of the matrix element. In (59.5) we have made use of a general relation between the matrix elements $\boldsymbol{p}_{n'n}$ and $\boldsymbol{r}_{n'n}$ of the momentum and position operators, respectively. This relation can be derived easily by explicit wave mechanical means[1]. We give instead a derivation using general operator manipulation[2], which we shall also find useful in later sections.

Consider a general HAMILTONian H of form

$$H = \sum_i \frac{p_i^2}{2m} + V(\boldsymbol{r}_1, \boldsymbol{r}_2, \ldots), \tag{59.17}$$

where the operators $\boldsymbol{p}_i$, $\boldsymbol{r}_i$ (for the i-th electron) satisfy the fundamental commutation relations

$$[y_i, p_{xj}] = 0, \qquad [x_i, p_{xj}] = i\hbar\,\delta_{ij}, \quad \text{etc.}, \tag{59.18}$$

and $[a, b] \equiv ab - ba$. Using (11.6), we then find

$$[\boldsymbol{r}, H] = \frac{i\hbar}{m}\,\boldsymbol{p}, \tag{59.19}$$

where $\boldsymbol{r} = \sum \boldsymbol{r}_i$ and $\boldsymbol{p} = \sum \boldsymbol{p}_i$. For a transition between two eigenstates of H with eigenvalues E_n and $E_{n'}$, we also have

$$[\boldsymbol{r}, H]_{n'n} = (E_n - E_{n'})\,\boldsymbol{r}_{n'n},$$

---

[1] One writes the two matrix elements as integrals over position space, as in (59.4) and (59.6), integrates by parts and makes use of the SCHRÖDINGER differential equation and the fact that (if at least n or n' is a *bound* state) the integrands approach zero at large distance (sec ref. [*10*], p. 249).

[2] See refs. [*1*] and [*5*].

which proves the desired relation

$$\boldsymbol{p}_{n'n} = -i\, m\, \omega_{n n'}\, \boldsymbol{r}_{n'n}. \tag{59.20}$$

A third alternative form for $D_{n'n}$ can be derived from another operator relation,

$$(E_n - E_{n'})\, \boldsymbol{p}_{n'n} = [\boldsymbol{p}, H]_{n'n} = [\boldsymbol{p}, V]_{n'n} = -i\hbar \sum_i (\mathrm{grad}_i\, V)_{n'n}, \tag{59.21}$$

where we have used the explicit wave mechanical representation for momentum in the last expression. For a general atom the potential V is of form

$$V = -Z \sum_i \frac{e^2}{r_i} + \sum_{i<j} \frac{e^2}{|\boldsymbol{r}_i - \boldsymbol{r}_j|}.$$

In this case, (59.4), (59.5) can also be rewritten as

$$\boldsymbol{D}_{n'n} = \frac{Z e^2}{\hbar\, \omega_{n n'}} \int u_{n'}^* \sum_i \frac{\boldsymbol{r}_i}{r_i^3}\, u_n\, d\tau. \tag{59.22}$$

We thus have three alternative forms for $D_{n'n}$ (with retardation neglected throughout) which involve integrals over the atomic wave functions of three different operators, the gradient operator in (59.4), $\boldsymbol{r}_i$ in (59.6) and $\boldsymbol{r}_i/r_i^3$ in (59.22). If we use exact eigenfunctions of H for u_n and $u_{n'}$ the three expressions are identical, but if we evaluate the integrals using only approximate wave functions the results can differ from each other (and from the correct expression) appreciably. Note that in the integral involving $\boldsymbol{r}_i$, the integrand is most important for rather *large* values of r_i—and in the integral involving $\boldsymbol{r}_i/r_i^3$ *small* values of r_i are important. For the integral (59.4) involving the gradient operator one finds that intermediate values of r_i are most important. Many approximate wave functions used in practice are most accurate for intermediate values of r_i. This is especially the case for wave functions of helium-like atoms obtained from the variational method (Sects. 32 and 33). These wave functions are most reliable for r_i of the order of the "atomic radius", but are poor approximations for very large or very small r_i (Sect. 36). In such cases we should expect (59.4) to be the most accurate of the three forms for $D_{n'n}$.

The three methods were compared explicitly by CHANDRASEKHAR[1] for transitions from the ground state to states in the continuum of the H^--ion. Using the most accurate (12 parameter variational) ground state wave function the three expressions for $D_{n'n}$ were indeed almost identical. Using a less accurate (six parameter) wave function, (59.4) still gave a fairly accurate value for $D_{n'n}$, but the other two expressions for $D_{n'n}$ were in error by a considerable amount. Thus (59.4) is usually the most reliable form, if approximate wave functions are used, but the form involving (59.6) is usually easier to evaluate and is most commonly used in practice (and in the following sections).

60. Selection rules for orbital and magnetic quantum numbers. *α) One-electron spectra.* First we shall consider an atom having a single electron, and in usual fashion shall express the eigenfunctions in polar coordinates:

$$u_{n l m} = R_{n l}(r)\, \mathcal{P}_{l m}(\vartheta)\, e^{i m \varphi} \frac{1}{\sqrt{2\pi}}. \tag{60.1}$$

The matrix element of the coordinate z corresponding to a transition from the state having quantum numbers $n\, l\, m$ to the state $n'\, l'\, m'$, since $z = r \cos\vartheta$, is

[1] S. CHANDRASEKHAR: Astrophys. J. **102**, 223 (1945).

given by

$$\left.\begin{aligned} z_{nlm}^{n'l'm'} &= \int u_{n'l'm'}^{*}\, z\, u_{nlm}\, d\tau = \int_0^{\infty} r^2\, dr\, R_{n'l'}(r)\, R_{nl}(r) \cdot r \times \\ &\times \int_0^{\pi} \mathcal{P}_{l'm'}(\vartheta)\, \mathcal{P}_{lm}(\vartheta) \cos\vartheta \cdot \sin\vartheta\, d\vartheta \cdot \int_0^{2\pi} \frac{1}{2\pi}\, e^{i(m-m')\varphi}\, d\varphi. \end{aligned}\right\} \tag{60.2}$$

If $m' \neq m$ the integral over φ vanishes and we obtain the following selection rule for the magnetic quantum number for radiation emitted with polarization parallel to z

$$\Delta m \equiv m' - m = 0. \tag{60.3}$$

If the selection rule is fulfilled, the integration over φ gives exactly 1. For the purpose of evaluating the integral over ϑ we employ formula (A.22),

$$\mathcal{P}_{lm} \cos\vartheta = \sqrt{\frac{(l+1)^2 - m^2}{(2l+3)(2l+1)}}\, \mathcal{P}_{l+1\,m} + \sqrt{\frac{l^2 - m^2}{(2l+1)(2l-1)}}\, \mathcal{P}_{l-1\,m} \tag{60.4}$$

and the orthogonality relations obeyed by the associated LEGENDRE functions, viz.,

$$\int_0^{\pi} \mathcal{P}_{l'm}\, \mathcal{P}_{lm} \sin\vartheta\, d\vartheta = \delta_{ll'}. \tag{60.5}$$

From the above we obtain the result that the integral over ϑ vanishes unless the selection rule for the orbital quantum number

$$\Delta l \equiv l' - l = \pm 1 \tag{60.6}$$

is fulfilled, in which case (60.2) reduces to

$$\left.\begin{aligned} z_{nlm}^{n'l+1\,m} &= \sqrt{\frac{(l+1)^2 - m^2}{(2l+3)(2l+1)}}\, R_{nl}^{n'l+1}, \\ z_{nlm}^{n'l-1\,m} &= \sqrt{\frac{l^2 - m^2}{(2l+1)(2l-1)}}\, R_{nl}^{n'l-1}, \\ z_{nlm}^{n'l'm} &= 0 \quad \text{for all other } l', \end{aligned}\right\} \tag{60.7}$$

in which

$$R_{nl}^{n'l'} = \int R_{n'l'}(r)\, R_{nl}(r)\, r^3\, dr. \tag{60.8}$$

The integration with respect to r is more complicated and is deferred to Sect. 63.

The matrix elements of the coordinates x and y may be evaluated in a similar manner. Actually, it is more convenient to obtain the matrix elements of the linear combinations

$$x + i\,y = r \sin\vartheta\, e^{i\varphi} \quad \text{and} \quad x - i\,y = r \sin\vartheta\, e^{-i\varphi},$$

because this leads to a simplification of the integrals with respect to φ. One obtains

$$(x \pm i\,y)_{nlm}^{n'l'm'} = R_{nl}^{n'l'} \int_0^{\pi} \mathcal{P}_{l'm'}\, \mathcal{P}_{lm} \sin\vartheta \cdot \sin\vartheta\, d\vartheta \int_0^{2\pi} e^{i(m\pm1-m')\varphi}\, \frac{d\varphi}{2\pi}. \tag{60.9}$$

The integral with respect to φ vanishes unless

$$\Delta m = m' - m = \pm 1. \tag{60.10}$$

Thus, unless the selection rule for the magnetic quantum number is fulfilled there can be no radiation which is polarized parallel to the x and y axes. Evaluating the ϑ-integrals again with the help of formulas (A.20), (A.21) of the appendix, one again obtains the selection rule (60.6) for the orbital quantum number and also the following explicit expressions for the intensities

$$\left.\begin{aligned}
(x+iy)_{nlm}^{n'l+1\,m+1} &= \sqrt{\frac{(l+m+2)\,(l+m+1)}{(2l+3)\,(2l+1)}}\,R_{nl}^{n'l+1},\\
(x-iy)_{nlm}^{n'l+1\,m-1} &= -\sqrt{\frac{(l-m+2)\,(l-m+1)}{(2l+3)\,(2l+1)}}\,R_{nl}^{n'l+1},\\
(x+iy)_{nlm}^{n'l-1\,m+1} &= -\sqrt{\frac{(l-m)\,(l-m-1)}{(2l+1)\,(2l-1)}}\,R_{nl}^{n'l-1},\\
(x-iy)_{nlm}^{n'l-1\,m-1} &= \sqrt{\frac{(l+m)\,(l+m-1)}{(2l+1)\,(2l-1)}}\,R_{nl}^{n'l-1}.
\end{aligned}\right\}\qquad(60.11)$$

All other matrix elements vanish.

From formulas (60.11) one may draw the conclusion that a change in l and in $|m|$ in the same sense is more probable than a transition in the opposite sense.

Formulas (60.7) and (60.11) have the following consequences:

1. If one adds the intensities of the transitions from a certain state nlm to all the substates m' of the level $n'l'$ without regard to the direction of polarization of the emitted radiation, one finds that the sum is independent of m:

$$\left.\begin{aligned}
\sum_{m'} |\mathbf{r}_{nlm}^{n'l+1\,m'}|^2 &= |z_{nlm}^{n'l+1\,m}|^2 + |x_{nlm}^{n'l+1\,m+1}|^2 + |x_{nlm}^{n'l+1\,m-1}|^2 +\\
&\quad + |y_{nlm}^{n'l+1\,m+1}|^2 + |y_{nlm}^{n'l+1\,m-1}|^2\\
&= \frac{(R_{nl}^{n'l+1})^2}{(2l+3)\,(2l+1)}\cdot\Big[(l+1)^2 - m^2 + \tfrac{1}{2}(l+m+2)\,(l+m+1) +\\
&\quad + \tfrac{1}{2}(l-m+2)\,(l-m+1)\Big] = \frac{l+1}{2l+1}\,(R_{nl}^{n'l+1})^2.
\end{aligned}\right\}\qquad(60.12)$$

Similarly,

$$\sum_{m'} |\mathbf{r}_{nlm}^{n'l-1\,m'}|^2 = \frac{l}{2l+1}\cdot(R_{nl}^{n'l-1})^2. \qquad (60.13)$$

An immediate corollary of the above theorem is that the life time of a state is independent of its magnetic quantum number and depends only on n and l.

2. The sum of the intensities of all the ZEEMAN components of a spectral line which are polarized in the same direction is independent of that direction of polarization. (Thus, the summation which in case 1 was performed over all the directions of polarization (and m') with m held fixed, is now taken over m (and m') with the direction of polarization held fixed.) In view of (60.7) and (60.11) one obtains

$$\left.\begin{aligned}
\sum_m |z_{nlm}^{n'l-1\,m}|^2 &= (R_{nl}^{n'l-1})^2 \sum_{m=-l}^{+l} \frac{l^2-m^2}{(2l+1)\,(2l-1)} = \frac{1}{3}\,l\,(R_{nl}^{n'l-1})^2,\\
\sum_m \left(|x_{nlm}^{n'l-1\,m+1}|^2 + |x_{nlm}^{n'l-1\,m-1}|^2\right) &= \frac{1}{3}\,l\,(R_{nl}^{n'l-1})^2.
\end{aligned}\right\}\qquad(60.14)$$

One conclusion which we may draw from the above is that the total intensity[1] is the same for each of the three components of the LORENTZ triplet in the normal ZEEMAN effect.

[1] The intensity obtained by integrating over all directions of propagation.

β) General atom and helium. The results of Sect. 60α were derived for a single electron in a central (but otherwise arbitrary) field. In alkali atoms the transitions of most practical importance are those between states in which only the loosely bound valence electron is excited. For such transitions the alkali atom can be treated, to a good approximation, as a system with only one (the valence) electron which moves in a central potential $V(r)$. Although $V(r)$ is not a pure COULOMB field, but a HARTREE potential, the results of Sect. 60α still apply.

There are some selection rules which apply generally (in the dipole approximation) even to complex atoms and can be derived by general operator methods (see [*5*]). Consider an arbitrary many-electron atom, but treated by the RUSSELL-SAUNDERS approximation (see Sect. 43α, 48α and 64β), i.e. the spin-orbit coupling is small and L and S (the quantum numbers for total orbital and spin angular momentum, respectively) are good quantum numbers. The following selection rules then apply (for proof see ref. [*5*], Chap. 9):

1. The parity (defined in Sect. 51α) of the wave function must change in the transition (LAPORTE'S rule)[1].

2. The total orbital angular momentum changes at most by unity, i.e. $\Delta L = 0, \pm 1$.

3. The magnetic quantum number (component in the z-direction of the total orbital angular momentum) remains unchanged ($\Delta m = 0$) if the emitted radiation is polarized parallel to z and changes by unity ($\Delta m = \pm 1$) if the radiation is polarized perpendicular to z.

4. The total spin quantum number S remains unchanged, $\Delta S = 0$. For helium for instance, this means that transitions between an ortho- and a para-state are forbidden.

From symmetry considerations one also finds the additional selection rule that transitions between two states with $L = 0$ are forbidden.

For a one-electron atom these general selection rules reduce[2] to (60.3), (60.6) and (60.10).

For a helium-like atom the situation is as follows, for transitions from an initial level in the discrete spectrum in which at least one electron is in the ground state ($l_1 = m_1 = 0$): For emission spectra the final level must have lower energy than the initial one and must therefore also have at least one electron in the ground state. For such transitions the general selection rules again reduce exactly to Eqs. (60.3), (60.6) and (60.10). For *absorption* spectra, the general selection rules also allow transitions to doubly excited states (e.g. l_1 can change by 1, l_2 by 2, etc.). However, if one uses for both initial and final state the familiar (but approximate) product type wave functions (28.2), one finds that the matrix elements for such "double excitations" vanish. Such matrix elements are non-zero only by virtue of the polarization of the wave functions and should therefore be small. Explicit calculations[3] for He verify that transitions probabilities for double excitation are indeed small.

61. Sum rules. *α) Statement of sum rules.* In this section we state four different sum rules. The first rule is stated for any general atom, the other three

[1] If we are considering a wave function in the form of products (symmetrized, etc.) of single-electron wave functions with orbital quantum numbers $l_1, l_2, \ldots$, then LAPORTE'S rule states that $\sum_i l_i$ changes by an odd integer in the transition. For a single-electron atom it states that Δl is odd.

[2] $\Delta l = 0$ is forbidden, since the parity is unchanged in such a transition.

[3] J. P. VINTI: Phys. Rev. **42**, 632 (1932).

are stated for a one-electron atom (with an arbitrary central potential) and some results specific to hydrogen-like atoms derived from them. These sum rules will be proved in Sect. 62 and their generalizations to complex atoms discussed.

1. The most important sum rule is the THOMAS-REICHE-KUHN rule for the sum of the oscillator strengths for *all* transitions which start from a definite state n of the atom. This is a very general rule which holds for *any* atom or molecule, with or without external fields, for any polarization direction and no matter which (if any) of the various angular momentum operators are constants of the motion. Let Z be the total *number of electrons* in the system (for an ion this is *not* equal to the nuclear charge) and let n be a *particular* eigenstate of the total HAMILTONian and n' any one of a complete set of eigenstates[1]. The sum rule then states

$$\sum_{n'} f_{n'n} = Z. \tag{61.1}$$

2. Referring to the definition (59.14) we see that the oscillator strength corresponding to a transition $n \to n'$ depends on the orientation of the x-axis, i.e., on the direction of polarization, and therefore also on the magnetic quantum numbers m and m' of the initial and final state. Let us define an *average oscillator strength* of the transition $nl \to n'l'$, which is independent of polarization and m, as follows

$$\left.\begin{aligned} \bar{f}_{n'n} &= \frac{1}{2l+1} \sum_{m'=-l'}^{l'} \sum_{m=-l}^{l} f_{nm}^{n'm'} = \frac{2m}{3\hbar}\,\omega_{n'l'}^{nl} \sum_{m'=-l'}^{l'} |\boldsymbol{r}_{nlm}^{n'l'm'}|^2 \\ &= \frac{1}{3}\cdot\frac{\max(l,l')}{2l+1}\cdot\frac{\nu_{n'l'}^{nl}}{\mathrm{Ry}}\cdot\frac{(R_{nl}^{n'l'})^2}{a^2} \end{aligned}\right\} \tag{61.2}$$

[cf. Eqs. (59.14) and (60.12) to (60.14)], $g_n = 2l+1$ is the degree of degeneracy of the initial state.

It should be noted that $\bar{f}_{nn'}$ is not equal to $\bar{f}_{n'n}$ because, in the first place, the former is obtained by averaging over m' and summing over m, and secondly—as may be seen from the definition (59.14)—the sign of $f_{n'n}$ changes when the indices are interchanged:

$$\bar{f}_{nn'} = \frac{1}{2l'+1} \sum_{m'=-l'}^{l'} \sum_{m=-l}^{l} f_{n'm'}^{nm} = -\frac{2l+1}{2l'+1}\,\bar{f}_{n'n} = -\frac{g_n}{g_{n'}}\,\bar{f}_{n'n}. \tag{61.3}$$

The average oscillator strengths (61.2) obey a sum rule[2] which is stronger than the f sum rule. One can calculate the sum of the oscillator strengths of all the transitions from a certain level nl to the levels of a fixed orbital quantum number, with the result [cf. Eq. (61.2)]:

$$\sum_{n'} \bar{f}_{nl}^{n'l-1} = \frac{2m}{3\hbar}\,\frac{l}{2l+1} \sum_{n'} \omega_{n'l-1,nl} (R_{nl}^{n'l-1})^2 = -\frac{1}{3}\,\frac{l(2l-1)}{2l+1}, \tag{61.4}$$

$$\sum_{n'} \bar{f}_{nl}^{n'l+1} = \frac{1}{3}\,\frac{(l+1)(2l+3)}{2l+1}. \tag{61.5}$$

If the above two equations are added, one obtains the f sum rule (61.1) again.

The "partial f sum rules" (61.4), (61.5) show that among the transitions $nl \to n'l-1$ the ones which lead to energetically lower states ($\nu_{n'l-1,nl} < 0$,

[1] n and n' again denote all the quantum numbers, not only the principal one.

[2] Cf., J. G. KIRKWOOD: Phys. Z. **33**, 521 (1932). — E. WIGNER: Phys. Z. **32**, 450 (1931).

emission) predominate, whereas in the transitions $nl \to n'l+1$ absorption ($\nu_{n'l+1,nl} > 0$) makes the larger contribution; absorption predominates also in the summation of all oscillator strengths (the ordinary f sum rule). Since the energy increases with increasing principal quantum number, the sum rules (61.4) and (61.5) show that a change of principal and orbital quantum number in the same sense is more probable than a jump in the opposite sense. While we have stated the above sum rules for atoms in which a single electron makes the transitions, it should be noted that the sum rules can be generalized[1].

3. In addition to the sum rules for the oscillator strengths we can also obtain sum rules for the squares of the dipole moment; thus it can be shown [cf. Eq. (60.8)] that:

$$\sum_{n'} (R_{nl}^{n'\,l-1})^2 = \sum_{n'} (R_{nl}^{n'\,l+1})^2 = \overline{r_{nl}^2} = \int r^2 R_{nl}^2 r^2\,dr, \tag{61.6}$$

i.e., the average value of r^2 for the initial state. Substituting from (3.26) the average value of r^2 for hydrogen we obtain

$$\sum_{n'} (R_{nl}^{n'\,l-1})^2 = \sum_{n'} (R_{nl}^{n'\,l+1})^2 = a^2 \frac{n^2}{2} \cdot (5n^2 + 1 - 3l(l+1)) \tag{61.7}$$

in which a is the radius of the hydrogen atom. Using (60.12) and (60.13) one obtains

$$\left.\begin{aligned}
\sum_{n'm'} |r_{nlm}^{n'\,l-1\,m'}|^2 &= a^2 \frac{l}{2l+1} \cdot \frac{n^2}{2} (5n^2 + 1 - 3l(l+1)),\\
\sum_{n'm'} |r_{nlm}^{n'\,l+1\,m'}|^2 &= a^2 \frac{l+1}{2l+1} \cdot \frac{n^2}{2} (5n^2 + 1 - 3l(l+1)),\\
\sum_{n'l'm'} |r_{nlm}^{n'l'm'}|^2 &= a^2 \frac{n^2}{2} (5n^2 + 1 - 3l(l+1)).
\end{aligned}\right\} \tag{61.8}$$

Whereas (61.6) is valid for any atom having a single transition electron, (61.7) and (61.8) hold only for hydrogen.

4. Finally, for the purpose of getting some additional orientation about the distribution of the energy levels which combine with a level of a given n, the following sum rule is useful:

$$\sum_{n'} (E_{n'l'} - E_{nl})^2 (R_{nl}^{n'l'})^2 = 4\,\text{Ry} \cdot a^2 (E_{nl} - \overline{V}_{nl}), \tag{61.9}$$

in which $\overline{V}_{nl}$ is the average value of the potential energy with respect to the eigenfunction R_{nl}. For hydrogen-like atoms this quantity is given by the virial theorem (3.29), viz.,

$$\overline{V}_{nl} = \int V R_{nl}^2 r^2\,dr = 2E_{nl} = -\,\text{Ry} \cdot \frac{Z^2}{n^2} \tag{61.10}$$

(Z is the nuclear charge), from which we obtain

$$\sum_{n'} (E_{n'l'} - E_{nl})^2 (R_{nl}^{n'l'})^2 = 4\,\text{Ry}^2 \cdot a^2 \cdot \frac{Z^2}{n^2} \tag{61.11}$$

and

$$\sum_{n'} \nu_{n'l'nl} f_{nl}^{n'l'} = \frac{4}{3(2l+1)} \cdot \frac{Z^2}{n^2} \text{Ry} \cdot \begin{cases} l & \text{for } l' = l-1, \\ l+1 & \text{for } l' = l+1. \end{cases} \tag{61.12}$$

All the quantities are expressed in c.g.s. units, and a is the radius of the hydrogen atom.

[1] Cf., E. WIGNER, loc. cit. and our Sect. 62.

β) Examples of the application of the sum rules. 1. For the lines coming from the ground state $n=1$, $l=0$ we obtain

from (61.7) $$\sum_n (R_{10}^{n1})^2 = 3a^2,$$

from (61.4) $$\sum_n (E_{n1}-E_{10})(R_{10}^{n1})^2 = 3\,\mathrm{Ry}\cdot a^2,$$

from (61.11) $$\sum_n (E_{n1}-E_{10})^2 (R_{10}^{n1})^2 = 4\,\mathrm{Ry}^2 a^2.$$

Thus, on the average, the energy difference between the excited and the ground state is given by

$$\frac{\sum_n (E_n - E_1)(R_{10}^{n1})^2}{\sum_n (R_{10}^{n1})^2} = \mathrm{Ry},$$

i.e., the "center of gravity" of the LYMAN series lies at the point of separation between the discrete and the continuous spectrum. The square root of the average value of the square of the excitation energy is equal to $\sqrt{\frac{4}{3}}$ Ry.

Next, we shall consider the problem of using the above sum rules for obtaining an estimate for the sum

$$\sum \frac{(R_{10}^{n1})^2}{E_n - E_1} = S \tag{61.13}$$

which is of importance in the STARK effect of the ground level. If we replace $E_n - E_1$ by its average value 1 Ry, then we surely shall get a value of S which is too small, since transitions corresponding to a small energy difference $E_n - E_1$ make a larger contribution than the ones corresponding to a large energy difference[1]. This lower limit of S is given by

$$S_{\min} = \frac{\sum (R_{10}^{n1})^2}{\overline{E_n - E_1}} = \frac{[\sum (R_{10}^{n1})^2]^2}{\sum (E_n - E_1)(R_{10}^{n1})^2} = \frac{3}{\mathrm{Ry}} = 6\ \text{at. un.}$$

On the other hand, if we set $E_n - E_1$ equal to its smallest possible value $E_2 - E_1 = \frac{3}{4}$ Ry, we obtain a value of S which is surely too large:

$$S_{\max} = \frac{\sum_n (R_{10}^{n1})^2}{E_2 - E_1} = \frac{4}{\mathrm{Ry}} = 8\ \text{at. un.}$$

The correct value is actually equal to 6.75 atomic units[2] corresponding to an average energy difference of $\frac{8}{9}$ Ry.

2. We shall now investigate the transition probabilities for high quantum numbers for transitions from a certain level nl to a neighboring level. In particular, we shall obtain a more quantitative result for the assertion made in subsection α2, that the transitions in which both n and l change in the same direction are more frequent than the ones in which the change is in the opposite direction.

(61.8) represents an evaluation of the sum of the squares of the dipole moments for all transitions from nl to $n'l\pm1$ including the transition $n'=n$. If we subtract the latter we are left with the amount given by (63.6) and (63.7). For very

---

[1] The average value of $\frac{1}{E_n - E_1}$ is always greater than the reciprocal of the average of $E_n - E_1$.

[2] Formula (52.3) for the quadratic STARK effect for $n=1$, $n_1=n_2=m=0$ yields the perturbation energy $E_2 = -\frac{9}{4}F^2$ atomic units. On the other hand, $E_2 = -F^2 \sum_n \frac{(z_{10}^{n1})^2}{E_n - E_1} = -\frac{1}{3}F^2 S$, since the spherical symmetry of u_{100} results in $z_{10}^{n1} = (1/\sqrt{3})\,R_{10}^{n1}$.

large n and l, (63.6) and (63.7) may be written as follows

$$\sum_{n'} (R_{nl}^{n'l+1})^2 = \sum_{n'} (R_{nl}^{n'l-1})^2 = \tfrac{1}{4} n^2 (n^2 + 3l^2)\, a^2. \tag{61.14}$$

Furthermore, according to (61.11) we have

$$\sum_{n'} (E_{n'} - E_n)^2 (R_{nl}^{n'l\pm 1})^2 = \frac{4}{n^2} \mathrm{Ry}^2 a^2. \tag{61.15}$$

Next, we note that[1] surely

$$\left.\begin{aligned} \sum_{n'} |E_{n'} - E_n| (R_{nl}^{n'l\pm1})^2 &< \sqrt{\sum_{n'} (R_{nl}^{n'l\pm1})^2 \cdot \sum_{n'} (E_{n'} - E_n)^2 (R_{nl}^{n'l\pm1})^2} \\ &= \sqrt{n^2 + 3l^2}\, \mathrm{Ry} \cdot a^2. \end{aligned}\right\} \tag{61.16}$$

On the other hand, if we assume that $l \gg 1$ in (61.5) we obtain:

$$\sum_{n'} (E_{n'} - E_n) (R_{nl}^{n'l+1})^2 = 2l\, \mathrm{Ry} \cdot a^2. \tag{61.17}$$

From (61.16) and (61.17), taking into consideration the definition of the oscillator strength (59.14), follows:

$$\frac{\sum\limits_{n'>n} f_{nl}^{n'l+1}}{\sum\limits_{n'<n} |f_{nl}^{n'l+1}|} = \frac{\sqrt{n^2 + 3l^2} + 2l}{\sqrt{n^2 + 3l^2} - 2l}. \tag{61.18}$$

Thus, for very small l (eccentric orbits) the transitions with a change of n and l in the same sense are as frequent as the ones with changes in the opposite sense. For $l = n$ (circular orbits), n and l always change in the same sense. For intermediate eccentricities, say $l = \frac{1}{2}n$, a change in the same direction is, on the average, about 7 times as frequent as a change in the opposite sense.

From (61.14) and (61.15) we can also tell by how many units, on the average, the principal quantum number changes in an optical transition. Since

$$\overline{(E_{n'} - E_n)^2} = \frac{\sum\limits_{n'} (E_{n'} - E_n)^2 (R_{nl}^{n'l\pm1})^2}{\sum\limits_{n'} (R_{nl}^{n'l\pm1})^2} = \frac{16}{n^4 (n^2 + 3l^2)} \mathrm{Ry}^2 \tag{61.19}$$

and since $E_n = -\frac{1}{n^2}$ Ry, i.e.,

$$E_{n'} - E_n \approx \frac{2(n'-n)}{n^3} \mathrm{Ry},$$

the mean square of the change in the principal quantum number is given by

$$\sqrt{\overline{(n'-n)^2}} = \frac{n^3}{2} \sqrt{\overline{(E_{n'} - E_n)^2}} = \frac{2}{\sqrt{1 + 3l^2/n^2}}. \tag{61.20}$$

Thus, for circular orbits ($l = n$) the principal quantum number always changes by unity—a result which also follows from the correspondence principle. For very eccentric orbits ($l \ll n$) the average change in n is equal to 2. and for orbits of intermediate eccentricity ($l \approx \frac{1}{2}n$) the average change amounts to about 1.5. (However, on account of the factor ν^3 [cf. Eq. (59.7)] the transition probabilities emphasize the transitions corresponding to a large jump.)

62. Proof of the sum rules. Explicit wave mechanical derivations for the four sum rules stated in Sect. 61α will be found in [*10*], Sect. 40a. We give, instead,

[1] The mean of the square is always greater than the square of the mean.

derivations based on general operator manipulation[1], some of which illustrate the use of projection operators. Rule 1 will be proved for a general system, rules 2, 3 and 4 for a one-electron atom[2].

1. Using the relation (59.20), we can rewrite the definition (59.14) for the oscillator strength in the form[3]

$$f_{n'n} = -f_{nn'} = +\frac{2i}{\hbar}(p_x)_{nn'}\,x_{n'n} = -\frac{2i}{\hbar}x_{nn'}(p_x)_{n'n}. \tag{62.1}$$

Now the states n' form a complete set of eigenstates and the following general sum rule applies for any two operators A and B

$$(A\,B)_{mn} = \sum_{n'} A_{mn'}\,B_{n'n}. \tag{62.2}$$

Taking half the sum of the last two expressions in (62.1) and using (62.2) we find

$$\sum_{n'} f_{n'n} = \frac{i}{\hbar}[p_x, x]_{nn}. \tag{62.3}$$

The operators p_x and x are sums of operators for each of the Z electrons and (59.18) gives

$$[p_x, x] = -i\hbar\sum_{i,j=1}^{Z}\delta_{ij} = -Z\,i\hbar \tag{62.4}$$

which is a number (not an operator). Substituting (62.4) into (62.3) gives the desired relation (61.1). Note that we have used no specific property of V in the HAMILTONian (59.17), but merely the fact that the states n' form a complete set[4].

2. We now prove the sum rules (61.4) and (61.5) for a one-electron system in a central potential, so that the square $\boldsymbol{k}^2$ of the orbital angular momentum operator is a constant of the motion. We shall use the fact that the matrix element of x (or p_x) for a transition between states[5] $n\,l\,m$ and $n'\,l'\,m'$ is non-zero only if $l'=l-1$ or $l+1$. We abreviate the eigenvalues of $\boldsymbol{k}^2$ for states with orbital quantum number l, $l+1$ and $l-1$ by

$$c_0 = l(l+1), \quad c_+ = (l+1)(l+2), \quad c_- = (l-1)\,l.$$

We further define the "projection operator" $(\boldsymbol{k}^2 - c_-)(c_+ - c_-)^{-1}$, which is equivalent to a multiplying factor of unity and zero, respectively, when operating on a state with orbital quantum number $l+1$ and $l-1$. Using the fact that this projection operator gives zero for $l-1$ and that the matrix element of x is zero unless $l'=l\pm 1$, we can apply the general sum rule (62.2) to derive

$$\sum_{n'm'}^{(l'=l+1)}(p_x)_{nn'}\,x_{n'n} = \sum_{n'm'l'}\left(p_x\frac{\boldsymbol{k}^2-c_-}{c_+-c_-}\right)_{nn'}x_{n'n} = \left(p_x\frac{\boldsymbol{k}^2-c_-}{c_+-c_-}x\right)_{nn}, \tag{62.5}$$

and a similar relation with the order of x and p_x interchanged. The sum on the left hand side is carried over all values of n' and m', but with $l'=l+1$, for a fixed initial state $n\,l\,m$. The symbol $n\,n$ on the right hand side denotes the expectation value over the state $n\,l\,m$. We are interested in the *sum* of the

---

[1] For more general proofs of these sum rules and a discussion of operator manipulation, see [*1*] and [*5*]; M. BORN, W. HEISENBERG and P. JORDAN, Z. Physik **35**, 557 (1926) and E. WIGNER, Phys. Z. **32**, 450 (1931).

[2] For other sum rules and their derivation see J. M. HARRIMAN, Phys. Rev. **101**, 594 (1956).

[3] Note that $A_{n'n}$ is the matrix element of A for a transition *from* n to n'.

[4] In the above relations n stands for *all* the quantum numbers specifying a particular state. Note that the state n in (62.3) need not be a member of the set of states n'.

[5] Here n denotes the principal quantum number only.

mean oscillator strength $\bar{f}_{nl}^{n'l'}$, defined in (61.2), over all values of n' with l' (and $n\,l$) fixed. Using (62.1) we find that this sum equals $2i/\hbar$ times the *average* over m of the left hand side of (62.5). (60.14) shows that this average is independent of the polarization direction and we can also average over this direction. We then have

$$\sum_{n'} \bar{f}_{nl}^{n',l+1} = \frac{i}{3\hbar}\left(\boldsymbol{p}\cdot\frac{\boldsymbol{k}^2-c_-}{c_+-c_-}\boldsymbol{r}-\boldsymbol{r}\cdot\frac{\boldsymbol{k}^2-c_-}{c_+-c_-}\boldsymbol{p}\right)_{n\,n}. \tag{62.6}$$

Making use of (11.5) and (11.7), one can show that

$$\boldsymbol{p}\cdot k^2\boldsymbol{r}-\boldsymbol{r}\cdot k^2\boldsymbol{p}=(k^2\boldsymbol{p}\cdot\boldsymbol{r}-\boldsymbol{r}\cdot\boldsymbol{p}\,k^2)+2i(\boldsymbol{k}\times\boldsymbol{p}\cdot\boldsymbol{r}-\boldsymbol{r}\cdot\boldsymbol{p}\times\boldsymbol{k})+2(\boldsymbol{p}\cdot\boldsymbol{r}-\boldsymbol{r}\cdot\boldsymbol{p}). \tag{62.7}$$

Using (11.3), (11.4) and $\boldsymbol{k}\times\boldsymbol{p}\cdot\boldsymbol{r}=\boldsymbol{k}\cdot\boldsymbol{p}\times\boldsymbol{r}$, (62.7) and the term independent of $\boldsymbol{k}^2$ in (62.6) can be simplified further. Using the fact that the matrix element in (62.6) is a diagonal one for an eigenstate of $\boldsymbol{k}^2$ with eigenvalue c_0, we finally find (after some algebra)

$$\sum_{n'} \bar{f}_{nl}^{n',l\pm1} = \frac{\frac{7}{3}c_0+2-c_\mp}{c_\pm-c_\mp}. \tag{62.8}$$

In (62.8) the upper signs refer to the sum (62.6) with $l'=l+1$, the lower signs to an equivalent calculation with $l'=l-1$. Substituting the explicit values for c_0, c_+ and c_-, (62.8) with the upper signs reduces to (61.5) and with the lower signs to (61.4).

3. To prove the sum rule (61.6) we note that the radial matrix element $R_{nl}^{n'l'}$ for the dipole moment can be considered as a matrix element of r between two one-dimensional wave functions χ_{nl} and $\chi_{n'l'}$, (r times the radial wave function)

$$R_{nl}^{n'l'} = \int_0^\infty dr\,\chi_{n'l'}(r)\,r\,\chi_{nl}(r) \equiv r_{nl}^{n'l'}.$$

Now $\chi_{n'l'}$ satisfies the equation

$$\left[\frac{d^2}{dr^2}-\frac{l'(l'+1)}{r^2}+\frac{2m}{\hbar^2}\left(E_{n'l'}-V(r)\right)\right]\chi_{n'l'}(r)=0,$$

where $V(r)$ is a given central potential. Now, any bounded function of the variable r only, which also vanishes at $r=0$, can be expressed as a linear superposition of the functions $\chi_{n'l'}$ for any *fixed* values of l' but all values of n'. The $\chi_{n'l'}$ thus form a complete set (for radial functions only) and we can use the general sum rule (62.2) on the following sum over n' (with l' *fixed*)

$$\sum_{n'}(R_{nl}^{n'l'})^2=\sum_{n'} r_{n'l'}^{nl}\,r_{nl}^{n'l'}=(r^2)_{nl}^{nl}\equiv\int_0^\infty dr\,r^2\chi_{nl}^2. \tag{62.9}$$

This sum is thus independent of the value of l' and (61.6) is a special case of (62.9).

4. To derive the relations (61.9) to (61.12) we first use (59.14) and (59.20) to write

$$\omega_{n'n}f_{n'n}=\frac{2}{\hbar m}(p_x)_{nn'}(p_x)_{n'n}. \tag{62.10}$$

As in sum rule (62.8) we are again interested in the sum of this expression over all values of the principal and magnetic quantum numbers n' and m', but for *fixed* $l'(=l+1$ or $l-1)$, averaged over all values of m. We again average over directions, use a projection operator as in (62.5) and apply (62.2) to get for this sum

$$\sum_{n'}\bar{f}_{nl}^{n',l+1}\omega_{n'n}=\frac{2}{3\hbar m}\left(\boldsymbol{p}\cdot\frac{\boldsymbol{k}^2-c_-}{c_+-c_-}\boldsymbol{p}\right)_{nn}.$$

Using (11.5), (11.7) and the fact that n is an eigenstate of $\boldsymbol{k}^2$ with eigenvalue c_0, we find

$$\sum_{n'} \omega_{n'n} \bar{f}_{nl}^{n',l+1} = \frac{2}{3\hbar m} (p^2)_{nn} \frac{c_0 + 2 - c_-}{c_+ - c_-}. \tag{62.11}$$

Writing $T = p^2/2m$ for the kinetic energy operator and substituting the values for c_0, $c_\pm$ into (62.11) (and in the equivalent expression with c_- and c_+ interchanged for $l' = l - 1$), we have

$$\sum_{n'} \omega_{n'l',nl} \bar{f}_{nl}^{n'l'} = \frac{4}{3(2l+1)} \frac{\bar{T}_{nl}}{\hbar} \begin{Bmatrix} l & \text{for} \quad l' = l - 1, \\ l + 1 & \text{for} \quad l' = l + 1, \end{Bmatrix} \tag{62.12}$$

where $\bar{T}_{nl} = E_{nl} - \bar{V}_{nl}$ is the expectation value for the state $n\,l$ of the kinetic energy operator. For a COULOMB potential, $\bar{T}/\hbar$ equals $Z^2/2n^2$ atomic units of frequency (or $2\pi Z^2/n^2$ Ry) and (62.12) reduces to (61.12). For *any* potential, (61.2) shows that (61.9) and (62.12) are identical.

63. The transition probabilities for hydrogen in polar coordinates. *α) Formulas.* In order to arrive at the absolute values of the transition probabilities we must evaluate the integrals defined in (60.8), viz.:

$$R_{nl}^{n'l-1} = \int_0^\infty R_{nl} R_{n'l-1} r^3 \, dr. \tag{63.1}$$

In the above, the radial eigenfunctions are the associated LAGUERRE functions which we considered in Sects. 3 and 4. The calculation is not at all simple if it is carried out in complete generality leading to a result in closed form. Therefore, we shall at once quote the final formula obtained by GORDON[1] (for $n' \neq n$)

$$\left.\begin{aligned} R_{nl}^{n'l-1} &= \frac{(-1)^{n'-l}}{4(2l-1)!} \sqrt{\frac{(n+l)!\,(n'+l-1)!}{(n-l-1)!\,(n'-l)!}} \frac{(4nn')^{l+1} (n-n')^{n+n'-2l-2}}{(n+n')^{n+n'}} \times \\ &\times \left\{ F\left(-n_r, -n_r', 2l, -\frac{4nn'}{(n-n')^2}\right) - \left(\frac{n-n'}{n+n'}\right)^2 F\left(-n_r - 2, -n_r', 2l, -\frac{4nn'}{(n-n')^2}\right) \right\}. \end{aligned}\right\} \tag{63.2}$$

In the above,

$$F(\alpha, \beta, \gamma, x) = \sum_\nu \frac{\alpha(\alpha+1)\ldots(\alpha+\nu-1)\,\beta\ldots(\beta+\nu-1)}{\gamma\ldots(\gamma+\nu-1)\,\nu!} x^\nu \tag{63.3}$$

is the hypergeometric function and $n_r = n - l - 1$, $n_r' = n' - l$ are the radial quantum numbers of the two states. Because these numbers are integers, the series for the hypergeometric function terminate.

We shall list individually the squares of the radial integrals for the LYMAN and BALMER series, which are obtained by inserting the appropriate special values for n, n' and l in (63.2) and (63.3):

$$\left.\begin{aligned} &\text{LYMAN series:} & 1s - np \quad (R_{10}^{n1})^2 &= \frac{2^8 n^7 (n-1)^{2n-5}}{(n+1)^{2n+5}}, \\ &\text{BALMER series:} & 2s - np \quad (R_{20}^{n1})^2 &= \frac{2^{17} n^7 (n^2-1)(n-2)^{2n-6}}{(n+2)^{2n+6}}, \\ && 2p - nd \quad (R_{21}^{n2})^2 &= \frac{2^{19} n^9 (n^2-1)(n-2)^{2n-7}}{3(n+2)^{2n+7}}, \\ && 2p - ns \quad (R_{21}^{n0})^2 &= \frac{2^{15} n^9 (n-2)^{2n-6}}{3(n+2)^{2n+6}}. \end{aligned}\right\} \tag{63.4}$$

[1] W. GORDON: Ann. d. Phys. (5) **2**, 1031 (1929). The radial integrals will always be expressed in terms of the atomic unit a.

Furthermore, according to (59.14), (59.15) and (61.2), the mean oscillator strengths for the LYMAN series are given by

$$\bar{f}_{1\,0}^{n\,1} = \frac{2^8 n^5 (n-1)^{2n-4}}{3(n+1)^{2n+4}},$$

and the transition probability by

$$A_{1\,0}^{n\,1} = 8\times 10^9 \frac{2^8 n (n-1)^{2n-2}}{3(n+1)^{2n+2}} \sec^{-1},$$

provided the ground state is regarded as the initial state. The above is related to the probability for the absorption of radiation by a hydrogen atom in the ground state. (The latter quantity is obtained by multiplying the transition probability by $\frac{c^3}{4h\nu^3}\varrho_\nu$ in which ϱ_ν is the density of radiation.) On the other hand, the probability for the radiative transition of an excited np electron to the ground state is obtained by dividing the above by 3, the statistical weight of the p state

$$A_{n\,1}^{1\,0} = 8\times 10^9 \frac{2^8 n (n-1)^{2n-2}}{9(n+1)^{2n+2}} \sec^{-1}$$

and the emitted intensity per np electron [cf. Eq. (59.10)] is given by

$$J_{n\,1}^{1\,0} = 0.173 \frac{2^8 (n-1)^{2n-1}}{9n(n+1)^{2n+1}} \frac{\text{erg}}{\text{sec}}.$$

The expression (63.2) is not valid for transitions in which the principal quantum number does not change ($n\,l \to n, l\pm 1$). The radial integration for such a transition can be evaluated easily and gives

$$R_{n,l-1}^{n\,l} = R_{n\,l}^{n,l-1} = \tfrac{3}{2} n \sqrt{n^2-l^2}. \tag{63.5}$$

In hydrogen the frequency of the radiation emitted (or absorbed) in such transitions is in the radio or microwave region and such transitions form the basis of modern precision measurements of the fine structure and LAMB shift (Sect. 21). The square of $R_{n\,l}^{n,l-1}$ is, in many cases, even larger than the sum of the squares of all other matrix elements $R_{n\,l}^{n',l-1}$. Using the sum rule (61.7) and subtracting the square of (63.5), we find

$$\sum_{n'\neq n} (R_{n\,l}^{n',l-1})^2 = \tfrac{1}{4} n^2 \left[n^2 - 1 + 3(l-1)^2\right], \tag{63.6}$$

and similarly

$$\sum_{n'\neq n} (R_{n\,l}^{n',l+1})^2 = \tfrac{1}{4} n^2 \left[n^2 - 1 + 3(l+2)^2\right]. \tag{63.7}$$

For $n=2$, for instance, we get

$$(R_{2\,0}^{2\,1})^2 = (R_{2\,1}^{2\,0})^2 = 27, \quad \sum_{n'\neq 2} (R_{2\,1}^{n'0})^2 = 3, \quad \sum_{n'\neq 2} (R_{2\,0}^{n'1})^2 = 15, \quad \sum_{n'\neq 2} (R_{2\,1}^{n'2})^2 = 30.$$

For a fixed initial state $n\,l$, the transition probability to a final state with principal quantum number n' decreases roughly as n'^{-3} with increasing n'. Note that the energy separation of levels with n' and $(n'+1)$ is also proportional to n'^{-3} for large n' (and so are the fine structure and hyperfine structure splittings).

β) Tables. We give below some tables for various quantities connected with transition probabilities in the hydrogen spectrum. Numerical values for the radial integrals, oscillator strengths, line intensities, and lifetimes have been tabulated

Table 13. *Squares of the dipole moments* $(R_{nl}^{n'l'})^2 = (\int R_{nl} R_{n'l'} r^3\, dr)^2$ *for hydrogen.*

Initial	1s	2s	2p		3s	3p		3d	
Final	np	np	ns	nd	np	ns	nd	np	nf
$n=1$	—	—	1.67	—	—	0.3	—	—	—
2	1.666	27.00	27.00	—	0.9	9.2	—	22.5	—
3	0.267	9.18	0.88	22.52	162.0	162.0	101.2	101.2	—
4	0.093	1.64	0.15	2.92	29.9	6.0	57.2	1.7	104.6
5	0.044	0.60	0.052	0.95	5.1	0.9	8.8	0.23	11.0
6	0.024	0.29	0.025	0.41	1.9	0.33	3.0	0.08	3.2
7	0.015	0.17	0.014	0.24	0.9	0.16	1.4	0.03	1.4
8	0.010	0.10	0.009	0.15	0.5	0.09	0.8	0.02	0.8
$n=9$ to ∞ together	0.032	0.31	0.025	0.42	1.4	0.22	2.0	0.05	1.8
asymptotic	$4.7n^{-3}$	$44.0n^{-3}$	$3.7n^{-3}$	$58.6n^{-3}$	$169n^{-3}$	$28n^{-3}$	$248n^{-3}$	$5n^{-3}$	$198n^{-3}$
Discrete spectrum	2.151	39.30	29.820	27.62	202.56	179.18	174.54	125.88	122.85
Continuous spectrum	0.849	2.70	0.180	2.38	4.44	0.82	5.46	0.12	3.15
Total	3.000	42.00	30.00	30.00	207.00	180.00	180.00	126.00	126.00

Initial	4s	4p		4d		4f	
Final	np	ns	nd	np	nf	nd	ng
$n=1$	—	0.09	—	—	—	—	—
2	0.15	1.66	—	2.9	—	—	—
3	6.0	29.8	1.7	57.0	—	104.7	—
4	540.0	540.0	432.0	432.0	252.0	252.0	—
5	72.6	21.2	121.9	9.3	197.8	2.75	314.0
6	11.9	2.9	19.3	1.3	26.9	0.32	27.6
7	5.7	1.4	7.7	0.5	8.6	0.08	7.3
8	2.1	0.6	3.2	0.2	3.9	0.04	3.0
$n=9$ to ∞ together	4.3	1.0	5.9	0.3	6.9	0.07	4.5
asymptotic	$445n^{-3}$	$102n^{-3}$	$655n^{-3}$	$33n^{-3}$	$687n^{-3}$	$6n^{-3}$	$393n^{-3}$
Discrete spectrum	642.7	598.7	591.7	503.50	496.0	359.95	356.4
Continuous spectrum	5.3	1.3	8.3	0.50	8.0	0.05	3.6
Total	648.0	600.0	600.0	504.00	504.0	360.00	360.0

by KUPPER[1], SUGIURA[2], SLACK[3] and MAXWELL[4]. Our tables are taken from these papers with a few corrections. Much more accurate values for the oscillator strengths (our Table 14) have been tabulated recently by HARRIMAN[5] for initial states up to $4f$ and final states up to $n=50$.

In Table 13 we have tabulated the squares of the radial integral

$$(R_{nl}^{n'l'})^2 = \left(\int_0^\infty R_{nl} R_{n'l'} r^3\, dr\right)^2$$

in terms of the atomic unit a^2 for $n=1$ to 4, $n'=1$ to 8. In addition, we list the sum of the squares for the transitions from a fixed state to the higher discrete states ($n' \geq 9$), and a corresponding sum for the transitions from nl to all the discrete states, and finally the sum of $(R_{nl}^{n'l'})^2$ for all the transitions into the continuous spectrum. The last sum is evaluated by taking the difference between

[1] A. KUPPER: Ann. d. Phys. **86**, 511 (1928).
[2] V. SUGIURA: J. Phys. Radium **8**, 113 (1927).
[3] F. G. SLACK: Phys. Rev. **31**, 527 (1928).
[4] L. R. MAXWELL: Phys. Rev. **38**, 1664 (1931).
[5] J. M. HARRIMAN: Phys. Rev. **101**, 594 (1956).

Table 14. *Oscillator strengths for hydrogen.*

Initial	1s	2s	2p		3s	3p		3d	
Final	np	np	ns	nd	np	ns	nd	np	nf
$n=1$	—	—	−0.139	—	—	−0.026	—	—	—
2	0.4162	—	—	—	−0.041	−0.145	—	−0.417	—
3	0.0791	0.4349	0.014	0.696	—	—	—	—	—
4	0.0290	0.1028	0.0031	0.122	0.484	0.032	0.619	0.011	1.016
5	0.0139	0.0419	0.0012	0.044	0.121	0.007	0.139	0.0022	0.156
6	0.0078	0.0216	0.0006	0.022	0.052	0.003	0.056	0.0009	0.053
7	0.0048	0.0127	0.0003	0.012	0.027	0.002	0.028	0.0004	0.025
8	0.0032	0.0081	0.0002	0.008	0.016	0.001	0.017	0.0002	0.015
$n=9$ to ∞ together	0.0109	0.0268	0.0007	0.023	0.048	0.002	0.045	0.0007	0.037
asymptotic	$1.6\,n^{-3}$	$3.7\,n^{-3}$	$0.1\,n^{-3}$	$3.3\,n^{-3}$	$6.2\,n^{-3}$	$0.3\,n^{-3}$	$6.1\,n^{-3}$	$0.07\,n^{-3}$	$4.4\,n^{-3}$
Discrete spectrum	0.5650	0.6489	−0.119	0.928	0.707	−0.121	0.904	−0.402	1.302
Continuous spectrum	0.4350	0.3511	0.008	0.183	0.293	0.010	0.207	0.002	0.098
Total	1.000	1.000	−0.111	1.111	1.000	−0.111	1.111	−0.400	1.400
$\overline{E}$	0.54	0.61	0.6	0.42	0.78	0.47		0.39	

Initial	4s	4p		4d		4f	
Final	np	ns	nd	np	nf	nd	$n'g$
$n=1$	—	−0.010	—	—	—	—	—
2	−0.009	−0.034	—	−0.073	—	—	—
3	−0.097	−0.161	−0.018	−0.371	—	−0.727	—
4	—	—	—	—	—	—	—
5	0.545	0.053	0.610	0.028	0.890	0.009	1.345
6	0.138	0.012	0.149	0.006	0.187	0.0016	0.183
7	0.060	0.006	0.063	0.002	0.072	0.0005	0.058
8	0.033	0.003	0.033	0.001	0.037	0.0003	0.027
$n=9$ to ∞ together	0.082	0.006	0.075	0.002	0.081	0.0006	0.045
asymptotic	$9.3\,n^{-3}$	$0.7\,n^{-3}$	$9.1\,n^{-3}$	$0.3\,n^{-3}$	$8.6\,n^{-3}$	$0.05\,n^{-3}$	$3.5\,n^{-3}$
Discrete spectrum	0.752	−0.126	0.912	−0.406	1.267	−0.715	1.658
Continuous spectrum	0.248	0.015	0.199	0.006	0.133	0.001	0.056
Total	1.000	−0.111	1.111	−0.400	1.400	−0.714	1.714
$\overline{E}$	1.25	0.72		0.45		0.32	

the total sum of all R^2 [which may be obtained from the sum rules (61.7)] and the sum for the transitions to the discrete spectrum. Finally, the asymptotic formula for $(R_{nl}^{n'l'})^2$ is given for high values of n', for fixed $n\,l\,l'$, under the heading "asymptotic".

Table 14 contains the average oscillator strengths, as defined in (61.2), for the (partial) Lyman, Balmer, Paschen, and Brackett series. The arrangement of the table is the same as that of Table 13; however, we have added a row on the bottom which contains the average energy of the states in the continuum which combine with the state $n\,l$ (the particular values of $n\,l$ are specified at the top of each column). The average energy expressed in terms of the absolute value of the energy of the state $n\,l$ is given by

$$\overline{E} = \frac{\int\limits_{\text{cont. spectr.}} E'(R_{nl}^{E'l'})^2\,dE'}{\int (R_{nl}^{E'l'})^2\,dE'} \cdot \frac{n^2}{\mathrm{Ry}}\,.$$

Table 15. *Transition probabilities for hydrogen in 10^8 sec^{-1}.*

Initial	Final	$n=1$	2	3	4	5	Total	Lifetime in 10^{-8} sec
$2s$	$n\,p$	—	—	—	—	—	0	∞
$2p$	$n\,s$	6.25	—	—	—	—	6.25	0.16
2	mean	4.69	—	—	—	—	4.69	0.21
$3s$	$n\,p$	—	0.063	—	—	—	0.063	16
$3p$	$n\,s$	1.64	0.22	—	—	—	1.86	0.54
$3d$	$n\,p$	—	0.64	—	—	—	0.64	1.56
3	mean	0.55	0.43	—	—	—	0.98	1.02
$4s$	$n\,p$	—	0.025	0.018	—	—	0.043	23
$4p$	$n\,s$	0.68	0.095	0.030	—	—	0.81	1.24
	$n\,d$	—	—	0.003	—	—		
$4d$	$n\,p$	—	0.204	0.070	—	—	0.274	3.65
$4f$	$n\,d$	—	—	0.137	—	—	0.137	7.3
4	mean	0.12_8	0.083	0.089	—	—	0.299	3.35
$5s$	$n\,p$	—	0.012_7	0.008_5	0.006_5	—	0.027_7	36
$5p$	$n\,s$	0.34	0.049	0.016	0.007_5	—	0.415	2.40
	$n\,d$	—	—	0.001_5	0.002	—		
$5d$	$n\,p$	—	0.094	0.034	0.014	—	0.142	7.0
	$n\,f$	—	—	—	0.000_5	—		
$5f$	$n\,d$	—	—	0.045	0.026	—	0.071	14.0
$5g$	$n\,f$	—	—	—	0.042_5	—	0.042_5	23.5
5	mean	0.040	0.025	0.022	0.027	—	0.114	8.8
$6s$	$n\,p$	—	0.007_3	0.0051	0.0035	0.0017	0.0176	57
$6p$	$n\,s$	0.195	0.029	0.0096	0.0045	0.0021	0.243	4.1
	$n\,d$	—	—	0.0007	0.0009	0.0010		
$6d$	$n\,p$	—	0.048	0.0187	0.0086	0.0040	0.080	12.6
	$n\,f$	—	—	—	0.0002	0.0004		
$6f$	$n\,d$	—	—	0.0210	0.0129	0.0072	0.0412	24.3
	$n\,g$	—	—	—	—	0.0001		
$6g$	$n\,f$	—	—	—	0.0137	0.0110	0.0247	40.5
$6h$	$n\,g$	—	—	—	—	0.0164	0.0164	61
6	mean	0.0162	0.0092	0.0077	0.0077	0.0101	0.0510	19.6

For example, the states of the continuum which combine with the level $3s$ have an average energy of $\bar{E}=0.78\times\frac{1}{9}$ Ry$=0.087$ Ry. However, it is not claimed that these numbers have a high degree of accuracy.

In Table 15 are listed the transition probabilities [with regard to their evaluation from the f values compare (59.15)] from the sublevels $s, p, d\,\ldots$ of the states $n=2, 3, 4, 5, 6$ to all the lower states in terms of 10^8 sec^{-1}. By summing the individual transition probabilities one obtains the decay constants given in the next to the last column under the heading "Total". The reciprocal of the decay constant is equal to the lifetime and is given in the last column. In addition, we have calculated the average value of the transition probabilities from the states of a certain principal quantum number n to that of another principal quantum number n', namely

$$A_{n'n}=\sum_{l l'}\frac{2l+1}{n^2}A_{nl}^{n'l'}\,. \tag{63.8}$$

The average transition probability, as given above, assumes importance if the excited atoms suffer a great many collisions during their lifetime or if some other perturbation, such as an electric field, assures that the atoms occupy the substates of various orbital quantum numbers l in proportion to their statistical weights (see below).

Table 16. *Intensities for hydrogen in 10^{-4} erg/sec.*

	LYMAN series	BALMER series				PASCHEN series					
	$1s-np$	$2s-np$	$2p-ns$	$2p-nd$	total	$3s-np$	$3p-ns$	$3p-nd$	$3d-np$	$3d-nf$	total
a) *Absorption or emission*, if one electron is *present* in the initial state (on the average).											
$n=2$	304	—	—	—	—	—	—	—	—	—	—
3	94	1.97	0.19	9.6	11.8	—	—	—	—	—	—
4	41	1.15	0.10	4.13	5.38	0.096	0.019	0.37	0.011	1.01	1.51
5	21	0.67	0.06	2.14	2.87	0.074	0.013	0.261	0.007	0.483	0.84
6	12	0.42	0.035	1.15	1.50	0.052	0.009	0.168	0.004_5	0.265	0.500
7	8	0.27	0.02	0.75	1.04	0.035	0.007	0.109	0.002_5	0.162	0.315
8	5	0.18	0.01_5	0.53	0.73	0.024	0.005	0.077	0.001_5	0.113	0.220
9 to ∞	19	0.64	0.05	1.70	2.4	0.09	0.01	0.25	0.006	0.34	0.70
b) Emission, if one electron per second is *put into* the initial state.											
$n=2$	48.6	—	—	—	—	—	—	—	—	—	—
3	50.5	1.06	3.0	15.0	19.0	—	—	—	—	—	—
4	51.0	1.42	2.3	15.0	18.7	0.12	0.44	1.35	0.014	7.4	9.3
5	50.5	1.61	2.2	15.0	18.8	0.17	0.45	1.85	0.017	6.8	9.3
6	49.5	1.73	2.0	14.4	18.1	0.21	0.51	2.10	0.018	6.4	9.2

Finally, Table 16 gives the line intensities under various conditions of excitation: If the electrons are distributed according to the statistical weights, i.e., if on the average there is exactly one electron in each excited state $n\,l\,m$, the intensity of the line $n\,l \to n'\,l'$ is given by

$$J_{nl}^{n'l'} = (2l+1)\,h\,\nu_{nl,n'l'}\,A_{nl}^{n'l'}. \tag{63.9}$$

These so-called statistical intensities are listed in Table 16a. If, on the other hand, precisely one electron arrives in each state $n\,l\,m$ per unit of time (for example, through collisions, absorption of radiation, cascading from higher states, etc.), then the number of electrons which, on the average, occupy the state $n\,l\,m$ is equal to the lifetime T_{nl} of that state, and the emitted intensity is given by

$$[J_{nl}^{n'l'}] = J_{nl}^{n'l'}\,T_{nl} = (2l+1)\,\frac{A_{nl}^{n'l'}}{\sum\limits_{n'l'} A_{nl}^{n'l'}}\,h\,\nu_{nl,n'l'}\,. \tag{63.10}$$

These so-called dynamical intensities are listed in Table 16b.

γ) Discussion of the tables. 1. By inspecting Tables 13 and 14, the frequently mentioned rule (Sects. 61α2, 61β2) may be verified, which states that the transitions in which n and l change in the same sense are more frequent than those in which there is a change in the opposite sense. For example, the transition probabilities for $2p \to 3s$ and $2p \to 3d$ are as 1:25. The rule also applies to transitions to the continuous spectrum. In such transitions l is practically always increased by unity.

2. For high orbital quantum numbers (the circular orbits of the BOHR theory), jumps of unity in the principal quantum number are by far the most frequent [cf. Eq. (61.20)]; transitions into the continuum are very rare. For small orbital quantum numbers (eccentric orbits), transitions to the continuum are more frequent.

One may compare, for example, the oscillator strengths of the lines having initial levels $4s$ and $4f$. For $4f \rightarrow 5g$ the oscillator strength is about $2\frac{1}{2}$ times as large as that of $4s \rightarrow 5p$. On the other hand, the transitions from $4s$ to the continuum have oscillator strengths about 5 times as large as the ones initiated at $4f$. Thus, circular orbits are difficult to ionize.

3. For a fixed value of l, the total oscillator strengths for all the transitions into the continuous spectrum generally decrease with increasing principal quantum number. Thus for the initial level $1s$ it amounts to 0.436, for $4s$ to 0.248. The average energy of the levels in the continuum which combine with a certain discrete level, is roughly half the magnitude of the ionization potential of the discrete level in question. More precisely, the ratio (last row of Table 14) increases somewhat with increasing principal quantum number and declines fairly rapidly with increasing orbital quantum number.

The transition probabilities may be obtained by multiplying the oscillator strengths by ν^2. As a consequence, the transitions corresponding to a high frequency ν are the most probable, in spite of the fact that the oscillator strengths are largest when the principal quantum number changes by the least amount, i.e., when ν is as small as possible. For example, in the transitions from $4p \rightarrow 1s$, $2s$ and $3s$, the ratio of the oscillator strengths is 1:3.5:16, whereas the ratio of the transition probabilities is 23:3:1 (see Tables 14 and 15). The above has several important consequences as follows:

4. Of all the possible transitions (in emission) from an initial state $n\,l$, the transition to the state of lowest energy (compatible with the selection rules) is by far the most probable one, i.e. to the state $n' = l$, $l' = l - 1$. *Cascade transitions*, which involve a series of transitions before the atom ends up in its ground state, are likely only insofar as they are required by the l-selection rule. I.e. the most likely form of cascade from a state $n\,l$ is the shortest possible one with l steps (via $n' = l$, $l' = l - 1$, then $n'' = l - 1$, $l'' = l - 2$) down to the ground state. Hence, states with $n > l + 1$ are more easily obtained by direct excitation from the ground state, rather than indirectly by excitation to a higher state followed by a radiative transition[1] (or ionization plus recombination). However, states with $n = l + 1$ are likely to be produced by such cascade from higher states, if the excitation conditions allow appreciable excitation to higher states[2].

As an example we give in Table 17 the theoretical relative probabilities of various cascade processes, which all start from the $5d$ level in hydrogen. All

Table 17. *Relative probabilities of various transitions from the 5d-state.*

$4f \rightarrow 3d \rightarrow 2p \rightarrow 1s$	0.3%	$4p \rightarrow 2s$	1.1%
$4p \rightarrow 3d \rightarrow 2p \rightarrow 1s$	0.1%	$3p \rightarrow 2s$	2.9%
$4p \rightarrow 3s \rightarrow 2p \rightarrow 1s$	0.3%		4.0%
$4p \rightarrow 1s$	8.0%		
$3p \rightarrow 1s$	21.2%		
$2p \rightarrow 1s$	66.1%		
	96.0%		

[1] An important exception is the metastable $2s$-state, which cannot be excited by a direct radiative transition from the ground state. States with $l > 1$ also cannot be obtained by direct radiative excitation from the ground state. Such states, as well as the $2s$-state, can be obtained by electronic excitation.

[2] For experimental confirmation see L. Ornstein and H. Lindemann, Z. Physik **63**, 8 (1930). A study of cascade transitions is also important in connection with "mesic atoms" where negatively charged mesons are captured by the nuclear Coulomb field to form atomic states with large values of n.

cascades end either in the ground state or the $2s$-state and the $5d \to 2p \to 1s$ cascade has indeed the largest probability.

5. Of all the sublevels nl of the n-th quantum state, the p level has by far the shortest life-time because it combines with the $1s$ ground state, and the probability corresponding to that transition is by far greater than any other. The lifetimes of all the other levels arrange themselves according to their orbital quantum numbers, except for the lifetime of the ns levels which do not fit into the regular scheme. Their lifetimes are always very long since the transitions $ns \to n'p$ are very rare, as n and l change in the opposite sense (cf. Table 15).

6. The lifetimes of the quantum states go up with increasing principal quantum number. This is true both for a fixed orbital quantum number and for the average over l. For a fixed value of l, we have with pretty good accuracy

$$T_{nl} \sim n^3,$$

whereas the following holds for the average lifetime of the n-th quantum state[1]:

$$T_n = \left(\sum_l \frac{2l+1}{n^2} \frac{1}{T_{nl}}\right)^{-1} \sim n^{4.5}.$$

7. Within a given series the line intensities decline strongly, if the number of electrons which on the average occupy an excited state, is the same for all the levels (Table 16a). This assumption is fulfilled when thermodynamic equilibrium exists and the temperature is very (infinitely) high. That condition is nearly fulfilled in the hot stars. When one talks about the "intensities" of spectral lines (e.g., SCHRÖDINGER), what is usually meant is the intensities at infinitely high temperature excitation.

On the other hand, if thermodynamic equilibrium does not exist, and the excitation process is of such a nature that the same number of electrons arrive in each excited state per second, then the line intensities in a given series are constant within the accuracy of the calculation (Table 16b). Thus, the decline of the intensities within a given series has its origin solely in the different excitation probabilities of the different levels.

8. We consider finally the sum of the oscillator strengths $f_{nlm}^{n'l'm'}$, summed over *all* l, l', m' and m, with fixed n and $n' (n \neq n')$. The following approximate formula[2] represents this sum accurately for large n and n' (and to within a factor of about two for *all* values of $n \neq n'$)

$$F_{n'n} \equiv \sum_{l l' m m'} f_{nlm}^{n'l'm'} \approx \frac{2^6}{3\sqrt{3}\pi} \left(\frac{1}{n^2} - \frac{1}{n'^2}\right)^{-3} \frac{1}{n^3} \frac{1}{n'^3} = 3.92 \left(\frac{E_{n'} - E_n}{\mathrm{Ry}}\right)^{-3} \frac{1}{n^3} \frac{1}{n'^3}. \tag{63.11}$$

64. Intensity of fine structure lines.

α) *The* PAULI *and dipole approximations.* We consider next the effect of the electron's spin on the transition probabilities. In (59.3) we have essentially taken the matrix element between the nonrelativistic wave functions[3] for two atomic states of $e^{i\boldsymbol{k}\cdot\boldsymbol{r}}\boldsymbol{p}$, where $\boldsymbol{p}$ is the electron's momentum operator and $\boldsymbol{k}$ is the propagation vector (k the wave number) of the photon. According to the relativistic DIRAC theory for electrons, in this matrix element the operator $\boldsymbol{p}$ is replaced by mc times the DIRAC operator $\boldsymbol{\alpha}$

---

[1] The more rapid rise of the average lifetime with n is explained by the fact that when n is increased by 1, a circular orbit having a long lifetime is included with the other values of the orbital quantum number.

[2] A. UNSÖLD: Physik der Sternatmosphären, 2nd ed. Berlin: Springer 1955.

[3] We again use units such that $\hbar = 1$.

(and the wave functions by DIRAC spinors). We consider, for simplicity, a one-electron system. Written in momentum space representation, the matrix element is then (apart from numerical factors)

$$\xi = m c \int d^3p \langle u_{n'}^* (\boldsymbol{p} + \boldsymbol{k}) \boldsymbol{\alpha} u_n (\boldsymbol{p}) \rangle, \tag{64.1}$$

where $\langle\ \rangle$ denotes the scalar product of the four-component DIRAC spinors $u_{n'}^*$ and $\boldsymbol{\alpha} u_n$.

We restrict ourselves now to an "essentially nonrelativistic" system, so that the important values of momentum p in the atomic DIRAC wave functions are small compared with mc and we shall only work to the accuracy of the PAULI approximation (Sects. 12 and 13). Following the work of Sect. 16, we then approximate the wave functions $u_n(\boldsymbol{p})$ by eigenfunctions of the operator $\beta m c + \boldsymbol{\alpha} \cdot \boldsymbol{p}$ with positive eigenvalue (and similarly for $u_{n'}(\boldsymbol{p}+\boldsymbol{k})$). We can then reduce (64.1) to a matrix element involving only two-component PAULI spinors and operators. Using further the approximation (16.14), the matrix element (64.1) reduces to

$$\xi = \int d^3p \left\langle u_{n'}^* (\boldsymbol{p} + \boldsymbol{k}) \left[\boldsymbol{p} + \frac{1}{2} \boldsymbol{k} + \frac{i}{2} \boldsymbol{k} \times \sigma\right] u_n (\boldsymbol{p}) \right\rangle, \tag{64.2}$$

where u_n and $u_{n'}$ are now PAULI spinors and σ is the two-by-two PAULI spin matrix. It can be shown that the errors made in replacing (64.1) by (64.2) are of relative order of magnitude $(p/mc)^2$ and $(|\boldsymbol{p}+\hbar\boldsymbol{k}|/mc)^2$. For an electron in a COULOMB potential (charge Z) this error is of order $(Z\alpha)^2$, as is the case generally for the PAULI approximation.

The matrix element (64.2) can be simplified further if, in addition to the PAULI approximation, we also use the "electric dipole" approximation discussed in Sect. 59. In position space this involves neglecting $k r_0$ compared with unity, where r_0 is of the order of the "atomic radius". In momentum space the important values of p are of order $\hbar/r_0$ and the dipole approximation consists of neglecting $\hbar k$ compared with p. Thus, if we replace $\boldsymbol{k}$ by zero in (64.2), this expression reduces to

$$\xi = \int d^3p \langle u_{n'}^* (\boldsymbol{p}) \boldsymbol{p} u_n (\boldsymbol{p}) \rangle = \int d^3r \langle u_{n'}^* (\boldsymbol{r}) \boldsymbol{p} u_n (\boldsymbol{r}) \rangle = \boldsymbol{p}_{n' n}. \tag{64.3}$$

We have thus shown that, in the electric dipole (and PAULI) approximation, the matrix element obtained in the DIRAC theory is identical with that of the nonrelativistic theory [see Eq. (59.5)], except that the wave functions are now PAULI spinors. For a COULOMB potential the relative error made in replacing (64.2) by (64.3) is of order $Z\alpha$ (which is larger than the error due to using the PAULI approximation).

The expression (64.2) can also be simplified somewhat even if we want to keep terms of relative order $Z\alpha$. We only need the component ξ_e of the vector matrix element (64.2) in the polarization direction $\boldsymbol{e}$ of the photon. The photon's propagation direction $\boldsymbol{k}$ is always perpendicular to $\boldsymbol{e}$, and $k_e = 0$; also $(\boldsymbol{k} \times \sigma)_e = k \sigma_\perp$, where $\perp$ denotes the direction perpendicular to both $\boldsymbol{k}$ and $\boldsymbol{e}$. We can rewrite the matrix element ξ_e in terms of a position space integral and get

$$\xi_e = (p_e e^{i \boldsymbol{k} \cdot \boldsymbol{r}})_{n' n} + \frac{i}{2} k (\sigma_\perp e^{i \boldsymbol{k} \cdot \boldsymbol{r}})_{n' n}. \tag{64.2a}$$

The first term in (64.2a) is the *full* nonrelativistic matrix element (without neglect of retardation). The second term in (64.2a) is a correction term (of relative order $Z\alpha$), characteristic of the DIRAC theory, and will be discussed in Sect. 66α in connection with magnetic dipole radiation. The neglect of retardation (replacing the exponential by unity) in this *second* term only introduces errors of order $(Z\alpha)^2$.

For electrons moving in a central potential the electron's spin affects the selection rules, etc. for radiative transitions even if the approximation (64.3) is used, i.e. even if specific relativistic effects are neglected. This is due to the degeneracy of the nonrelativistic energy of states differing only by their quantum number m_l (see Sect. 13).

β) Selection rules. For a system of any number of electrons in a central potential, the z-components of the total orbital angular momentum (quantum number m_L) and of the total spin (m_S) are *not* constants of the motion individually. On the other hand $m=m_L+m_S$ and J [eigenvalue of $\boldsymbol{M}^2=(\boldsymbol{K}+\boldsymbol{S})^2$ is $J(J+1)$] *are* good quantum numbers for any atom (in the absence of external fields). This change in the quantization rules immediately leads to new selection rules. If we restrict ourselves to the dipole approximation, i.e. use the matrix element (59.5) or (64.3), one can prove some general selection rules using only the commutation properties of $\boldsymbol{p}$, $\boldsymbol{r}$ and $\boldsymbol{M}$ (for proofs see [3] and [5]). For any atom the following rigorous selection rules hold

$$\Delta m = 0, \quad \pm 1 \quad \text{(for polarization parallel and perpendicular, resp., to } z) \tag{64.4}$$

and

$$\Delta J = 0 \quad \text{or} \quad \pm 1, \tag{64.5}$$

$$J=0 \rightarrow J=0 \quad \text{forbidden.} \tag{64.6}$$

As discussed in Sect. 48α, for many atoms (especially for low Z) the Russell-Saunders approximation is a fairly good one. I.e. the spin-orbit coupling is treated as a small perturbation and the quantum numbers L and S are (almost) "good" quantum numbers. In this approximation the four selection rules at the beginning of Sect. 60β also apply. For a single-electron atom[1] the first two of these rules again reduce to (60.6).

We merely outline how some of the above selection rules can be verified explicitly for a single-electron atom in the Pauli approximation. The wave function for a stationary state can be written in the form

$$u_{nljm} = \sum_{m_l+m_s=m} \alpha_{m_s}^{ljm} \, v_{nlm_l}(\boldsymbol{r}) \, \xi_{m_s}, \tag{64.7}$$

where the α_{m_s} are numerical coefficients, $v(\boldsymbol{r})$ spatial wave functions (for quantum numbers n, l, and m_l) which do not depend on the spin coordinates. ξ_{m_s} for $m_s=\pm\frac{1}{2}$ are two ortho-normal Pauli spinors which are eigenstates of s_z with eigenvalues $\pm\frac{1}{2}$. One can then write out the matrix element (64.3) of the operator $\boldsymbol{p}$ (or similarly for $\boldsymbol{r}$) for the transition from a state $nljm$ to $n'l'j'm'$ as a double sum over m_s and m_s', using (64.7) for the initial and final wave functions. Using the fact that the operator $\boldsymbol{p}$ (or $\boldsymbol{r}$) does *not* contain any Pauli matrices and that the ξ_{m_s} form an orthonormal set, one finds

$$\boldsymbol{r}_{nljm}^{n'l'j'm'} = \sum_{m_s} \alpha_{m_s}^{ljm} \left(\alpha_{m_s}^{l'j'm'}\right)^* \boldsymbol{r}_{nl,m-m_s}^{n'l',\,m'-m_s} \tag{64.8}$$

where the term in $\boldsymbol{r}$ on the right hand side denotes the spatial matrix element (59.6) of $\boldsymbol{r}$ between the wave functions

$$v_{nl,\,m-m_s} \quad \text{and} \quad v_{n'l',\,m'-m_s}^*.$$

From the form of (64.8) and the work of Sect. 60α, the selection rules (64.4) and $\Delta l=\pm1$ follow immediately. Since $j=l\pm\frac{1}{2}$, the selection rule $\Delta l=\pm1$

[1] In this case the Russell-Saunders and Pauli approximations are identical.

does not, by itself, forbid transitions with $\Delta j = \pm 2$. That the matrix element (64.8) for such transitions is in fact zero, as stated in (64.5), can be verified explicitly by substituting the explicit expressions for the coefficients α_{m_s} into (64.8).

γ) Sum rules. For any many-electron atom, to which the RUSSELL-SAUNDERS approximation is applicable, we have the following sum rule:

(I) The total probability of all transitions from a fixed state $nLJm$ to all states with fixed $n'L'$ (but all possible values of $J'm'$) is independent of the total angular momentum J and magnetic quantum number m of the initial state. Further, this total probability is the same as the total probability of transitions in the theory *without* spin from the state nLm_L to all states with fixed $n'L'$ (but all values of m'_L).

We merely outline the proof of this rule for a one-electron system. We have to evaluate the sum over all j' and m' of the square of (64.8). From the definition (64.7) of the coefficients α_{m_s} and the fact that both the functions u_{nljm} and $v_{nlm_l}\,\xi_m$ form complete orthonormal sets, follow the relations

$$\sum_{j'} (\alpha_{m_s}^{l'j'm'})^* \alpha_{m'_s}^{l'j'm'} = \delta_{m_s m'_s}, \qquad \sum_{m_s} |\alpha_{m_s}^{ljm}|^2 = 1 .$$

From (60.12) and (60.13) we also find that

$$\sum_{m'} |\boldsymbol{r}_{nl,\, m-m_s}^{n'l',\, m'-m_s}|^2 \equiv |\boldsymbol{r}_{nl}^{n'l'}|^2$$

is independent of $m - m_s$. Using these relations and (64.7) one finally obtains

$$\sum_{j'm'} |\boldsymbol{r}_{nljm}^{n'l'j'm'}|^2 = |\boldsymbol{r}_{nl}^{n'l'}|^2, \tag{64.9}$$

which is the required relation.

It should be remembered that the sum rule I above holds also for a many-electron system, but only in the RUSSELL-SAUNDERS approximation, i.e. if L is (to a good approximation) a good quantum number and the (spin-orbit) splitting of multiplets small. For X-ray levels (inner electrons) in heavy atoms (large Z), relativistic effects are quite appreciable and the spacing of multiplets large. The wave functions deviate appreciably from the PAULI approximations and the sum rule I is not a very good approximation. We shall only consider cases where the above approximations are applicable (see, however, Sects. 66 and 68).

It follows from the sum rule I that the lifetime of any fine structure component of a level with fixed quantum numbers n and L is *independent* of the "total" and magnetic quantum numbers J and m (at least for unperturbed atoms) and has the same value as in the theory without spin. At least under the usual excitation conditions (no preferred spatial direction), the probability of excitation of a component $nLJm$ is also independent of J and m. In this case, for fixed values of n and L, the *number* of electrons *present in* a state $nLJm$ is also independent of J and m. The following sum rule also holds in this case:

(II) The total intensity of all spectral lines for transitions from a level nLJ (summed over all ZEEMAN components, i.e. all m) to all levels with fixed $n'L'$ (all J', m') is proportional to $(2J+1)$, the statistical weight of the initial level.

The sum rule II has been verified experimentally for closely spaced multiplets in different types of atoms, especially for alkali atoms. For hydrogen-like atoms, however, the assumptions leading to the rule II do *not* apply under the usual *practical* conditions although the fine structure splitting is small and the PAULI approximation good (for unperturbed atoms): This is due to the degeneracy of the nonrelativistic energy of levels with the same n but different l. This degeneracy is only removed to a slight extent by the fine structure and LAMB shift and the wave functions are perturbed severely by the presence of even quite weak external electric fields or other pertubations (see Sect. 55). We shall show in Sect. 67 that such perturbations also affect the lifetimes of the various fine structure levels and hence also the number of electrons present in various excited states.

δ) Intensity formulas. For doublet spectra, such as the spectrum of hydrogen, the sum rules in conjunction with the selection rules suffice to determine completely the transition probabilities for all the lines.

We shall consider the transitions from the states $n\,l$, $j=l+\frac{1}{2}$ and $j=l-\frac{1}{2}$ to the states n', $l-1$, $j'=l-\frac{3}{2}$ and $j=l-\frac{1}{2}$ (cf. Fig. 31). One of these, $j=l+\frac{1}{2}\rightarrow j'=l-\frac{3}{2}$ is forbidden by the j selection rule. Thus, only one line is initiated at the level $j=l+\frac{1}{2}$ (a in Fig. 31). On the other hand, there are two lines from the initial level $j=l-\frac{1}{2}$ (b, c). According to our sum rule, the ratio of the sum of the transition probabilities of the two lines b and c to that of a, must be the same as the ratio of the statistical weights, viz.,

$$(b+c):a=2l:(2l+2). \tag{64.10}$$

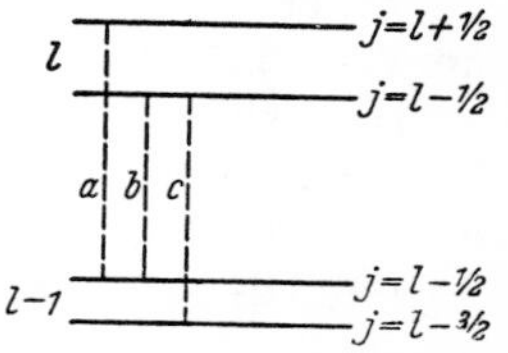

Fig. 31. Diagram of the transitions from a state with orbital quantum number l to one with $l-1$ for a one-electron atom (doublet spectrum), including fine structure.

On the other hand, if we regard the primed levels as initial states, we obtain in an analogous fashion

$$(a+b):c=l:(l-1). \tag{64.11}$$

From (64.10) and (64.11) follows the ratio of the three transition probabilities, namely

$$a:b:c=[(l+1)\,(2l-1)]:1:[(l-1)\,(2l+1)]. \tag{64.12}$$[1]

The ratios of line intensities and transition probabilities are the same, provided the initial states are excited in proportion to their statistical weights. The most important special cases are the following:

$$\left.\begin{aligned}
&s\,p \text{ transitions: } s\,p_{\frac{3}{2}}:s\,p_{\frac{1}{2}}=2:1\\
&\qquad(=a:b;\ c \text{ does not exist, since } s \text{ levels do not split}),\\
&p\,d \text{ transitions: } p_{\frac{3}{2}}d_{\frac{5}{2}}:p_{\frac{3}{2}}d_{\frac{3}{2}}:p_{\frac{1}{2}}d_{\frac{3}{2}}=9:1:5,\\
&d\,f \text{ transitions: } d_{\frac{5}{2}}f_{\frac{7}{2}}:d_{\frac{5}{2}}f_{\frac{5}{2}}:d_{\frac{3}{2}}f_{\frac{5}{2}}=20:1:14.
\end{aligned}\right\} \tag{64.13}$$

For large values of l, the intensity of the line b, i.e., the transition in which j does not change, is very small compared to the intensity of the transition in which j and l change by the same amount. This statement is a companion of the rule (60.11) which states that l and m change predominantly in the same sense, and also of the theorem in Sect. 63γ1 which makes the same claim for n and l.

The intensity ratios (64.13) have been verified in many instances, for example for the alkali spectra. For a comparison with experiment see Sect. 67ε and Sect. 68.

The absolute intensities may be obtained by evaluating first the intensities without considering spin and then multiplying the results by the relative intensities given in (64.12) and dividing by $\frac{1}{2}(2l+1)\,(2l-1)$.

[1] This was obtained at an early date. See, for example, H. HÖNL, Ann. d. Phys. **79**, 273 (1925).

Table 18. *Fine structure intensities of H_α.*
($\Delta\nu$ is the line frequency in cm^{-1} relative to that of line c. $2j+1$ is the statistical weight of the initial level.)

	Initial state	Final state	$\Delta\nu$	Transition	Oscillator strength	$2j+1$	Total oscillator strength	
a)	$j=\frac{1}{2}$	$j'=\frac{3}{2}$	-0.144	$3s \to 2p_{\frac{3}{2}}$	$\frac{2}{3}\times 0.041$	2	0.05	2.83
b)	$\frac{3}{2}$	$\frac{3}{2}$	-0.036	$3d_{\frac{3}{2}} \to 2p_{\frac{3}{2}}$	$\frac{1}{6}\times 0.417$	4	0.28	
c)	$\frac{5}{2}$	$\frac{3}{2}$	0	$3d_{\frac{5}{2}} \to 2p_{\frac{3}{2}}$	1×0.417	6	2.50	
d)	$\frac{1}{2}$	$\frac{1}{2}$	0.220	$3s \to 2p_{\frac{1}{2}}$	$\frac{1}{3}\times 0.041$	2	0.03	0.31
				$3p_{\frac{1}{2}} \to 2s$	1×0.142	2	0.28	
e)	$\frac{3}{2}$	$\frac{1}{2}$	0.328	$3p_{\frac{3}{2}} \to 2s$	1×0.142	4	0.57	1.96
				$3d_{\frac{3}{2}} \to 2p_{\frac{1}{2}}$	$\frac{5}{6}\times 0.417$	4	1.39	

As an example, the intensities[1] of the components of the hydrogen line H_α are given in Table 18.

It will be seen that the intensity of the line a is too small and that line b lies too close to the strong line c to permit separate observation. Line d occupies an asymmetric position among the short wave components of H_α. Under the assumption of statistical distribution, the intensity ratios are

$$(a+b+c):d:e = 1:0.11:0.69.$$

The center of gravity of the complex $a+b+c$ is shifted by $-0.006\ \text{cm}^{-1}$ relative to the line c, the center of gravity of $d+e$ is shifted by $-0.015\ \text{cm}^{-1}$ relative to e, and the separation between the two centers of gravity amounts to $0.319\ \text{cm}^{-1}$.

The intensities may be derived without the help of the sum rules directly from the PAULI eigenfunctions (13.19) in a way which we used in Sect. 64β for the verification of the selection rule for j. This yields, at the same time, the intensities of the ZEEMAN components: For transitions in which j changes by unity that intensity is given, as before, by (60.7) and (60.11) provided we replace l by j and m by the z component of the total angular momentum. For transitions in which there is no change in j, one obtains

$$z_{nljm}^{n'l'jm} = m\, C_{lj}^{l'j} R_{nl}^{n'l'}, \tag{64.14}$$

$$(x+iy)_{nljm}^{n'l'jm+1} = (x-iy)_{n'l'jm+1}^{nljm} = \sqrt{(j+m+1)(j-m)}\, C_{lj}^{l'j} R_{nl}^{n'l'}. \tag{64.15}$$

Formulas (64.14) and (64.15) have general validity for any multiplet spectrum. In the case where there is only one valence electron, $R_{nl}^{n'l'}$ is the radial integral (60.8). For a doublet spectrum the C factors are given by

$$C_{lj}^{l-1j} = \frac{1}{2j(j+1)}, \quad C_{lj}^{l-1j-1} = \frac{1}{2j}. \tag{64.16}$$

Even for hydrogen, transitions between fine structure components with the *same* principal quantum number n and with $\Delta l = \pm 1$, $\Delta j = 0, \pm 1$ are not forbidden by the selection rules. But the frequency of "photons" emitted or absorbed in such transitions is extremely low (radio waves rather than light) and depends strongly on the j-values of the two states (for $\Delta j = \pm 1$ the energy difference is of the order of the fine structure, for $\Delta j = 0$ of the order of the LAMB shift). *Induced* transitions of this sort are of great importance in modern experiments on the LAMB shift and fine structure (Sect. 21), but the probability A of a *spontaneous* transition is extremely small, since the frequency ν is so low, ($A_{n'n}$

[1] A. SOMMERFELD and A. UNSÖLD: Z. Physik **38**, 237 (1926).

is proportional to $\nu^3 x^2_{n'n}$). The radial integral for a transition with $\Delta n = 0$ is given by (63.5), and (64.16) still holds. For $n=2$ in hydrogen, for instance, a spontaneous transition from $2P_{\frac{3}{2}}$ to $2S_{\frac{1}{2}}$ is possible with the emission of a "photon" of frequency 9912 Mc/sec. The transition probability is about 10^{-6} sec^{-1}, which is negligible compared with the probability of 6×10^8 sec^{-1} for the transition $2P_{\frac{3}{2}}$ to the ground state. Similarly a spontaneous transition from $2S_{\frac{1}{2}}$ to $2P_{\frac{1}{2}}$ is possible with a "photon" frequency of 1058 Mc/sec and a transition probability of about 10^{-9} sec^{-1} (lifetime of about 30 years). Although transitions from the $2S$-state to the ground state are forbidden in the dipole approximation, two-quantum transitions to the ground state, etc., have a much larger probability than 10^{-9} sec^{-1} (see Sect. 67β).

ε) The intensities of the helium fine structure lines. The intensities in triplet spectra cannot be immediately derived from the sum rules, except for the combinations between S and P levels. Since S terms are not split by the interaction with the spin, the ratio of the intensities of the transitions from the one ^3S term to the three ^3P terms $j=0, 1, 2$ is equal to the ratio of the statistical weights

$$^3S_1\,{}^3P_2 : {}^3S_1\,{}^3P_1 : {}^3S_1\,{}^3P_0 = 5:3:1.$$

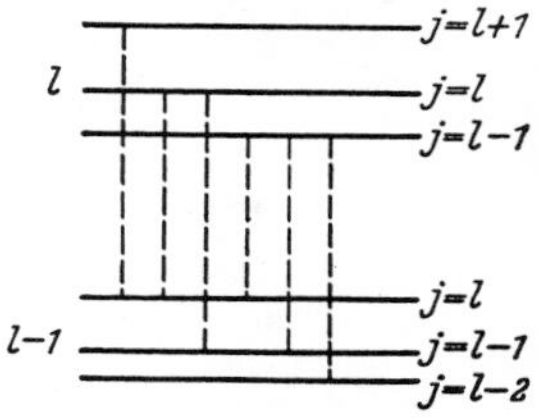

Fig. 32. Diagram of the transitions from a state with orbital quantum number l to one with $l-1$ for a triplet spectrum.

More generally, the intensity ratio of the lines which arise in the transition from the triplet nl to the triplet $n'l-1$ (cf. Fig. 32) is given in Table 19a.

Table 19a. *Relative intensities of the multiplet components in triplet spectra.*

Final state	j of initial state			Sum
	$j=l+1$	l	$l-1$	
$j'=l$	$(2l+3)(2l-1)l^2$	$(2l+1)(2l-1)$	1	$(2l+1)^2 l^2$
$l-1$	—	$(2l+1)(2l-1)(l+1)(l-1)$	$(2l+1)(2l-1)$	$(2l+1)(2l-1)l^2$
$l-2$	—	—	$(2l+1)(2l-3)l^2$	$(2l+1)(2l-3)l^2$
Sum	$(2l+3)(2l-1)l^2$	$(2l+1)(2l-1)l^2$	$(2l-1)^2 l^2$	$3(2l+1)(2l-1)l^2$

Naturally, the intensity ratios are again valid only if the initial states are occupied in proportion to their statistical weights. As a specific example we shall put down the intensity relationships for a PD transition.

Table 19b. *Relative intensities of the components of the multiplet* $^3D \to {}^3P$.

Final state	Initial state			Sum
	$^3D_3$	$^3D_2$	$^3D_1$	
$^3P_2$	84	15	1	100
$^3P_1$	—	45	15	60
$^3P_0$	—	—	20	20
Sum	84	60	36	180

Both in the special example given in Table 19b and in the more general case of Table 19a, we have included the sum of the intensities of all the lines which arise from the same initial state in order to show that these sums are indeed proportional to the statistical weight $2j+1$ of the initial level. Furthermore, it will readily be seen from the tables that the transitions in which j and l change in the same sense are the most frequent; that the transitions in which there is no change in j are rarer; and that the transitions in which j and l change in the opposite sense are extremely weak. For large values of l only the transitions of the first type occur.

65. Intensities in parabolic coordinates (STARK effect). We consider next the effect of a moderately strong uniform external electric field on the intensities of spectral lines. We discuss only hydrogen-like atoms[1], for which the effect is very marked because of the l-degeneracy of the nonrelativistic energies. The effect in very weak electric fields (STARK effect $\ll$ fine structure splitting, see Sect. 55) is discussed in Sect. 67. We consider here only field strengths such that the STARK effect splitting is large compared with the fine structure and the linear STARK effect (Sect. 51) approximation holds. The atomic eigenstates are then those described by the wave functions expressed in parabolic coordinates (Sect. 6) with quantum numbers n_1, n_2 and m.

The intensities of the STARK components of the BALMER lines were first calculated by E. SCHRÖDINGER[2] and have been put to an extensive experimental test[3]. There are fewer selection rules for an atom in an external field than for a free atom. There exists only one selection rule with respect to the magnetic quantum number m, which determines the component of the orbital angular momentum about the direction of the electric field, namely,

$\Delta m = 0$ for radiation polarized in a direction parallel to the field,

$\Delta m = \pm 1$ for radiation polarized in a perpendicular direction.

There is no strict selection rule with respect to the parabolic quantum numbers n_1 and n_2; however, there is a quasi-selection rule which predicts that the outermost components, which according to the term scheme may be expected to appear in the line pattern, will generally have unobservably small intensities. This is the case, for example, with the components $\pi 8$ of H_α which are shifted by $8F/15620\ \text{cm}^{-1}$ relative to the unperturbed line and correspond to the transition from the state $n=3$, $n_1=2$, $n_2=m=0$ to the state $n=2$, $n_1=0$, $n_2=1$, $m=0$.

The general formula for the coordinate matrix element has been obtained by GORDON[4], and for radiation polarized parallel to the field is given by

$$\left.\begin{aligned} z_{n_1 n_2 m}^{n_1' n_2' m} &= (-)^{n_1'+n_2'} \frac{a}{4(m!)^2} \sqrt{\frac{(n_1+m)!}{n_1!}\,\frac{(n_2+m)!}{n_2!}\,\frac{(n_1'+m)!}{n_1'!}\,\frac{(n_2'+m)!}{n_2'!}} \left(\frac{4nn'}{(n-n')^2}\right)^{m+2} \left(\frac{n-n'}{n+n'}\right)^{n+n'} \times \\ &\times \left\{\left[2(n_1'-n_2')\frac{n^2+n'^2}{(n+n')^2} - (n_1-n_2)\frac{4nn'}{(n+n')^2}\right] \Psi_m(n_1 n_1')\,\Psi_m(n_2 n_2') - \right. \\ &\left. - 2\left[n_1' \Psi_m(n_1, n_1'-1)\,\Psi_m(n_2, n_2') - n_2' \Psi_m(n_1 n_1')\,\Psi_m(n_2, n_2'-1)\right]\right\} \end{aligned}\right\} \tag{65.1}$$

and for radiation polarized perpendicularly to the field by

$$\left.\begin{aligned} x_{n_1 n_2 m}^{n_1' n_2' m-1} &= (-)^{n_1'+n_2'} \frac{a}{4(m-1!)^2} \sqrt{\frac{(n_1+m)!}{n_1!}\,\frac{(n_2+m)!}{n_2!}\,\frac{(n_1'+m-1)!}{n_1'!}\,\frac{(n_2'+m-1)!}{n_2'!}} \left(\frac{4nn'}{(n-n')^2}\right)^{m+1} \left(\frac{n-n'}{n+n'}\right)^{n+n'} \times \\ &\times \left\{\Psi_{m-1}(n_1 n_1')\,\Psi_{m-1}(n_2 n_2') - \left(\frac{n-n'}{n+n'}\right)^2 \Psi_{m-1}(n_1+1, n_1')\,\Psi_{m-1}(n_2+1, n_2')\right\}. \end{aligned}\right\} \tag{65.2}$$

In the above, Ψ is the hypergeometric function

$$\Psi_m(n_i n_i') = F\left(-n_i, -n_i', m+1, -\frac{4nn'}{(n-n')^2}\right) = 1 - \frac{n_i n_i'}{m+1}\cdot\frac{4nn'}{(n-n')^2} + \cdots. \tag{65.3}$$

---

[1] For He see S. FOSTER, Proc. Roy. Soc. Lond., Ser. A **117**, 137 (1927).

[2] E. SCHRÖDINGER: Ann. d. Phys. **80**, 468 (1926).

[3] H. MARK and R. WIERL: Z. Physik **53**, 526; **55**, 126; **57**, 494 (1929) referred to as I, II and III respectively. See also J. STARK, Ann. d. Phys. **48**, 193 (1915); Handbuch der Experimentalphysik, Bd. XXI, 427; J. ST. FOSTER and L. CHALK, Proc. Roy. Soc. Lond. **123**, 108 (1929); Nature, Lond. **118**, 693 (1926).

[4] W. GORDON: Ann. d. Phys. **2**, 1031 (1929). A numerical error in this paper was corrected by A. B. UNDERHILL, Publ. Dominion Astrophys. Obs. **8**, 386 (1951).

For the LYMAN series ($n'=1$, $n'_1=n'_2=m'=0$) the formulas for the squares of the coordinate matrix elements are especially simple and are given by

$$\left.\begin{aligned}(z^{n_1 n_2 0}_{000})^2 &= a^2 \cdot \frac{2^8 n^6 (n-1)^{2n-6}}{(n+1)^{2n+6}} (n_1-n_2)^2,\\ (x^{n_1 n_2 1}_{000})^2 = (x^{n_1, n_2, -1}_{000})^2 &= a^2 \cdot \frac{2^8 n^6 (n-1)^{2n-6}}{(n+1)^{2n+6}} (n_1+1)(n_2+1).\end{aligned}\right\} \quad (65.4)$$

By summing over the values of n_1 and n_2 which belong to the same principal quantum number ($n_1=0 \ldots n-1$, $n_2=n-1-m-n_1$), one arrives again at the intensity formula (63.4) for the LYMAN series which we have previously derived in polar coordinates.

Below we give a table of the intensities of the STARK effect components of the second LYMAN line L_β, and of the first BALMER line H_α which has the same initial level ($n=3$). The former was obtained from (65.4), the latter from the tables of SCHRÖDINGER.

The first part of the Table, 20a, enables one to calculate the lifetime of the STARK effect terms having principal quantum number $n=3$. In it are entered the probabilities for a transition from each term to the first and second quantum states. The second part of the Table, 20b, is to be used in the calculation of the actual intensities of the components of H_α under two different assumptions (cf. Table 16) as follows:

Table 20a. *Probabilities for transitions starting from the* STARK *effect levels with* $n=3$. ($n_1 n_2 m$ denote the quantum numbers of the initial state; π and σ the two polarization possibilities; A_{rel} is the transition probability in arbitrary units, A_{abs} in units of 10^8 sec^{-1} and T is the mean lifetime in 10^{-8} sec.

$n_1 n_2 m$	LYMAN series			BALMER series						A_{abs}	T
	pol.	A_{rel}	A_{abs}	pol. π: Final state	pol. π: A_{rel}	pol. σ: Final state	pol. σ: A_{rel}	$\pi+2\sigma$: A_{rel}	$\pi+2\sigma$: A_{abs}		
002	—	0	0	—	0	001	2304	4608	0.64	0.64	1.56
110	—	0	0	100 010	729 729	001	882	3222	0.45	0.45	2.22
101	σ	4	0.82	001	1152	100 010	968 8	3104	0.43	1.25	0.80
200	π	4	0.82	100 010	1681 1	001	18	1718	0.24	1.06	0.94

Table 20b. *The intensities of the* STARK *effect components of the* H_α*-line.* ($\Delta\nu$ is the displacement of the line, relative to the field-free line, in units of $F/15620$ cm^{-1}; J_S and J_D are the statistical and dynamical intensities, respectively, in units such that the strongest component has intensity 100; $\bar{J}_S$ is the calculated J_S in the units given by SCHRÖDINGER.)

Initial state	Statis. weight	Final state	$\Delta\nu$	Calculated $\bar{J}_S$	Calculated J_S	Calculated J_D	Observed J_S	Observed J_D
				Polarization parallel to the field				
110	1	010	2	729	32	89	31	79
101	2	001	3	2304	100	100	100	100
200	1	100	4	1681	73	86	76	92
200	1	010	8	1	0	0	0	0
				Polarization perpendicular to the field				
002 110	2 1	001 001	0 0	4608 882	100	100	100	100
101	2	100	1	1936	35	17	38	38
101	2	010	5	16	0	0	0	0
200	1	001	6	18	0	0	0	0

1. The occupation of each of the STARK effect levels is proportional to its statistical weight (i.e., on the average each level is occupied by the same number of atoms).

2. The excitation of each level is proportional to its statistical weight (i.e., the same number of atoms arrive in each level per unit time).

Under assumption 1, the intensities, the so-called statistical intensities, are calculated by multiplying the transition probabilities of Table 20a by the statistical weight of the initial state, and the results agree with those of SCHRÖDINGER. One arrives at the intensities under assumption 2, the dynamical intensities, by multiplying the statistical intensities by the lifetime of the initial state. The statistical and dynamical intensities differ considerably. The measured intensities of MARK and WIERL (loc. cit. II) are also included in the Table. They are the results of two different experiments: In the first, a hydrogen-nitrogen mixture is maintained at a considerable pressure (0.02 to 0.03 mm Hg) and the hydrogen atoms are continually excited by collisions. In the second experiment, the emission takes place essentially in a vacuum (10^{-4} mm Hg), and, accordingly, only those atoms emit which are already in an excited state when they enter the region of space under observation. It will be noted that the pressure experiments agree well with SCHRÖDINGER's statistical intensities, the experiments in vacuum with the dynamical intensities. That is to be expected. In the experiments which are carried out under pressure, the continual collisions assure a uniform distribution of the atoms over the STARK levels. On the other hand, in the vacuum experiments one may probably assume that there is a fairly uniform distribution ln the beginning which in the course of time shifts in favor of the long-lived ievels 110 and 002.

66. Higher multipole radiation[1]. *α) The multipole expansion.* As discussed in Sects. 59 and 64α, we have used throughout the "dipole approximation" (neglect of retardation). Let $\boldsymbol{k}_\omega$ be the[2] propagation vector of the photon. We have replaced the operator $e^{i\boldsymbol{k}_\omega\cdot\boldsymbol{r}}mc\boldsymbol{\alpha}$, occurring in the DIRAC theory, by the nonrelativistic operator $e^{i\boldsymbol{k}_\omega\cdot\boldsymbol{r}}\boldsymbol{p}$ and have further replaced the exponential by unity. This replacement is based on the assumption that $k_\omega a$ is small, where a (the "atomic radius") is a distance characteristic of the linear dimensions of the atomic wave functions.

The neglect of retardation is a poor approximation for X-ray radiation emitted by the inner electrons of an atom with large Z. For such atoms $Z\alpha$ is not very small and relativistic effects are important[3]. The effects of retardation are also important for the continuous spectrum (e.g., photoeffect), where photons of high frequency (wave length not necessarily larger than a) are emitted or absorbed. This will be discussed in Sects. 72 and 73. In this section we restrict ourselves to the discrete spectrum for atoms with $Z \ll 137$. In this case $k_\omega a$ is indeed small and the effect of retardation is small in general. However, in the dipole approximation used so far some types of transitions are forbidden completely by selection rules. For some of these "forbidden" transitions the more exact theory will give non-zero probabilities (although small compared with dipole probabilities for "allowed" transitions).

We consider first the operator $e^{i\boldsymbol{k}_\omega\cdot\boldsymbol{r}}\boldsymbol{p}$ of the SCHRÖDINGER theory. The product $\boldsymbol{k}_\omega\cdot\boldsymbol{r}$ is small and, instead of neglecting it completely, we expand the

[1] For details see [5], Chap. 4, 9 and 11; [7], p. 728 to 743; H. C. BRINKMAN, Ph. D. Diss. Utrecht, 1932 and M. E. ROSE, Multipole Fields. New York: John Wiley & Sons 1955.

[2] We denote the constant propagation vector by $\boldsymbol{k}_\omega$, the orbital angular momentum operator by $\boldsymbol{k}$.

[3] E. SEGRÈ: Rend. Lincei (6) **14**, 501 (1931).

exponential in a TAYLOR series,

$$e^{i\boldsymbol{k}_\omega\cdot\boldsymbol{r}} = 1 + i\,\boldsymbol{k}_\omega\cdot\boldsymbol{r} - \tfrac{1}{2}(\boldsymbol{k}_\omega\cdot\boldsymbol{r})^2 + \cdots. \tag{66.1}$$

The first term (unity) in this expansion leads exactly to the electric dipole approximation of the previous sections. The higher terms in the expansion lead to transitions which are somewhat analogous to the types of radiation obtained by a multipole expansion in classical radiation theory. We shall consider only the effect of the second term of the expansion (66.1) on the matrix element (59.3). We call the propagation direction $\boldsymbol{k}_\omega$ of the photon the x-axis and its polarization direction $\boldsymbol{e}$ the y-axis ($\boldsymbol{k}_\omega$ and $\boldsymbol{e}$ are always perpendicular) and consider a transition of the atom from a state n to n'. From the BOHR energy relation (59.1) the wave number k_ω of the emitted photon equals $\omega_{n'n}/c$. We then have to add to the electric dipole matrix element (59.5) the correction term

$$D'_{n'n} = \frac{i}{\hbar}\Big(\sum_j i\,k_\omega\,x_j\,p_{y,j}\Big)_{n'n} = -\frac{\omega_{n'n}}{c\hbar}\sum_j (x_j\,p_{y,j})_{n'n}, \tag{66.2}$$

where j denotes the j-th electron and $n'n$ denotes the matrix element of an operator.

The matrix element (66.2) can be rewritten as follows. We first write (for one electron)

$$x\,p_y = \tfrac{1}{2}(x\,p_y + p_x\,y) + \tfrac{1}{2}(x\,p_y - p_x\,y).$$

Using (59.19), the explicit definition (11.4) for the operator $\boldsymbol{k}$ for the orbital angular momentum, and the fact that x commutes with p_y, we find

$$x\,p_y = \frac{i\,m}{2\hbar}(H\,x\,y - x\,y\,H) + \frac{\hbar}{2}\,k_z, \tag{66.3}$$

where k_z is the z-component of the operator $\boldsymbol{k}$ for the particular electron[1]. Since the states n and n' are eigenstates of the HAMILTONian H with eigenvalues E_n and $E_{n'}$, we have [using (59.1)]

$$D'_{n'n} = -\frac{\omega_{n'n}}{2c\hbar}\sum_j \left[-i\,m\,\omega_{n'n}(x_j\,y_j)_{n'n} + \hbar\,(k_{zj})_{n'n}\right]. \tag{66.4}$$

The matrix element (66.4) was obtained using the nonrelativistic operator $\boldsymbol{p}$ instead of $mc\boldsymbol{\alpha}$, which occurs in the DIRAC theory. This replacement was discussed in Sect. 64α and is equivalent to replacing the vector in square brackets in (64.2) by $\boldsymbol{p}$. If the DIRAC theory is used, as it should be, one has to evaluate the component of the vector matrix element (64.2) in the polarization direction[2] $\boldsymbol{e}$, which results in the expression (64.2a). The first term in this expression is the full nonrelativistic matrix element, whose expansion leads to the electric dipole expression plus (66.4) plus higher terms. The second term in (64.2a) is of the same (small) order of magnitude as (66.4) and we approximate it by replacing the exponential by unity. If this term is added to the matrix element (66.4), the operator k_z in (66.4) is replaced by $k_z + \sigma_z = k_z + 2s_z$, where s is the PAULI spin-operator for the particular electron. $D'_{n'n}$ plus this additional term is then

[1] An error in a similar derivation in [*10*], p. 473, was kindly pointed out by Dr. M. A. PRESTON.

[2] $\boldsymbol{e}$ is perpendicular to $\boldsymbol{k}_\omega$, which is called $\boldsymbol{k}$ in Sect. 64.

the sum of two matrix elements

$$\left.\begin{aligned} D_{n'n}^{(e2)} &= \frac{i\,m\,\omega_{n'n}^2}{2c\hbar}\sum_i (x_j\,y_j)_{n'n}; \\ D_{n'n}^{(m1)} &= -\frac{\omega_{n'n}}{2c}\,(K_z+2\,S_z)_{n'n} \end{aligned}\right\} \tag{66.5}$$

where $\boldsymbol{K}=\sum_j \boldsymbol{k}_j$ and $\boldsymbol{S}=\sum_j \boldsymbol{s}_j$ are the operators for the total orbital and spin angular momentum, respectively.

The matrix elements (66.5) are to be compared with the electric dipole matrix element [see (59.5)]

$$D_{n'n}^{(e1)} = \frac{m}{\hbar}\,\omega_{n\,n'}\sum_j (y_j)_{n'n}.$$

These matrix elements bear some analogy to expressions found in classical radiation theory: The matrix element $e\,y_{n'n}$ corresponds to the classical electric dipole moment in the direction of polarization of the emitted radiation. Similarly $e(xy)_{n'n}$ corresponds to the electric quadrupole moment and $D^{(e2)}$ is called an electric quadrupole matrix element. Note that $D^{(e2)}$ depends both on the propagation (x) and polarization (y) directions of the photon. Finally, $(e/2mc)\times(K_z+2S_z)_{n'n}$ is the quantum mechanical equivalent of the magnetic dipole moment of a charge and current distribution possessing angular momentum[1]. Note that the magnetic dipole matrix element $D^{(m1)}$ depends on the direction (z) perpendicular to the plane containing the propagation and polarization directions. Apart from selection rules, the order of magnitude of both $D^{(e2)}$ and $D^{(m1)}$ should be smaller than that of $D^{(e1)}$ by $k_\omega a\sim\omega a/c\sim\hbar/mca\sim Z\alpha$. The selection rules are discussed below.

β) Electric quadrupole radiation. We consider now the selection rules for $D^{(e2)}$, the electric quadrupole matrix element. We restrict ourselves to single-electron atoms, but consider different orientations of the polarization and propagation directions relative to the quantization direction of the atom (to which the magnetic quantum number m refers). We also restrict ourselves to the PAULI approximation, so that l is a good quantum number.

The selection rules for the magnetic quantum number m are an immediate consequence of (66.5). If, for example, the direction of quantization is along z, then the following rules hold:

Observation direction	Polarization direction	Matrix element of	Selection rule for m
parallel to the field (z)	x or y	$xz=r^2\cos\vartheta\sin\vartheta\cos\varphi$	$\Delta m=\pm 1$
perpendicular to the field (x)	parallel (z)	same	$\Delta m=\pm 1$
	perpendicular (y)	$xy=\frac{1}{2}r^2\sin^2\vartheta\sin 2\varphi$	$\Delta m=\pm 2$
at 45° to the field $\left(\frac{1}{\sqrt{2}}(x+z)\right)$	45° to the field $\left(\frac{1}{\sqrt{2}}(z-x)\right)$	$\frac{1}{2}(z^2-x^2)=\frac{1}{2}r^2\left(\frac{3}{2}\cos^2\vartheta-\frac{1}{2}\right)-\frac{1}{4}r^2\sin^2\vartheta\cos 2\varphi$	$\Delta m=0$ and $\Delta m=\pm 2$
	perpendicular (y)	$\frac{1}{\sqrt{2}}(xy+zy)$	$\Delta m=\pm 1$ and ± 2

[1] Note that this magnetic moment combination also occurs in the ZEEMAN effect.

As in the case of the dipole radiation of Sect. 60, the above selection rules follow simply from a consideration of the φ integral which occurs in the matrix element.

The integrals with respect to ϑ give rise to the selection rules for l. Examining, for example, the integral which corresponds to the transition $\Delta m=0$

$$\int R^*_{n'l'}(r)\,\mathscr{P}_{l'm}(\vartheta)\,r^2\left(\tfrac{3}{2}\cos^2\vartheta-\tfrac{1}{2}\right)R_{nl}(r)\,\mathscr{P}_{lm}(\vartheta)\,r^2\,dr\,\sin\vartheta\,d\vartheta,$$

it is readily seen that l' and l may only differ by an even integer since $P_2(\vartheta)=\frac{3}{2}\cos^2\vartheta-\frac{1}{2}$ is an even function of $\cos\vartheta$, and, furthermore, they may differ by at most by 2 since $P_2(\vartheta)$ contains only the second power of $\cos\vartheta$. Therefore,

$$\Delta l=0 \quad \text{or} \quad \pm 2 \quad \text{and} \quad l=0\to 0 \quad \text{is forbidden.} \tag{66.6}$$

The above selection rule may also be arrived at in another way. According to the usual rules of matrix multiplication we have

$$(x\,y)_{n'n}=\sum_{n''} x_{n'n''}\,y_{n''n}.$$

Applying the selection rule for dipole radiation $\Delta l=\pm 1$ we obtain

$$l''-l=\pm 1 \quad \text{and} \quad l''-l'=\pm 1$$

from which (66.6) follows immediately. Similarly, one obtains the J selection rule for quadrupole radiation from the rule for dipole radiation (64.5):

$$\Delta J=0,\quad \pm 1 \quad \text{or} \quad \pm 2. \tag{66.7}$$

Evidently, in similar fashion one can also derive specialized intensity formulas for the ZEEMAN components, fine structure components, etc. There are also sum rules which correspond exactly to those derived for dipole radiation. For example, for reasons of symmetry the quadrupole radiation is independent of the direction of propagation and polarization if all the ZEEMAN components are summed. The quadrupole radiation within a given multiplet is independent of the magnetic and total angular momentum quantum numbers of the initial state, if a summation over all the directions of propagation and polarization is performed. For the details we refer the reader to the papers by RUBINOWICZ[1] and for experimental verifications to the work of SEGRÈ[2] and others.

In order to obtain a notion of the magnitude of the line intensities in question, we shall calculate the intensity of the transition from the ground state to the $3d$ state of hydrogen. Carrying out the integrations over angles and over the directions of propagation and polarization of the emitted light, one obtains

$$\int d\Omega \sum |D^{kj}_{n'n}|^2=\left(\frac{m}{2\hbar c}\,\omega^2\right)^2\frac{8\pi}{15}\left(\int_0^\infty R_{10}(r)\,r^2\,R_{32}(r)\,r^2\,dr\right)^2.$$

Inserting the eigenfunctions (3.18) into the radial integral yields $\frac{81}{256}\times\sqrt{30}\,a^2$, in which a is the radius of the hydrogen atom. Defining the oscillator strength as

$$\bar{f}_{n'n}=\frac{2}{3}\,\frac{\hbar}{m\,\omega_{nn'}}\,\frac{1}{8\pi}\int d\Omega\sum_j |D^{kj}_{n'n}|^2 \tag{66.8}$$

---

[1] A. RUBINOWICZ: Z. Physik **61**, 338 (1930); **65**, 662 (1930); with J. BLATON, Ergebn. exakt. Naturwiss. **11**, 176 (1932) which also contains additional references.

[2] E. SEGRÈ: Z. Physik **66**, 827 (1930); with C. J. BAKKER, Z. Physik **72**, 724 (1931); S. SAMBURSKY, Z. Physik **68**, 774 (1931); **76**, 132, 266 (1932).

[for dipole radiation the definition goes over to (59.14)], one obtains after some numerical computation, for the transition $1s \to 3d$

$$f_{1s}^{3d} = 0.033\,\alpha^2 = 1.8 \times 10^{-6}. \tag{66.9}$$

Transitions which have an oscillator strength of such a small magnitude can, of course, be observed only in two ways: either in absorption—this has been done, for example, by SEGRÈ for the transition $3s \to 3d$ of Na—or if the upper level is metastable. If, for example, the $3d$ state of hydrogen were metastable (assuming for a moment that the transition $3d \to 2p$ does not exist), the lifetime of the $3d$ state would be given by[1] [cf. Eq. (59.15)]:

$$T = \left(\frac{\nu}{\mathrm{Ry}}\right)^{-2} 1.25 \times 10^{-10} \times \frac{5}{1.8 \times 10^{-6}} = 4.4 \times 10^{-4}\,\mathrm{sec}. \tag{66.10}$$

The above agrees in order of magnitude with the lifetimes of metastable states as generally found experimentally.

γ) Magnetic dipole radiation. We consider first the most general selection rules for the magnetic dipole matrix element $D^{(m1)}$. For any complex atom (without external fields), $\boldsymbol{M}^2$ and M_z are constants of the motion ($\boldsymbol{M} = \boldsymbol{K} + \boldsymbol{S}$) with eigenvalues $J(J+1)$ and m, respectively. In addition, the atomic states can be classified into states with even or odd parity (for a nonrelativistic product wave function the parity is even (odd) if $\sum_j l_j$ is even (odd), where l_j is the orbital quantum number for the j-th electron). We need the matrix element, between two atomic states, of the component of $\boldsymbol{K} + 2\boldsymbol{S} = \boldsymbol{M} + \boldsymbol{S}$ in the direction ξ which is perpendicular to the plane containing the propagation and polarization directions of the photon. One can derive (see [5]) the following three general selection rules:

(1) $$\Delta m = 0 \quad (\text{if } \xi \parallel z), \quad \pm 1 \quad (\text{if } \xi \perp z), \tag{66.11}$$

(2) $$\Delta J = 0 \quad \text{or} \quad \pm 1 \quad (J = 0 \to 0 \text{ forbidden}). \tag{66.12}$$

and (3) the parity must remain unchanged in the transition[2].

If the RUSSELL-SAUNDERS approximation (see Sects. 43α, 48α and 64β) holds, much more restrictive selection rules apply. Consider first the HARTREE product type wave functions belonging to a particular "configuration" i.e., with *given* values of the quantum numbers $n_1 l_1, n_2 l_2$, etc. for the various electrons, but arbitrary values of m_{1l}, m_{1s}; m_{2l}, m_{2s}; etc. The spatial part of each single-electron wave function (in this approximation) is independent of m_s and the radial part is also independent of m_l. In the RUSSELL-SAUNDERS approximation one then forms a linear superposition of these wave functions (from a particular configuration), for which L, S and J are good quantum numbers (as well as $n_1 l_1, n_2 l_2$, etc.). Now the operator $\boldsymbol{K} + 2\boldsymbol{S}$ commutes with $\boldsymbol{K}^2$, $\boldsymbol{S}^2$ and also with $\boldsymbol{k}_2^2, \boldsymbol{k}_1^2$, etc. One then finds the following selection rule for a matrix element of $\boldsymbol{K} + 2\boldsymbol{S}$,

$$\Delta L = \Delta S = \Delta l_1 = \Delta l_2 = \cdots = 0, \tag{66.13}$$

in addition to (66.11) and (66.12). But in our present approximation the radial part of a wave function is simply a product of single-particle radial functions

[1] The factor 5 has its origin in the fact that the oscillator strength 1.8×10^{-6} must be shared by the five magnetic substates of the $3d$ level.

[2] For electric dipole transitions (see Sect. 64β), we also have rules (1) and (2) (with the polarization direction taking the place of ξ) but (3) is replaced by the rule that the parity must change. For electric quadrupole transitions the rule (3) also applies, but (1) is replaced by $\Delta m = 0, \pm 1, \pm 2$ and in (2), $\Delta J = \pm 2$ is now also possible.

which depend only on $n_1 l_1, n_2 l_2$, etc. Now the operator $\boldsymbol{K}+2\boldsymbol{S}$ leaves the radial part of any wave function unchanged and two radial wave functions with the same l, but different n, are orthogonal. We then find the additional selection rule

$$\Delta n_1 = \Delta n_2 = \cdots = 0. \tag{66.14}$$

We have thus found that, in the RUSSELL-SAUNDERS approximation, magnetic dipole transitions are only possible between two states belonging to the *same* configuration and having the *same* values of L and S. Two such states belong to the same fine structure multiplet and their energy difference is extremely small (compared with 1 Ry, say). The emitted radiation is then in the microwave or radio region, *not* in the optical region, and $\omega_{nn'}$ in (66.5) is extremely small. Spontaneous transitions of this type thus have a negligibly small probability, but induced transitions of this type can be important: For an atom in a weak external magnetic field, for instance, the energy of a level depends on the magnetic quantum number m. Magnetic dipole transitions are then possible between two ZEEMAN components of the same[1] fine structure level ($\Delta L = \Delta S = \Delta J = 0$, $\Delta m = \pm 1$) and can be used to measure the ZEEMAN effect energy splitting (see Sect. 49). For an atom whose nucleus has a magnetic moment, one can also get magnetic dipole transitions between two hyperfine structure components of the same fine structure level ($\Delta L = \Delta S = \Delta J = 0$, $\Delta f = \pm 1$) (see [16] and our Sect. 22).

δ) Applications. The transition probabilities for electric quadrupole transitions with $\Delta l = \pm 2$ (or 0) are an order of $(Z\alpha)^2$ smaller than for "allowed" electric dipole transitions with $\Delta l = \pm 1$. For hydrogen-like atoms the frequencies of quadrupole lines coincide with those of much stronger dipole lines (because of the l-degeneracy) and cannot be investigated experimentally. For alkali and more complex atoms the frequencies of quadrupole lines are distinct and have been measured in absorption (see [5], Chap. 9, Sect. 5). Electric octupole transitions with $\Delta l = \pm 3$ have probabilities an order of $(Z\alpha)^4$ smaller than dipole transitions and are of little interest for atomic spectra.

We have already discussed magnetic dipole transitions between components of the same fine structure multiplet. Magnetic dipole transitions in the optical region (between different fine structure multiplets) have probabilities an order of $(Z\alpha)^2 \xi^2$ smaller than electric dipole transitions, where ξ is the order of magnitude of the matrix element $(K_z + 2S_z)_{n'n}$. In the RUSSELL-SAUNDERS approximation, ξ is zero—and is generally very small for atoms with small nuclear charge Z. Magnetic dipole transitions thus have very small probabilities, but occur nevertheless in interstellar gas[2] (emission nebulae): Interstellar gas contains some doubly ionized O^{++}-ions at extremely low pressure, so that atomic collisions are very rare. The ground state configuration of O^{++} has two valence electrons in p-states which can form a $^1D_2$ state, as well as ^3P-states with $J = 0, 1$ or 2 at lower energies. This $^1D_2$-state is metastable since electric dipole transitions to the ^3P-states are strictly forbidden (parity unchanged) and higher order transitions are also forbidden in a pure RUSSELL-SAUNDERS approximation ($\Delta S = 1$). The exact wave functions deviate slightly from pure RUSSELL-SAUNDERS coupling and the exact singlet $^1D_2$-state has a slight admixture of the triplet $^3P_2$ wave functions (and vice versa). The order ξ of the matrix elements for magnetic

[1] For a single-electron atom in an S-state, for instance, $l = 0$ and $s = j = \frac{1}{2}$ for both states and $m = -\frac{1}{2}$ and $+\frac{1}{2}$ respectively. For such a transition the matrix element $(K_z + 2S_z)_{n'n}$ is simply unity if z is perpendicular to the axis of quantization.

[2] See ref. [5], Chap. 11, Sect. 5 and J. A. HYNEK, Astrophysics, Chap. 13. New York: McGraw-Hill 1951.

dipole transitions is then not exactly zero, but small (less than 0.01). Spontaneous magnetic dipole transitions from the $^1D_2$-state to $^3P_2$ and $^3P_1$ are responsible for the "nebular emission lines" in interstellar gas and the lifetime of the $^1D_2$-state is about 40 sec. The lifetime of the metastable $2\,^2S_{\frac{1}{2}}$-state in hydrogen is discussed in Sect. 67α.

Radiative transitions of higher multipole type are much more common between energy levels of *nuclei* than in atoms[1]: "Metastable states" occur very frequently and in some cases the J-value of a first excited state differs by ± 3 from that of the ground state. Such states (called nuclear isomers) may decay by electric octupole transitions. Electric quadrupole transitions are more common still in nuclear spectroscopy. In complex nuclei spin-orbit coupling is very much stronger than in atoms and the nuclear wave functions are not of RUSSELL-SAUNDERS type. The selection rules (66.13) and (66.14) do not apply and the probabilities for magnetic dipole transitions may be quite appreciable.

67. Lifetimes of excited states in hydrogen. In Sect. 63 we have calculated the probabilities for transitions between states in hydrogen which are eigenstates of $\boldsymbol{k}^2$ (l is a good quantum number, wave function separable in spherical polar coordinates). The corresponding mean lifetimes for such states are given in Table 15 and depend strongly on the orbital quantum number l. In Sect. 64 we have taken the electron's spin into account and shown that the lifetime of a state with a definite l-value (in the PAULI approximation) is the same as in nonrelativistic theory and the same for the states with $j=l-\frac{1}{2}$ and $l+\frac{1}{2}$. The lifetimes of excited states of hydrogen atoms in a reasonably strong electric field (STARK effect $\gg$ fine structure) were discussed in Sect. 65. In this case l is not at all a good quantum number (we have instead the parabolic quantum numbers) and the lifetimes are quite different from those of Table 15. In the absence of any perturbations or in *very* weak electric fields, levels with different j-values are well separated in energy. On the other hand, the two states of given j value (with $l=j-\frac{1}{2}$ and $j+\frac{1}{2}$) have the same energy, if the LAMB shift is neglected. We shall discuss in this section under what circumstances these two degenerate states (with l differing by unity) decay separately with the different lifetimes given in Table 15. We restrict ourselves throughout to weak enough electric fields so that the STARK effect is smaller than the fine structure splitting.

We shall use in our discussion the concept of the "radiation width" Γ of an energy level: If an atomic state of energy E decays exponentially with a mean lifetime of $\hbar/\Gamma$ seconds, the time dependence of its wave function will be proportional to

$$\exp\left[-i\left(E-\tfrac{1}{2}\,i\,\Gamma\right)t/\hbar\right]. \tag{67.1}$$

The quantity $\frac{1}{2}\Gamma$ has the dimensions of energy and is called the "half-width" of the level. In the language of the uncertainty principle, Γ corresponds to a spread or uncertainty in the energy of the level. Radiation theory leads to the following related result: Consider a radiative transition from the excited state of energy E and mean lifetime $\hbar/\Gamma$ to the ground state of energy E_0 (and infinite lifetime). The energy $h\nu$ of the emitted photon is then not exactly $(E-E_0)$, but photons of different energies can be emitted with a probability approximately proportional to

$$\left[(h\,\nu-E+E_0)^2+(\tfrac{1}{2}\Gamma)^2\right]^{-1}. \tag{67.2}$$

For hydrogen-like atoms of nuclear charge Z, the width Γ (see Sect. 59α) is of order $\alpha(Z\alpha)^2\,W_Z$, where $W_Z=Z^2\,\mathrm{Ry}$ is the ionization potential. Thus Γ is extremely small compared with the energy differences (E_2-E_1) between levels

[1] See J. BLATT and V. WEISSKOPF, Theoretical Nuclear Physics, Chap. 12. New York: Wiley 1952; R. G. SACHS, Nuclear Theory, Chap. 9 (Cambridge- Addison-Wesley 1953), and Vols. XXXIX to XLII of this Encyclopedia.

with different principal quantum numbers n, and Γ is even one order of α smaller than the fine structure splitting. We are also interested in the ratio of Γ for excited states to the LAMB shift splitting S_L between the two states $l=j+\frac{1}{2}$ and $j-\frac{1}{2}$ for fixed j. This ratio is roughly independent of n (both Γ and S_L are roughly proportional to n^{-3}) but depends strongly on j: For $j \geqq \frac{3}{2}$ and for any n, the LAMB shift splitting S_L is appreciably smaller than the width Γ of either of the two states (for $j=\frac{3}{2}$, for instance, Γ for the $P_{\frac{3}{2}}$-state is about 10 times the splitting energy S_L). For $j=\frac{1}{2}$ and any n, on the other hand, S_L is appreciably larger than the width Γ of the $P_{\frac{1}{2}}$-state (the width Γ is smaller still for the $S_{\frac{1}{2}}$-state). For $n=2$, for instance, the mean-life $\hbar/\Gamma$ of the $2P_{\frac{1}{2}}$-state is

$$\frac{\hbar}{\Gamma}=\frac{3c^2}{4\alpha\,\omega_{21}^3\,|\boldsymbol{r}_{12}|^2}=1.595\times 10^{-9}\,\text{sec}. \tag{67.3}$$

The width in frequency units is then $\Gamma/h=99.8$ Mc/sec (corresponding to 0.0033 cm^{-1}), compared with the LAMB shift splitting[1] between $2S_{\frac{1}{2}}$ and $2P_{\frac{1}{2}}$ of $S_L/h=1058$ Mc/sec.

We shall discuss separately the case of levels with $j=\frac{1}{2}$ and those with $j>\frac{1}{2}$. For all $j=\frac{1}{2}$ states (see Table 15) the lifetime (without perturbations) of the S-state is appreciably longer than that of the P-state. The situation is particularly interesting for $n=2$ where the 2 S-state is metastable.

α) The unperturbed 2S-state. We consider first the lifetime of a hydrogen atom in the metastable $2S_{\frac{1}{2}}$-state in the absence of any perturbations such as an electric field or atomic collisions. The only states with lower energy are the $1S$ ground state and the $2P_{\frac{1}{2}}$-state. Spontaneous transitions to the 2 P-state have a negligibly small probability (lifetime about 20 years), since the energy difference is so small. Electric dipole transitions to the ground state are strictly forbidden, since the $1S$ and $2S$-states have the same parity. In the PAULI approximation, $2S_{\frac{1}{2}}-1S_{\frac{1}{2}}$ electric quadrupole transitions (Sect. 66β) are forbidden[2] (since both states have $l=0$) and magnetic dipole transitions (Sect. 66γ) are also forbidden since the radial wave functions of the two states are orthogonal in this approximation. If the exact DIRAC wave functions are used, the matrix element ξ of the spin operator is not exactly zero, but the relative deviations of the exact from the PAULI wave functions, and hence ξ, are only of order $(Z\alpha)^2$. Magnetic dipole transitions from $2S_{\frac{1}{2}}$ to $1S_{\frac{1}{2}}$ are therefore not strictly forbidden, but their probability is smaller than those for allowed electric dipole transitions by an order of $(Z\alpha)^6$ or about 10^{-13} for hydrogen. An explicit calculation[3] of this effect leads to a lifetime of the $2S_{\frac{1}{2}}$-state in hydrogen of about 2 days!

The largest probability for a $2S-1S$ transition comes from a type of process which we have neglected so far, namely the simultaneous emission of two photons whose combined energies equal the energy difference between the two atomic states. For such two-quantum processes $l=0\to l=0$ transitions are not forbidden, but their probabilities turn out to be smaller than those of *allowed* single quantum transitions by an order of $\alpha(ka)^2\sim\alpha(Z\alpha)^2$. The total probability for two-quantum transitions from $2S$ to $1S$ in hydrogen has been calculated[4] and

---

[1] We shall neglect any hyperfine structure splitting in hydrogen, which is less than the LAMB shift for all $j=\frac{1}{2}$ states and less than the radiation width Γ for all states with $j\ \ \frac{3}{2}$.

[2] In fact, electric quadrupole transitions are strictly forbidden unless $j_1+j_2 \geqq 2$ (here $j_1=j_2=\frac{1}{2}$).

[3] G. BREIT and E. TELLER: Astrophys. J. **91**, 215 (1940).

[4] G. BREIT and E. TELLER: Astrophys. J. **91**, 215 (1940). For a discussion of other two-quantum processes see M. GÖPPERT-MAYER, Ann. Phys. **9**, 273 (1931).

is about 7 $\sec^{-1}$. The mean lifetime of $\frac{1}{7}$ sec of the $2S$-state is thus extremely long compared with that of the $2P$-state (1.6×10^{-9} sec).

The effect of electric fields on the lifetime of the metastable state in hydrogen is discussed below. The effect of collisions transferring hydrogen atoms from the $2S$ to other states has been investigated by various authors[1]. In a partially ionized hydrogen gas under conditions of thermal equilibrium the main effect is due to collisions of the atom in the $2S$-state with hydrogen ions (protons) resulting in a transition to either of the $2P$-states. At temperatures around 10000 °K the probability for the removal of a hydrogen atom from the $2S$-state by collisions[2] is about $7\times10^{-4}\,N_i\,\sec^{-1}$, where N_i is the number of positive ions per cm³. The lifetime of an atom in the $2S$-state is then appreciably longer than for the $2P$-state if N_i is much less than 10^{12} ions/cm³. Collisions with neutral hydrogen atoms contribute only a removal probability of the order of $10^{-8}N\,\sec^{-1}$ $\sim10^{7}p\,\sec^{-1}$, where N is the number of atoms/cm³ and p the pressure in mm Hg. In terrestrial low pressure discharge tubes with *low* ion densities (and also in the outermost atmospheres of stars) the removal rate of $2S$-state atoms by collisions is appreciably less than the inverse lifetime of about $10^9\,\sec^{-1}$ of the $2P$-state. In interstellar gas clouds N and N_i are only of the order of about 100 and removal by collisions is even slower than the two-quantum decay to the ground state. In the LAMB shift experiments (Sect. 21) unidirectional atomic beams in a very good vacuum are used and the effect of collisions can be neglected.

β) The $j=\frac{1}{2}$ states in an electric field. We consider next the effect of a uniform, constant and weak electric field of field strength F on the lifetime of the metastable $2S_{\frac{1}{2}}$-state in hydrogen. In the absence of the electric field (and all other perturbations) the two $n=2$, $j=\frac{1}{2}$ states decay separately with vastly different lifetimes: $t_P=1.6\times10^{-9}$ sec for the $2P_{\frac{1}{2}}$-state and $t_S=\frac{1}{7}$ sec for the $2S_{\frac{1}{2}}$-state. If, for instance, at time $t=0$ we have a wave function which is a linear superposition of the $2S$ and $2P$ eigenfunctions,

$$u(0)=a\,u_{2S}+b\,u_{2P}, \tag{67.4}$$

the two parts of the wave function decay quite independently. At a later time t where $t_P\ll t\ll t_S$, for instance, the $2P$ part has practically all decayed to the ground state ($1S$) and the $2S$ part practically not at all. The wave function is then approximately

$$u(t)=a u_{2S}\,e^{-iE_{2S}t/\hbar}+b u_{1S}\,e^{-iE_{1S}t/\hbar}. \tag{67.5}$$

We consider now the two stationary states with $n=2$, $j=\frac{1}{2}$ in the presence of an electric field F, weak enough so that the STARK effect is small compared with the fine structure splitting (but not necessarily smaller than the LAMB shift). We neglect the effect[3] of hyperfine structure and of the radiation width of the $2P$-state, which are smaller than the (field free) LAMB shift splitting S_L between $2S$ and $2P$ of 1058 Mc/sec (in frequency units). In the presence of the electric field F (but neglecting radiation) there are two stationary states with $n=2$, $j=\frac{1}{2}$ and given m ($+\frac{1}{2}$ or $-\frac{1}{2}$), which are discussed in Sect. 55α. The wave function for each of these two states is a linear superposition of form (67.4). The ratio a/b for each of these states as a function of F is given by (55.7) and their energy

[1] See E. M. PURCELL: Astrophys. J. **116**, 457 (1952).

[2] Collisions with electrons (instead of protons) contribute only about 10% of this probability.

[3] For states with $j \gtrless \frac{3}{2}$ we shall use a different approximation in Sect. 67γ. More general expressions (which neglect neither the LAMB shift nor the radiation width) have been obtained by W. LAMB and R. RETHERFORD, Phys. Rev. **79**, 549 (1950) (see their Appendix II) and by G. LÜDERS, Z. Naturforsch. **5a**, 608 (1950); see also (67.14).

difference by (55.8). For $n=2$, the ratio 2ξ of the STARK effect splitting $2\sqrt{3}F$ to the (field-free) LAMB shift splitting S_L is about $F/475$ Volt/cm. (55.7) then gives for the ratio a/b

$$\frac{a_\pm}{b_\pm} = + \frac{2\xi}{1 \pm \sqrt{1+4\xi^2}}, \tag{67.6}$$

where the plus sign refers to the stationary state which reduces to $2P$ for $\xi=0$ and the minus sign to that which reduces to $2S$.

(55.8) shows that the energy separation between the two stationary states with $n=2$, $j=\frac{1}{2}$ increases with increasing field strength F and is larger than the radiation width of the $2P$-state for all F. Each of the two states, with wave functions given by (67.4) and (67.6), will then decay to the ground state separately with its own lifetime $t_\pm(F)$. The transition matrix element from the part of the wave function involving u_{2S} is negligible and the transition probability essentially all comes from the admixture of u_{2P} in the wave function. The lifetimes of the two states are then given by

$$t_\pm(F) = t_P \frac{a_\pm^2 + b_\pm^2}{b_\pm^2}, \tag{67.7}$$

where t_P is the lifetimes of the field-free $2P$-state and $a_\pm$, $b_\pm$ are given by (67.6). For $\xi \gg 1$, both t_+ and t_- are nearly equal to $2t_P$ and no trace of metastability remains in either state. For $\xi \ll 1$, one of the two states is almost pure $2P$ and t_+ nearly equals the field-free t_P. The other state is almost pure $2S$ with a small admixture of $2P$ which gives a lifetime of (neglecting again the direct $2S-1S$ transition probability)

$$t_-(F) = \xi^{-2} t_P = \left(\frac{F}{475\ \text{Volt/cm}}\right)^{-2} t_P. \tag{67.8}$$

Under the conditions of the LAMB shift experiment all external electric fields can be kept down to about 5 Volt/cm or less and the $2S$-state is almost pure and has a much longer lifetime than the $2P$-state[1]. The situation is more complicated if a uniform and constant weak magnetic field $\mathcal{H}$ is also present: In the presence of the magnetic (and the absence of an electric) field the components with $m=\frac{1}{2}$ and $-\frac{1}{2}$ of both the $2S_{\frac{1}{2}}$ and $2P_{\frac{1}{2}}$ energy levels split as shown in Fig. 33 (see also Sect. 46α). At about 575 Gauss the $m=-\frac{1}{2}(S)$ and the $m=\frac{1}{2}(P)$ levels coincide and the $m=\frac{1}{2}(S)$ and $m=-\frac{1}{2}(P)$ levels are separated by about 2150 Mc/sec (compared with 1058 Mc/sec for zero field). If an additional electric field, with direction *perpendicular* to that of the magnetic field, is applied it will couple the m-component of the S-level with the $P_{\frac{1}{2}}$-level with $m'=-m$. In a very weak electric field the mixing of the wave functions is much larger[2] for the $m=-\frac{1}{2}(S)$ level (whose energy coincides with that of the relevant P-level)

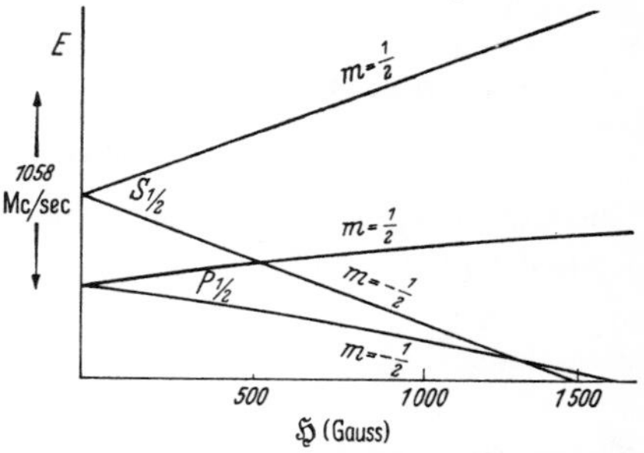

Fig. 33. ZEEMAN effect on the levels with $n=2$, $j=\frac{1}{2}$ in hydrogen for weak magnetic fields $\mathcal{H}$ (including the LAMB shift).

[1] Although we have assumed a uniform and constant electric field, the results can be extended to apply to the varying electric fields produced in a discharge tube or atomic beam apparatus by passing electrons and ions. Note, however, that these fields would have to be less than about 0.05 Volt/cm for the lifetime of the $2S$-state to have its field-free value of $\frac{1}{7}$ sec.

[2] In our approximation by an infinite factor, in reality by a factor of $\sqrt{1850}$ [see Sect. 67γ and also W. E. LAMB, Rep. Progr. Phys. **14**, 19 (1951)].

than for the $m=\frac{1}{2}(S)$ level. The lifetime of the $m=-\frac{1}{2}(S)$ level is then much shorter than for $m=\frac{1}{2}(S)$. The experimental conditions in the LAMB shift experiment can be so arranged that the $m=-\frac{1}{2}(2S)$ and all $(2P)$ levels decay in flight to the ground state and a polarized beam of $2S$-atoms with $m=\frac{1}{2}$ reaches the detector.

We have considered so far only the $j=\frac{1}{2}$ levels with $n=2$. For $j=\frac{1}{2}$ but larger values of n (in an electric, but no magnetic, field) the situation is *qualitatively* similar. The field-free lifetime of the nS-state is no longer (practically) infinite, but nevertheless appreciably larger than that of the nP-state and the LAMB shift is much larger than the radiation widths. The lifetimes of the two states again become comparable with each other for field strengths F for which the STARK effect is comparable with the LAMB shift. However, the STARK effect increases and the LAMB shift decreases with increasing principal quantum number n. The critical field strength thus decreases very rapidly (inversely as $n^4\sqrt{n^2-1}$) with increasing n and is approximately 475, 58, 12 and 1.7 Volt/cm for $n=2, 3, 4$ and 6, respectively.

γ) Lifetimes of other excited states. We now consider the effect of a weak electric field on the "mixing" of the wave functions and the lifetimes of the two states with $l=j+\frac{1}{2}$ and $j-\frac{1}{2}$ in hydrogen for $j\geqq\frac{3}{2}$. The field-free LAMB shift is small compared with the radiation widths for such states and, for simplicity, we neglect the LAMB shift completely. Since the two energy levels are assumed to coincide in the absence of an external field, one might at first sight expect that an external electric field of *arbitrarily* small strength F would "mix up" the wave functions and lifetimes of the two field-free states. We shall now show that this is *not* the case until the field strengths are large enough so that the STARK effect splitting is larger than the difference between the radiation widths of the two states.

Let $u_1(\mathbf{r},t)$ and $u_2(\mathbf{r},t)$ be the wave functions of the states with $l=j+\frac{1}{2}$ and $j-\frac{1}{2}$ (and fixed m) in the absence of both the electric field and the interaction with radiation. We consider a state of the atom in the electric field whose wave function is a linear superposition of u_1, u_2 and wave functions for levels of lower energy. The part of this wave function which contains u_1 and u_2 is then

$$u(t) = a_1(t)\,u_1 + a_2(t)\,u_2, \tag{67.9}$$

where the coefficients a_1 and a_2 satisfy[1] the coupled differential equations (derived from the wave equations)

$$\left.\begin{aligned} \frac{da_1}{dt} &= -i f a_2 - 2\beta_1 a_1, \\ \frac{da_2}{dt} &= -i f a_1 - 2\beta_2 a_2. \end{aligned}\right\} \tag{67.10}$$

The coefficients f and β in (67.10) have the following meaning: $\hbar f$ is the magnitude of the matrix element between the states 1 and 2 of the perturbation HAMILTONian due to the presence of a weak electric field of strength F parallel to the quantization direction. From (55.3) we have

$$\hbar f = \left|\pm\frac{3}{4}\sqrt{n^2-\left(j+\frac{1}{2}\right)^2}\,\frac{n\,m}{j(j+1)}\,F\right|. \tag{67.11}$$

$4\beta_1$ and $4\beta_2$ are the reciprocal mean lifetimes of the pure states 1 and 2 as given in Table 15 (and $\beta_1>\beta_2$). In the absence of the electric field, $a_1(t)$ would be a multiple of $e^{-2\beta_1 t}$ and similarly for a_2.

[1] E. WIGNER and V. WEISSKOPF: Z. Physik 63, 54 (1930).

We can look for a solution of (67.10) for which a_1 and a_2 have the *same* purely exponential (but possibly complex) time dependence. One finds two different solutions satisfying this requirement and the corresponding two wave functions (67.9) are

$$\left.\begin{aligned} u_a &= [f u_1 + i(\beta_- - \gamma)\, u_2]\, e^{-(\beta_1+\beta_2+\gamma)t}, \\ u_b &= [f u_1 + i(\beta_- + \gamma)\, u_2]\, e^{-(\beta_1+\beta_2-\gamma)t}; \\ \beta_- &\equiv \beta_1 - \beta_2, \qquad \gamma = \sqrt{\beta_-^2 - f^2}. \end{aligned}\right\} \tag{67.12}$$

The general solution of (67.9) with (67.10) is a linear superposition of the wave functions u_a and u_b. Note, however, that u_a and u_b are in general *not* orthogonal except in the limits of $\beta_-^2 \ll f^2$ and of $\beta_-^2 \gg f^2$.

It is convenient to consider separately the two cases of β_-^2 larger than and smaller than f^2:

(i) $\beta_-^2 > f^2$: In this case, γ and the exponents in the exponentials in (67.12) are real. The time dependence of u_a (and of u_b) represents a purely exponential decay. The real energies of the two states a and b are then equal (as in the absence of the electric field) but the lifetimes of the two exponential decays are different (except in the limit of $\beta_-^2 = f^2$). (67.12) simplifies if we assume $\beta_-^2 \gg f^2$, i.e. if the Stark effect splitting is small compared with the difference between the radiation widths. The states a and b are then almost identical with the two field-free states: The ratio $|a_2/a_1|$ is then approximately $f/2\beta_-$ for u_a and $2\beta_-/f$ for u_b and the lifetimes t_a and t_b differ little from the field-free values,

$$t_a^{-1} \approx 4\beta_1 - \frac{f^2}{\beta_-}, \qquad t_b^{-1} \approx 4\beta_2 + \frac{f^2}{\beta_-}. \tag{67.13}$$

(ii) $\beta_-^2 < f^2$: In this case, γ is purely imaginary and the exponents in the exponentials in (67.12) are complex. The terms $e^{\pm i|\gamma|t}$ represent energy shifts of the two states in opposite directions and their energy difference is $2|\gamma|\hbar$. If $\beta^2 \ll f^2$ then $2|\gamma|$ reduces to $2f - \beta_-^2/f$, compared with $2f$ in the absence of radiation. The inverse lifetimes of the two states a and b are then the same and equal to $2(\beta_1 + \beta_2)$. Note also that $|a_2/a_1|$ is unity for both states in this limit.

The above equations would also hold for states with $j = \frac{1}{2}$ if the Lamb shift (in the absence of an electric field) were zero. More general relations can also be derived which take into account both the Lamb shift and the radiation widths. We only give a special case of these relations for $n = 2$ and $j = \frac{1}{2}$: Let $\Gamma_P = 4\hbar\beta_P = \hbar/t_P$ be the radiation width of the $2P$-state and $\hbar L$ the energy separation between $2S$ and $2P$ in the absence of the electric field. If the Stark effect is small compared with the Lamb shift and/or Γ_P and if we neglect Γ_S completely, one then finds for the lifetime t_b of the state which is "almost pure $2S$",

$$\frac{t_P}{t_b} = \frac{f^2}{4\beta_P^2 + L^2}. \tag{67.14}$$

This expression for t_b reduces to (67.13) if $L \ll \beta_P$ and to (67.8) if $L \gg \beta_P$. In the absence of any magnetic field the ratio $L/2\beta_P$ is about 21; in a magnetic field of about 575 Gauss (see end of Sect. 67β) this ratio is zero and about 43, respectively, for the $m = -\frac{1}{2}$ and $+\frac{1}{2}$ states.

We can summarize the dependence on electric field strength F of the lifetimes of the various states with $n = 3$, for instance, as follows. For the levels with $j = m = \frac{3}{2}$, $\beta_- = 0.31 \times 10^8\ \text{sec}^{-1}$ and f, as given by (67.11), equals β_- for the critical field strength of $F_c = 1.9$ Volt/cm. For $F \ll F_c$ the inverse lifetimes (in $10^8\ \text{sec}^{-1}$) are as given in Table 15, i.e. 0.06 for $S_{\frac{1}{2}}$, 1.86 for $P_{\frac{1}{2}}$ and $P_{\frac{3}{2}}$ and 0.64

for $D_{\frac{3}{2}}$ and $D_{\frac{5}{2}}$. As F approaches F_c the $P_{\frac{3}{2}}$ and $D_{\frac{3}{2}}$ states are "mixed" into two different states and the inverse of the lifetime of each of these states (in $10^8\,\text{sec}^{-1}$) approaches 1.25 (and remains 1.25 for $F > 1.9$ Volt/cm). As F approaches 60 Volts/cm (see Sect. 67β) the $S_{\frac{1}{2}}$ and $P_{\frac{1}{2}}$ states also begin to be "mixed" and the inverse lifetime of each of the two resulting states approaches 0.96 for F much larger than this value (the $D_{\frac{5}{2}}$ lifetime is unchanged). Finally, for F of the order of 500 Volt/cm or larger, mixing of the states with different values of j sets in and the lifetimes approach those given in Table 20. For larger values of n the situation is qualitatively similar, but the critical values of field strength are roughly proportional to n^{-5}.

δ) Occupation numbers and excitation conditions. We have only discussed so far the effect of perturbations such as a weak electric field on the lifetimes of two states in hydrogen which have identical values of n and j. We have found the linear combinations u_a and u_b of the field-free wave functions u_1 and u_2 which have a purely exponential time-dependence. Another quantity of interest is the occupation number n_1 (and similarly n_2), i.e. the time average of the number of atoms per cm^3 which are in the state u_1 (and u_2, respectively). These occupation numbers are of importance since the intensities of different spectral lines (both in absorption and in emission) depend on them for the following reason: The states u_1 and u_2 correspond to different values of the orbital quantum number, $l=j+\frac{1}{2}$ and $j-\frac{1}{2}$ respectively, and combine optically with different states. Consider, for instance, transitions from the two levels with $n=3$ and $j=\frac{3}{2}$ to various levels with $n=2$. The part of the $n=3$ wave function involving $u_2(3\,P_{\frac{3}{2}})$ gives transitions only to the levels with $j=\frac{1}{2}$ (to the $2\,S_{\frac{1}{2}}$-component). The part involving $u_1(3\,D_{\frac{3}{2}})$, however, can also give transitions to the level with $j=\frac{3}{2}\,(2\,P_{\frac{3}{2}})$.

The occupation numbers n_1 and n_2 depend not only on the perturbing electric field, but also on the excitation conditions, and can be calculated as follows. Consider a particular excitation process which excites at time $t=0$ one electron into a state which is a definite superposition of the field-free states 1 and 2,

$$u(0) = a_1(0)\,u_1 + a_2(0)\,u_2; \qquad |a_1(0)|^2 + |a_2(0)|^2 = 1. \tag{67.15}$$

We consider, for simplicity, states with $j \gtrless \frac{3}{2}$, so that we can neglect the LAMB shift. Using the solutions (67.12) of (67.9) and (67.10), one can then find the wave function $u(t)$, Eq. (67.9), at later times t which satisfies the Eq. (67.10) and the boundary condition (67.15) at $t=0$. One can then evaluate the time integral I_1 of the partial probability that the electron be in the state u_1. The result is

$$I_1 \equiv \int\limits_0^\infty |a_1(t)|^2\,dt = \frac{f^2 + 4(\beta_1+\beta_2)\,\beta_2\,|a_1(0)|^2 - 4f\beta_2\,\mathrm{Im}\,[a_1(0)\,a_2^*(0)]}{4(\beta_1+\beta_2)\,(4\beta_1\beta_2+f^2)}, \tag{67.16}$$

where Im denotes the imaginary part of an expression and f, β_1, and β_2 are defined in Sect. 67γ. A similar expression holds for I_2, the time integral of $|a_2(t)|^2$.

If N excitations of the type (67.15) take place per sec per cm^3, then the occupation number n_1 (average number of atoms in state 1 per cm^3) is simply NI_1 and similarly $n_2 = NI_2$. In practice, excitation conditions are usually such that different excitations can occur with different ratios of $a_1(0)/a_2(0)$ for an *individual* process but with definite *average* values for $|a_1(0)|^2$, $|a_2(0)|^2$ and for the phase relation between $a_1(0)$ and $a_2(0)$. Note that I_1 (in an electric field) for an individual process depends not only on $|a_1(0)|^2$ but also on the phase relation through the term $\mathrm{Im}\,(a_1 a_2^*)$. Under most practical excitation conditions, the *average* of $\mathrm{Im}\,(a_1 a_2^*)$ is zero: (i) Excitation by collisions with electrons. A linear combination of u_1 and u_2 is excited in an individual collision, but the phase relation varies in a random manner from one collision to the next. (ii) Excitation from a lower atomic state by light absorption. Because of the selection rule on l, either u_1 alone or u_2 alone is excited in an individual transition so that Im $(a_1 a_2^*)$ is zero for each transition[1].

We assume now that the average of $\mathrm{Im}(a_1 a_2^*)$ in (67.16) is zero and denote the average number $N|a_1(0)|^2$ of excitations to state u_1 per sec cm³ by N_1 (similarly for N_2). We then get for the average occupation number n_1 from (67.16),

$$n_1 = \frac{N_1[4(\beta_1+\beta_2)\beta_2 + f^2] + N_2 f^2}{4(\beta_1+\beta_2)(4\beta_1\beta_2+f^2)}, \tag{67.17}$$

and a similar expression for n_2. Note that n_1 depends in general on N_2 as well as N_1, i.e. even if only states 2 are excited directly ($N_1=0$) some probability for the electron being in state 1 is built up by the mixing effect of the electric field. For weak enough fields, so that $f^2 \ll 4\beta_1\beta_2$, we have approximately

$$n_1 = \frac{N_1}{4\beta_1}\left[1 + \frac{N_2}{N_1}\frac{f^2}{4(\beta_1+\beta_2)\beta_2}\right]. \tag{67.18}$$

Unless N_2/N_1 is very large, (67.18) approximates the field-free values of $n_1 = N_1/4\beta_1$ ($4\beta_1$ is the inverse lifetime) and also $n_2 = N_2/4\beta_2$. If, on the other hand, the electric field is strong enough so that $f^2 \gg 2(\beta_1^2+\beta_2^2)$, then (67.17) and the equivalent relation for n_2 reduce (approximately) to

$$n_1 = n_2 = \frac{N_1+N_2}{4(\beta_1+\beta_2)}. \tag{67.19}$$

The relations (67.16) to (67.19) hold only in the absence of a Lamb shift (field-free energy separation between the states 1 and 2), but the situation is *qualitatively* similar if such a shift is present (e.g. for states with $j=\frac{1}{2}$): (i) If either the Lamb shift or the radiation widths are large compared with the Stark effect splitting, the occupation numbers are given approximately by their field-free values. (ii) If the Stark effect is large compared with both the Lamb shift and the two radiation widths, the occupation numbers n_1 and n_2 are approximately equal and given by (67.19). In case (i) the two states with the same l and $j=l\pm\frac{1}{2}$ have the same lifetime and the total intensity of all lines from all Zeeman components of the level with either j-value is proportional to the statistical weight $(2j+1)$ under the usual excitation conditions (rule II, Sect. 64β). Note that this is *not* true in case (ii), where levels with different j-values have different lifetimes.

The situation is again different if the Stark effect is even large compared with the total fine structure splitting of the levels with fixed n (e.g. for $F \gg 500$ Volt/cm if $n=3$ and $F \gg 10$ Volt/cm if $n=6$). If the electric field F is constant in magnitude and direction we deal with the Stark effect components, whose energies are discussed in Sect. 51 and their lifetimes in Sect. 65. Under many practical conditions the perturbing electric field varies in direction and magnitude in a random manner, (e.g. the field due to electrons and ions passing by). In this case the spectral lines coming from states with fixed n are broadened (rather than shifted) and the *average* lifetimes of *all* levels with the same n should be

[1] If we neglect the mixing by the electric field of states with different l values in the lower states from which absorption takes place. Even with mixing the average of Im $(a_1 a_2^*)$ is usually still zero (this is certainly the case if the orientation of the electric field varies in a random manner).

approximately the same. Under most excitation conditions, the occupation number of a component with particular values of n, l, j and m will then only depend on n.

ε) Summary. In the last few sections we have mainly discussed oscillator strengths, transition probabilities and line intensities for transitions between states of a single-electron atom which can be characterized by the orbital quantum number l. In Sect. 63 we have evaluated the required radial matrix elements explicitly for the special case of hydrogen-like atoms (pure COULOMB potential). As we discussed in Sect. 67, experimental verification of the theoretical results for hydrogen are very difficult in practice, because of the l-degeneracy. Under most practical conditions some weak perturbations, such as fluctuating electric fields or atomic collisions are present. These perturbations "mix up" the two fine structure levels with the same j-value (except, possibly, for $j=\frac{1}{2}$ and small values of n where the LAMB shift is appreciable) to an extent which depends on the details of the experimental conditions. Further, the thermal motions of the atoms give a DOPPLER shift to the frequency of a spectral line, with sign and magnitude varying from one atom to the next, so that each experimental spectral line is broadened considerably (DOPPLER broadening). The line broadening due to the DOPPLER effect may even be larger than the fine structure separations for large principal quantum number n.

We shall not discuss the many experiments on the line intensities in hydrogen, which have been carried out by means of optical spectroscopy in spite of these difficulties (they are described in Sect. 44 of [*10*]). It should be mentioned, however, that the LAMB shift experiments (Sect. 21) verify at least one entry for hydrogen in Table 15 quite accurately: The natural line width and shape for the $2P_{\frac{1}{2}}$- (and also the $2P_{\frac{3}{2}}$) level in H, D, and He^+ are measured accurately under (atomic beam) conditions where the DOPPLER and STARK broadening is kept to a minimum. The natural width is related to the lifetime of the level by (67.1) and (67.2) and the LAMB experiments agree well with the theoretical lifetime of 1.595×10^{-9} sec.

68. Alkali and X-ray spectra. There are two other kinds of spectra, to which the theory of single-electron spectra is often applied, which are not complicated by any l-degeneracy. These are the spectra of valence electrons in alkali atoms and the X-ray spectra due to transitions of inner electrons in heavy atoms. We shall not discuss these spectra in detail, but merely outline to what extent the theory of single-electron atoms applies and how these spectra differ from the hydrogen spectrum.

α) Alkali spectra. An alkali atom in its ground state consists of one or more closed shells of electrons plus one single (valence) electron in a new shell in a ns-state ($n=2$ for Li, $n=3$ for Na, etc.). We shall only consider those excited states of alkali atoms which contain the same closed shells with only the valence electron excited. The closed shells have zero total orbital angular momentum and zero total spin and are essentially unchanged in a transition between two states of the valence electron. In Sect. 17β we outlined briefly how one can calculate (most accurately by the HARTREE method) the effective central potential $V(r)$, due to the closed shells plus the nuclear COULOMB potential, which acts on the valence electron. Alkali spectra are usually treated theoretically by simply assuming that the valence electron makes transitions between stationary states in a *fixed* central potential $V(r)$. This treatment is, of course, only an approximation: The field of the valence electron acts on the electrons in the closed shells and the radial HARTREE wave functions of the closed shell electrons depend very slightly on the state in which the valence electron is. Hence the closed shells are not completely unaffected by a transition of the valence electron and the effective potential $V(r)$ acting on this electron depends slightly on its state. Further, the total wave function cannot be exactly of the assumed product form, but can be written as a superposition of all possible product wave functions. In this superposition, terms (with small coefficients) will occur in which more than one electron is excited ("configuration mixing", see Sect. 49β). For all alkali atoms these effects are very small and the single-electron approximation is excellent.

The effective potential $V(r)$ for alkali atoms is radically different from a COULOMB potential, especially for *large* nuclear charge Z: At very small distances r the effective charge $Z_p = r\,V(r)$ is close to Z, whereas at large distances the screening is almost complete and the effective charge is close to unity. The dependence of the level energies on the orbital quantum number is very strong (much larger than the fine structure splittings). The radial dipole matrix elements, and especially the oscillator strengths $f_{n'n}$, are numerically quite different from the hydrogenic ones. Some approximate oscillator strengths, as calculated from HARTREE wave functions[1], for the principal series in Li ($2S-nP$) and Na ($3S-nP$) are compared with the hydrogenic ones (Table 14) below:

n	2	3	4	5	6
Li$-2S$	0.75	0.006	0.005	0.003	0.00_2
H$-2S$	0	0.43	0.10	0.042	0.022
Na$-3S$		0.98	0.014	0.002	0.001
H$-3S$		0	0.48	0.12	0.05

One striking feature of the alkali spectra is the fact that the oscillator strength for a transition between an S- and a P-state with the *same* principal quantum number n is not only non-zero, but actually close to unity. The oscillator strengths for $nS-n'P$ with $n \neq n'$ are very much smaller than for $n=n'$ and also much smaller than the equivalent strengths in hydrogen. The most prominent line in the absorption spectrum of an alkali, with a nS valence electron for its ground state, is the doublet corresponding to the transitions to the $nP_{\frac{3}{2}}$ and $nP_{\frac{1}{2}}$ states. According to the discussion of Sect. 64, the matrix elements for the transitions to $P_{\frac{3}{2}}$ and $P_{\frac{1}{2}}$ should be identical. This leads to the simple rule that the intensities of the two components of the doublet should have the same ratios as the statistical weights $(2j+1)$ of the final states, i.e., a ratio of $1:2$ for $P_{\frac{1}{2}}:P_{\frac{3}{2}}$. This rule is satisfied very well by the experimental intensity ratios for the first member of the principal series for alkalis ($nS-nP$).

This rule is violated for the doublets $nS-n'P$ with $n'>n$ (at least for alkalis with large Z) for the following reason[2]. Because of the relativistic spin-orbit interaction, a nonrelativistic $n'P$ wave function is not an exact eigenfunction of the total HAMILTONian, but the correct eigenfunction is a linear superposition of various wave functions. Although the $n'P$ function is by far the leading term in this superposition, a small admixture of nP is also contained. The expansion coefficient for nP is of order $(Z\alpha)^2$ and its value is *different* for the $P_{\frac{1}{2}}$ and $P_{\frac{3}{2}}$ states. Although this coefficient is small, the transition matrix element for $nS-nP$ is much larger than for $nS-n'P$. For alkalis with large Z, most of the transition probability then comes from this small admixture and the probability,

[1] B. TRUMPY: Z. Physik **61**, 54 (1930), **66**, 720 (1930).
[2] E. FERMI: Z. Physik **59**, 680 (1929).

like the admixture coefficient, is *different* for $P_{\frac{1}{2}}$ and $P_{\frac{3}{2}}$. For Cs, for instance, ($Z=55$, $n=6$ for the ground state) the intensity ratio for $6S-7P_{\frac{3}{2}}$ to $6S-7P_{\frac{1}{2}}$ is about 3.5:1 (but 2:1 for the $6S-6P$ doublet).

β) X-ray spectra. In a heavy atom (large Z) in its ground state a number of the innermost shells are completely filled and only some outer shells are partially unfilled. Thus, for $Z>30$ all possible electronic states with $n=1, 2$ and 3 (and $4s$) are occupied and for $Z>70$ all states with n up to 4 (also $5s$, $5p$ and $6s$) are occupied, etc. Consider now a highly excited state of such an atom in which one of the electrons in an inner shell has been removed (either completely by ionization or by excitation to one of the outermost partially empty shells), say a $1s$-electron (K-shell). Spontaneous radiative transitions can then take place in which one electron from one of the filled shells outside the K-shells makes a transition to the vacant $1s$-state. In the initial state we have a single "hole" in the K-shell, in the final state a single hole in the L- or M-shell ($n=2$ or 3), etc. For such a transition the effect of the very outermost shells, which are only partially filled, can be neglected and the closed shells can be replaced (to a good approximation) by a central screening potential. As regards angular momentum quantum numbers, selection rules, etc., a single hole in a closed shell behaves similarly to a single electron in the shell (because of the exclusion principle). To quite a good approximation such transitions can be treated theoretically as transitions of a single electron in some effective central potential $V(r)$.

The effective potentials $V(r)$ to be used for the initial and final states are not quite the same but, since the nuclear charge Z is much larger than unity, this difference is not important. Also, for large Z, the deviation of $V(r)$ from the nuclear COULOMB potential Z/r is not very marked at the small distances r at which the wave function of an inner electron is concentrated. We have discussed the energies of X-ray levels in Sect. 17γ and seen that the energy splitting of levels with different l and same j (due to the non-COULOMB screening potential) becomes less marked as Z increases and the wave functions approach hydrogenic ones. On the other hand relativistic effects (e.g. the energy splitting of levels with the same l and different j) become more important as Z increases.

Exact matrix elements have been calculated recently[1] for a single electron in a completely *unscreened* COULOMB potential. These calculations use relativistic DIRAC wave functions and do *not* neglect retardation in evaluating matrix elements (operator $m c \boldsymbol{\alpha} e^{i\boldsymbol{k}\cdot\boldsymbol{r}}$ not replaced by $\boldsymbol{p}$, see Sects. 64 and 66). For $Z=82$ (Pb, screening neglected) and for transitions between $1s$ and $2p_{\frac{3}{2}}$ or $2p_{\frac{1}{2}}$ (called the $K\alpha_1$ or $K\alpha_2$ lines, respectively) the results are as follows. The completely nonrelativistic and non-retarded oscillator strengths f (valid only for low Z) of Table 14 for these two transitions are $\frac{2}{3}$ and $\frac{1}{3}$ of 0.416, respectively, i.e. 0.277 and 0.139. The corresponding relativistic values for $Z=82$ are 0.195 and 0.112 (ratio of 1.73 instead of 2). The frequency ω of the $K\alpha_1$ X-ray line is larger than that of the $K\alpha_2$ by a factor of 1.035 for this value of Z and the calculated *intensity* ratio for the two lines (intensity proportional to $\omega^3 f$) is 1.93.

For electrons in the K- and L-shells for heavy atoms, the effects of screening are not very important and the above mentioned calculation for the intensities of the $K\alpha$-doublet should be quite a good approximation. For transitions to electron states in higher shells (M, N, etc.) screening should not be neglected[2]

[1] W. B. PAYNE: Ph. D. Thesis. Louisiana State Univ. 1955. — W. PAYNE and J. LEVINGER: Phys. Rev. **101**, 1020 (1956).

[2] Screening reduces the overlap between the K-shell and the higher shells. The oscillator strengths in the discrete spectrum are thus reduced and those in the continuum enhanced by screening.

even for the heaviest atoms. Intensity ratios are then rather complicated functions of Z (since both the effect of screening and relativistic and retardation effects depend on Z) and are only in qualitative agreement with the nonrelativistic hydrogenic results of Sect. 63. Rather few accurate calculations[1] and experiments are available for the various intensity ratios.

In practice another process, called the AUGER effect, which has no analogue in single-electron spectra, competes with the emission of X-rays: Consider again a spontaneous transition of an electron from, say, the L, M or N shell to a state in a lower shell. In heavy atoms the energy release of such an electronic transition is larger than the ionization potential of electrons in the *outermost* shells. This energy release can then be taken up by the ejection from the atom of one of the outer electrons unaccompanied by any radiation (instead of a photon taking up the energy release). The relative probabilities[2] of radiative and AUGER effect transitions depend strongly on Z and on the particular states involved. For very large Z and for electronic transitions between the innermost shells, the AUGER effect is less likely than the emission of X-rays.

b) The photoeffect.

69. General survey[3]. In Sect. 59 we gave general formulae for radiative transitions of an atom from any state of higher to one of lower energy, accompanied by the spontaneous emission of a photon. In the last few sections we have largely restricted ourselves to transitions between atomic states in the *discrete* spectrum (or "bound-bound" transitions). We shall consider in the next few sections the case where one of the two atomic states is in the discrete, but the other in the *continuous*, spectrum ("bound-free" transitions). Transitions from a free to a bound state with the emission of a photon (called recombination or radiative capture) are discussed in Sect. 75. We shall mainly be concerned with the inverse process, the photoeffect, i.e., the absorption of radiation by an atom in a bound state accompanied by the ejection of one of the atom's electrons into a "free" state (i.e., a state of positive energy in the continuum).

Consider electromagnetic radiation of definite frequency ν, propagation vector $\boldsymbol{k}_\nu$ and polarization direction $\boldsymbol{j}$, incident on an atom in some bound state b. Let I_b be one of the ionization potentials of this atomic state, i.e., the energy required to remove one electron to the free state with zero kinetic energy with the remaining electrons forming *some* bound state of the remaining positive ion[4]. If $h\nu > I_b$, an absorption process can take place to this state of the positive ion plus a free electron of kinetic energy W. W is related to the energy $h\nu$ of the absorbed photon by

$$W = h\nu - I_b, \tag{69.1}$$

and, since the energy W is in the continuous spectrum, absorption is possible for a continuous range of frequencies ν.

The continuous spectrum for the ejected electron is highly degenerate (even for a *non*-COULOMB potential), i.e., there are infinitely many electronic states each with energy W. We can take as a set of linearly independent states of energy

---

[1] H. MASSEY and E. BURHOP: Proc. Roy. Soc. Lond., Ser. A **153**, 661 (1936).

[2] For calculations see E. RAMBERG and F. RICHTMYER, Phys. Rev. **51**, 913 (1937).

[3] For more detailed accounts of the photoeffect and for further references, see ref. [7], Chap. 6 and ref. [6], Chap. IV and V; also H. HALL, Rev. Mod. Phys. **8**, 358 (1936); G. R. WHITE, U. S. Nat. Bur. Stand. Circular 1003 (May 1952, Washington 25, D.C.) and K. H. SPRING, Photons and Electrons (London: Methuen 1954).

[4] We shall often consider the special case of a single-electron atom, where the remaining positive ion is simply a bare nucleus and there is only one ionization potential I_b.

W those with wave functions separable in spherical polar coordinates, characterized by quantum[1] numbers l and m. Let u_W denote the wave function for a particular one of these states (definite l and m, as well as energy W), normalized per unit energy interval [see Eqs. (4.11) and (4.19)]. Let $D_{Wb}^{\boldsymbol{k}_\nu j}$ be the matrix element (59.3) with $u_{n'}$ replaced by u_W (and u_n by the wave function u_0 for the bound state). We form the following quantity, which has the dimensions of cm² and is called a cross-section,

$$\sigma_W = \frac{2\pi e^2 \hbar^2}{m^2 c \nu} |D_{Wb}^{\boldsymbol{k}_\nu j}|^2. \tag{69.2}$$

From the transition probability (59.2) and the EINSTEIN relations between the probabilities of inverse processes (see [5] to [7]), one can derive the following physical significance for the absorption cross-section σ_W: Let N_0 be the number of photons in the incident beam of radiation (considered monochromatic) which cross 1 cm² per sec (energy flux of $N_0 h\nu$ per cm² per sec) and $\mathcal{N}$ the number of atoms per cm³ in state b. Let w_W be the probability per sec for one such atom being excited to state W and τ_W the probability for one photon being absorbed in a path length of 1 cm (in a $b \to W$ transition). One then finds that

$$w_W = N_0 \sigma_W, \qquad \tau_W = \mathcal{N} \sigma_W. \tag{69.3}$$

The expressions (69.2) and (69.3) refer to absorption processes which lead to a continuum state of the ejected electron with *specific* values of l and m. To get the total absorption coefficient τ (for fixed ν and initial atomic state b) we have to sum τ_W (and similarly for w_W and σ_W) over all possible values of l and m. In the dipole approximation, which we discuss below, the selection rules of Sect. 60 apply and (since the initial state b has fixed values of l and m) only a few terms in this sum are non-zero.

There is an alternative scheme for classifying the final states and evaluating the absorption probabilities, which involves the continuum wave functions discussed in Sects. 6γ, 7β and 9β. One can show[2] that the wave functions representing plane waves plus *incoming* spherical waves should be used for the electron's continuum wave function, which appears as the *final* state in the transition[3]. The angular distribution of the ejected electron can be obtained as follows in this method: Let $\hbar \boldsymbol{k}$ be a possible momentum of the electron with $\hbar^2 k^2/2m = W$ and with the direction of $\boldsymbol{k}$ inside a cone of infinitesimal solid angle $d\Omega$ (axis of the cone denoted by Ω). Let $D_{\Omega b}^{\boldsymbol{k}_\nu j}$ denote the matrix element (59.3) with $u_{n'}$ (in atomic units) replaced by

$$u_\Omega(\boldsymbol{r}) = \sqrt{\frac{k}{(2\pi)^3}}\,[e^{i\boldsymbol{k}\cdot\boldsymbol{r}} + v(\boldsymbol{r})], \tag{69.4}$$

where $v(\boldsymbol{r})$ is the "scattered part" of this eigenstate[4] of the atomic HAMILTONian. Instead of (69.2), we then have a partial cross-section, for absorption processes

---

[1] We are considering the nonrelativistic theory at present and are neglecting spin.

[2] See ref. [7], p. 457 and also G. BREIT and H. BETHE, Phys. Rev. **93**, 888 (1954) and H. A. BETHE, Ann. d. Phys. **4**, 443 (1930).

[3] A wave packet can be formed by a superposition of electronic wave functions of this type, which approximates a plane wave without *any* spherical waves for large *positive* times. This wave packet would contain incoming spherical waves at large *negative* times, but, since it occurs as a *final* state in a transition, the wave packet is only built up after a certain time (at which the photon wave packet is absorbed).

[4] The normalization factor under square roots in (69.4) is the "density of states per unit energy" ϱ_E; see, for instance, ref. [6], p. 205.

in which $\boldsymbol{k}$ lies within the solid angle $d\Omega$, given by

$$\sigma_\Omega \, d\Omega = \frac{2\pi e^2 \hbar^2}{m^2 c \nu} \, |D^{k_\nu j}_{\Omega b}|^2 \, d\Omega. \tag{69.5}$$

The total cross-section σ is the integral of the differential cross-section σ_Ω over $d\Omega$ and the total absorption coefficient is $\tau = \mathcal{N}\sigma$.

Exact expressions for the photoeffect cross-sections are not available and a number of different approximations are usually used under different circumstances. A list of some common approximations, and their range of applicability, follows.

α) Single-electron approximation and screening. The calculations are simplified enormously if hydrogenic wave functions can be used both for the initial and final states of the photo-electron. Besides being exact for one-electron ions, such wave functions yield quite good approximations also for the photo-electric absorption of high-frequency radiation (X-rays) by atoms with fairly large Z. It will be shown in Sects. 70 and 71 that the *inner* electrons (mainly the K- and L-shells) contribute most to the absorption of X-rays. As for transitions in the discrete spectrum (Sect. 68β), the photo-ejection of an inner electron from an atom with large Z can be described fairly well by using single-electron HARTREE wave functions both for the initial (bound) and final states of this electron. Further, if Z is fairly large, the HARTREE potential acting on one electron depends very little on the state of the electron and the same potential $V(\boldsymbol{r})$ can be used for the electron's initial and final states.

The wave function u_b for a bound state with small principal quantum number n is concentrated in a small range of radial distances r around some value r_{0n}. The integrand in the matrix element (59.3) is then most important also for r near r_{0n}. As discussed in Sect. 17β, the HARTREE potential can be approximated, in this region, by (17.5),

$$V_n(r) = -\frac{(Z - s_n)}{r} + V_{0n}. \tag{69.6}$$

For atoms with large Z, the effect of the "inner screening" constant s_n is rather small and we shall choose $s_1 = 0.3$ for $n = 1$ (K-shell) and $s_2 = 4.1_5$ for $n = 2$ (L-shell). The "outer screening" constant V_{0n} is chosen most conveniently such that the ionization potential (17.6),

$$I_n = \left[\left(\frac{Z - s_n}{n}\right)^2 - 2V_{0n}\right] \text{Ry}, \tag{69.7}$$

agrees with the experimental ionization potential. For Cu ($Z = 29$) and $n = 1$, for instance, the experimental I_1 is 662 Ry and $2V_0 = 161$ Ry.

For the initial bound state wave function u_b for an electron in the potential (69.6), we shall then use a hydrogenic one with principal quantum number n and nuclear charge $Z - s_n$. For the wave function u_W or u_Ω of the final state in the continuum we shall use the following approximation. The *total* energy W of the electron in the final state is given by (69.1), where I_n is the experimental ionization potential which is also given by (69.7). At very large radial distances r the kinetic energy of the electron equals W, at intermediate distances r the potential energy is given by the rather complicated HARTREE potential and only in the neighbourhood of the small distance r_{0n} is the potential approximated by (69.6). Since the integrand of the matrix element D, (59.3), is needed mainly for r of order r_{0n} we shall approximate the final state by a wave function for total energy W in the potential (69.6). This approximate wave function is then identical with a hydrogenic one for nuclear charge $Z-s_n$ and for an *apparent* total energy $\hbar^2 k'^2/2m$ of

$$\frac{\hbar^2 k'^2}{2m} = W - 2V_{0n} = h\nu - I_n - 2V_{0n} = h\nu - \left(\frac{Z-s_n}{n}\right)^2 \text{Ry}. \qquad (69.8)$$

This approximation for the final continuum state is a more drastic one than for the bound state, since the correct potential in the asymptotic region (large r) does *not* approach V_{0n}, as given by (69.6), but approaches zero. In the frequency region $I_n < h\nu < (Z-s_n)^2 n^{-2}$ Ry, in particular, W is positive and the photoeffect is possible but the *apparent* total energy (69.8) is *negative*. We shall see in Sect. 71 that the final results are not very sensitive to the value and sign of k'^2 in this region and we shall simply substitute (69.8) for k'^2 (even when negative) into the final expressions for the matrix elements.

The hydrogenic approximation is rather poor for electrons of principal quantum number n much larger than 2 or 3, especially if the nuclear charge Z is not very large. Fortunately these cases are not of very great importance[1], except for calculations on the opacity in stellar atmospheres. In particular, photoeffect from the outer electrons of *negative* atomic ions takes place in stellar atmospheres, for which the single-electron approximation breaks down completely. More accurate calculations for such cases will be discussed in Sect. 74α.

β) Nonrelativistic treatment. As discussed before, the bound state of the electron can be treated nonrelativistically and its spin neglected, if $p_0/mc \sim Z\alpha \ll 1$, where p_0 is the BOHR momentum for nuclear charge Z and electronic mass m. If, in addition, the kinetic energy W of the ejected electron is small compared with the electron's restmass energy mc^2, the ejected electron can also be treated nonrelativistically (Sects. 70 to 72 and 74). Calculations for $Z\alpha$ of the order of unity are very difficult (see Sect. 73) but, if $Z\alpha \ll 1$, the case of arbitrarily large W can be treated (Sect. 73α).

γ) Neglect of retardation. We restrict ourselves, for the moment, to cases with $Z\alpha \ll 1$. We then have the following inequalities between three different orders of magnitude of energy, the ground state ionization potential I_1, c times the BOHR momentum p_0 and the electron's restmass energy mc^2.

$$I_1 \sim (Z\alpha)^2 mc^2 \ll p_0 c \sim (Z\alpha)\, mc^2 \ll mc^2. \qquad (69.9)$$

If the energy of the incident photon $h\nu$ is small compared to mc^2, then also $W \ll mc^2$ [see Eq. (69.1)] and the nonrelativistic approximation applies. If the more stringent condition $h\nu \ll p_0 c \sim Z\alpha mc^2$ is also satisfied, then the wave length of the photon is also large compared with the "radius" of the bound state of the electron and the photon's momentum small compared with the BOHR momentum p_0. In this case we can again neglect retardation, i.e., replace the factor $e^{i\boldsymbol{k}_\nu\cdot\boldsymbol{r}}$ in the matrix element (59.3) by unity, just as for the electric dipole approximation to the discrete spectrum.

In this approximation we can again write the matrix element (59.3) in the form (59.5), which involves $\boldsymbol{r}$ instead of the momentum operator. Calculations with retardation neglected are discussed in Sects. 70 and 71. Note that in this dipole approximation the matrix element does not depend explicitly on the propagation direction of the photon and the angular distribution of the ejected

[1] For the photoeffect from the valence electron in an alkali atom, the single-electron approximation is again applicable, but the appropriate single-electron wave functions differ radically from hydrogenic ones (Sect. 68α).

electrons is rather simple. The effect of retardation on the angular distribution is discussed in Sect. 72.

*δ) The "*BORN *approximation".* If $h\nu \gg I_1$, then the kinetic energy W of the ejected electron is also large compared with the ionization potential I_1. In this case the wave function of the ejected electron can be treated by BORN approximation (see Sects. 7 and 9). In fact, for the photoeffect from a bound state with zero orbital angular momentum the effect of the nuclear potential on the ejected electron can be neglected completely if $h\nu \gg I_1$. If $Z\alpha \ll 1$, it follows from (69.9) that there is a range of $h\nu$ for which *both* the BORN approximation can be used *and* retardation neglected. The BORN approximation is discussed in Sects. 70 and 72β.

We shall neglect throughout higher order radiative corrections, i.e., treat the interaction with the radiation field in lowest order perturbation theory (with α as the coupling constant). Besides neglecting radiative corrections, we also do not treat processes involving two (or more) real photons, although one such process, the COMPTON scattering of photons, is of great importance (see Sect. 73β).

70. The BORN approximation. We consider first the photoeffect from a single-electron atom with $Z\alpha \ll 1$ and for a photon frequency ν such that $mc^2 \gg h\nu \gg I_1 = Z^2$ Ry. We shall use the matrix element $D_{\Omega b}^{\boldsymbol{k}_\nu \boldsymbol{j}}$ which involves the wave function u_Ω (69.4), which represents a plane wave plus scattered waves. We discuss first the simplest approximation to u_Ω, a plane wave.

α) Plane wave approximation. Consider the wave function u_Ω for an electron with asymptotic momentum $\hbar k$, where

$$W = \frac{\hbar^2 k^2}{2m} = h\nu - I_b \tag{70.1}$$

and I_b is the ionization potential of the initial bound state b. If $h\nu \gg Z^2$Ry, then $\hbar k$ is large compared with the BOHR momentum p_0. In this case the second part $v(\boldsymbol{r})$ of the wave function (69.4) is small compared with the first part $e^{i\boldsymbol{k}\cdot\boldsymbol{r}}$, which simply represents a plane wave state of the electron in the absence of any COULOMB potential. We first evaluate the part of the matrix element D which involves only the plane wave part of (69.4). We shall see later that this gives a good approximation to D *only* if the bound state b is an S-state.

Let u_b be any normalized bound state wave function. The matrix element $D_{\Omega b}^{\boldsymbol{k}_\nu \boldsymbol{j}}$, with $v(r)$ in (69.4) neglected completely, is then given by

$$D_{\Omega b}^{\boldsymbol{k}_\nu \boldsymbol{j}} = i\sqrt{\frac{k}{(2\pi)^3}} \int d^3r\, e^{-i\boldsymbol{k}\cdot\boldsymbol{r}}\, e^{i\boldsymbol{k}_\nu\cdot\boldsymbol{r}}\, p_j\, u_b(\boldsymbol{r}), \tag{70.2}$$

where $\hbar p_j$ is the component of the electron's momentum operator in the polarization direction $\boldsymbol{j}$ of the photon. $\boldsymbol{j}$ is perpendicular to the photon's propagation vector $\boldsymbol{k}_\nu$, so that p_j commutes with $e^{i\boldsymbol{k}_\nu\cdot\boldsymbol{r}}$. The function $e^{i\boldsymbol{k}\cdot\boldsymbol{r}}$ is an eigenstate of p_j with eigenvalue $k\cos\vartheta$, where ϑ is the angle between the vectors $\boldsymbol{k}$ and $\boldsymbol{j}$. We can then rewrite (70.2) in the form

$$D_{\Omega b}^{\boldsymbol{k}_\nu \boldsymbol{j}} = i\, k^{\frac{3}{2}} \cos\vartheta\, \psi_b(\boldsymbol{k} - \boldsymbol{k}_\nu), \tag{70.3}$$

where $\psi_b(\boldsymbol{p})$ is the FOURIER-transform of $u_b(\boldsymbol{r})$, i.e., the normalized momentum-space wave function for the state b (discussed in Sect. 8). For a state b, characterized by the quantum numbers n, m, l, in a central potential, $\psi_b(\boldsymbol{p})$ is of form $F_{nl}(p)\, Y_{lm}(\vartheta, \varphi)$ where Y_{lm} is a *normalized* spherical harmonic.

We consider now the special case of a COULOMB potential with nuclear charge Z and an initial bound state b with principal quantum number n and with $l=0$

(S-state). We are only considering the case of k large compared with the BOHR momentum and can use the asymptotic approximation (8.11) for F_{n0}. The wave function ψ_b is then, in *atomic* units,

$$\psi_b(\boldsymbol{k}-\boldsymbol{k}_\nu) = \frac{2\sqrt{2}}{\pi n^{\frac{3}{2}}} \frac{Z^{\frac{5}{2}}}{|\boldsymbol{k}-\boldsymbol{k}_\nu|^4}. \tag{70.4}$$

On substituting (70.3) with (70.4) into (69.5), we obtain the differential cross-section σ_Ω. The momentum $|\boldsymbol{k}|$ in (70.3) and (70.4) is given by (70.1), but $I_b = I_1/n^2 \ll h\nu$ and we can replace $(\hbar k)^2$ by $2mh\nu$ in the final expression for σ_Ω.

If we had neglected retardation, the k_ν would have been replaced by zero in (70.2) and hence also in (70.3) and (70.4). As discussed in Sect. 69γ this neglect of retardation is always justified if $h\nu \ll Z\alpha mc^2$, in which case $\hbar k_\nu$ is much smaller than the BOHR momentum. But k_ν enters our expressions only through (70.4) and the neglect of k_ν in (70.4) causes a small error as long as $k_\nu = 2\pi\nu/c \ll k$. From (70.1) this is the case as long as $h\nu \ll mc^2$, *even* if $\hbar k_\nu$ is *not* smaller than the BOHR momentum. If we replace k_ν by zero[1] in (70.4), our approximation for the differential cross-section σ_Ω (from a bound S-state) becomes (in C.G.S. units):

$$\sigma_\Omega = \frac{2^4}{\pi n^3} \frac{e^2}{mc} \frac{\nu_1^{\frac{5}{2}}}{\nu^{\frac{7}{2}}} \cos^2\vartheta, \tag{70.5}$$

where $\nu_1 = Z^2$ Rydberg is $Z^2(4\pi)^{-1}$ times one atomic unit of frequency. The total cross-section σ, obtained by integrating σ_Ω over all solid angles, is then

$$\sigma = \frac{2^6}{3n^3} \frac{e^2}{mc} \frac{\nu_1^{\frac{5}{2}}}{\nu^{\frac{7}{2}}}. \tag{70.6}$$

In our present approximation the cross-section for the photoeffect decreases with the minus third power of the principal quantum number n (for an S-state) and with the minus $\frac{7}{2}$ power of the frequency ν of the photon. If we use the hydrogenic approximation for complex atoms and if $\nu \gg \nu_1$, then the contribution to the photoeffect from the two $1s$-electrons is appreciably larger than from all other ns-electrons combined. In deriving (70.5) and (70.6) we have used the asymptotic expression for the momentum space wave function ψ_b, which is valid only if $W \sim h\nu \gg I_b$ $(k \gg p_0)$. It is interesting to note the energy dependence of the cross-section near the long-wave-length limit ($h\nu$ near I_b), obtained by substituting the exact expression for ψ_b into (70.3), even though the BORN approximation expression (70.3) is not valid in this energy range: For k less than the BOHR momentum, the correct ψ_b does not increase indefinitely with decreasing k but [unlike (70.4)] approaches a constant limit as $k \to 0$. Thus, for $W = h\nu - I_b \ll I_b$, the main energy dependence of the BORN approximation matrix element (70.3) is the factor $k^{\frac{3}{2}}$ and the cross-section is approximately proportional to $W^{\frac{3}{2}}$, where W is the energy of the ejected electron. Thus the BORN approximation cross-section is zero at threshold ($h\nu = I_b$, $W = 0$), rises to a maximum at W of the order of I_b and then decreases as $W^{-\frac{7}{2}}$ for large W, (70.6). For a $1s$-electron in hydrogen, for instance, we find, using the explicit wave function (8.10),

$$\sigma \propto \frac{W^{\frac{3}{2}}}{(W+I_1)^5} \propto \frac{(\nu-\nu_1)^{\frac{3}{2}}}{\nu^5}. \tag{70.6a}$$

In (70.6a), $I_1 = h\nu_1$ is the ionization potential for the $1s$-state. We shall see that the correct cross-section for hydrogen-like atoms (Sect. 71α) has a *finite* value

[1] The effect of the term dropped here is discussed in Sect. 72β.

(and a maximum) at threshold ($W=0$), but for negative atomic ions (Sect. 74α) the energy dependence is similar to that given by the BORN approximation (70.6a).

For an initial bound state b with non-zero orbital quantum number l, one again obtains (70.3) for the matrix element D, *if* one again neglects $v(\boldsymbol{r})$ in (69.4) completely. In the region $h\nu \sim W \gg Z^2$ Ry, we can use the asymptotic expression (8.12) with (8.4) for ψ_b. For a bound p-state ($n, l=1, m$), for instance, with retardation (i.e., k_ν) neglected, we have

$$D_{\Omega b}^{\boldsymbol{k}_\nu \boldsymbol{j}} = i\,\frac{8}{3}\sqrt{\frac{2}{\pi}}\sqrt{\frac{n^2-1}{n^5}}\left(\frac{Z}{k}\right)^{\frac{7}{2}}\cos\vartheta\, Y_{1m}(\vartheta,\varphi), \tag{70.7}$$

where (k, ϑ, φ) are spherical polar coordinates (with $\boldsymbol{j}$ as polar axis) for $\boldsymbol{k}$ and Y_{1m} is the normalized spherical harmonic. On substituting (70.7) into (69.5) one again obtains the lowest order BORN approximation for the differential cross-section σ_Ω. If one *averages* σ_Ω over the three possible values of the magnetic quantum number m for the initial bound state and uses the appendix Eq. (A.42), one finds (for $l=1$) instead of (70.5),

$$\sigma_\Omega = \frac{2^6(n^2-1)}{9\pi n^5}\,\frac{e^2}{m c}\,\frac{\nu_1^{\frac{7}{2}}}{\nu^{\frac{9}{2}}}\cos^2\vartheta\,. \tag{70.8}$$

In the present approximation one obtains qualitatively similar results for bound states with higher values of l: σ_Ω, averaged over all possible values of m from $-l$ to l, is proportional to $\cos^2\vartheta$ and to $\nu^{-l-\frac{7}{2}}$ and approximately proportional to n^{-3} (for $n \gg l$). We shall see below that the neglect of $v(\boldsymbol{r})$ in (69.5) is *not* justified for $l \gtreqless 1$ even if $h\nu \sim W \gg Z^2$ Ry so that (70.8) and similar expressions for $l > 1$ are *wrong*, (although the dependence on n and ν and the order of magnitude is correct).

β) First order BORN *approximation.* We now investigate the effect of the second term $v(\boldsymbol{r})$ in (69.4), which we have omitted in Sect. 70α. We shall neglect retardation, i.e., omit the factor $e^{i\boldsymbol{k}_\nu\cdot\boldsymbol{r}}$ in the matrix element D, which can then be written as an integral over momentum space

$$D_{\Omega b}^{\boldsymbol{k}_\nu \boldsymbol{j}} = i\int d^3r\, u_\Omega^*(\boldsymbol{r})\, p_j\, u_b(\boldsymbol{r}) = i\sqrt{k}\int d^3p\, \psi_\Omega^*(\boldsymbol{p})\, p_j\, \psi_b(\boldsymbol{p})\,. \tag{70.9}$$

In (70.9), $\sqrt{k}\,\psi_\Omega(\boldsymbol{p})$ is the FOURIER transform of the exact continuum wave function $u_\Omega(\boldsymbol{r})$, Eq. (69.4), and ψ_b that of u_b. In Sect. 9β we have discussed the first order BORN approximation expression for ψ_Ω. If $V'(p)$ is $(2\pi)^{-\frac{3}{2}}$ times the FOURIER transform of the central potential (not necessarily COULOMB) in which the electron moves, then the BORN approximation [see Eqs. (9.7) and (9.11)] is

$$\psi_\Omega(\boldsymbol{p}) = \delta^{(3)}(\boldsymbol{p}-\boldsymbol{k}) + \frac{2}{k^2-p^2}\,V'(|\boldsymbol{p}-\boldsymbol{k}|)\,. \tag{70.10}$$

On substituting the delta-function part (zero order BORN approximation) of (70.10) into (70.9), we again obtain (70.3), after neglecting k_ν. We now investigate the additional contribution D' to (70.9), obtained by substituting the second part of (70.10), in the region where $W=k^2/2m$ is much larger than the ionization potential.

In this energy region, k is large compared with the "average momentum" p_0. One can then show that the main contribution to the integral

$$D' = 2i\sqrt{k}\int d^3p\,\frac{V'(|\boldsymbol{p}-\boldsymbol{k}|)}{k^2-p^2}\,p_j\,\psi_b(\boldsymbol{p}) \tag{70.11}$$

comes from values of p of the order of $p_0 \ll k$, where the bound wave function ψ_b is large. For a bound S-state one can show that (70.11) is small compared with (70.3), if $p_0 \ll k$. For a bound p-state ($l=1$), the following approximation to (70.11) is sufficient: For $p \sim p_0 \ll k$, the functions $V'(|\boldsymbol{p}-\boldsymbol{k}|)$ and k^2-p^2 vary very slowly with p and we replace p by zero in these expressions. In this approximation we have

$$D' = 2i\,k^{-\frac{3}{2}}\,V'(k)\int d^3p\,p_j\,\psi_b(\boldsymbol{p}). \tag{70.12}$$

After a partial integration we have

$$p_x\,\psi_b(\boldsymbol{p}) = -\frac{i}{(2\pi)^{\frac{3}{2}}}\int d^3r\,e^{-i\boldsymbol{r}\cdot\boldsymbol{p}}\,\frac{\partial u_b(\boldsymbol{r})}{\partial x},$$

where u_b is the FOURIER transform of ψ_b and the x-axis is parallel to $\boldsymbol{j}$. Using the relation

$$\int d^3p\,e^{-i\boldsymbol{r}\cdot\boldsymbol{p}} = (2\pi)^3\,\delta^{(3)}(\boldsymbol{r})$$

we find

$$D' = 2(2\pi)^{\frac{3}{2}}\,k^{-\frac{3}{2}}\,V'(k)\left[\frac{\partial u_b(\boldsymbol{r})}{\partial x}\right]_{r=0}. \tag{70.13}$$

The approximate expression (70.13) is non-zero only if the bound state b has quantum numbers $l=1$ and $m=0$ ($u \propto x$) where the quantization (x) direction is along $\boldsymbol{j}$. For the special case of a COULOMB potential, $V'(k)$ is given by (8.6a) and the derivative at the origin of $u_b(\boldsymbol{r})$ can be obtained from (1.3), (1.8) and the expansion (3.17). For a bound state ($n, l=1, m$) of a hydrogen-like atom with charge Z we find[1]

$$D' = -i\,\frac{2}{\pi}\sqrt{\frac{2}{3}}\sqrt{\frac{n^2-1}{n^5}}\left(\frac{Z}{k}\right)^{\frac{5}{2}}\delta_{m0}, \tag{70.14}$$

where δ_{m0} is the KRONECKER delta function. The first order BORN expression (70.14) has to be added to the zero order expression (70.7). Note that the two expressions are of the *same* order of magnitude (for $l=1$). We substitute the sum of the two expressions into (69.5) and again *average* σ_Ω over the three values -1, 0 and 1 of m. Using the explicit expressions (1.8) for Y_{lm}, we find

$$\sigma_\Omega = \frac{2^4}{9\pi}\,\frac{n^2-1}{n^5}\,\frac{e^2}{mc}\,\frac{\nu_1^{\frac{7}{2}}}{\nu^{\frac{9}{2}}}. \tag{70.15}$$

The angular distribution is thus *isotropic* [unlike the incorrect result (70.8)], and the total cross section is $\sigma = 4\pi\sigma_\Omega$. The range of validity of (70.15) is given by $\nu_1 \ll \nu \precsim \nu_1/Z\alpha$.

For bound states with $l > 1$, the approximation (70.12) to (70.11) vanishes. For these higher l-values one can expand $V'(\boldsymbol{p}-\boldsymbol{k})/(k^2-p^2)$ in terms of spherical harmonics and powers of p/k and keep only the lowest order term which gives a non-zero contribution to the integral (70.11). This term will again be of the same order of magnitude as (70.3) for all values of l except zero: This can be seen

[1] Since we will have to add this matrix element to (70.7) we must take for $u_b(\boldsymbol{r})$ *exactly* the FOURIER transform of ψ_b, given by (8.12) with (8.4), which was used in deriving (70.7). This form for u_b is i times the wave function defined by (3.17) with (1.8).

most easily by considering the continuum wave functions which are separable in spherical polar coordinates (used in the next sections) with quantum numbers l' and m': For $l>0$, transitions are possible with $l'=l+1$ and $l-1$. For $l'=l-1$, the first order BORN wave function $F_{l'}(p)\,Y_{l'm'}(\vartheta\,\varphi)$ is still sufficiently large "far off the energy shell" (i.e., for $p\sim p_0\ll k$) so that the first order contribution is of the same order as the zero order one. For $l'=l+1$, on the other hand, $F_{l'}(p)$ is so small for $p\ll k$ that the first order contribution is negligible. The transitions to $l'=l-1$ are absent only if $l=0$.

Note how rapidly the total cross-section σ *per electron* decreases with increasing n and l. For s- and p-states, for instance,

$$\sigma_{1s}=n^3\sigma_{ns}=3\,\frac{n^5}{n^2-1}\,\frac{\nu}{\nu_1}\,\sigma_{np}\,. \tag{70.16}$$

This dependence on n and l reflects the behavior of the bound state wave functions in momentum space at large momenta (or in position space at small radial distances r).

71. The absorption coefficient without retardation. We shall neglect retardation and relativistic effects throughout this section. However, we shall *not* replace the continuum wave functions by their BORN approximation, but use the exact hydrogenic nonrelativistic wave functions which give valid results also very near threshold (i.e., near the long wave length limit, $h\nu=I_b$). We consider a bound state b and a wave function u_W, separable in spherical polar coordinates, for the continuum state. With retardation neglected, (69.2) and (69.3) with (59.5) then gives for the absorption coefficient τ_W,

$$\tau_W=\frac{8\pi^3e^2\mathcal{N}\nu}{c}\left|\int u_W^*\sum_i x_i\,u_b\,d\tau\right|^2, \tag{71.1}$$

where x is the polarization direction of the photon.

α) The K-shell. We shall evaluate the above integral for the hydrogen atom. Let u_b be the eigenfunction of the ground state. The continuum eigenfunction depends not only on the energy but also on two additional quantum numbers such as l and m. In order to obtain the total absorption coefficient, (71.1) must be evaluated for all values of l and m and the results must be summed. However, in our particular case, since the eigenfunction of the ground state is spherically symmetric, only those continuum eigenfunctions contribute which have an angular dependence of the form $\sin\vartheta\cos\varphi$; otherwise the integrals over angles in (71.1) vanish. Accordingly, the orbital quantum number of the contributing continuum state is $l=1$. The integral in (71.1) becomes

$$\left.\begin{aligned}x_{W1}&=\int_0^\infty r^3\,dr\,R_{W,l=1}(r)\cdot 2e^{-Zr}\cdot Z^{\frac{3}{2}}\int_0^\pi\sin\vartheta\,d\vartheta\int_0^{2\pi}d\varphi\,\times\\&\quad\times\sqrt{\frac{3}{4\pi}}\sin\vartheta\cos\varphi\cdot\sqrt{\frac{1}{4\pi}}\cdot\sin\vartheta\cos\varphi=\frac{4Z^2\sqrt{1+n'^2}}{\sqrt{3}\sqrt{1-e^{-2\pi n'}}}\,\times\\&\quad\times\frac{1}{2\pi}\int_0^\infty(2kr)^{-2}r^3\,dr\,e^{-Zr}\oint\left(\xi+\frac{1}{2}\right)^{-in'-2}\left(\xi-\frac{1}{2}\right)^{in'-2}e^{-2ikr\xi}\,d\xi.\end{aligned}\right\} \tag{71.2}$$

In the above, we have inserted the expressions for the spherical harmonics Y_{00} Y_{11} as given by (1.8) and the continuum eigenfunction from (4.22). The contour integral is defined in Sect. 4, $n'=Z/\sqrt{2W}$ and $k=\sqrt{2W}$. Interchanging the order of integration with respect to r and ξ, and disregarding for the moment the coefficient in front of the first integral sign, we obtain

$$J = \frac{1}{4k^2} \oint d\xi \frac{(\xi+\frac{1}{2})^{-in'-2}(\xi-\frac{1}{2})^{in'-2}}{(Z+2ik\xi)^2}$$
$$= \frac{-1}{16k^4} \int d\xi \left(\xi+\frac{1}{2}\right)^{-in'-2} \left(\xi-\frac{1}{2}\right)^{in'-2} \left(\xi - \frac{1}{2} i n'\right)^{-2}.$$

The integrals must be taken around the two branch points $\xi = \frac{1}{2}$ and $\xi = -\frac{1}{2}$[1]; however, since the integrand goes to zero as ξ^{-6}, the contour may be extended to infinity. The contour goes around the pole $\xi = \frac{1}{2} i n'$ in the negative sense and the integration therefore yields simply the residue at that pole, namely

$$\left.\begin{aligned} J &= \frac{2\pi i}{16k^4} \cdot \frac{d}{d\xi} \left[\left(\xi+\frac{1}{2}\right)^{-in'-2} \left(\xi-\frac{1}{2}\right)^{in'-2}\right]_{\xi=\frac{1}{2}in'} \\ &= \frac{64n' \cdot 2\pi}{16k^4(1+n'^2)^3} \left(\frac{in'-1}{in'+1}\right)^{in'} = \frac{8\pi k Z}{(Z^2+k^2)^3} \cdot e^{-2n' \operatorname{arc\,cot} n'}. \end{aligned}\right\} \tag{71.3}$$

Substitution into (71.2) yields

$$|x_{W1}|^2 = \frac{2^8}{3} \cdot \frac{Z^6}{(Z^2+k^2)^5} \frac{e^{-4\frac{Z}{k}\arctan\frac{k}{Z}}}{1-e^{-2\pi Z/k}} = \frac{2^8}{3Z^4}\left(\frac{n'^2}{1+n'^2}\right)^5 \cdot \frac{e^{-4n' \operatorname{arc\,cot} n'}}{1-e^{-2\pi n'}} \text{ at. un.} \tag{71.4}$$

The dimensions are those of an area divided by an energy; in atomic units the dimensions are a^3/e^2.

Next, we substitute (71.4) into (71.1). In doing so we note that the long wave length limit of the photoeffect is given by

$$\nu_1 = \frac{E_1}{h} = Z^2\,\text{Ry} = \frac{Z^2}{4\pi} \text{ at. un. of frequency} \tag{71.5}$$

according to the photoelectric equation (69.1). Furthermore, according to the definition of n', $W = k^2 = Z^2/n'^2$ Rydberg, and thus

$$\nu = (Z^2+k^2)\,\text{Ry} = \nu_1 \cdot \left(1+\frac{1}{n'^2}\right), \qquad n' = \sqrt{\frac{\nu_1}{\nu-\nu_1}}. \tag{71.6}$$

Taking into consideration that an atom has two K electrons, the absorption coefficient becomes

$$\tau = 2\cdot(2\pi a)^3 \mathcal{N} \frac{\nu}{c} |x_{W1}|^2 = \frac{2^8 \pi e^2}{3mc} \mathcal{N} \cdot \frac{\nu_1^3}{\nu^4} \cdot \frac{e^{-4n'\operatorname{arc\,cot} n'}}{1-e^{-2\pi n'}}, \tag{71.7}$$

in which a is the radius of the hydrogen atom. If ϱ denotes the density and A the atomic weight of the absorbing substance, the total absorption by the K shell has the value

$$\tau = 4.1 \times 10^8 \cdot \frac{\varrho}{AZ^2}\left(\frac{\nu_1}{\nu}\right)^4 \cdot f(n'), \tag{71.8}$$

in which $f(n')$ is the last fraction in (71.7). For small and intermediate values of k (say, $k < 3Z$), $f(n')$ is closely approximated by

$$f(n') = f(k) = e^{-4}\left(1+\frac{4}{3n'^2}\right) = e^{-4}\left(1+\frac{4}{3}\frac{k^2}{Z^2}\right), \tag{71.9}$$

[1] See Fig. 6. For more details compare A. SOMMERFELD and G. SCHUR, Ann. d. Phys. 4, 409 (1930).

and for very large values of k by

$$f(n') = \frac{1}{2\pi n'} = \frac{k}{2\pi Z}. \tag{71.10}$$

For $k \ll Z$, i.e. so close to the long wave length limit that the energy of the photoelectrons is small compared to the ionization potential of the atom, we obtain, in view of (71.9), (71.5) and (71.6),

$$f(n') = e^{-4}\left(\frac{\nu}{\nu_1}\right)^{\frac{4}{3}},$$

and thus

$$\frac{\tau}{\varrho} = \frac{7.6\times 10^6}{A Z^2}\left(\frac{\nu_1}{\nu}\right)^{\frac{8}{3}}. \tag{71.11}$$

The absorption coefficient at the K absorption limit is seen to decline about as Z^{-3} with increasing atomic number. For a fixed value of Z, τ varies as $\nu^{-\frac{8}{3}}$ in the immediate neighborhood of the absorption edge[1]. At a more considerable distance from the edge, for example, if the energy of the photoelectrons is approximately equal to the ionization potential, then (71.9) is nearly $\frac{4}{3}e^{-4}\frac{\nu}{\nu_1}$ and the absorption coefficient goes as the inverse third power of ν. Finally, if the incident frequency becomes very high, say 100 times as great as the frequency corresponding to the K absorption edge, then in view of (71.10),

$$\frac{\tau}{\varrho} = \frac{6.5\times 10^7}{A Z^2}\left(\frac{\nu_1}{\nu}\right)^{\frac{7}{2}}.$$

This expression is identical with the BORN approximation result, obtained from (70.6). Thus, the decline with growing frequency becomes increasingly steeper, and this agrees with experiment. However, if the frequency ν of the incident light becomes so high that retardation plays a role, the decline becomes less steep again.

The results above are strictly valid only for hydrogen-like atoms, but we shall adapt them to give approximate results for the photoeffect for K-shell electrons in complex atoms. Following the discussion of Sect. 69α, we use hydrogenic wave functions for the bound and continuum state of the photoelectron, both for the same nuclear charge $Z - s$ where we take $s_1 = 0.3$, SLATER's inner screening constant for the K-shell. Following (69.8) we simply use (71.7) with ν still standing for the actual frequency of the photon but with ν_1 and n' modified to

$$\nu_1 = (Z - s_1)^2 \,\text{Rydberg}, \qquad n'^2 = \frac{\nu_1}{\nu - \nu_1}. \tag{71.12}$$

We then have for τ_K, the absorption coefficient for both K-shell electrons, instead of (71.8)

$$\tau_K = 4.1\times 10^8 \frac{\varrho}{A}(Z-0.3)^6\left(\frac{\text{Ry}}{\nu}\right)^4 f\left(\sqrt{\frac{\nu_1}{\nu-\nu_1}}\right). \tag{71.13}$$

Note, however, that the experimental K-absorption edge or threshold frequency $\nu_K = I_1/h$ (at which the *actual* energy W of the ejected electron is zero) does *not* equal ν_1, as defined by (71.12). In fact, ν_K is *smaller* than ν_1 and the difference

[1] Not as ν^{-4} as has been frequently claimed in the literature, e.g., B. M. STOBBE and F. SAUTER, loc. cit.

is due to the outer screening constant V_{01}, Eq. (69.7). Near the absorption edge ν_K, the function $f(n')$ is well represented by (71.9) and no difficulty is encountered by substituting a negative (or zero) value for n'^{-2} from (71.12) into (71.9).

In Fig. 34a the theoretical absorption coefficient τ_K, Eq. (71.13), is plotted against wavelength of the incident photon for Sn ($Z=50$).

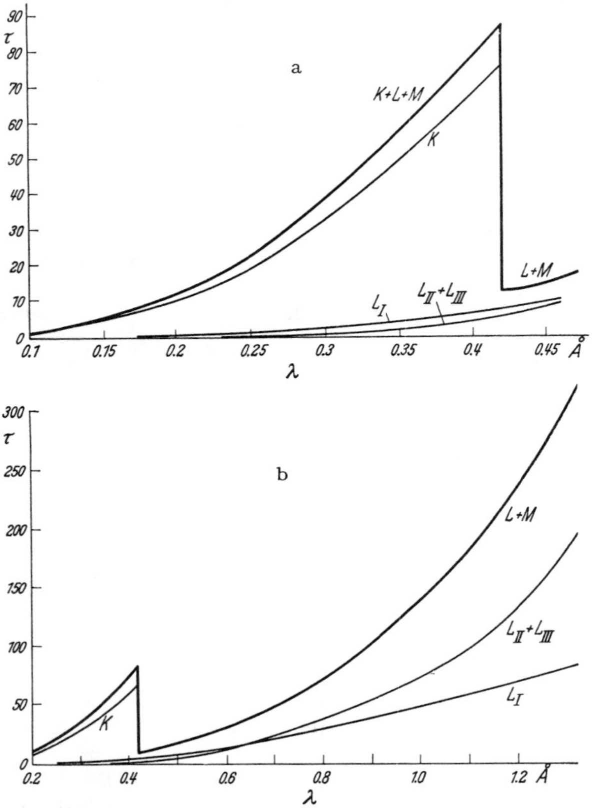

Fig. 34a and b. The theoretical photoelectric absorption coefficient τ (actually absorption cross-section in units of 10^{-22} cm²/atom) for Sn, plotted against photon wave-length λ (in Ångström units). The letters K, L, etc. denote the contribution to τ from the corresponding electron shells

β) Contribution of higher shells. The contribution to the absorption coefficient due to the $2s$- and $2p$-electrons has been calculated by STOBBE[1]. His calculations are similar to those for the K-shell electrons—retardation effects are neglected and hydrogenic wave functions are used. The contribution of the L_{I}-shell (the two $2s$-electrons) to the absorption coefficient τ is

$$\tau_{L_{\mathrm{I}}}=\frac{2^{11}\pi e^2\mathcal{N}}{3mc}\,\frac{\nu_2^3}{\nu^4}\left(1+3\,\frac{\nu_2}{\nu}\right)\frac{e^{-4n_2'\operatorname{arc\,cot}\left(\frac{1}{2}n_2'\right)}}{1-e^{-2\pi n_2'}}\,, \tag{71.14}$$

and that of the L_{II}- and L_{III}-shell combined (the six $2p$-electrons) is[2]

$$\tau_{L_{\mathrm{II}}}+\tau_{L_{\mathrm{III}}}=\frac{2^{11}\pi e^2\mathcal{N}}{3mc}\,\frac{\nu_2^4}{\nu^5}\left(3+8\frac{\nu_2}{\nu}\right)\frac{e^{-4n_2'\operatorname{arc\,cot}\left(\frac{1}{2}n_2'\right)}}{1-e^{-2\pi n_2'}}\,. \tag{71.15}$$

[1] M. STOBBE: Ann. d. Phys. 7, 661 (1930).
[2] The formula in STOBBE's paper is too large by a factor of two.

In these expressions, ν_2 and n_2' are defined by

$$\nu_2 = \frac{1}{4}(Z - s_2)^2 \,\mathrm{Ry}, \quad n_2' = 2\sqrt{\frac{\nu_2}{\nu - \nu_2}}, \tag{71.16}$$

where we use $s_2 = 4.15$ for SLATER's inner screening constant[1]. A similar calculation for the eighteen electrons in the M-shell ($3s$, $3p$ and $3d$) has been carried out by HALL[2].

In Fig. 34 we have plotted the contribution to the absorption coefficient τ for Sn ($Z = 50$) of the K, L_{I} and $L_{\mathrm{II}} + L_{\mathrm{III}}$ shells, as well as the total from the K, L and M shells, using the above formulae[3]. The units for τ are 10^{-22} cm²/atom [actually the absorption cross section σ, Eq. (69.3)]. The agreement with experiment[4] is quite good, in spite of the simple screening approximations used in the calculations.

At high frequencies ($\nu \gg \nu_1$), the expressions (71.14) and (71.15) reduce to those obtained from the BORN approximation, (70.6) and (70.15). As discussed in Sect. 70, the contribution to the absorption coefficient of the higher shells is small compared with that of the K-shell at high frequencies (in spite of the larger number of electrons in the higher shells). Including the effects of screening we find for the L-shell (for $\nu \gg \nu_1$)

$$8\tau_{L_{\mathrm{I}}} = \frac{8}{3}\frac{\nu}{\nu_2}(\tau_{L_{\mathrm{II}}} + \tau_{L_{\mathrm{III}}}) = \left(\frac{Z - s_2}{Z - s_1}\right)^5 \tau_K. \tag{71.17}$$

Another quantity of interest is the "K-absorption jump" δ_K, i.e., the ratio of the absorption coefficient just above and just below the experimental threshold frequency ν_K for the photoeffect from the K-shell,

$$\delta_K = \left(\frac{\tau_K + \tau_L + \tau_M + \cdots}{\tau_L + \tau_M + \cdots}\right)_{\nu = \nu_K}. \tag{71.18}$$

If we neglect both outer and inner screening (i.e., put ν_K equal to ν_1 and $s_1 = s_2 = 0$) and neglect the contributions from the M- and higher shells, we have

$$\delta_K = 1 + \frac{8}{3}\exp\left(\frac{8}{\sqrt{3}}\arctan\sqrt{3} - 4\right) = 7.15.$$

The effect of screening on δ_K is quite appreciable, except for very large Z. We use $s_1 = 0.3$, $s_2 = 4.1_5$ and evaluate δ_K at a value of the frequency ν equal to the experimentally *observed* ν_K. Still omitting the contribution from the M-shell, one finds $\delta_K = 11.2$, 9.3 and 8.5, respectively, for Fe ($Z = 26$), Ag ($Z = 47$) and W ($Z = 74$). Including a rough estimate for absorption from the M-shell, one finally gets

$$\delta_K = 9._2 \text{ for Fe}, \quad 7._4 \text{ for Ag}, \quad 6._5 \text{ for W},$$

in fair agreement with experiment[5].

The absorption coefficient $\tau_{L_{\mathrm{I}}}$ for the L_{I}-subshell, Eq. (71.14), is proportional to $\nu^{-3.5}$ for high frequencies ($\nu \gg \nu_1$) and approximately proportional to $\nu^{-2.1}$ for

---

[1] Actually, a slightly larger value of s_2 should be used for $2p$- than for $2s$-electrons. In any case the present screening approximation is accurate only for fairly large Z, say, $Z > 20$.

[2] H. HALL: Rev. Mod. Phys. **8**, 358 (1936). More detailed expressions for the states with $n = 3$ and $n = 4$ are given by J. HARRIMAN, Phys. Rev. **101**, 594 (1956).

[3] More accurate graphs and tables for the K- and L-shells are given in HALL's review article and total absorption coefficients are given by G. WHITE, U.S. Nat. Bur. Stand. Circ. 1003 (May 1952, Washington, D.C.).

[4] S. J. ALLEN: Phys. Rev. **27**, 266; **28**, 907 (1926) and HALL's article.

[5] E. JÖNSSEN: Diss. Upsala 1928.

ν near the frequency ν_2, defined in (71.16). The ratio $\delta = (\tau_{L_{II}} + \tau_{L_{III}})/\tau_{L_I}$ equals $3\nu_2/\nu$ for $\nu \gg \nu_1$ and is thus very small for high frequencies. The ratio δ is still approximately proportional to ν^{-1} even at lower frequencies and equals 2.75 for $\nu = \nu_2$. The experimental L-shell absorption edge lies at a frequency ν_L which is still *lower* than ν_2 (due to outer screening) and at this frequency δ is even larger than 2.75. The calculated values for δ for radiation of wavelength 1.54 Å (the Cu $K\alpha$-line) for two elements follow: For Cu ($Z=29$), $\nu/\nu_2 = 3.80$ and $\delta = 0.75$; for Ba ($Z=56$), $\nu/\nu_2 = 0.87$ and $\delta = 3.1$. The calculated values for δ for various elements and frequencies are in moderate, but *not* good, agreement with experiment (see HALL's article).

Exact calculations for the photoelectric cross section from shells higher than the M-shell are tedious, but an approximate formula, for frequencies not much larger than the threshold frequency, can be derived as follows[1]. Consider the photoelectric cross-section $\sigma_{nl}(\nu)$ from a single nl-level in a hydrogen-like atom. Using (69.2) and the definition of the mean oscillator strengths (Sect. 61), we can write[2]

$$\sigma_{nl}(\nu) = \frac{2\pi^2 e^2 \hbar}{m c} \frac{d\bar{f}_{nl}}{dE}, \tag{71.19a}$$

where df/dE is the oscillator strength per unit energy interval for a transition from the state nl to a continuum state of energy $E = h\nu - E_n$. Similarly the cross-section σ_{nl}, summed over all $2n^2$ electrons with principal quantum number n, is

$$\sigma_n(\nu) = \frac{2\pi^2 e^2 \hbar}{m c} \frac{dF_n}{dE}, \tag{71.19}$$

where F is the summed oscillator strength discussed at the end of Sect. 63.

Consider now the approximate expression (63.11) for large values of n'. The number of integral values of n' per unit energy interval is proportional to n'^3 and $dF_n/dE_{n'}$, as given by (63.11), is a slowly varying function of $E_{n'}$. We can therefore expect this expression to be still reasonably accurate for small *positive* values $h\nu - E_n$ of $E_{n'}$. With the frequency ν expressed in units of ν_1 (i.e., $\nu' \equiv h\nu/Z^2\,\mathrm{Ry} = \nu/\nu_1$) we then have

$$\frac{dF_n}{d\nu'} \approx 1.96\,\nu'^{-3} n^{-3}. \tag{71.20}$$

This very simple approximate expression is reasonably accurate[3] even for low n and for ν a few times the threshold frequency. For $n=1$, for instance, the correct expression for low ν, (71.7) with (71.9) and (71.19), gives

$$\frac{dF_1}{d\nu'} = \frac{2^8 e^{-4}}{3} \nu'^{-2.7} = 1.56\,\nu'^{-2.7},$$

compared with $1.96\,\nu'^{-3}$ from (71.20). Similarly (71.14) and (71.15) give, for $n=2$ and for ν not much larger than ν_2, $dF_2/d\nu' = 0.282\,\nu'^{-2.9}$, compared with $0.245\,\nu'^{-3}$ from (71.20).

72. Angular distribution and retardation. *α) Angular distribution without retardation*[4]. The angular distribution of the ejected photoelectron is given by the differential cross-section σ_Ω, Eq. (69.5): For a fixed propagation direction $\boldsymbol{k}_\nu$

[1] See also the end of Sect. 78.

[2] H. BETHE, L. BROWN and J. STEHN: Phys. Rev. **77**, 370 (1950).

[3] For corrections to this expression see D. MENZEL and C. PEKERIS, M.N.R. Astron. Soc. **96**, 77 (1935). See also J. A. GAUNT, Phil. Trans. Roy. Soc. Lond., Ser. A **229**, 163 (1930).

[4] For further details, and for references to the experimental literature, see ref. [*10*], Sect. 47d and HALL's review article, p. 369.

and polarization direction $\boldsymbol{j}$ of the incident photon, the cross-section for the ejection of an electron with momentum $\boldsymbol{k}$ (per unit solid angle around this direction) is σ_Ω with u_Ω given by (69.4). We discuss first general results which can be obtained from symmetry considerations if retardation and relativistic effects are neglected.

We consider first a single-electron atom with an arbitrary central potential $V(r)$ and an initial bound state b with wave function $u_{nlm}(\boldsymbol{r})$ separable in spherical polar coordinates. If we take the polarization direction $\boldsymbol{j}$ of the photon as our x-axis, the matrix element to be substituted into (69.5) becomes, with retardation *neglected*,

$$D^{\boldsymbol{j}}_{\Omega b} \propto \int d^3r\, u^*_\Omega(\boldsymbol{r})\, x\, u_{nlm}(\boldsymbol{r}). \tag{72.1}$$

This matrix element, and hence σ_Ω, does not depend explicitly on the propagation direction of the incident photon, but does depend on the angle ϑ between the polarization (x-) direction of the photon and the propagation direction $\boldsymbol{k}$ of the emitted electron. For a single initial state u_{nlm}, (72.1) also depends on the quantization direction and magnetic quantum number m for this state. We now restrict ourselves to the *average* σ_Ω, averaged over all possible m values from $-l$ to l for the initial state u_{nlm} (but with n and l fixed). For a closed subshell in a complex atom, the state with each m-value is occupied (twice) and the cross-section from the whole subshell is $2(2l+1)$ times this average. For a partially filled subshell the average occupation number is also independent of the m-value, as long as no external (or crystal lattice) fields are present. Such an average over all m-values is independent of the quantization direction used for the initial state. The angular distribution for the averaged $\bar{\sigma}_\Omega$ thus depends only on the single angle ϑ between $\boldsymbol{k}$ and $\boldsymbol{j}$ ($\cos\vartheta = k_x/k$ in our notation).

We show first that σ_Ω remains *unchanged* when the electron's propagation direction is changed from $\boldsymbol{k}$ to $-\boldsymbol{k}$ (with the direction of $\boldsymbol{j}$, the x-axis, fixed): We change the variable of integration in (72.1) from $\boldsymbol{r}$ to $-\boldsymbol{r}$ and reverse the quantization direction of u_{nlm}. The integrand is then unchanged except for a change of sign, *each* integral of form (72.1) changes sign and $\bar{\sigma}_\Omega$ is unchanged. Changing the sign of $\boldsymbol{k}$ changes the sign of $\cos\vartheta$ and $\bar{\sigma}_\Omega$ is thus an *even* function of $\cos\vartheta$. We show next that this function must be of form $(\alpha+\beta\cos^2\vartheta)$: We use a spherical polar coordinate system $(r, \vartheta', \varphi')$ for the variable $\boldsymbol{r}$ in (72.1) with the direction of $\boldsymbol{k}$ as polar axis (and quantization direction for u_{nlm}). Using the spherical harmonics addition theorem we can write x in (72.1) in the form

$$x = \boldsymbol{r}\cdot\boldsymbol{j} = r(\cos\vartheta\cos\vartheta' + \sin\vartheta\sin\vartheta'\cos\varphi'), \tag{72.2}$$

where we have taken $\varphi'=0$ for the azimuthal plane which contains the unit polarization vector $\boldsymbol{j}$. The matrix elements (72.1) thus depend on ϑ only through the two terms in (72.2) which are linear in $\cos\vartheta$ and $\sin\vartheta$, respectively. The averaged cross-section $\bar{\sigma}_\Omega$ is obtained by summing the absolute squares of these matrix elements over all m-values. From the above symmetry argument the coefficient of the cross-term $\cos\vartheta\sin\vartheta$ must vanish and we have

$$\bar{\sigma}_\Omega \propto \alpha\sin^2\vartheta + \beta'\cos^2\vartheta = \alpha + \beta\cos^2\vartheta. \tag{72.3}$$

More explicitly, the coefficients α and β are given by the following expressions. The exact continuum wave function u_Ω for a central potential can be written as a sum of wave functions $u_{\Omega l'}$, where $u_{\Omega l'}$ is expressible in spherical polar coordinates (with $\boldsymbol{k}$ as polar axis) with orbital quantum number l' and zero magnetic quantum number m' [see (7.2)]. Using the orthogonality properties of spherical harmonics, we then find

$$\left.\begin{aligned}\alpha &= \tfrac{1}{4}\sum_{m=-1,1}\Big|\sum_{l'=l-1,\,l+1}\int d^3r\, u^*_{\Omega l'}\, r\sin\vartheta'\, e^{-im\varphi'}\, u_{nlm}\Big|^2\\ \beta' &= \beta+\alpha = \Big|\sum_{l'=l-1,\,l+1}\int d^3r\, u^*_{\Omega l'}\, r\cos\vartheta'\, u_{nl0}\Big|^2.\end{aligned}\right\}\qquad (72.4)$$

If the initial bound state is an s-state ($l=0$), then there are no states u_{n0m} with $m=\pm 1$ and the coefficient α in (72.3) and (72.4) vanishes. Thus the angular distribution is proportional to $\cos^2\vartheta$ for an s-state in any central potential. For a p-state we have already shown in Sect. 70β that the angular distribution is isotropic ($\beta=0$) in BORN approximation. An explicit calculation[1], valid also at low frequencies ν near the threshold ν_2, Eq. (71.16), for $2p$-electrons ($L_{\mathrm{II}}+L_{\mathrm{III}}$-shell) gives[2]

$$\bar{\sigma}_\Omega \propto 1 + \frac{2(Z-s_2)^2\,\mathrm{Ry}}{\nu}\cos^2\vartheta. \qquad (72.5)$$

β) Retardation effects. Let (Θ, Φ) be the spherical polar coordinates of the propagation direction $\boldsymbol{k}$ of the ejected electron in a coordinate system with the photon's propagation direction $\boldsymbol{k}_\nu$ as polar (z-) axis and its polarization direction $\boldsymbol{j}$ as x-axis ($\Phi=0$ plane). We have seen that the angular distribution $\bar{\sigma}_\Omega$ only depends on $\cos^2\vartheta$, if retardation is neglected, where

$$\cos^2\vartheta = \sin^2\Theta\cos^2\Phi. \qquad (72.6)$$

With retardation included, $\bar{\sigma}_\Omega$ also depends on Θ itself, although we shall see that the retardation effects are small at nonrelativistic velocities. We still restrict ourselves to the nonrelativistic SCHRÖDINGER theory for both the initial and final states of the electron. *Exact* (within the frame work of the nonrelativistic theory) calculations are available[3] for the differential cross-section σ_Ω for the K- and L-shells of hydrogen-like atoms. These results take retardation into account fully and are also valid for low photon frequencies. We shall merely evaluate the retardation correction in the BORN approximation for s-electrons and also restrict ourselves to nonrelativistic velocities for the ejected electron[4], i.e., $(Z\alpha)^2 mc^2 \ll h\nu \ll mc^2$.

In zero order (plane wave) BORN approximation, the differential cross section σ_Ω from a bound s-state is given by (69.5) with (70.3), if retardation is taken into account fully. The only effect of retardation is that $\psi_b(\boldsymbol{k}-\boldsymbol{k}_\nu)$ occurs in (70.3) instead of $\psi_b(\boldsymbol{k})$. This effect can be pictured physically by saying that the absorbed photon imparts its own momentum $\hbar\boldsymbol{k}_\nu$ to the ejected electron (in addition to the momentum it receives in the dipole approximation)[5]. The angular distribution is no longer symmetric about the polarization direction, but the direction of maximum intensity is shifted towards the direction of propagation of the photon: Using the explicit hydrogenic wave function (70.4), the

[1] G. SCHUR: Ann. d. Phys. **4**, 433 (1930).

[2] (72.5) is exact only for a COULOMB potential $(Z-s_2)/r$. In a complex atom the actual effective (HARTREE) potential deviates appreciably from $(Z-s_2)/r$ for large r. The coefficient β in (72.4) is quite sensitive to the exact shape of the potential at large r, especially at low frequencies. Thus (72.5) is not very accurate for complex atoms and the correct coefficient β of $\cos^2\vartheta$ is smaller than that given by (72.5).

[3] J. FISCHER, Ann. d. Phys. **8**, 821; **11**, 489 (1931); F. SAUTER, Ann. d. Phys. **9**, 217; **11**, 454 (1931) and especially A. SOMMERFELD and G. SCHUR, Ann. d. Phys. **4**, 409 (1930) and ref. [7], Chap. 6, Sects. 4 and 6.

[4] J. FRENKEL: Phys. Rev. **37**, 1276 (1931).

[5] This picture must not be taken too seriously: The factor $k^{\frac{3}{2}}$ in (70.3) is *not* replaced by $|\boldsymbol{k}-\boldsymbol{k}_\nu|^{\frac{3}{2}}$, as the picture might imply.

differential cross-section σ_Ω with retardation equals the dipole approximation (70.5) times the correction factor F,

$$F = \frac{k^8}{|\boldsymbol{k} - \boldsymbol{k}_\nu|^8}. \qquad (72.7)$$

$\hbar k$ is given by (70.1) and the photon momentum $\hbar k_\nu$ equals $h\nu/c$. Neglecting I_b compared with $h\nu$ [we are assuming $h\nu \gg (Z\alpha)^2 mc^2$], we have

$$\frac{k_\nu}{k} = \frac{\hbar k}{2mc} = \frac{1}{2}\frac{v}{c}, \qquad (72.8)$$

where v is the velocity of the ejected electron. Since $v \ll c$ (we assume $h\nu \ll mc^2$) we find, after expanding (72.7) in powers of v/c and keeping only the first two terms,

$$F = \left(1 - \frac{v}{c}\cos\Theta\right)^{-4} \approx 1 + 4\frac{v}{c}\cos\Theta. \qquad (72.9)$$

We have thus shown that the angular distribution from s-state electrons is not given by (72.6), but by

$$\sigma_\Omega \propto \sin^2\Theta\cos^2\Phi\left(1 + 4\frac{v}{c}\cos\Theta\right). \qquad (72.10)$$

Note that the correction factor in (72.9) is quite small still even when the photon's wavelength is comparable with the atomic radius. We have so far neglected all other specifically relativistic effects, but the correction factor (72.9) is nevertheless meaningful since it is linear in v/c, whereas the other relativistic effects (see Sect. 73) are of order $(v/c)^2$ or smaller. For the *total* cross-section σ, (72.10) integrated over all angles, however, the correction linear in v/c integrates to zero and the retardation correction is also only of order $(v/c)^2$.

In the same energy region, $Z^2\,\mathrm{Ry} \ll h\nu \ll mc^2$, the angular distribution for the $L_{\mathrm{II}} + L_{\mathrm{III}}$ shell (the six $2p$-electrons) is given by ([7], p. 477)

$$\bar{\sigma}_\Omega \propto \left(1 + 2\frac{v}{c}\cos\Theta\right) + \sin^2\Theta\cos^2\Phi\left[2\frac{(Z-s_2)^2\,\mathrm{Ry}}{\nu} + 4\frac{v}{c}\cos\Theta\right]. \qquad (72.11)$$

SOMMERFELD and SCHUR, and SCHUR[1], respectively, have calculated more accurate results for K- and for L-electrons, which do not neglect $Z^2\,\mathrm{Ry}/\nu$ at all, but omit higher powers of v/c. These results reduce to (72.10) and (72.11) for small $Z^2\,\mathrm{Ry}/\nu$ (and small v/c).

For s-state electrons, the maximum of the differential cross-section (72.10) still lies at zero azimuthal angle Φ. For constant Φ, however, the maximum intensity is obtained not at $\Theta = \frac{1}{2}\pi$ ($\cos\Theta = 0$), but at an angle $\Theta_{\max}$, given by (for $v \ll c$)

$$\cos\Theta_{\max} \approx \frac{\pi}{2} - \Theta_{\max} \approx 2\frac{v}{c} = 2\beta. \qquad (72.12)$$

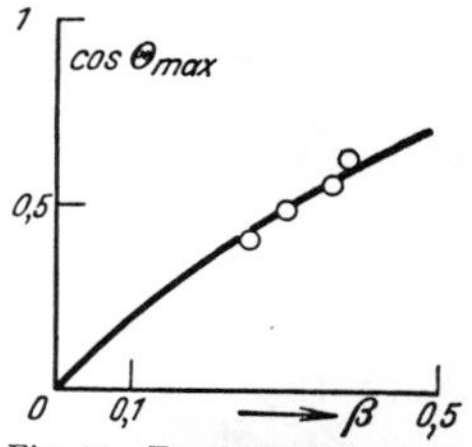

Fig. 35. Forward shift of the maximum of the photoelectric cross-section. The function $\cos\vartheta_{\max}$ is plotted against $\beta = v/c$ (v is the velocity of the photoelectron).

$\cos\Theta_{\max}$ is plotted against β in Fig. 35. For larger values of β, the more accurate relativistic expression (73.3) was used to evaluate the plotted expression of $\cos\Theta_{\max}$.

73. Relativistic effects. We discuss now the effects introduced by using the relativistic DIRAC theory for the electron instead of the nonrelativistic SCHRÖDINGER theory. The matrix element D to be substituted into (69.5) is modified in two ways. Relativistic DIRAC spinor wave functions must be used for u_Ω and for u_b and the momentum operator $\boldsymbol{p}$ is to be replaced by $mc\boldsymbol{\alpha}$, i.e.

$$D_{\Omega b}^{\boldsymbol{k}_\nu j} = \frac{i\,m\,c}{\hbar}\int u_\Omega^* \sum_i e^{i\boldsymbol{k}_\nu\cdot\boldsymbol{r}_i}\,\alpha_j^{(i)}\,u_b\,d\tau. \qquad (73.1)$$

[1] G. SCHUR: Ann. d. Phys. **4**, 433 (1930).

No exact analytic calculations have been carried out so far using the DIRAC theory, but various useful formulae are available. We discuss first approximate analytic formulae, which hold if $Z\alpha \ll 1$.

α) Relativistic BORN *approximation.* We restrict ourselves to hydrogenic wave functions with $Z\alpha \ll 1$. Relativistic effects for the bound state wave function u_b are only of relative order $(Z\alpha)^2$ and we shall ignore them (e.g. by using the PAULI approximation for u_b). On the other hand we require expressions which are also valid for $h\nu \gtrsim mc^2$ and have to use DIRAC wave functions u_Ω for the continuum state. Since $h\nu_1 \sim (Z\alpha)^2 mc^2$ and since the relativistic effects are small if $h\nu \ll mc^2$, we can also restrict ourselves to the energy region $\nu \gg \nu_1$, where the BORN approximation can be used. Such a calculation, analogous to those of Sect. 70, [except that a DIRAC wave function u_Ω and (73.1) was used] has been carried out by SAUTER[1] for K-electrons. We discuss first the angular distribution of SAUTER's results.

We define the following dimensionless variables,

$$\beta = \frac{v}{c}, \quad \gamma = \frac{1}{\sqrt{1-\beta^2}} \approx 1 + \frac{h\nu}{mc^2}, \tag{73.2}$$

where v is the velocity of the ejected electron [neglecting $I_b/h\nu$ in (69.1)]. SAUTER's angular distribution is then given by

$$\sigma_\Omega \propto \frac{\sin^2\Theta}{(1-\beta\cos\Theta)^4}\left\{\frac{\cos^2\Phi}{\gamma}\left[1 - \frac{1}{2}(\gamma-1)(1-\beta\cos\Theta)\right] + \frac{1}{4}(\gamma-1)^2(1-\beta\cos\Theta)\right\}, \tag{73.3}$$

where Θ and Φ are the angles defined at the beginning of Sect. 72β. At relatively low energies, $\beta \ll 1$, the parameter γ is approximately unity and $\gamma - 1 \approx \frac{1}{2}\beta^2 \ll \beta$. In this case the first term in (73.3) is the leading one and this expression reduces to (72.10). At extremely relativistic energies, on the other hand, we have

$$\frac{h\nu}{mc^2} \approx \gamma \gg 1, \qquad 1 - \beta \approx \frac{1}{2\gamma^2} \ll 1. \tag{73.4}$$

The last term in (73.3) is then the leading one and the angular distribution is strongly peaked in the forward direction (Θ small). For $\Theta \ll 1$ and $\gamma \gg 1$, (73.3) then gives, instead of (72.10) and (72.12),

$$\sigma_\Omega \propto \frac{\Theta^2}{(1+\gamma^2\Theta^2)^3}, \quad \Theta_{\max} = \frac{1}{\sqrt{2}\,\gamma}. \tag{73.5}$$

Note that, in this limit, σ_Ω is independent of the photon's polarization direction (i.e. of Φ).

The total cross-section σ_K per electron (σ_Ω integrated over angles) for the K-shell (τ_K equals $2\mathcal{N}\sigma_K$) according to SAUTER's formula, can be written in the following form

$$\frac{\sigma_K}{\varphi_0} = Z^5\alpha^4\left(\frac{mc^2}{h\nu}\right)^5(\beta\gamma)^3\left[1 + \frac{3}{4}\frac{\gamma(\gamma-2)}{\gamma+1}\left(1 - \frac{1}{2\beta\gamma^2}\log\frac{1+\beta}{1-\beta}\right)\right]. \tag{73.6}$$

In this expression, φ_0 is a constant of dimensions cm², called the THOMSON scattering cross-section,

$$\varphi_0 = \frac{8\pi}{3} r_0^2 = 6.65\times 10^{-25}\,\text{cm}^2, \qquad r_0 = \frac{e^2}{mc^2} = \alpha\,\lambda_c = 2.818\times 10^{-13}\,\text{cm}, \tag{73.7}$$

[1] F. SAUTER: Ann. d. Phys. **11**, 454; **9**, 217 (1931). See also ref. [7], Chap. 6, Sect. 8.

where r_0 is the "classical radius" and $\lambda_c = \hbar/mc = 3.86 \times 10^{-11}$ cm is the "rationalized COMPTON wave length" of the electron. In the nonrelativistic region, $\beta \ll 1$, $\gamma \approx 1$ and the expression in square brackets in (73.6) reduces to unity. Using the fact that $h\nu = \frac{1}{2} m c^2 \beta^2$, (73.6) for $\beta \ll 1$ reduces to

$$\sigma_K = 2^{\frac{3}{2}} Z^5 \alpha^4 \left(\frac{m c^2}{h \nu}\right)^{\frac{7}{2}} \varphi_0 . \tag{73.8}$$

Using the fact that $h\nu_1 = \frac{1}{2}(Z\alpha)^2 mc^2$ and the definition (73.7), one finds that (73.8) is identical with the nonrelativistic BORN approximation (70.6). For extremely relativistic energies, on the other hand, (73.4) applies and (73.6) reduces to

$$\sigma_K = \frac{3}{4} Z^5 \alpha^4 \left(\frac{m c^2}{h \nu}\right) \varphi_0 = Z^5 \alpha^6 \lambda \lambda_c , \tag{73.9}$$

where λ_c is defined in (73.7) and λ is the wave length of the incident photon. At relativistic energies $h\nu$ of the photon, the absorption cross-section thus decreases only with the minus *first* power of this energy.

β) Attenuation of photons. We have been mainly concerned with the photoelectric absorption of high frequency radiation (X-rays and γ-rays of a few keV and more) in elements with medium and large Z. In this energy region the photoeffect comes mainly from the inner electrons of the atoms (especially the two K-electrons). There are two other effects which also contribute to the attenuation of X-rays and γ-rays while passing through matter[1]. We shall not discuss these in detail, but merely mention some results. One of these is the *scattering* of a photon by an electron[2]. For a single *free* electron in the nonrelativistic energy region $h\nu \ll mc^2$ the photon is scattered with only a small decrease of frequency ν and the total scattering cross-section is simply φ_0, Eq. (73.7), and is independent of ν. Note that the THOMSON scattering cross-section φ_0 is proportional to e^4, since the electron interacts with the radiation field *twice* (absorption of the incident and emission of the scattered photon).

For an electron bound in an atom, the scattering of the photon is still given approximately by φ_0, if the wave length λ of the photon is small compared with the "radius" of the bound state electronic wave function. In this case the electron is ejected from the atom, but with energy small compared with that of the photon (still for $h\nu \ll mc^2$). At smaller frequencies (larger λ), the effect of the binding of the electron is more important (and complicated), both coherent and incoherent scattering of the photon takes place and the total scattering cross section is somewhat larger than φ_0. In elements with large Z, most of the Z electrons are in the outer shells with large radii and the total scattering cross-section from the whole atom is roughly $Z\varphi_0$ for frequencies larger than the K-shell absorption edge[3]. In the energy region $(Z\alpha)^2 mc^2 \ll h\nu \ll mc^2$, the ratio of the total photoelectric absorption cross-section σ_{ph} [approximately twice σ_K, Eq. (73.8)] to the scattering cross-section σ_{sc} is then

$$\frac{\sigma_{ph}}{\sigma_{sc}} = 2^{\frac{5}{2}} (Z\alpha)^4 \left(\frac{m c^2}{h\nu}\right)^{\frac{7}{2}} . \tag{73.10}$$

[1] See E. SEGRÈ, Experimental Nuclear Physics, Vol. 1, Part II by J. ASHKIN and H. BETHE. New York: J. Wiley 1953.

[2] See ref. [6], Sects. 19 and 22; see also G. R. WHITE, U.S. Nat. Bur. Stand. Circular 1003 (May 1952, Washington, D.C.).

[3] For the *coherent* scattering of photons from K-shell electrons in atoms with very large Z, see S. BRENNER, G. BROWN, R. PEIERLS and J. WOODWARD, Proc. Roy. Soc. Lond., Ser. A **227**, 51, 57 (1954).

This ratio is of order $(Z\alpha)^{-3}$ for ν near the K-absorption edge and is also large for even lower frequencies (photoeffect mainly from the L-shell). At large frequencies, however, this ratio is small [of order $(Z\alpha)^4$ for $h\nu \sim mc^2$] and most of the attenuation is due to photon-scattering. The ratio (73.10) is unity at an energy of approximately

$$h\nu = 1.6\,(Z\alpha)^{1.14}\, m c^2 = 0.84\,(Z\alpha)^{1.14}\,\text{MeV}. \tag{73.11}$$

At relativistic photon energies $h\nu > mc^2$, the scattered photon has an appreciably lower frequency than the incident one (the electron takes up the momentum difference). The total cross-section σ_{sc} for scattering from the Z electrons (which can certainly be considered as though they are unbound) is given by the KLEIN-NISHINA formula for the COMPTON effect ([6], Sect. 22) in this energy range. σ_{sc} decreases with increasing ν slightly less rapidly than σ_{ph}, Eq. (73.9), and the

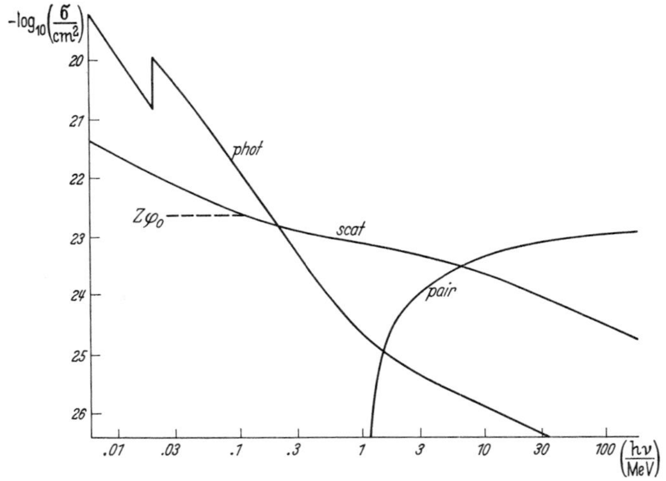

Fig. 36. The cross-sections σ for various processes undergone by a photon of energy $h\nu$ in passing through molybdenum ($Z=42$), plotted on a log-log scale. The curves labelled "phot", "scat" and "pair" are for photoelectric absorption, photon scattering and pair creation, respectively. The dotted line labelled $Z\varphi_0$ is the THOMSON cross-section from Z free electrons.

photoeffect is much less important than COMPTON scattering for all $h\nu \gtrsim mc^2$. In the extreme relativistic region $h\nu \gg mc^2$,

$$\sigma_{sc} = \frac{3}{8\gamma}\left(\log 2\gamma + \frac{1}{2}\right) Z\varphi_0, \tag{73.12}$$

where γ is given by (73.4).

At relativistic energies, photon attentuation by pair creation ([6], Sect. 26) competes with scattering and the photoeffect (see also Sect. 79γ). This is an effect specific to DIRAC pair theory and the creation of the electron-positron pair can be thought of as follows: An (unobservable) electron in the sea of negative-energy states (under the influence of the nuclear COULOMB potential) absorbs the photon and makes a transition to a positive-energy state (the "hole in the sea" is observed as the positron). The effect of pair creation by a photon depends only on the presence of the nuclear COULOMB potential, *not* on the presence of any real atomic electrons. The total pair creation cross-section σ_{pair} rises rapidly at first with increasing ν from zero at the threshold $h\nu = 2mc^2 = 1.02$ MeV. For $h\nu/mc^2 \approx \gamma \gg 1$, σ_{pair} *increases* logarithmically with increasing γ and is of order $Z\alpha\gamma\sigma_{sc}$. At extremely relativistic energies, pair creation is thus more important than the COMPTON effect (and the photoeffect is negligible). In Fig. 36

the three cross-sections σ_{ph}, σ_{scat} and σ_{pair} are plotted against $h\nu$ on a logarithmic scale for Mo ($Z=42$, $Z\alpha=0.31$).

γ) Deviations from BORN *approximation.* For elements with small enough Z, so that $Z\alpha \ll 1$, we have discussed quite accurate approximation formulae for the photoeffect which cover the whole range of photon frequencies ν. Thus, for $h\nu \ll mc^2$ the STOBBE formulae of Sect. 71 (relativity neglected), and for $h\nu \gg (Z\alpha)^2 mc^2$ the SAUTER formula (73.6) may be used. Since $Z\alpha \ll 1$, the range of validity of the two approximations overlap and one can even combine them in a semi-empirical way: For the K-shell multiply (73.6) by $2\pi\sqrt{\nu_1/\nu}\, f(n')$ with $f(n')$ defined by (71.7). This formula then reduces to (71.7) for small frequencies ν and to (73.6) for[1] large ν. However, both the SAUTER and STOBBE formulae neglect some relativistic effects of relative order $(Z\alpha)^2$ and, for very heavy elements, $Z\alpha$ is by no means very small (although never larger than unity, e.g. $Z\alpha=0.67$ for U, $Z=92$).

HULME *et al.*[2] have evaluated the exact DIRAC expressions (no neglect of $Z\alpha$) for the total photoelectric absorption cross-section σ_K for the K-shell for a few values of Z and of $h\nu$. Since no analytic DIRAC continuum wave functions separable in parabolic coordinates are available, these calculations involved summing a number of terms in the multipole expansion and some numerical work had to be carried out separately for each value of Z and $h\nu$. HALL[3] has obtained an analytic expression for σ_K, valid for all $Z\alpha$, for the limit of high frequency $h\nu \gg mc^2$. His expression for σ_K equals the limit (73.9) of the SAUTER formula multiplied by the factor

$$F=\exp\left[-\pi Z\alpha+2Z^2\alpha^2(1-\log Z\alpha)\right]. \quad (73.13)$$

Table 21. *Correction factors F_n and F to the* SAUTER *formula for Pb.*

$\frac{h\nu}{mc^2}$	0.69	2.2	∞
F_n	0.28	0.47	1
F	0.27	0.53	0.46

In Table 21, we give the ratio F (for two frequencies) of HULME's numerical values of σ_K to those obtained from SAUTER's expression (73.6) [and HALL's factor (73.13) for $h\nu \gg mc^2$] for Pb, $Z=82$, $Z\alpha=0.60$. In the same table, F_n is the factor $2\pi\sqrt{\nu_1/\nu}\, f(n')$, Eqs. (71.7) and (71.8), with n' given by the nonrelativistic formula (71.6). The empirical factor F_n is quite close to the correct expression F at moderately low energies, even for such large values of Z. The departure of F_n from F for large values of the energy and of Z is not surprising: As $h\nu/mc^2 \to \infty$, the relativistic expression $Ze^2/\hbar v$ for n' tends to $Z\alpha$, whereas the nonrelativistic value for n', used in F_n, tends to zero.

It should be noted that the frequency dependence $\nu^{-3.5}$ of the nonrelativistic BORN approximation (70.6) for σ_K does not hold for *any* frequencies ν for elements with large Z: The BORN approximation factor (71.10) would be accurate only for rather large values of ν/ν_1, (say, $\nu \gg 10\nu_1$) and for such large frequencies the nonrelativistic approximation is no longer accurate. If we write $\sigma_K \propto \nu^{-n}$, then n varies almost monotonically from $n \approx 2.7$ at $\nu \sim \nu_1$, to $n=1$ for $h\nu \gg mc^2$ (see also Fig. 36) without ever attaining the value $n=3.5$, if Z is larger than about 30 or 40.

74. The optical region. *α) Negative ions and helium.* We have considered so far mainly the photoelectric absorption of X-rays and γ-rays in atoms with large Z. In such cases most of the contribution comes from the innermost atomic

[1] For large ν, $n' \approx \sqrt{\nu_1/\nu}$ and $2\pi n' f(n') \approx 1$ from (71.10).

[2] H. HULME, J. MCDOUGAL, R. BUCKINGHAM and R. FOWLER: Proc. Roy. Soc. Lond., Ser. A **149**, 131 (1935).

[3] H. HALL: Phys. Rev. **45**, 620 (1934) and Rev. Mod. Phys. **8**, 358 (1936).

electrons for which screening effects are not too important and one obtains good results by using single-electron hydrogenic wave functions for both the initial and the final state of the photoelectron. For radiation of frequency much lower than the threshold for the ejection of inner electrons, the photoeffect can take place only from the more loosely bound outer electrons, for which the hydrogenic approximation is rather poor. Few calculations have been done for such states in complex atoms, but the photoeffect from the negative hydrogen ion H^- (see Sect. 34), a loose structure for which the hydrogenic approximation breaks down, has been studied extensively.

As discussed in Sect. 34, the negative hydrogen ion has only one bound state with ionization potential $I_1 = h\nu_1 = 0.75$ eV and its wave function is represented rather poorly by a simple product of two single-electron wave functions (polarization effects are important). CHANDRASEKHAR[1] has calculated the photoelectric cross-section $\sigma(\nu)$ for H^-, using different approximations for the bound state wave function. He finds that rather accurate bound state wave functions are required (the best one being an eleven-parameter variational one) to obtain reliable results for $\sigma(\nu)$. The continuum wave function for the final state of the electron is also very different from a hydrogenic one for ν near the threshold value ν_1 and the frequency dependence near threshold is drastically different from that of Sect. 71α. This can be seen as follows.

The final state wave function represents an electron of positive energy $k^2/2m$ moving in the potential $V(r)$ due to a *neutral* hydrogen atom in its ground state. This potential $V(r)$ approximates e/r for small r but approaches zero very rapidly for r larger than the BOHR radius a_0 (complete screening). Since the ground state of H^- is an s-state, the final state is a p-state. For $r > a_0$, where $V \to 0$, r times the radial wave function for the p-state is approximately of the form

$$\sqrt{\frac{\pi}{2}}\,\chi(r) = \frac{\sin(kr+\delta)}{kr} - \cos(kr+\delta)\,, \tag{74.1}$$

if we use the same normalization for $kr \to \infty$ as in (4.18). For such a "short-range" potential $V(r)$, one finds that the phase shift δ in (74.1) is very small if $ka_0 \ll 1$, i.e. δ is of the order of $(ka_0)^3$. For $r \sim a_0$, the range of radial distances of importance for the photoelectric matrix element, one then finds $\chi(a_0) \sim (ka_0)^2$. For such small values of k, i.e. near the low-frequency limit $\nu \approx \nu_1$, the cross-section $\sigma(\nu)$ is then proportional to $k^3 \propto (\nu - \nu_1)^{\frac{3}{2}}$ and goes to *zero* at threshold, just as the BORN approximation result of Sect. 70α. In fact, if we replace δ by zero in (74.1), we obtain exactly the wave function used in the BORN approximation calculation (solution for zero potential). If δ were small compared with $(ka_0)^3$, $\sigma(\nu)$ would not only be of the same order of magnitude as, but very close to, the BORN approximation result. If, on the other hand, the final state electron moves in a potential which is COULOMBic at large distances, then $\chi(a_0)$ is[2] of order $(ka_0)^{\frac{1}{2}}$ [instead of $(ka_0)^2$] and $\sigma(\nu)$ tends to a *finite* limit at threshold ($k \to 0$), as for the hydrogenic calculations of 71α.

Explicit calculations[3], using more accurate final state wave functions, show that the BORN approximation result for $\sigma(\nu)$ is in fact within 5% of the correct value for a large range of frequencies ν. CHANDRASEKHAR's cross-section is plotted against ν/ν_1 (in arbitrary units) in Fig. 37, where $h\nu_1$ is the ionization potential of H^-. It rises from zero at threshold (wavelength about 16500 Å) to a maximum at a wavelength of about 8500 Å.

[1] S. CHANDRASEKHAR: Astrophys. J. **100**, 176 (1944); **102**, 223 (1945).
[2] This can be seen by comparing (4.19) and (4.23) for $n' \gg 1$.
[3] S. CHANDRASEKHAR: Astrophys. J. **102**, 395 (1945).

The situation is different again for the photoeffect from the ground state of neutral helium: Even at large radial distances r the potential acting on the photoelectron is not zero but $-e/r$, the Coulomb potential of the nucleus ($Z=2$) minus that of *one* electron. The cross-section $\sigma(\nu)$ has a finite value (in fact, a maximum) at the threshold frequency ν_1 as for hydrogen. This cross-section[1] is plotted against ν/ν_1 in Fig. 37, together with the hydrogenic expression (71.7) (normalized to agree at $\nu=1.5\nu_1$). Note that the He-curve is closer to the hydrogenic one than to that for H^-.

β) Stellar opacity[2]. The photoeffect is one of the most important causes of opacity (i.e. the attenuation of electromagnetic radiation) in the interior and atmosphere of the sun and of stars. Typical stellar matter consists largely of hydrogen plus about 10% (by mass) of helium and of the order of a few percent (or less) by mass for the elements with $Z\sim 6$ to $Z\sim 30$ combined. The stellar matter is partly ionized and photons can also be absorbed by a process we have not discussed so far, the "free-free" transitions:

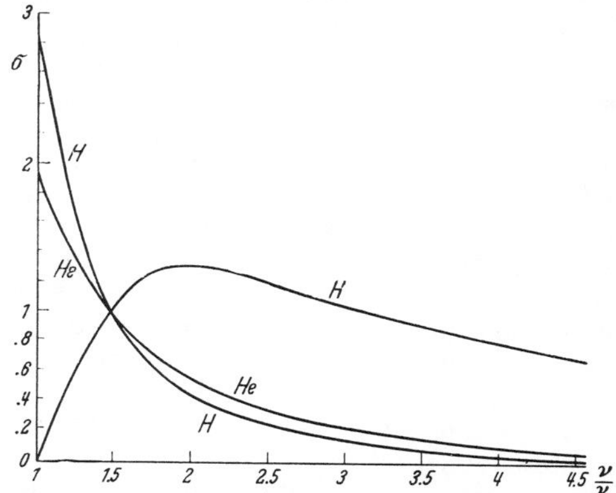

Fig 37. The cross-section σ for the photoelectric absorption from the ground states of H^-, He and H. The abscissa is the frequency ν divided by the threshold frequency ν_1 for the particular atom or ion, the ordinate is σ in units such that $\sigma=1$ for $\nu=1.5\nu_1$.

An electron of *positive* energy moving in a *continuum* state in some atomic potential can make a transition to another continuum state with higher energy and simultaneously absorb a photon. This process is thus the analogue of the photoeffect for an initial state of the electron in the continuum (instead of in the discrete spectrum) and there is no minimum threshold value for the frequency ν of the photon to be absorbed. This process is the inverse of Bremsstrahlung (discussed in Sects. 76 to 79) and the photon absorption cross-section can be derived from related expressions for Bremsstrahlung. We shall not discuss calculations[3] for the photon absorption cross-section $\sigma_{FF}(\nu)$ due to free-free transitions under stellar conditions, but merely note that for an electron with initial velocity v in a Coulomb potential of charge Z the approximate relation

$$\sigma_{FF}(\nu) \propto Z^2 v^{-1} \nu^{-3} \tag{74.2}$$

holds[4].

In the interior of a typical star, where most of its mass is concentrated, the temperature is of the order of 10^6 to 10^7 °K ($kT\sim 10^2$ to 10^3 eV) and the density of the order of 10^{-2} to 10^2 gm/cm³. Energy is transported outwards from the interior by electromagnetic radiation, which is continually absorbed and re-emitted and has a thermal frequency distribution. Under these circumstances

[1] Calculated by using a six-parameter variational wave function for the ground state and Coulomb wave function with charge $Z-1=1$ for the continuum state; S. Huang, Astrophys. J. **108**, 354 (1948).

[2] L. H. Aller: Astrophysics, Vol. I and II. New York: Ronald Press Co. 1953 and 1954. G. Keller and R. Meyerott: Argonne Nat. Lab. Rep 4771 and 4856 (1952). — A. Unsöld: Physik der Sternatmosphäre, 2nd ed. Berlin: Springer 1955.

[3] H. Zirin: Astrophys. J. **119**, 371 (1954). — R. Kulsrud: Astrophys. J. **119**, 386 (1954).

[4] See also the end of Sect. 78 and (78.10).

essentially all the hydrogen and helium is completely ionized. The heavier atoms with $Z \sim 6$ to 30 are ionized to a high degree and only the innermost electrons remain bound. The photoeffect then is due only to the bound electrons of these heavier atoms and the photoelectric cross-sections can be obtained approximately from (71.19) and (71.20) and small corrections to this formula have also been calculated. If the abundance of these heavier atoms is very low, the free-free transitions of an electron in the potentials of ionized hydrogen and helium are an important source of photon absorption [especially at low photon frequencies where only bound states with large principal quantum number n could contribute to the photoeffect, cf. Eq. (71.20)]. For large photon frequencies, the *scattering* of photons by the free electrons is more important than either the photoeffect or free-free transitions, and the scattering cross-section per electron is given to a good approximation by φ_0, Eq. (73.7).

The absorption of radiation in the atmospheres of the sun and of other stars is also of interest. The temperature T_s in the "photosphere" (i.e. depths from which radiation has about an equal chance of escaping and of being absorbed) of most stars lies between 3000 and 20000 °K and the density is very low. In reasonably hot stars ($T_s \sim 10^4$ °K) the hydrogen is only partly ionized and most photons are absorbed by the photoelectric effect from bound hydrogen atoms. In cooler stars, such as the sun, most of the hydrogen is neutral and in its *ground* state, but the outermost electrons of the heavier atoms have been removed by ionization. Some of these electrons are captured by neutral hydrogen atoms to form H^--ions. Most photons in the thermal radiation have frequencies well below threshold for the photoeffect from neutral hydrogen in the ground state and such photons are mainly absorbed by the photoeffect from the bound H^--ions. For photons of very low frequency ($h\nu < 0.75$ eV) absorption by free-free transitions from the H^--continuum (positive energy electrons moving in the field of a *neutral* hydrogen atom) is also important[1].

γ) The average excitation energy for the LAMB *shift.* We consider first a bound S-state with principal quantum n_0 and energy E_0 of a hydrogen-like atom. In (19.10) we have defined a dimensionless quantity K_0/Z^2 Ry which represents, in some sense, the "average excitation energy" in units of the ground state energy. Using the definition (59.14) of the oscillator strength f_{0n} and (59.20), we can rewrite (19.10) as

$$\log \frac{K_0}{Z^2 \,\mathrm{Ry}} = \frac{\sum\limits_n f_{0n} \nu_{0n}^2 \log |\nu_{0n}|}{\sum\limits_n f_{0n} \nu_{0n}^2}, \tag{74.3}$$

where $\nu_{0n} = (E_n - E_0)/Z^2$ Ry. The sums over n are to be carried over *all* stationary states of the hydrogen atom, including those in the continuum, and can be written as

$$\sum_n f_{0n} \nu_{0n}^2 = {\sum_n}' f_{0n} \nu_{0n}^2 + \int\limits_{-2\log n}^{\infty} \frac{df}{d\nu} \nu^3 \, d \log \nu, \tag{74.4}$$

with a similar relation for the sum involving $\log\nu$. In (74.4), $\sum'$ denotes summation over bound states n only and $df/d\nu$ is the oscillator strength per unit frequency interval and is related to the photoelectric absorption cross-section from the state n_0 by (71.19a). It should be remembered that the calculations of Sect. 19β were nonrelativistic ones with retardation neglected and hence f_{0n} in (74.3) is also the nonrelativistic, non-retarded oscillator strength.

[1] S. CHANDRASEKHAR and F. BREEN: Astrophys. J. **104**, 430 (1946).

Analytic expressions for f_{0n} for the discrete spectrum were given in Sect. 63 and $df/d\nu$ for the continuum can be derived from STOBBE's analytic formulae for the photoelectric cross-section, discussed in Sect. 71. The sums and integrals in (74.3) with (74.4) can then be evaluated by numerical work, separately for each value of n_0. Such calculations have been carried out[1] for $n_0=1$ to 4. The results are

n_0	1	2	3	4	∞
K_0/Z^2 Ry	19.770	16.640	15.921	15.640	15.2

including an extrapolated value for $n_0\to\infty$. Note that the values of K_0/Z^2 Ry are numerically rather large and do not depend on the value of n_0 very strongly. This result is at first sight somewhat surprising: Using (19.13) and (21.1) we can write

$$\sum_n f_{n0}\,\nu_{0n}^2 = \frac{16\,\pi}{3\,Z^3}\,\delta^{(3)}(r)_{n_0 n_0} = \frac{16}{3\,n_0^3}\,. \tag{74.5}$$

Since $\sum_n f_{n0}=1$, the square root of the expression (74.5) also represents an average of ν, in some sense. This "average" is only about 2.3 for $n_0=1$ and decreases with increasing n_0 as $n_0^{-1.5}$ quite unlike the other "average", K_0/Z^2 Ry.

The dependence on n_0 of K_0 and of (74.5) can be understood as follows: Table 14, and also (63.11), shows that f_{0n} is of order unity if n is close to n_0 but falls off rapidly with increasing $n-n_0$, if n_0 is large. For small $n-n_0$, the energy difference ν_{0n} in (74.4) is very small and the sum over the discrete spectrum $\sum' f_{0n}\,\nu_{0n}^2$ is of order n_0^{-6}. On the other hand $df/d\nu$ is roughly proportional to n_0^{-3} and $\nu^3 df/d\nu$ increases with ν, for ν of the order unity, and has a maximum at a rather large numerical value ν_m of ν. Only for very large values of ν does $\nu^3\, df/d\nu$ approach its BORN approximation expression (see Sect. 70α), which is proportional to $\nu^{-0.5}$. The deviation from the BORN approximation is largely due to the effect of the COULOMB potential on the *continuum* wave function. Consequently ν_m does not depend very strongly on n_0 and is rather large ($\nu_m\sim 7$ for $n_0=2$). The ratio ϱ of the first (discrete sum) to the second (continuum integral) term on the right side of (74.4) thus decreases rapidly with increasing n_0 (and ϱ is already only 0.068 for $n_0=1$). Thus the major contribution to both the numerator and denominator of (74.3) comes from the continuum and K_0/Z^2 Ry is of order (actually larger than) ν_m, which is almost independent of n_0.

The situation is different for states $n_0 l_0$ with non-zero orbital quantum number l_0. In this case the dimensionless quantity K_0/Z^2 Ry, to be substituted into (21.3), is defined by

$$\log\frac{K_0(n_0,\,l_0)}{Z^2\,\mathrm{Ry}} = \frac{3\,n_0^3}{16}\sum_n \bar f_{0n}\,\nu_{0n}^2\log|\nu_{0n}|\,, \tag{74.6}$$

where $\bar f_{0n}$ is the mean oscillator strength for $n_0 l_0 m_0\to n,\, l_0\pm 1,\, m$ (averaged over m_0 or over the polarization direction). If $\log|\nu_{0n}|$ were replaced by a constant on the right hand side of (74.6), it follows from (74.5) that the sum $\sum f\nu^2$ would vanish exactly[2] since the wave function at the origin is zero for $l_0\neq 0$. For non-zero l_0, the integral over the continuous spectrum [cf. (74.4)] contributes very *little*, since $\nu^3 df/d\nu$ *decreases* with increasing ν already at threshold ($\nu=n_0^{-2}$) and decreases even more strongly in the BORN approximation region (as $\nu_0^{-l_0-0.5}$, see

[1] H. BETHE, L. BROWN and J. STEHN: Phys. Rev. **77**, 370 (1950). — J. M. HARRIMAN: Phys. Rev. **101**, 594 (1956).

[2] Note that f_{0n} is negative for negative ν_{0n}.

Sect. 70 and 71 β). The negative and positive contributions in the sum (74.6) cancel to an appreciable extent and the total sum is rather small for all n_0. Some of the numerical results are

$n_0 l_0$	$2P$	$4P$	$3D$
$\log(K_0/Z^2\,\text{Ry})$	-0.0300	-0.0419	-0.0052

Similar calculations are required for evaluating the LAMB shift (41.7) for the ground state of helium-like atoms. K_0 is again defined by (74.3) and the dipole matrix elements (or oscillator strengths) are required for transitions from the ground state to excited states of the two-electron atom. These matrix elements are not known exactly, but reasonably good approximations are available. The calculation of K_0 has to be carried out separately for each value of the nuclear charge Z. One finds that the most important transitions are those to singly excited states and especially to those in the continuum. The oscillator strengths for the continuum for He ($Z=2$) can be obtained from HUANG's expression for the photoelectric cross-section, discussed in Sect. 74α, and plotted in Fig. 37. One check for the accuracy of the oscillator strengths is the sum rule corresponding to (74.5),

$$\sum_n f_{0n}\,\nu_{0n}^2 = \frac{16\pi}{3Z^3}\left(\delta^{(3)}(\boldsymbol{r}_1) + \delta^{(3)}(\boldsymbol{r}_2)\right)_{n_0 n_0}. \tag{74.7}$$

The expectation value over the ground state wave function on the right hand side of (74.7) is known quite accurately (see Table 10, Sect. 36). The numerical results[1] for He ($Z=2$) are

$$K_0 = (84.3 \pm 5)\ \text{Ry}. \tag{74.8}$$

For large Z, K_0/Z^2 Ry must approach the hydrogenic value for $n_0=1$, $l=0$. Combined with (74.8) this gives the semi-empirical result

$$K_{0(Z)} \approx 19.77\,(Z+0.06)^2\ \text{Ry}. \tag{74.9}$$

75. Recombination. α) *General formulas for the probability of the processes.* In the preceding sections we discussed the absorption processes in the continuous spectrum. Now we shall deal with the emission processes. If an electron is incident on a bare nucleus the following events may occur:

The electron may be captured by the nucleus with the emission of light, i.e., the electron may reach a discrete energy level;

or the electron may merely have its velocity reduced—with the emission of light—and continue on its flight in a different direction;

or, finally, the electron may simply be deflected without change in velocity.

The third process has already been dealt with in Sect. 6γ, and is of no interest to us here since it is not accompanied by the emission of light. The probability of the first two processes is directly given by (59.2):

$$w(\Omega, j)\,d\Omega = \frac{e^2\hbar\omega}{2\pi m^2 c^3}\,|D_{n'n}^{\boldsymbol{k}\boldsymbol{j}}|^2\,d\Omega \tag{75.1}$$

is the probability that the electron undergoes the transition from the state n to the state n' and emits light, of frequency $\nu_{nn'}$ and polarization $\boldsymbol{j}$, into the solid angle $d\Omega$.

[1] P. KABIR and E. SALPETER: Bull. Amer. Phys. Soc. 1, 46 (1956).

In the evaluation of D, the eigenfunctions u_n and $u_{n'}$ must be taken to be those of an electron in the field of the nucleus which causes the emission. Furthermore, u_n must have the form of an incident plane wave at large distances from the nucleus. This condition is fulfilled by the eigenfunction in parabolic coordinates (cf. Sect. 6γ):

$$u_k = \sqrt{\frac{2\pi n'}{1-e^{-2\pi n'}}}\, e^{\frac{1}{2}ik\xi} \cdot \frac{1}{2\pi i\sqrt{v}} \int d\zeta\, e^{-ik\eta\zeta}\left(\zeta+\frac{1}{2}\right)^{-in'}\left(\zeta-\frac{1}{2}\right)^{in'-1}, \quad (75.2)$$

in which z is the direction of incidence of the electron, $\xi = r+z$, $\eta = r-z$, $k=\sqrt{\frac{W}{\mathrm{Ry}}}$ is the wave number, $n = -in' = -iZ/k$ is the "principal quantum number". The normalization of the wave function differs from the usual one and is chosen so that one electron is incident on a unit of area per unit of time [see the remark following Eq. (6.24)]. With this normalization (75.1) simply becomes the cross-section of the nucleus for the processes under consideration.

It is also possible, of course, to express the wave of the incident electron (75.2) in terms of the eigenfunctions in polar coordinates[1]:

$$u_k = \frac{\sqrt{h}}{2k}\sum_l (2l+1)\, i^l P_l(\cos\vartheta)\,\frac{\Gamma(l+1-in')}{|\Gamma(l+1-in')|}\cdot R_{Wl}(r). \quad (75.3)$$

In general, the above representation is not as convenient as (75.2).

β) Recombination processes[2]. The probability of capturing the incident electron in a $1s$ orbit may be written down at once, since we have already calculated the pertinent matrix elements in the treatment of the photoelectric effect (Sect. 71). Assuming that the velocity of the incident electron is not too large, the retardation factor may again be neglected in the evaluation of the matrix element D, and we obtain [cf. Eq. (75.3)]

$$|D^{kj}_{1W}| = \frac{m\omega}{\hbar}\int u_1 z\, u_{W10}\, d\tau \cdot \sqrt{3}\cdot\sqrt{4\pi}\cdot\frac{\sqrt{h}}{2k}. \quad (75.4)$$

Evidently, in a transition to the ground state only radiation which is polarized in the z direction—the direction of incidence—is emitted, as in all other cases the matrix element D vanishes, provided the retardation is neglected. For the same reason only the part of the eigenfunction (75.3) of the incident electron which corresponds to $l=1$ makes a contribution (l selection rule). Thus, we finally arrive at

$$u_{W10} = R_{W1}(r)\, Y_{10}(\vartheta,\varphi) = \sqrt{\frac{3}{4\pi}}\, R_{W1}(r)\, P_1(\cos\vartheta), \quad (75.5)$$

[1] Cf., for example, B. M. STOBBE, Ann. d. Phys. **7**, 682 (1930). For large z, u_k must behave as an incident plane wave; thus, using the well known expansion of a plane wave in terms of spherical waves

$$u_k = \frac{1}{\sqrt{v}}\cdot e^{ikz} = \sqrt{\frac{\pi}{2v}}\cdot\frac{1}{\sqrt{kr}}\cdot\sum_l (2l+1)\, i^l P_l(\cos\vartheta)\, J_{l+\frac{1}{2}}(kr)$$

$$= \frac{1}{\sqrt{v}}\cdot\frac{1}{kr}\cdot\sum_l (2l+1)\cdot i^l P_l(\cos\vartheta)\cdot\cos\left(kr-(l+1)\frac{\pi}{2}\right).$$

(75.3) is obtained by comparing the above expression with the asymptotic representation of the eigenfunction normalized per unit energy.

[2] M. STOBBE, loc. cit., E. C. G. STÜCKELBERG and P. M. MORSE: Phys. Rev. **35**, 116 (1930). — W. WESSEL: Ann. d. Phys. **5**, 611 (1930).

in which Y_{10} is the normalized spherical harmonic and P_1 is the unnormalized LEGENDRE polynomial. Next, we insert the value of the matrix element (71.4) into (75.4) and the resulting expression into (75.1), and integrate over all possible directions of propagation of the emitted light quantum.

Then we obtain the following expression for the cross-section for recombination

$$\left.\begin{aligned} \sigma_1(\nu) &= \frac{2^7\pi}{3}\,\frac{e^2}{m c^2}\,\frac{h}{m c}\,\frac{\nu_1^3}{\nu^2(\nu-\nu_1)}\cdot\frac{e^{-4\sqrt{\frac{\nu_1}{\nu-\nu_1}}\,\mathrm{arc\,tg}\sqrt{\frac{\nu-\nu_1}{\nu_1}}}}{1-e^{-2\pi\sqrt{\frac{\nu_1}{\nu-\nu_1}}}} \\ &= 9.1\times10^{-21}\frac{\nu_1^3}{\nu^2(\nu-\nu_1)}\cdot f\left(\sqrt{\frac{\nu_1}{\nu-\nu_1}}\right). \end{aligned}\right\} \tag{75.6}$$

We note that e^2/mc^2 is the classical electron radius, and h/mc the COMPTON wave length of the electron. For hydrogen, the cross-section is equal to $2.1\times10^{-21}\,\mathrm{cm}^2$ if the velocity of the incident electron corresponds to 1 electron volt. Thus, the cross-section is seen to be very small, and is inversely proportional to the square of the velocity for low speeds and to the fifth power for high velocities. The recombination processes in which the electron is caught in a higher shell are even rarer[1].

As for the photoeffect, we can get a *rough* approximation from (71.19) and (71.20) for the total cross-section σ_n for recombination with the electron being captured into any of the bound states with principal quantum number n. This approximation, roughly valid up to frequencies ν about $10\nu_1$, is ($\nu_n=\nu_1/n^2$)

$$\sigma_n = 1.96\pi^2\frac{e^2\hbar}{m^2c^3}\,\frac{\nu_1^2}{\nu(\nu-\nu_n)}\,n^{-3}. \tag{75.7}$$

For large frequencies, $\nu\gg10\nu_1$, the BORN approximation applies and (75.7) breaks down. In this region the correct cross-section decreases with increasing ν more rapidly than (75.7) by approximately one power of $\nu^{-\frac{1}{2}}$.

The RUTHERFORD scattering formula (6.24) shows that the cross-section for radiationless scattering of the electron by the COULOMB potential, through large angles (say, $\vartheta>90°$), is of the order of magnitude of $\sigma_R=(Ze^2/E)^2$, where E is the energy of the incident electron. (75.7) then gives the following order of magnitude relation

$$\sigma_n \sim Z^2\alpha^3\frac{\nu-\nu_n}{\nu}\,n^{-3}\,\sigma_R\,. \tag{75.8}$$

Although recombination is much less likely than RUTHERFORD scattering, it is nevertheless important in a partially ionized gas in thermal equilibrium. Atoms are continuously ionized by the photoeffect (photons from the thermal radiation) and electrons must be recaptured at an equal rate (at equilibrium).

We have only discussed so far the radiative capture of an electron by a bare nucleus. For the capture of an electron by a positive ion, screening corrections must be applied as for the photoeffect. Since the recombination cross-section decreases rapidly with increasing principal quantum number n, the electron is most likely to be captured into the innermost empty (or partially unfilled) shell.

[1] If the velocity of the incident electron is low, the small magnitude of the cross-section has its origin in the factor ν^3 which multiplies the square of the matrix element of the coordinate [cf. Eqs. (75.1), (75.4)]. If the initial velocity is high, the matrix elements D become small through destructive interference.

c) Bremsstrahlung.

76. General survey[1]. We consider now the case of radiative transitions of an electron between two states in the continuum. We shall discuss mainly transitions in which a photon is emitted, i.e. the following process called Bremsstrahlung: An electron of positive kinetic energy E_0 and momentum $\boldsymbol{p}_0$ impinges on an atomic ion (or bare nucleus), emits a photon of momentum $\boldsymbol{k}$ (energy $h\nu = kc$) and polarization direction $\boldsymbol{j}$ (perpendicular to $\boldsymbol{k}$) and the electron emerges with momentum $\boldsymbol{p}$ and energy E. The energies of the photon and the electron are related by the expression

$$h\nu = E_0 - E, \tag{76.1}$$

but there is no conservation of momentum for the electron-photon system. If the electron impinges on an atom or ion (instead of a bare nucleus) we have, strictly speaking, a many-electron problem. In most cases the polarization of the atomic electrons by the incident electron is unimportant and we shall always replace the atom or ion by a fixed central potential $V(r)$.

Let $u_0(\boldsymbol{r})$ be the wave function for a stationary state of the electron in the potential $V(r)$, which behaves asymptotically like a plane wave of momentum $\boldsymbol{p}_0$ plus scattered outgoing spherical waves. We normalize u_0 per unit current crossing unit area, so that (75.2) is the special case of u_0 for a COULOMB potential. Similarly $u(\boldsymbol{r})$ is a wave function which behaves asymptotically like a plane wave of momentum $\boldsymbol{p}$ plus *incoming* spherical scattered waves. As discussed in the beginning of Sect. 69, the "incoming" type of solution must be used, since it is to represent a *final* state[2]. Further, we shall normalize $u(\boldsymbol{r})$ per unit *energy* interval, as for the wave function (69.4). Following (75.1), we write

$$\left.\begin{aligned} \sigma(E, \Omega_p, \Omega_k, \boldsymbol{j}) &= \frac{e^2 h\nu}{2\pi m^2 c^3} |D|^2, \\ D &= \frac{i}{\hbar} \int u^*(\boldsymbol{r})\, p_j\, e^{-i\boldsymbol{k}\cdot\boldsymbol{r}/\hbar} u_0(\boldsymbol{r})\, d^3r. \end{aligned}\right\} \tag{76.2}$$

For fixed initial momentum $\boldsymbol{p}_0$, consider a Bremsstrahlung process in which the outgoing electron has its energy in an energy interval dE (centered around E) and the direction of its momentum in an infinitesimal cone of solid angle $d\Omega_p$ (centered around $\boldsymbol{p}$, denoted by Ω_p) and the photon has polarization direction $\boldsymbol{j}$ and momentum direction $\boldsymbol{k}$ in a cone of solid angle $d\Omega_k$ (axis direction denoted by Ω_k). The probability per unit time for such a process is then given by

$$\sigma(E, \Omega_p, \Omega_k, \boldsymbol{j})\, dE\, d\Omega_p\, d\Omega_k. \tag{76.3}$$

Since u_0 is normalized per unit current density, (76.3) is of the dimensions of cm^2 and we shall call $\sigma(E, \Omega_p, \Omega_k, \boldsymbol{j})$ the differential cross-section for short. We shall also be interested in the expression obtained by summing (76.3) over two polarization directions perpendicular to $\boldsymbol{k}$ and integrating this expression over both $d\Omega_p$ and $d\Omega_k$. We shall write this integrated cross-section in either of two forms,

$$\sigma(E)\,|dE| = \sigma(\nu)\,|d\nu| \tag{76.4}$$

where ν is related to E by (76.1).

---

[1] For more detailed discussions of Bremsstrahlung, see ref. [7], Chap. 7 and ref. [6], Sect. 25; also the article by H. A. BETHE and J. ASHKIN in E. SEGRÈ, Experimental Nuclear Physics, Vol. 1, Part II (New York: J. Wiley 1953), and L. P. SMITH, Rev. Mod. Phys. **6**, 69 (1934).

[2] See, however, H. OLSEN, Phys. Rev. **99**, 1335 (1955).

We have already made one approximation, namely to replace the atom on which the electron impinges by a fixed central potential $V(r)$. Calculations of Bremsstrahlung cross-sections are more difficult still than for the photoeffect (a larger number of momentum variables are involved) and various additional approximations have to be used under different circumstances. Two regions for the incident energy E_0 are of greatest practical interest. (1) For the production of the continuous X-ray spectrum in X-ray tubes, nonrelativistic energies $E_0 \ll mc^2$ are most important. In this case E_0 may not be large compared with the K-shell ionization potential of the struck atom. (2) For the passage of electrons from cosmic rays or from high energy accelerators through matter, the relativistic effects for $E_0 \gg mc^2$ are of greatest interest. In both cases 1 and 2, the struck atom is usually neutral and has a reasonably large nuclear charge Z. We outline now some of the approximations made under different circumstances.

α) Nonrelativistic treatment. If $Z\alpha \ll 1$ and if $E_0 \ll mc^2$, then both the initial and final states of the electron can be treated nonrelativistically. (E is always less than E_0.) In this case SCHRÖDINGER wave functions can be used and the various energies and momenta are related by [see Eq. (76.1)],

$$E_0 = \frac{p_0^2}{2m}, \qquad E = \frac{p^2}{2m}, \qquad k = \frac{p_0^2 - p^2}{2mc}. \tag{76.5}$$

Since $p_0 \ll mc$, (76.5) shows that the photon momentum k is always small compared with the momentum change $|\boldsymbol{p}_0 - \boldsymbol{p}|$ of the electron. As for the photoeffect, the neglect of retardation (neglecting $k/|\boldsymbol{p}_0 - \boldsymbol{p}|$) then introduces rather small errors at nonrelativistic energies. Nevertheless, the effect of retardation on the *angular* distribution is of relative order p_0/mc, whereas specifically relativistic effects are of order $(p_0/mc)^2$ and $(Z\alpha)^2$. These retardation effects are discussed briefly in Sect. 77γ. For a COULOMB potential and with retardation and relativistic effects omitted, both the differential and integrated cross sections have been evaluated analytically. These results are discussed in Sect. 78.

If the incident electron energy is relativistic, $E_0 \gtrsim mc^2$, the DIRAC theory has to be used for the electrons. Thus DIRAC spinor wave functions must be used for u_0 and u in the matrix element D, (76.2), and the momentum operator $\boldsymbol{p}$ is replaced by the DIRAC matrix $mc\boldsymbol{\alpha}$. We also have to use the relativistic relation $E = \sqrt{m^2c^4 + p^2c^2}$ between energy and momentum and (76.1) takes the form

$$k = \sqrt{(mc)^2 + p_0^2} - \sqrt{(mc)^2 + p^2}. \tag{76.6}$$

At extremely relativistic energies, $p \gg mc$, the photon momentum k is approximately equal to $p_0 - p$, which can be very close to the electron's momentum transfer $|\boldsymbol{p}_0 - \boldsymbol{p}|$ and retardation effects are extremely important. No exact relativistic calculations for arbitrary values of $Z\alpha$ are available. Approximate calculations, which neglect $(Z\alpha)^2$ compared with unity, have been carried out for arbitrary energy and arbitrary potential $V(r)$. The results of these calculations, the so-called BETHE-HEITLER formula, are discussed in Sect. 79α. Some calculations for extremely relativistic energies, which neglect only $Z\alpha\, mc/p_0$ (not $Z\alpha$), are discussed in Sect. 79β.

β) The BORN *approximation.* If $Z\alpha \ll 1$ and if both E_0 and E are large compared with the K-shell ionization potential $I_1 \sim \frac{1}{2}(Z\alpha)^2 mc^2 = Z^2$ Ry, the BORN approximation (Sect. 7 and 9) can be used for the wave functions u_0 and u. We shall see (Sect. 77α) that u_0 and u can not *both* be replaced by plane waves, but methods somewhat similar to those of Sect. 70β have to be used. The BORN approximation results are reasonably simple even for an arbitrary potential $V(r)$ (see Sects. 77β and 79α).

At relativistic momenta $p_0 \gg mc$, the expansion parameter for the BORN approximation to the DIRAC wave functions is no longer $Z\alpha\, mc/p$, but $Ze^2/\hbar v$, where v is the velocity corresponding to the momentum p. Since v approaches the velocity of light c (not ∞) as $p/mc \to \infty$ the expansion parameter is of order $Z\alpha$ at extreme relativistic energies. The BETHE-HEITLER formula (Sect. 79α) is based on such a BORN approximation expansion and is in error by a factor of relative order $(Z\alpha)^2$ even at the highest energies.

γ) Screening. We consider next the various approximations used for the effective central potential $V(r)$ due to the struck atom (see also the discussion of Sect. 17β). This potential can also be written in the form

$$V(r) = -\frac{Ze^2}{r} + e^2 \int d^3r' \frac{\varrho(\boldsymbol{r}')}{|\boldsymbol{r} - \boldsymbol{r}'|}, \tag{76.7}$$

where Z is the nuclear charge and $e\varrho(r')$ is the (spherically symmetric) average charge distribution of the atomic electrons in the struck atom or ion. In Bremsstrahlung calculations which employ the BORN approximation, the quantity required is $V'(\boldsymbol{q})$, the three-dimensional FOURIER transform of $V(\boldsymbol{r})$ times $(2\pi)^{-\frac{3}{2}}$. Working in atomic units, we find from (76.7)

$$V'(q) = -\frac{Z - F(q)}{2\pi^2 q^2}, \qquad F(q) = \int d^3r\, \varrho(r)\, e^{i\boldsymbol{q}\cdot\boldsymbol{r}}. \tag{76.8}$$

As discussed in Sect. 7γ, the differential cross-section for *radiationless* scattering of an electron by the potential $V(r)$ is proportional to the quantity $|V'(q)|^2$, if $\boldsymbol{q}$ is the momentum change of the electron and if BORN approximation is used [see (7.11)]. The most accurate expressions for $V(r)$ and $\varrho(r)$ are obtained by means of the HARTREE method. The quantity $V'(q)$, or the atomic form-factor $F(q)$, can be obtained by numerical integration from the HARTREE potentials, but the integrations have to be carried out separately for each atom or ion and for each value of q. This HARTREE form-factor has been evaluated for a number of light and medium-heavy atoms (see [9], p. 188). For atoms with large nuclear charge Z, the THOMAS-FERMI approximation to the effective potential $V(r)$ is sufficiently accurate. For a neutral atom, $V(r)$ is given by a single function of $Z^{\frac{1}{3}}r$ for all Z and $F(q)$ as a function of $Z^{-\frac{1}{3}}q$. These functions have been tabulated ([9], p. 190); $V(r)$ falls off rapidly for $r \gg Z^{-\frac{1}{3}}$ (in atomic units) and $F(q)$ approaches Z rapidly for $q \ll Z^{\frac{1}{3}}$, so that $V'(q)$ in (76.8) is much smaller than the expression for the unscreened COULOMB potential ($F=0$). Note that the BOHR momentum for charge Z is $Z \gg Z^{\frac{1}{3}}$ (in atomic units). A very simple form for the effective potential, which only gives a *qualitative* account of screening, is

$$V(r) = -\frac{Z}{r}\, e^{-Qr}, \qquad V'(q) = -\frac{Z}{2\pi^2 (q^2 + Q^2)}, \tag{76.9}$$

where Q is a constant of the order of magnitude of $Z^{\frac{1}{3}}$.

In Sect. 78 we shall discuss exact nonrelativistic results, valid for the special case of a COULOMB potential. These calculations can be adapted to take screening into account, at least in a very crude way, by choosing $V(r)$ of form (69.6)

$$V(r) = \left(-\frac{Z - s}{r} + V_0\right) \text{a.u.} \tag{76.10}$$

The wave functions in the matrix element (76.2) are needed most accurately for radial distances r of the order of $\hbar|\boldsymbol{p}_0 - \boldsymbol{p}|^{-1}$ ($\boldsymbol{p}_0$ and $\boldsymbol{p}$ are the initial and final electron momenta). One can then choose s and V_0 so that (76.10) approximates the THOMAS-FERMI potential most closely for these radial distances. For atoms with large Z, the values of $|\boldsymbol{p}_0 - \boldsymbol{p}|$ of most practical interest are usually large compared with $Z^{\frac{1}{3}}$. In this case[1] one puts $s=0$ in (76.10).

The replacement of a complex atom by a fixed effective potential $V(r)$ only takes account of the influence of the atomic electrons for processes in which these atomic electrons remain in their bound orbits after the emission of the photon (coherent effects). We are thus omitting "electron-electron Bremsstrahlung", where the momentum change of the incident electron is not taken up by the fixed potential, but by one of the atomic electrons, which is ejected from the atom in the process. In such a process the ejected atomic electron also carries away energy. The ratio of the cross-section for such processes to that of ordinary "potential Bremsstrahlung" is proportional to $1/Z$ and at nonrelativistic energies[2] is very small even if Z is small (see also Sect. 79γ).

77. Nonrelativistic BORN approximation. *α) The matrix element.* We first rewrite the matrix element (76.2) as an integral over momentum space. We use atomic units and denote the FOURIER transforms of the two wave functions $u_0(\boldsymbol{r})$ and $u(\boldsymbol{r})$ by $(2\pi)^{\frac{3}{2}} p_0^{-\frac{1}{2}} \psi_0(\boldsymbol{p}')$ and by $p^{\frac{1}{2}} \psi(\boldsymbol{p}')$, respectively. With u_0 and u normalized per unit current density and per unit energy interval, respectively, the asymptotic "plane wave parts" of both $\psi_0(\boldsymbol{p}')$ and $\psi(\boldsymbol{p}')$ are then simply three-dimensional DIRAC delta functions. Using the fact that the photon's momentum $\boldsymbol{k}$ is perpendicular to its polarization direction $\boldsymbol{j}$, one can rewrite the matrix element D in (76.2) in the form

$$D = i\sqrt{\frac{p\,(2\pi)^3}{p_0}} \int d^3p'\, \psi^*(\boldsymbol{p}')\, p_j'\, \psi_0(\boldsymbol{p}' + \boldsymbol{k}), \tag{77.1}$$

where p_j' is the component of $\boldsymbol{p}'$ in the direction of $\boldsymbol{j}$.

ψ_0 and ψ are momentum space wave functions for eigenstates of the electron in the potential (76.7) which have "asymptotic momentum" $\boldsymbol{p}_0$ and $\boldsymbol{p}$, respectively. If both p_0 and p are *large* compared with the BOHR momentum Z (E_0 and E large compared with the ground state binding energy Z^2 Ry), then we can replace ψ_0 and ψ by their BORN approximation expressions [see (9.7) and (9.11)],

$$\left.\begin{aligned} \psi_0(\boldsymbol{p}') &= \delta^{(3)}(\boldsymbol{p}' - \boldsymbol{p}_0) + \frac{2}{p_0^2 - p'^2} V'(\boldsymbol{p}' - \boldsymbol{p}_0), \\ \psi(\boldsymbol{p}') &= \delta^{(3)}(\boldsymbol{p}' - \boldsymbol{p}) + \frac{2}{p^2 - p'^2} V'(\boldsymbol{p}' - \boldsymbol{p}), \end{aligned}\right\} \tag{77.2}$$

where $V'(q)$ is given[3] by (76.8). The terms involving V' in (77.2) represent the second term in an expansion in powers of Z/p_0 (or Z/p). On substituting (77.2) into (77.1) we obtain the sum of four integrals. Since $Z \ll p_0$, p we might expect the leading term (cf. Sect. 70α) to be the one involving both $\delta^{(3)}(\boldsymbol{p}_0 - \boldsymbol{p}' - \boldsymbol{k})$ and $\delta^{(3)}(\boldsymbol{p} - \boldsymbol{p}')$. However, $\boldsymbol{p}_0 - \boldsymbol{p} - \boldsymbol{k}$ can never vanish if the equation of energy conservation (76.6) [or (76.5) if $p_0, p \ll mc$] is satisfied. The "leading" term in (77.1) is then identically zero: Physically speaking, this is due to the fact that an absolutely free electron cannot emit a photon without violating the conservation of either energy or momentum. For Bremsstrahlung to take place

[1] V_0 can then be chosen so that (69.7) with $s=0$, $n=1$ agrees with the experimental K-shell ionization potential.

[2] J. KATZENSTEIN: Phys. Rev. **78**, 161 (1950).

[3] In the denominators in (77.2) we have omitted the infinitesimal imaginary parts $\pm i\,\varepsilon$, since we shall not need these functions for p' equal to p_0 or p in our approximate calculations.

the atomic potential V must then "absorb some momentum", i.e. we have to consider the effect of the potential V' on at least one of the wave functions ψ_0 and ψ.

We shall see that the two terms involving one delta function and one power of V', obtained by substituting (77.2) into (77.1), are non-zero. The fourth term involving two powers of V is smaller by a factor of order Z/p and we shall omit it. Carrying out the integrals for these two terms, we find

$$D = 2i\, V'(q) \sqrt{\frac{p\,(2\pi)^3}{p_0}} \left(\frac{p_{0j}}{p^2 - |\boldsymbol{p}_0 - \boldsymbol{k}|^2} + \frac{p_j}{p_0^2 - |\boldsymbol{p} + \boldsymbol{k}|^2} \right), \tag{77.3}$$

where

$$\boldsymbol{q} = \boldsymbol{p}_0 - \boldsymbol{p} - \boldsymbol{k} \tag{77.4}$$

is the "momentum transfer absorbed by the atomic potential". (77.3) is the required BORN approximation result for the matrix element (expressed in atomic units) and can be substituted into (76.2) to give the differential cross-section.

Identically the same BORN approximation result (77.3) can also be obtained by a slightly different method (see [6], p. 242). One considers *both* the atomic potential $V(r)$ and the electron's interaction with the radiation field as perturbations on the HAMILTONian $H_0 = p^2/2m$. One then uses second order perturbation theory to calculate the probability amplitude for the transition of the electron from a free state of momentum $\boldsymbol{p}_0$ to one of momentum $\boldsymbol{p}$ with the emission of the photon. The two terms in (77.3) correspond to the photon being emitted by the electron before or after the electron is scattered by the potential V.

β) Cross-section without retardation. The following inequalities can be derived from the nonrelativistic relation (76.5),

$$\frac{k}{|\boldsymbol{p}_0 - \boldsymbol{p}|} \leq \frac{p_0}{m\,c}, \quad (2\boldsymbol{p}_0 \cdot \boldsymbol{k}) \frac{m\,c}{p_0} \leq p_0^2 - p^2 \geq (2\boldsymbol{p} \cdot \boldsymbol{k}) \frac{m\,c}{p}.$$

Since $p < p_0 \ll m c$, we can then neglect retardation with only a small loss of accuracy. I.e. we can replace k by zero both in (77.4) and in the two denominators in (77.3).

With retardation neglected, (77.3) reduces to

$$D = -2i\, V'(|p_0 - p|) \sqrt{\frac{p}{p_0}\,(2\pi)^3}\; \frac{p_0 x_0 - p\,x}{p_0^2 - p^2}, \tag{77.5}$$

where x_0 and x are the cosines of the angles which $\boldsymbol{p}_0$ and $\boldsymbol{p}$, respectively, make with the polarization direction $\boldsymbol{j}$. Note that (77.5) does not depend explicitly on the propagation direction $\boldsymbol{k}$ of the photon (except that $\boldsymbol{j}$ must be perpendicular to $\boldsymbol{k}$). Substituting (77.5) into (76.2), using (76.1) and reverting to C.G.S. units, we find for the differential cross-section

$$\sigma(E, \Omega_p, \Omega_k, j) = [Z - F(q)]^2\, \alpha^3\, \frac{\hbar^2}{\pi^2} \frac{p}{p_0} \frac{1}{E_0 - E} \frac{(p_0 x_0 - p\,x)^2}{q^4}, \tag{77.6}$$

where $\boldsymbol{q} = \boldsymbol{p}_0 - \boldsymbol{p}$ and F is defined in (76.8).

The differential cross-section (77.6), for fixed p_0, depends on a number of variables: On one energy variable E [or p or k, since E, p, k are connected by (76.5)], on the direction of $\boldsymbol{p}$ through the factor $q = |\boldsymbol{p}_0 - \boldsymbol{p}|$, on the polarization direction $\boldsymbol{j}$ through the cosine factors x_0 and x, and indirectly on the electron's propagation direction $\boldsymbol{k}$ (since $\boldsymbol{j}$ and $\boldsymbol{k}$ must be perpendicular). We shall outline a few properties of the Bremsstrahlung spectrum, derivable from (77.6), all for a fixed value of $\boldsymbol{p}_0$ (directed along the x-axis, say).

We consider first the polarization of photons which are emitted with a given momentum $\boldsymbol{k}$. The absolute value, but not the direction Ω_p, of $\boldsymbol{p}$ is then fixed. If one neglects screening [i.e. replaces F in (77.6) by zero], the integral over $d\Omega_p$ can be carried out[1]. If, for instance, $\boldsymbol{k}$ is perpendicular to the direction of incidence $\boldsymbol{p}_0$ of the electron ($\boldsymbol{p}_0$ in the x-direction, $\boldsymbol{k}$ in the y-direction), then the polarization direction $\boldsymbol{j}$ must lie in the xz-plane. Let $J_\parallel$ and $J_\perp$ be the relative probabilities for polarization $\boldsymbol{j}$ in the x-direction and z-direction, respectively. After integrating over $d\Omega_p$, one finds the following expression for P, a measure of the degree of polarization,

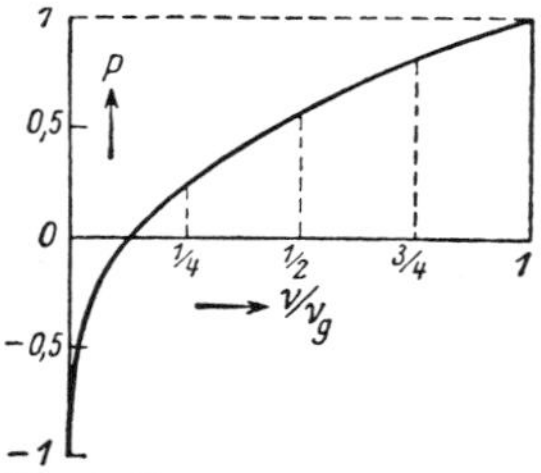

Fig. 38. The measure P, defined in (77.7), of polarization of Bremsstrahlung photons emitted at right angles to the momentum of the incident electron. The abscissa is the photon frequency ν divided by the high-frequency limit ν_g (called ν_0 in the text).

$$P \equiv \frac{J_\parallel - J_\perp}{J_\parallel + J_\perp} = \frac{(p_0^2 - 3p^2)\log\dfrac{p_0+p}{p_0-p} + 6p_0 p}{(3p_0^2 - p^2)\log\dfrac{p_0+p}{p_0-p} + 2p_0 p}. \tag{77.7}$$

As $p/p_0 \to 0$, i.e. near the high-frequency limit ν_0 of the photon spectrum,

$$h\nu_0 = k_0 c = E_0 = p_0^2/2m, \tag{77.8}$$

P approaches $+1$, i.e. the photons are all polarized in the x-direction. As $p \to p_0$ (i.e. as ν and k approach zero) P approaches -1, i.e. the photons are all polarized in the z-direction. In Fig. 38 the quantity P, Eq. (77.7), is plotted against $\nu/\nu_0 = 1 - p^2/p_0^2$.

For a fixed direction and absolute value of $\boldsymbol{p}$, the indirect dependence of the cross-section on the photon's propagation direction $\boldsymbol{k}$ is obtained as follows. Let ϑ and ϑ_0 be the angles which $\boldsymbol{k}$ makes with $\boldsymbol{p}$ and $\boldsymbol{p}_0$, respectively, and φ the angle between the $(\boldsymbol{p}, \boldsymbol{k})$ and $(\boldsymbol{p}_0, \boldsymbol{k})$ planes. Further, let χ be the angle between $\boldsymbol{k}$ and the fixed vector (momentum transfer) $\boldsymbol{q} = \boldsymbol{p}_0 - \boldsymbol{p}$. We now have to sum the expression $(p_0 x_0 - p x)^2 = (p_{0j} - p_j)^2$ in (77.6) over two polarization directions $\boldsymbol{j}$, perpendicular to each other and to $\boldsymbol{k}$. The result can be written in various forms,

$$\left.\begin{aligned} \sum_{j \perp k} (p_{0j} - p_j)^2 &= q^2 - (\boldsymbol{q}\cdot\boldsymbol{k})^2/k^2 = q^2 \sin^2\chi \\ &= p_0^2 \sin^2\vartheta_0 + p^2 \sin^2\vartheta - 2p_0 p \sin\vartheta_0 \sin\vartheta \cos\varphi. \end{aligned}\right\} \tag{77.9}$$

The intensity ($\propto \sin^2\chi$) thus has a maximum for $\boldsymbol{k}$ in (and is symmetric about) the plane perpendicular to the direction of the momentum transfer $\boldsymbol{q}$. If $p \ll p_0$ (ν near the high frequency limit ν_0), the direction of $\boldsymbol{q}$ is almost parallel to $\boldsymbol{p}_0$ (direction of incidence) and $\chi \approx \vartheta_0$. The expression (77.9) holds with or without screening.

With screening neglected and for a fixed absolute value of p and fixed vector $\boldsymbol{k}$, one can integrate the differential cross-section over $d\Omega_p$ and sum over polarization directions. The dependence of the resulting cross-section on the direction of $\boldsymbol{k}$ is then proportional to

$$J_\parallel \sin^2\vartheta_0 + J_\perp (1 + \cos^2\vartheta_0), \tag{77.10}$$

where the ratio of $J_\perp$ to $J_\parallel$ is given by (77.7). This distribution for $\boldsymbol{k}$ is again symmetric about the yz-plane ($\vartheta_0 = \pi/2$).

For a fixed direction and momentum $\boldsymbol{p}$ of the outgoing electron, one can also integrate (77.6) over the photon's propagation direction $d\Omega_k$ (after summing over

[1] For details, see ref. [7], Chap. 7, Sect. 3.

polarization directions), using (77.9). The angular distribution of the outgoing electrons[1] is then given by the cross-section

$$\sigma(E, \Omega_p)\, dE\, d\Omega_p = \alpha^3 \frac{8\hbar^2}{3\pi} \frac{dE}{E_0 - E}\, d\Omega_p \frac{[Z - F(q)]^2}{q^2}, \tag{77.11}$$

in which expression only the last fraction depends on the direction of $\boldsymbol{p}$. If we neglect screening (put $F=0$), this factor reduces to

$$Z^2 q^{-2} = Z^2 (p_0^2 + p^2 - 2 p_0 p \cos\alpha)^{-1}, \tag{77.12}$$

where α is the angle between $\boldsymbol{p}_0$ and $\boldsymbol{p}$. According to (77.12), the intensity of the scattered electrons has a maximum for forward scattering ($\alpha=0$) and a minimum for backward scattering ($\alpha=\pi$) and the dependence of the intensity on α is strongest if $p_0 - p$ is small (small photon energy).

We consider next the effect of screening, i.e. of the atomic form factor $F(q)$, on (77.11). Our BORN approximation is in any case only valid for p_0 and p large compared with the BOHR momentum, Z atomic units. As discussed in Sect. 76γ, $F(q) \ll Z$ if $q \gg Q$, where Q is a momentum of the order of $Z^{\frac{1}{3}}$ atomic units. Q is thus small compared with p_0 and p, especially for atoms with large Z. Since $q \gtrsim p_0 - p$, we can neglect screening over most of the range of values of p (0 to p_0) and need consider it only for $p_0 - p \lesssim Q \ll p_0$. If we use the very approximate form (76.9) for the screening potential, we get for the last fraction in (77.11)

$$Z^2 q^2 (q^2 + Q^2)^{-2}, \tag{77.13}$$

instead of (77.12). The situation is qualitatively similar if more accurate screening potentials are used: The approximation (77.12) is accurate for $q \gg Q$, but for $p \to p_0$ the last fraction in (77.11) has a *finite* maximum value of the order of $Z^2 Q^{-2}$.

We finally come to the integrated cross-section (76.4). If we neglect screening, (77.11) with (77.12) can easily be integrated over $d\Omega_p$ to give

$$\sigma_B(\nu)\, d\nu = \sigma_0 \frac{d\nu}{\nu} \log \frac{p_0 + p}{p_0 - p}, \tag{77.14}$$

where $\nu = kc/h$ is related to p_0, p by (76.5) and

$$\sigma_0 = \frac{16}{3} Z^2 \alpha^3 \left(\frac{\hbar}{p_0}\right)^2. \tag{77.15}$$

The BORN approximation $\nu\sigma_B(\nu)/\sigma_0$ is plotted against ν in Fig. 39, Sect. 78. As ν approaches the high frequency limit ν_0, Eq. (77.8), this function approaches zero as $2p/p_0$. However, the BORN approximation breaks down for $p \ll Z$ atomic units and we shall see in the next section that the correct cross-section approaches a *finite* limit as $\nu \to \nu_0$.

As ν approaches the low frequency limit zero ($p \to p_0$), $\nu\sigma_B(\nu)/\sigma_0$ for an unscreened COULOMB potential approaches infinity as $\log(2p_0/(p_0 - p))$. For an actual neutral atom, however, (77.13) shows that $\nu\sigma(\nu)/\sigma_0$ with screening included deviates from the unscreened expression for very low values of ν ($p_0 - p \lesssim Q$) and approaches a *finite* value of the order[2] of $\log(p_0/Q)$ as $\nu \to 0$.

---

[1] O. SCHERZER: Ann. d. Phys. **13**, 137 (1932).

[2] For a more detailed account of screening see F. SAUTER, Ann. d. Phys. **18**, 486 (1933); **20**, 404 (1934).

We finally compare the order of magnitude of the cross-section σ_0, Eq. (77.15), with that of large-angle COULOMB scattering and of recombination. We find

$$\sigma_0 \sim \alpha \left(\frac{p_0}{m c}\right)^2 \sigma_R \sim \left(\frac{p_0}{Z \text{ at. un.}}\right)^2 \sigma_{\text{rec}}, \tag{77.16}$$

where $\sigma_R \sim (Z e^2/E_0)^2$ is the cross-section for radiationless RUTHERFORD scattering through large angles and σ_{rec} the order of magnitude for the cross-section for recombination or radiative capture [cf. Eq. (75.7)]. Thus, although σ_0 decreases in absolute value with increasing p_0, its ratios to σ_R and to σ_{rec} increase. σ_0 is small compared with σ_R at all nonrelativistic energies E_0, but is larger than σ_{rec} if E_0 is much larger than the K-shell ionization potential of the atom.

We have seen that, with screening included, the quantity $\nu\sigma(\nu)$ approaches a finite, but *non*-zero, limit as $\nu \to 0$. Hence the integral $\int d\nu\, \sigma(\nu)$ diverges logarithmically at the low-frequency limit. One also finds a similar result if one keeps the direction of the final momentum $\boldsymbol{p}$ of the electron fixed (rather than integrating over it): The relative probability that the scattering of an electron from momentum $\boldsymbol{p}_0$ to $\boldsymbol{p}_0 - \boldsymbol{q}$ be accompanied by the emission of a photon of very low frequency (between ν and $\nu + d\nu$) is of the order of magnitude of $\alpha (q/m c)^2 d\nu/\nu$. The *total* number of low frequency photons which are emitted in a scattering process is thus infinite, but only of the order of one photon is emitted in the enormous fractional frequency range ν to $\nu \exp(-137\, m^2 c^2/q^2)$. This so called infrared catastrophe was discussed in Sect. 18γ in connection with radiative corrections to elastic scattering.

Another quantity of interest is the average energy loss, due to Bremsstrahlung radiation, of an electron passing through matter. This energy loss per unit length of path is

$$-\frac{dE_0}{dx} = N \int_0^{\nu_0} h\nu\, \sigma(\nu)\, d\nu, \tag{77.17}$$

where N is the number of atoms per unit volume. Using the BORN approximation (77.14) for $\sigma(\nu)$, the result of the integration gives (see [*6*], p. 252)

$$-\frac{1}{\log 2}\frac{dE_0}{dx} = 2N E_0 \sigma_0 = \frac{16}{3} N Z^2 \alpha \frac{e^4}{m c^2} = \frac{32}{3} N Z^2 \alpha^3 \frac{\text{Ry}}{a_0}. \tag{77.18}$$

The last expression in (77.18) holds if N is expressed in atoms per a_0^3 and length in the atomic unit a_0. Note that the energy loss per unit length is *independent* of the energy E_0 (for energies for which the nonrelativistic BORN approximation holds). In atomic units, N is of the order of 0.01 for most solids (e.g. $N = 0.009$ for Al, $N = 0.005$ for Pb). The energy loss is then of the order of $100 Z^2$ electron volts per cm in solids. We shall not discuss the energy loss due to radiationless ionization of bound atomic electrons[1], which is actually much more important at nonrelativistic energies: The ionization energy loss per unit length is of order $N Z e^4/E_0$, i.e. larger than the Bremsstrahlung energy loss by a factor of order $m c^2/Z \alpha E_0$.

γ) Retardation[2]. Within the framework of nonrelativistic BORN approximation, retardation effects are included rigorously in the matrix element (77.3). In the discussion of Sect. 77β, we have neglected retardation in going from (77.3) to (77.5), i.e. by replacing the photon momentum $\boldsymbol{k}$ by zero both in the

[1] See ref. [*6*], Sect. 37; ref. [*9*], Chap. 11 and ref. [*10*], Sect. 56.

[2] For further details see ref. [*7*], Chap. 7, Sect. 6.

term $V'(q)$ and in the last two denominators in (77.3). From (76.5) we find the following expression, valid only for nonrelativistic energies,

$$k = (p_0 - p)\frac{p_0 + p}{2mc} \lessgtr |\boldsymbol{p}_0 - \boldsymbol{p}|\frac{p_0}{mc} = |\boldsymbol{p}_0 - \boldsymbol{p}|\frac{v_0}{c}, \qquad (77.19)$$

where v_0 is the velocity of the incident electron. Retardation affects the angular distribution of the emitted photons, but (as for the photoeffect) the effect is only of relative order v_0/c.

We discuss only two special cases, for which the angular distribution of the photons is relatively simple and the effect of retardation is relatively important: (1) The initial and final momenta $\boldsymbol{p}_0$ and $\boldsymbol{p}$ are parallel to each other. (2) The inequality $p \ll p_0$ holds (high frequency limit) and the direction of $\boldsymbol{p}$ is arbitrary. We sum the differential scattering cross-section over the two possible polarization directions. With retardation neglected, this cross-section for both cases is then [see (77.9)] proportional to $\sin^2\vartheta_0$, where ϑ_0 is the angle between $\boldsymbol{p}_0$ and $\boldsymbol{k}$, i.e. the intensity has a maximum in the plane perpendicular to $\boldsymbol{p}_0$. We now take for $V'(q)$ in (77.3) an unscreened Coulomb potential ($V' \propto q^{-2}$) and take the ratio R of the retarded matrix element (77.3) and the unretarded one (77.5). Using (77.19), expanding the ratio R in powers of v_0/c and keeping only the first two terms, we find in both cases

$$R^2 = 1 + 4\frac{v_0 + v}{c}\cos\vartheta_0, \qquad (77.20)$$

where v is the electron's velocity in the final state.

The angular distribution is then given by a cross-section which is proportional to $R^2 \sin^2\vartheta_0$. The intensity thus no longer has a maximum for $\vartheta_0 = \frac{1}{2}\pi$, but for an angle $\vartheta_{0,\max}$, given by (for $v_0 \ll c$)

$$\frac{\pi}{2} - \vartheta_{0,\max} = 2\frac{v_0 + v}{c}. \qquad (77.21)$$

Near the high-frequency limit ($v \ll v_0$), these nonrelativistic expressions for the angular distribution become identical with those for the photoeffect (after averaging over polarization directions) in nonrelativistic approximation (Sect. 72β). In fact, the angular distributions for the photoeffect and for Bremsstrahlung remain identical even at relativistic energies, as long as $v \ll v_0$. Thus Fig. 35 also applies to Bremsstrahlung near the high-frequency limit.

78. Calculations for low energies. As mentioned before, the Born approximation results of the previous section break down unless both the initial and final momenta p_0 and p of the electron are large compared with the Bohr momentum of the struck atom. Neglecting only retardation and relativistic effects, Sommerfeld[1] has obtained an exact analytic expression for the differential cross-section (76.2) for an unscreened Coulomb potential. This general expression is rather complicated and we shall only quote some of the results derivable from it (for details see [7], Chap. 7).

We discuss first the integrated cross-section (76.4). By a very ingenious method[2] Sommerfeld's differential cross-section for a pure Coulomb potential can be integrated over all electron and photon angles. Let

$$n_0 = \frac{Z \text{ at. un.}}{p_0}, \qquad n = \frac{Z \text{ at. un.}}{p}, \qquad \frac{v}{v_0} = 1 - \frac{n_0^2}{n^2}, \qquad (78.1)$$

[1] A. Sommerfeld: Ann. d. Phys. **11**, 257 (1931).
[2] A. Sommerfeld and A. Maue: Ann. d. Phys. **23**, 589 (1935).

where ν_0 is the high-frequency limit (77.8). The general result for the integrated cross-section $\sigma(\nu)$ is

$$\frac{\nu\,\sigma(\nu)}{\sigma_0} = \frac{\pi^2 x_0}{(e^{2\pi n_0}-1)(1-e^{-2\pi n})}\,\frac{d}{dx}\,|F(i\,n_0,\,i\,n,\,1,\,x)|^2_{x=x_0}, \tag{78.2}$$

where

$$x_0 = -\frac{4 n_0 n}{(n-n_0)^2} = -\frac{4 p_0 p}{(p_0-p)^2}, \tag{78.3}$$

and σ_0 is defined by (77.15). F is the general (*not* the confluent) hypergeometric function whose power series expansion is (for $x<1$)

$$F(a,b,c,x) = 1 + \frac{a\,b}{c}\,x + \frac{a\,(a+1)\,b\,(b+1)}{c\,(c+1)}\,\frac{x^2}{2!} + \cdots. \tag{78.4}$$

The general expression (78.2), which is a complicated function of the two variables n_0 and n, can be simplified for various limiting values of n_0 and n, using various properties of the hypergeometric function, such as

$$\frac{d}{dx}\,|F|^2_{x=x_0} = -2 n_0\,n\,\mathrm{Re}\,[F(1-i\,n_0,\,1-i\,n,\,2,\,x_0)\,F(i\,n_0,\,i\,n,\,1,\,x_0)] \tag{78.5}$$

and

$$F(1,1,2,x_0) = -x_0^{-1}\log(1-x_0). \tag{78.6}$$

In the limit $2\pi\,n_0 \ll 1$, one finds

$$\frac{\nu\,\sigma(\nu)}{\sigma_0} = \frac{2\pi\,n}{1-e^{-2\pi n}}\log\left(\frac{n+n_0}{n-n_0}\right). \tag{78.7}$$

If we also have $2\pi\,n \ll 1$, then (78.7) reduces to the BORN approximation expression (77.14). Note, however, that (78.7) goes to a finite *non*-zero value at the high frequency limit $n\to\infty$ ($p\to 0$). ELWERT[1] finds that the following more accurate approximation to (78.2) is in error by less than about 10% for values of n_0 up to about 0.5,

$$\frac{\nu\,\sigma(\nu)}{\sigma_0} = \frac{n}{n_0}\,\frac{1-e^{-2\pi n_0}}{1-e^{-2\pi n}}\log\left(\frac{n+n_0}{n-n_0}\right). \tag{78.8}$$

(78.8) is identical with the BORN approximation result near the low-frequency limit ($n\to n_0$) and approaches the following limit as $n\to\infty$ ($\nu\to\nu_0$, $p\to 0$)

$$\frac{\nu_0\,\sigma(\nu_0)}{\sigma_0} = 2\,(1-e^{-2\pi n_0}). \tag{78.9}$$

If $2\pi\,n_0 \ll 1$, ELWERT's expression (78.8) reduces to (78.7).

For values of n_0 near the upper limit of validity of (78.8), $n_0 \sim 1$, the two exponential terms in (78.8) are rather small and the ratio of (78.8) to the BORN approximation is approximately n/n_0. ELWERT has also shown that (78.8) holds even if n_0 is *not* small, as long as $n - n_0 \ll 1$. Thus the BORN approximation holds very close to the low-frequency limit even for very low initial momenta p_0 of the electron.

In the limit of $p_0 \to 0$ and *away* from the low-frequency limit, i.e. for $n_0 \gg 1 \ll n - n_0$, one can derive[2] another approximation to (78.2): One uses (78.5) and the integral representation for the general hypergeometric function F. Using the fact that n, $n_0 \gg 1$, one can simplify the contour integrals by a method similar

[1] G. ELWERT: Ann. d. Physik **34**, 178 (1939).

[2] See also J. A. GAUNT, Phil. Trans. Roy. Soc. Lond. Ser. A **229**, 163 (1930).

to the method of stationary phase (see [7], appendix Sect. 16). Using such relations as

$$\int_0^\infty dx \frac{\cos x}{x^{\frac{2}{3}}} = \Gamma\left(\frac{1}{3}\right) \sin\frac{\pi}{3}, \qquad \int_0^\infty dx \frac{\sin x}{x^{\frac{1}{3}}} = \Gamma\left(\frac{2}{3}\right) \sin\frac{\pi}{3},$$

one finds the following constant value

$$\frac{\nu\,\sigma(\nu)}{\sigma_0} = \frac{\pi}{\sqrt{3}} = 1.82, \tag{78.10}$$

valid if $n - n_0 \gg 1$, as well as $n_0 \gg 1$.

To summarize the situation: The high-frequency limit of $\nu\sigma(\nu)/\sigma_0$ is $4\pi n_0$ for $2\pi n_0 \ll 1$, increases to a maximum value of about two for n_0 of the order of unity and then approaches 1.82 as n_0 approaches infinity. The dependence on ν of $\nu\sigma(\nu)/\sigma_0$ becomes less marked as n_0 increases, except near the low-frequency limit where the function approaches $\log\left(2n/(n-n_0)\right)$ for all values of n_0. In Fig. 39 we have plotted the function $\nu\sigma(\nu)/\sigma_0$ as a function of ν for various values of n_0: "BORN" denotes the BORN approximation ($n_0 \to 0$), "hard" denotes a value of $n_0 \approx 0.04$, "medium" denotes n_0 about 0.5 and "soft" denotes an *estimated* curve for fairly large values of n_0 (of the order of 5).

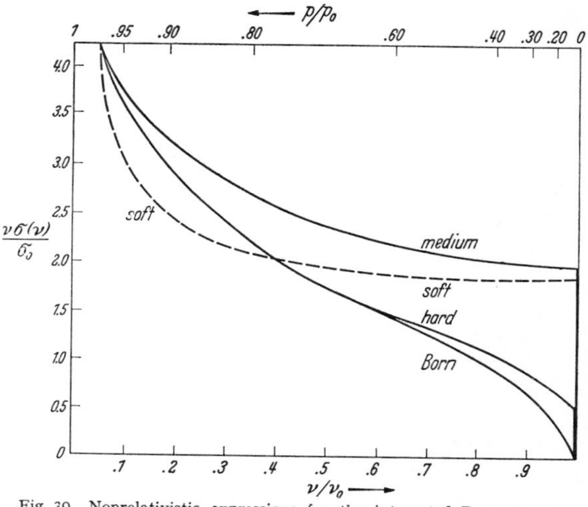

Fig. 39. Nonrelativistic expressions for the integrated Bremsstrahlung cross-section $\sigma(\nu)$ times ν/σ_0 plotted against frequency ν in units of the high-frequency limit ν_0. The curves marked BORN, hard, medium and soft are for values of n_0 of 0, 0.04, 0.5 and approximately 5, respectively.

The constant σ_0, defined by (77.15), which gives the order of magnitude of Bremsstrahlung cross-sections, can also be written as

$$\sigma_0 = \frac{16}{3} Z^2 \alpha^3 a_0^2 \frac{\text{Ry}}{E_0} = \frac{16}{3}\alpha\left(\frac{\hbar}{m c}\right)^2 \frac{Z^2\,\text{Ry}}{E_0} = \left(\frac{Z^2\,\text{Ry}}{E_0}\right) 5.8\times 10^{-23}\,\text{cm}^2, \tag{78.11}$$

where a_0 is the atomic unit of distance and E_0 the initial energy of the electron.

From SOMMERFELD's differential cross-section one can also obtain the polarization and angular distribution of the emitted photons, by integrating this cross-section over $d\Omega_p$, the direction of the electron's final momentum (for fixed photon momentum $\boldsymbol{k}$ and polarization $\boldsymbol{j}$). For general n_0 and n, the result of this integration cannot be expressed in closed analytical form [unlike the *total* cross-section (78.2)]. However, these integrals have been carried out by semi-numerical methods for a number[1] of values of n_0 and n and analytic expressions are available in limiting cases: The measure $P = (J_\parallel - J_\perp)/(J_\parallel + J_\perp)$ is given by the BORN approximation expression (77.7), plotted in Fig. 38, if $2\pi n_0 \ll 1$. At

[1] R. WEINSTOCK, Phys. Rev. **61**, 585 (1942), ELWERT's paper, and especially P. KIRKPATRICK and L. WIEDMANN, Phys. Rev. **67**, 321 (1945), who also give numerical values for (78.2) for various values of n_0 and $\boldsymbol{n}$.

the low-frequency limit ($\nu=0$), $P=-1$ for all values of n. If $2\pi n_0$ is not very small, P increases more rapidly with increasing ν than (77.7) for small ν and then approaches a constant value less than unity as $\nu\to\nu_0$ (high-frequency limit). For $n_0\gg 1$ (very low initial electron energy), P approaches the constant value of $\frac{3}{5}$ for all except very small frequencies ν (valid as long as $n-n_0\gg 1$). For $P=\frac{3}{5}$, the polarization is not complete, but $J_{\parallel}=4J_{\perp}$. The angular distribution of the emitted photons is given in terms of $J_{\parallel}/J_{\perp}$ by (77.10) for all values of n_0 and n.

SOMMERFELD's differential cross-section, and the total cross-section (78.2) derived from it, is valid only for an unscreened COULOMB potential. However, these formulas can be adapted to a potential of the form (76.10), which takes account of the atomic screening at least over a reasonable range of radial distances. In SOMMERFELD's formula, and in the definition (77.15) for σ_0 one simply replaces Z by $Z-s$ and defines n_0 and n (instead of 78.1) by

$$n_0=\frac{Z-s}{\sqrt{E_0-2V_0}}, \qquad n=\frac{Z-s}{\sqrt{E-2V_0}}, \tag{78.12}$$

with E_0 and E expressed in Ry. In the differential cross-section one chooses s and V_0 in (76.10) to represent the atomic potential $V(r)$ for values of r of the order of $\hbar|\boldsymbol{p}_0-\boldsymbol{p}|^{-1}$ (all in atomic units). Unfortunately this method is neither very accurate nor very convenient, especially at very low energies where screening is most important.

For atoms with reasonably large nuclear charge Z, one can account for screening by the following argument: ELWERT has shown that the BORN approximation is valid near the low-frequency limit (at least for a COULOMB potential) even at low energies, when n_0 is large, as long as $n-n_0\ll 1$ [with n_0, n defined by (78.1)]. On the other hand, we have seen in Sect. 77β that screening is unimportant if $p_0-p\gg Q\sim Z^{\frac{1}{3}}$ (all in atomic units). One then finds, *if* $n_0\ll Z^{\frac{1}{3}}$ (but not necessarily $n_0\ll 1$), that one can use the BORN approximation with screening near the low-frequency limit (say, up to $n-n_0\sim n_0\,Z^{-\frac{1}{3}}\ll 1$, i.e. $p_0-p\sim Z^{\frac{2}{3}}\,n_0^{-1}\gg Z^{\frac{1}{3}}$) and the SOMMERFELD formula without screening for larger frequencies. Near the low-frequency limit, $\nu\,\sigma(\nu)/\sigma_0$ is no longer given by (78.8), but has a finite[1] limit of order $\log(p_0/Q)\sim\log(Z^{\frac{2}{3}}/n_0)$. No accurate approximations are available for very low energies, where $n_0\gg Z^{\frac{1}{3}}$, but screening depresses the value of $\nu\,\sigma(\nu)/\sigma_0$ greatly [below the value in (78.10) for an unscreened COULOMB potential] if $n_0\gg Z^{\frac{2}{3}}$ ($p_0\ll Z^{\frac{1}{3}}$). In fact, $\nu\,\sigma(\nu)$ for a neutral atom remains finite as $E_0\to 0$, whereas $\sigma_0\to\infty$.

For astrophysical applications (see Sect. 74β) the inverse process to Bremsstrahlung, "free-free absorptive transition", is also of interest. The fundamental process is as follows. Consider one (unscreened) atomic nucleus of charge Z at rest, immersed in a stream (of infinite extent) of electrons with density $\mathcal{N}$ per unit *volume* and velocity v, energy E. We are interested in the absorption cross-section $\sigma_{FF}(\nu)$ for a photon of frequency ν, presented by the combination of one nucleus plus the electron stream. In the process, one of the incident electrons makes a transition to a state of higher energy $E_0=E+h\nu$ (to obtain σ_{FF}, we integrate the differential cross-section over all directions of the final momentum of the electron). The matrix elements which enter into the formula for σ_{FF} are identical with those for the Bremsstrahlung process (transition from E_0 to E), but the various normalization factors are different.

---

[1] For details see P. KIRKPATRICK and L. WIEDMANN, Phys. Rev. **67**, 321 (1945).

If we average $\sigma_{FF}(\nu)$ over the angle between the momentum of the photon and that of the incident electrons, we find[1]

$$\sigma_{FF}(\nu) = \frac{\mathcal{N} v c^2}{\nu^3} \frac{E_0}{E} \frac{\nu\,\sigma(\nu)}{8\pi}, \tag{78.13}$$

where $\sigma(\nu)$ is the total Bremsstrahlung cross-section, defined in (76.3), (76.4). If we use the low-energy approximation (78.10) for $\sigma(\nu)$, we find

$$\sigma_{FF}(\nu) = \frac{2\mathcal{N}}{3\sqrt{3}} \frac{Z^2 e^6}{m^2 \hbar c v \nu^3} = \frac{2}{3\sqrt{3}} Z^2 \alpha \left(\frac{\mathcal{N}}{\nu^3 v}\right)_{\text{a.u.}}, \tag{78.14}$$

where the last expression holds if all quantities are expressed in atomic units (unit of frequency is 4π Ry). It is interesting to compare this expression with the low-energy approximation for $\sigma_n(\nu)$, the cross-section for the photoeffect from a shell of *bound* electrons with principal quantum number n, obtained from (71.19) and (71.20). In atomic units we have,

$$\sigma_n(\nu) = \frac{2}{3\sqrt{3}\,\pi^2} \frac{Z^4 \alpha}{\nu^3 n^3}. \tag{78.15}$$

The two cross-section are thus of the same order of magnitude, if (in atomic units) $\mathcal{N}$ is of order Z, v of order Z and n of order unity, for all Z and ν [at least in the range of ν not much larger than Z^2, where (78.14) and (78.15) are valid].

One can also *combine* expressions (78.14) and (78.15) in the following manner. We consider first the photoeffect from bound electron states with high principal quantum numbers n (total energy E negative and small compared with Z^2 Ry): If all the shells with principal quantum numbers from $n-y$ to $n+y$, say, are filled (with $n \gg y \gg 1$), then all the electronic states in the energy interval (in atomic units)

$$\Delta E = \frac{Z^2}{2(n-y)^2} - \frac{Z^2}{2(n+y)^2} = \frac{2yZ^2}{n^3}$$

are occupied. The photon absorption cross-section (78.15) from one closed shell thus represents the absorption from occupied electron states in the energy interval Z^2/n^3. We can then rewrite (78.15) in the following more general form: If a fraction ξ of all the electronic states in an energy interval ΔE are occupied, then the photon absorption cross-section from these electrons is

$$\sigma(\nu)\,\xi\,\Delta E = \frac{2}{3\sqrt{3}\,\pi^2} \frac{Z^2\alpha}{\nu^3} \xi\,\Delta E. \tag{78.16}$$

Consider next free-free transitions from electrons with positive (but small) total energies near the energy E (momentum p, velocity v, all in atomic units). The total number of possible electronic states per unit energy interval per unit volume is then (cf. the theory of a degenerate FERMI gas)

$$\frac{8\pi}{(2\pi)^3} p^2 \frac{dp}{dE} = \frac{v}{\pi^2}.$$

If $\mathcal{N}$ free electrons per unit volume with energies in a small energy interval ΔE are present, the fraction ξ of states in this energy interval which are filled is then given by $\xi\,\Delta E = \pi^2 \mathcal{N}/v$. Substituting this relation into (78.14), we *also* obtain (78.16) for photon absorption from free electrons.

[1] See ref. [7], p. 566.

79. Relativistic effects[1]. If the electron is to be treated relativistically, the following changes have to be made in our previous treatment. We denote now by E_0 and E the total (including rest mass) initial and final energy of the electron, divided by c. We then have, instead of (76.5),

$$E_0=\sqrt{p_0^2+\mu^2}, \quad E=\sqrt{p^2+\mu^2}, \quad h\nu/c\equiv k=E_0-E, \tag{79.1}$$

where $\mu=mc$. We further have to use DIRAC wave functions and replace the operator $\boldsymbol{p}$ by $\mu\boldsymbol{\alpha}$ in the matrix element D, Eq. (76.2).

As discussed before, the exact DIRAC wave functions, which behave asymptotically like plane waves, for an electron in a COULOMB potential cannot be written in closed analytic form. Thus the DIRAC matrix element D cannot be evaluated analytically. The partial wave solutions (in spherical polar coordinates) of the DIRAC equation are expressible in analytic form and, in principle, D could be evaluated as an infinite sum of matrix elements which involve these solutions. Even this method is impractical, except for special cases such as extremely high energies (Sect. 79β). However, if BORN approximation is used, the calculations become relatively simple. The main results of such calculations are described below.

α) *The* BETHE-HEITLER *formula.* As in Sect. 77 we assume that $Z\alpha\ll 1$ and that the initial and final momenta p_0 and p are large compared with the BOHR momentum $Z\alpha\,\mu$ for nuclear charge Z. The BORN approximation to the DIRAC wave functions, which are the relativistic generalizations of (77.2), for an electron in *any* potential $V(r)$ can then be obtained analytically, if the FOURIER transform $V'(p)$ of the potential is known. By methods analogous to those leading to (77.3), one can then derive the BORN approximation to the DIRAC matrix element D. However, retardation must not be neglected since retardation effects are extremely important at relativistic energies. As in the nonrelativistic case, the same result for D can also be obtained by second-order perturbation theory, the method used by BETHE and HEITLER[2].

In the relativistic BORN approximation, the differential cross-section also depends on the initial and final spin-states of the electron as well as on the polarization direction of the photon. Summing over the final spin states and over photon polarization[3] and averaging over the initial spin-states, one obtains the BETHE-HEITLER result

$$\sigma(\nu,\Omega_p,\Omega_k)\,d\nu\,d\Omega_p\,d\Omega_k=\alpha^3\frac{\hbar^2}{\pi^2}\,d\Omega_p\,d\Omega_k\,\frac{d\nu}{\nu}\,\frac{p}{p_0}\,\frac{[Z-F(q)]^2}{q^4}\,\Gamma, \tag{79.2}$$

where Γ is the expression

$$\left.\begin{aligned}\Gamma=p^2\sin^2\vartheta\left(\frac{4E_0^2-q^2}{4\varepsilon^2}+\frac{k^2}{2\varepsilon\,\varepsilon_0}\right)+p_0^2\sin^2\vartheta_0\left(\frac{4E^2-q^2}{4\varepsilon_0^2}+\frac{k^2}{2\varepsilon\,\varepsilon_0}\right)-\\ -2p\,p_0\sin\vartheta\sin\vartheta_0\cos\varphi\left(\frac{4E_0E-q^2+2k^2}{4\varepsilon\,\varepsilon_0}\right)\end{aligned}\right\} \tag{79.3}$$

with

$$\boldsymbol{q}=\boldsymbol{p}_0-\boldsymbol{p}-\boldsymbol{k}, \qquad \varepsilon_0=E_0-p_0\cos\vartheta_0, \quad \varepsilon=E-p\cos\vartheta. \tag{79.4}$$

---

[1] Bremsstrahlung and pair creation calculations at relativistic energies are described in more detail in ref. [7], Chap. 7, Sect. 7; ref. [6], Sects. 25 and 26; B. ROSSI aud K. GREISEN, Rev. Mod. Phys. **13**, 240 (1941) and J. ASHKIN und H. A. BETHE in E. SEGRÈ: Experimental Nuclear Physics, Vol. 1, Part II. New York; J. Wiley 1953.

[2] H. A. BETHE and W. HEITLER: Proc. Roy. Soc. Lond., Ser. A **146**, 83 (1934).

[3] Photon polarization is discussed by M. MAY and G. WICK, Phys. Rev. **81**, 628 (1951).

The screening function F is defined in (76.8), ϑ_0 (or ϑ) is the angle between $\boldsymbol{k}$ and $\boldsymbol{p}_0$ (or $\boldsymbol{p}$), φ the angle between the $(\boldsymbol{p}, \boldsymbol{k})$ and $(\boldsymbol{p}_0, \boldsymbol{k})$ planes and E, E_0, p, p_0 and k are connected by (79.1).

For nonrelativistic momenta, $p_0, p \ll \mu$, each of the three expressions in brackets in (79.3) can be expanded in powers of p_0/μ and p/μ. The leading term in each of these expansions is unity and the expression (79.3) for Γ reduces to the nonrelativistic, non-retarded expression (77.9). If terms linear in p_0/μ and p/μ are kept, and also terms linear in $k/|\boldsymbol{p}_0 - \boldsymbol{p}|$ in the expressions in (79.2) involving q [see Eq. (77.19)], the nonrelativistic retardation effects of Sect. 77γ are obtained.

If screening is neglected (F replaced by zero), the differential cross-section (79.2) with (79.3) can be integrated analytically [see [6], p. 245) over $d\Omega_p$ and also over $d\Omega_k$ for arbitrary values of p_0 and p. We shall discuss in detail only the limiting case of extremely large momenta.

For p_0 and p of the order of magnitude of μ the analytic expressions for the angular distribution of the photons and for the integrated cross-section are very involved, but the main effect is a shift in the forward direction of the angular distribution of the emitted photon and outgoing electron. For such momenta, the effect of screening is small, except near the low-frequency limit (ν and $p_0 - p$ small).

The expressions simplify somewhat in the extreme relativistic case of p_0, $p \gg \mu$. This case is of practical importance both for showers produced by the electronic component of cosmic rays in its passage through matter and for many high energy electron accelerators where the electron beam is made to strike an internal target and the emerging beam of Bremsstrahlung photons is used in experiments. For such extremely relativistic momenta the differential cross-section (79.2) is appreciably large only for small values of the angles ϑ and ϑ_0. This is due to the fact that the quantities ε and ε_0 in (79.4), as well as q, increase rapidly with increasing ϑ and ϑ_0 if p and p_0 are large. We simplify the expressions occuring in (79.2) to (79.4) by expanding E_0 and E in powers of μ/p_0 and μ/p and by making the small-angle approximation $\sin\vartheta \to \vartheta$ and $\cos\vartheta \to 1 - \frac{1}{2}\vartheta^2$. Carrying only the first two terms in the expansion in powers of μ/p_0 and μ/p, we get from (79.1)

$$E_0 = p_0 + \frac{1}{2}\frac{\mu^2}{p_0}, \qquad E = p + \frac{1}{2}\frac{\mu^2}{p}, \qquad k = (p_0 - p)\left(1 - \frac{1}{2}\frac{\mu^2}{p_0 p}\right). \tag{79.5}$$

From (79.4) we find

$$\left.\begin{aligned} 2\varepsilon_0 &= \frac{\mu^2}{p_0} + p_0\vartheta_0^2, \qquad 2\varepsilon = \frac{\mu^2}{p} + p\,\vartheta^2; \\ q^2 &= q_{\min}^2 + (p_0\vartheta_0 - p\,\vartheta)^2 + 2p_0 p\,\vartheta_0\vartheta\,(1 - \cos\varphi) \end{aligned}\right\} \tag{79.6}$$

where

$$q_{\min} = (p_0 - p)\,\frac{\mu^2}{2p_0 p} \approx \frac{k\,\mu^2}{2p_0 p}. \tag{79.7}$$

Instead of quoting the exact results, we shall derive some simple expressions, illustrating the angular distribution of the photon and outgoing electron. We consider a fixed direction (and magnitude) of the photon momentum $\boldsymbol{k}$ for fixed $\boldsymbol{p}_0$ (ϑ_0 fixed). Let ξ be the angle which the outgoing electron momentum $\boldsymbol{p}$ makes with the fixed vector $\boldsymbol{p}_0 - \boldsymbol{k}$. Using the fact that ϑ_0 and ϑ are small, one can derive from (79.6) an alternative approximation for q,

$$q^2 = q_{\min}^2 + p^2\xi^2. \tag{79.8}$$

Now ε_0 (or ε), given by (79.6), increases rapidly with increasing ϑ_0 (or ϑ) if $\mu \ll p_0\vartheta_0$ (or $p\,\vartheta$) and the most important values of $p_0\vartheta_0$ (or $p\,\vartheta$) are of the order of μ.

On the other hand, q^2 [given by (79.8)] increases with increasing ξ for ξ larger than $k\mu^2/p_0 p^2$ ($\ll \mu/p$). We shall see that the important range of values of ξ is

$$\frac{k\,\mu^2}{p_0\,p^2} \ll \xi \ll \frac{\mu}{p}\;(\sim\vartheta), \qquad q \ll \mu \ll k,\, p,\, p_0 .$$

For $\xi \ll \vartheta$, (79.6) and (79.8) show that

$$p\,\vartheta \approx p_0\,\vartheta_0, \quad p\,\varepsilon \approx p_0\,\varepsilon_0 .$$

We now replace $p\,\varepsilon$ by $p_0\,\varepsilon_0$ in (79.3) and omit q. Using (79.5) and (79.6), the expression (79.3) for Γ reduces approximately to

$$\Gamma = \frac{2 p_0^3\, p^3\, \xi^2}{(p_0^2\,\vartheta_0^2 + \mu^2)^2}$$

if $p \ll p_0$. Integrating over the azimuthal angles which correspond to ξ and ϑ_0 and substituting this expression for Γ into (79.2), we find

$$\left.\begin{aligned} &\sigma(\nu, \Omega_p, \Omega_k)\, d\nu\, 2\pi\,\xi\, d\xi\, 2\pi\,\vartheta_0\, d\vartheta_0 \equiv \sigma(\nu, \xi, \vartheta_0)\, d\nu\, d\xi\, d\vartheta_0 \\ &\quad = 8 Z^2 \alpha^3 \left(\frac{\hbar}{\mu}\right)^2 \frac{d\nu}{\nu} \left\{\frac{\xi^3\, d\xi}{\left[\xi^2 + \left(\frac{k\,\mu^2}{2 p_0\, p^2}\right)^2\right]^2}\right\} \left\{\frac{(\mu/p_0)^2\, \vartheta_0\, d\vartheta_0}{\left[\vartheta_0^2 + \left(\frac{\mu}{p_0}\right)^2\right]^2}\right\}. \end{aligned}\right\} \tag{79.9}$$

Although (79.9) is strictly valid only if $p \ll p_0$, it gives the right order of magnitude of the cross-section for *all* values of p/p_0, as long as $\xi \ll \vartheta \ll 1$.

The angular distribution of the outgoing electron, as given by the first curly bracket in (79.9), behaves like $d\xi/\xi$ for $k\mu^2/2 p_0 p^2 \ll \xi$. For $\xi > \mu/p$, the approximation (79.9) breaks down and the cross-section decreases more rapidly with increasing ξ. After integrating over ξ, the first curly bracket in (79.9) reduces to an expression of the order of $\log(p_0 p/k\mu) \gg 1$. The angular distribution of the photon is thus largely given by the second curly bracket in (79.9), i.e. most of the photons are emitted in a cone of semi-angle $\mu/p_0 \ll 1$ about the forward direction. The *exact* cross-section, integrated over ξ, for *arbitrary* p/p_0 (but for $p \gg \mu$, $\vartheta_0 \ll 1$) is (see [7], p. 551).

$$\begin{aligned} \sigma(\nu, \vartheta_0)\, d\nu\, d\vartheta_0 &= 4 Z^2 \alpha^3 \left(\frac{\hbar}{\mu}\right)^2 \frac{d\nu}{\nu} \frac{y^2\, \vartheta_0\, d\vartheta_0}{(\vartheta_0^2 + y^2)^2} \times \\ &\times \left\{2\left[1 + x^2 - 4x\left(\frac{\vartheta_0\, y}{\vartheta_0^2 + y^2}\right)^2\right] \log\left(\frac{2 p_0\, p}{\mu\, k}\right) - \left[(1+x)^2 - 16x\left(\frac{\vartheta_0\, y}{\vartheta_0^2 + y^2}\right)^2\right]\right\}, \end{aligned}$$

where $x = p/p_0$ and $y = \mu/p_0$. Note that the angular distribution of the photons does not depend very strongly on the ratio x. In particular, even for very low frequency $\nu\,(x \to 1)$ do most of the photons emerge in a narrow cone of semi-angle μ/p_0 around the forward direction.

By integrating the above expression over $d\vartheta_0$, one can obtain the integrated cross-section $\sigma(\nu)\, d\nu$, which we discuss below. However, one can also carry out the integrations in a different order: We again consider the initial vector momentum $\boldsymbol{p}_0$ and also the photon frequency ν (hence also p and k) as fixed. The vectors $\boldsymbol{p}$ and $\boldsymbol{k}$ for an elementary process can also be specified by giving the absolute value q and direction of the momentum transfer $\boldsymbol{q}$, defined in (79.4) (which fixes the vector $\boldsymbol{p} + \boldsymbol{k}$), as well as the azimuthal angle of the $(\boldsymbol{p}, \boldsymbol{k})$ plane. Keeping the absolute value q fixed, one can carry out the angular integrations analytically[1]. The range of possible values of q extends from $q_{\min}$ ($\ll \mu$), defined

[1] This is done by H. A. BETHE, Proc. Cambridge Phil. Soc. **30**, 524 (1934). Since the screening factor F depends only on the absolute value q, the same analytic integrations hold even if screening is included (see Sect. 79β).

in (79.7), up to $p_0+p+k(\gg\mu)$. With screening neglected and for $p\ll p_0$, the dependence of the cross-section on q is given by

$$\sigma(\nu, q)\, d\nu\, dq \propto \frac{dq}{q}\left(\frac{q-q_{\min}}{q}\right)^2$$

for $q\ll\mu$, and the cross-section decreases more rapidly with increasing q for $q>\mu$. The dependence on q is qualitatively very similar for arbitrary values of p/p_0, i.e. the important range of q extends from about $2q_{\min}$ to about μ.

We finally quote the limit of the exact integrated cross-section for $p\gg\mu$, which is

$$\sigma(\nu)\, d\nu = \bar\sigma \frac{d\nu}{\nu}\left(1+\frac{p^2}{p_0^2}-\frac{2}{3}\frac{p}{p_0}\right)\left(\log\frac{2p_0 p}{k\mu}-\frac{1}{2}\right), \tag{79.10}$$

$$\bar\sigma = 4Z^2\alpha^3\left(\frac{\hbar}{\mu}\right)^2 = 4Z^2\alpha\left(\frac{e^2}{m c^2}\right)^2 = Z^2\times 2.32\times 10^{-27}\ \mathrm{cm}^2. \tag{79.11}$$

The expression (79.10) is not valid very close to the high-frequency limit where $p\gtrsim\mu$. For $p\ll\mu$, the cross-section is of the form

$$\nu\,\sigma(\nu) = \tfrac{1}{2}(p/\mu)\,\bar\sigma \tag{79.12}$$

and approaches zero as $p\to 0$ $(k\to p_0-\mu)$, as does the nonrelativistic BORN approximation (for corrections see Sect. 79β). After a sharp rise from $p=0$ to $p\sim\mu$, the function $\nu\,\sigma(\nu)$ increases rather slowly with increasing p and diverges logarithmically at the low-frequency limit.

β) Screening. We now have to consider the effect of screening, i.e. of the atomic form factor $F(q)$ in (79.2), which we have neglected so far. As discussed in Sects. 76γ and 77β, $F(q)\ll Z$ only if $q\gg Q$, where Q is a momentum of the order of $Z^{\frac{1}{3}}\alpha\mu$. For $q<Q$, $(Z-F)$ decreases rapidly with decreasing q. In the nonrelativistic calculations we have found that, for fixed p_0 and p, the minimum value of the momentum transfer q is approximately p_0-p. At nonrelativistic energies the effect of screening becomes relatively less important with increasing energy E_0. In the relativistic region this is *not* the case, in fact the importance of screening *increases* with increasing energy E_0: Consider fixed values of p_0 and p with $p_0, p\gg\mu$. The minimum value $q_{\min}$ of q is then given by (79.7), which is very much *smaller* than p_0-p for extremely relativistic momenta. We have seen that the important values of the photon angle ϑ_0 are of order μ/p_0. For ϑ_0 of this order, the important values of the angle ξ are of order $\vartheta\sim p_0\vartheta_0/p$ and smaller. In this range the momentum transfer q varies from $q_{\min}$ if $\xi=0$ ($q_{\min}$ is independent of ϑ_0) to $q\sim\mu$ if $\xi\sim\vartheta$. Now, for all elements, $Q\sim Z^{\frac{1}{3}}\alpha\mu\ll\mu$ and screening is unimportant for the larger values of ξ. On the other hand, if

$$\frac{\mu k}{p_0 p}\ll Z^{\frac{1}{3}}\alpha, , \tag{79.13}$$

then $q_{\min}\ll Q$ and the cross-section for $\xi\lesssim Q/p$ in (79.9) is depressed by screening.

If we integrate this differential cross-section over $d\xi$, the angular distribution of the emitted photons is not affected very strongly by screening[1]. In the integrated cross-section, finally, a term of order $\log(\mu/q_{\min})\sim\log(p_0 p/k\mu)$ is replaced by a term of order $\log(\mu/Q)\sim\log(1/Z^{\frac{1}{3}}\alpha)$. For the limit of "complete

[1] For further details on the angular distribution see P. V. HOUGH, Phys. Rev. **74**, 80 (1948) and M. STEARNS, Phys. Rev. **76**, 836 (1949).

screening" [i.e. if the inequality (79.13) holds] the integrated BETHE-HEITLER cross-section, using the THOMAS-FERMI values for the atomic form-factor F, is

$$\nu\,\sigma(\nu) = \bar{\sigma}\left[\left(1 + \frac{p^2}{p_0^2} - \frac{2}{3}\,\frac{p}{p_0}\right)\log\left(183\,Z^{-\frac{1}{3}}\right) + \frac{1}{9}\,\frac{p}{p_0}\right], \tag{79.14}$$

whereas (79.10) holds if the opposite inequality to (79.13) applies. For a number of intermediate values of the parameter $\mu k/p_0 p Z^{\frac{1}{3}}\alpha$, the integrated cross-section for the THOMAS-FERMI atomic form-factor has been obtained by numerical integration (see references at beginning of Sect. 79α).

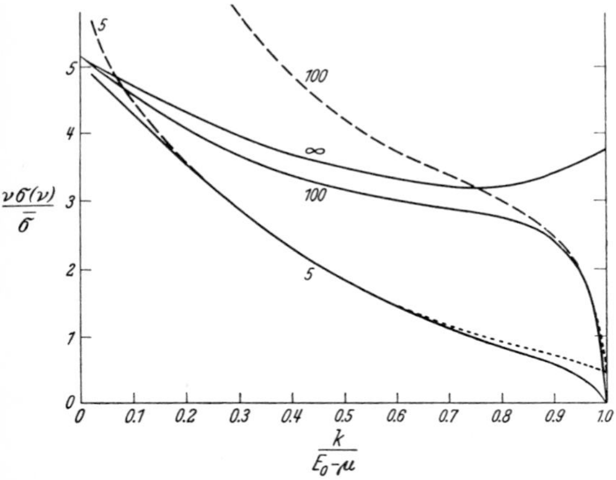

Fig. 40.

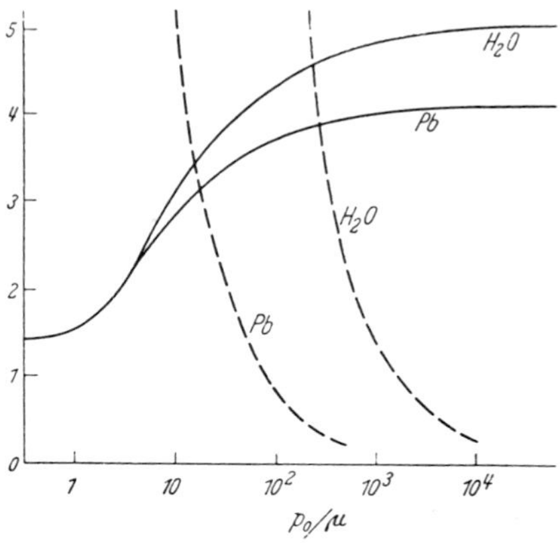

Fig. 41.

Fig. 40. The BETHE-HEITLER integrated Bremsstrahlung cross-section $\sigma(\nu)$ times $\nu/\bar{\sigma}$, plotted against photon momentum in units of the high-frequency limit The number against each curve is the primary energy E_0 in units of the rest-mass energy μ. The solid curves are for Pb ($Z=82$), the dotted curves are those with screening neglected. The solid circles near the high-frequency limit denote ELWERT's *estimated* deviations from the BORN-approximation results.

Fig. 41. Energy loss per cm divided by $N E_0 \bar{\sigma}$ is plotted against primary momentum in units of μ. The solid curves are the Bremsstrahlung energy loss, the dotted curves the ionization energy loss.

To summarize the behavior of the function $\nu\,\sigma(\nu)/\bar{\sigma}$ for different initial momenta p_0: With screening neglected, this function depends on p_0, but not on Z. For p_0 not much larger than μ, this function is similar to that for the nonrelativistic BORN approximation. For $p_0 \gg \mu$, the function rises sharply from zero at the high-frequency limit ($\nu=\nu_0$, $p=0$) to a value of order unity for $p \sim \mu$ and then rises only logarithmically. Screening becomes important when the inequality (79.13) holds. $\nu\,\sigma(\nu)$ is finite at the low-frequency limit for all values of p_0, if screening is included. If $\mu/p_0 \gg Z^{\frac{1}{3}}\alpha \ll 1$, then screening is important only near the low-frequency limit. If $p_0 \gg 137\,Z^{-\frac{1}{3}}\mu$, then screening is important everywhere except near the high-frequency limit (screening sets in for $p \gtrsim 137\,Z^{-\frac{1}{3}}\mu$). In Fig. 40, the function $\nu\sigma(\nu)/\bar{\sigma}$ is plotted against $\nu/\nu_0 = k/(E_0-\mu)$ for $E_0/\mu = 5$ and 100 respectively, with and without screening. The curves with screening are for $Z=82$ (Pb). The curve marked ∞ is a plot of the function (79.14) for $Z=82$ (Pb), which holds in the limiting case of $p_0 Z^{\frac{1}{3}}/137\mu \approx E_0/32\mu \to \infty$, if screening is included.

We finally mention the average energy loss $-dE_0/dx$ of an electron passing through matter due to Bremsstrahlung. This quantity is defined by the integral (77.17). General results for this quantity are discussed in [6], p. 252. We merely give two limiting cases, both for $E_0 \approx p_0 \gg \mu$ (the nonrelativistic limit of $p_0 \ll \mu$

is given by (77.18)]: We write

$$-\frac{dE_0}{dx} = N E_0 \sigma_{\mathrm{rad}}, \quad \sigma_{\mathrm{rad}} = \int_0^{\nu_0} \frac{\nu}{\nu_0} \sigma(\nu)\, d\nu. \tag{79.15}$$

If $p_0 \ll 137 Z^{-\frac{1}{3}} \mu$, then screening can be neglected and one finds

$$\sigma_{\mathrm{rad}} = \left(\log \frac{2p_0}{\mu} - \frac{1}{3}\right) \bar{\sigma}, \tag{79.16}$$

where $\bar{\sigma}$ is defined by (79.11). If $p_0 \gg 137 Z^{-\frac{1}{3}} \mu$, the screening is complete and σ_{rad} tends to a limit independent of p_0,

$$\sigma_{\mathrm{rad}} = \left(\log \frac{183}{Z^{\frac{1}{3}}} + \frac{1}{18}\right) \bar{\sigma}. \tag{79.17}$$

In Fig. 41, σ_{rad} is plotted against p_0/μ for Pb ($Z=82$) and for H_2O (mainly $Z=8$). Apart from the logarithmic factor in (79.16) the energy loss per atom is proportional to $Z^2 E_0$. The energy loss due to ionization is proportional to Z and roughly independent of energy E_0 in the relativistic region. The radiation energy loss is one order of $Z\alpha$ smaller than the ionization loss for $p_0 \sim \mu$, the two losses are equal for p_0 of the order $137\mu/Z$ and the radiation loss is more important at larger energies still. For comparison, the ionization energy loss, divided by NE_0, is also plotted in Fig. 41.

γ) Deviations from Born *approximation.* The Bethe-Heitler cross-sections are based on the Born approximation which is accurate only if the following parameter n,

$$n = \frac{Ze^2}{\hbar v} = Z\alpha \frac{c}{v}, \quad \frac{v}{c} = \sqrt{\frac{E^2-\mu^2}{E^2}} = \sqrt{\frac{p^2}{p^2+\mu^2}}, \tag{79.18}$$

and a similar parameter n_0 for the initial momentum, is small. Close to the high-frequency limit, n is by no means small, even if n_0 is, and the Born approximation breaks down even for relativistic E_0. Especially if p_0 is not very much larger than μ, then $n \gtrsim 1$ over an appreciable part of the frequency range. Elwert[1] has given some arguments that the correct integrated cross-section $\sigma(\nu)$ is approximated fairly closely by the Bethe-Heitler expression multiplied by the factor

$$\frac{n}{n_0} \frac{1-e^{-2\pi n_0}}{1-e^{-2\pi n}}, \tag{79.19}$$

for fairly small values of Z [see Eq. (78.8)]. Using this factor and (79.12) one finds an expression for $\nu\sigma(\nu)$ which tends to a *finite* limit (at the high-frequency limit) of

$$\nu\sigma(\nu) = \frac{1}{2}\bar{\sigma} Z\alpha \frac{1-e^{-2\pi n_0}}{n_0} = \frac{1}{2}\bar{\sigma}\frac{v_0}{c}\left(1-e^{-2\pi n_0}\right). \tag{79.20}$$

In Fig. 40 the cross-sections corrected by Elwert's factor (79.19) are shown as the dotted curves (points) for Pb ($Z=82$). Experiments[2] for $E_0 = 2\mu$ and 3μ are at least in semi-quantitative agreement with Elwert's cross-section for fairly small p if Z is not too large.

For extremely relativistic energies $E_0 \gg \mu$, Elwert's semi-empirical factor (79.19) is close to unity over most of the frequency range. For large Z this factor is not accurate and appreciable deviations from the Bethe-Heitler formula

[1] G. Elwert: Ann. d. Phys. **34**, 178 (1939).
[2] J. W. Motz: Phys. Rev. **100**, 1560 (1955).

could be expected; for Pb for instance, even when E_0, $E \gg \mu$, both n_0 and n are about 0.64, which is by no means small compared with unity. Approximate analytic calculations have been carried out recently, which are quite accurate for *arbitrary* values of $Z\alpha$, as long as both p_0 and p are large compared with μ: The calculation for the differential cross-section[1], with screening neglected, is based on the following arguments. The exact initial and final state DIRAC wave functions in a COULOMB field, which behave asymptotically like plane waves (plus outgoing and incoming spherical ones, respectively), can each be expressed as an infinite sum of partial wave solutions (whose analytic form is known) with all values of the orbital quantum numbers l_0 and l. We have seen that the important values of the momentum transfer q are of order μ (or less) and one finds, for the corresponding matrix element, the important values of l_0 and l are of order p_0/μ and p/μ (or larger). By neglecting only terms of relative order $(Z\alpha/l_0)^2$ and $(Z\alpha/l)^2$ in these partial wave solutions, one can sum the series over l_0 (or l) to get an analytic wave function[2] separable in parabolic coordinates, which is approximate but far more accurate than the BORN approximation wave function. Using these wave functions one can evaluate the matrix element for the differential cross-section. Since large values of l_0 and l are most important, one finds that these results are in error only by a fraction of order $Z\alpha\mu/p$, i.e. are very accurate in the extreme relativistic case even for $Z\alpha \sim 1$. These results are smaller than the BETHE-HEITLER ones at all angles, appreciably so for small q near $q_{\min}$, Eq. (79.7), and almost identical with the BETHE-HEITLER ones for larger values of q.

These "COULOMB corrections" to the BETHE-HEITLER differential cross-section are rigorously valid only for an unscreened COULOMB potential. If $p_0 \gg 137 Z^{-\frac{1}{3}}\mu$, screening is important just at small values of q, where the COULOMB corrections are appreciable and these corrections have not yet been calculated reliably[3]. However, for the integrated cross section $\sigma(\nu)$ one can use a different set of final state electron wave functions (involving outgoing spherical waves), with which the COULOMB and screening corrections occur for different ranges of q, so that the two effects are additive[4]. We merely quote a simple form of the result: The BETHE-HEITLER integrated cross-section is multiplied by a correction factor F which is, for arbitrary strength of screening,

$$F = 1 - \frac{(Z\alpha)^2}{L} g(Z\alpha) \tag{79.21}$$

where L is a factor in the general BETHE-HEITLER formula which is approximately $\log(2p_0 p/k\mu)$ for no screening and $\log(183 Z^{-\frac{1}{3}})$ for complete screening. g is a slowly varying function of $Z\alpha$ and $g \approx 1.202$ for $Z\alpha \ll 1$ and $g = 0.926$ for $Z\alpha = 0.60$ (Pb). The correct cross-section for $p \gg \mu$ is thus *lower* than the BETHE-HEITLER one (unlike the result for $p \to 0$), but F is not much smaller than unity even for large Z (e.g. $F \approx 0.91$ for $Z = 82$ and complete screening)[5].

δ) Bremsstrahlung in the field of an electron. We have discussed so far only Bremsstrahlung processes in which the recoil momentum q is taken up by the

[1] H. BETHE and L. MAXIMON: Phys. Rev. **93**, 768 (1954).

[2] W. H. FURRY: Phys. Rev. **46**, 391 (1934).

[3] The implication, given in the paper by BETHE and MAXIMON, that the COULOMB and screening corrections are additive, is incorrect.

[4] H. DAVIES, H. BETHE and L. MAXIMON: Phys. Rev. **93**, 788 (1954). — H. OLSEN: Phys. Rev. **99**, 1335 (1955).

[5] For references to the experimental literature see the paper by BETHE and MAXIMON; also K. L. BROWN, Phys. Rev. **103**, 243 (1956).

atom as a whole and the atom remains in its ground state (the recoil energy of the whole atom is negligible because of the large nuclear mass). Bremsstrahlung processes "in the field of an electron" are also possible, i.e. a single atomic electron absorbs the recoil momentum q and is ejected (or at least excited). For extremely relativistic momenta p_0 of the incident electron we have seen that values of q of the order of $\mu \ll p_0$ or less are most important. In such cases the recoil energy of the atomic electron is not very important and this process cannot be distinguished experimentally from "potential" Bremsstrahlung. If screening and binding is neglected, i.e. if we replace the atomic electron by a free electron initially at rest, the differential and integrated cross-sections for Bremsstrahlung in the field of the electron can be evaluated, at least approximately[1]. For $p_0 \gg \mu$ and for small momentum transfer $q \gtrsim \mu$, the differential cross-section is almost the same as from a heavy particle (fixed COULOMB field) of unit charge. For larger values of q, the cross-section for an electron is smaller than from a fixed unit charge. For very small values of q, where screening and binding effects are important, these effects depress the cross-section *less*[2] for a single atomic electron than for the process from the atom as a whole. If the integrated cross-section for these processes from the Z atomic electrons (proportional to Z) is added to the ordinary "potential" cross-section $\sigma(\nu)$ (proportional to Z^2), the result is as follows: The factor Z^2 in the "potential" formula is replaced by $Z(Z+\xi)$, where ξ is a factor slightly less than unity for $\mu \ll p_0 \ll 137\, Z^{-\frac{1}{3}}\, \mu$ and slightly larger than unity for $p_0 \gg 137\, Z^{-\frac{1}{3}}\, \mu$, where screening is important. (For nonrelativistic momenta $p_0 \ll \mu$, ξ is very small.) These electron processes are thus important only for fairly small values of the nuclear charge Z.

ε) Pair creation by photons. The calculations for Bremsstrahlung at relativistic energies are mathematically very similar to those for another process, the creation of an electron-positron pair accompanied by the absorption of a photon in the COULOMB field of a nucleus. This is a process predicted only by the DIRAC pair theory and can be thought of as an inverse process to Bremsstrahlung: The photon is absorbed instead of emitted, and the initial electron wave function is replaced by one for a negative energy state (the absence of this state is observed as a positron). The calculations of the relativistic BORN approximation (BETHE-HEITLER formula), and even of the COULOMB corrections to it, proceed in an analogous manner to those for Bremsstrahlung. Detailed discussions of pair creation will be found in the various references given in Sects. 79α and β. We merely quote some of the most important results for the integrated cross-section in BORN approximation.

Let $h\nu = kc$ be the energy of the photon incident on an atom with nuclear charge Z and let cE_0 and cE be the energies (including restmass) of the created positron and electron. We then have the equation of energy conservation,

$$k = E_0 + E. \tag{79.22}$$

The threshold for this process is thus $k = 2\mu = 2mc$. Let $\sigma(E)\, dE$ be the cross-section for pair creation processes where the electron's energy lies between E

[1] A. BORSELLINO, Nuovo Cim. **4**, 112 (1947), and Revista univ. nac. Tucuman (Argentina) A **6**, 7 (1947). See also M. L. REDHEAD, Proc. Phys. Soc. Lond. A **66**, 196 (1953), and ref. [*6*], p. 414. See also V. VOTRUBA, Phys. Rev. **73**, 1468 (1948).

[2] J. WHEELER and W. LAMB: Phys. Rev. **55**, 858 (1939). — D. BERNSTEIN and W. K. PANOFSKI: Phys. Rev. **102**, 522 (1956).

and $E+dE$, integrated over all directions of the electron and positron momenta. For $k \gg \mu$, this cross-section can be written in the form

$$\sigma(E)\,dE = \bar{\sigma}\,\frac{dE}{k}\left(1 - \frac{4}{3}\,\frac{E_0 E}{k^2}\right) L\,, \tag{79.23}$$

where $\bar{\sigma}$ is defined by (79.11) and L is a factor which is approximately $\log(2p_0 p/k\mu)$ if screening is unimportant and $\log(183 Z^{-\frac{1}{3}})$ if screening is complete. Note the similarity between this expression and (79.10) or (79.14). For $k \gg \mu/Z\alpha$, pair creation is a more important cause of photon attenuation than the COMPTON effect and photoeffect (see Sect. 73 and Fig. 36). Pair creation by photons and Bremsstrahlung of electrons and positrons are the causes of "soft component showers" in cosmic radiation: A photon of extremely high energy (produced, for instance, by the decay of a neutral π-meson) is absorbed in its passage through matter and creates a high energy pair. The electron and positron suffer Bremsstrahlung, giving up a reasonable fraction of their energy to the produced photons. These photons in turn produce more pairs, etc.

Appendix on spherical harmonics.

Throughout the text we have made extensive use of a number of formulae involving spherical harmonics. We give below the definitions we have used and a collection of useful formulae, most of them without proofs. Proofs will be found in, or can be derived from, the standard mathematical texts[1].

α) LEGENDRE polynomials. We define the LEGENDRE polynomial, $P_l(x)$, of l-th order as the l-th expansion coefficient in the following expansion (with $r<1$)

$$\frac{1}{\sqrt{1-2rx+r^2}} = \sum_{l=0}^{\infty} r^l P_l(x)\,. \tag{A.1}$$

The variable x is to lie in the range -1 to 1. For $x=\pm 1$, we have

$$P_l(1) = 1\,, \qquad P_l(-1) = (-1)^l\,. \tag{A.2}$$

$P_l(x)$ is a polynomial in x of the l-th degree, given by

$$P_l(x) = \frac{1}{2^l\, l!}\,\frac{d^l\,[(x^2-1)^l]}{dx^l} \tag{A.3}$$

or, more explicitly, by

$$P_l(x) = \frac{(2l)!}{2^l\cdot l!^2}\left[x^l - \frac{l(l-1)}{2(2l-1)}\,x^{l-2} + \frac{l(l-1)(l-2)(l-3)}{2\cdot 4\cdot(2l-1)(2l-3)}\,x^{l-4} + \cdots\right]. \tag{A.4}$$

The LEGENDRE polynomials and their first derivatives satisfy the following recursion relations.

$$(2l+1)\,x P_l = (l+1)\,P_{l+1}(x) + l\,P_{l-1}(x)\,. \tag{A.5}$$

$$P_l = P'_{l-1} - 2x P'_l + P'_{l+1}\,. \tag{A.6}$$

$$(2l+1)\,P_l(x) = P'_{l+1}(x) - P'_{l-1}(x)\,. \tag{A.7}$$

$$\left.\begin{aligned} x P'_l &= P'_{l-1} + l P_l \\ &= P'_{l+1} - (l+1)\,P_l\,. \end{aligned}\right\} \tag{A.8}$$

[1] J. MEIXNER: Spezielle Funktionen, Vol. I of this Encyclopedia. — E. W. HOBSON: Spherical and Ellipsoidal Harmonics. Cambridge 1931. — W. MAGNUS and F. OBERHETTINGER: Spezielle Funktionen der Mathematischen Physik, Chap. 4, 2nd ed. Berlin-Göttingen-Heidelberg: Springer 1948. — E. T. WHITTAKER and G. N. WATSON: Modern Analysis, Chap. 15. Cambridge 1927. See also Sect. 65 of ref. [*10*].

The LEGENDRE polynomials satisfy the following second order differential equation

$$(1-x^2)P_l''-2xP_l'+l(l+1)P_l=0 \tag{A.9}$$

or, written in terms of ϑ, where $\cos\vartheta = x$

$$\frac{1}{\sin\vartheta}\frac{d}{d\vartheta}\left(\sin\vartheta\frac{dP_l}{d\vartheta}\right)+l(l+1)P_l=0. \tag{A.10}$$

The first part of (A.10) is clearly r^2 times the ϑ-part of the LAPLACE-operator Δ [cf. Eq. (1.2)], written in terms of spherical polar coordinates (r, ϑ, φ). In fact, the differential equation

$$r^{2-l}\Delta\,[r^l P_l(\cos\vartheta)]=0$$

reduces, after carrying out the r-differentation, exactly to (A.10).

The LEGENDRE polynomials satisfy the orthogonality relations

$$\int_{-1}^{1} dx\,P_n(x)\,P_m(x)=\begin{cases}0 & \text{if } n\neq m,\\ \dfrac{2}{2n+1} & \text{if } n=m.\end{cases} \tag{A.11}$$

The inverse distance between two points with polar coordinates $(r, 0, 0)$ and $(\varrho, \vartheta, \varphi)$ can be expressed in terms of LEGENDRE polynomials,

$$\frac{1}{\sqrt{r^2-2r\varrho\cos\vartheta+\varrho^2}}=\begin{cases}\sum\limits_l \dfrac{\varrho^l}{r^{l+1}}P_l(\cos\vartheta), & \text{if } \varrho<r,\\ \sum\limits_l \dfrac{r^l}{\varrho^{l+1}}P_l(\cos\vartheta), & \text{if } \varrho>r.\end{cases} \tag{A.12}$$

β) Associated LEGENDRE *polynomials.* For positive integers m, we define the (unnormalized) associated LEGENDRE polynomial $P_l^m(x)$ by[1]

$$P_l^m(x)=(1-x^2)^{m/2}\frac{d^m P_l(x)}{dx^m}. \tag{A.13}$$

The function P_l^m satisfies the following differential equation

$$(1-x^2)(P_l^m)''-2x(P_l^m)'+\left[l(l+1)-\frac{m^2}{1-x^2}\right]P_l^m=0. \tag{A.14}$$

We also define the *normalized* associated LEGENDRE polynomial P_{lm} by

$$\mathscr{P}_{lm}=\sqrt{\frac{2l+1}{2}\cdot\frac{(l-m)!}{(l+m)!}}P_l^m=\sqrt{\frac{2l+1}{2}\cdot\frac{(l-m)!}{(l+m)!}}\frac{1}{2^l\cdot l!}(1-x^2)^{m/2}\frac{d^{l+m}}{dx^{l+m}}(x^2-1)^l. \tag{A.15}$$

We further define the (unnormalized) spherical harmonic

$$\Phi_{lm}=P_l^m e^{im\varphi}, \tag{A.16}$$

which satisfies the following differential equation, written in terms of ϑ instead of $x=\cos\vartheta$,

$$\frac{1}{\sin\vartheta}\frac{d}{d\vartheta}\left(\sin\vartheta\frac{d\Phi}{d\vartheta}\right)+\frac{1}{\sin^2\vartheta}\frac{d^2\Phi}{d\varphi^2}+l(l+1)\Phi=0. \tag{A.17}$$

[1] The definition used by some authors differs from ours by a factor $(-1)^m$.

Note that the functions $r^l \Phi_{lm}$ and $r^{-(l+1)} \Phi_{lm}$ both satisfy LAPLACE'S equation. We also define the normalized spherical harmonic Y_{lm} by

$$Y_{lm}(\vartheta, \varphi) = \frac{1}{\sqrt{2\pi}} \mathscr{P}_{lm} e^{im\varphi} \tag{A.18}$$

which satisfies the normalization condition,

$$\int_0^\pi \sin\vartheta \, d\vartheta \int_0^{2\pi} d\varphi \, |Y_{lm}|^2 = \int_{-1}^{+1} \mathscr{P}_{lm}^2(x)\, dx = 1 . \tag{A.19}$$

Any two associated LEGENDRE polynomials with different lower index l, but the *same* upper index m, are orthogonal. Hence

$$\int_0^\pi \sin\vartheta \, d\vartheta \int_0^{2\pi} d\varphi \, Y_{lm}^* \, Y_{l'm'} = 0$$

unless both $l = l'$ and $m = m'$.

For negative m we define $\mathscr{P}_{lm}$ and Y_{lm} still[1] by (A.15) and (A.18). Many authors use instead, for negative m,

$$Y'_{lm} = \frac{1}{\sqrt{2\pi}} \mathscr{P}_{l,|m|} e^{im\varphi} .$$

The two forms are related by

$$\mathscr{P}_{l,-m} = (-1)^m \mathscr{P}_{lm}; \qquad Y'_{lm} = (-1)^{\frac{|m|-m}{2}} Y_{lm} .$$

Our definition for Y_{lm} has the advantage that the same formulae hold for positive and negative m, which is not the case for the conventional Y'_{lm}. Note, however, that $Y_{lm}^* = (-1)^m Y_{l,-m}$.

γ) Coordinate matrix elements. For evaluating matrix elements involving the coordinates (x, y, z), the following formulae are of use:

$$\left.\begin{aligned} &\sin\vartheta\, \mathscr{P}_{lm}(\cos\vartheta) \\ &= \sqrt{\frac{(l+m+1)(l+m+2)}{(2l+1)(2l+3)}}\, \mathscr{P}_{l+1,m+1} - \sqrt{\frac{(l-m)(l-m-1)}{(2l+1)(2l-1)}}\, \mathscr{P}_{l-1,m+1} , \end{aligned}\right\} \tag{A.20}$$

$$\left.\begin{aligned} &\sin\vartheta\, \mathscr{P}_{lm}(\cos\vartheta) \\ &= -\sqrt{\frac{(l-m+1)(l-m+2)}{(2l+1)(2l+3)}}\, \mathscr{P}_{l+1,m-1} + \sqrt{\frac{(l+m)(l+m-1)}{(2l+1)(2l-1)}}\, \mathscr{P}_{l-1,m-1} , \end{aligned}\right\} \tag{A.21}$$

$$\left.\begin{aligned} &\cos\vartheta\, \mathscr{P}_{lm}(\cos\vartheta) \\ &= \sqrt{\frac{(l+m+1)(l-m+1)}{(2l+1)(2l+3)}}\, \mathscr{P}_{l+1,m} + \sqrt{\frac{(l+m)(l-m)}{(2l+1)(2l-1)}}\, \mathscr{P}_{l-1,m} . \end{aligned}\right\} \tag{A.22}$$

A double application of (A.20) to (A.22) gives

$$\left.\begin{aligned} \frac{z^2}{r^2} \mathscr{P}_{lm} = \cos^2\vartheta\, \mathscr{P}_{lm} &= \sqrt{\frac{[(l+1)^2 - m^2][(l+2)^2 - m^2]}{(2l+1)(2l+3)^2(2l+5)}}\, \mathscr{P}_{l+2,m} + \\ &+ \frac{2l^2 + 2l - 2m^2 - 1}{(2l+3)(2l-1)} \mathscr{P}_{lm} + \sqrt{\frac{[l^2 - m^2][(l-1)^2 - m^2]}{(2l+1)(2l-1)^2(2l-3)}}\, \mathscr{P}_{l-2,m} , \end{aligned}\right\} \tag{A.23}$$

---

[1] For negative m, we must use the definition on the right hand side of (A.15); the definition (A.13) would be meaningless in this case.

$$\left.\begin{aligned}\cos\vartheta\sin\vartheta\,\mathscr{P}_{lm} &= \sqrt{\frac{(l+m+3)(l+m+2)(l+m+1)(l-m+1)}{(2l+5)(2l+3)^2(2l+1)}}\,\mathscr{P}_{l+2,m+1} + \\ &+ \frac{2m+1}{(2l+3)(2l-1)}\sqrt{(l+m+1)(l-m)}\,\mathscr{P}_{l,m+1} - \\ &- \sqrt{\frac{(l+m)(l-m)(l-m-1)(l-m-2)}{(2l+1)(2l-1)^2(2l-3)}}\,\mathscr{P}_{l-2,m+1},\end{aligned}\right\} \quad (A.24)$$

$$\left.\begin{aligned} &= -\sqrt{\frac{(l+m+1)(l-m+1)(l-m+2)(l-m+3)}{(2l+5)(2l+3)^2(2l+1)}}\,\mathscr{P}_{l+2,m-1} + \\ &+ \frac{2m-1}{(2l+3)(2l-1)}\sqrt{(l+m)(l-m+1)}\,\mathscr{P}_{l,m-1} + \\ &+ \sqrt{\frac{(l+m)(l+m-1)(l+m-2)(l-m)}{(2l+1)(2l-1)^2(2l-3)}}\,\mathscr{P}_{l-2,m-1},\end{aligned}\right\} \quad (A.25)$$

$$\left.\begin{aligned}\sin^2\vartheta\,\mathscr{P}_{lm} &= \sqrt{\frac{(l+m+4)(l+m+3)(l+m+2)(l+m+1)}{(2l+5)(2l+3)^2(2l+1)}}\,\mathscr{P}_{l+2,m+2} - \\ &- \frac{2}{(2l+3)(2l-1)}\sqrt{(l+m+2)(l+m+1)(l-m)(l-m-1)}\,\mathscr{P}_{l,m+2} + \\ &+ \sqrt{\frac{(l-m)(l-m-1)(l-m-2)(l-m-3)}{(2l+1)(2l-1)^2(2l-3)}}\,\mathscr{P}_{l-2,m+2},\end{aligned}\right\} \quad (A.26)$$

$$\left.\begin{aligned} &= \sqrt{\frac{(l-m+4)(l-m+3)(l-m+2)(l-m+1)}{(2l+5)(2l+3)^2(2l+1)}}\,\mathscr{P}_{l+2,m-2} - \\ &- \frac{2}{(2l+3)(2l-1)}\sqrt{(l-m+2)(l-m+1)(l+m)(l+m-1)}\,\mathscr{P}_{l,m-2} + \\ &+ \sqrt{\frac{(l+m)(l+m-1)(l+m-2)(l+m-3)}{(2l+1)(2l-1)^2(2l-3)}}\,\mathscr{P}_{l-2,m-2}.\end{aligned}\right\} \quad (A.27)$$

Eqs. (A.23) to (A.27) can be used to evaluate matrix elements of expressions quadratic in the coordinates (like x^2, z^2, xy and xz), which occur especially in the treatment of the fine structure problem. Consider, for instance the matrix-element of the expression $f(r)\,(x+iy)\,z/r^2$, where $f(r)$ is any function of radial distance r only, between any two states with the *same* value of l (quantum number of total orbital angular momentum). If the initial and final eigenfunctions are of the form

$$u_i = R_{nl}(r)\,Y_{lm}, \qquad u_f = R_{n'l}(r)\,Y_{lm'},$$

then the matrix element, for $m' = m+1$,

$$[f(r)\,(x+iy)\,z/r^2]_{lm}^{l,m+1} = \int d\tau\, u_f^*\, f(r)\cos\vartheta\sin\vartheta\, e^{i\varphi}\, u_i,$$

can be written as the product of a radial integral and an integral over angles. If we write for the radial integral

$$\bar{f} = \int_0^\infty dr\, r^2 R_{n'l}(r)\, f(r)\, R_{nl}(r),$$

we then obtain

$$[(x+iy)\,z\,f/r^2]_{lm}^{l,m+1} = \bar{f}\,\frac{2m+1}{(2l+3)(2l-1)}\sqrt{(l+m+1)(l-m)}\,. \quad (A.28)$$

Similarly

$$[z^2 f/r^2]_{lm}^{lm} = \overline{f}\,\frac{2l^2 + 2l - 1 - 2m^2}{(2l+3)(2l-1)} \tag{A.29}$$

and so on.

The matrix elements of products of the various components of the operator $\boldsymbol{k}$ for orbital angular momentum, on the other hand, can be obtained by ordinary matrix multiplication, using (1.10) and (1.14). We find, for instance,

$$\left.\begin{aligned} &[k_z(k_x+ik_y)]_{l,m}^{l,m+1} = (k_z)_{l\,m+1}^{l\,m+1}(k_x+ik_y)_{lm}^{l\,m+1} = -(m+1)\sqrt{(l+m+1)(l-m)},\\ &[(k_x+ik_y)k_z]_{l,m}^{l,m+1} = (k_x+ik_y)_{lm}^{l\,m+1}(k_z)_{lm}^{lm} = -m\sqrt{(l+m+1)(l-m)},\\ &\qquad (k_z^2)_{lm}^{lm} = m^2, \qquad\qquad (\boldsymbol{k}^2)_{lm}^{lm} = l(l+1) \end{aligned}\right\} \tag{A.30}$$

where $\boldsymbol{k}^2 \equiv k_x^2 + k_y^2 + k_z^3$.

By comparison we find[1]

$$\left.\begin{aligned} &[(x+iy)z]_{lm}^{l\,m+1} = -\frac{\overline{r^2}}{(2l+3)(2l-1)}\,[k_z(k_x+ik_y)+(k_x+ik_y)k_z]_{lm}^{l\,m+1},\\ &\qquad (z^2)_{lm}^{lm} = \frac{1}{3}\,\overline{r^2} - \frac{\overline{r^2}}{(2l+3)(2l-1)}\cdot 2\cdot\left(k_z^2 - \frac{1}{3}\,k^2\right)_{lm}^{lm}, \end{aligned}\right\} \tag{A.31}$$

Similar relations hold between the matrix-elements of *all* quadratic expressions of the coordinates on the one hand and quadratic expressions of the components of the orbital angular momentum on the other, for any transitions between states of the *same* orbital quantum number l. These relations can be collected together to give

$$r^2\delta_{ij} - 3x_i x_j = -\frac{\overline{r^2}}{(2l+3)(2l-1)}\cdot[2k^2\delta_{ij} - 3(k_i k_j + k_j k_i)], \tag{A.32}$$

where $i, j = 1, 2, 3$ denote the three CARTESian coordinates x, y, z and δ_{ij} is the KRONECKER delta-symbol ($\delta_{ij} = 1$ and 0 for $i = j$ and $i \neq j$, respectively). If $\boldsymbol{a}$ and $\boldsymbol{b}$ are any two vectors which commute with $\boldsymbol{r}, \boldsymbol{k}$ and each other, then (A.32) can be rewritten in the form

$$\left.\begin{aligned} (\boldsymbol{a}\cdot\boldsymbol{b})\,r^2 - 3(\boldsymbol{a}\cdot\boldsymbol{r})(\boldsymbol{b}\cdot\boldsymbol{r}) &= \sum_{ij=1}^{3} a_i b_j (r^2\delta_{ij} - 3x_i x_j)\\ &= -\frac{\overline{r^2}}{(2l+3)(2l-1)}\,[2k^2(\boldsymbol{a}\cdot\boldsymbol{b}) - 3(\boldsymbol{a}\cdot\boldsymbol{k})(\boldsymbol{b}\cdot\boldsymbol{k}) - 3(\boldsymbol{b}\cdot\boldsymbol{k})(\boldsymbol{a}\cdot\boldsymbol{k})]. \end{aligned}\right\} \tag{A.33}$$

Eq. (A.33) should be considered as a matrix equation in the sense that the matrix elements of the left and right hand side are equal for any transition between two states of the *same* orbital quantum number l (for any value of l and for all combinations of principal and magnetic quantum numbers n, n', m, m').

δ) Other relations. The derivatives with respect to ϑ of the associated LEGENDRE polynomials are

$$\left.\begin{aligned} -\frac{dP_l^m(\cos\vartheta)}{d\vartheta} &= P_l^{m+1} - \frac{m\,x}{\sqrt{1-x^2}}\,P_l^m\\ &= -(l+m)(l-m+1)P_l^{m-1} + \frac{m\,x}{\sqrt{1-x^2}}\,P_l^m \end{aligned}\right\} \tag{A.34}$$

---

[1] For simplicity we write the following formulae for the special choice $f(r) = r^2$. Equivalent equations hold for *any* $f(r)$, with $\overline{r^2}$ replaced by $\overline{f}$.

where $x = \cos\vartheta$. For the normalized functions we have

$$-\frac{d\mathscr{P}_{lm}}{d\vartheta} = \sqrt{(l+m+1)(l-m)}\,\mathscr{P}_{l,m+1} - m\cot\vartheta\,\mathscr{P}_{lm}, \tag{A.35}$$

$$= -\sqrt{(l+m)(l-m+1)}\,\mathscr{P}_{l,m-1} + m\cot\vartheta\,\mathscr{P}_{lm}. \tag{A.36}$$

In the DIRAC wave equation, derivatives of the wave function with respect to the coordinates occur. These derivatives can be rewritten, using

$$\frac{\partial}{\partial z} = \cos\vartheta\frac{\partial}{\partial r} - \sin\vartheta\frac{1}{r}\frac{\partial}{\partial\vartheta},$$

$$\frac{\partial}{\partial x} = \sin\vartheta\cos\varphi\frac{\partial}{\partial r} + \cos\vartheta\cos\varphi\frac{1}{r}\frac{\partial}{\partial\vartheta} - \frac{\sin\varphi}{r\sin\vartheta}\frac{\partial}{\partial\varphi},$$

$$\frac{\partial}{\partial y} = \sin\vartheta\sin\varphi\frac{\partial}{\partial r} + \cos\vartheta\sin\varphi\frac{1}{r}\frac{\partial}{\partial\vartheta} + \frac{\cos\varphi}{r\sin\vartheta}\frac{\partial}{\partial\varphi}.$$

If f is any function of the radial distance r alone, we find,

$$\left.\begin{aligned}\frac{\partial}{\partial z}[f(r)\,Y_{lm}(\vartheta,\varphi)] &= \sqrt{\frac{(l+m+1)(l-m+1)}{(2l+3)(2l+1)}}\,Y_{l+1,m}\left(\frac{df}{dr} - l\frac{f}{r}\right) + \\ &+ \sqrt{\frac{(l+m)(l-m)}{(2l+1)(2l-1)}}\,Y_{l-1,m}\left(\frac{df}{dr} + (l+1)\frac{f}{r}\right).\end{aligned}\right\} \tag{A.37}$$

Similarly we get

$$\left.\begin{aligned}\left(\frac{\partial}{\partial x} + i\frac{\partial}{\partial y}\right)(f\,Y_{lm}) &= \sqrt{\frac{(l+m+2)(l+m+1)}{(2l+3)(2l+1)}}\,Y_{l+1,m+1}\left(\frac{df}{dr} - l\frac{f}{r}\right) - \\ &- \sqrt{\frac{(l-m)(l-m-1)}{(2l+1)(2l-1)}}\,Y_{l-1,m+1}\left(\frac{df}{dr} + (l+1)\frac{f}{r}\right),\end{aligned}\right\} \tag{A.38}$$

$$\left.\begin{aligned}\left(\frac{\partial}{\partial x} - i\frac{\partial}{\partial y}\right)(f\,Y_{lm}) &= -\sqrt{\frac{(l-m+2)(l-m+1)}{(2l+3)(2l+1)}}\,Y_{l+1,m-1}\left(\frac{df}{dr} - l\frac{f}{r}\right) + \\ &+ \sqrt{\frac{(l+m)(l+m-1)}{(2l+1)(2l-1)}}\,Y_{l-1,m-1}\left(\frac{df}{dr} + (l+1)\frac{f}{r}\right).\end{aligned}\right\} \tag{A.39}$$

We finally state the spherical harmonics addition theorem in our notation. Let (Θ, Φ) and (ϑ, φ) be the angle coordinates of two vectors $\boldsymbol{R}$ and $\boldsymbol{r}$ in spherical polar coordinates ,with some other vector chosen as polar axis. Let (ϑ', φ') be the polar coordinates of the vector $\boldsymbol{r}$ in a coordinate system with the vector R as polar axis, so that

$$\cos\vartheta' = \cos\Theta\cos\vartheta + \sin\Theta\sin\vartheta\cos(\Phi - \varphi). \tag{A.40}$$

The spherical harmonics addition theorem then states that

$$Y_{l0}(0)\,Y_{l0}(\vartheta') = \sum_m Y_{lm}^*(\Theta,\Phi)\,Y_{lm}(\vartheta,\varphi). \tag{A.41}$$

For the special case of $\vartheta' = 0$ we have

$$\sum_m |Y_{lm}(\Theta,\Phi)|^2 = (Y_{l0}(0))^2 = \frac{2l+1}{4\pi}. \tag{A.42}$$

Bibliography.

[1] DIRAC, P. A. M.: The Principles of Quantum Mechanics, 3rd ed. Oxford: Clarendon Press 1947.

[2] KRAMERS, H. A.: Quantentheorie des Elektrons und der Strahlung. In Hand- und Jahrbuch der Chemischen Physik, Bd. 1, Abschn. I und II. Leipzig: Akademische Verlagsgesellschaft 1938.

[3] PAULI, W.: Die Allgemeinen Prinzipien der Wellenmechanik, this Encyclopedia, Vol. V.

[4] SCHIFF, L. I.: Quantum Mechanics, 2nd ed. New York: McGraw-Hill 1955.

[5] CONDON, E. U., and G. H. SHORTLEY: Theory of Atomic Spectra. Cambridge: Cambridge University Press 1951. — Discusses mainly discrete spectra and also deals with general operator manipulation.

[6] HEITLER, W.: The Quantum Theory of Radiation, 3rd ed. Oxford: Clarendon Press 1954. — Discusses in detail the application of quantum electrodynamics to various radiation processes.

[7] SOMMERFELD, A.: Atombau und Spektrallinien, 2. Aufl., Bd. 2. Braunschweig: Vieweg & Sohn 1939. — Gives a detailed account of the quantum mechanics of the hydrogen atom (up to 1938) and also of Bremsstrahlung and the photoeffect.

[8] WHITTAKER, E. T., and G. N. WATSON: A Course of Modern Analysis, 4th ed. Cambridge: Cambridge University Press 1927.

[9] MOTT, N. F., and H. S. W. MASSEY: The Theory of Atomic Collisions. Oxford: Clarendon Press 1949. — Also contains detailed discussions of positive energy states of a DIRAC electron in a COULOMB field.

[10] Bethe, H. A.: Quantenmechanik der Ein- und Zwei-Elektronenprobleme. In Handbuch der Physik, Bd. 24/1. Berlin: Springer 1933. — This is the forerunner of the present work and contains more details on some of the older calculations and experiments.

[11] WENTZEL, G.: Einführung in die Quantentheorie der Wellenfelder. Vienna: Deuticke 1943. — An account of the older formulation of quantum field theory.

[12] SCHWEBER, S. S.; H. A. BETHE and F. DE HOFFMANN: Mesons and Fields, Vol. I (Fields). Evanston: Row, Peterson & Co. 1955. — An introduction to the modern formulations of quantum field theory.

[13] JAUCH, J. M., and F. ROHRLICH: Theory of Photons and Electrons, Cambridge (Mass): Addison-Wesley 1955. — A text on modern quantum field theory and especially on quantum electrodynamics.

[14] KÄLLEN, G.: Quantum electrodynamics. This Encyclopedia, Vol. V. — A discussion of the more fundamental aspects of quantum electrodynamics.

[15] MOTT, N. F., and I. N. SNEDDON: Wave Mechanics and its Applications. Oxford: Clarendon Press 1948.

[16] RAMSEY, N. F.: Nuclear Moments. New York: John Wiley 1953. — Also gives a discussion of the ZEEMAN effect and of hyperfine structure and of relevant microwave experiments.

Addenda and Errata.

17γ. The fine structure formula for X-ray levels. On p. 88 of our text we discussed the fine structure splitting between the L_{II} and L_{III} subshells ($2P_{\frac{1}{2}}$ to $2P_{\frac{3}{2}}$) in atoms with large nuclear charge Z. This splitting has been remeasured recently[1] to an accuracy of better than one part in 10^4 for a number of atoms with Z between 74 and 94. Theoretical calculations have not reached anywhere near this accuracy: One can start with the exact DIRAC expression (17.1) for the splitting in an unscreened hydrogen-like atom. One can evaluate next the effect on the splitting due to the interaction between a $2p$-electron and all the other atomic electrons, using hydrogen-like DIRAC wave functions and the *first* order perturbation methods outlined in Sect. 43 of our text. These effects are of relative order $1/Z$ and can be evaluated for arbitrary values of $Z\alpha$. Essentially this calculation had been performed by CHRISTY and KELLER, but not to very high numerical accuracy. Terms of relative order $1/Z^2$ are still missing after such a calculation. There are two other kinds of interesting correction terms whose relative contributions to the splitting *increase* (rather than decrease) with increasing Z: One is the effect of the finite nuclear size (which increases with Z) on the energy of the $2p_{\frac{1}{2}}$-electron (whose wave function at small distances from the nucleus increases very strongly with increasing Z). The other effect is due to the variation with $Z\alpha$ of radiative corrections such as the electron's anomalous magnetic moment, vacuum polarization and the "LAMB shift proper". Except for vacuum polarization, these radiative corrections have not yet been calculated for arbitrarily large values of $Z\alpha$. For $Z\sim 90$ the nuclear size and radiative corrections are of the order of 10^{-3} of the total splitting.

18β. Covariant calculations of radiative corrections. On p. 93 of our text we quoted theoretical results for the anomalous moment g_1 of the electron, including the fourth order contribution $-2.973\,\alpha^2/\pi^2$ as calculated by KARPLUS and KROLL. The evaluation of this fourth order moment contribution involves extremely lengthy and intricate calculations and it now appears likely that KARPLUS and KROLL's numerical coefficient of -2.973 is incorrect. SOMMERFIELD[2] has recalculated this coefficient and obtained -0.328 instead of -2.973. This difficult calculation is now being redone by a number of theorists, using different methods, in order to establish the theoretical value of the fourth order moment beyond any doubt. If we accept the result of SOMMERFIELD's calculation we obtain, instead of (18.5),

$$1+g_1=1+\frac{\alpha}{2\pi}-0.328\,\frac{\alpha^2}{\pi^2}=1.0011596. \tag{18.5 A}$$

20β. Corrections for nuclear structure. In the text we have shown that there is a contribution to the level shift of S-states, due to the finite size of a nucleus, which is proportional to the mean square radius $\langle r^2\rangle$ of the charge distribution inside the nucleus. We have stated that a similar but smaller spread of charge of the proton cannot yet be calculated from meson theory. This is still true but

[1] R. L. SHACKLETT and J. W. DUMOND: Phys. Rev. **106**, 501 (1957).
[2] C. M. SOMMERFIELD: Phys. Rev. **107**, 328 (1957).

experiments on high energy scattering of electrons by protons do give an experimental value for the mean square radius $\langle r^2 \rangle$ of the proton charge distribution. This value is somewhat larger than one might have suspected on purely theoretical grounds and is[1]

$$\langle r^2 \rangle = (0.77 \pm 0.10)^2 \times 10^{-26}\ \mathrm{cm}^2 \approx 2.1 \times 10^{-10}\, a^2 \tag{20.3 A}$$

for the proton, while the equivalent quantity $\langle r^2 \rangle$ for the neutron is almost exactly zero. This spread of the proton charge contributes an amount[2] of $(+0.12 \pm 0.03)$ Mc to the shift of the $2S$-state in hydrogen.

We quoted in our text a contribution of $+0.73$ Mc to the shift of the $2S$-state in deuterium, due to the charge spread inside the deuteron (made up of one proton and one neutron). This calculation also had not taken into account the charge spread of the proton and recent experiments[3] on electron-deuteron scattering indicate that this contribution of $+0.73$ Mc for deuterium should also be increased by approximately 0.12 Mc.

21. Fine structure and the LAMB shift. The theoretical expression (21.5) for the fine structure separation $2P_{\frac{3}{2}} - 2P_{\frac{1}{2}}$ in deuterium can be written in the form

$$F = \frac{c R_D}{16} \alpha^2 \left[1 + 2g_1 + \frac{5}{8}\alpha^2 - \frac{m}{M_D}\frac{\alpha}{\pi} \right], \tag{21.5 A}$$

where g_1 is the anomalous magnetic moment of the electron. If we accept the change in the theoretical value of g_1 from expression (18.5) in the text to expression (18.5 A) in these Addenda, we have to modify the value in (21.6) for the fine structure constant to

$$\frac{1}{\alpha} = 137.0390 \pm 0.0012. \tag{21.6 A}$$

The change of the fourth order moment contribution to g_1 from $-2.973\,\alpha^2/\pi^2$ to $-0.328\,\alpha^2/\pi^2$ affects the LAMB shift markedly: The fourth order moment contributes about -0.94 Mc to the $n=2$ LAMB shift in H and in D if we use the old value of g_1, but only -0.10 Mc if we use the new one. Further, the change in the fine structure constant from (21.6) to (21.6 A) decreases the LAMB constant L in (21.8) by about 43 ppm and decreases $S_\infty^{(1)}$ by about 0.05 Mc. If we accept these changes and add the contributions due to nuclear size, discussed in Sect. 20β of these Addenda, the theoretical values in Table 3 for the LAMB shift (in Mc/sec) are changed to

H	D	He⁺
1058.03 ± 0.15	1059.38 ± 0.15	14055 ± 3

Comparison with Table 3 shows that these changes decrease the magnitude and change the sign of the discrepancy between theory and experiment.

22. Hyperfine structure splitting. As (22.13) and the table at the bottom of p. 110 show, the ratio of the hyperfine splittings ΔE in the $1S_{\frac{1}{2}}$ and $2S_{\frac{1}{2}}$ states of any hydrogenlike atom should be 8 according to the simple FERMI formula. Accurate measurements of the hyperfine splitting in the metastable $2S_{\frac{1}{2}}$ state are now available[4] for both H and for D and the experimental ratios are

$$\left(\frac{8\Delta E_{2S}}{\Delta E_{1S}}\right)_{\mathrm{exp}} = \begin{Bmatrix} 1 + (34.6 \pm 0.3) \times 10^{-6}\ (H) \\ 1 + (34.2 \pm 0.6) \times 10^{-6}\ (D) \end{Bmatrix}. \tag{22.13 A}$$

[1] D. YENNIE, M. LÉVY and D. RAVENHALL: Rev. Mod. Phys. **29**, 144 (1957).
[2] W. ARON and A. ZUCHELLI: Phys. Rev. **105**, 1681 (1957).
[3] J. MCINTYRE and S. DHAR: Phys. Rev. **106**, 1074 (1957).
[4] J. HEBERLE, P. KUSCH and H. REICH: Phys. Rev. **101**, 612 (1956); **104**, 1585 (1956).

There are no corrections of order α to the theoretical ratio but there is a correction of $(\frac{5}{8})\alpha^2$ from purely relativistic effects and some radiative corrections of order α^3 which have not been calculated yet. For D at least, there are appreciable corrections (about 2×10^{-4}) due to nuclear structure both in the $1S$ and $2S$ states but these corrections should be almost exactly 8 times larger in the $1S$ state so they should have little effect on the ratio. The present theoretical ratio, both for H and D, is then

$$\left(\frac{8\Delta E_{2S}}{\Delta E_{1S}}\right)_{\text{theor}} = 1 + \frac{5}{8}\alpha^2 = 1 + 33.3\times 10^{-6}. \tag{22.13 B}$$

The discrepancy between theory and experiment is seen to be only about 1 *ppm*.

We have to discuss next the effect of a change in the theoretical anomalous magnetic moment g_1 of the electron on Eqs. (22.15) to (22.20) of our text. To compound the confusion there are some misprints in some of the equations in the text: The last term $\alpha^2(\frac{5}{2}-\log 2)$ in the first line of (22.15) should have a minus sign instead of a plus sign and (22.17) should read

$$\left.\begin{aligned}\frac{\nu_{\mathrm{H}}}{c R_\infty} &= \frac{16}{3}\alpha^2\left(\frac{M_p}{M_p+m}\right)^3\left(\frac{g_p\mu_N}{g_s\mu_0}\right)\times\\ &\times(1+g_1)\left[1+g_1+\alpha^2(\log 2-1)-0.2\times 10^{-5}+\delta\right]\end{aligned}\right\} \tag{22.17 A}$$

where we have written $1+g_1$ for $g_s/2$. Further, in (22.19) we quoted the experimental value for protons in a liquid sample. For substitution into (22.17A) we need the value for free protons. This value, obtained by applying diamagnetic corrections to (22.19), is

$$\left(\frac{g_s\mu_0}{g_p\mu_N}\right)_{\text{free}} = 658.2096 \pm 0.0010. \tag{22.19 A}$$

However, in evaluating (22.20) we had used the correct expressions (22.17A) and (22.19A), and (22.20) would be correct[1] if we use the "old" theoretical value for the anomalous moment $g_1 = 0.001\,1453$. If, on the other hand, we accept the "new" value (see Sect. 18β of these Addenda) of $g_1 = 0.001\,1596$ we get, instead of (22.20),

$$\frac{1}{\alpha} = 137.0387\left(1+\frac{1}{2}\delta \pm 2\times 10^{-5}\right). \tag{22.20 A}$$

It should be noted that a comparison between (21.6A) and (22.20A) gives almost exactly the same "experimental" value for the proton structure correction δ as obtained with the "old" value of g_1: Dividing Eq. (22.17A) by (21.5A) and dropping only terms smaller than 10^{-7} we get

$$\left.\begin{aligned}&\frac{3}{256}\,\frac{\nu_{\mathrm{H}}}{F}\left(\frac{g_s\mu_0}{g_p\mu_N}\right)_{\text{free}}\\ &= \frac{(1+m/M_D)}{(1+m/M_p)^3}\left[1+g_1^2+\alpha^2\left(\log 2-\frac{13}{8}\right)+\frac{\alpha}{\pi}\,\frac{m}{M_D}-0.2\times 10^{-5}+\delta\right],\end{aligned}\right\} \tag{22.22 A}$$

where F is the fine structure separation $2P_{\frac{1}{2}}-2P_{\frac{3}{2}}$ for deuterium, discussed in Sect. 21. The anomalous moment g_1 only occurs in the very small term g_1^2 in this expression and the velocity of light c and the value of the RYDBERG constant are also not needed. Using the experimental value $(10971.59 \pm 0.20)\,Mc/\text{sec}$ for F, (22.18), (22.19A) and the accurately known electron, proton and deuteron masses m, M_p and M_D, we find

$$\delta = (0.4 \pm 2.0)\times 10^{-5}. \tag{22.23 A}$$

[1] Except for another misprint: The error should read $\pm 2\times 10^{-5}$, instead of $\pm 2\times 10^{-6}$.

In our text we had stated that the proton structure correction δ cannot be calculated explicitly from presentday meson theories. In the strictest sense this is still true, but an expression has recently been derived[1] for δ in terms of just two physical parameters related to the proton structure. This theoretical expression is

$$\delta = -\frac{2\langle r\rangle_{\mathrm{em}}}{a} - 0.33\times 10^{-5}\log\frac{2K}{M_p}, \qquad (22.24\,\mathrm{A})$$

where $\langle r\rangle_{\mathrm{em}}$ is the "mean radius" of the proton, defined in a certain manner, and must be positive. $2K$ is a cut-off parameter, also related to the proton structure, which should be of the order of magnitude of M_p. Assuming $2K/M_p$ to lie between 0.1 and 10, we get from (22.23 A) an "experimental" value for $\langle r\rangle_{\mathrm{em}}$ of $(-0.1\pm 0.7)\times 10^{-13}$ cm. The correct value of $\langle r\rangle_{\mathrm{em}}$ must be positive and might be expected to be only slightly smaller than the root mean square radius of about 0.8×10^{-13} for the proton's charge distribution, given in (20.3 A) of these Addenda.

28. First order HEISENBERG's method: Misprint correction: In Table 4, Sect 28 δ p. 136, the last column should be labelled $\frac{1}{2}(\delta_p-\delta_0)$ instead of $\frac{1}{2}(\delta_0-\delta_p)$.

30. FOCK's method (excited S-states). In the text we described SMITH's calculation of the HARTREE-FOCK wave functions and the corresponding RYDBERG corrections δ for highly excited nS-states $(n\to\infty)$ of ortho- and para-helium. This calculation has been repeated recently[2], with the same method but higher numerical accuracy[3]. The theoretical and experimental values for $(-\delta)$ are

	theory	experiment[4]
ortho	0.292_9	0.297 ± 0.02
para	0.123_0	0.140 ± 0.01

The sign of the discrepancy between the theoretical and experimental results for δ is such that the actual (experimental) energy level lies lower (larger ionization potential) than the calculated one, both for ortho- and para-helium. This (rather small) discrepancy must be due to the correlation (polarization) effects between the two electrons, which are not included in the HARTREE-FOCK (HF) wave function. For *excited* states of an atom one cannot in general prove rigorously that the HARTREE-FOCK method gives an upper limit to the correct energy, but for *singly* excited discrete states $(1s, nl)$ in helium we might in fact expect this to be the case: The correct wave function for a state $(1s, nl)$ could be pictured as the HF-function U_F plus an infinite sum of product-type functions (which take account of polarization effects). It follows from the fact that the expressions in curly brackets in (30.2) vanish that the matrix element $\langle U_F^* H\psi\rangle$ vanishes, where ψ is any product wave function which contains as a factor either of the two single-particle functions u_1 or u_2. We thus might except that in the infinite sum of product functions, to be added to U_F, only those functions will occur which correspond, in some sense, to "*doubly* excited states". Since all the real doubly excited states of the helium atom have higher energies than our $(1s, nl)$ state, we might expect any second order perturbation energy which involves matrix elements to these "doubly excited functions" to give a *negative* correction to the HF-energy.

[1] A. C. ZEMACH: Phys. Rev. **104**, 1771 (1957).
[2] R. T. BRADEN: Unpublished report (Engineering Physics Dept., Cornell U., 1957).
[3] The value obtained for δ for para-helium from SMITH's wave function is approximately -0.124, not -0.160 as quoted in his paper and our text.
[4] The experimental values are extrapolations to principal quantum number $n\to\infty$ from the experimental δ_n for various n up to about 10.

32 and 33. Ground state of He and helium-like ions. The work of KINOSHITA, quoted in Sect. 32 of the text, has meanwhile been published[1]. This work on the ground state of He ($Z=2$) has been extended to include 39 parameters, but the numerical values are almost identical with those quoted in the text (from a 38 parameter function). HART and HERZBERG[2] have obtained variational wave functions with 20 parameters for a number of helium-like ions ($Z=1, 2, 3, 6, 8, 10$ and 12). Their values for the ionization potentials J are in good agreement with the interpolation formula (33.12) of our text, which was based on the work of HYLLERAAS and MIDTDAL. For $Mg^{(10+)}$ ($Z=12$), for instance, the explicit 20-parameter calculation gives $J=129.313866$ Ry while (33.12) gives 129.313894 Ry. HART and HERZBERG have also evaluated the mass-polarization corrections ε_M (see Sect. 37γ of our text) with their wave functions.

36β. Expansion in LEGENDRE polynomials. The exact wave function for any state of a two-electron atom can (in principle) be written as a superposition of central field functions (i.e. of products of two single-particle functions). For S-states of the atom the angular dependence of each central field function is simply $P_l(\cos\vartheta_{12})$ and the wave function is of the form (36.4) of our text. More work has been and is being done[3] on the evaluation of wave functions of this form (with a finite number of terms), especially for the ground state and the metastable $2S$-state of helium. Values obtained with such functions for the energy eigenvalue do not seem to converge as rapidly with the number of terms carried as with variational wave functions of the type discussed in Sect. 33 and 35. However, wave functions of such type can have some other advantages over the variational ones which employ r_{12} as one of the coordinates: First, these methods can be generalized for higher states or more complicated atoms where the variation method is not practical. Second, the various terms in a superposition of central field functions are orthogonal to each other, which the HYLLERAAS-type terms in a variational function are not, and have a more direct physical significance. Finally, such wave functions may yield more reliable expectation values of some operators (such as a high power of r_1) which weight heavily regions in position or momentum space which are unimportant for the energy expectation value and are therefore not given very accurately by the variational functions. Unfortunately no wave functions of this kind of very high accuracy are available as yet for helium.

40. Fine structure splitting of helium. We merely add a few references to those quoted in the text: New microwave techniques for measuring fine structure separations in the rather short-lived excited triplet states of helium are described in a paper by LAMB[4], who also reviews the status of theoretical fine structure calculations. Calculations of the effect of radiative corrections on the theoretical fine structure splitting are also being carried out[5]. More accurate wave functions for the excited triplet states of helium are badly needed for the accurate evaluation of the main theoretical splitting (order $Z^2\alpha^2$ Ry), before effective use can be made of accurate experiments and of higher order calculations.

---

[1] T. KINOSHITA: Phys. Rev. **105**, 1490 (1957).

[2] J. HART and G. HERZBERG: Phys. Rev. **106**, 79 (1957).

[3] P. O. LÖWDIN and H. SCHULL: Phys. Rev. **101**, 1730 (1956). — L. C. GREEN et al.: Phys. Rev. **104**, 1593 (1956). — D. H. TYCKO: Ph. D. Thesis, Columbia U., 1957. — E. HOLØIEN: Phys. Rev. **104**, 1301 (1956).

[4] W. E. LAMB: Phys. Rev. **105**, 559 (1957). — W. E. LAMB and T. H. MAIMAN: Phys. Rev. **105**, 573 (1957).

[5] G. ARAKI: Phys. Rev. **101**, 1410; **103**, 1906 (1956). — H. ARAKI: Progr. Theor. Phys. **17**, 619 (1957).

41. Relativistic corrections for the ground state. *β) The* LAMB *shift.* Misprint correction: In (41.7) on p. 190 of the text, the first fraction on the right-hand side should read $\frac{16}{3}$ instead of $\frac{3}{16}$.

γ) Numerical results. Details on the evaluation of $E_J - \varepsilon_M$ for He ($Z=2$) will be found in KINOSHITA's paper[1]. There has been some slight numerical improvements in the evaluation of $E_J - \varepsilon_M$ and ΔE_J for helium-like ions of $Z>2$: The small mass-polarization term ε_M has been evaluated accurately[2], using 20-parameter wave functions for a number of ions; ε_M increases slowly from 4.9_6 cm^{-1} for Li$^+$ to 7.1_6 cm^{-1} for O$^{(6+)}$. E_J and ΔE_J have not yet been evaluated using these accurate wave functions, but all the relevant expectation values have been evaluated[3] for Li$^+$ and O$^{(6+)}$ ($Z=3$ and 8) using 10 parameter wave functions[4]. These expectation values, together with (74.9A) in Sect. 74 of these Addenda, give E_J and ΔE_J. From these results for $Z=3$ and 8 and from the more accurate ones for $Z=2$ and for $Z\to\infty$, we have constructed interpolation formulae for other values of Z. These formulae, which should be slightly more accurate than (41.11) and (41.12) of our text, are

$$E_J = \frac{1}{4}\alpha^2 Z^2\left(Z^2 - 3.606Z + 3.29 + 0.05\,\frac{1}{Z}\right)\text{Ry}, \tag{41.11 A}$$

$$\left.\begin{aligned}\Delta E_J = -\frac{16Z^4\alpha^3}{3\pi}\Big[(3.745 - \log Z) - \frac{1}{Z}(5.97 - 1.31\log Z) + \\ + \frac{1}{Z^2}(3.08 - 0.28\log Z)\Big]\text{Ry}.\end{aligned}\right\} \tag{41.12 A}$$

We estimate the probable errors in the numerical values in the various terms contributing to the theoretical ionization potential J_{theor} for $Z=3$ to 8 to be as follows: A few cm^{-1} in J_{NR} for all Z; from about ± 3 cm^{-1} (for $Z=3$) to ± 60 cm^{-1} (for Z=8) in $E_J - \varepsilon_M$; from about ± 1 cm^{-1} (for $Z=3$) to ± 20 cm^{-1} (for $Z=8$) in ΔE_J. We reproduce below the part of Table 12 for $Z>2$, using our revised values for E_J and ΔE_J. The calculated ionization potentials agree with the experimental ones to within better than the quoted experimental errors.

Table 12A. *Experimental and theoretical ionization potentials for helium-like ions (in* cm^{-1}).

Z ion	3 Li$^+$	4 Be^{++}	6 C$^{(4+)}$	8 O$^{(6+)}$
J_{NR}	610072	1241177	3161660	5959980
$E_J - \varepsilon_M$	$+14._6$	$+98$	$+922$	$+3590$
ΔE_J	$-8._2$	-28	-134	-390
J_{theor}	610078	1241247	3162448	5963180
J_{exp}	610079 ± 25	1241225 ± 100	3162450 ± 300	5963000 ± 600

49δ. The absolute value of g_s. The largest contribution to the probable error in the experimental value in (49.9) for g_s comes from the measurement of the electron cyclotron frequency (in terms of the proton resonance frequency). An independent measurement of this quantity has been carried out recently[5] with slightly different results (and about the same accuracy) as the older measurement quoted in our text. The newer measurement leads to an experimental value for g_s of

$$g_s = 2(1.001165 \pm 0.000011). \tag{49.9A}$$

[1] T. KINOSHITA: Phys. Rev. **105**, 1490 (1957).
[2] J. HART and G. HERZBERG: Phys. Rev. **106**, 79 (1957).
[3] T. KINOSHITA, M. NAUENBERG and R. F. PEIERLS: Unpublished work.
[4] S. CHANDRASEKHAR and G. HERZBERG: Phys. Rev. **98**, 1050 (1955).
[5] P. FRANKEN and S. LIEBES: Phys. Rev. **104**, 1197 (1956).

The theoretical value (see Sect. 18β of these Addenda) for $g_s/2$ would be 1.001145 using the "old" KARPLUS-KROLL value of the fourth order electron moment, 1.001160 using the "new" SOMMERFIELD value.

50. The diamagnetism of helium. In the text we have shown that the diamagnetic susceptibility χ per gm mol of helium is related to $\overline{r^2}$, the expectation value of r^2 for one electron in the helium ground state. With $\overline{r^2}$ in atomic units (a^2) and χ in cm³ we have

$$\chi = -1.585 \times 10^{-6}\, \overline{r^2}. \tag{50.5 A}$$

We had found excellent agreement between the older measurements of χ and the approximate theoretical value of $\overline{r^2} = 1.19$ obtained from the HARTREE wave function. The excellence of the agreement is somewhat fortuitous, since the latest measurements[1] of χ lead to a slightly larger value of $\overline{r^2}$, namely

$$\chi_{\text{exp}} = -(1.93_3 \pm 0.01) \times 10^{-6}, \qquad (\overline{r^2})_{\text{exp}} = (1.22_0 \pm 0.006) \quad \text{a.u.} \tag{50.6 A}$$

$\overline{r^2}$ has not yet been evaluated directly with any ground state wave function more accurate than the HARTREE function, but DALGARNO and LYNN[2] have used some semi-empirical formulae for dipole oscillator strengths to evaluate a sum [see (61.22 A) of our Addenda] which, indirectly, leads to a value of about 1.22 for $\overline{r^2}$.

58. The dielectric constant of helium. In the text we have stated that the STARK effect energy $E_2 F^2$ for the helium ground state in an electric field F is related to the dielectric constant ε of helium. E_2 is defined as [see (56.1)]

$$-\frac{\alpha'}{2} \equiv E_2 = \sum_k \frac{(z_1 + z_2)^2_{0k}}{E_0 - E_k}, \tag{58.12 A}$$

where $(\,)_{0k}$ is a matrix element between the ground state and a state k, and $\alpha' \equiv -2E_2$ is called the "polarizability of helium in atomic units" ($\alpha' a^3$ is the polarizability in C.G.S. units). We saw that the polarizability can also be calculated approximately by the perturbation-variation method and that SLATER and KIRKWOOD's calculated approximate value was $\alpha' = 1.43$. More recent measurements[3] of the dielectric constant yield a slightly lower experimental value for the polarizability than the older one quoted in the text, the present value being

$$\alpha' = 1.40 \pm 0.01. \tag{58.13 A}$$

Extrapolation of refractive index measurements in helium to infinite wavelengths yields a similar value for α'.

61 α. Statement of sum rules. A number of other sum rules, besides those stated in the text, have been derived by various authors[2,4]. We shall state without proof a few of these sum rules which apply to a general atom or ion: Let Z be the number of electrons, Z_c the nuclear charge, f_{n0} the oscillator strength

$$f_{n0} = +(2i/\hbar)\,(p_x)_{0n}\,(x)_{n0}$$

---

[1] G. G. HAVENS: Phys. Rev. **43**, 992 (1933). In evaluating HAVENS' results the more recent change in the CURIE constant for O_2 has to be taken into account.

[2] A. DALGARNO and N. LYNN: Proc. Phys. Soc. A (in print, 1957).

[3] L. ESSEN: Proc. Phys. Soc. B **66**, 189 (1953). — L. HARTSHORN: Precision Electrical Measurements. (London: H. M. Stationary Office, 1955.

[4] J. P. VINTI: Phys. Rev. **41**, 432 (1932). — H. MARGENAU: Phys. Rev. **56**, 1000 (1939). — A. DALGARNO and J. LEWIS: Proc. Roy. Soc. Lond., Ser. A **233**, 70 (1955).

and E_n the energy of the state n expressed in units of the RYDBERG (*not* in atomic units). The sum rules are

$$\sum_n f_{n0}(E_n - E_0)^{-2} = \tfrac{1}{4}\alpha', \tag{61.21 A}$$

$$\sum_n f_{n0}(E_n - E_0)^{-1} = \tfrac{1}{3}\left(\left|\sum_i \boldsymbol{r}_i\right|^2\right)_{00}, \tag{61.22 A}$$

$$\sum_n f_{n0} = Z, \tag{61.23 A}$$

$$\sum_n f_{n0}(E_n - E_0) = \tfrac{4}{3}\left[[|E_0| + \tfrac{1}{2}\sum_{i\neq j}(\boldsymbol{p}_i\cdot\boldsymbol{p}_j)_{00}\right], \tag{61.24 A}$$

$$\sum_n f_{n0}(E_n - E_0)^2 = \frac{16\pi Z_c}{3}\sum_i \left(\delta^{(3)}(\boldsymbol{r}_i)\right)_{00}. \tag{61.25 A}$$

On the left-hand sides of these equations the summation n goes over all the states of the atom, including those in the continuum, except for the ground state, i.e. $n \neq 0$. On the right-hand sides the summations i and j go over each of the Z electrons; $\boldsymbol{r}$ and $\boldsymbol{p}$ are position and momentum in atomic units; the symbol $(\ )_{00}$ denotes an expectation value for the ground state. The symbol α' in (61.21 A) is the "polarizability" of the atom, defined (for $Z=2$) in (58.12 A) of the present Addenda. As indicated in Sect. 58, the polarizability α' can (in principle) be calculated by means of the perturbation-variation method without explicit reference to transition matrix elements to excited states.

Of the above sum rules, (61.23 A) is simply the THOMAS-REICHE-KUHN sum rule (61.1); (61.22 A) is related to our sum rule (61.6); (61.25 A) is equivalent to (19.13) plus (21.1) of our text and is also restated in (74.5). The expectation values on the righthand sides of these equations are often evaluated much more easily than the sums on the left-hand sides and some of them (e.g. α') can also be obtained from experimental measurements. DALGARNO and LYNN[1], for instance, have used these sum rules, together with a few explicit calculations, to derive a semi-empirical formula for the oscillator strengths of dipole transitions from the ground state of helium to each of the various excited states (including $df/d\nu$ for the continuum, see Sect. 74γ of our text).

68. X-ray spectra. We merely add some recent references which deal with the dipole oscillator strengths and their sum rules in highly relativistic atoms[2].

73α. Relativistic Born approximation. Misprint correction: On p. 312, equation (73.3), the factor in square brackets should read $\left[1 - \tfrac{1}{2}\gamma(\gamma - 1)(1 - \beta\cos\Theta)\right]$.

74γ. The average excitation energy for the LAMB shift. In (74.8) of the text we stated the result of an approximate calculation of K_0, the "average excitation energy for the LAMB shift" for the ground state of He ($Z=2$). The probable error quoted in (74.8) is most probably too small[3]: The quantity $\nu^3\, df/d\nu$ for transitions to the continuum, which enters in the calculation of K_0, has its maximum at quite large frequencies ($h\nu$ about 25 times the ionization potential of He). The expressions used for $df/d\nu$ are quite reliable for moderately low values of ν and again for very large ν (where the BORN approximation applies), but they employ the approximate "full screening" wave functions for the continuum

[1] A. DALGARNO and N. LYNN: Proc. Phys. Soc. A (in print, 1957).

[2] J. S. LEVINGER, M. RUSTGI and K. OKAMOTO: Phys. Rev. **103**, 439 (1956), **106**, 1191 (1957). — G. E. BROWN and D. F. MAYERS: Proc. Roy. Soc. Lond., Ser. A **234**, 387 (1956). — I. P. GRANT: Phys. Rev. **106**, 754 (1957).

[3] P. KABIR and E. SALPETER: Phys. Rev. **108** (in press, 1957).

and may not be very accurate near the maximum of $\nu^3 \, df/d\nu$. The present value for He ($Z=2$) is

$$K_0 = (80.5 \pm 15)\ \text{Ry}, \qquad (74.8\,\text{A})$$

where the ± 15 Ry is only an estimate of the probable error. This value divided by $Z^2=4$ is quite close to the hydrogenic value of 19.77 Ry. An (even rougher) calculation for Li^+ ($Z=3$) also gave a value for K_0 close to $3^2 \times 19.8$ Ry and, within the present accuracy, we adopt for the ground state of helium-like ions of charge Z

$$K_{0(z)} \approx 19.77\, Z^2\ \text{Ry}. \qquad (74.9\,\text{A})$$

78. Bremsstrahlung calculations for low energies. In our text, Eq. (78.2), we have quoted SOMMERFELD's exact nonrelativistic formula for the integrated cross-section $\sigma(\nu)$, expressed in terms of the general hypergeometric function. In our text we gave the simplified expressions to which (78.2) reduces for various limiting values of the parameters n_0 and n. Very accurate numerical evaluations of SOMMERFELD's formula (78.2) are now also available[1] for arbitrary values of n_0 and n.

79γ. Relativistic deviations from BORN approximation. In our text we have discussed the "Coulomb effects", i.e. deviations from the BETHE-HEITLER BORN approximation formula for large values of $Z\alpha$, and stated that the calculations are very difficult when these COULOMB effects and screening effects are of importance simultaneously. Calculations for the differential cross-section at high energies for Bremsstrahlung and for pair-production, including both COULOMB and screening effects, have nevertheless been performed recently[2].

Another recent paper[3] tabulates numerical values for the *un*corrected BETHE-HEITLER formula, integrated over the direction of the radiated photon only.

---

[1] J. M. BERGER: Phys. Rev. **105**, 35 (1957).
[2] H. OLSEN, L. C. MAXIMON and H. WERGELAND: Phys. Rev. **106**, 27 (1957).
[3] P. MCCORMICK, D. KEIFFER and G. PARZEN: Phys. Rev. **103**, 29 (1956).

Further Addenda and Errata.

18β. Covariant calculations of radiative corrections. The fourth order contribution to the moment has been recalculated, by a different method, by A PETERMANN, He obtains the same result as SOMMERFIELD.

32 and 33. Ground state of helium. A much more accurate variational calculation was published by C. L. PEKERIS, Phys. Rev. **112**, 1649 (1958). Using a trial function with 203 terms, he finds for the non-relativistic energy

$$E = -2.903\,724\,353\,2 \text{ a.u.}$$

instead of (32.25). He also calculates relativistic corrections and mass polarization. Using a rough estimate of the LAMB shift, he finds for the ionization potential

$$J = 198\,310.67 \text{ cm}^{-1}$$

$$J_{\text{exp}} = 198\,310.82 \pm 0.15 \text{ cm}^{-1}$$

Many further improvements have been published by PEKERIS, CHARLES SCHWARTZ and others. The ground states of other two-electron atoms, from H^- to Ne IX, have also been calculated by PEKERIS with similar accuracy.

39. The PAULI approximation. In the expression for H_2 in Eq. (39.14) the sign convention is such that

$$r_{12} \cdot (r_{12} \cdot p_1) p_2 = + \sum_i \sum_k (x_{i1} - x_{i2})(x_{k1} - x_{k2}) p_{i1} p_{k2}$$

67α. The unperturbed 2S-state. The value for lifetime of $2S$-state against magnetic dipole *one-photon* decay, quoted on page 285, is in error by a factor of 9/4. The correct value [see G. W. F. DRAKE, Phys. Rev. **A3**, 908 (1971); G. FEINBERG and J. SUCHER, Phys. Rev. Lett. **26**, 681 (1971)] is about 4.5 days.

Author Index.

Subject Index.

Index of Tables.